P9-DNX-849

Discovering Algebra

THIRD EDITION

Jerald Murdock

Ellen Kamischke

Eric Kamischke

Discovering Mathematics

Cover image © Shutterstock, Inc.

www.kendallhunt.com
Send all inquiries to:
4050 Westmark Drive
Dubuque, IA 52004-1840
1-800-542-6657

Copyright © 2002, 2007 by Key Curriculum Press

Copyright © 2014 by Kendall Hunt Publishing Company

ISBN 978-1-4652-3905-1

All rights reserved. No part of this publication may be reproduced, stored in a retrieval system, or transmitted, in any form or by any means, electronic, mechanical, photocopying, recording, or otherwise, without the prior written permission of the copyright owner.

Printed in the United States of America

1 2 3 4 5 6 7 8 9 10 19 18 17 16 15 14

CONTENTS

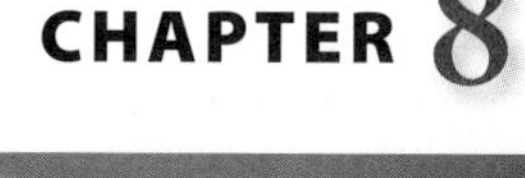

Quadratic Functions 525

Demonstrating the Standards for Mathematical Practice in *Discovering Algebra*

In *Discovering Algebra,* while learning the mathematical content you will learn how to utilize the ways of thinking about and doing mathematics emphasized in the Common Core State Standards for Mathematics (CCSSM). These ways of thinking about and doing mathematics are called mathematical practices, or SMPs, and are summarized below.

Use the **Bugs, Bugs, Everywhere Bugs Investigation in Lesson 6.1** to look at what these standards might mean to you.

Make sense of problems and persevere in solving them.

Figure out just what the problem means. You might need to use things you can move around or to draw a picture. Think about a strategy to use that will get you where you need to be before you start. If you get stuck or think you have hit a dead end, don't give up. Review your work for any errors, talk to your classmates to get a different perspective on the problem, and ask your teacher clarifying questions. As you go, make sure the solutions you are getting make sense. Would you get the same answer if you tried a different strategy? This is one of two SMPs that should be used with every problem you encounter, in mathematics and in life.

Reason abstractly and quantitatively.

When presented with a problem in mathematics, you sometimes have a situation and you have to write an equation. You often have an equation and you need to understand the meaning of the quantities, not just how to compute them. In **Step 3** you have to graph real-world data, in **Step 4** you explain the ratios in terms of the bug population, in **Step 5** you use a multiplier to calculate the population, and in **Step 8** you look back to see what the numbers mean in terms of the growth of a bug population.

Construct viable arguments and critique the reasoning of others.

In this course you will be asked to present your solutions to the investigation. You need to be able to make conjectures and use assumptions, definitions, and previous results to justify your conclusions and explain them to others. You will listen to or read other's arguments, determine if they make sense, and explain why you do or do not agree with them. You'll ask questions to get clarification of an explanation and use counterexamples in your argument that an answer isn't correct. In **Step 2** you explain whether the rate of change is linear and how you know.

Model with mathematics.

Modeling is applying the mathematics you know to solve everyday problems. Sharing a pizza involves fractions, yardage on third down involves integers, and how much more money you need to buy that special outfit involves decimals. In algebra, you'll use equations, graphs, tables, diagrams, etc., to show the mathematical relationships in a model. And you'll think about whether the model you have created makes sense and modify it if necessary. The investigation uses the growth of a bug population to model the mathematical concept of exponential growth, a growth pattern in which amounts increase by repeatedly multiplying by the same number.

Use appropriate tools strategically.

No one wants to measure the distance from Ohio to Maine with a ruler. You need to know which tools are available, what they each do, what the benefits and limitations of each are, and which would be best for solving the problem. You need to know where to find other resources that can help you solve the problem. And you need to know what might have gone wrong when an answer doesn't make sense—man cannot walk from Ohio to Maine in 3 hours so maybe your decimal point was off. In **Steps 6–8,** you use a calculator to find the population for extended periods of time.

Attend to precision.

Precision is not just about calculating accurately and efficiently, although that is certainly an important part of it. It means specifying units of measure and labeling axes. It also involves expressing numerical answers with an appropriate degree of precision. Beyond computation, it means communicating precisely to others, using clear and mathematically correct definitions in discussions, and explaining the meaning of the symbols you chose to use. This is the second of two SMPs that should be used with every problem you encounter, in mathematics and in life.

Look for and make use of structure.

Algebra is the study of patterns, finding a pattern and writing an equation to explain it. In this course, you will look closely to identify a pattern or structure, break things down to an easier problem to find a way to solve the bigger problem, and you'll step back regularly, take another look at your strategy, and change directions if necessary. In **Step 2,** you have to decide if the pattern is linear, and in **Step 8** you decide, based on the pattern, what will happen to a bug population over the long term.

Look for and express regularity in repeated reasoning.

To use your time efficiently, you should notice when calculations are repeated and look for both general methods and for short cuts. For example, in elementary school you probably noticed very quickly that multiplication was a short cut for repeated addition. As you work on investigations, keep track of where you need to be at the end of the problem while you are doing each step to get there and continually check to see it the results you get at each step are reasonable, rather than getting to the end and find out you made a mistake in Step 2! In **Steps 1–2** you are looking for a pattern in the data and in **Step 8** you use the pattern to predict the population growth in the future.

Lesson 6.1 Investigation Steps

Step 1 In a table like this one, record the total number of bugs at the end of each week for 4 weeks.

Step 2 The increase in the number of bugs each week is the population's rate of change per week. Calculate each rate of change, and record it in your table. Does the rate of change show a linear pattern? Why or why not?

Step 3 Let x represent the number of weeks elapsed, and let y represent the total number of bugs. Graph the data using (0, 16) for the first point. Connect the points with line segments, and describe how the slope changes from point to point.

Step 4 Calculate the ratio of the number of bugs each week to the number of bugs the previous week, and record it in the table. See the entry in the last column for week 1. Repeat this process to complete your table. How do these ratios compare? Explain what the ratios tell you about the bug population growth.

Step 5 What is the **constant multiplier** for the bug population? How can you use this number to calculate the population when 5 weeks have elapsed?

Step 6 Model the population growth by writing a recursive rule that shows the growing number of bugs. [▸ See **Calculator Note: Recursion on a List** to review recursive rules. ◂] Describe what each part of this calculator command does.

Step 7 By pressing ENTER a few times, check that your recursive rule gives the sequence of values in your table (in the column "Total number of bugs"). Use the rule to find the bug population at the end of weeks 5 to 8.

Step 8 What is the bug population after 20 weeks have elapsed? After 30 weeks have elapsed? What happens in the long run?

A Note to Students from the Authors

Jerald Murdock

Ellen Kamischke

Eric Kamischke

You are about to embark on an exciting mathematical journey. The goal of your trip is to reach the point at which you have gathered the skills, tools, confidence, and mathematical power to participate fully as a productive citizen in a changing world. Your life will always be full of important decision-making situations, and your ability to use mathematics and algebra can help you make informed decisions. You need skills that can evolve and adapt to new situations. You need to be able to interpret and make decisions based on numerical information and to find ways to solve problems that arise in real life, not just in textbooks. On this journey you will make connections between algebra and the world around you.

You're going to discover and learn much useful algebra along the way. Learning algebra is more than learning facts and theories and memorizing procedures. We hope you also discover the pleasure involved in mathematics and in learning "how to do mathematics." Success in algebra is a gateway to many varied career opportunities.

With your teacher as a guide, you will learn algebra by doing mathematics. You will make sense of important algebraic concepts, learn essential algebraic skills, and discover how to use algebra. This requires a far bigger commitment than just "waiting for the teacher to show you" or studying "worked-out examples."

During this journey, successful learning will come from your personal involvement, which will often come about when you work with others in small groups. Talk about algebra, share ideas, and learn from and with the members of your group. Work and communicate with others to strengthen your understanding of the mathematical concepts presented in this book. To gain respect in your role as a team player, respect differences among group members, listen carefully when others are sharing their ideas, stay focused during the process, be responsible and respectful, and share your own ideas and suggestions.

And now it is time to begin. You are about to discover some pretty fascinating things.

CHAPTER 0

Fractions and Fractals

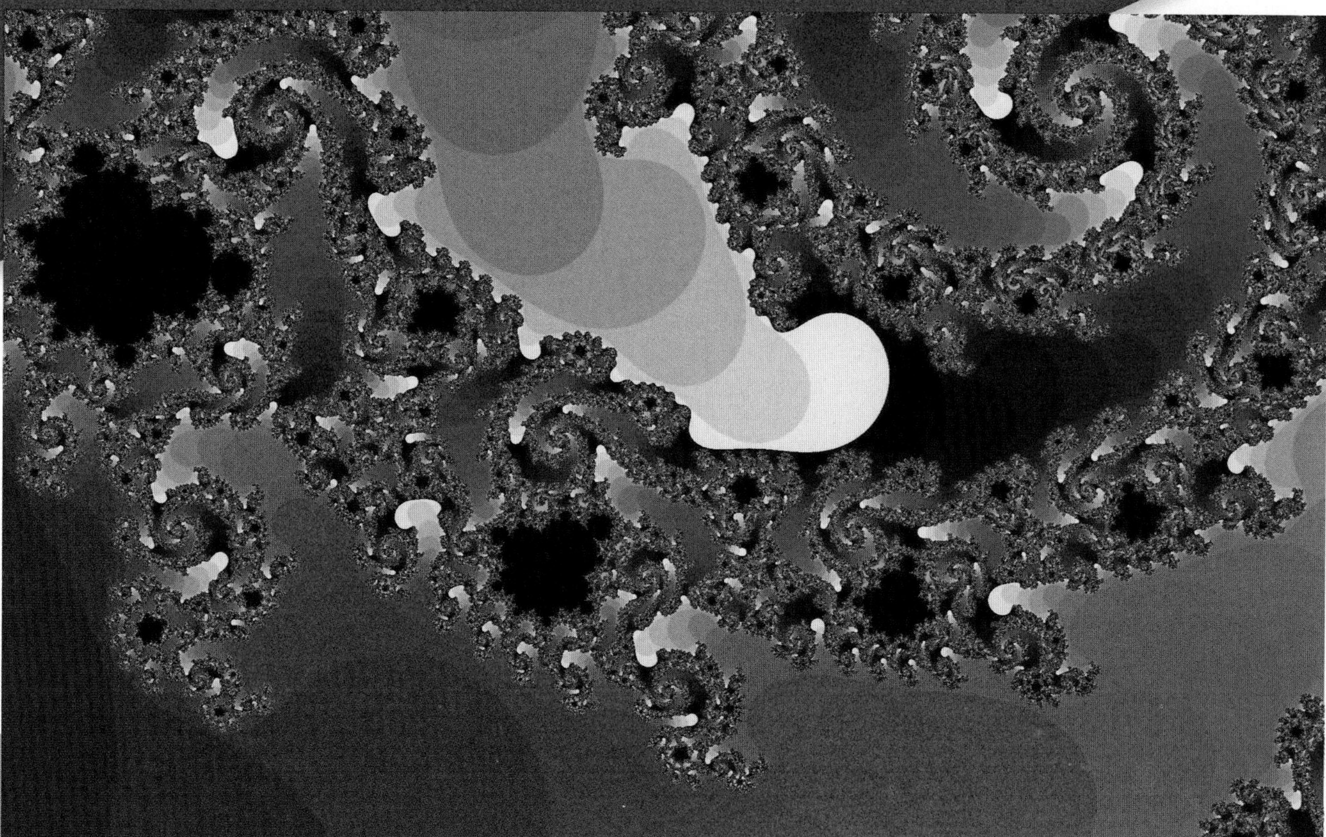

You have probably seen designs like this—you may even have heard the word *fractal* used to describe them. Complex fractals are created by infinitely repeating simple processes. Some fractals are created with basic geometric shapes such as triangles or squares. Using fractals, mathematicians and scientists can model the formation of clouds, the growth of trees, and the structure of human blood vessels.

OBJECTIVES

In this chapter you will

- investigate numeric, algebraic, and geometric patterns
- review operations with fractions and signed numbers
- review the rules for order of operations
- use exponents to represent repeated multiplication
- extend the ideas of recursion to algebraic expressions
- learn to use this book as a tool

LESSON 0.1

Recursive Fractions

A procedure that you do over and over, each time building on the previous stage, is **recursive.** You'll see recursion used in many different ways throughout this book. In this lesson you'll use a recursive procedure to draw a **fractal** design. After you draw the design, you'll review operations with fractions as you examine its parts.

Words in **bold** type are important mathematical terms. You can find definitions in the glossary.

Investigations are a very important part of this course. Often you'll discover new concepts in an investigation, so be sure to take an active role.

INVESTIGATION

Connect the Dots

YOU WILL NEED

- a ruler

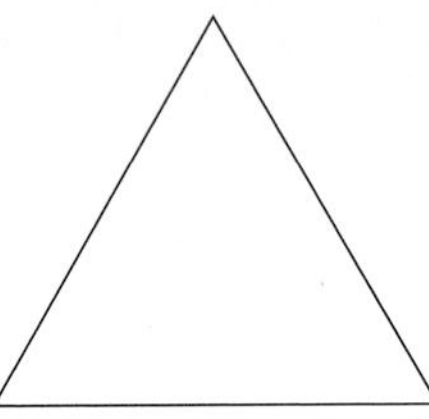

Stage 0

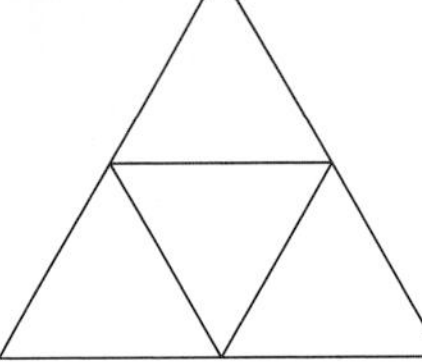

Stage 1

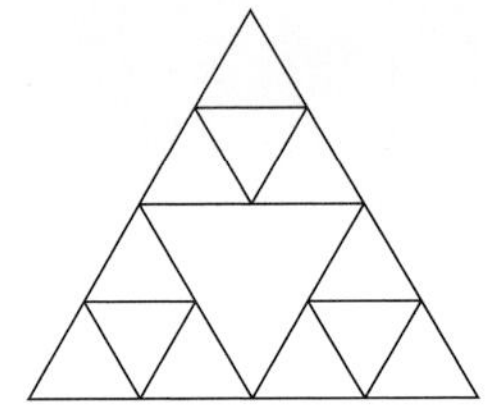

Stage 2

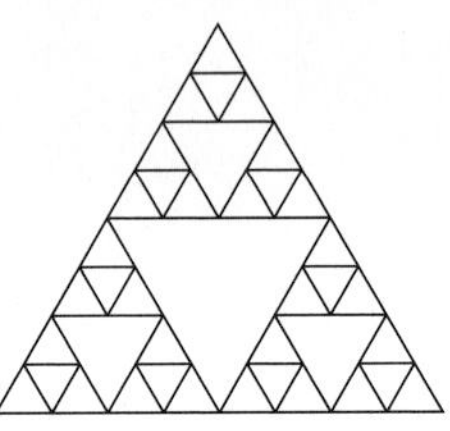

Stage 3

Step 1 Examine the figures above. The starting figure is the Stage 0 figure. To create the Stage 1 figure, you join the *midpoints* of the sides of the triangle. The Stage 1 figure has three small upward-pointing triangles. See if you can find all three.

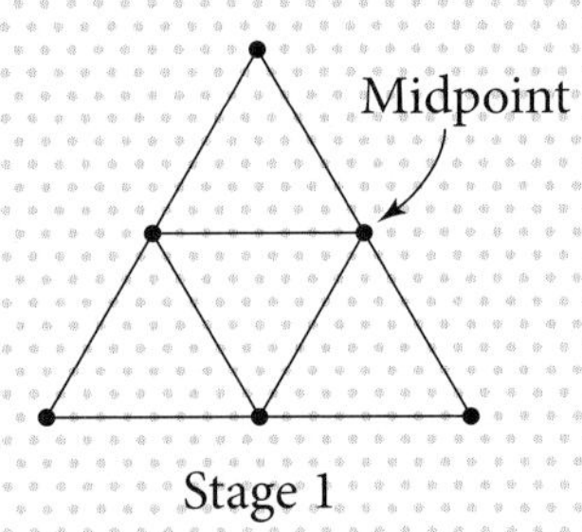

Stage 1

Step 2 At Stage 2, **line segments** connect the midpoints of the sides of the three upward-pointing triangles that showed up at Stage 1. What do you notice when you compare Stage 1 and Stage 2?

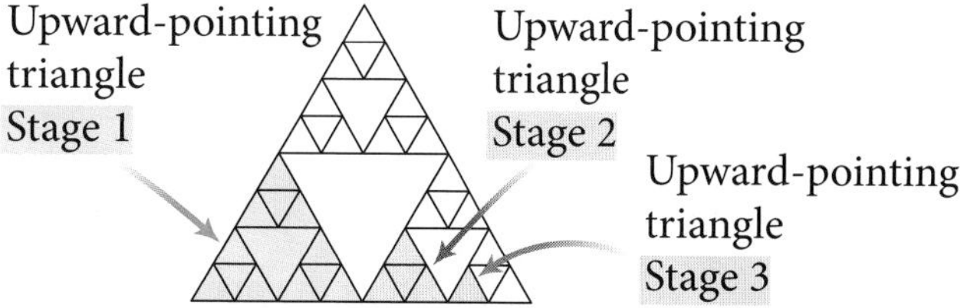

Step 3 How many new upward-pointing triangles are in the Stage 3 figure?

Step 4 Create the Stage 4 figure. A blank triangle is provided. Connect the midpoints of the sides of the large triangle, and continue connecting the midpoints of the sides of each smaller upward-pointing triangle at every stage. How many of the smallest upward-pointing triangles are in the Stage 4 figure?

Step 5 What would happen if you continued on to further stages? Describe any patterns you've noticed in drawing these figures.

Words in *italics* are words you may have seen before or could be new words that will not appear in the glossary.

You have been using a **recursive rule.** The rule is "Connect the midpoints of the sides of each upward-pointing triangle."

If you could continue this process forever, you would create a fractal called the *Sierpiński triangle.* At each stage the smallest upward-pointing triangles are *congruent*—the same shape and size.

This marker shows a convenient stopping place.

Step 6 If the Stage 0 figure has area equal to 1 square unit, what is the area of one new upward-pointing triangle at Stage 1?

Step 7 There are many different ways to find the combined area of the smallest upward-pointing triangles at Stage 1. For example, you could write the *addition expression* $\frac{1}{4}+\frac{1}{4}+\frac{1}{4}$. Write at least two other expressions to find this area. Use as many different operations (such as addition, subtraction, multiplication, or division) as you can.

Step 8 What is the area of one of the smallest upward-pointing triangles at Stage 2? How do you know?

Step 9 How many smallest upward-pointing triangles are at Stage 2? What is the combined area of these triangles?

Step 10 Repeat Steps 8 and 9 for Stage 3.

Step 11 If the Stage 0 figure has area 8 square units, what is the combined area of each of these?

a. One smallest upward-pointing triangle at Stage 1 plus one smallest upward-pointing triangle at Stage 2.

b. Two smallest upward-pointing triangles at Stage 2 minus one smallest upward-pointing triangle at Stage 3.

c. One smallest upward-pointing triangle at Stage 1 plus three smallest upward-pointing triangles at Stage 2 plus nine smallest upward-pointing triangles at Stage 3.

Step 12 Make up one problem like those in Step 11. Then exchange problems with a partner and solve.

This marker means the investigation is done.

The Polish mathematician Waclaw Sierpiński created his triangle in 1916. But the word *fractal* wasn't used until nearly 60 years later, when Benoit Mandelbrot drew attention to recursion that occurs in nature. Trees, ferns, and even the coastlines of continents can be modeled with fractals.

EXAMPLE A

Evan designed an herb garden. He divided each side of his garden into thirds and connected the points.

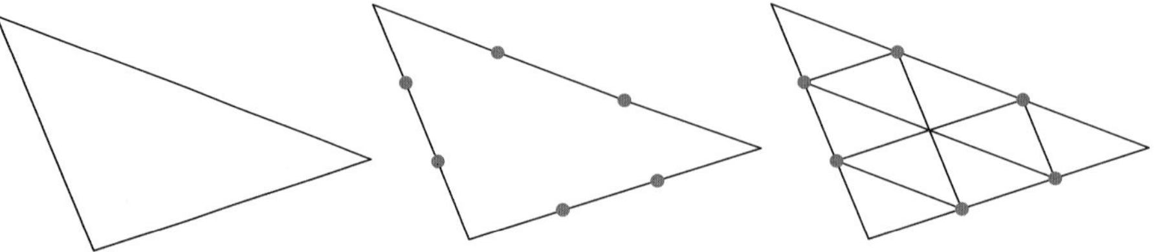

He planted oregano in the labeled sections. If the whole garden has area 1 square unit, what is the area of one oregano section? What is the total area planted in oregano?

Solution

Because there are nine equal-size sections, each oregano section is $\frac{1}{9}$ of the garden's area. To find the total area planted in oregano, you can either add, $\frac{1}{9} + \frac{1}{9} = \frac{2}{9}$, or multiply, $2 \times \frac{1}{9} = \frac{2}{9}$. So the oregano is planted in sections with a total area equal to $\frac{2}{9}$ of the garden's area. Explain how each expression represents the area.

Let's examine some features of Evan's garden in more detail. You can think of Evan's garden as a Stage 1 figure with six identical upward-pointing triangles, each with area $\frac{1}{9}$ square unit.

What is the area of the small shaded upward-pointing triangle at Stage 2?

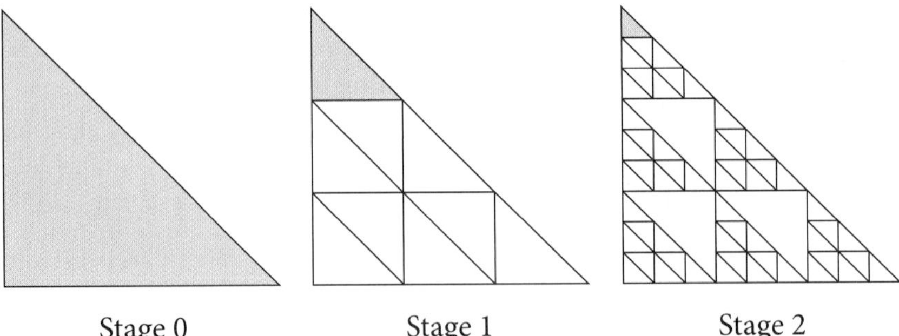

Stage 0 Stage 1 Stage 2

Benoit Mandelbrot (1924–2010) first used the word *fractal* in 1975 to describe irregular patterns in nature.

At Stage 2, nine smaller triangles are formed in each upward-pointing triangle from Stage 1. The area of the shaded triangle in Stage 2 is $\frac{1}{9}$ the area of the shaded triangle in Stage 1. This equals $\frac{1}{9}$ of $\frac{1}{9}$, which you can write as $\frac{1}{9} \times \frac{1}{9}$, which is equal to $\frac{1}{81}$.

To find combined areas, you'll be adding, subtracting, and multiplying fractions. Remember that you'll need *common denominators* to add fractions. You won't need common denominators to multiply fractions.

Operations with Fractions

To add fractions that have a common denominator, simply add the numerators. The denominator stays the same.

$\frac{a}{b} + \frac{c}{b} = \frac{a+c}{b}$ **For example,** $\frac{2}{7} + \frac{3}{7} = \frac{5}{7}$

To multiply fractions, multiply the numerator times the numerator and the denominator times the denominator.

$\frac{a}{b} \cdot \frac{c}{d} = \frac{a \cdot c}{b \cdot d}$ **For example,** $\frac{2}{3} \cdot \frac{5}{9} = \frac{10}{27}$

To change the denominator of a fraction, multiply or divide both the *numerator and the denominator* by the same number.

$\frac{a}{b} = \frac{a \cdot c}{b \cdot c}$ **or** $\frac{a}{b} = \frac{a \div c}{b \div c}$ **For example,** $\frac{2}{5} = \frac{2 \cdot 3}{5 \cdot 3}$ **or** $\frac{6}{15} = \frac{(6 \div 3)}{(15 \div 3)}$

Go to the calculator notes whenever you see this icon. The calculator notes explain how to use your graphing calculator. These notes are available from your teacher and in your ebook.

You should be able to do the calculations in this lesson with pencil and paper. Many calculators are programmed to give answers in fraction form, so use a calculator to check your answers. [▶ See **Calculator Note: Fractions.** ◀]

EXAMPLE B

If the largest triangle has area 1 square unit, what is the combined area of the shaded triangles?

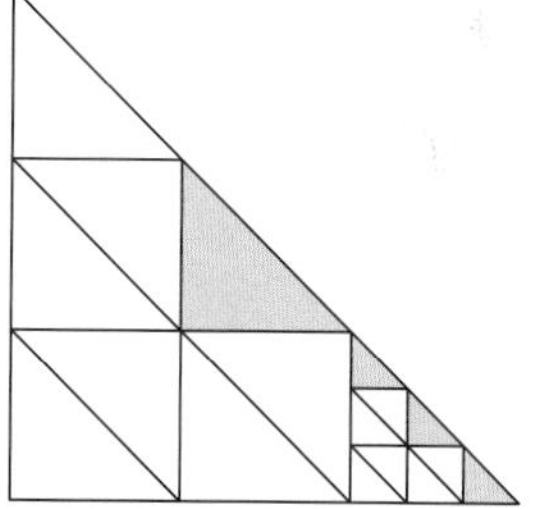

Solution

The area of the larger shaded triangle is $\frac{1}{9}$ square unit.

The area of each smaller shaded triangle is $\frac{1}{9} \times \frac{1}{9}$, or $\frac{1}{81}$ square unit.

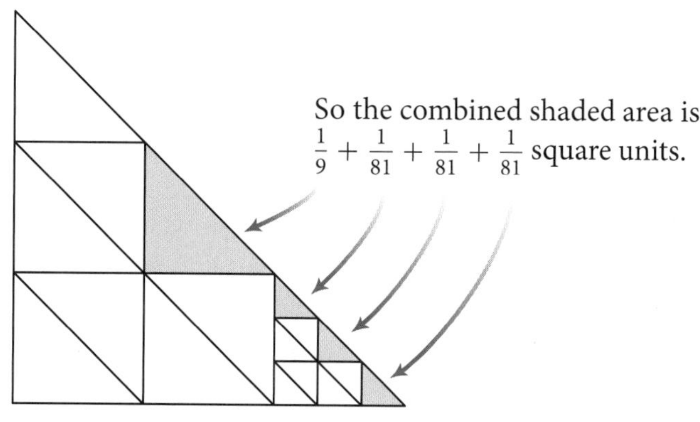

Notice that $\frac{1}{81} + \frac{1}{81} + \frac{1}{81} = \frac{3}{81}$, so the combined area is $\frac{1}{9} + \frac{3}{81}$ square unit.

Notice that you're asked to rework a problem. Check your method and your answer by sharing them with a classmate. Working together is a powerful learning strategy.

Change the denominator of $\frac{1}{9}$ so you have a common denominator and can add: $\frac{1 \cdot 9}{9 \cdot 9} = \frac{9}{81}$. Now you can rewrite the combined area as $\frac{9}{81} + \frac{3}{81}$, which equals $\frac{12}{81}$, or $\frac{4}{27}$ in *lowest terms.*

Think of another way to get the same answer. Check your method with a classmate to see if he or she agrees with you.

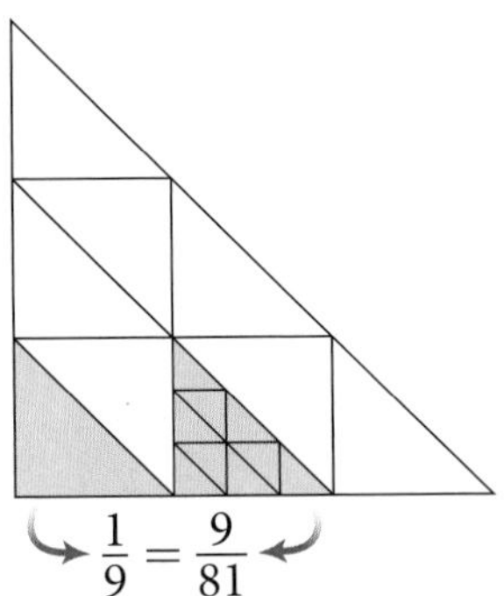

In the Sierpiński triangle, the design in any upward-pointing triangle looks just like any other upward-pointing triangle and just like the whole figure—they differ only in size. Objects like this are called **self-similar.** Self-similarity is an important feature of fractals, and you can find many examples of self-similarity in nature.

Science **CONNECTION**

The smallest leaves of a fern look very similar to the whole fern. This is an example of self-similarity in nature.

0.1 Exercises

If an exercise has an ⓐ, you can find an answer in Selected Answers and Hints at the back of the book. If an exercise has an ⓗ, you'll find a hint.

Practice Your Skills

In the Practice Your Skills exercises, you will practice basic skills that you'll need to solve exercises in the Reason and Apply section.

Do the calculations in Exercises 1–3 with paper and pencil. Check your work with a calculator.

1. Do each calculation. Then check your results with a calculator. Set your calculator to give answers in fraction form.

a. $\frac{1}{3} + \frac{2}{9}$ b. $\frac{3}{4} + \frac{1}{2} + \frac{1}{3}$ c. $\frac{2}{5} \times \frac{3}{5}$ d. $2 - \frac{4}{9}$

e. $\frac{5}{9} + \frac{2}{3}$ f. $\frac{1}{9} \times \frac{2}{5}$ g. $\frac{2}{5} \times 36$ h. $4 - \frac{7}{12}$

2. Find the total shaded area in each triangle. Write two expressions for each problem, one using addition and the other using multiplication. Assume that the area of each Stage 0 triangle is 1 square unit.

a. ⓐ

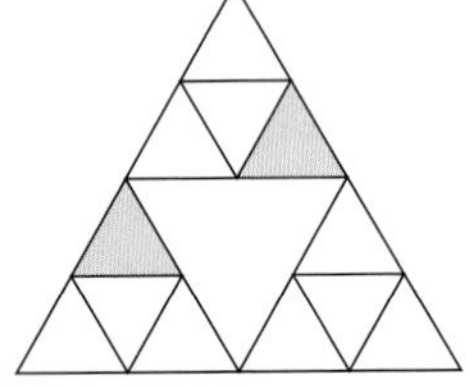

b.

c.

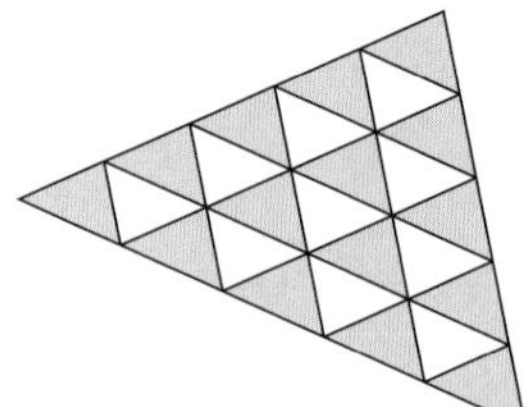

d. ⓐ

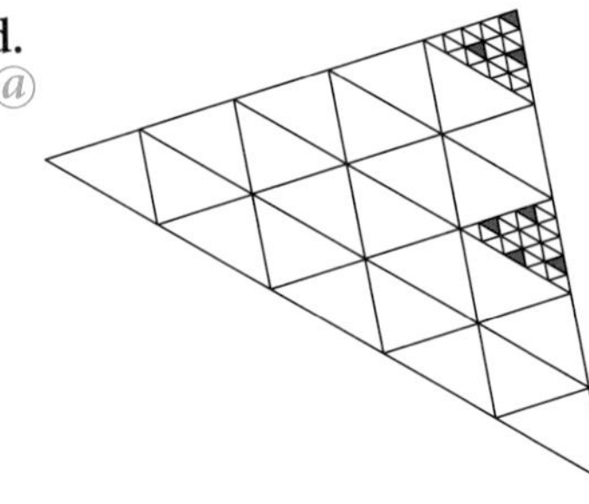

3. Write an expression for the total shaded area in each triangle, and then find that area. Assume that the area of each Stage 0 triangle is 1 square unit.

Sometimes it's easier and faster to do a calculation by hand than with a calculator.

a. @

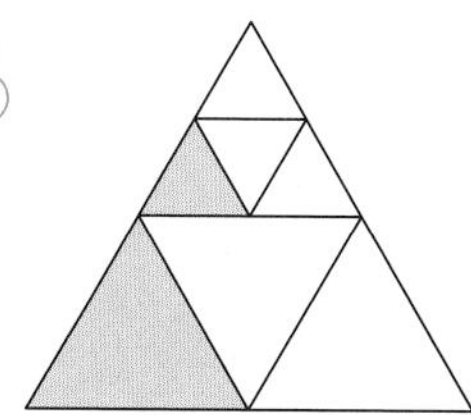

b.

c. @

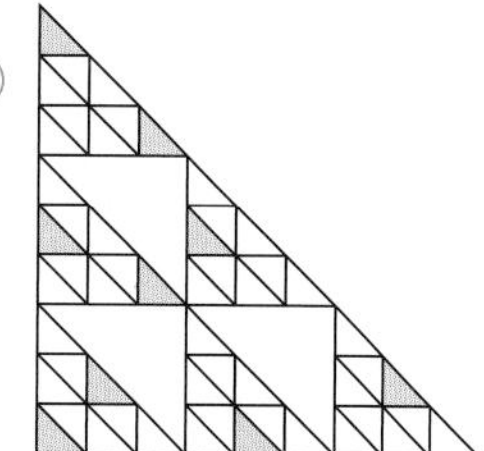

d.

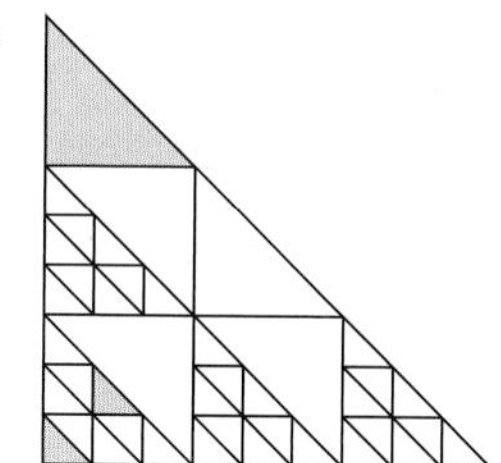

4. The first stages of a Sierpiński-like triangle are shown.

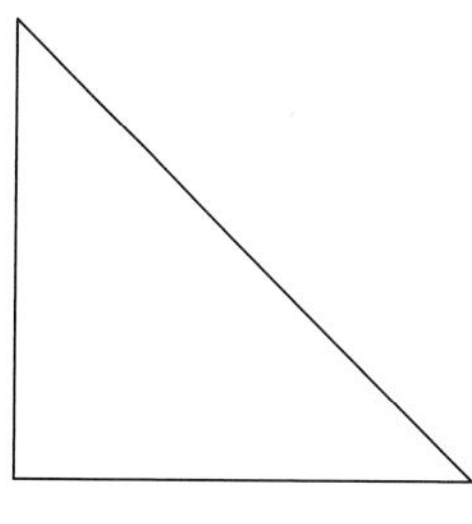

Stage 0

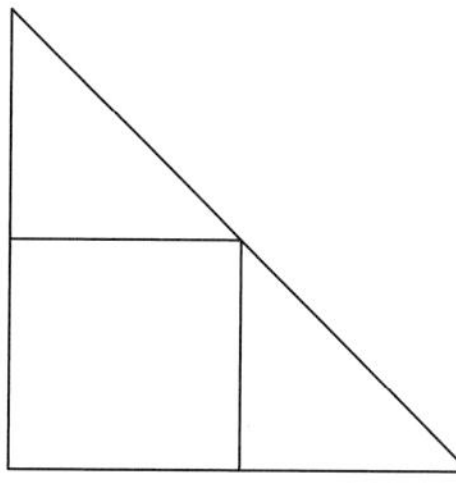

Stage 1

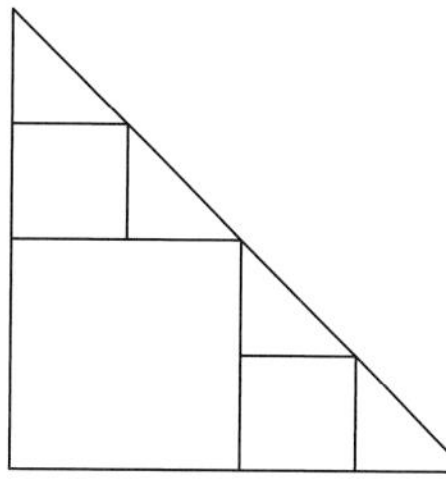

Stage 2

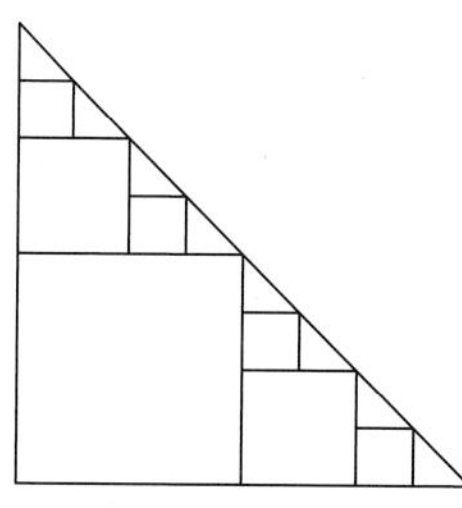

Stage 3

a. Draw Stage 4 of this pattern. You might find it easiest to start with a triangle that is about 8 cm or 4 in. along the bottom. @

b. If the Stage 0 triangle has area 64 square units, what is the area of the square at Stage 1? (h)

c. At Stage 2, what is the combined area of the squares? @

d. At Stage 3, what is the combined area of the squares?

Reason and Apply

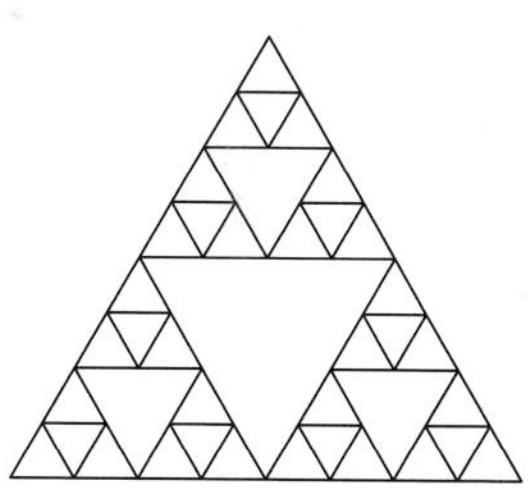

5. Suppose the area of the original large triangle in the fractal design at right is equal to 1 square unit. Copy the figure and shade parts to show each area.

a. $\frac{1}{4}$ b. $\frac{3}{16}$ (h) c. $\frac{5}{16}$ d. $1-\frac{7}{16}$

The exercises in this book may be different from what you're used to. There may be fewer exercises, but you'll probably have to spend more time on each one.

6. You have been introduced to the Sierpiński triangle. What are some aspects of this triangle that make it a fractal?

7. Rewrite each expression by using fractions. Then draw a Sierpiński triangle and shade the area described. In each case the Stage 0 triangle has area 32 square units.

You may need to refer back to examples or to work you did in an investigation as you work on an exercise.

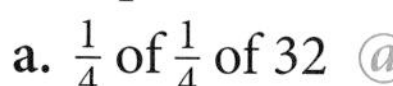

a. $\frac{1}{4}$ of $\frac{1}{4}$ of 32 @

b. $\frac{3}{4}$ of $\frac{1}{4}$ of $\frac{1}{4}$ of 32

c. $\frac{1}{2}$ of $\frac{1}{2}$ of $\frac{1}{4}$ of 32

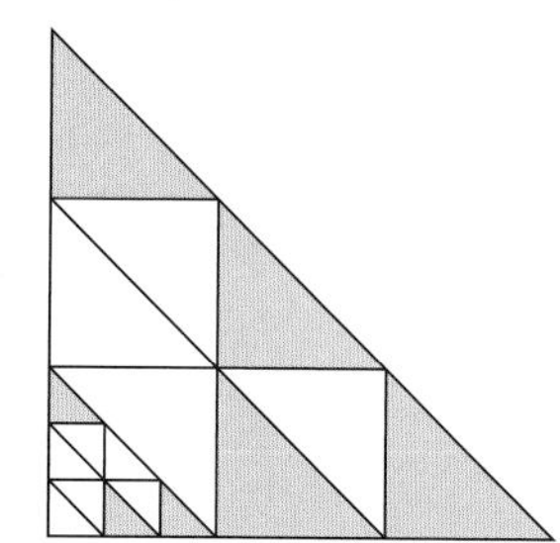

8. Suppose the original large triangle at right has area 24 square units.

a. What fraction of the area is the shaded triangle at the top?

b. What fraction of the area is each smallest shaded triangle?

c. What is the total shaded area? Find two ways to calculate this area.

9. Look at the Sierpiński-like pattern in the squares.

Stage 0

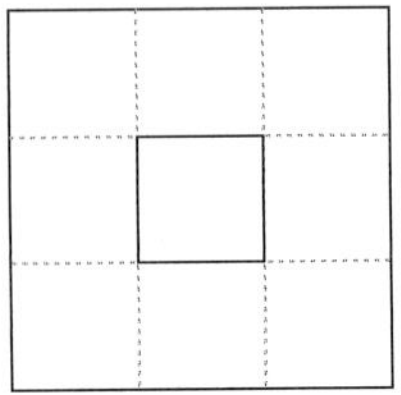
Stage 1

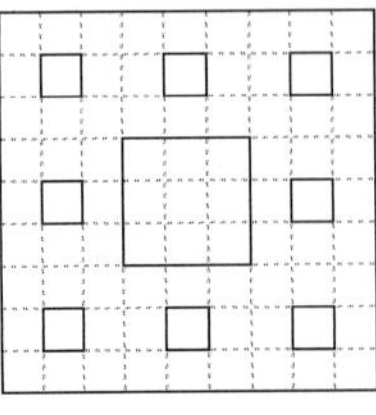
Stage 2

a. Describe the recursive rule used to create this pattern.

b. Carefully draw the next stage of the pattern.

c. Suppose the Stage 0 figure represents a square carpet. The new squares drawn at each stage represent holes that have been cut out of the carpet. If the Stage 0 carpet has area 1 square unit, what is the total area of the holes at each of Stages 1 to 3?

d. What is the area of the remaining carpet at each stage?

10. Suppose the area of the original large triangle at right is 8 square units.

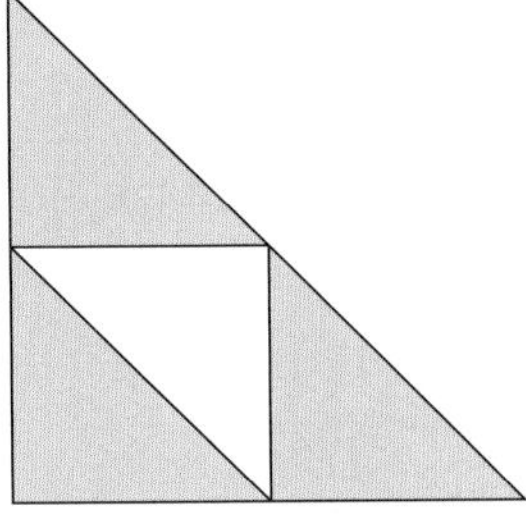

a. Write a division expression to find the area of one of the shaded triangles. What is the area? ⓐ

b. What fraction of the total area is each shaded triangle? Use this fraction in a multiplication expression to find the area of one of the shaded triangles. ⓐ

c. What is the difference between dividing by 4 and multiplying by $\frac{1}{4}$? ⓐ

d. Write a multiplication expression using the fraction $\frac{3}{4}$ to find the combined shaded area. ⓐ

11. Suppose the original large triangle at right has area 12 square units.

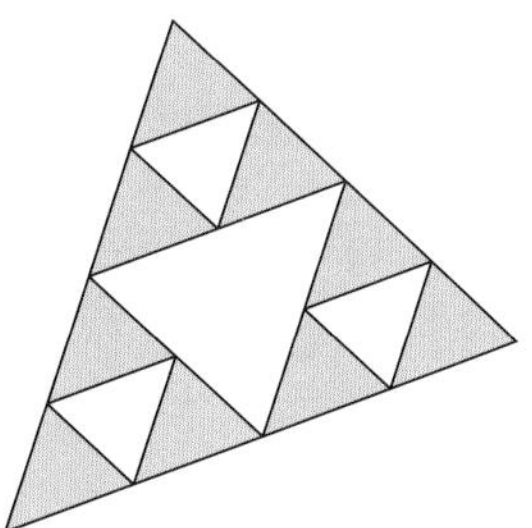

a. What fraction of the area is shaded?

b. Which is the best estimate of the combined area of the shaded triangles?

i. 4 square units **ii.** 6 square units **iii.** 9 square units **iv.** 10 square units

c. Find the combined area of the shaded triangles. Write two different expressions you could use to find this area.

Review

12. Assume the area of your desktop is 1 square unit. Your math book covers $\frac{1}{4}$ of your desktop, your calculator covers $\frac{1}{16}$ of your desktop, and your scrap paper covers $\frac{1}{32}$ of your desktop. What total area is covered by these objects? Write an addition expression, and then give your answer as a single fraction in lowest terms. ⓗ

13. Use the information from Exercise 12 to find the area of your desktop that is not covered by the materials. Write a subtraction expression, and then give your answer as a single fraction in lowest terms.

LESSON 0.2

Using Exponents

"A strong positive mental attitude will create more miracles than any wonder drug."
PATRICIA NEAL

Did you notice that at each stage of a Sierpiński design, you have more to draw than at the previous stage? The new parts get smaller, but the number of them increases quickly. Let's examine these patterns more closely.

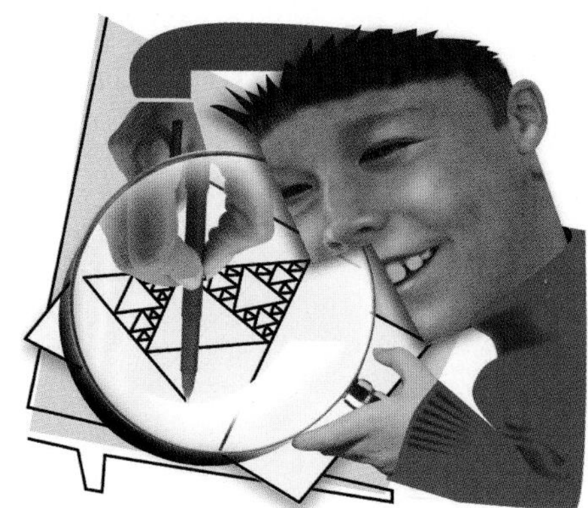

INVESTIGATION

How Many?

Explore how quickly the number of new triangles grows when you use multiplication repeatedly. Look for a pattern to help you *predict* the number of new triangles at each stage without counting them.

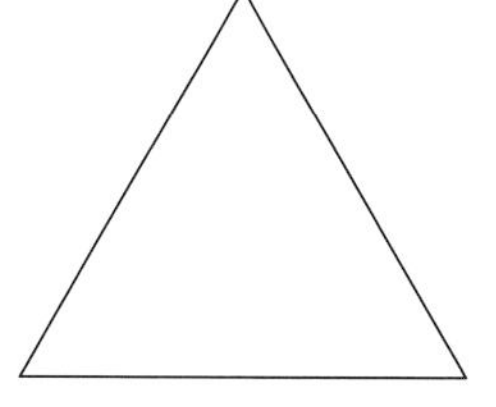
Stage 0

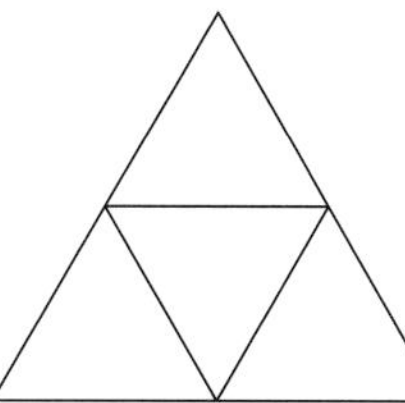
Stage 1

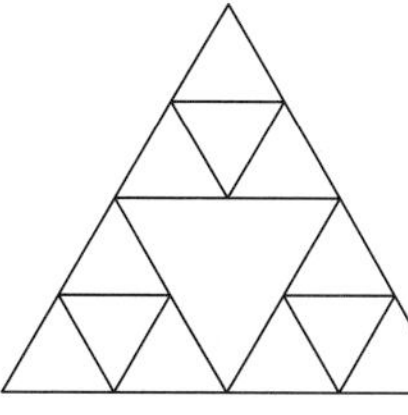
Stage 2

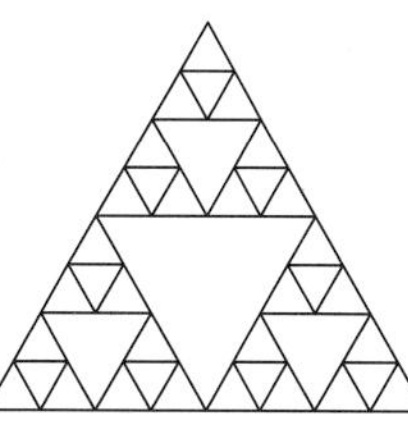
Stage 3

Stage 4

Step 1 Look at the fractal designs. Count the number of new upward-pointing triangles for each of Stages 0 to 4. Make a table like this to record your work.

Stage number	Number of new upward-pointing triangles
0	1
1	

Throughout this course you'll record results in tables. Tables provide a useful way for you to keep track of your work and see patterns develop.

Step 2 How does the number of new triangles at each stage compare to the number of new triangles at the previous stage?

Step 3 Using your answer to Step 2, find how many new upward-pointing triangles are at Stages 5, 6, and 7.

Step 4 Explain how you could find the number of upward-pointing triangles at Stage 15 without counting.

At each stage, three new upward-pointing triangles are drawn in each upward-pointing triangle from the previous stage. How is this the same as repeatedly multiplying by 3?

You can write the symbol for multiplication in different ways. For example, you can write 3×3 as $3 \cdot 3$ or $(3)(3)$ or $3(3)$. All of these expressions have the same meaning. Each expression equals 9.

EXAMPLE Describe how the number of new upward-pointing triangles is growing in this fractal.

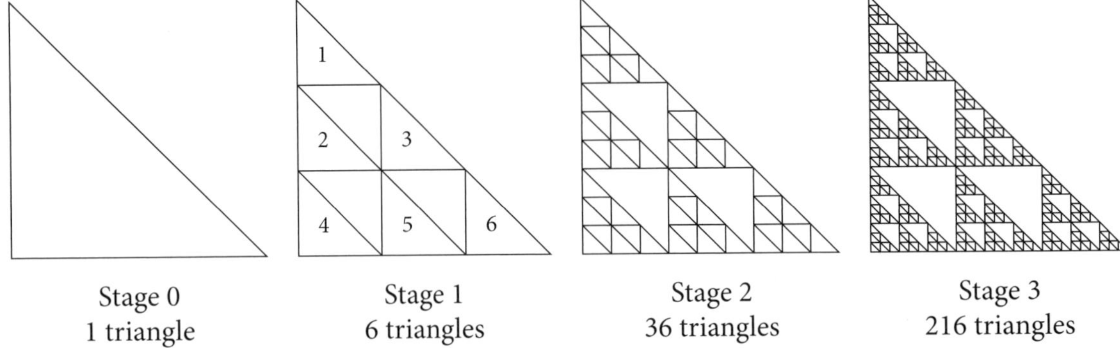

Stage 0 — 1 triangle; Stage 1 — 6 triangles; Stage 2 — 36 triangles; Stage 3 — 216 triangles

Solution At Stage 1, the six new upward-pointing triangles are numbered. At Stage 2, six new upward-pointing triangles are formed in each numbered Stage 1 triangle. At Stage 2, there are $6 \cdot 6$, or 36, new triangles. At Stage 3, six triangles are formed in each new upward-pointing Stage 2 triangle, so there are $36 \cdot 6$, or 216, new upward-pointing triangles.

Another way to look at the number of new upward-pointing triangles at each stage is shown in this table.

	Number of new upward-pointing triangles		
Stage number	**Total**	**Repeated multiplication**	**Exponent form**
1	6	6	6^1
2	36	$6 \cdot 6$	6^2
3	216	$36 \cdot 6$, or $6 \cdot 6 \cdot 6$	6^3

The last number in each row of the table is a 6 written with an **exponent.**

Exponent — Factors (the exponent tells you the number of times the base is used as a factor)

$$6^5 = 6 \cdot 6 \cdot 6 \cdot 6 \cdot 6$$

Base

What is the pattern that relates the stage number and the exponent? Do you think the pattern applies to Stage 0? Enter the number 6^0 into your calculator. [▶ See **Calculator Note: Exponents** to learn how to enter exponents. ◀] Does the result fit the pattern?

How many upward-pointing triangles are at Stage 4? According to the pattern, there should be 6^4. That's 1296 triangles! It's a lot easier to use the exponent pattern than to count all those triangles.

0.2 Exercises

Practice Your Skills

1. Write each multiplication expression in exponent form.

a. $5 \times 5 \times 5 \times 5$ @

b. $7 \times 7 \times 7 \times 7 \times 7$

c. $3 \cdot 3 \cdot 3 \cdot 3 \cdot 3 \cdot 3 \cdot 3$

d. $2(2)(2)$

2. Rewrite each expression as a repeated multiplication in three ways: using ×, ·, and parentheses.

a. 3^4 @

b. 5^6

c. $\left(\frac{1}{2}\right)^3$

3. Write each number with an exponent other than 1. For example, $8 = 2^3$.

a. 27 @

b. 32

c. 625

d. 343

e. 125

f. 128

g. 1000

h. 243

4. Do the calculations. Check your results with a calculator.

a. $\frac{2}{3} \cdot 12$

b. $\frac{1}{3} + \frac{3}{5}$

c. $\frac{3}{4} - \frac{1}{8}$

d. $5 - \frac{2}{7}$

e. $\frac{1}{4} \cdot \frac{1}{4} \cdot 8$

f. $\frac{3}{64} + \frac{3}{16} + \frac{3}{4}$

g. $\frac{1}{2} \cdot \frac{1}{4} \cdot \frac{3}{8}$

h. $\frac{4}{9} - \frac{1}{3}$

i. $\frac{3}{4} \cdot 28$

Reason and Apply

5. Another type of fractal drawing is called a *tree.* Study Stages 0 to 3 of this tree:

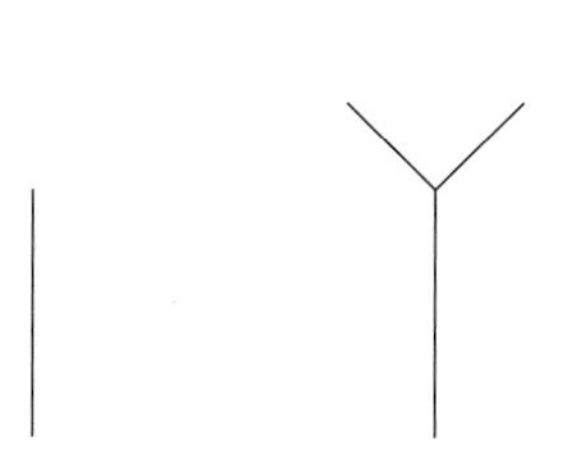

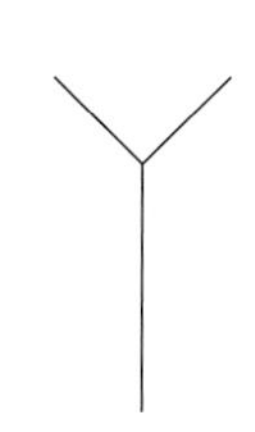

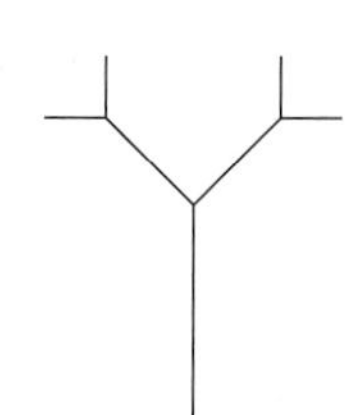

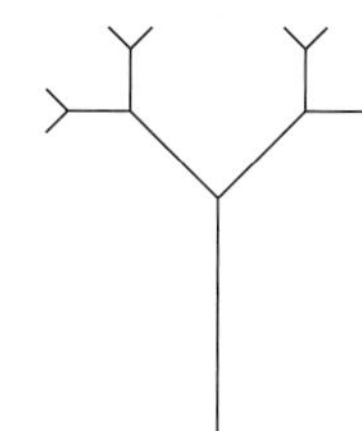

Stage 0 Stage 1 Stage 2 Stage 3

Complete a table like this one to help you answer the questions.

Stage number	New branches	Repeated multiplication	Exponent form
1	2	2	2^1
2			
3			
4			
5			

a. At Stage 1, two new branches are growing from the trunk. How many new branches are at Stage 2? At Stage 3?

b. How many new branches are at Stage 5?

6. This is another fractal tree pattern:

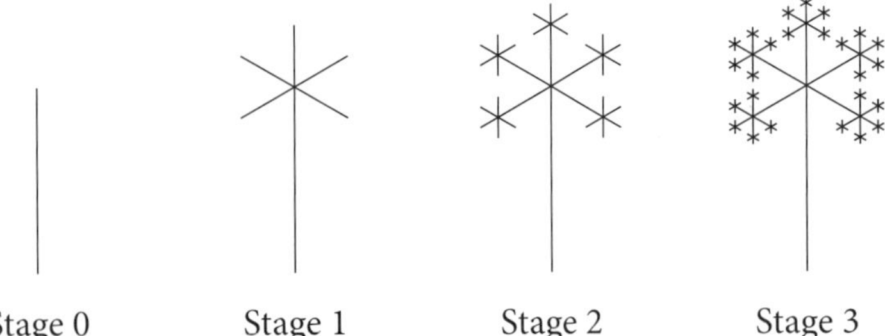

a. At Stage 1, five new branches are growing. How many new branches are at Stage 2? ⓐ

b. How many new branches are at Stage 3?

c. How many new branches are at Stage 5? Write your answer in exponent form.

7. Study Stages 0 to 3 of this fractal "weed" pattern. At Stage 1, two new branches are created.

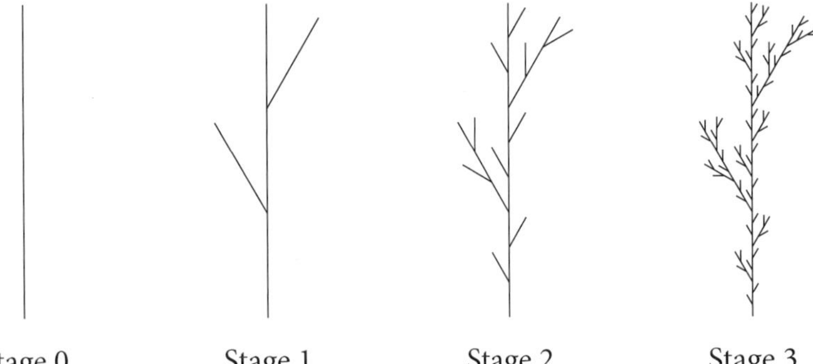

a. How many new branches are created at Stage 2? ⓐ

b. How many new branches are created at Stage 3?

c. You can write the expression $2 \cdot 5^1$ to represent the number of new branches in the Stage 2 figure. Write similar expressions to represent the number of new branches at each of Stages 3 to 5.

d. How are the 2 and the 5 in each expression related to the figure? ⓗ

Patterns like the "weed" in Exercise 7 can be used to create very realistic computer-generated plants, like this "seaweed." Graphic designers can use fractal routines to create realistic-looking trees and other natural features.

8. Look again at this familiar fractal design:

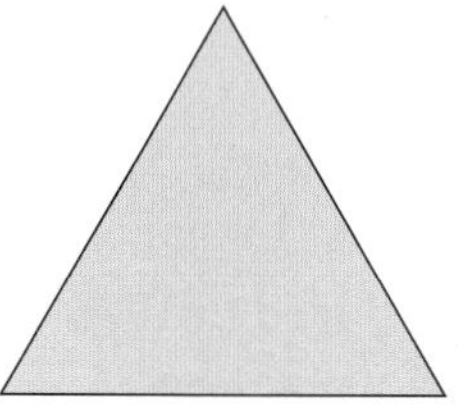
Stage 0

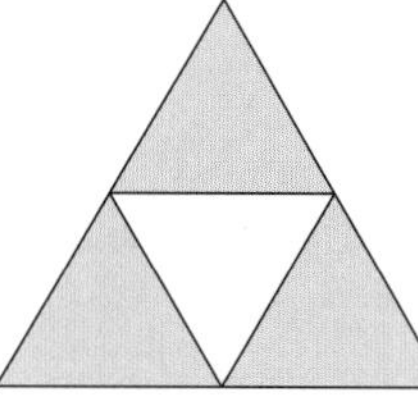
Stage 1

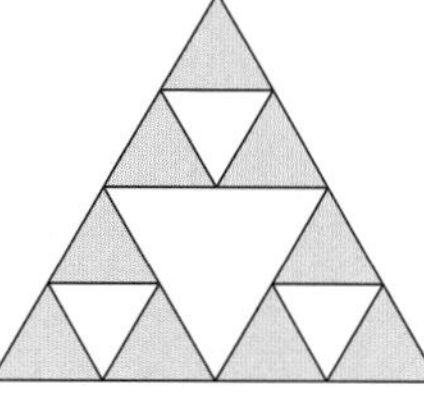
Stage 2

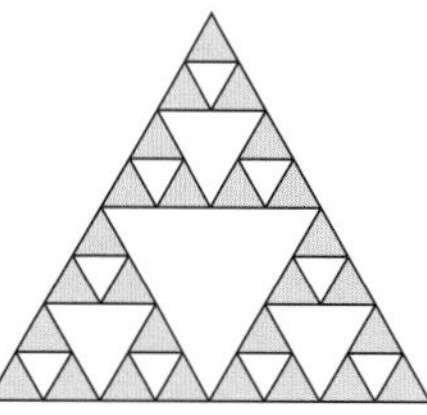
Stage 3

a. The area of the shaded triangle at Stage 0 is 1 square unit. Make a table like this to calculate and record the area of one shaded triangle at each Stage.

Stage number	Area of one shaded triangle	Total area of the shaded triangles
0	1	1
1		

b. Record the total shaded area for each figure in your table.

c. Describe at least two patterns you discovered.

Review

9. Ethan deposits \$2 in a bank account on the first day, \$4 on the second day, and \$8 on the third day. He will continue to double the deposit each day. How much will he deposit on the eighth day? Write your answer as repeated multiplication separated by dots, in exponent form, and as a single number.

10. Write a word problem or draw a diagram that illustrates $\frac{3}{4} + \frac{1}{5}$.

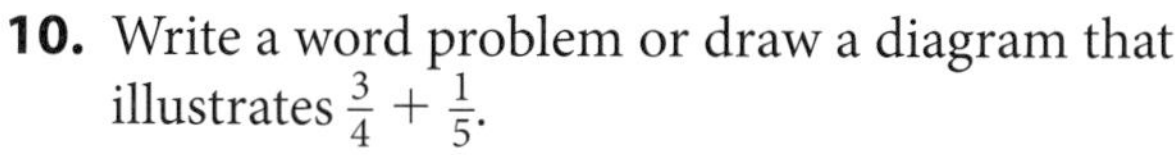

11. The large triangles in these figures each have area 1 square unit. Find the total shaded area in each.

a.

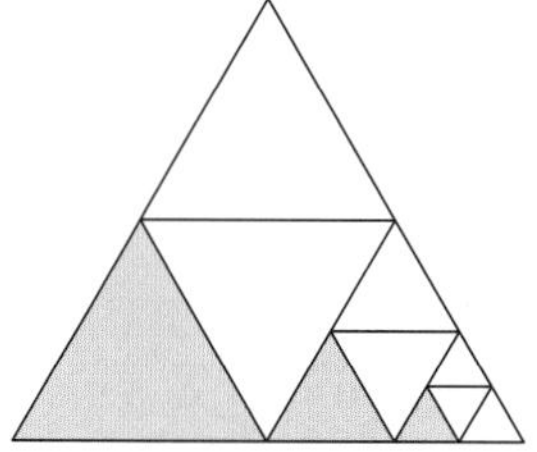

b. @

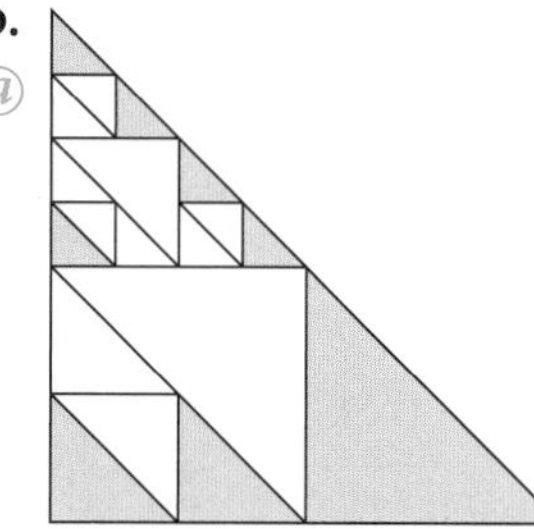

LESSON

0.3

Exponents and Fractions

"The number of distinct scales of length of natural patterns is for all practical purposes infinite."

BENOIT MANDELBROT

In fractals like the Sierpiński triangle, a new enclosed shape is formed at each stage. Not all fractals are formed this way. One example is the *Koch curve,* which is not a smooth curve but a set of connected line segments. It was introduced in 1906 by the Swedish mathematician Niels Fabian Helge von Koch. As you explore the Koch curve and other fractals, you'll continue to work with fractions and exponents.

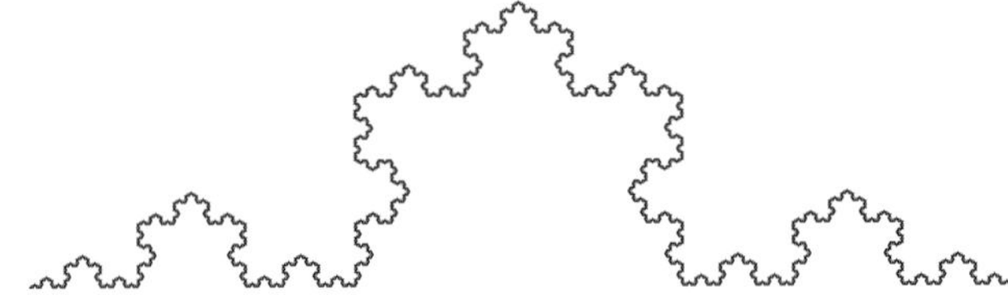

INVESTIGATION

How Long Is This Fractal?

Study how the Koch curve develops. One way to discover a fractal's recursive rule is to determine what happens from one stage to the next. Once you know the rule, you can build, or *generate,* later stages of the figure.

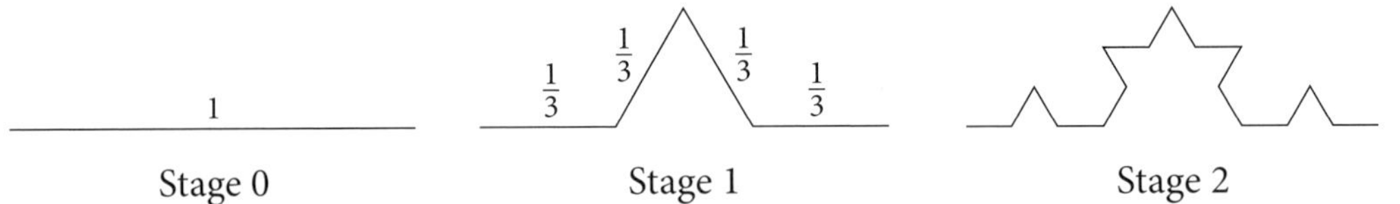

Step 1 Make and complete a table like this for Stages 0 to 2 of the Koch curve shown. How do the lengths change from stage to stage? If you don't see a pattern, try writing the total lengths in different forms.

			Total length (number of segments times length of segments)	
Stage number	Number of segments	Length of each segment	Fraction form	Decimal form
0				

Step 2 Look at Stages 0 and 1. Describe the curve's recursive rule so that someone could re-create the curve from your description.

Step 3 Which is the best estimate of the total length of the Stage 3 figure? Explain.

a. less than 2

b. 2

c. more than 2 but less than 3

d. more than 3 but less than 4

e. 4 or more

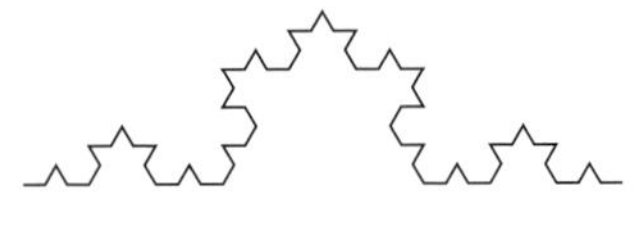

Stage 3

Step 4 Find the length of each small segment at Stage 3 and the total length of the Stage 3 figure.

Step 5 Use exponents to rewrite your numbers in the column labeled "Total length, Fraction form" for Stages 0 to 3.

Step 6 Predict the Stage 4 lengths. Explain your reasoning.

Step 7 Koch was attempting to create a "curve" that was nothing but line segments and angles. Do you think he succeeded? If the curve is formed recursively for many stages, what happens to its length?

Science CONNECTION

Because a coastline, like a fractal curve, is winding and irregular, it is not possible to measure its length accurately. The Koch curve helps geographers understand the structure of coastlines.

At later stages the Koch curve looks smoother and smoother. But if you magnify a section at a later stage, it is just as jagged as at Stage 1. Mandelbrot named figures like this *fractals,* based on the Latin word *fractus,* meaning broken or irregular.

EXAMPLE

Look at these beginning stages of a fractal:

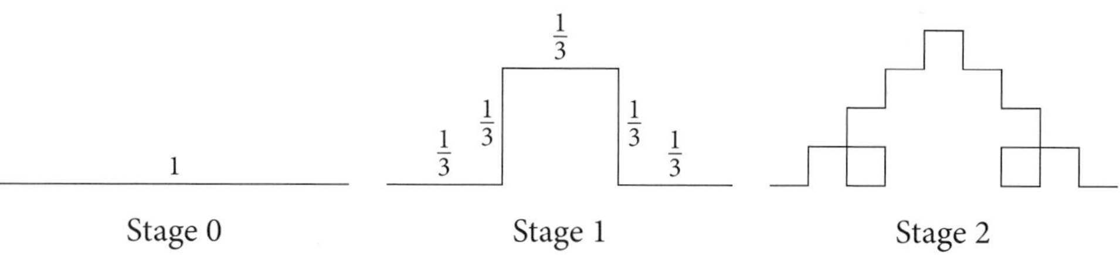

a. Describe the fractal's recursive rule.

b. Find its length at Stage 2.

c. Write an expression for its length at Stage 17.

[▶See the next few stages of this fractal by using the **Dynamic Algebra Exploration** in your ebook.◀]

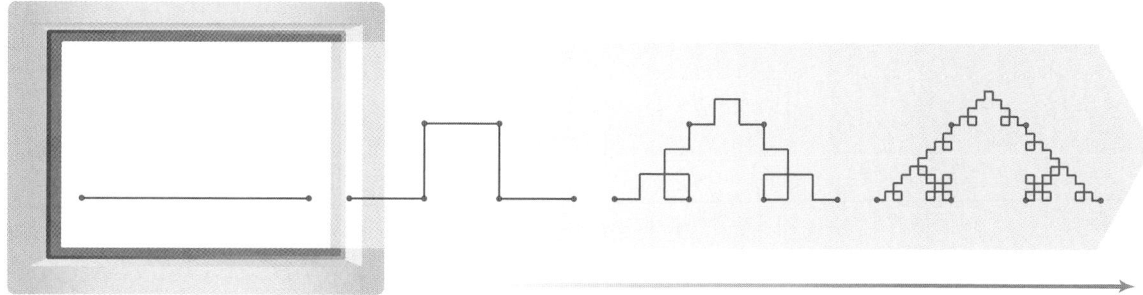

Solution

Don't forget to think through the solution and answer any questions.

a. Compare Stage 0 and Stage 1 to get the recursive rule. To create Stage 1, divide the Stage 0 segment into thirds. Build a square on the middle third and remove the bottom. The same procedure will create Stage 2 from Stage 1, so the recursive rule is "To get to the next stage, divide each segment from the previous stage into thirds and build a bottomless square on the middle third."

b. If you organize the information in a table, you may find patterns. You can use the recursive rule from part a to complete the rows for Stage 0 and Stage 1. (To compare total lengths, it's often easiest to express each length as a decimal rounded to the hundredths place.)

To get to the next stage, you replace each segment with 5 segments. Each new segment is $\frac{1}{3}$ the length of the previous segment. Use this reasoning to complete the row for Stage 2.

			Total length (number of segments times length of segments)	
Stage number	Number of segments	Length of each segment	Fraction form	Decimal form
0	1	1	$1 \cdot 1$	1.00
1	5	$\frac{1}{3}$	$5 \cdot \frac{1}{3} = \frac{5}{3}$	1.67
2	$5 \cdot 5$, or 5^2	$\frac{1}{3} \cdot \frac{1}{3}$, or $\left(\frac{1}{3}\right)^2$	$5^2 \cdot \left(\frac{1}{3}\right)^2$, or $\left(\frac{5}{3}\right)^2$	2.78

c. Look at the patterns developing in the table. How is the stage number related to the exponent? You can now find the length of the Stage 17 figure.

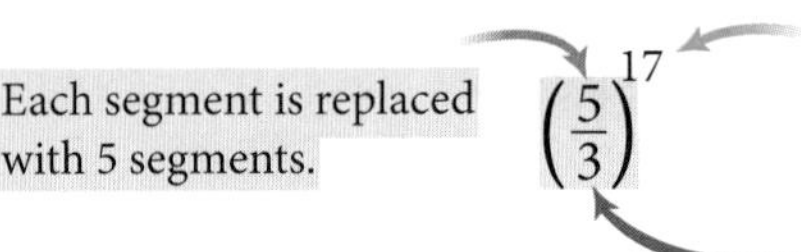

Now you can complete the row for Stage 17.

17	5^{17}	$\left(\frac{1}{3}\right)^{17}$	$\left(\frac{5}{3}\right)^{17}$	5907.84

The example demonstrates an important property of exponents.

Evaluating Fractions with Exponents

To evaluate a fraction with an exponent, apply the exponent to both the numerator and the denominator.

$\left(\frac{a}{b}\right)^3 = \frac{a^3}{b^3}$ **For example,** $\left(\frac{2}{5}\right)^3 = \frac{2^3}{5^3}$

0.3 Exercises

Practice Your Skills

1. Evaluate each expression. Write your answer as a fraction and as a decimal rounded to the nearest hundredth. Remember, if the third digit to the right of the decimal point is 5 or higher, round up.

a. $\frac{5^3}{2^3}$ b. $\left(\frac{5}{3}\right)^2$ @ c. $\left(\frac{7}{3}\right)^4$ d. $\left(\frac{9}{4}\right)^3$

e. $\frac{2^4}{3^4}$ f. $\left(\frac{3}{2}\right)^3$ g. $\left(\frac{4}{9}\right)^3$ h. $\frac{5^4}{4^4}$

2. The fractal from the example is shown. How much longer is the figure at Stage 2 than at Stage 1? Using the table on the previous page, find your answer as a fraction and as a decimal rounded to the nearest hundredth.

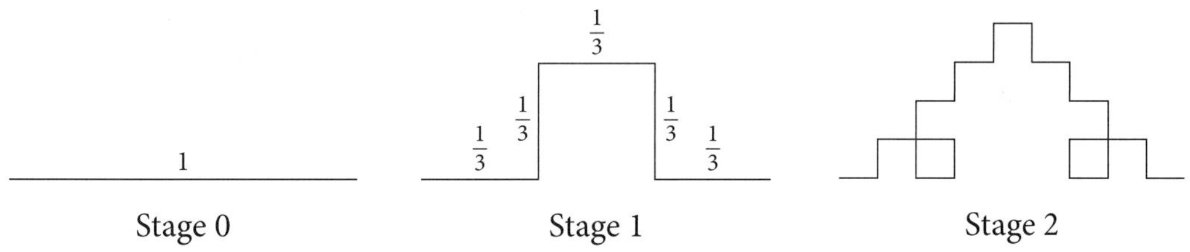

3. At what stage does the figure in Exercise 2 first exceed length 10?

4. Evaluate each expression, and check your results with a calculator.

a. $\frac{1}{5} + \frac{3}{4}$ b. $3^2 + 2^4$ c. $\frac{2}{3} \cdot \left(\frac{6}{5}\right)^2$ d. $4^3 - \frac{2}{5}$

e. $\left(\frac{3}{2}\right)^4$ f. $\frac{1}{5}\left(\frac{2}{5}\right)^3$ g. $3^3 + \frac{1}{4}$ h. $\left(\frac{1}{2}\right)^4 + \left(\frac{1}{4}\right)^2$

Reason and Apply

5. The Stage 0 figure below has length 1 unit. At Stage 1, each segment has length $\frac{1}{4}$ unit.

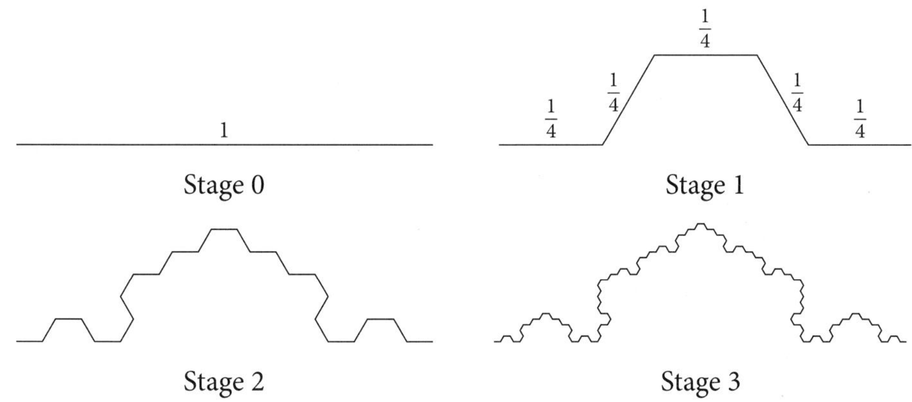

a. Complete a table like the one on the next page by calculating the lengths of the figure at Stages 2 and 3. Give each answer as a fraction in multiplication form, as a fraction in exponent form, and as a decimal rounded to the nearest hundredth. Try to figure out the total lengths at Stages 2 and 3 without counting. (h)

b. Which is the first stage to have a length greater than 3 units? A length greater than 10 units?

	Total length		
Stage number	**Multiplication form**	**Exponent form**	**Decimal form**
0	1	1^0	1.00
1	$5 \cdot \frac{1}{4} = \frac{5}{4}$	$\left(\frac{5}{4}\right)^1$	1.25
2	$5 \cdot 5 \cdot \frac{1}{4} \cdot \frac{1}{4} = \frac{25}{16}$		
3			

6. The Stage 0 figure below has length 1 unit.

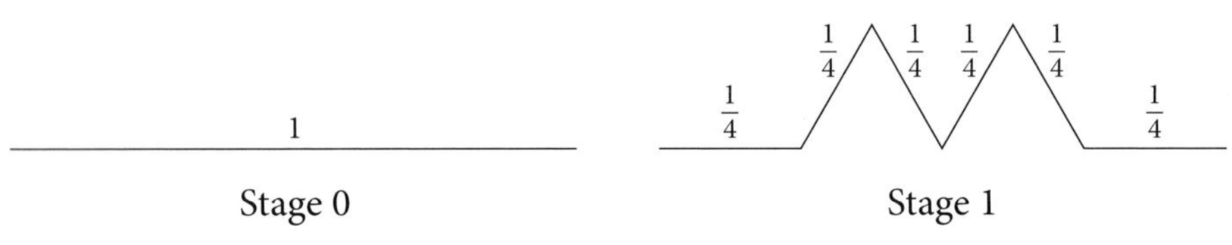

Stage 0 Stage 1

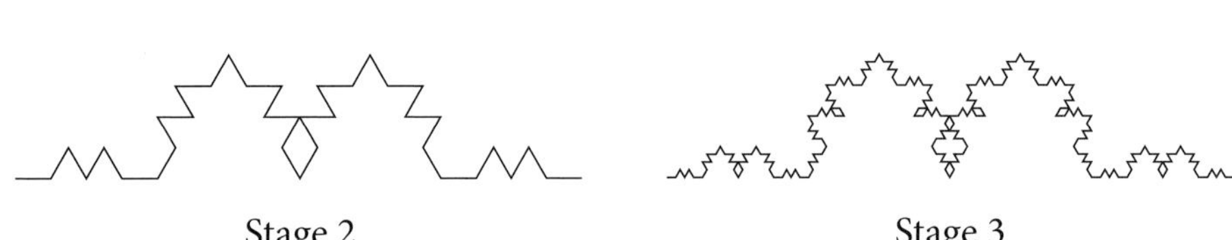

Stage 2 Stage 3

a. Complete a table like this one by calculating the total lengths of the figure at Stages 2 and 3. Give each answer as a fraction in multiplication form, as a fraction in exponent form, and as a decimal rounded to the nearest hundredth.

	Total length		
Stage number	**Multiplication form**	**Exponent form**	**Decimal form**
0	1	1^0	1.00
1	$6 \cdot \frac{1}{4} = \frac{6}{4} = \frac{3}{2}$	$6^1 \cdot \left(\frac{1}{4}\right)^1 = \left(\frac{6}{4}\right)^1 = \left(\frac{3}{2}\right)^1$	1.50
2			
3			

b. At what stage does the figure have length $\frac{243}{32}$ units?

c. At what stage is the length closest to 100 units?

7. The Stage 0 figure below has length 1 unit.

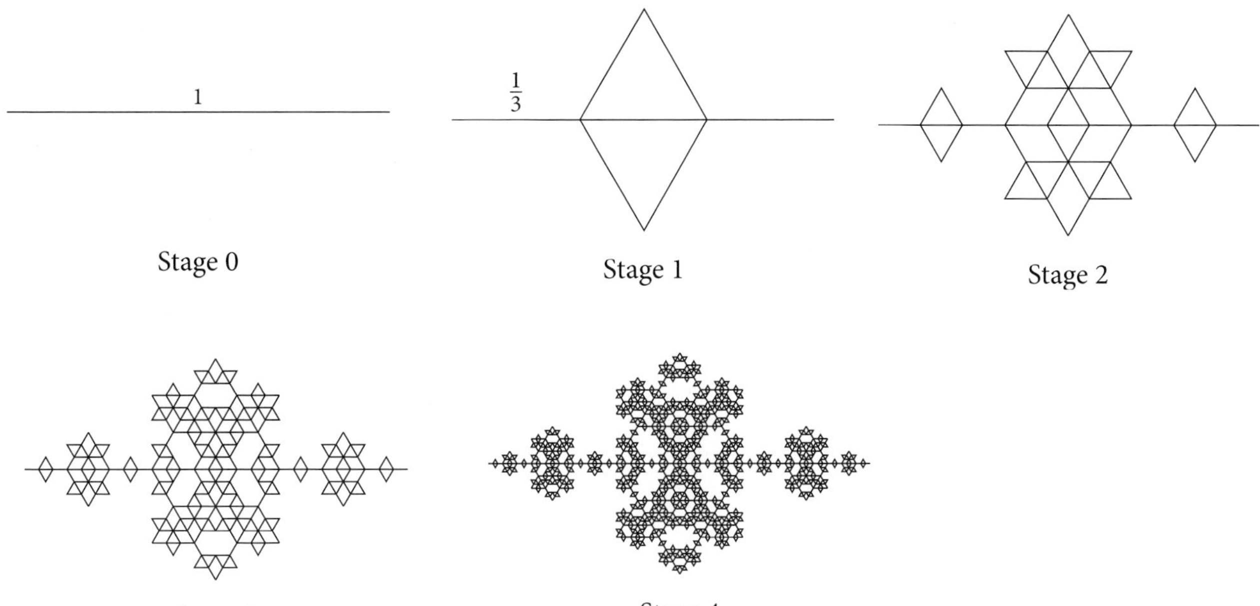

a. Complete a table like this one by calculating the total lengths at Stages 2 to 4. Give each answer as a fraction in multiplication form, as a fraction in exponent form, and as a decimal rounded to the nearest hundredth. Figure out the lengths at Stages 3 and 4 without counting.

	Total length		
Stage number	**Multiplication form**	**Exponent form**	**Decimal form**
0	1	1^0	1.00
1	$7 \cdot \frac{1}{3} = \frac{7}{3}$	$7^1 \cdot \left(\frac{1}{3}\right)^1 = \left(\frac{7}{3}\right)^1$	2.33
2			
3			
4			

b. At what stage does the figure have length $\frac{16{,}807}{243}$ units?

c. Will the figure ever have length 168 units? If so, at what stage? If not, why not?

Review

8. Write a word problem or draw a diagram that illustrates the multiplication expression $\frac{3}{4} \cdot \frac{1}{5}$.

9. Write $\frac{14}{5}$ as a decimal.

10. Suppose you need to buy $3\frac{2}{3}$ yd of fabric that costs \$3.99 per yard. You have \$15 in your wallet. Which reasoning is best for estimating whether you have enough money to buy the fabric?

a. The fabric costs about \$4 per yard. I need almost 5 yd, so it will cost just a little less than \$20. I probably don't have enough money.

b. The fabric costs about \$4 per yard. I need between 3 and 4 yd, so it will cost between \$12 and \$16. I might have enough money, but I can't tell without actually calculating the exact cost.

c. The fabric costs about \$4 per yard. Three yards will cost \$12, and 4 yd will cost \$16. So $3\frac{1}{2}$ yd will cost \$14. I need a little more than this, so I probably have enough money.

11. Look at this fractal "cross" pattern. At each stage, new line segments are drawn through the existing segments to create crosses.

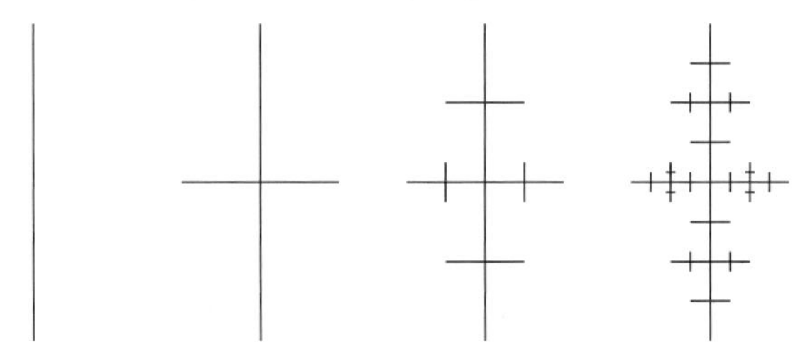

Stage 0 Stage 1 Stage 2 Stage 3

a. How many new segments are drawn at Stage 2? @

b. How many new segments are drawn at Stage 3?

c. How many new segments would be drawn at Stage 4?

d. Use exponents to represent the number of new segments drawn at Stages 2 to 4.

e. In general, how is the exponent related to the stage number for Stages 2 to 4? Does this rule apply to Stage 1?

LESSON

0.4

Operations with Signed Numbers

Leslie was playing miniature golf with her friends. First she hit the ball past the hole. Then she hit it back, but it went too far and missed again. She kept hitting the ball closer, but it still missed the hole. Finally she got so close that the ball fell in.

Some recursive number processes also get closer and closer to a final target until the result is so close that the number rounds to the target value or answer. You'll explore processes like these while reviewing operations with positive and negative numbers.

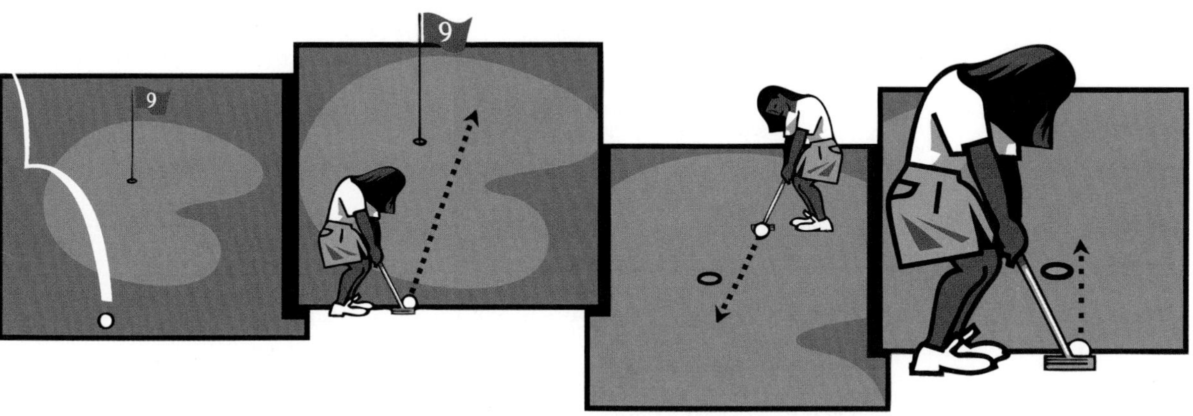

One way to investigate getting closer and closer is through graphs. In this course you will make and interpret many graphs. You can use graphs to see relationships or patterns that might not be clear if you looked only at the corresponding numbers or equations. One of the simplest graphs is a number-line graph. A **number line** allows you to order numbers. The values of the numbers increase as you move along the line from left to right. In the investigation you will use a number line to explore numbers that get closer to a target.

INVESTIGATION

A Strange Attraction

Step 1 Each member of your group should use one of these four expressions:

$2 \cdot \square + 1 \qquad 3 \cdot \square - 4 \qquad -2 \cdot \square + 3 \qquad -3 \cdot \square - 1$

Step 2 As a group, choose a starting number. Record your expression and starting number in a table like the one shown.

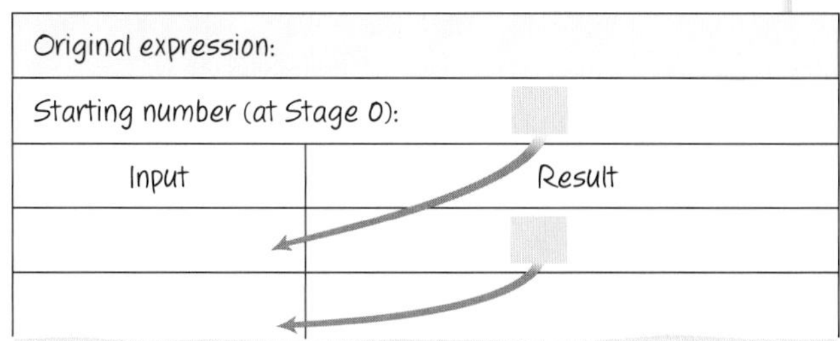

Original expression:	
Starting number (at Stage 0):	
Input	Result

Step 3 Put your starting number in the box, and do the computation. This process is called **evaluating the expression,** and the result is the **value of the expression.** Should you multiply first, or should you add or subtract first? Check your answer with a calculator, and record it in the table as your first result. [► See **Calculator Note: Negation and Subtraction** to learn about the difference between the negative key and the subtraction key. ◄]

Step 4 Take the result from Step 3, put it in the box in your expression, and evaluate your expression again. Place your new result in the table as your second result.

Step 5 Continue this recursive process, each time using your result from the previous stage as your input. Evaluate your expression. Each time, record the new result in your table. Do this ten times.

Step 6 Draw a number line, and scale it so that you can show the first five results listed in your table. Plot the first result from your table, and draw an arrow to the next result to show how the value of the expression changes. For example,

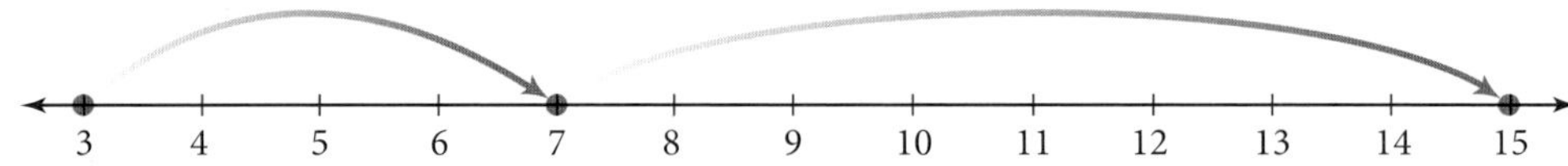

Step 7 How do the results in your group compare?

Step 8 Repeat Steps 1 to 6 with one of these expressions:

$0.5 \cdot \square - 3 \qquad 0.2 \cdot \square + 1 \qquad -0.5 \cdot \square + 3 \qquad -0.2 \cdot \square - 2$

Step 9 How do the results in your group compare? Do the results of evaluating these expressions differ from the results of evaluating your first expression?

In the investigation, you explored what happens when you recursively evaluate an expression. First you selected a starting number to put into your expression, and then you evaluated the expression. Then you put your result back into the same expression and evaluated the expression again. Calculators and computers are good tools for doing these repetitive operations.

EXAMPLE A What happens when you evaluate the expression $-2 + 0.5 \cdot \square$ recursively with different starting numbers?

Solution

Have your pencil and calculator in hand as you work through the solution to this example.

Choosing the starting number 1 gives the result shown here.

Original expression: $-2 + 0.5 \cdot \square$	
Starting number:	1
Input	Result
1	$-2 + 0.5 \cdot 1 = -2 + 0.5 = -1.5$
-1.5	$-2 + 0.5 \cdot (-1.5) = -2 + (-0.75) = -2.75$
-2.75	$-2 + 0.5 \cdot (-2.75) = -2 + (-1.375) = -3.375$
-3.375	$-2 + 0.5 \cdot (-3.375) = -2 + (-1.6875) = -3.6875$
-3.6875	$-2 + 0.5 \cdot (-3.6875) = -2 + (-1.84375) = -3.84375$

Each result of the recursion seems to get closer to a certain number. If you continue the process a few more times, you'll get approximately -3.9219, then -3.9609, then -3.9805. What do you think will happen after even more recursions?

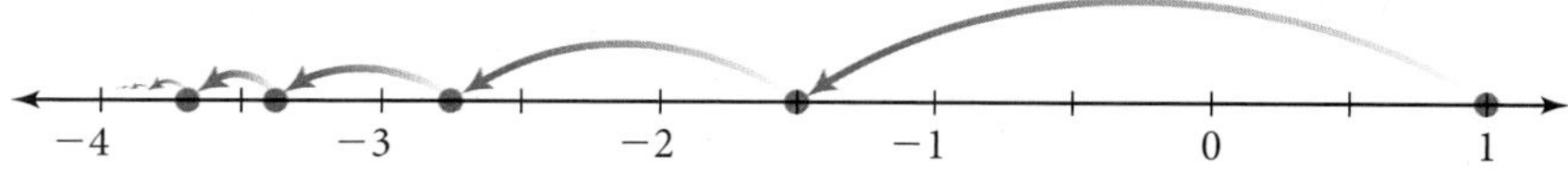

Using 6 as a starting number in the same expression, you get these results:

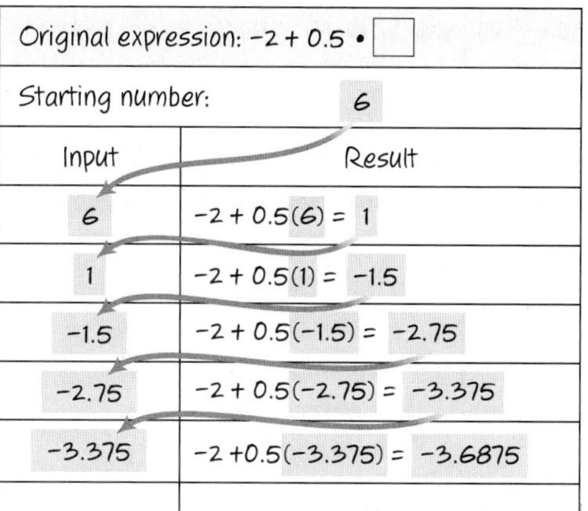

Original expression: $-2 + 0.5 \cdot \square$	
Starting number:	6
Input	Result
6	$-2 + 0.5(6) = 1$
1	$-2 + 0.5(1) = -1.5$
-1.5	$-2 + 0.5(-1.5) = -2.75$
-2.75	$-2 + 0.5(-2.75) = -3.375$
-3.375	$-2 + 0.5(-3.375) = -3.6875$

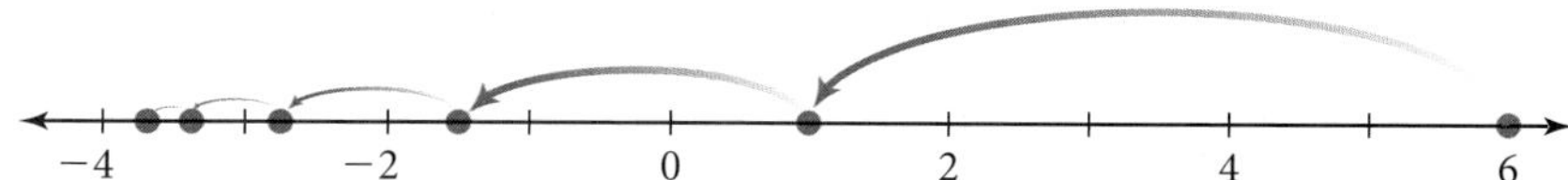

Again the values seem to get closer to one number, perhaps -4. If any starting number that you try (other than -4) eventually gets closer and closer to -4, then -4 is called an **attractor value** for this expression.

Now try using -4 as the starting number.

Using -4 as the starting number gives

$$-2 + 0.5 \cdot (-4) = -2 + (-2) = -4$$

Because you get back exactly what you started with, -4 is also called a **fixed point** for the expression $-2 + 0.5 \cdot \square$.

How do you know whether to multiply before adding or subtracting? In mathematics there is an agreed-upon order of doing things.

Order of Operations

1. **Evaluate all expressions within parentheses.**
2. **Evaluate all exponents.**
3. **Multiply and divide from left to right.**
4. **Add and subtract from left to right.**

The next example shows you how to apply this order of operations.

EXAMPLE B

Evaluate each expression.

a. $3 - 4 \cdot (5)^2$

b. $2 + \frac{10}{5} \cdot 4$

c. $(2 - 8)^2 - 2 \cdot -3$

Solution

To evaluate these expressions, you need to follow the order of operations.

a.

$3 - 4 \cdot (5)^2 = 3 - 4 \cdot 25$	Evaluate the exponent first.
$= 3 - 100$	Multiply.
$= -97$	Subtract.

b. Multiplication and division are done in order from left to right.

$2 + \frac{10}{5} \cdot 4 = 2 + 2 \cdot 4$	Divide.
$= 2 + 8$	Multiply.
$= 10$	Add.

c. The parentheses indicate that the exponent applies to -6, not just 6. You will need to enter parentheses if you use your calculator to evaluate powers of negative numbers.

$(2 - 8)^2 - 2 \cdot -3 = (-6)^2 - 2 \cdot -3$	Evaluate the expression within the parentheses first.
$= 36 - 2 \cdot -3$	Evaluate the exponent.
$= 36 - (-6)$	Multiply.
$= 42$	Subtract.

0.4 Exercises

Practice Your Skills

1. Do each calculation and use a calculator to check your results. Then use a number line to illustrate your answer.

a. $-4 + 7$ b. $5 + -8$ c. $-2 - 5$ d. $-6 - (-3)$

e. $-5 - 2 + 9$ f. $-6 + 4 - 11$ g. $4 + -7 - 7$ h. $9 - (-2) + (-4)$

2. Do each calculation and use a calculator to check your results.

a. $-2 \cdot 5$

b. $6 \cdot -4$

c. $-3 \cdot -4$

d. $-12 \div 3$

e. $36 \div -6$

f. $-50 \div -5$

g. $-4 \cdot 3 \div -2$

h. $24 \div -8 \cdot -3$

i. $-30 \div -5 \div -2$

3. Do each calculation. Check your results by entering the expression into your calculator exactly as it is shown.

a. $5 \cdot -4 - 2 \cdot -6$

b. $3 + -4 \cdot 7$

c. $-2 - 5 \cdot (6 + -3)$

d. $(-3 - 5) \cdot -2 + 9 \cdot -3$

4. Do each calculation, paying careful attention to the order of operations. Check your results by entering the expression into your calculator exactly as it is shown.

a. $4 \cdot 3 - 5^2 + 7$

b. $-3^4 + 2^3 \cdot 5 - (4 - 7)$

c. $(12 - 5^2) - (4 \cdot -3 + 7)$

d. $-7^2 - 4 \cdot -2 + 3(-5)$

5. Match each number-line diagram to the expression it illustrates. State the value of each expression.

a. $8 + -6$

b. $-8 + -6$

c. $8 - (-6)$

d. $-8 - 6$

e. $-8 - (-6)$

i.

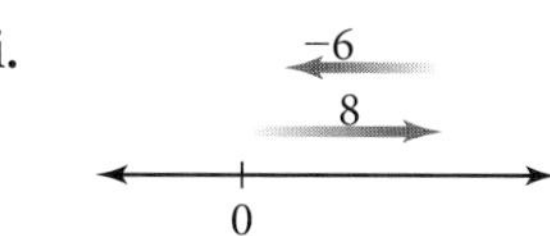

ii.

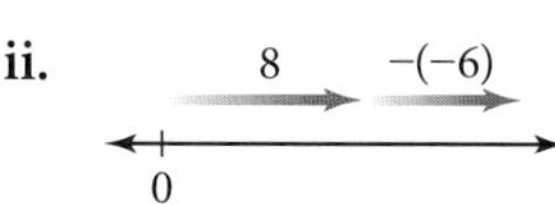

iii.

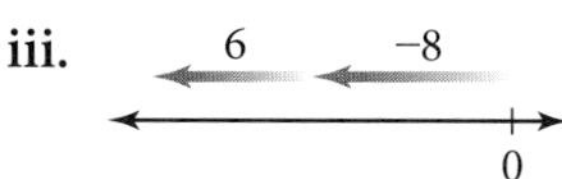

iv.

−6 −8

0

v.

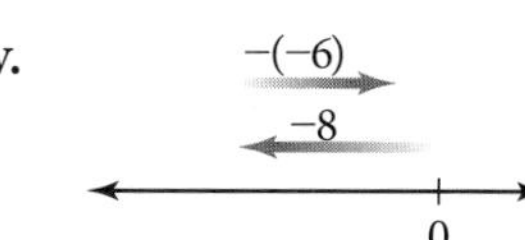

Reason and Apply

6. Explain how to do each operation described, and state whether the result is a positive or a negative number.

a. adding two negative numbers

b. adding a negative number and a positive number @

c. subtracting a negative number from a positive number

d. subtracting a negative number from a negative number

e. multiplying a negative number by a positive number

f. multiplying two negative numbers

g. dividing a positive number by a negative number

h. dividing two negative numbers

7. Pete Repeat was recursively evaluating this expression, starting with 2.

$-0.2 \cdot \square - 4$

a. Check his first two stages and describe what, if anything, he did wrong. ⓐ

$-0.2 \cdot 2 - 4 = 0.4 - 4 = -3.6$

$-0.2 \cdot -3.6 - 4 = -0.72 - 4 = -4.72$

b. Redo Pete's first two stages and do two more.

c. Now do three recursions starting with -1.

d. Do you think this expression has an attractor value? Explain.

8. To tell whether an expression has an attractor value, you often have to look at the results of several different starting values.

a. Evaluate this expression for different starting values:

$0.1 \cdot \square - 2$

Record the results for several recursions (stages) in a table like the one shown. ⓐ

Starting value	2	-1	10
First recursion			
Second recursion			
Third recursion			
⋮			

b. Based on your table, do you think this expression reaches an attractor value in the long run? If so, what is it? If not, why not? ⓐ

c. If you found an attractor value in 8b, use your calculator to see if substituting that value into the expression gives it back to you.

9. Investigate this expression:

$-2 \cdot \square + 1$

Starting value	2	-1	10
First recursion			
Second recursion			
Third recursion			
⋮			

a. Evaluate the expression for different starting values. Record your results in a table like the one shown.

b. Based on your table, do you think this expression reaches an attractor value in the long run? If so, what is it? If not, why not?

c. Try the starting value $\frac{1}{3}$. What is the result? What is the value $\frac{1}{3}$ called for this expression? ⓐ

10. MINI-INVESTIGATION Expressions like $\square^2 - 2$ can have a variety of results when evaluated recursively. [▸ See **Calculator Note: Recursion** to learn how to do recursion on your calculator. ◂]

a. Evaluate $\square^2 - 2$ recursively, starting with -1. Describe what happens.

b. Evaluate $\square^2 - 2$ recursively, starting with 3. Describe what happens.

c. Evaluate $\square^2 - 2$ recursively, starting with -2. Describe what happens.

d. Choose at least three other starting values and evaluate $\square^2 - 2$ recursively. Describe what happens.

e. Based on 10a–d, what are the attractor values for this expression?

11. How is the recursion process like drawing the Sierpiński triangle in Lesson 0.1 or like creating the Koch curve in Lesson 0.3?

12. Determine the missing value in each equation.

a. $-3(-5) + 6 = \square$

b. $0.2(-14) - (-3) = \square$ @

c. $\square + \frac{2}{3}(-9) = 7$

d. $\frac{\square}{0.5} - 6 = 0$ @

e. $\square - \frac{2}{3}(-6) = 10$

f. $\frac{10}{\square} - 3 = 2$

Review

13. What is $4 - 12 \div 4 \cdot \frac{1}{2} - 5^2$?

14. Find $(-3 \cdot -4) - (-4 \cdot 2)$.

15. What is $\frac{3}{8} - \frac{1}{2} + \left(\frac{3}{4}\right)^2$?

IMPROVING YOUR Reasoning SKILLS

As the Koch curve develops, the length of each segment decreases as the number of segments increases.

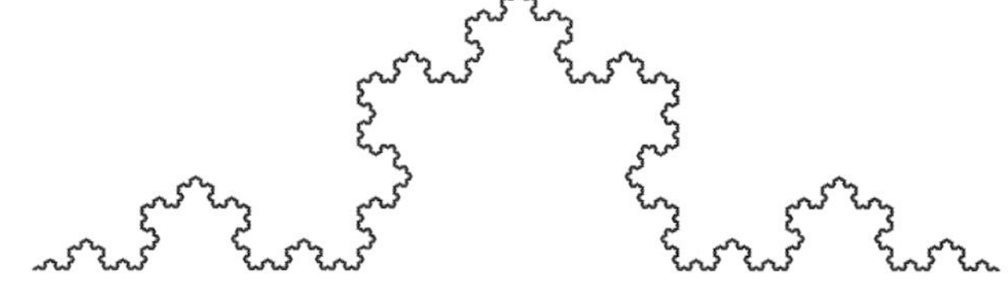

As you draw higher stages, the length of individual segments approaches, or gets closer and closer to, what number? What number does the number of line segments approach? Is it possible to draw the "finished" fractal? Why or why not? What would its total length be?

Now consider this pattern of polygons inscribed in circles:

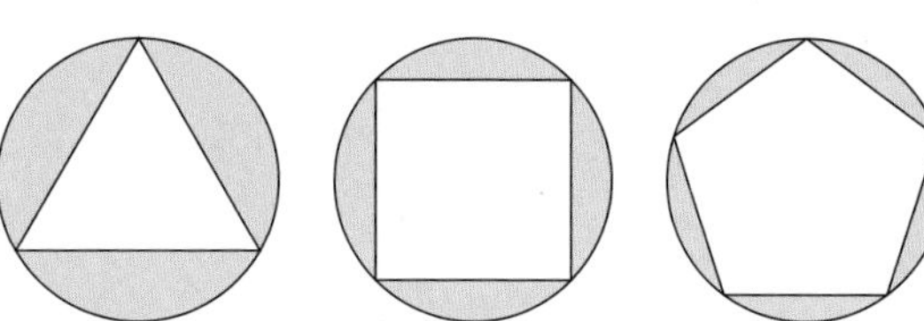

As you draw higher and higher stages, what does the length of each polygon side approach? What number does the number of sides approach? Is it possible to draw the "finished" polygon? If so, what would it look like? What would the total perimeter of the polygon be? Is this pattern recursive? Is the result a fractal? Why or why not?

LESSON 0.5

ACTIVITY DAY

"Nothing in nature is random....A thing appears random only through the incompleteness of our knowledge."
BARUCH SPINOZA

Out of Chaos

If you looked at the results of 100 rolls of a die, would you expect to find a pattern in the numbers? You might expect each number to appear about one-sixth of the time. But would you expect to see a pattern, for example, in the times when a 5 appears? You could not create a method to predict exactly when a 5 appears. It appears **randomly,** without order.

Many events that seem irregular and chaotic occur in nature and in our own lives. In this activity you'll take a look at one random process, rolling a die. You'll see if you can find any patterns when the rolls are interpreted as directions for a recursive process.

ACTIVITY

YOU WILL NEED
- a die
- a centimeter ruler
- document camera or a blank transparency and marker

A Chaotic Pattern?

What happens if you use a random process recursively to determine where you draw a point? Would you expect to see a pattern?

Work with a partner. One partner rolls the die. The other measures distance and marks points.

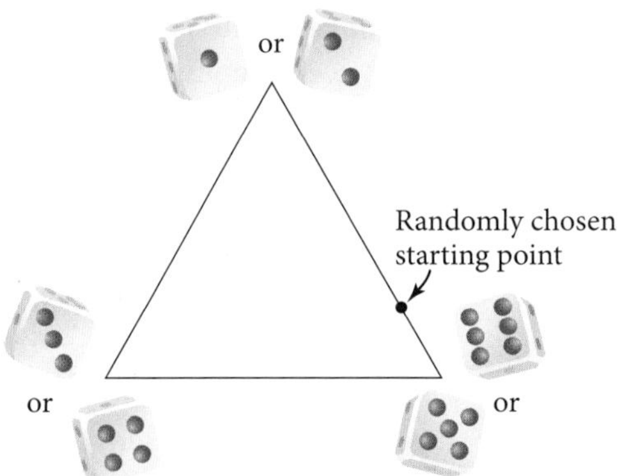

Step 1 Mark any point on the triangle as your starting point.

Step 2 Roll the die.

Step 3 In centimeters, measure the distance from your point to the corner, or *vertex,* labeled above with the number of dots, or pips, showing on the die. Mark a point halfway between your previous point and the vertex. This is your new point. Remember to measure accurately to get the best results.

Step 4 Repeat Steps 2 and 3 until you've rolled the die 20 times. Then switch roles with your partner and repeat the process 20 times. Remember to place the new point halfway between the previous point and the chosen vertex each time.

Step 5 How is this process recursive?

Step 6 Describe the arrangement of points.

Step 7 What would have happened if you had numbered the vertices of the triangle 1 and 3, 2 and 5, and 4 and 6?

Step 8 Place a transparency or patty paper over your drawing. Use a transparency marker and mark the vertices of the triangle. Carefully trace your points onto the transparency or patty paper.

Step 9 When you finish, use a document camera or overhead projector to display your work. Align the vertices of your triangle with the vertices of your classmates' triangles. This will allow you to see the results of many rolls of a die. Describe what happens when you combine everyone's points. How is this like the result in other recursion processes? Is the result as random as you expected? Explain.

Most people are surprised that after they plot many points, a familiar figure appears. When an orderly result appears out of a random process like this one, the figure is a *strange attractor.* No matter where you start, the points "fall" toward this shape. The shape acts like the attractor values in Lesson 0.4. It probably took many points to see the pattern in the investigation. Calculators can be programmed to do such recursive processes quickly and efficiently. [▶ See **Calculator Note: Chaos Game** to learn how to play The Chaos Game. Then use the link in your ebook to download the program file CHAOS. To learn how to link calculators, see **Calculator Note: Transferring Programs and Lists.** ◀]

In the activity a *random process* produced ordered-looking results. Sometimes, though, orderly processes can produce random-looking results. Mathematicians use the term *chaotic* to describe systematic, nonrandom processes that produce results that appear random. Chaos theory helps scientists understand, for example, the turbulent flow of water, the mixing of chemicals, and the spread of an oil spill.

The growth and movement of an oil spill may appear random, but scientists can use chaos theory to predict its boundaries. This can help with control and cleanup of the spill.

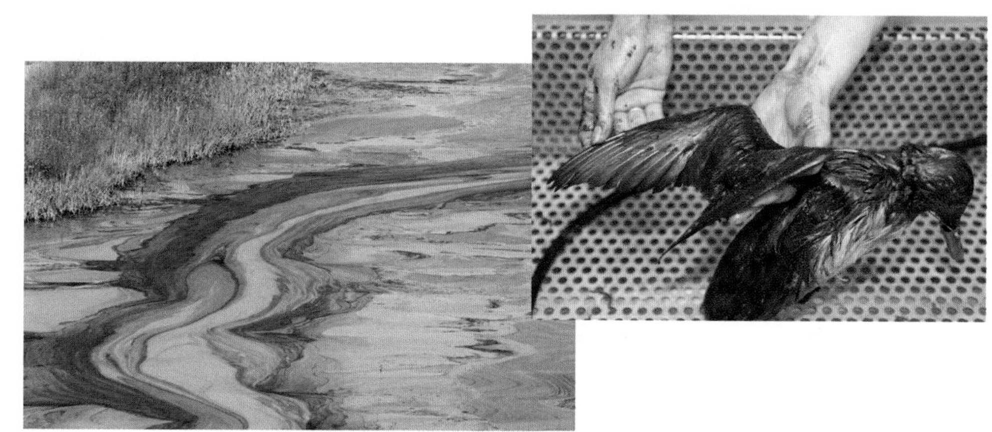

CHAPTER 0 REVIEW

In this chapter you saw many instances of how you can start with a figure or a number, apply a mathematical rule, get a result, and then apply the same rule to the result. This is called **recursion,** and it led you to find patterns in the results. When the recursive rule involved multiplication, you used an **exponent** as a shorthand way to show repeated multiplication.

Patterns in the results of recursion were often easier to see when you left them as common fractions. To add and subtract fractions, you needed a common denominator. You also needed to round decimals and measure lengths.

To **evaluate expressions** with any kind of numbers, you needed to know the **order of operations** that mathematicians use. The order is (1) evaluate what is in parentheses, (2) evaluate all exponents, (3) multiply and divide as needed, and (4) add and subtract as needed. You used your knowledge of operations (add, subtract, multiply, divide, raise to a power) to write several expressions that represented the same number. Having an expression for a recursive rule helped you predict a value later in a sequence without figuring out all the values in between.

In this chapter you also got a peek at some mathematics that are new even to mathematicians, including **fractals** like the Sierpiński triangle, attractor values, and chaos. You had to think about **random** processes and whether the long-term outcome of these processes was truly random.

Exercises

@ **Answers are provided for all exercises in this set.**

1. Match equivalent expressions.

a. $\frac{1}{9}+\frac{1}{9}+\frac{1}{9}$ b. $\frac{1}{9}+\frac{1}{9}+\frac{1}{3}$ c. $\frac{2}{9}+\frac{1}{9}+\frac{1}{27}$ d. $\frac{4}{9}+\frac{2}{27}+\frac{3}{81}$ e. $\frac{2}{81}+\frac{1}{3}+\frac{2}{27}$

i. $\frac{35}{81}$ ii. $\frac{10}{27}$ iii. $3\times\frac{1}{9}$ iv. $\frac{12}{27}+\frac{2}{27}+\frac{1}{27}$ v. $2\times\left(\frac{1}{9}\right)+\frac{1}{3}$

2. Evaluate these expressions.

a. $2\times(24+12)$ b. $2+24\times12$ c. $2-24+12$

d. $(2+24)\times12$ e. $(2+24)\div12$ f. $2-(24+12)$

3. Write a multiplication expression equivalent to each expression in exponent form.

a. $\left(\frac{1}{3}\right)^3$ b. $\left(\frac{2}{3}\right)^4$ c. $(1.2)^2$ d. 16^5 e. 2^7

4. Write an addition expression that gives the total shaded area in each figure. Then evaluate the expression. The area of each original figure is 1 square unit.

a. 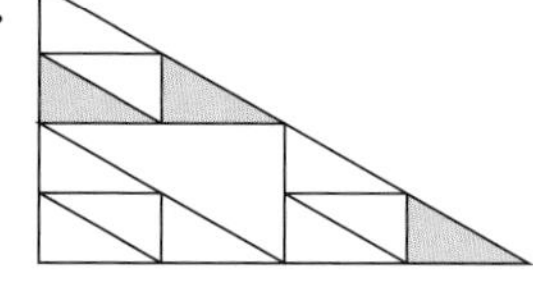

b. 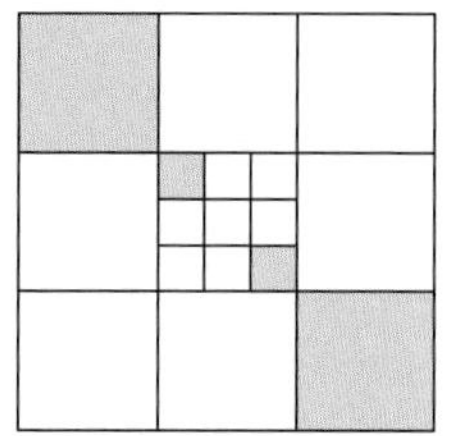

c. 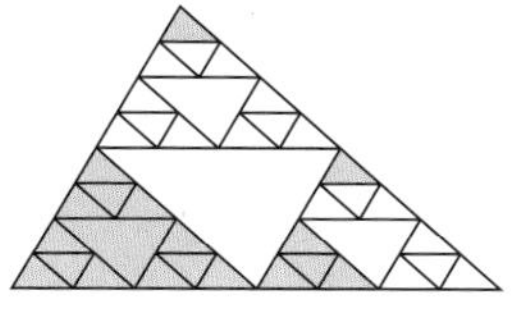

5. Do these calculations. Check your results with a calculator.

a. $-2 + 5 - (-7)$

b. $(-3)^2 - (-2)^3$

c. $\frac{3}{5} + \frac{-2}{3}$

d. $-0.2 \cdot 20 + 15$

e. $4 - 6(-2)$

f. $7 - 4(2 - 5)$

g. $-2\frac{1}{3} - 4\frac{1}{6}$

6. Draw the next stage of each fractal design. Then describe the recursive rule for each pattern in words.

a.

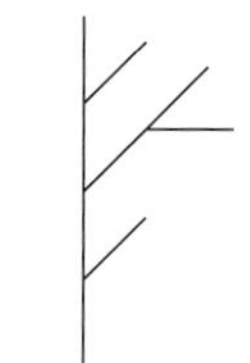

Stage 0 Stage 1 Stage 2

b.

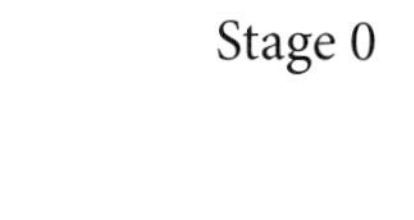

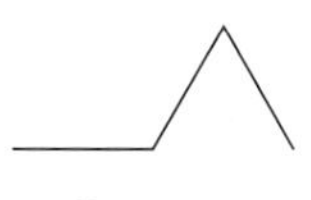

Stage 0 Stage 1 Stage 2

c.

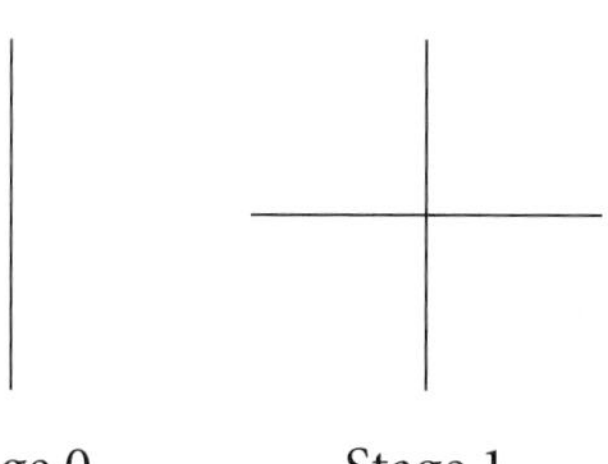

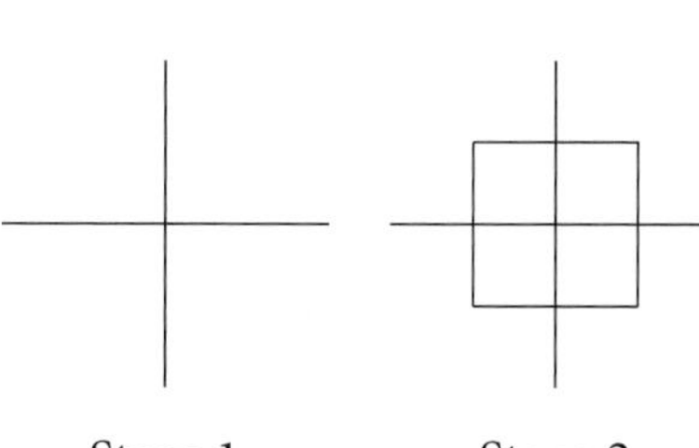

Stage 0 Stage 1 Stage 2

d.

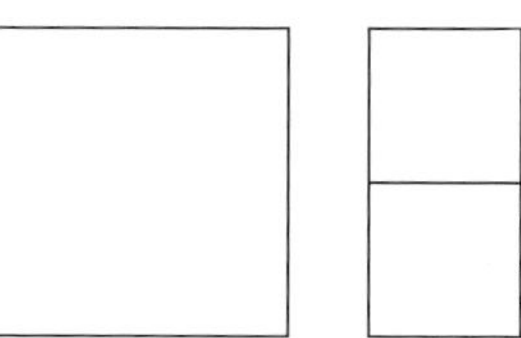

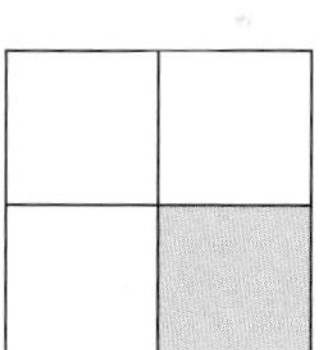

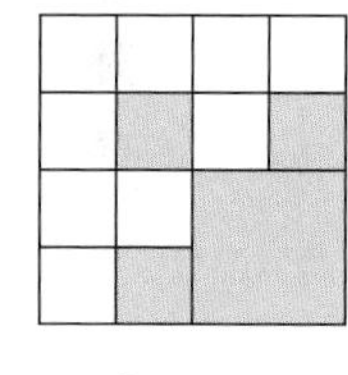

Stage 0 Stage 1 Stage 2

7. Investigate the behavior of this expression. Use recursion to evaluate the expression several times for different starting values. You might want to record your recursions in a table. Does the expression appear to have an attractor value?

$0.4 \cdot \square + 3$

8. Look at these figures.

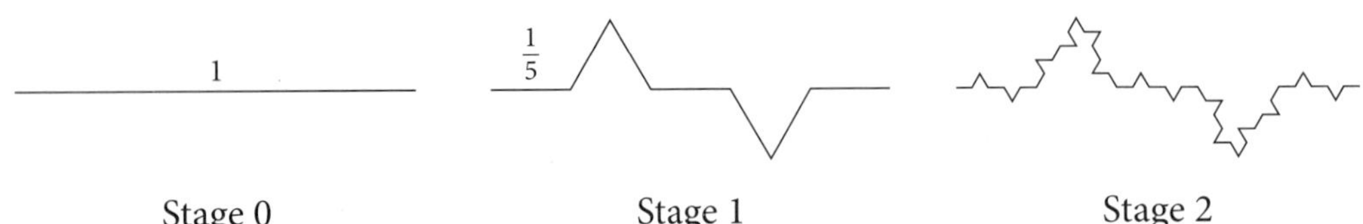

Stage 0 Stage 1 Stage 2

a. Complete a table like this one.

	Total length		
Stage number	**Multiplication form**	**Exponent form**	**Decimal form**
0			
1			
2			

b. If you were to draw Stage 20, what expression with an exponent could you write to represent the total length? Evaluate this expression by using your calculator, and round the answer to the nearest hundredth.

Take Another Look

- If a number gets larger when it is raised to a power, what kind of number is it?
- If a number gets smaller when it is raised to a power, what kind of number is it?
- What numbers stay the same when they are raised to a power?

To investigate these questions, choose positive and negative numbers, zero, and positive and negative fractions to put into the box, and evaluate the expressions

$\square^3$ and $\square^4$

You might want to use a table like the one at right to save your results.

$\square$	$\square^3$
1	$1^3 = 1$
2	$2^3 = 8$

You know that if the denominator of a fraction increases, the value of the fraction decreases. Why is that? Are there any exceptions?

Look again at your results for the expression $\square^3$. What would the numerator of the fraction have to be so that $\frac{\bigcirc}{\square^3}$ is smaller than $\square^3$? Greater than $\square^3$?

Now do the same thing with $\frac{\bigcirc}{\square^4}$. Display your results in a table.

Assessing What You've Learned

BEGIN YOUR PORTFOLIO If you look up *assess* in a dictionary, you'll find that it means to estimate or judge the value of something. The value you've gained by the end of a chapter is not what you studied but what you remember and what you feel confident about. You may not remember some ideas but you will be able to reconstruct them in appropriate situations. That's mathematical confidence.

One way to hold on to the value you've gained is to start a portfolio. Like an artist's portfolio, a mathematics portfolio shows off what you can do. It also collects work that you found interesting or rewarding (even if it isn't a masterpiece!). It also reminds you of ideas worth pursuing. The fractal designs that you figured out or invented are worth collecting and showing. Your study of patterns in fractals is a rich example of investigative mathematics that is also a good reference for how to work with fractions and exponents.

Choose one or more pieces of your work for your portfolio. Your teacher may have specific suggestions. Document each piece with a paragraph that answers these questions:

- What is this piece an example of?
- Does it represent your best work? Why else did you choose it?
- What mathematics did you learn or gain confidence in with this work?
- How would you improve the piece if you wanted to redo it?

Portfolios are an ongoing and ever-changing display of your work and growth. As you finish other chapters, remember to update your portfolio with new work.

CHAPTER 1 Data Exploration

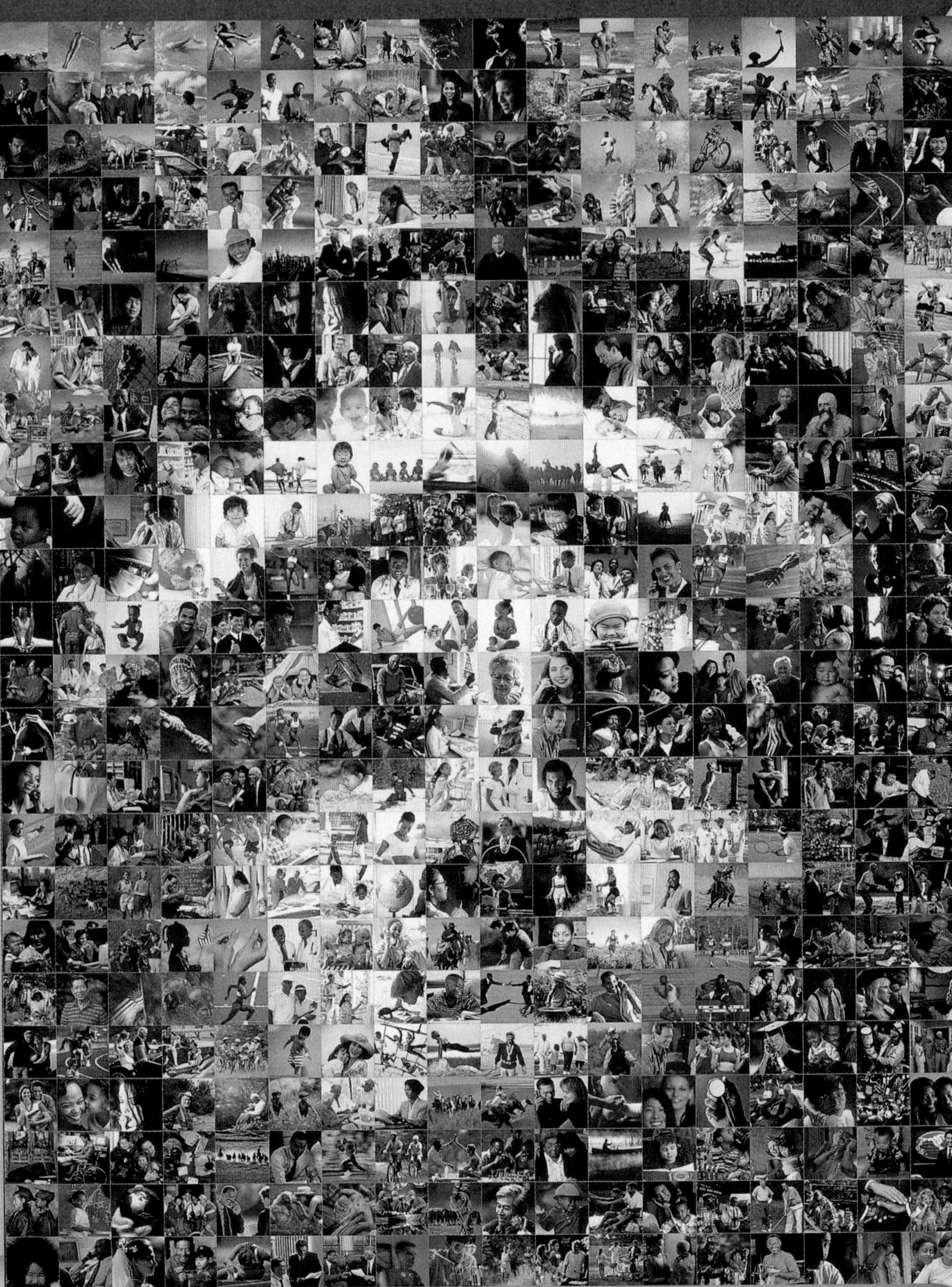

You are surrounded by information in many forms—in pictures, in graphs, in words, and in numbers. This information can influence what you eat, what you buy, and what you think of the world around you. This photo collage by Robert Silvers shows a lot of information.

OBJECTIVES

In this chapter you will

- interpret and compare a variety of graphs
- find summary values for a data set
- draw conclusions about a data set based on graphs and summary values
- create and interpret relative frequency graphs
- use statistics to compare center and spread of two or more data sets

Number-Line Graphs

Plotting a single value on a number line is not a difficult task because there is no need to consider placement, scale, and where your number line starts and stops. But if you need to plot two or more values on the same line, you must consider placement, scale, and where your number line starts and stops. The number line is infinitely long and holds all real values, so when you draw a representation, put an arrow on each end. Yours should focus attention on the values you are graphing. For example, you would not use the same graph to plot the values −3 and 5 as you would to plot only the values 1997 and 2012.

EXAMPLE A Identify an error in each of these number-line graphs.

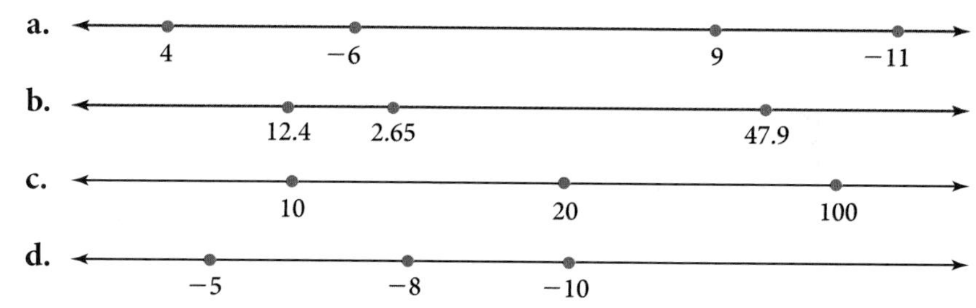

Solution

a. The negative values should be to the left of the positive values.

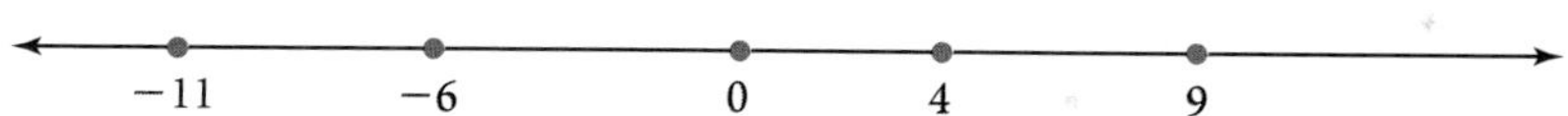

b. The value 12.4 should be between 2.65 and 47.9 and closer to 2.65 than to 47.9.

c. The gap between 20 and 100 should be eight times as large as the gap between 10 and 20.

d. Smaller numbers go to the left of larger numbers. −10 is smaller than −8, which is smaller than −5.

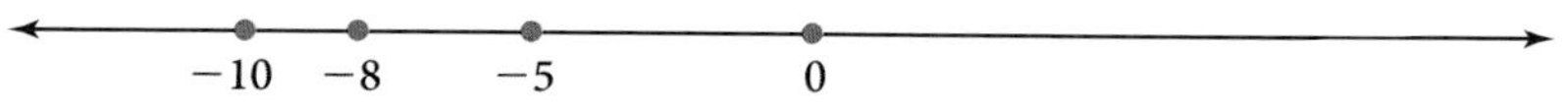

Before you begin plotting values on a number line, you need to think about the range of values to be plotted. Identify the smallest value (minimum) and the largest value (maximum). Use this range to mark an appropriate interval, and then use your markings to place your values.

EXAMPLE B

Your class has collected temperatures at six airports. Describe the steps you would take to create a number-line graph of these data.

Aalborg, Denmark (AAL): 55°F

Anchorage, Alaska (ANC): −12°F

Boston, Massachusetts (BOS): 62°F

Bangalore, India (BLR): 72°F

Cap Haitien, Haiti (CAP): 94°F

Casper, Wyoming (CPR): 47°F

Solution

The temperatures vary from −12°F to 94°F, a range of 106°. If you were to mark every degree, the graph would have 106 marks. Marking every 10° would use 13 marks, still too many. A mark at multiples of 20° is about right.

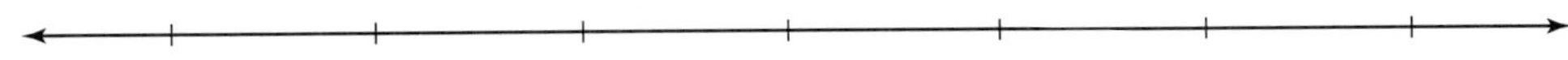

There should be one mark to the left of the lowest data value. This means that the left-most mark is at −20. There should be one mark to the right of the highest data value. This means that the right-most mark is at 100.

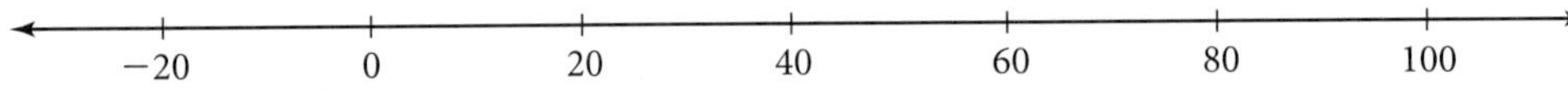

Now plot the points within the intervals you've set.

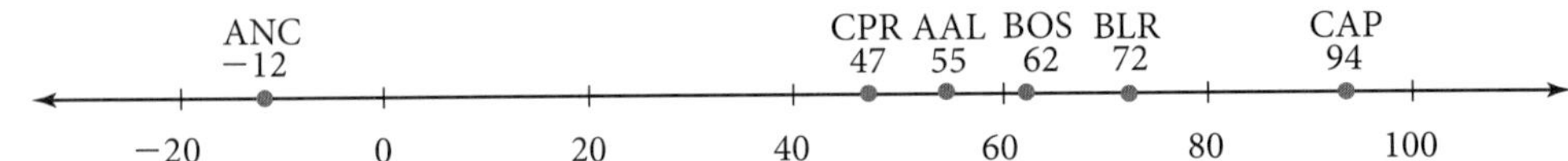

When you are making a number line, it is sometimes helpful to include zero for comparison, even if zero wouldn't otherwise appear in the interval. For example, suppose three teams in a science class built rockets and then measured the initial speeds of their rockets. These two graphs show different views for Team A, 12.8 m/s; Team B, 16.4 m/s; and Team C, 14.3 m/s.

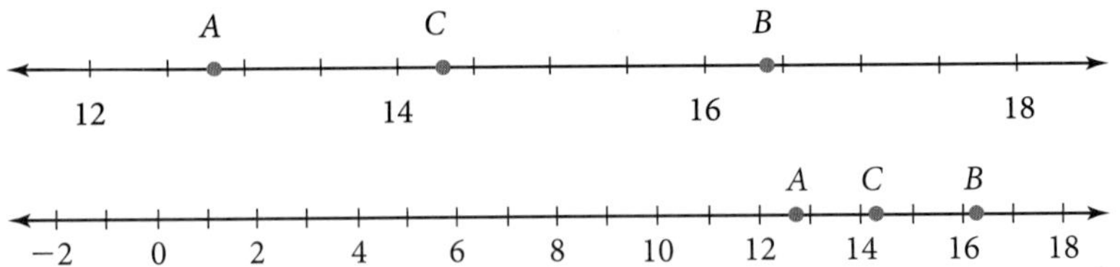

The first graph shows the separation of the three values, but the second graph shows how similar these three speeds are.

Exercises

1. Describe what is wrong with the plotting of the points on each graph, and then redraw the graph correctly.

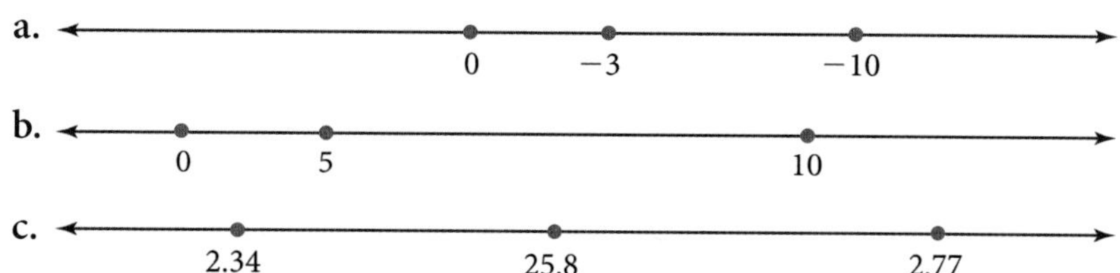

2. For each set of values, identify an appropriate range of numbers to use on the number line and indicate how to space the marks. Then plot the values.

   a. 16, 23, 8, 47, 33

   b. 90, 39, 152, 247

   c. −20, −75, 52, 82

3. Decide whether each number line should include zero, and then plot the values.

   a. Years in which the price of first-class postage changed: 1932, 1958, 1963, 1968, 1971, 1974, 1975, 1978, 1981, 1985, 1988, 1991, 1995, 1999, 2001, 2002, 2006, 2007, 2008, 2009, 2011, 2012, 2013

   b. Frequency of the word *of* per 1000 words in six texts written by the same author: 37, 40, 36, 48, 39, 41

   c. Area of the continents:

Continent	Area (km^2)
Africa	30,065,000
Antarctica	13,209,000
Asia	44,579,000
Australia	7,687,000
Europe	9,938,000
North America	24,256,000
South America	17,819,000

(*www.worldatlas.com*)

LESSON 1.1

Bar Graphs and Dot Plots

"I've always felt rock and roll was very, very wholesome music."

ARETHA FRANKLIN

This **pictograph** shows the number of CDs sold at Sheri's Music Store in one day. Can you tell just by looking which *type* sold the most? How many CDs of this type were sold?

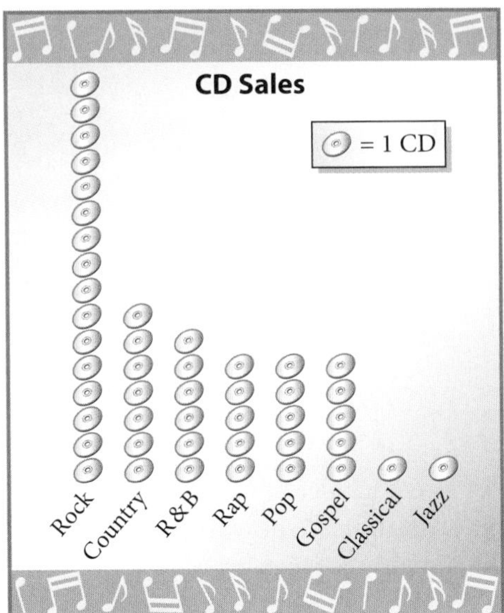

This specific information, the kind that Sheri may use later to make decisions, is sometimes called **data.** You use data every day when you answer questions like "Where is the cheapest place to buy a can of soda?" or "How long does it take to walk from class to the lunchroom?"

In this lesson you'll interpret and create graphs. Throughout the chapter you'll learn more ways to organize and represent data.

EXAMPLE

Joaquin's school posts a pictograph showing how many students celebrate their birthdays each month. Here is part of this pictograph. Create a table of data and a **bar graph** from the pictograph.

Solution

This table lists the birthday data.

Number of Birthdays in Each Month

Jan	Feb	Mar	Apr
15	10	0	25

In the pictograph, there are three figures for January. Each figure represents five students. So 3 times 5 tells us that 15 students have a birthday in January.

Career CONNECTION

In 2010 there were more than 225,000 paramedics in the United States, a number predicted to grow to 300,000 by 2020. Paramedics need to be able to read values from graphs and to make decisions based on numerical data.

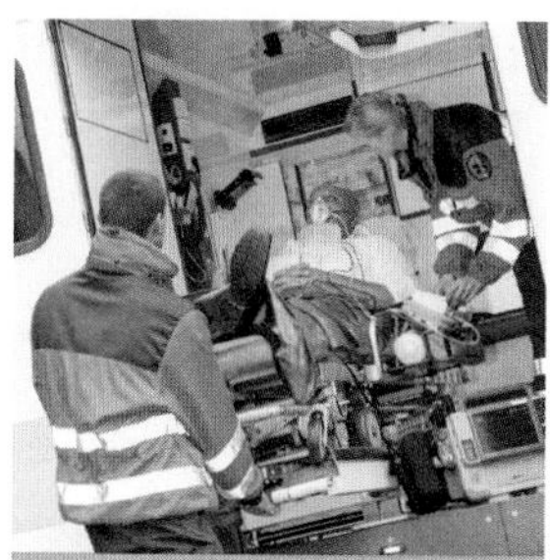

This bar graph shows the same data. The height of a bar shows the total in that **category,** in this case, a particular month. You use the *scale* on the *vertical axis* to measure the height of each bar. The vertical axis extends slightly past the greatest number of birthdays in any one month so that the data do not go beyond the scale.

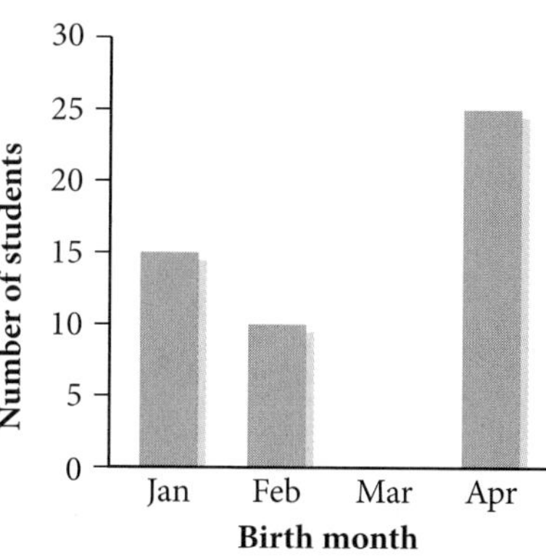

Bar graphs gather data into categories and make it easy to present a lot of information in a compact form. With a bar graph you can quickly compare the quantities for each category.

Different types of data require different types of graphs. Bar graphs are appropriate for nonnumeric data, that is, data that fall into categories, such as *Jan, Feb, Mar, Apr*. When all the data recorded are numbers, you can use a different type of graph. For example, see Step 4 of the investigation. In a **dot plot** each item of numerical data is shown above a number line or *horizontal axis*. Dot plots make it easy to see gaps and clusters in the data set, as well as how the data **spread** along the axis.

In the investigation you'll gather and plot data about pulse rates. People's pulse rates vary, but a healthy person at rest usually has a pulse rate between certain values. A pulse that is too fast or too slow could tell a paramedic that a person needs immediate care.

INVESTIGATION

YOU WILL NEED

- a watch or clock with a second hand

Picturing Pulse Rates

Use the Procedure Note to learn how to take your pulse. Practice a few times to make sure you have an accurate reading.

Procedure Note

How to Take Your Pulse

1. Find the pulse in your neck.
2. Count the number of beats for 15 seconds.
3. Multiply the number of beats by 4 to get the number of beats per minute (bpm). This number is your pulse rate.

Step 1 Collect pulse-rate data for 10 to 20 students.

Step 2 Find the **minimum** (lowest) and **maximum** (highest) values in the pulse-rate data. The minimum and maximum describe the spread of the data. For example, you could say, "The pulse rates are between 56 and 96 bpm."

Based on your data, do you think a paramedic would consider a pulse rate of 80 bpm to be "normal"? What about a pulse rate of 36 bpm?

Step 3 Construct a number line with the minimum value near the left end. Select a scale, and label equal **intervals** until you reach the maximum.

Step 4 Put a dot above the number line for each data value. When a data value occurs more than once, stack the dots.

Here is an example for the pulse rates 56, 60, 60, 68, 76, 76, and 96 bpm. Your line will probably have different minimum and maximum values.

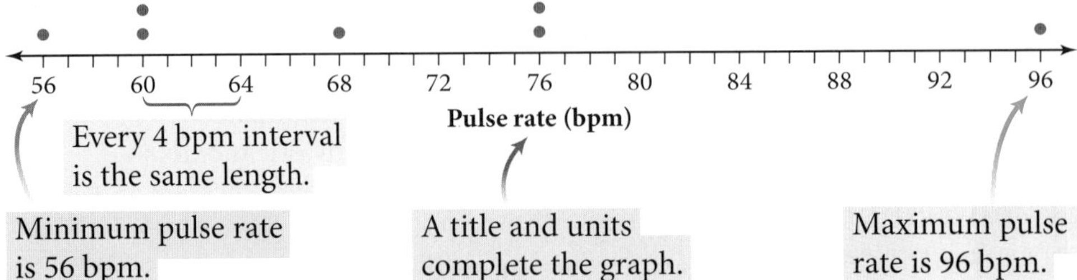

The **range** of a data set is the difference between the maximum and minimum values. The data on the example graph have a range of 96 minus 56, or 40 bpm.

Step 5 What is the range of your data? Suppose a paramedic says normal pulse rates have a range of 12. Is this range more or less than your range? What information is the paramedic not telling you when she mentions a range of 12?

Step 6 For your class data, are there data values between which a lot of points cluster? What do you think these clusters would tell a paramedic? What factors might affect whether your class data are more or less representative of all people?

Step 7 How could you change your data-collection method to make it appear that your class's pulse rates are much higher than they really are?

The word *statistics* was first used in the late 18th century to mean the collection of data about a state or country.

Statistics are the measures you gather from your **sample** and any values you calculate using these measures. For example, you did not measure the average and the range of the pulse-rate data, but they are statistics because they were calculated from the data. A new sample of the same measures (such as a new sample of pulse rates) may produce somewhat different statistics.

Valid statistics can help describe a much larger group than the sample group. This larger group is called the **population.** The population is not those sampled, but the group the sample represents. For example, using pulse-rate data from a large random sample of people allows us to generalize about the pulse rates of all people. Do you think the information from the investigation represents everyone in the world? Everyone your age? Everyone at your school? If the values of your sample are not like those of the population, your sample is **biased.**

1.1 Exercises

Practice Your Skills

1. Angelica has taken her pulse 11 times in the last six hours. Her results are 69, 92, 64, 78, 80, 82, 86, 93, 75, 80, and 80 bpm. Find the maximum, minimum, and range of the data. (h)

2. The table shows the percentages of the most common elements found in the human body. Make a bar graph to display the data.

Elements in the Human Body

Oxygen	Carbon	Hydrogen	Nitrogen	Calcium	Phosphorus	Other
65%	18%	10%	3%	2%	1%	1%

3. Use this bar graph to answer each question.

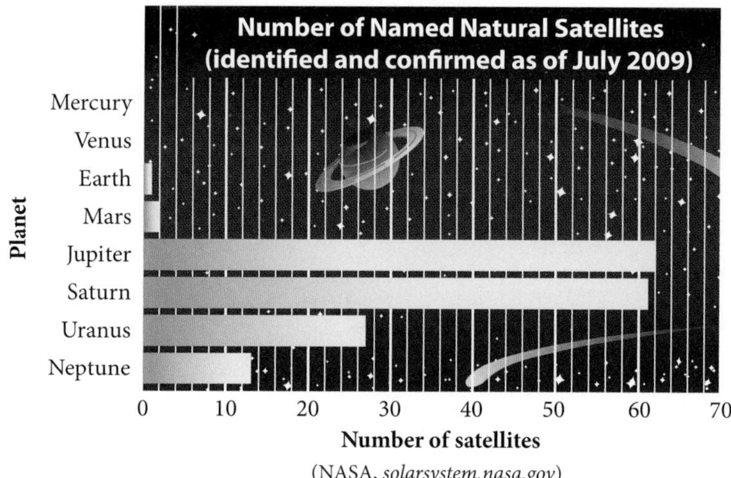

(NASA, *solarsystem.nasa.gov*)

a. Which planet has the most satellites?

b. What does this graph tell you about Mercury and Venus?

c. How many more satellites does Jupiter have than Neptune?

d. Saturn has how many times as many satellites as Mars?

4. This table shows how long it takes the students in one of Mr. Matau's math classes to get to school.

a. Construct a dot plot to display the data. Your number line should show time in minutes. ⓐ

b. How many students are in this class?

c. What is the combined time for Mr. Matau's students to travel to school? ⓗ

d. What is the average time for Mr. Matau's students to travel to school?

Travel Time to School

Time (min)	Number of students
1	2
3	2
5	6
6	1
8	6
10	7
12	3
14	2
15	1

Reason and Apply

5. This graph is a dot plot of Angelica's pulse-rate data.

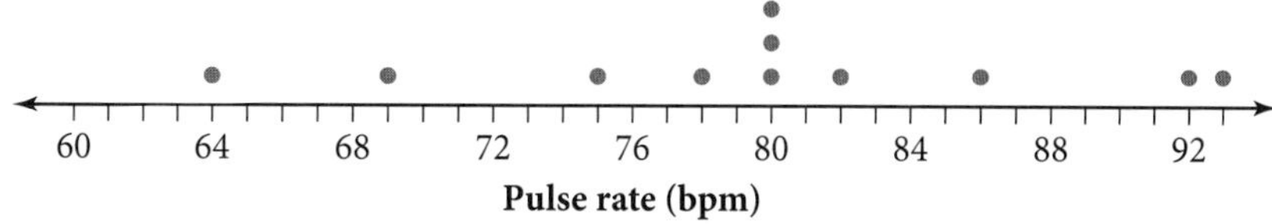

a. What pulse rate appeared most often?

b. What is the range of Angelica's data?

c. If your class followed the directions for the investigation, your pulse rates should be multiples of four. Angelica's are not. How do you think she took her pulse?

d. How would your data change if everyone in your class had taken his or her pulse for a full minute? How would the dot plot be different?

e. Do you think medical professionals measure pulse rates for 1 minute or for 15 seconds? Why?

6. Each of these graphs displays information from a recent class survey. Determine which graph best represents each description.

a. Number of people living in students' homes

b. Students' heights in inches

c. Students' pulse rates in beats per minute

d. Number of working television sets in students' homes @

i.

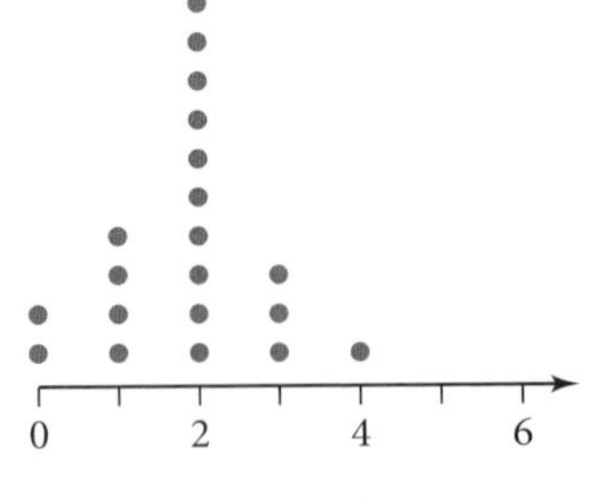

ii.

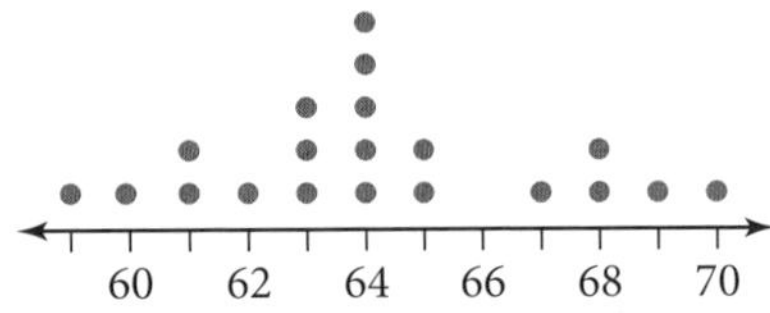

iii.

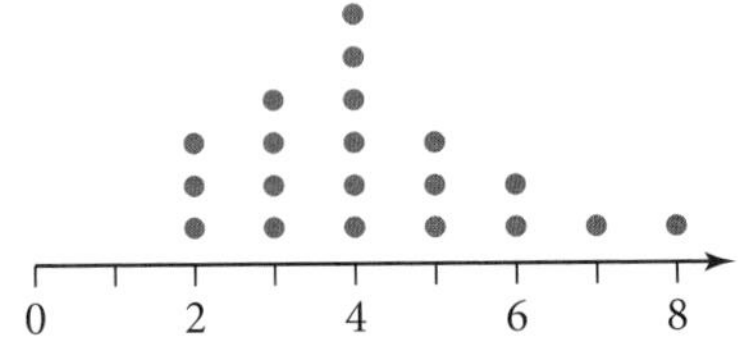

iv.

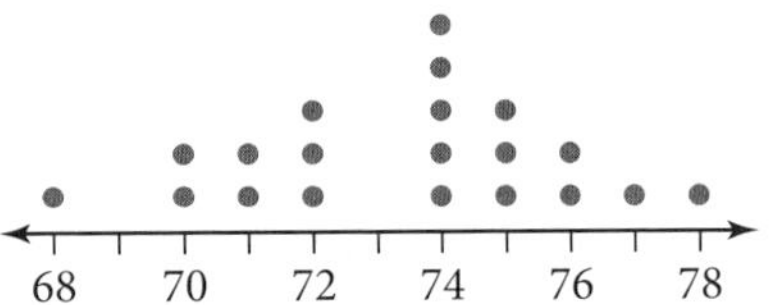

7. Reporter "Scoop" Presley of the school paper polled 20 students about their favorite type of music—classical, pop/rock, R&B, rap, or country. He delivered his story to his editor, Rose, just under the deadline. Rose discovered that Scoop, in his haste, had ripped the page with the bar graph showing his data. The vertical scale and one category were missing! Unfortunately, the only thing Scoop could remember was that three students had listed R&B as their favorite type. Reconstruct the graph so that it includes the vertical axis and the missing category with the correct count.

8. Suppose you collect information on how each person in your class gets to school. Would you use a bar graph or a dot plot to show the data? Explain why you think your choice would be the better graph for displaying this information. @

9. Each of these three graphs represents heights, in inches, of a sample of students from Jonesville School, which has students in kindergarten to 12th grade. Each sample was taken from a particular class or group of students. The title of a graph should indicate the sample.

Group A

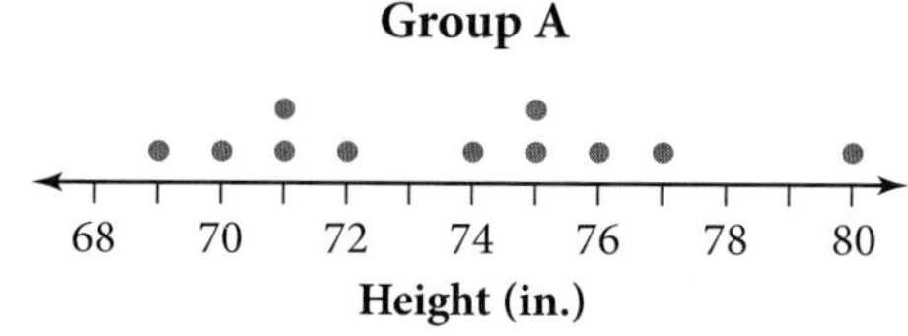

Group B

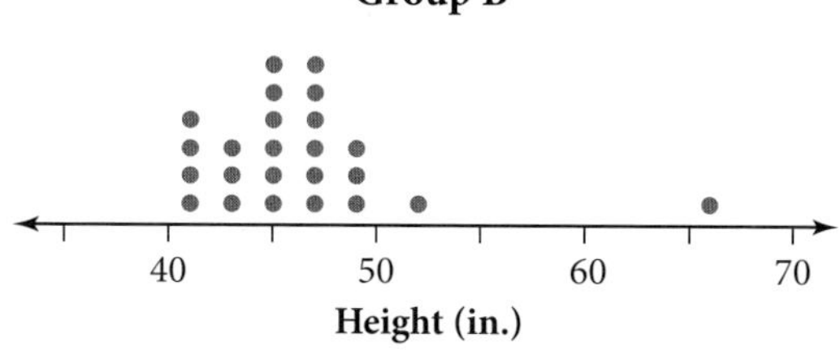

Group C

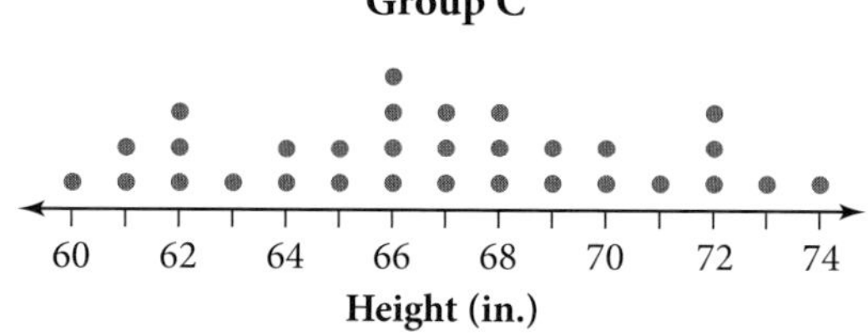

a. Write a more descriptive title for the Group A graph. (*Hint:* Think about different groups or classes in your school, such as clubs, sports teams, or grade levels.) @

b. Write a more descriptive title for the Group B graph.

c. Write a more descriptive title for the Group C graph.

d. A sample is biased if the values in the sample are not like those in the population. If the title of each of these graphs was "Students from Jonesville School," would you think the sample represented by each graph was biased low, biased high, or unbiased?

Review

10. Rewrite and simplify each of these multiplication expressions by using exponents.

a. $10 \times 10 \times 10 \times 10$

b. $2 \cdot 2 \cdot 2 \cdot 5 \cdot 5 \cdot 5 \cdot 5 \cdot 5 \cdot 5$

c. $\dfrac{3^2(3^4)}{8(8)(8)}$

d. $5 \cdot 5^6$

e. $(7^2)(9^2)(7^3)$

f. $\dfrac{4 \cdot 4 \cdot 4 \cdot 4 \cdot 7^8}{4 \cdot 4 \cdot 7^3}$

11. Use the order of operations to evaluate each expression.

a. $7 + (3 \cdot 2) - 4$

b. $8 + 2 - 4 \cdot 12 \div 16$

c. $1 - 2 \cdot 3 + 4 \div 5$

d. $1 - (2 \cdot 3 + 4) \div 5$ @

e. $1^2 \cdot 3 + (4 \div 5)$

12. The early Egyptian *Ahmes Papyrus* (1650 B.C.E.) shows how to use a doubling method to divide 696 by 29. (George Joseph, *The Crest of the Peacock,* 2000, pp. 61–66)

Doubles of 29	58	116	**232**	**464**	928
Doubles of 1	2	4	**8**	**16**	32

Double the divisor (29) until you go past the dividend (696). Find doubles of 29 that sum to 696: $232 + 464 = 696$. Then sum the corresponding doubles of 1: $8 + 16 = 24$. So 696 divided by 29 is 24.

a. Divide 4050 by 225 with this method. @

b. Divide 57 by 6 with this method. (*Hint:* Use doubles and halves.)

13. Write an addition expression that gives the combined total of the shaded area. Then evaluate the expression. The area of the large triangle is 1 square unit.

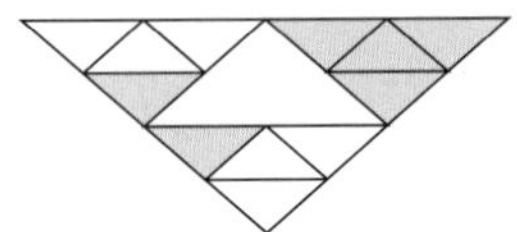

IMPROVING YOUR Reasoning SKILLS

Janet and JoAnn used the same data set of high and low temperatures for cities in a month in early spring. Which graph shows the low temperatures better? Is either graph better for showing the differences between the high and low temperatures?

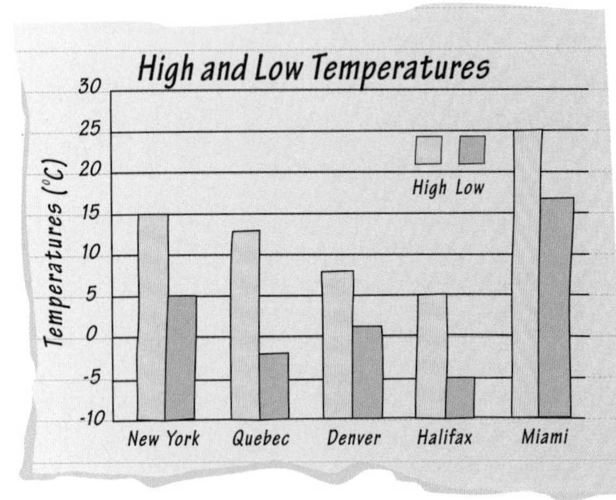

Janet's graph

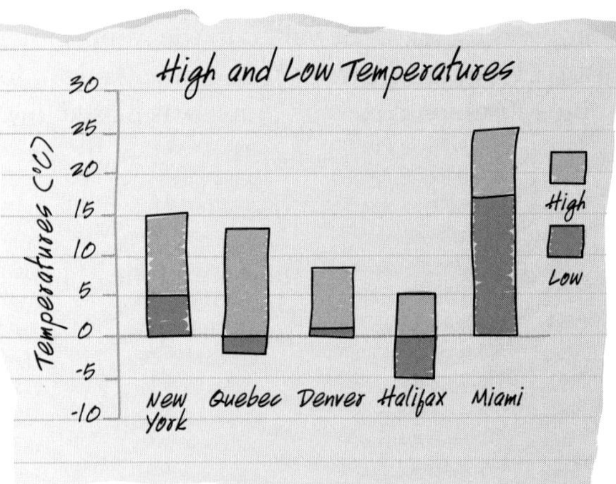

JoAnn's graph

LESSON

1.2

Summarizing Data with Measures of Center

"Americans watch an average of four hours of television each day."

"Half of the participants polled had five or more people living in their home."

"When graduating seniors were asked how many colleges they applied to, the most frequent answer they gave was three."

Statements like these try to say what is typical. They summarize a lot of data with one number, called a **measure of center** or **measure of central tendency.** The first statement uses the **mean,** or **average.** The second statement uses the **median,** or middle value. The third statement uses the **mode,** or most frequent value.

INVESTIGATION

Making "Cents" of the Center

YOU WILL NEED

- 20 to 30 pennies

In this investigation you'll learn to find the mean, median, and mode of a data set. You may already be familiar with measures of center.

Procedure Note

Finding the Median

If you have an odd number of pennies, the median is the year on the middle penny. If you have an even number of pennies, the median is the sum of the dates on the two pennies closest to the middle divided by two.

Step 1 Sort your pennies by mint year. Make a dot plot of the years.

Step 2 Put your pennies in a single line from oldest to newest. Find the median, or middle value. Does the median have to be a whole-number year? Why or why not? Would you get the same median if you arranged the pennies from newest to oldest?

Step 3 On your dot plot, circle the dot or dots that represent the median. Write the value you got in Step 2 beside the circled dot(s), and label this value "median."

Step 4 Now stack pennies with the same mint year. The year of the tallest stack is called the mode. If there are two tallest stacks, your data set is **bimodal.** If every stack has two pennies in it, you might say there is "no mode" because no year occurs most often. How many modes does your data set have? What are they? Does a mode have to be a whole number?

Step 5 Draw a square around the year corresponding to the mode(s) on the number line of your dot plot. Label each value "mode."

Step 6 Find the sum of the mint years of all your pennies, and divide by the number of pennies. The result is called the mean. What is the mean of your data set?

Step 7 Show where the mean falls on your dot plot's number line. Draw an arrowhead under it, and write the number you got in Step 6. Label it "mean."

Step 8 Now enter your data into a calculator list, and use your calculator to find the mean and the median. Are they the same as what you found using pencil and paper? [► Refer to **Calculator Note: Setting the Mode** to check the settings on your calculator. See **Calculator Notes: Entering Lists and Median, Mean and Five Number Summary** to enter data into lists and find the mean and median. ◄]

Step 9 Suppose your friend's teacher has been using the same set of pennies for this investigation for the last ten years. How would the mean, median, and mode of the penny data from her class be different from what you found?

Save the dot plot you created. You will use it in Lesson 1.3.

Measures of Center

Mean

The mean is the sum of the data values divided by the number of data items. The result is often called the average.

Median

For an odd number of data items, the median is the middle value when the data values are listed in order. For an even number of data items, the median is the average of the two middle values.

Mode

The mode is the data value that occurs most often. Data sets can have two modes (bimodal) or more. Some data sets have no mode.

Each measure of center has its advantages. The mean and the median may be quite different, and the mode, if it exists, may or may not be useful. You will have to decide which measure is most meaningful for each situation.

EXAMPLE

This data set shows the number of people who attended a movie theater over a period of 16 days:

114	192	123	114
110	126	121	121
107	138	180	120
132	135	130	121

a. Find the measures of center.

b. The theater's management wants to compare its attendance to that of other theaters in the area. Which measure of center best represents the data?

Moviegoers wear special glasses to watch 3-D movies.

Solution | **a.** The mean is approximately 130 people.

Sum of the data values

$$\frac{114 + 192 + 123 + 114 + 110 + 126 + 121 + 121 + 107 + 138 + 180 + 120 + 132 + 135 + 130 + 121}{16} = 130.25$$

Number of data values — Mean

The median is 122 people.

Data values listed in order

107, 110, 114, 114, 120, 121, 121, 121, 123, 126, 130, 132, 135, 138, 180, 192

The median is in the middle, or halfway between 121 and 123.

The most frequent value, 121 people, is the only mode.

b. To determine which measure of center best summarizes the data, look for patterns in the data and look at the shape of the graph.

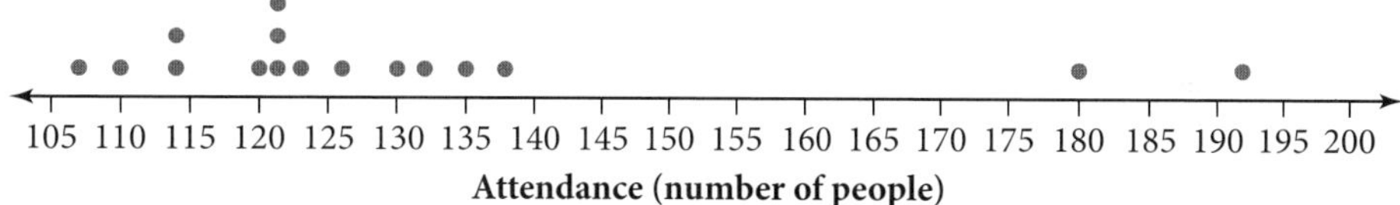

The dot plot clearly shows that, except for two items, the data are clustered between 107 and 138. The items with values 180 and 192 are far outside the range of most of the data and are called **outliers.**

Either the median, 122, or the mode, 121, could be used by the management to compare this theater's attendance to that of other theaters. The management could say, "Attendance was about 121 or 122 people per day over a 16-day period." The mean, 130, is too far to the right of most of the data to be the best measure of center. Yet the theater's management might prefer to use the mean, 130, in an advertisement. Why?

In the example, the mean is much larger than the median or the mode. This is because the mean is influenced by outliers in the data. To see how, recalculate the mean using 145 and 150, instead of 180 and 192, as the two largest values. What would happen to the median and mode with this change? What happens if you remove these outliers and find the mean for the remaining 14 values? Using the mean to describe a data set that includes outliers can be misleading.

1.2 Exercises

Practice Your Skills

1. Find the mean, median, and mode for each data set.

a. {1, 5, 7, 3, 5, 9, 6, 8, 10} @

b. {6, 1, 3, 9, 2, 7, 3, 4, 8, 8}

c. {12, 6, 11, 7, 18, 5, 2, 21} @

d. {10, 10, 20, 20, 20, 25}

e. {6, 3, 4, 6, 3, 5, 6, 4}

f. {46, 42, 47, 46, 43, 45, 46, 44}

g. {12, 7, 11, 8, 6, 8, 9, 7, 7}

h. {1200, 700, 1100, 800, 600, 800, 900, 700, 700}

2. Find the mean, median, and mode for each dot plot.

a.

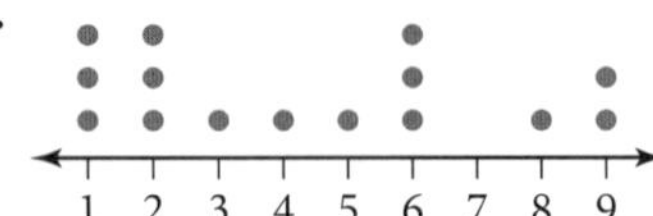

b.

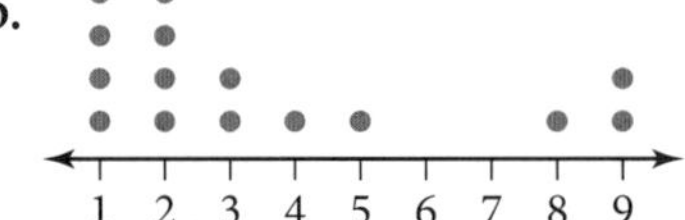

3. Students were asked how many pets they had. Their responses are shown in this dot plot.

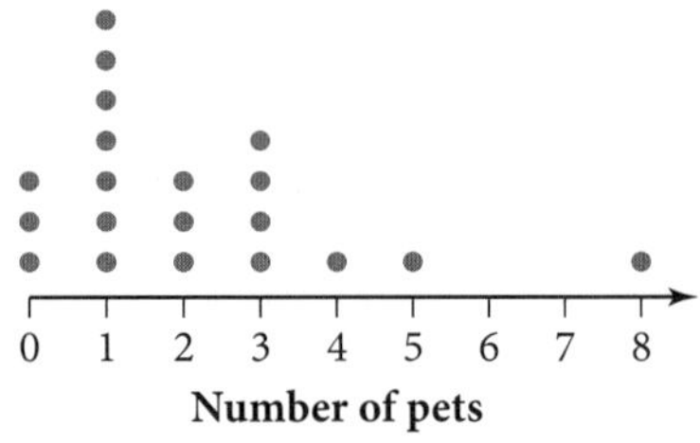

a. How many students were surveyed?

b. What is the range of responses?

c. What was the most common response?

4. This graph gives the lift heights and vertical drops of the five tallest roller coasters at Cedar Point Amusement Park in Ohio in September 2009.

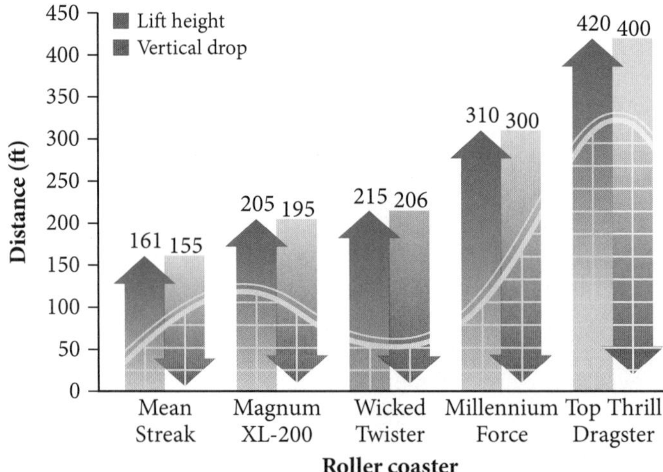

(Cedar Point Amusement Park, *www.cedarpoint.com*)

a. Find the mean and median for the lift heights. @

b. Find the mean and median for the vertical drops.

5. If you purchase 16 grocery items at an average cost of $1.14 per item, what is your grocery bill? Explain how you found the total bill.

Reason and Apply

6. An ocean wave caused by an earthquake, a landslide, or a volcano is called a tsunami. The heights of the 20 tallest tsunamis on record are given in the table. The December 26, 2004, Indian Ocean tsunami caused the most damage and loss of life of any tsunami in recorded history.

Tallest Tsunamis

Location	Year	Height (m)
Koborinai, Japan	2011	37.88
Indonesia	2004	50.9
Paatuut, Greenland	2000	50
Kashiwazakiko, Japan	1993	54
Spirit Lake West, Washington	1980	250
Valdez Inlet, Alaska	1964	67.1
Lituya Bay, Alaska	1958	524.26
Unimak Island, Alaska	1946	35.05
Lituya Bay, Alaska	1936	149.35
Nesodden, Norway	1936	74

Location	Year	Height (m)
Nesodden, Norway	1905	40.5
Lituya Bay, Alaska	1899	60.96
Shirahama, Japan	1896	38.2
Java, Indonesia	1883	35
Lituya Bay, Alaska	1853	120
Shimabara, Japan	1792	55
Ishigaki Island, Japan	1771	85.4
Sado Island, Niigata, Japan	1741	90
Bering Island, Russia	1737	64
Hila, Indonesia	1674	100

(National Geophysical Data Center, *www.ngdc.noaa.gov*) [Data set: **TSUHT**]

Many of the data sets in this book are available in your ebook for you to download onto your graphing calculator.

a. Calculate the mean and median for the height data.

b. Which measure of center is most appropriate for the height data? Explain your reasoning.

7. The first three members of the stilt-walking relay team finished their laps of the race with a mean time of 53 seconds per lap. What mean time for the next two members will give an overall team mean of 50 seconds per lap? (h)

8. Noah scored 88, 92, 85, 65, and 89 on five tests in his history class. Each test was worth 100 points. Noah's teacher usually uses the mean to calculate each student's overall score. How might Noah argue that the median is a better measure of center for his test scores?

9. At a state political rally, a speaker announced, "We should raise test scores so that all students are above the state median." Analyze this statement.

10. This table gives information about ten of the largest saltwater fish species that have been caught. The approximate mean weight of these fish is 1527.4 lb.

a. Explain how to use the mean to find an approximate total weight for these ten fish. What is the total weight? ⓐ

b. The median weight of these fish is about 1449 lb. Assuming that no two weights are the same, what does the median tell you about the individual weights of the fish? ⓐ

c. The range of weights is 1673 lb, and the minimum weight is 991 lb. What is the weight of the great white shark, the largest fish caught?

Largest Saltwater Fish Species

Species	Location where caught
Swordfish	Chile
Bluefin tuna	Nova Scotia
Great white shark	South Australia
Atlantic blue marlin	Brazil
Greenland shark	Norway
Black marlin	Peru
Hammerhead shark	Florida
Tiger shark	California
Pacific blue marlin	Hawaii
Mako shark	Mauritius

(International Game Fish Association, in *The Top 10 of Everything 2001*, p. 41)

11. Create a data set that fits each description.

a. The mean age of a family is 19 years, and the median age is 12 years. There are five people in the family. ⓗ

b. Six students in the Mathematics Club compared their family sizes. The mode was five people, and the median was four people.

c. The points scored by the varsity football team in the last seven games have a mean of 20 points, a median of 21 points, and a mode of 27 points.

12. These data sets give the ages of the top 10 highest-paid athletes in the United States and the top 10 highest-paid actors in the United States. (Forbes, *www.forbes.com*) [Data sets: **ATHPY, ACTPY**]

Athletes: {35, 33, 32, 40, 35, 29, 26, 32, 29, 28}
Actors: {47, 45, 54, 44, 36, 21, 45, 48, 47, 49}

a. Make dot plots of these data.

b. Give the mean, median, and mode for the data.

c. Which measure or measures of center best summarize each data set? Explain your reasoning.

d. Describe how the two data sets compare, using both dot plots and measures of center.

Review

13. Fifteen students gave their ages in months:

{168, 163, 142, 163, 165, 164, 167, 153, 149, 173, 163, 179, 155, 162, 162}

a. Would you use a bar graph, pictograph, or dot plot to display these data? Explain. ⓐ

b. Create the graph you chose in 13a.

14. Use this segment to measure or calculate in 14a–c.

a. What is the length in centimeters of the segment?

b. Draw a segment that is $\frac{2}{3}$ as long as this segment. What is the length of your new segment?

c. Draw a segment that is $\frac{1}{5}$ as long as the original segment. What is the length of this new segment?

LESSON

1.3

Graphical and Numeric Measures of Spread

"To talk sense is to talk quantities. It is no use saying a nation is large—how large?"

ALFRED NORTH WHITEHEAD

Michael Jordan is regarded as one of the all-time greatest athletes. He played in more than 1,000 basketball games, scored more than 32,000 points, was the National Basketball Association (NBA) Most Valuable Player five times, and helped the Chicago Bulls win six NBA championships. During the 1997–98 season, he scored almost three times as many points as the next highest scorer on his team. Does any measure of center give a complete description of how the Bulls scored as a team? A **five-number summary** could give a better picture. It uses five boundary points: minimum, maximum, median, **first quartile** (the median of the first half), and **third quartile** (the median of the second half).

Points Scored by Chicago Bulls Team Members Who Played More Than 40 Games (1997–98 Season)

Team members	Total points scored	Team members	Total points scored
Michael Jordan	2357	Steve Kerr	376
Toni Kukoc	984	Dennis Rodman	375
Scottie Pippen	841	Randy Brown	288
Ron Harper	764	Jud Buechler	198
Luc Longley	663	Bill Wennington	167
Scott Burrell	416		

(National Basketball Association, *www.nba.com*)

Michael Jordan

EXAMPLE Find the five-number summary for the number of points scored by Chicago Bulls team members during the 1997–98 season (use the table).

Solution

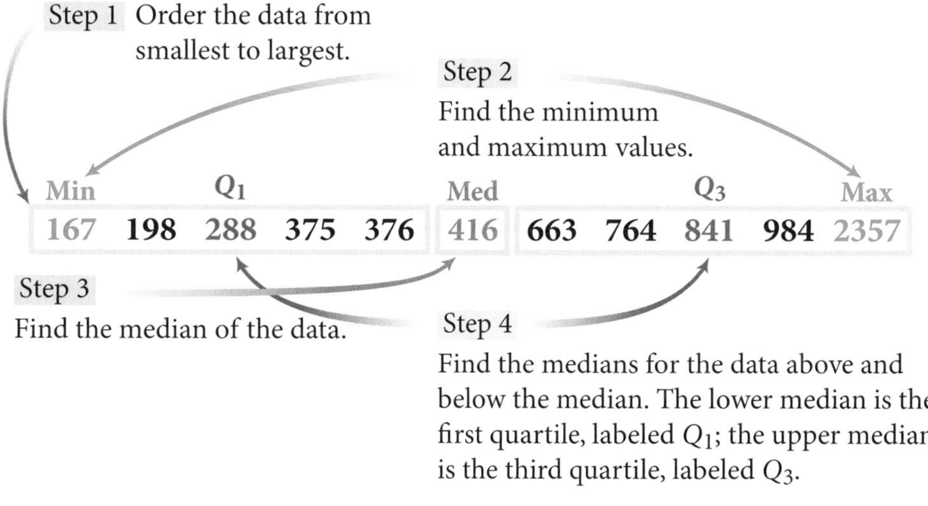

Because the Bulls data consist of 11 values, the middle value is ignored in finding Q_1 and Q_3. If there were only 10 values, then Q_1 would still be the median of the smallest 5 values, and Q_3 would be the median of the largest 5 values.

The five-number summary is 167, 288, 416, 841, 2357. This is the minimum, first quartile, median, third quartile, and maximum in order from smallest to largest. The first quartile, median, and third quartile divide the data into four equal groups. Each of the four groups has the same number of values, in this case two.

A five-number summary helps you better understand the spread of the data along the number line. It also helps you compare different sets of data. A **box plot** is a visual way to show a five-number summary. This box plot shows the data for the 1997–98 Bulls.

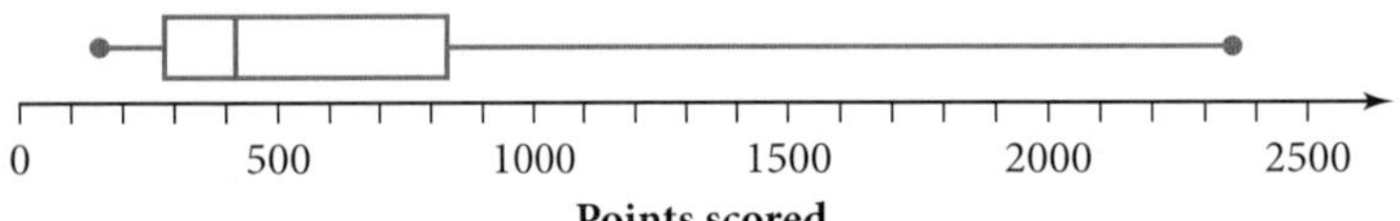

Notice how the box plot shows both the spread of data and Michael Jordan as an extreme outlier. How does the box plot represent the five-number summary values? Can you see why this type of graph is sometimes called a **box-and-whisker plot?** In the investigation you'll see how to use the five-number summary to construct a box plot.

To find Q_1 and Q_3 when the sample size is even, split the data in the middle to form two equal groups and find the median in each group. If the sample size is odd, ignore the value of the median and form two equal groups with the remaining data. Find the median of each group. For example, with a sample of 10 data values, list them in order of size and divide them into two groups with 5 values in each group. With a sample of 11 values, list them in order of size, find the median, and divide the remaining values into two groups with 5 values in each group. The medians of each of the sets of 5 are the quartiles.

INVESTIGATION

Pennies in a Box

YOU WILL NEED

- your dot plot from Investigation 1.2: Making "Cents" of the Center

The illustrations are examples only. Your box plot should look different.

Step 1 Find the five-number summary values for your penny data.

Step 2 Place a clean sheet of paper over your dot plot and trace the number line. Using the same scale will help you compare your dot plot and box plot.

Step 3 Find the median value on your number line, and draw a short vertical line segment just above it. Repeat this process for the first quartile and the third quartile.

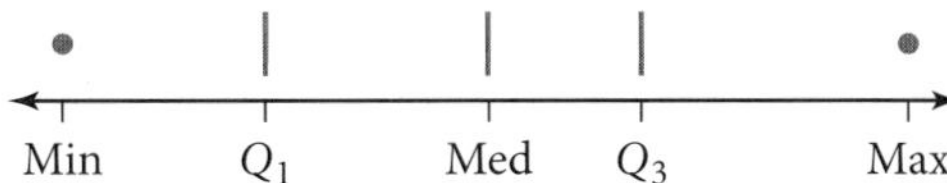

Step 4 Place dots above your number line to represent the minimum and maximum values from your dot plot.

Step 5 Draw a rectangle with ends at the first and third quartiles. This is the "box." Finally, draw horizontal segments that extend from each end of the box to the minimum and maximum values. These are the "whiskers."

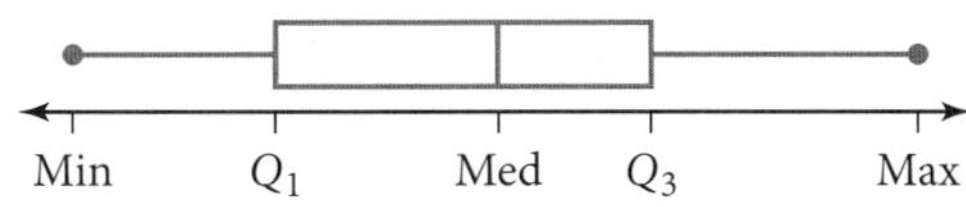

This worker is counting and bagging pennies at the U.S. Mint in Denver, Colorado.

Step 6 Compare your dot plot and box plot. On which graph is it easier to locate the five-number summary? Which graph helps you see the spread of data better?

Remember that the first quartile, median, and third quartile divide the data items into four equal groups. Although each section has the same number of data items, your boxes and whiskers may vary in length. Some box plots will be more *symmetric* than others. When would that happen?

Step 7 Enter your penny mint years into a calculator list, and draw a calculator box plot. [▸ Follow the procedure outlined in **Calculator Note: Box Plots.** ◂] Does your calculator box plot look equivalent to the plot you drew by hand?

Step 8 Use the trace function on your calculator. What values are displayed as you trace the box plot? Are the five-number summary values the same as those you found before?

The difference between the first quartile and the third quartile is the **interquartile range,** or ***IQR.*** Like the range, the interquartile range helps describe the spread in the data.

Step 9 Complete this investigation by answering these questions.

a. What are the range and *IQR* of your data?

b. How many pennies fall between the first and third quartiles of the box plot? What fraction of the total number of pennies is this number? Will this fraction always be the same? Explain.

c. Under what conditions will exactly $\frac{1}{4}$ of the pennies be in each whisker of the box plot?

[▶ You can explore relationships between a data set and its box plot using the **Dynamic Algebra Exploration** in your ebook. ◀]

Box plots are a good way to compare two data sets. These box plots summarize the final test scores for two of Mr. Werner's algebra classes. Use what you have learned to compare these two graphs. Which class has the greater range of scores? Which has the greater *IQR*? In which class did the greatest fraction of students score above 80?

Notice that neither graph shows the number of students in the class or the individual scores. If knowing each data value is important, a box plot is not the best choice to display your data.

Mr. Werner's Algebra Test

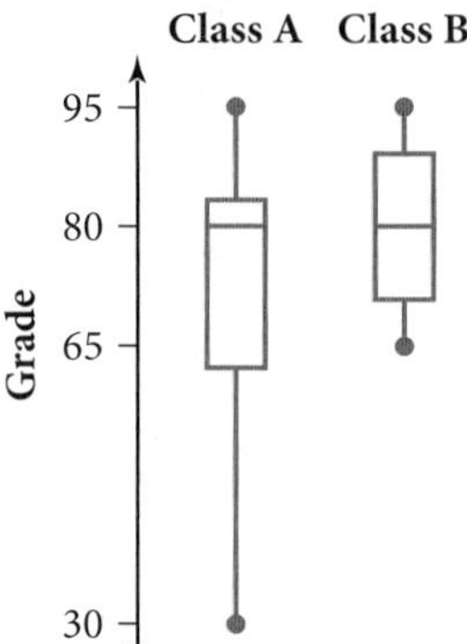

In Lesson 1.2 you looked at measures of center, but another important feature of any set of values is the spread of those values. In this lesson you explored range and *IQR*, which are called measures of spread. If you are given such measures for two groups, you know which group has values that are closer together. But range and *IQR* depend on only two values—max and min, or Q_3 and Q_1—and sometimes they don't describe the spread of the values very well.

A **deviation** is a measure of how far from center an observation is. If you are in Mr. Werner's Class B above where the mean test score was 80 and you have a score of 86, then your deviation is 6. Usually this is a signed number indicating direction. A test score of 78 has a deviation of negative 2, telling us that it is 2 below the mean. Since every value in a set has deviation, you could *also* measure spread by reporting some average of these deviations. Do you see a problem with this idea?

Scores:	65, 70, 72, 75, 85, 87, 91, 95 −80 −80 −80 −80 −80 −80 −80 −80	The mean of the set is $\overline{x} = \dfrac{640}{8} = 80$.
Deviations:	−15 −10 −8 −5 5 7 11 15	The sum of these is zero.

Can you explain why the sum will always be zero? What is the average deviation?

The **absolute deviation** is the positive value of the deviation—that is, the distance from the mean without the direction from the mean. A way to measure spread that uses all values is to give the **mean absolute deviation (MAD).**

$$MAD = \frac{15 + 10 + 8 + 5 + 5 + 7 + 11 + 15}{8} = \frac{76}{8} = 9.5$$

This value tells us that the average value is 9.5 from the mean. (Some more and some less.) If you were given another sample with a much larger MAD, what would you know about that sample?

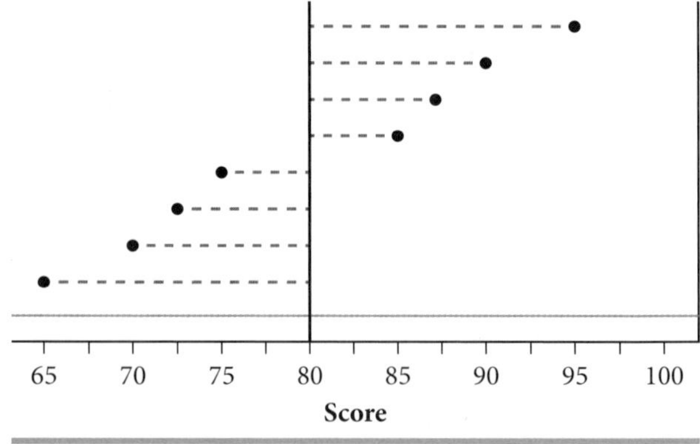

The sum of the deviations, a measure of how far from the mean an observation is, will always be zero.

You have now learned three measures of spread: range, interquartile range, and mean absolute deviation. Statisticians would tell us that we have missed the two most important measures of spread, the **variance** and the **standard deviation.** The sum of the squares of the deviations, divided by one less than the number of values, is called the variance of the data. The measurement units of variance, however, are squares of the data units. The square root of variance—the *standard deviation*—has the same units as the data and is less affected by outliers, so it is the most commonly used measure of spread. You will learn more about these two in the mini-investigation in the Reason and Apply exercises.

1.3 Exercises

Practice Your Skills

1. Find the five-number summary for each data set.

a. {5, 5, 8, 10, 14, 16, 22, 23, 32, 32, 37, 37, 44, 45, 50} @

b. {10, 15, 20, 22, 25, 30, 30, 33, 34, 36, 37, 41, 47, 50}

c. {44, 16, 42, 20, 25, 26, 14, 37, 26, 33, 40, 26, 47} @

d. {47, 43, 35, 34, 32, 21, 17, 16, 11, 9, 5, 5}

2. Sketch each graph on your own paper.

i.

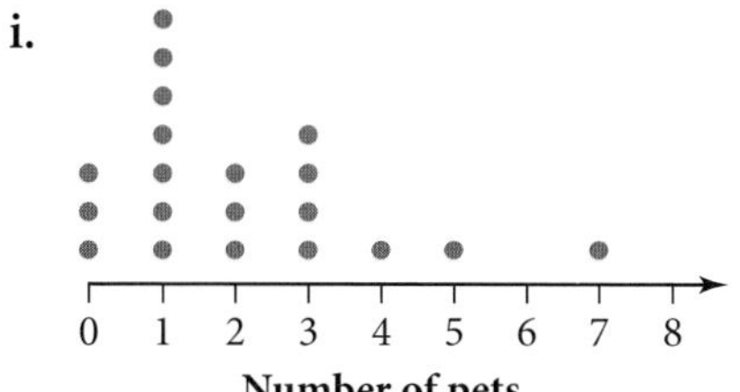

ii.

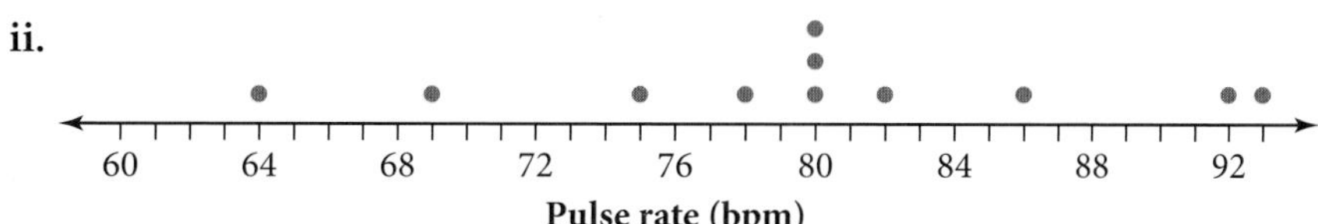

a. Circle the points that represent the five-number summary values. If two data points are needed to calculate the median, first quartile, or third quartile, draw a circle around both points.

b. List the five-number summary values for each data set. @

3. Give the five-number summary and create a box plot for the listed values in each data set.

a. {4.1, 4.3, 4.4, 4.4, 4.5, 4.5, 4.6, 4.6, 4.7, 4.7, 4.9}

b. {22, 16, 25, 27, 19, 22, 23, 23, 31, 21, 15, 19, 22, 28}

c. {2, 6, 4, 9, 1, 6, 4, 7, 2, 8, 5, 6, 9, 3, 6, 7, 5, 4, 8}

d. {4, 8, 12, 14, 16}

4. Which data set matches this box plot? (More than one answer may be correct.)

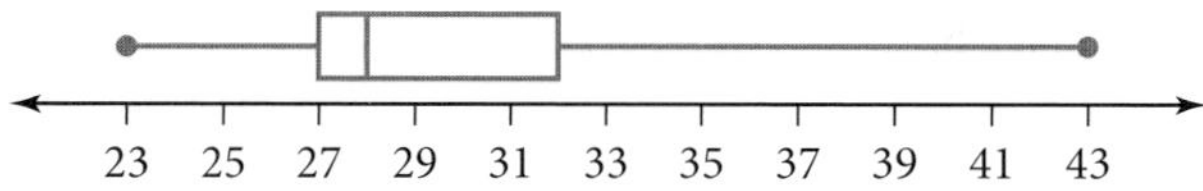

a. {23, 25, 26, 28, 28, 28, 28, 30, 31, 33, 41, 43}

b. {23, 23, 24, 25, 26, 27, 29, 30, 31, 33, 41, 43}

c. {23, 27, 28, 28, 33, 43}

d. {23, 27, 28, 28, 29, 32, 43}

5. Check your vocabulary understanding by answering these questions.

a. How does the term *quartile* relate to how data values are grouped when using a five-number summary? @

b. What is the name of the difference between the minimum and maximum values in a five-number summary? @

c. What is the name of the difference between the third quartile and first quartile in a five-number summary?

d. How are outliers of a data set related to the whiskers of its box plot?

6. Find each of these for the data set {1, 2, 3, 5, 9}

a. The mean of the sample.

b. The five absolute deviations.

c. The mean absolute deviation (MAD). @

Reason and Apply

7. APPLICATION The table gives the points scored by the top-scoring Chicago Bulls players in the 2011–12 season.

Points Scored by Chicago Bulls Team Members Who Played More Than 40 Games (2011–12 Season)

Chicago Bulls Player	Total Points Scored	Chicago Bulls Player	Total Points Scored
Carlos Boozer	991	Taj Gibson	484
Derrick Rose	852	C. J. Watson	474
Luol Deng	828	Ronnie Brewer	455
Joakim Noah	652	John Lucas	369
Kyle Korver	529	Richard Hamilton	326

(*http://www.basketball-reference.com/teams/CHI/2012.html*)

a. The five-number summary for the Chicago Bulls 1997–98 season is 167, 288, 416, 841, 2357. (See the table and example at the beginning of this lesson.) Find the five-number summary for the Chicago Bulls 2011–12 season.

b. Find and compare the measures of center for the two Chicago Bulls teams.

c. Decide which measure of center best describes each team's performance. Explain your answer.

d. These box plots compare the points scored by the 1997–98 Chicago Bulls players to the points scored by the 2011–12 Chicago Bulls players. Compare the two teams' performance based on what you see in the box plots.

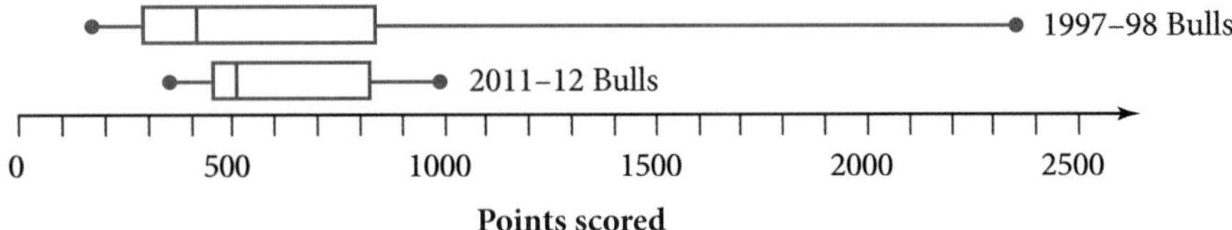

e. Remove Michael Jordan's points from the data table for the 1997–98 Chicago Bulls and make a new box plot. How does this new box plot compare to the original box plot for the 1997–98 Bulls? How does it compare to the box plot for the 2011–12 Bulls?

8. Stu had a mean score of 25.5 on four 30-point papers in English. He remembers three scores: 23, 29, and 27.

a. Estimate the fourth score without actually calculating it.

b. Check your estimate by calculating the fourth score. @

c. What is the five-number summary for this situation?

d. Does it make sense to have a five-number summary for this data set? Explain why or why not.

9. APPLICATION This table lists median weekly earnings of full-time workers by occupation and gender for 2008.

a. Make two box plots, one for men's salaries and one for women's salaries, above the same number line. Use them to compare the two data sets. Use the terms you have learned in this chapter. @

b. What do the data tell you about women's and men's wages for the same type of work in 2008?

c. Do the box plots help you identify characteristics of the data better than the table does? Are there any aspects of the data that are seen better in the table?

d. How could you use the box plots to explain the slogan "Equal pay for equal work"?

Median Weekly Earnings, 2008

Occupation	Men	Women
Management	$1384	$979
Business and financial operations	1167	885
Computer and mathematical	1320	1088
Architecture and engineering	1286	1001
Community and social services	860	753
Legal	1696	962
Education, training, and library	1020	818
Healthcare practitioner and technical	1210	909
Protective service	794	594
Food preparation and serving-related	432	376
Sales and related	796	516
Office and administrative support	651	590
Farming, fishing, and forestry	427	392
Installation, maintenance, and repair	774	779
Production	659	464
Transportation and material moving	615	455

(U.S. Bureau of Labor Statistics, *www.bls.gov*)

During World War II many women took nontraditional jobs to support war industries. Some started the fight for equal pay for equal work. The Lilly Ledbetter Fair Pay Act was signed in 2009, more than 60 years later.

10. These box plots display the lengths of 19 snakes that are longer than the average human is tall. Ten of the snakes live in the eastern hemisphere and the other nine live in the western hemisphere.

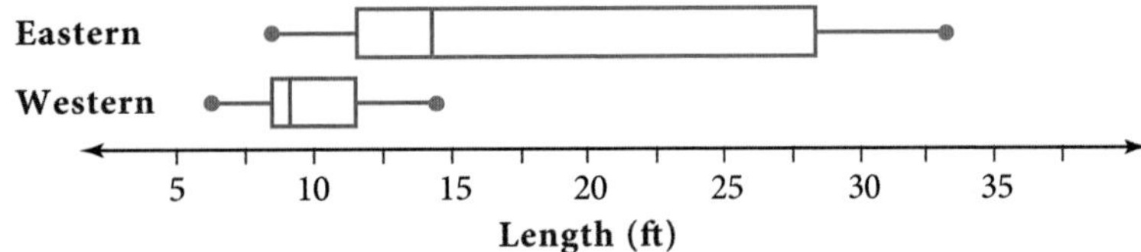

(*Smithsonian Handbooks: Reptiles and Amphibians, 2002*)

a. The longest snakes in the world are the reticulated python and the green anaconda. How long are these snakes?

b. The fifth-longest snake in the eastern hemisphere is the carpet python, and the fifth-longest in the western hemisphere is the indigo snake. Can you determine the length of these snakes? Explain.

c. Which hemisphere has the longer snakes? Explain your choice.

d. Which hemisphere has the greater variation in long snakes? Explain your choice.

11. The average weights of the 10 largest land animals are found in the table.

a. Calculate the mean and MAD for this set of values.

b. It is hard to get these animals to step up on the scale and hold still so you can weigh them, so they are usually weighed in a harness. The weight of the harness is 100 kg. Add 100 kg to each of the values and calculate the mean and MAD again.

c. Write a conjecture about adding the same value to each data value based on your answers to parts a and b.

d. To convert the weight to lb, you need to multiply each value by 2.2 lb/kg. Do that to each and calculate the mean and MAD of the weight in lbs.

Animal	Average weight
African elephant	8500 kg
Asian elephant	4200 kg
Hippo	2500 kg
White Rhino	2350 kg
Gaur	1600 kg
Giraffe	1400 kg
Walrus	1200 kg
Black Rhino	1150 kg
Saltwater crocodile	785 kg
Wild Asian water buffalo	770 kg

(*http://oddstuffmagazine.com/top-10-largest-land-animals-in-the-world.html*)

e. Write a conjecture about multiplying each data value based on your answer to parts a and d.

12. As a general rule, if the distance of a data point from the nearest end of the box is more than 1.5 times the length of the box (or *IQR*), then it is a potential outlier.

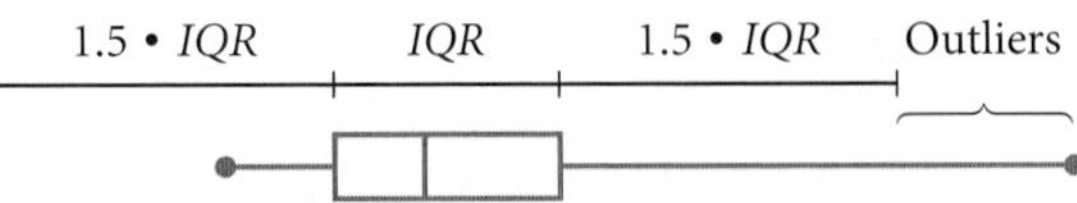

a. The five-number summary for the number of points scored by the 1997–98 Chicago Bulls players is 167, 288, 416, 841, 2357. What is 1.5 times the interquartile range?

b. What is the value of the first quartile minus 1.5 times the interquartile range?

c. What is the value of the third quartile plus 1.5 times the interquartile range?

d. The values you found in 10b and 10c are the limits of outlier values. Identify any 1997–98 Chicago Bulls players who are outliers.

13. MINI-INVESTIGATION Five women whose heights are 68 in., 67 in., 62 in., 67 in., and 61 in. were given shoes with heel heights of 4 in., 1 in., 2 in., 4 in., and 4 in. respectively.

a. Find the mean heights of the women, of the shoes, and of the women wearing their assigned shoes. @

b. Find the mean absolute deviation of the heights of the women, the shoes, and the women wearing their assigned shoes.

c. What do you observe about the three means? Is your observation also true about the MADs?

d. Use your calculator to find the variance of the heights of the women, the shoes, and the women wearing their assigned shoes.

e. Does the relationship of the means work with these variances?

f. To find the variance by hand you must do the following.

1. Find all the deviations.

2. Square all the deviations.

3. Add those together.

4. Divide by one less than the sample size.

Show the calculations for each step of the procedure using the heights of the women without shoes.

The units of variance are the square of the units of the data. An easier way to interpret this value is called the standard deviation. It is found by taking the square root of the variance. It has the same units as the data.

g. Find the standard deviation of the heights of the women, the shoes, and the women wearing their assigned shoes. Take the square root of the values you found in 13d. @

h. Now do it again using the standard deviation command on your calculator.

i. How do these values compare to the MADs you found in part (b).

The variance is the only measure of spread where the sum of the variances of two independent sets is equal to the variance of their sum. The standard deviation is the way we can put an interpretation on the variance.

Review

14. Create a data set for a family of five with mean age 22 years and median age 14.

15. The majority of pets in the United States are cats.

a. How many pet cats are in the United States? Use the pictograph below. @

b. How many fewer dogs are there?

c. If small mammals (21 million) were added to the pictograph, how many paw prints would be drawn to represent them? ("Small mammals" include rabbits and small rodents.) @

Pets in the United States

(American Pet Products Manufacturers Association, *www.petplace.com*)

Histograms and Stem-and-Leaf Plots

This dot plot provides information about the amount of pocket money 16 students had with them on a given day. If you collected similar data for all the students in your school, you probably wouldn't want to make a dot plot because you would have too many dots. A box plot could be used to show the spread of the data set, but it wouldn't show whether you polled 16 or 600 students.

Pocket Money

0 1.00 2.00 3.00 4.00 5.00

Amount of pocket money ($)

A **histogram** is related to a dot plot but is more useful than a dot plot when you have a large data set. Histograms use columns to display how data are distributed and reveal clusters and gaps in the data. Unlike bar graphs, which use categories, the data for histograms must be numeric and ordered along the horizontal axis.

This histogram shows the same data as the dot plot.

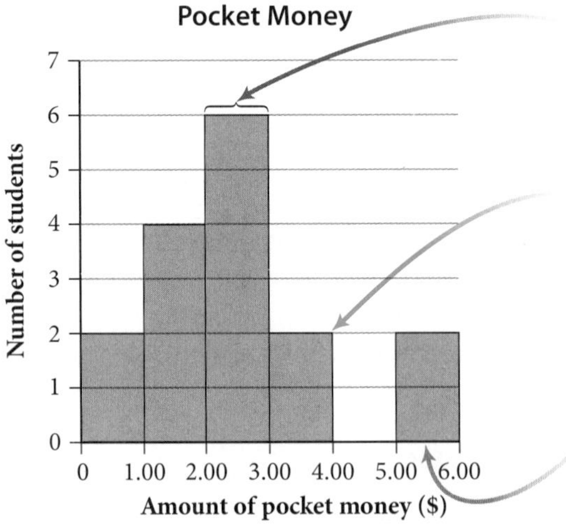

The width of each column represents an interval of $1.00. These intervals are also called **bins.**

The height of each column shows the number of students whose money falls in that bin. This is the **frequency** of each bin.

Boundary values fall in the bin to the right. For example, this bin is $5.00 to $5.99.

All bins in a histogram have the same width, and the columns are drawn next to each other without any space between them. A gap between columns indicates a bin with frequency 0. You can't name the individual values represented in a histogram, so a histogram summarizes data. You *can* determine the total number of data items. The sum of the column heights in the histogram shown tells you the total number of students.

When you construct a histogram, you have to decide what bin width works best. These histograms show the same data set but use different bin widths. Use each of the three histograms presented to answer the question "Between what values did the most students have pocket money?" How do the bin widths of each histogram affect your answers?

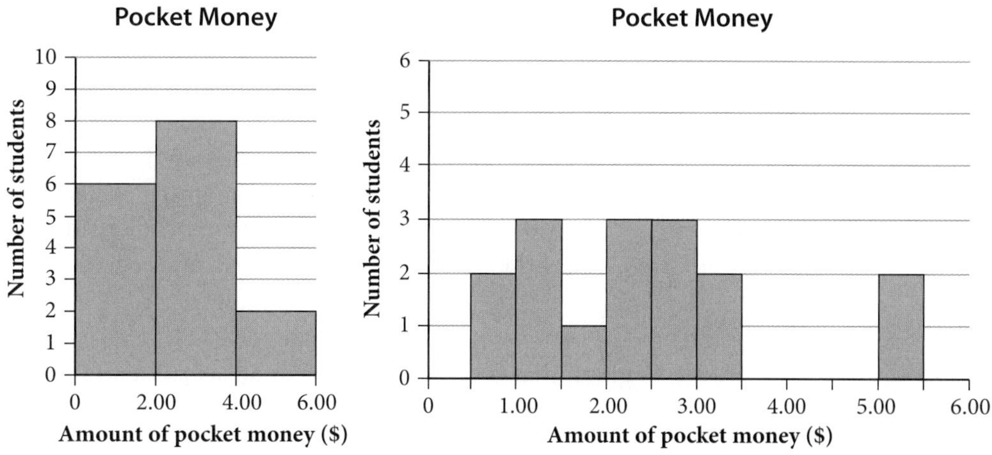

Having too many bins may create an information overload. Having too few bins may hide some features of the data set. As a general rule, try to have five to ten bins. There are exceptions, however.

INVESTIGATION

Hand Spans

YOU WILL NEED

- graph paper
- a centimeter ruler

In this investigation you'll collect hand-span measurements and make a histogram. You'll organize the data using different bin widths and compare the results to a box plot.

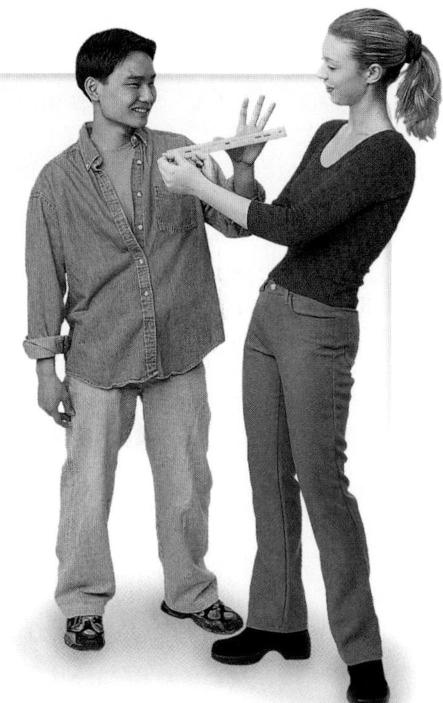

Step 1 Measure your hand span in centimeters. Post your hand-span measurement in a classroom data table.

Step 2 Mark a zero point on your graph paper. Draw a horizontal axis to the right and a vertical axis up from the zero point.

Step 3 Scale the horizontal axis for the range of your data. Clearly divide this range into five to ten equal bins. Label the boundary values of each bin.

Step 4 Count the data items that will fall into each bin. For example, in a bin ranging from 20 cm to 22 cm, you would count all the items with the values 20.0, 20.5, 21.0, and 21.5. Items with the value 22.0 are counted in the next bin.

Step 5 Scale the vertical axis for the frequency, or count, of data items. Label it from zero to at least the largest bin count.

Step 6 Draw columns showing the correct frequency of each bin.

Step 7 Enter your hand-span measurements into a calculator list. Create several versions of the histogram using different bin widths. [▶ See **Calculator Note: Histograms** for instructions on creating a histogram. ◀]

Step 8 How did you select a bin width for your graph-paper histogram? Now that you have experimented with calculator bin widths, would you change the bin width of your paper graph? Write a paragraph explaining how to pick the "best" bin width.

Step 9 Add a box plot of your hand-span data to both your graph-paper and your calculator versions of the histogram. What information does the histogram provide that the box plot does not? Consider gaps in the data and the shape of the histogram.

A graph that is often useful for small sets of data is a **stem plot,** or **stem-and-leaf plot.** A stem plot, like a dot plot, displays each individual item. But like a histogram, data values are grouped into intervals, or bins. You need a **key** to interpret a stem plot.

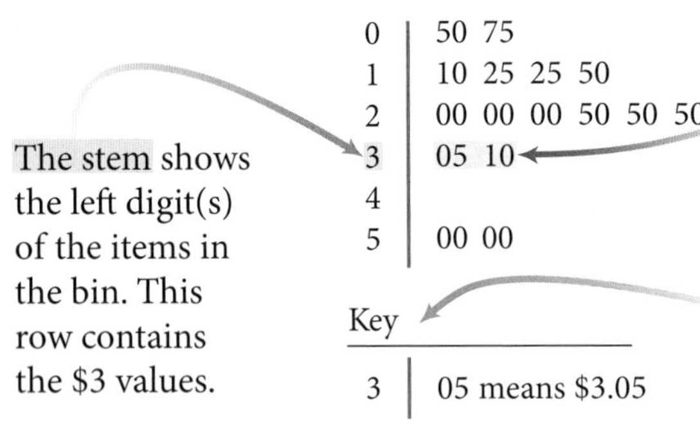

The leaves show the digits that complete each value. One value was $3.05, and one value was $3.10.

The key helps you read the information.

EXAMPLE

This stem-and-leaf plot gives data about Canadian universities. Draw a histogram representing the same data.

Establishment Dates of Canadian Universities (1800–1950)

Stem	Leaves
180	2 4
181	8 8
182	1 7
183	6 8 9
184	1 3 8 8
185	2 2 3 7
186	3 5
187	1 3 3 6 6 7 8 8
188	7 7
189	0 9
190	0 3 5 6 7 7 8
191	0 0 1 1 3 3 7 9
192	1 5 5
193	6
194	2 5 8

Key

191 | 3 means 1913

(Association of Universities and Colleges of Canada, *www.aucc.ca*)

Solution

First, find the range of the data: $1948 - 1802 = 146$ yr. Then consider a "friendly" bin width. For a bin width of 10 yr, you'd need at least 15 bins, which is too many. For a bin width of 25 yr, you'd need 6 bins, which is more manageable.

You could start the first bin with the minimum value, 1802. However, it may be better to round down to 1800 so that each boundary will be a multiple of 25 and the century 1900 will fall on a boundary.

Count the frequency of each bin. You could use a table like this:

Bin	1800–1824	1825–1849	1850–1874	1875–1899	1900–1924	1925–1949
Frequency	5	8	9	9	16	6

Then create your histogram.

Establishment Dates of Canadian Universities (1800–1950)

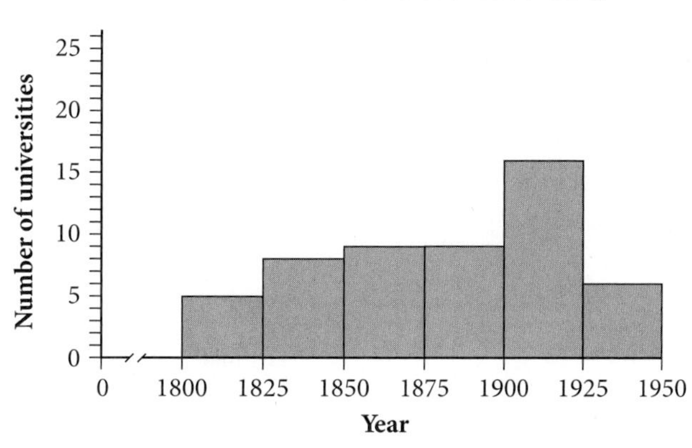

This histogram may or may not use the best bin width. Use your calculator to experiment with other bin widths for the data. Which bin width do you think highlights the spread of the data? Which do you think highlights the clustering of data? Does one bin width show an increasing trend?

When making a histogram, you might need to experiment with different bin widths. As you do this, you may wish to change your minimum value so that it is a multiple of the bin width.

Exercises

Practice Your Skills

1. Maive surveyed people attending matinee and evening ballet performances. She made these two graphs showing the ages of the attendees she surveyed.

Matinee Attendance

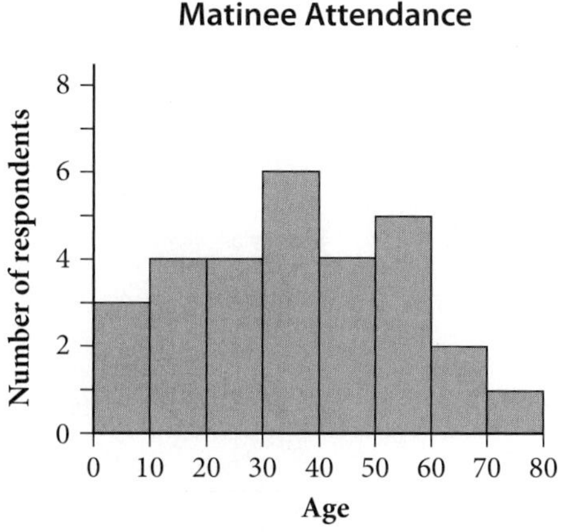

Evening Attendance

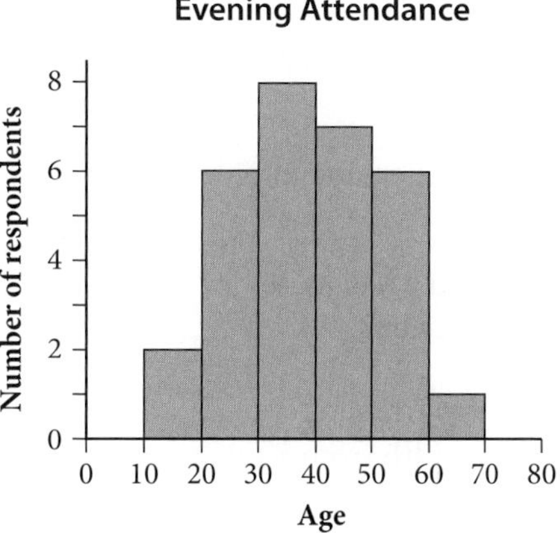

a. How many people did she survey at each performance? (h)

b. At which performance did the ages of survey respondents vary more?

c. How many children younger than age 10 responded to the survey at the evening performance? ⓐ

d. What can you say about the number of 15-year-olds surveyed at the matinee?

2. What bin width should you use to make histograms with the given minimum and maximum values and number of bins?

a. Minimum = 20, maximum = 94, number of bins = 8

b. Minimum = 20, maximum = 94, number of bins = 13

c. Minimum = 42, maximum = 161, number of bins = 10

d. Minimum = 28, maximum = 35, number of bins = 15

3. This box plot and histogram reflect the life expectancy in 2009 for countries with a population greater than 10 million.

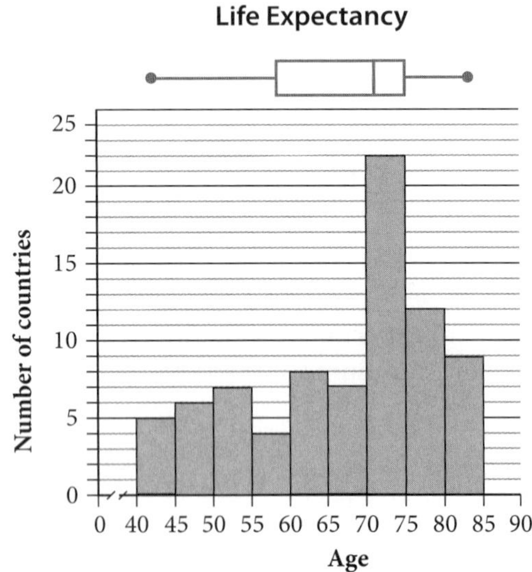

(United Nations Population Fund, in *The New York Times Almanac 2009*, pp. 487–489)

a. How many countries are represented? ⓐ

b. The box that spans from the median to the third quartile of the box plot is very short. What does this mean? ⓐ

c. How many countries had life expectancies of less than 60 years?

d. How can you tell that no country had a life expectancy of greater than 85 years?

4. Imagine that you redrew the histogram for Exercise 3 and changed the bin width from 5 to 10.

a. How many bins would you have?

b. How would the values on the vertical axis need to change?

c. Would the shape of the graphs be different or similar?

d. Sketch the new graph.

5. Suppose some class members measure the lengths of their ring fingers. The measurements are 6.5, 6.5, 7.0, 6.0, 7.5, 7.0, 8.5, and 7.0 cm.

a. Identify the minimum, maximum, and range values of the data.

b. Create a stem plot of these data values. @

Reason and Apply

6. Thirty students participated in a 20-problem mathematics competition. Here are the numbers of problems they got correct:

{12, 7, 8, 3, 5, 7, 10, 13, 7, 10, 2, 1, 11, 12, 17, 4, 11, 7, 6, 18, 14, 17, 11, 9, 1, 12, 10, 12, 2, 15}

a. Construct two histograms for the data. Use different bin widths for each.

b. What patterns do you notice in the data? What do the histograms tell you about the number of problems students tend to get correct?

c. Give the five-number summary for the data and construct a box plot.

d. Give the mode(s) for the data.

7. Sketch what you think a histogram looks like for each situation. Remember to label values and units on the axes.

a. The outcomes when rolling a die 100 times @

b. The estimates of the height of the classroom ceiling made by 100 different students

c. The ages of the next 100 people you meet in the school hallway

d. The 100 data values used to make this box plot (Use a bin width of 1.)

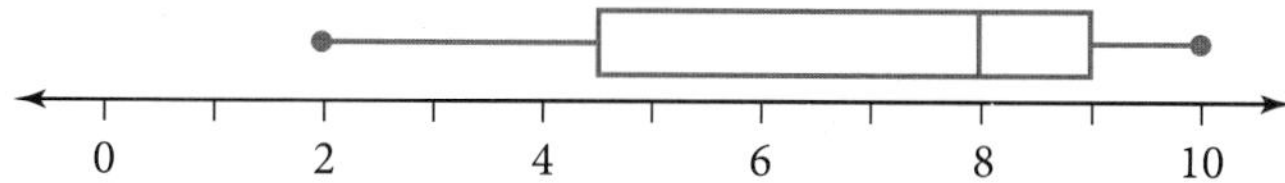

8. For each graph, create a data set with eight data values.

a. (h)

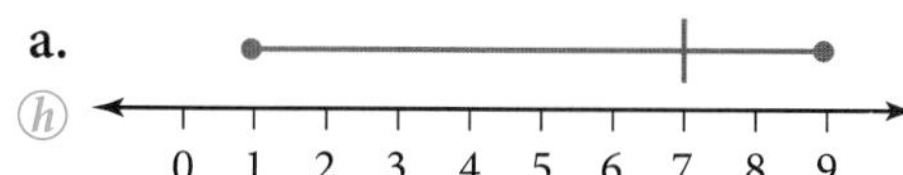

b.

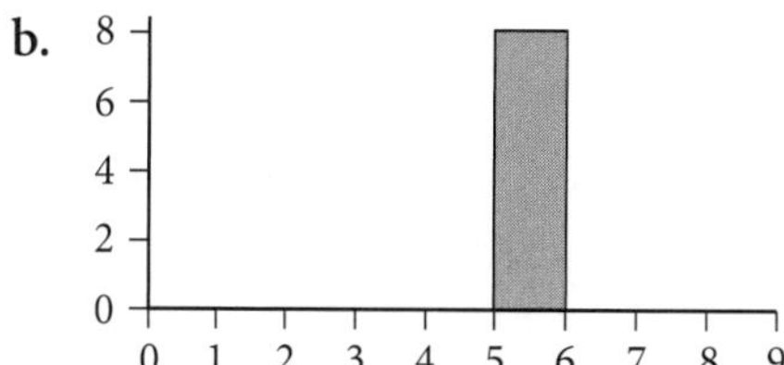

c.

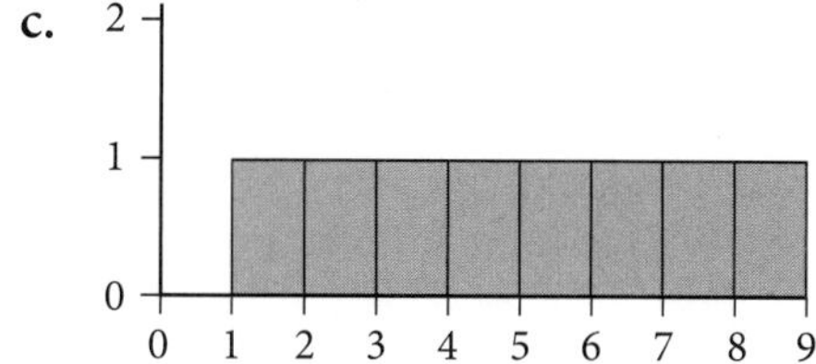

d. (h)

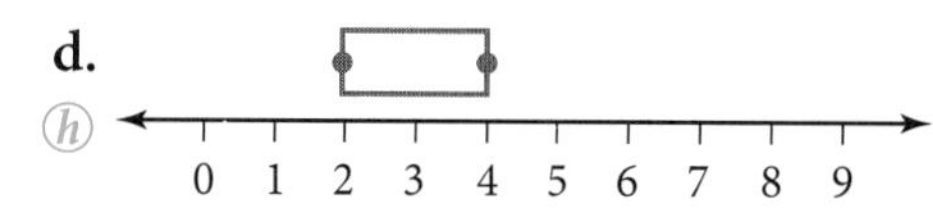

e.

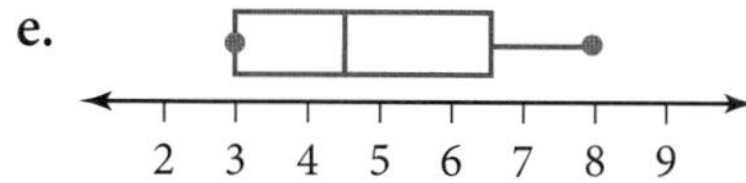

f.

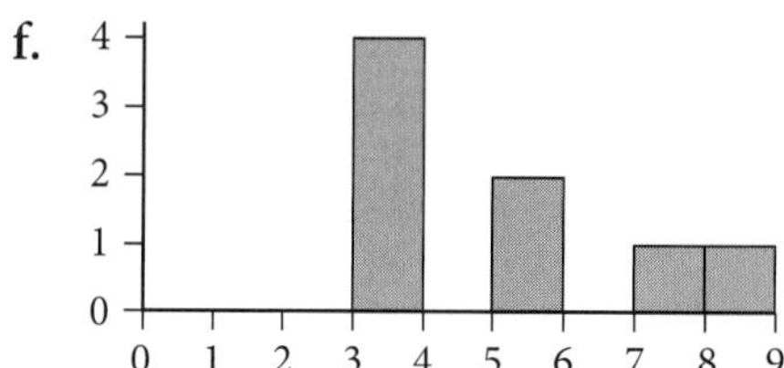

9. APPLICATION The histogram shows the results of an assessment on which 30 points were possible.

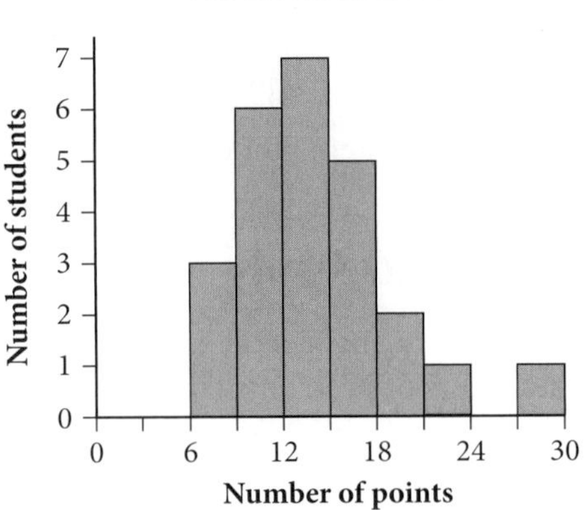

a. Explain your reasoning as you estimate the median and mean scores from this graph.

b. The most "influential" values in a set of data are the values that greatly change the statistics, such as the mean, when they are removed from the calculation. Which score is most influential?

c. Which score is least influential?

10. Chip and Dale, two algebra students, visited four different stores and recorded the prices on 1 lb bags of potato chips. They organized their data in the stem plot at right.

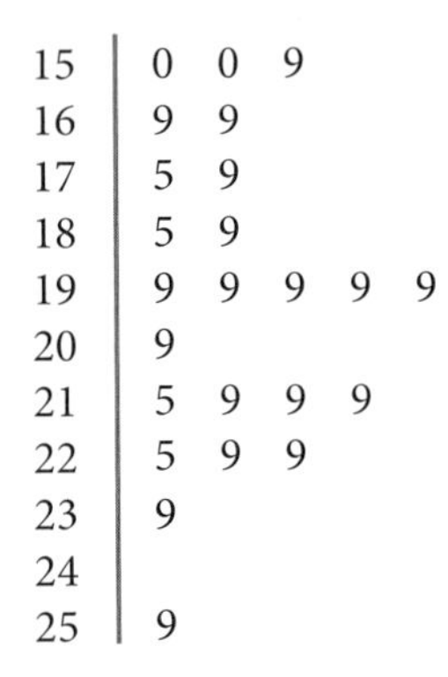

a. What is the lowest price they found? @

b. What do the entries in the third line from the top represent?

c. How many bags cost less than $2?

d. What is the most common price?

e. What is the range of prices for these chips?

11. Mac and Ida each weighed all the apples in a basket. One of them weighed apples bought from the farmers' market. The other weighed apples gathered from a backyard tree. Each found they had the same number of apples and their apples had the same mean weight. They created histograms showing their apple weights.

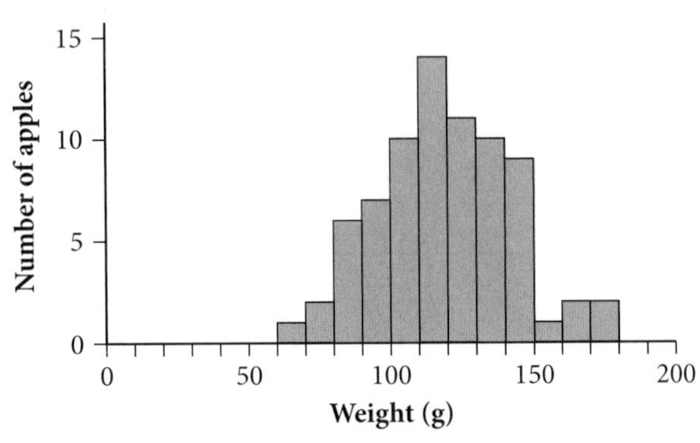

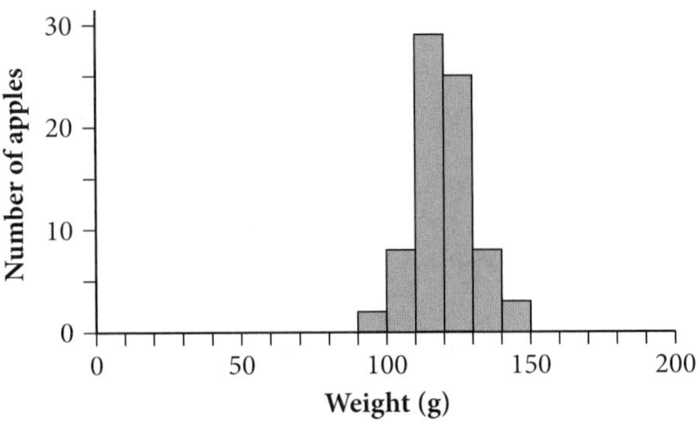

a. Who weighed the backyard apples and who weighed the purchased apples? Explain your reasoning. @

b. What differences in the two baskets of apples are indicated by the histograms?

c. What is similar about the shapes of the histograms? What might explain this similarity?

12. APPLICATION Four hospital emergency rooms collected data on how long patients on a given day waited before being seen. They created these histograms:

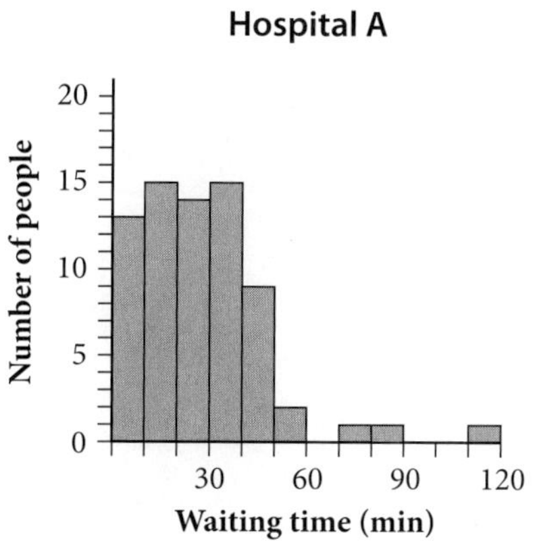

Hospital B

Number of people

Waiting time (min)

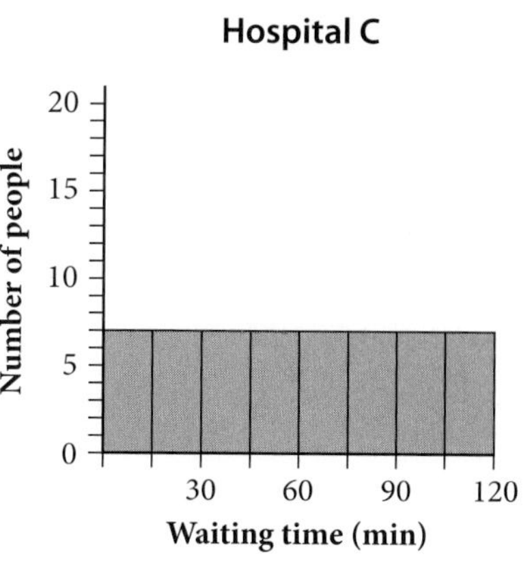

a. Describe the shape of each histogram. @

b. What do the histograms tell you about waiting times at each hospital?

c. Did patients at Hospital A generally have shorter waiting times than patients at Hospital B? Explain.

d. In an emergency, which hospital would you want to go to?

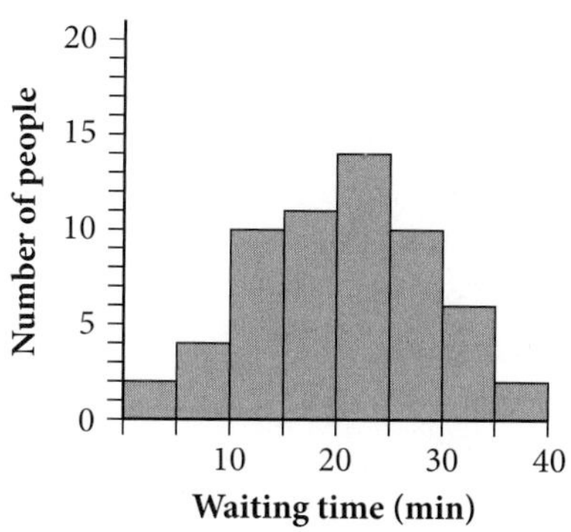

Review

13. This dot plot represents ages (in months) of students in an algebra class. Make a box plot of this data. Create a second box plot that pictures another algebra class with a youngest student who just turned 13 years old. The two classes have the same median student age and interquartile range. The new class has a range of 16 months and first quartile 3 months less than the median age.

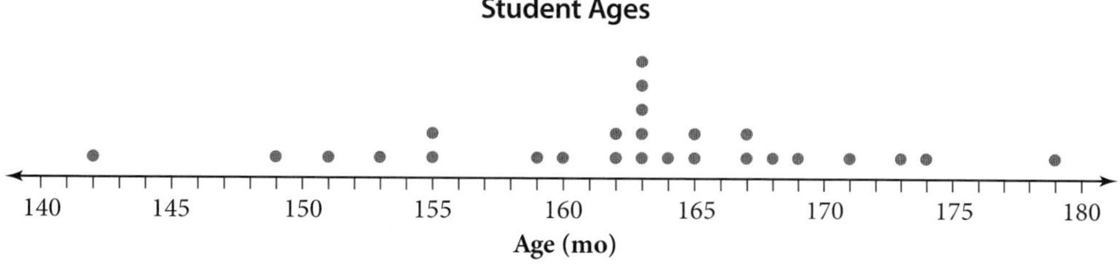

14. Create a data set of nine test scores with the five-number summary 64, 72, 82, 82, 95 and mean 79.

LESSON

1.5

Relative Frequency Graphs

"In this world nothing is certain but death and taxes."

BENJAMIN FRANKLIN

Earlier, in Chapter 1, you learned to display categorical data (data that are sorted into categories) in bar graphs. **Relative frequency graphs** also summarize data in categories, but instead of including the actual number for each category, they compare the number in that category to the total for all the categories. Relative frequency graphs can be bar graphs or circle graphs, and they show fractions or percents, not values.

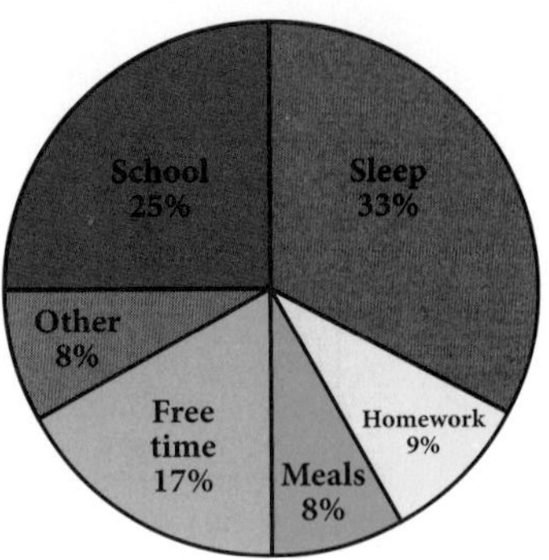

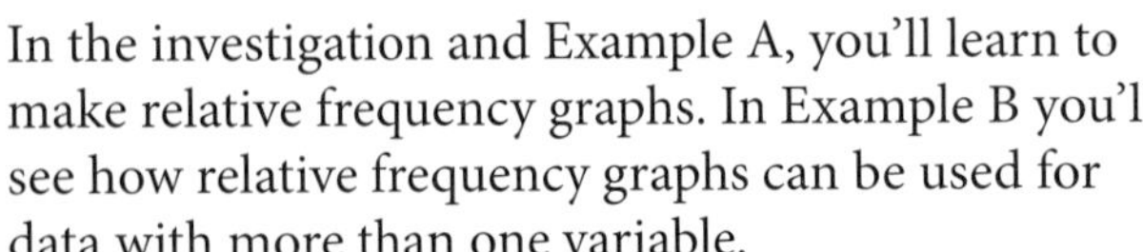

In the investigation and Example A, you'll learn to make relative frequency graphs. In Example B you'll see how relative frequency graphs can be used for data with more than one variable.

INVESTIGATION

Circle Graphs and Bar Graphs

YOU WILL NEED

- graph paper
- a protractor
- a compass or circle template
- a ruler

This bar graph shows the approximate land area of the seven continents.

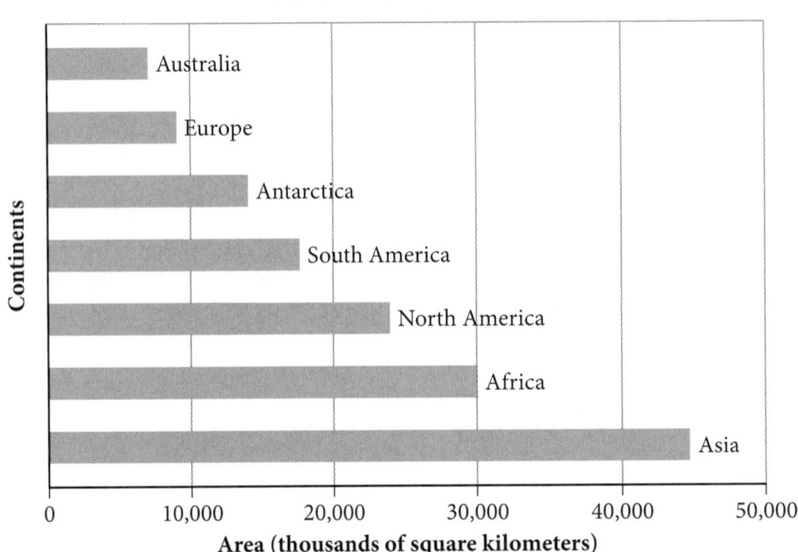

Step 1 Determine from the bar graph the approximate area of each continent and the total land area.

Step 2 Convert the data in the bar graph to a circle graph. Use the fact that there are 360 degrees in a circle. Write proportions to find the number of degrees in each sector of the circle graph. Then use a protractor to accurately draw each sector.

Step 3 Convert the data in the bar graph to a relative frequency circle graph. Instead of showing the land area, the graph will show percents of total land area.

Step 4 Convert the data from the bar graph to a relative frequency *bar* graph that shows percents rather than land areas.

Step 5 Compare the graphs you made with the original graph. What advantages are there to each kind of graph?

EXAMPLE A

Randy has been asked to create a graphical display showing the distribution of the library's collection in six categories. His boss has asked him to create two rough drafts. Together they will decide which one to finalize for the display.

He organized the data in a table.

Library Collection

Category	Number of items
Children's fiction	35,994
Children's nonfiction	28,106
Adult fiction	48,129
Adult nonfiction	69,834
Media	11,830
Other	5,766
Total	**199,659**

Solution

Randy decides to first create a circle graph. He puts the number of items in each category into *list1*. He wants the calculator to determine in *list2* the number of degrees needed for each sector. He writes a proportion to find the number of degrees in the sector for a particular category.

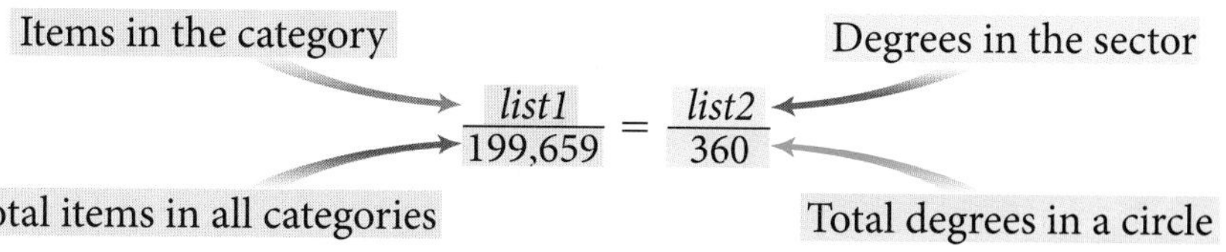

By multiplying by 360, he finds the formula to enter into *list2*.

$$list2 = list1 \cdot \frac{360}{199{,}659}$$

Randy's calculator quickly determines the number of degrees for each sector of the circle graph. Using a protractor to measure the angles, Randy creates the graph.

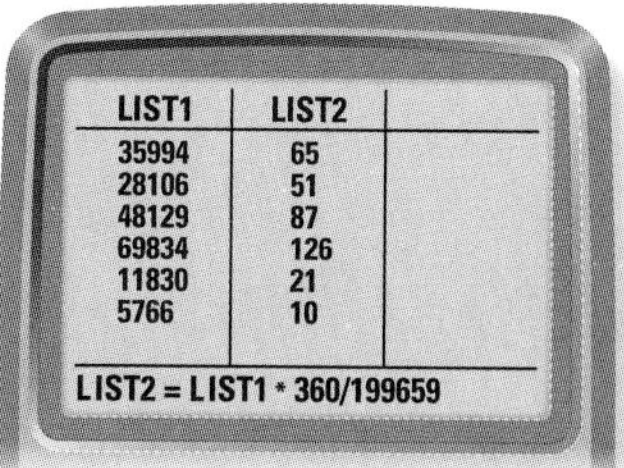

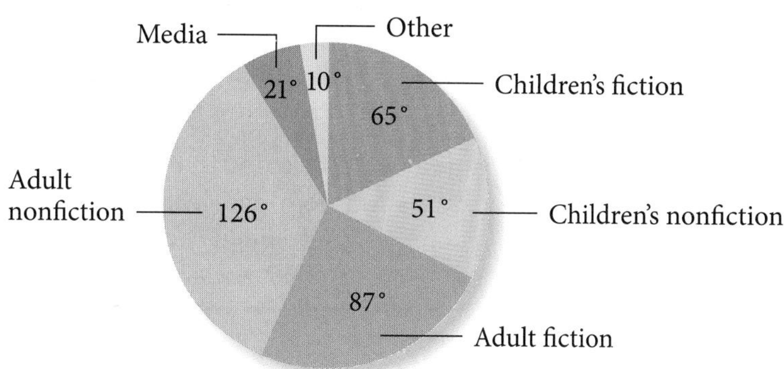

To make a relative frequency graph, Randy finds the percent of the total each category represents. He uses *list1* again and the proportion:

$$\frac{list1}{199{,}659} = \frac{list3}{100}$$

He solves the proportion for *list3* and enters the formula that will give him the percents.

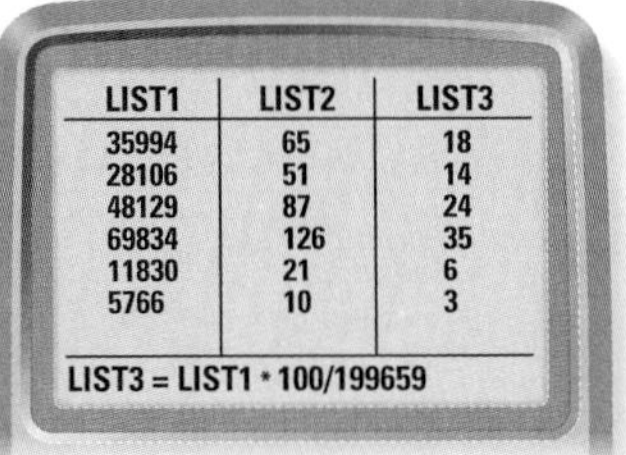

He makes a relative frequency circle graph by putting these percents in his circle graph. He then uses the same percents to create a relative frequency bar graph.

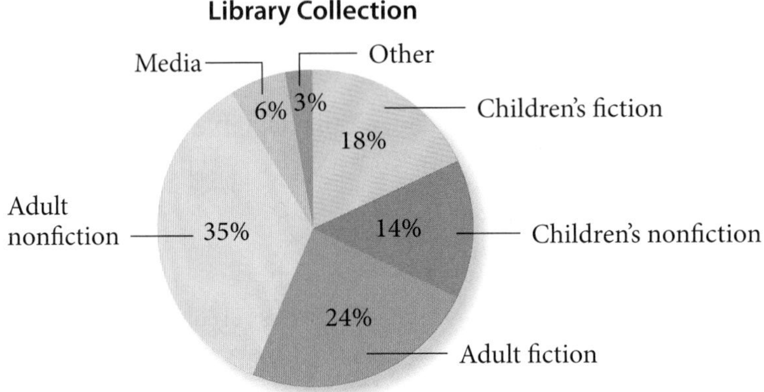

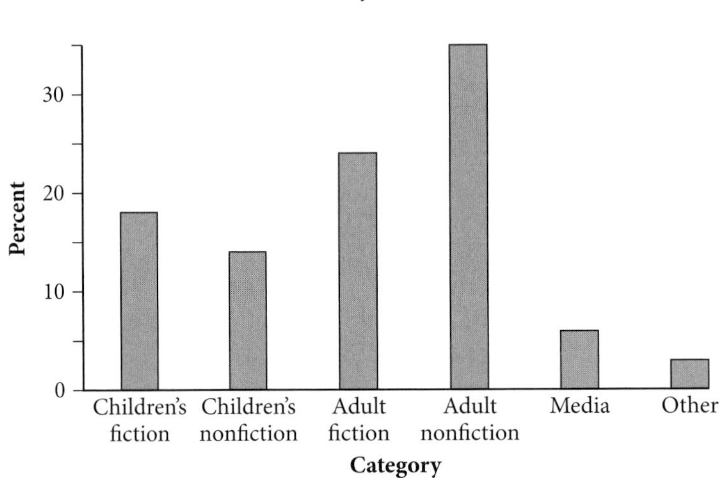

In Example A, do you think the relative frequency circle graph or the bar graph shows the data more clearly?

Like the box plots you studied in Lesson 1.3, relative frequency graphs give a visual summary of the data but don't show actual data values.

In the investigation, you worked with data that had only one variable. In Lesson 1.4 you used histograms and stem-and-leaf plots to display the number of times a value appears in a data set, or the frequency of that value. In Example B you will use a two-way frequency table to summarize data for two categories.

EXAMPLE B

This two-way frequency table shows the number of male and female students who wear glasses, wear contacts, or wear neither glasses nor contacts. Use the information in the table to answer the questions.

	Glasses	Contacts	Neither
Male	18	5	30
Female	8	12	35

a. How many of the female students surveyed wear contacts?

b. What is the total number of male students surveyed?

c. What percent of the students surveyed wear neither glasses nor contacts?

d. What percent of the students surveyed are male students who wear glasses?

e. What percent of students who wear glasses are female?

f. The Better Vision Eyewear store in Dubuque has decided to open a branch that caters just to women. How will the owners change their inventory to accommodate their female customers?

Solution

First, calculate the totals for each row and column. The totals report the marginal frequencies, or marginal distribution.

	Glasses	Contacts	Neither	Total
Male	18	5	30	53
Female	8	12	35	55
Total	26	17	65	108

a. The number of students that are jointly female and in the wears-contacts group is 12. Each cell of a two-way frequency table displays a **joint frequency,** in this case, the joint frequency of female students who wear contacts.

b. The total number of male students is 53. The totals of each row and column are the **marginal frequencies.**

c. The percent of students who wear neither glasses nor contacts is $\frac{65}{108}$, approximately 60%. This ratio is called the **marginal relative frequency,** a ratio of the marginal total to the table total. Relative frequencies are reported as ratios or percents.

d. The percent of the students surveyed who are male students who wear glasses is $\frac{18}{108}$, or about 17%. This ratio of the value in a cell to the table total is called the **joint relative frequency,** in this case the number of male students who wear glasses out of the total number of students surveyed.

e. The percent of students who wear glasses that are female is $\frac{8}{26}$, or about 31%. The ratio of the relative frequency for a condition to the marginal frequency of that condition is called **conditional relative frequency.** The conditional relative frequency compares data with respect to one specific condition, in this case the number of students who wear glasses and who are female.

f. The inventory should include more contacts than glasses because a greater number of women wear contacts than glasses, and women choose contacts more often than men, who usually choose glasses.

1.5 Exercises

Practice Your Skills

1. APPLICATION There are four basic blood types. The distribution of these types in the general population is shown in the relative frequency circle graph. In a city of 75,000 people, about how many people with each blood type would you expect to find? ⓐ

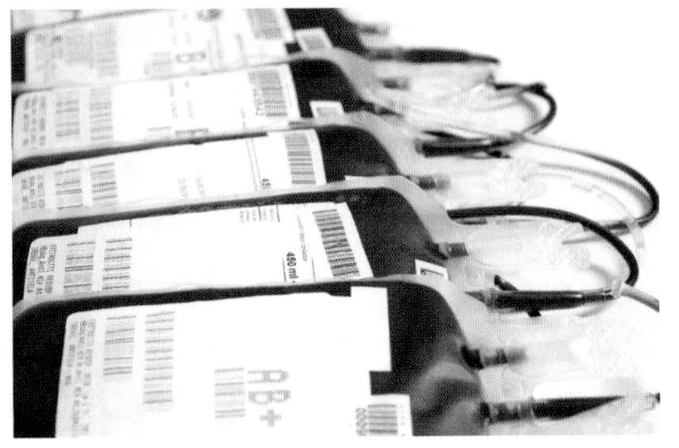

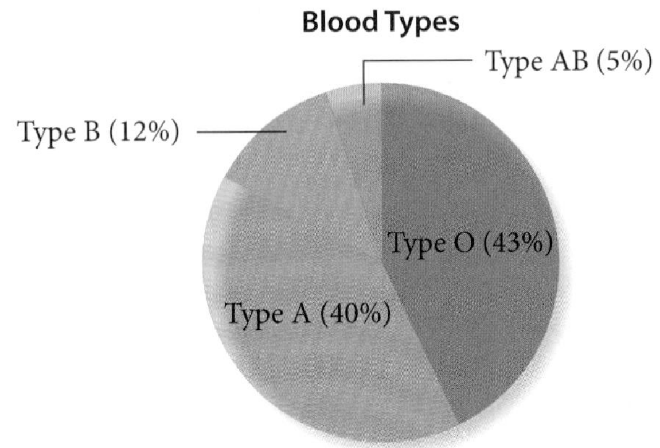

2. Which data set matches the relative frequency circle graph at right? ⓗ

i. {15, 18, 22, 25, 28} ii. {20, 24, 30, 36, 45}

iii. {12, 18, 24, 30, 36} iv. {9, 12, 18, 20, 24}

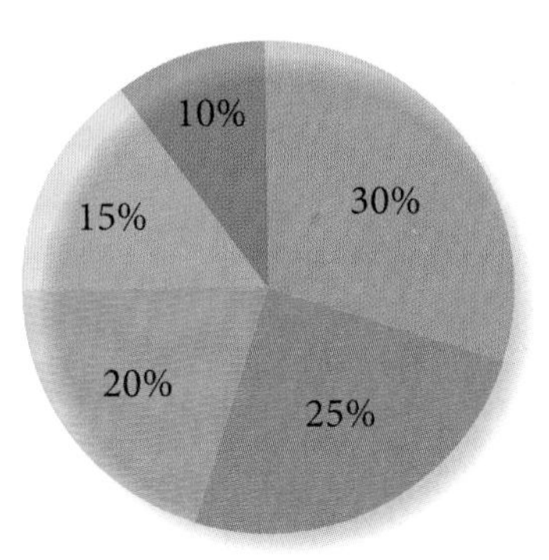

3. In the relative frequency bar graph of the library's collection created in Example A, the bar for adult fiction represents 24%. Could there be a situation in which all the bars represented 24%? Explain your thinking. ⓐ

Reason and Apply

4. A manufacturer states that it produces colored candies according to the percents listed in this table. Create a relative frequency circle graph to show this information. Label the degree measure of each sector.

Colored Candies Manufactured

Orange	Yellow	Blue	Red	Green	Brown
10%	20%	10%	20%	10%	30%

5. Chloe bought a small package of the candies described in Exercise 4 and counted the number of each color. Her count is listed in the table at right.

Chloe's Colored Candies

Orange	Yellow	Blue	Red	Green	Brown
11	10	4	12	7	14

a. Construct a relative frequency bar graph for Chloe's package of candies.

b. Construct a relative frequency bar graph that shows on one graph both Chloe's small package of candies and the percents stated by the candy manufacturer. Use one color for the bar representing Chloe's candies and a different color for the bar representing the manufacturer's. Include a key showing what each bar color means. What conclusions can you draw? ⓐ

6. This table shows the number of students in each grade at a high school.

Class Size

Ninth grade	Tenth grade	Eleventh grade	Twelfth grade
185	175	166	150

a. What percent of the school is represented in each grade? (h)

b. After the semester break, the student population has changed. The ninth grade has increased by 2%, the tenth grade has decreased by 1.5%, the eleventh grade has increased by 2.5%, and the twelfth grade has decreased by 2%. How many students are in each grade at the beginning of the second semester? By what percent has the total school population changed? What is the actual change in the number of students?

c. Construct a relative frequency circle graph for the situation at the beginning of the year and another circle graph for the situation at the beginning of the second semester. How has the distribution of students changed?

7. Match each bar graph with its corresponding circle graph. Try to do this without calculating the actual percents.

a.

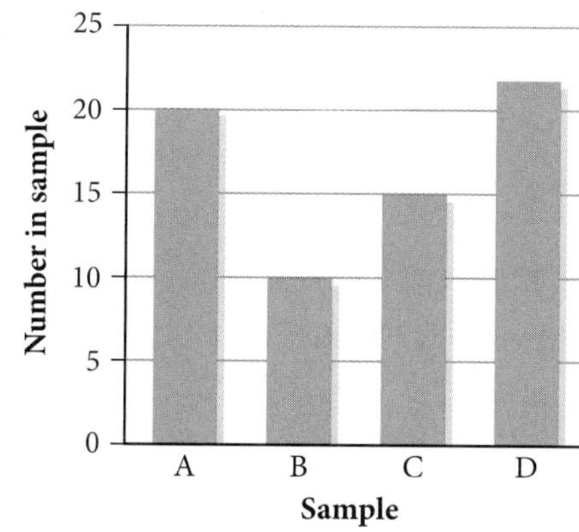

b. (a)

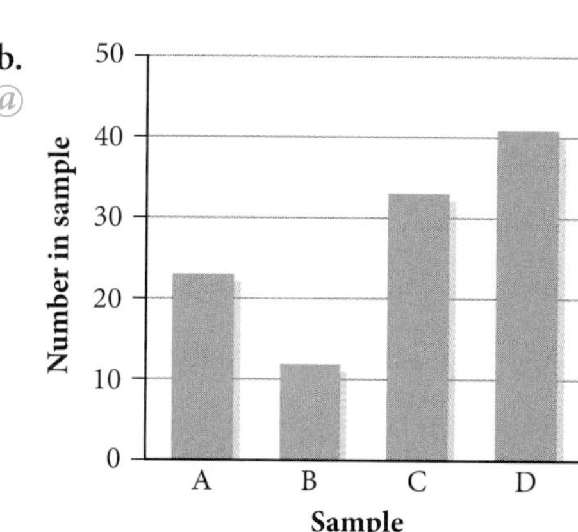

c.

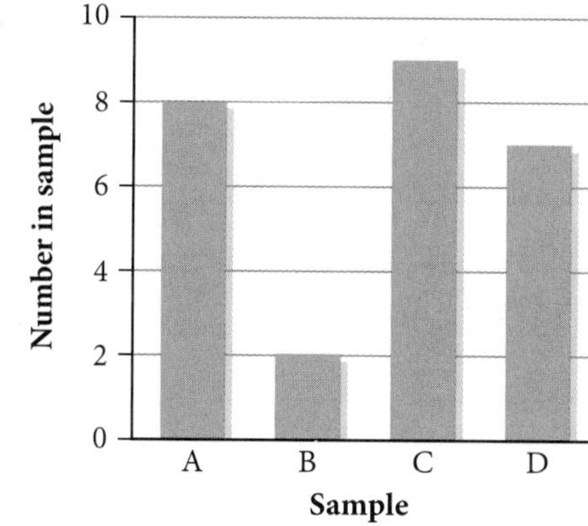

d.

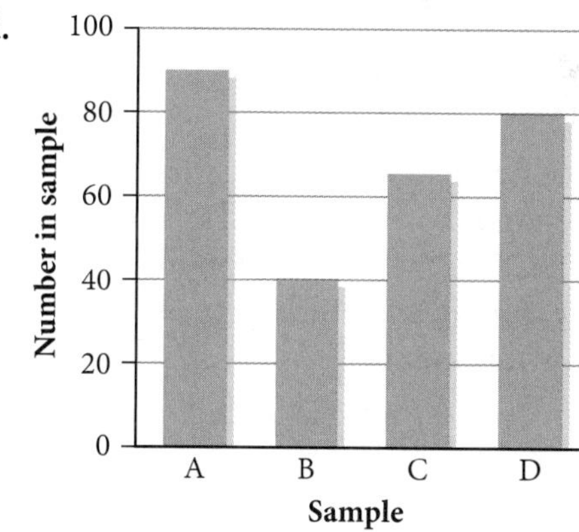

i.

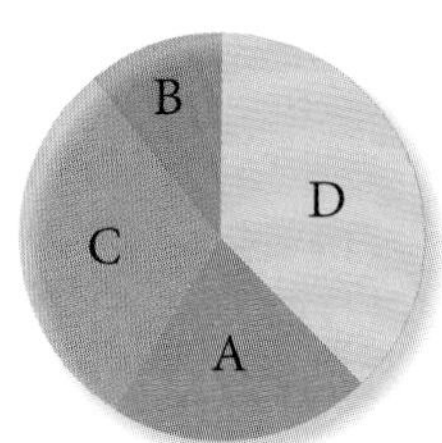

ii.

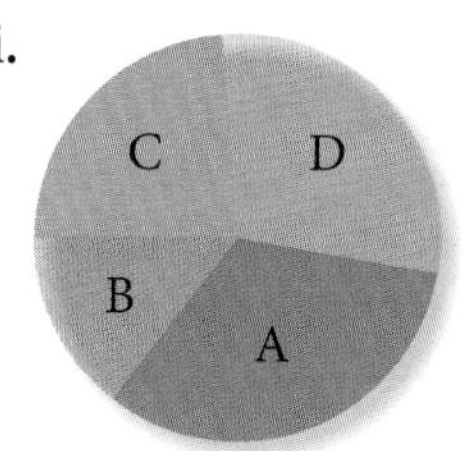

iii.

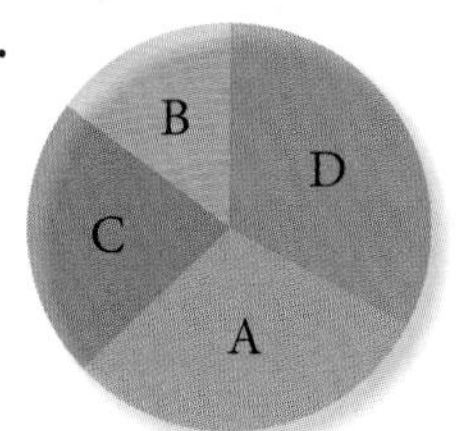

iv.

C D B A

8. This two-way table gives the voter turnout for the 2010 U.S. elections, rounded to the nearest thousand.

	White (non-Hispanic)	Black (non-Hispanic)	Hispanic	Asian (non-Hispanic)
Voted in 2010	74,372,000	11,149,000	6,646,000	2,354,000
Registered but did not vote	29,944,000	4,952,000	4,336,000	1,411,000
Citizens not registered to vote	48,613,000	9,531,000	10,982,000	3,874,000

(U.S. Census Bureau, 2010)

a. Calculate the conditional relative frequencies of the number of people of each ethnicity in the table who voted in 2010.

b. What pattern do you see in the frequency results in 8a?

9. This two-way table gives the number of male and female students participating in a variety of after-school activities.

	Chess	Mu Alpha Theta	Science	Fine Arts
Female	8	18	10	21
Male	23	22	12	5

a. What is the marginal relative frequency of students who prefer Mu Alpha Theta?

b. What is the joint relative frequency of male students who prefer the chess club?

c. What is the conditional relative frequency of female students who prefer the fine arts club?

d. An all-girl charter school is opening in town. How should the school assign staff to after-school activities to meet the needs of the students?

10. Complete the two-way table for exercise habits of Shenandoah High School's freshman class. Use the information to answer these questions. Which frequency is reported by the answer?

	Male	Female	Totals
Exercises regularly		115	300
Does not exercise regularly	135	160	
Totals		275	

a. How many females were included in the survey?

b. How many males exercise regularly?

c. What percent of the total number of females do not exercise regularly?

d. What percent of the total number of students exercise regularly?

11. This two-way table lists the favorite genres of television shows of the Linden Fire Auxiliary.

	Drama	Comedy	Sports	Total
Men	2	8	10	20
Women	16	8	6	30
Total	18	16	16	50

When asked to identify a conditional relative frequency from the table, Parker said the conditional relative frequency of women who prefer dramas is $\frac{16}{30}$. Caleb said the conditional relative frequency of drama for women is $\frac{16}{18}$. Describe how they got their answers. Who is correct? Explain.

Review

12. Mr. Chin and Mrs. Shapiro had their classes collect data on the amount of change each student had in class one day. The students graphed the data on the back-to-back stem plot at right.

a. How many students are in each class?

b. Find the range of the data in each class.

c. How many students had more than $1?

d. What do the entries in the last row represent?

e. Without adding, make an educated guess as to which class has the most money altogether. Explain your thinking.

f. How much money does each class have?

Mrs. Shapiro's class		Mr. Chin's class
0 0 0 0	0	0 0 0 0 5 8
2 0	1	0 5 6
5 5 5	2	0 0 5 5 5 7
9 6 5 0 0	3	5 5
5	4	0 0 0 6
5 2 0 0	5	0 0 5 5 8
7 3 0 0	6	0 2 5 5
5 0	7	0 5 5 6
2 0 0	8	
4 1	9	
4 0 0	10	0 0 5
5 0	11	0
6 4 1	12	1 5 5
5 0	13	

Key

5 | 4 | 0 0 0 6

means 45¢ in Mrs. Shapiro's class; 40¢, 40¢, 40¢, and 46¢ in Mr. Chin's class

13. Create a data set that fits the information. (h)

a. Ten students were asked the number of times they had flown in an airplane. The range of data values was 7. The minimum was 0, and the mode was 2.

b. Eight students each measured the length of his or her right foot. The range of data values was 8.2 cm, and the maximum value was 30.4 cm. There was no mode.

LESSON 1.6

ACTIVITY DAY

Exploring a Conjecture

data
measures of center
mean
median
mode
measure of spread
range
interquartile range (IQR)
MAD

five-number summary
minimum
maximum
first quartile (Q_1)
third quartile (Q_3)
outlier

pictograph
bar graph
dot plot
box-and-whisker plot
histogram
frequency
stem-and-leaf plot

Statistics is a branch of applied mathematics dedicated to collecting and analyzing numerical data. The **data analysis** that statisticians do is used in science, government, and social services like health care. In this chapter you have learned concepts fundamental to statistics: measures of center, summary values, and types of graphs to organize and display data. Terms you have learned are in the box at left.

Each measure or graph tells part of the story. Yet having too much information for a data set might not be helpful. Statisticians, and other people who work with data, must choose which measures and graphs give the best picture of a particular situation. Carefully chosen statistics can be informative and persuasive. Poorly chosen statistics, ones that don't show important characteristics of the data set, can be accidentally or deliberately misleading.

ACTIVITY

The Conjecture

YOU WILL NEED

- two books
- graph paper
- colored pencils or pens
- poster paper

A **conjecture** is a statement that might be true but has not been proved. Your group's goal is to come up with a conjecture relating two things and then to collect and analyze the numerical evidence to either support your conjecture or cast doubt on it.

In this activity you'll review the measures and graphs you have learned. Along the way, you will be faced with questions that statisticians face every day.

Step 1 Your group should select two books on different subjects or with different reading levels. Flip through the books, but do not examine them in depth. State a conjecture comparing these two books. Your conjecture should deal with a quantity that you can count or measure—for example, "The history book has more words per sentence than the math book."

Step 2 Decide how much data you'll need to convince yourself and your group that the conjecture is true or doubtful. Design a way to choose data to count or measure. You will want your data to reflect the whole book. A sample that includes only pages from Chapter 1 or only the first page of each chapter, for example, might be biased. You might use your calculator to randomly select a page or a sentence. [▶ See **Calculator Note: Generating Random Integers** to learn how to generate random numbers. ◀]

Step 3 Collect data from both books. Be consistent in your data collection, especially if more than one person is doing the collecting. Assign tasks to each member of your group. Trade tasks partway through to avoid bias in the data collection.

Step 4 Calculate three measures of center and three measures of spread.

Step 5 Create a dot plot or stem-and-leaf plot for each data set.

Step 6 Make box plots for both data sets above the same horizontal axis.

Step 7 Make a histogram for each data set.

Be sure that you have used descriptive units for all your measures and clearly labeled your axes and plots before going on to the next step.

Step 8 Choose one or two of the measures and one pair of graphs that you feel give the best evidence for or against your conjecture. Prepare a brief report or a poster that includes each of the following.

a. Your conjecture.

b. A description of how you collected your data and why your sample is unbiased.

c. Tables showing all the data you collected.

d. The measures and graphs that seem to support or disprove your conjecture.

e. Your conclusion should contrast the centers of the two data sets. If possible, express the difference between the centers in terms of a measure of spread.

Step 9 You took care in your procedure to guard against bias. Suppose you want your data to reach a different conclusion. How might you change your procedures to bias your data?

LESSON

1.7 Two-Variable Data

In statistics a **variable** is a trait that can take on different values. For example, age will vary from person to person. A data set that contains measures of only one trait is called **one-variable data.** In Lessons 1.1 to 1.6, you learned to graph and summarize one-variable data. These data may be either **quantitative** (numeric) or **qualitative** (such as hair color or gender).

Often we get more than one piece of information from a source, such as height and shoe size. In this lesson you will explore **two-variable data** in situations where both variables are numeric. To look for relationships between these variables, you will use the **coordinate plane** to create graphs called **scatter plots.**

Scatter plots involve plotting **coordinates,** written as (x, y), such as $(-1, 2)$ plotted here. The coordinates tell a point's horizontal distance x and vertical distance y from the origin. The horizontal distance x is always listed first, so (x, y) is called an **ordered pair.** This first coordinate is also called the **abscissa,** and the second coordinate, the **ordinate.** The two **axes** intersect at the **origin,** (0, 0), and divide the **coordinate plane** into four **quadrants.**

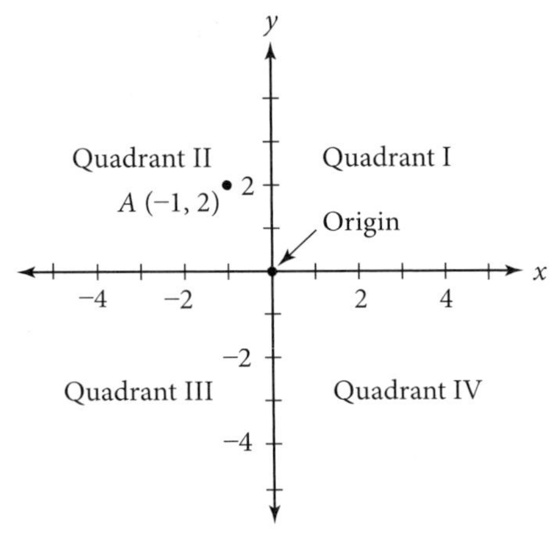

INVESTIGATION

Let It Roll!

YOU WILL NEED

- a centimeter ruler
- a centimeter tape measure
- a ramp, such as a book, notebook, or stiff piece of cardboard
- an object that rolls, such as a pencil, soda can, or toy with wheels
- graph paper

Just how far will an object roll? If you roll it from a different height, will this distance change? One way to begin to answer questions like these is to collect some data. In this investigation you'll collect two-variable data: The first variable will be the release height of the ramp, and the second variable will be the distance from the ramp at which the object stops rolling. A graph of these data points may help you see a relationship between the two variables.

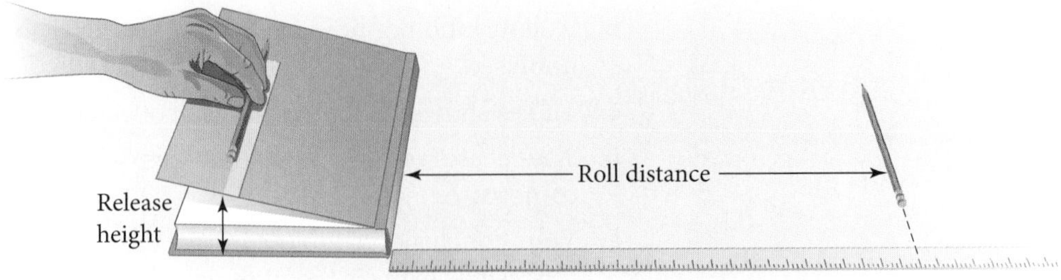

Step 1 Set up your experiment as shown in the diagram on the previous page. Mark the point on the ramp from which you will release your rolling object. Make sure that you have plenty of room in front of your ramp for the object to roll freely. Record the release height of the object in a table like the one at right.

Release height (cm)	Roll distance (cm)

Step 2 Release the object and let it roll to a stop. Measure the distance the object traveled from the base of the ramp to its stopping point. Record this roll distance in your table.

Step 3 Repeat the experiment at least five times, using a different release height each time. Record the data in your table.

Step 4 Create a set of axes on your graph paper. Label the axes as shown.

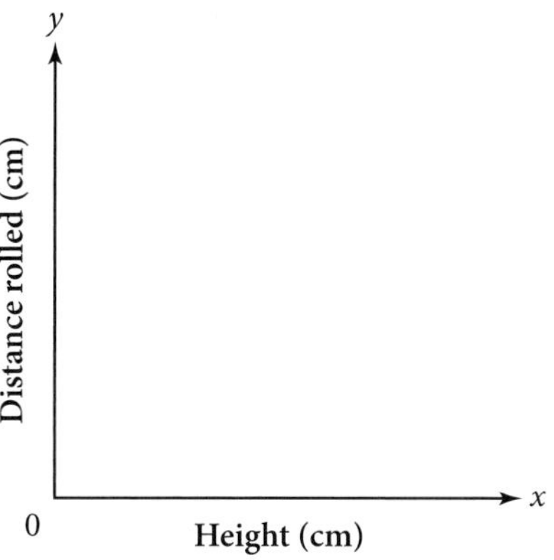

Step 5 Scale the x-axis appropriately to fit all your height values. For example, if your greatest height was 8.5 cm, you might make each grid unit represent 0.5 cm. Scale the y-axis to fit all your roll-distance values. For example, if your longest roll length was 80 cm, you might use 10 cm for each vertical grid unit.

Step 6 Plot each piece of two-variable data from your table. Think of each row in your table as an ordered pair. Locate each point by first moving along the horizontal axis to the release-height measurement. Then move up vertically to the corresponding roll distance. Mark this point with a small dot.

Step 7 Describe any patterns you see in the graph. Is there a relationship between the two variables?

Step 8 Enter the information from your table into two calculator lists. Make a scatter plot. The calculator display should look like the graph you drew by hand. [▶ See **Calculator Note: Scatter Plots** to learn how to display this information on your calculator screen. ◀]

This police officer is using a radar device that measures the speed of oncoming cars.

There are many ways to collect data. Have you ever seen a police officer measuring the speed of an approaching car? Have you wondered how technicians measure the speed of a baseball pitch? Did you know that satellites collect information about Earth from distances of over 320 miles? Each of these measurements involves the use of remote sensors that collect data. In this course you may have the opportunity to work with portable sensor equipment.

EXAMPLE

This scatter plot shows how the distance from a motion sensor to a person varies over a period of 6 s. Describe where the person is in relation to the sensor at each second.

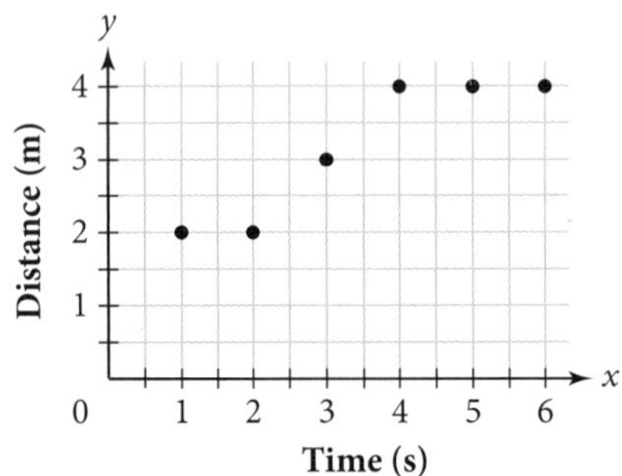

Solution

The first point, (1, 2), shows that after 1 s, the person was 2 m away from the sensor.

The next point, (2, 2), indicates that after 2 s, the person was still 2 m away.

The point (3, 3) means that after 3 s, the person was 3 m away.

The point (4, 4) means that at 4 s, the person was 4 m away. He or she remained 4 m away until 6 s had passed, as indicated by the points (5, 4) and (6, 4).

The graph in the example is a **first-quadrant graph** because all the values are positive. A lot of real-world data are described with only positive numbers, so first-quadrant graphs are very useful. However, you could graph the person's distances *in front of* the sensor as positive values and his or her distances *behind* the sensor as negative values. That would require more than one quadrant to show the data. How would you interpret a graph showing negative values of time?

1.7 Exercises

You will need your graphing calculator for Exercise **9.**

Practice Your Skills

1. Draw and label a coordinate plane so that the x-axis extends from -9 to 9 and the y-axis extends from -6 to 6. Represent each of these points with a dot, and label the point using its letter name.

$A(-5, -3.5)$ ⓐ	$B(2.5, -5)$ ⓐ	$C(5, 0)$ ⓐ	$D(-1.5, 4)$	$E(0, 4.5)$
$F(2, -3)$	$G(-4, -1)$	$H(-5, 5)$	$I(4, 3)$	$J(0, 0)$

2. Give the coordinates of each point on the scatter plot, and identify either the quadrant or the axis where the point is located. If you would like more practice with this skill, run the program POINTS.
[▸ Use the link in your ebook to download the program file POINTS. ◂]

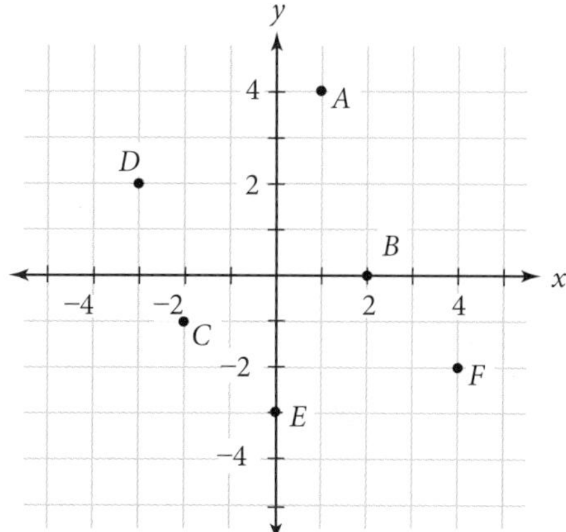

3. Sketch a coordinate plane. Label the axes and each of the four quadrants—I, II, III, and IV. Identify the axis or quadrant location of each point described.

a. The first coordinate is positive, and the second coordinate is 0.

b. The abscissa is negative, and the ordinate is positive.

c. Both coordinates are positive.

d. Both coordinates are negative.

e. The coordinates are (0, 0).

f. The ordinate is negative, and the abscissa is 0.

Reason and Apply

4. This graph represents a walker's distance from a stationary motion sensor.

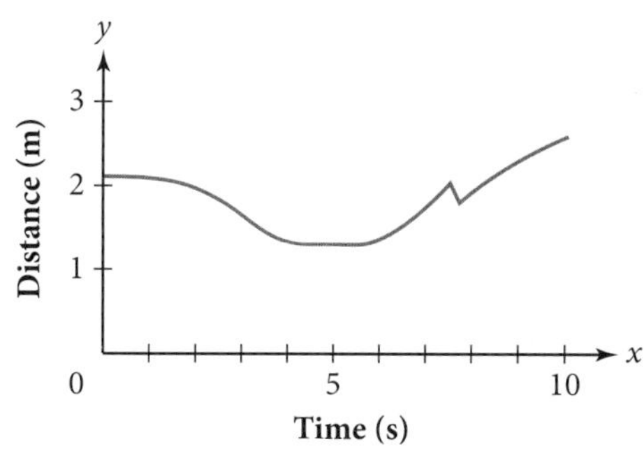

These people are running and walking in a fund-raiser to support cancer research.

a. How far away was the walker after 2 s? ⓐ

b. At what time was the walker closest to the motion sensor? ⓐ

c. Approximately how far away was the walker after 10 s? ⓐ

d. When, if ever, did the walker stop? ⓐ

5. Look at this scatter plot.

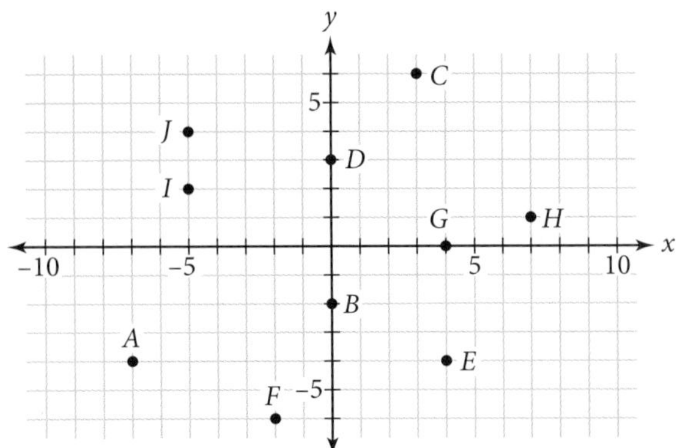

a. Name the (x, y)-coordinates of each point pictured.

b. Enter the x-coordinates of the points you named in 5a into the first calculator list and the corresponding y-coordinates into the second. Set your graphing window to the values suggested in the pictured graph, and make a scatter plot of the points.

c. Which points are on an axis?

d. List the points in Quadrant I, Quadrant II, Quadrant III, and Quadrant IV.

6. Write a paragraph explaining how to make a calculator scatter plot and how to identify point locations in the coordinate plane.

7. APPLICATION This graph is created by connecting the points in a scatter plot as you move from left to right. Describe the patterns you see in the graph. How would you explain these patterns?

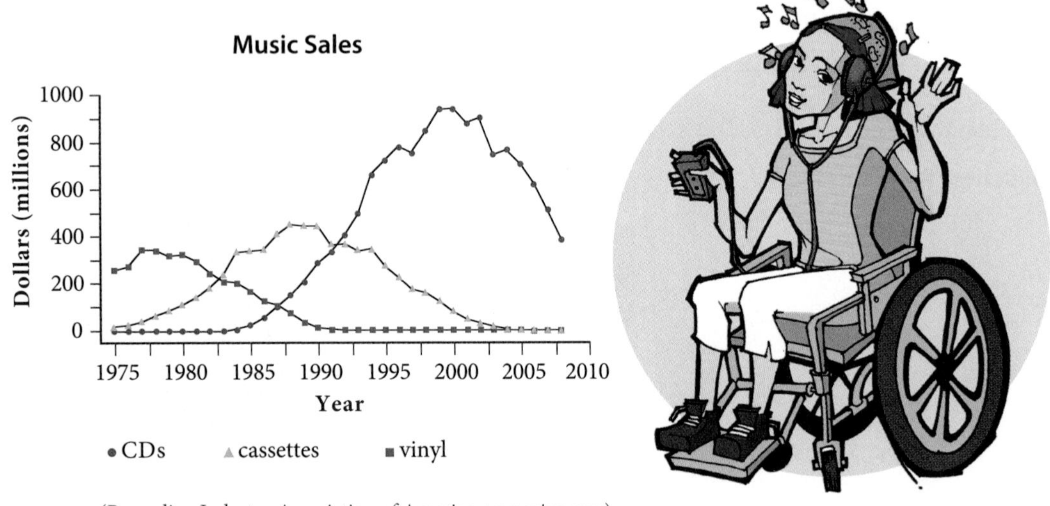

(Recording Industry Association of America, *www.riaa.com*)

8. The data in this table show the average number of miles traveled per gallon of gasoline (mi/gal) for new cars in the United States during the indicated years.

a. Make a scatter plot on your paper. Use the year as the abscissa and the miles per gallon as the ordinate. Carefully label and scale your axes. Give your graph a title.

b. Connect each point in your scatter plot with a line segment from left to right.

c. Based on any pattern you see in the graph, estimate the new U.S. automobile miles per gallon for 2020.

Average Miles per Gallon for New U.S. Automobiles

Year	Miles per gallon
1980	24.3
1985	27.6
1990	28.0
1995	28.6
2000	28.5
2003	29.5
2004	29.5
2005	30.3
2006	30.1
2007	31.2
2008	31.2

(U.S. Department of Transportation, *www.dot.gov*) [Data set: **AMPG**]

Technology CONNECTION

New technologies are being developed to improve car gas mileage. Car manufacturers are now producing cars that run on electricity or a combination of gasoline and electricity. Some cars and buses run on natural gas, or even recycled vegetable oil!

9. The graph at right is a hexagon whose vertices are six ordered pairs. Two of the points are (3, 0) and (1.5, 2.6). The hexagon is centered at the origin.

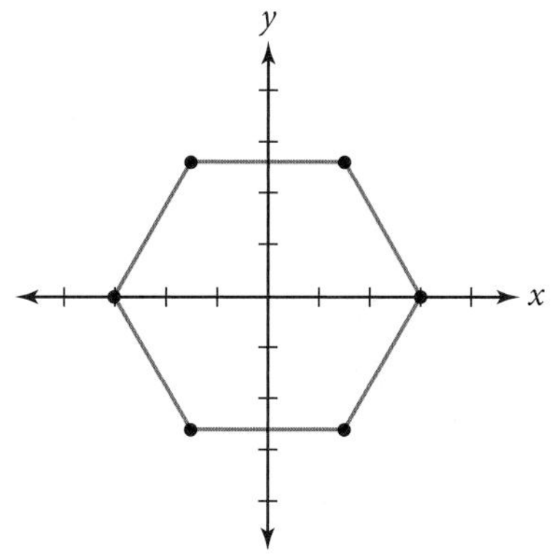

a. What are the coordinates of the other points?

b. Create this connected graph on your calculator. Add a few more points and line segments to make a piece of calculator art. Identify the points you added. [See **Calculator Note: Connecting the Points** to learn how to connect a scatter plot.]

10. Anthony's dad braked suddenly to avoid hitting a squirrel as he drove Anthony to school. The speed during the trip to school is shown on the graph at right.

a. At what time did Anthony's dad apply the brakes? @

b. What was his fastest speed during the trip?

c. How long did it take Anthony to get to school? @

d. Find one feature of this graph that you think is unrealistic.

Anthony's Trip to School

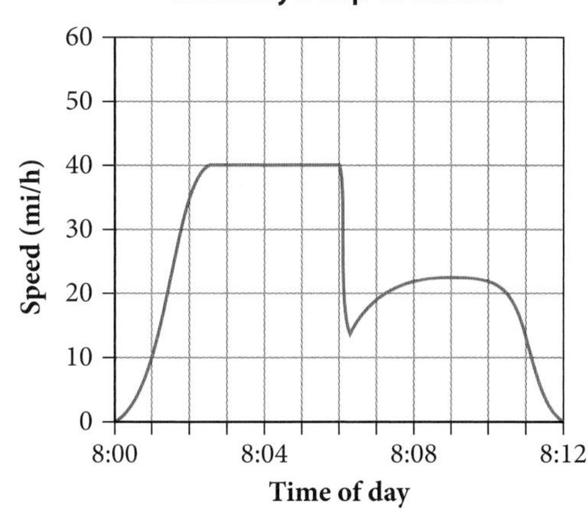

Review

11. Create a data set with the specified number of items and the five-number summary values 5, 12, 15, 30, 47.

a. 7 **b.** 10 **c.** 12

12. The table at right gives results for eighth-grade students in the 2007 Trends in International Mathematics and Science Study.

a. Find the five-number summary for this data set.

b. Construct a box plot for these data.

c. Between which five-number summary values is there the greatest spread of data? The least spread?

d. What is the interquartile range?

e. List the countries between the first quartile and the median. List those above the third quartile.

Results of the 2007 Trends in International Mathematics and Science Study (8th Grade)

Country	Mean score	Country	Mean score
Singapore	567	Lithuania	519
Japan	554	Australia	515
Korea, Republic of	553	Sweden	511
England	542	Scotland	496
Hungary	539	Norway	487
Czech Republic	539	Romania	462
Slovenia	538	Iran	459
Hong Kong SAR	530	Cyprus	452
Russian Federation	530	Colombia	417
United States	520		

(National Center for Education Statistics, *www.nces.ed.gov*)

IMPROVING YOUR Reasoning SKILLS

A *glyph* is a symbol that presents information nonverbally. These weather glyphs show data values for several variables in one symbol. How many variables can you identify? The diagram shows data for 12 hours starting at 12:00 noon. Which characteristics would you call categorical? Which are numeric? Is it possible to show all or some of the data using one or more of the graph types you learned to use in this chapter? How would you do that? Which types of graphs have the greatest advantages in this situation? Why?

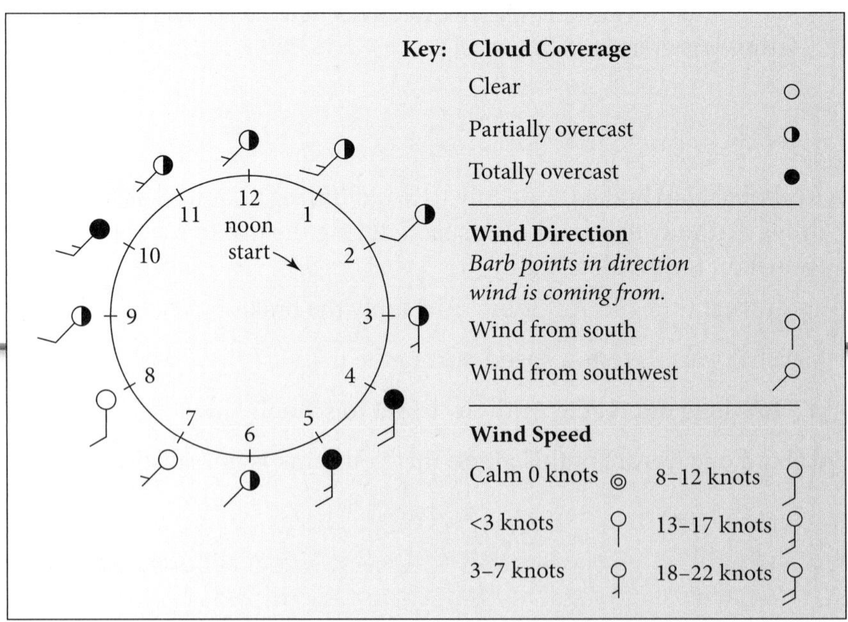

LESSON

1.8

Lines and Data

"Statistics are no substitute for judgment."

HENRY CLAY

Suppose you asked a friend her age and she said she was 15.436612 years old. You'd laugh. Or suppose a classmate said he lived 7.442761 miles from school. Maybe then you wouldn't laugh. In each case, you expect an estimate rather than an exact value. In this lesson you'll use scatter plots to make estimates. You will also discover how to compare these scatter plots to a graph of $y = x$.

INVESTIGATION

Guesstimating

YOU WILL NEED

- a meterstick, tape measure, or motion sensor

In this investigation you will estimate and measure distances around your room. As a group, select a starting point for your measurements. Choose nine objects in the room that appear to be less than 5 m away.

	x	y
Description	Actual distance (cm)	Estimated distance (cm)
(item 1)		
(item 2)		
(item 3)		

Step 1 List the objects in the description column of a table like this one.

Step 2 Estimate the distance in centimeters from your starting point to each object. If group members disagree, find the mean of your estimates. Record the estimates in your table.

Step 3 Measure the actual distance to each object, and record it in the table.

Step 4 Draw coordinate axes and label the x-axis *actual distance* and the y-axis *estimated distance.* Use the same scale on both axes. Carefully plot your nine points.

Step 5 Describe what this graph would look like if each of your estimates had been exactly the same as the actual measurement. How could you indicate this pattern on your graph?

Step 6 Make a calculator scatter plot of your data. Use your paper-and-pencil graph as a guide for setting a good graphing window.

Step 7 On your calculator, graph the line $y = x$. What does this *equation* represent? [▶ See **Calculator Note: Equations** to learn how to graph a scatter plot and an equation simultaneously. ◀]

Step 8 What do you notice about the points representing distances that were underestimated? What about the points representing distances that were overestimated?

Step 9 How would you recognize a point representing an estimated distance that exactly matched its actual measurement? Explain why this point would fall where it does.

Step 10 Suppose you were estimating a distance that was exactly 350 cm. Based on your plot, how accurate is your estimate likely to be? Write the interval in which your estimate would fall (between _____ cm and _____ cm, or ±_____ cm).

Throughout this course you will create useful and informative graphs. Sometimes adding other elements to a graph as a basis for comparison can help you interpret your data. In the investigation, you added the line $y = x$ to your graph. When a line can be used to describe the apparent pattern in a set of data, we say that the data have a **linear relationship.** Do you think the data in the investigation have a linear relationship?

Accuracy indicates how close estimates or measurements are to the actual values. Accuracy can be described by an interval, as in Step 10 of the investigation. Scientists often express accuracy by indicating an amount of possible **error,** such as (350 ± _____ cm). Remember that answers calculated based on estimated measurements should not show more **precision** than the measurements themselves.

1.8 Exercises

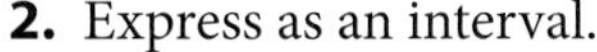

Practice Your Skills

1. Lucia and Malcolm each estimated the weights of five different items found in a grocery store. Each of Lucia's estimates was too low. Each of Malcolm's was too high. The scatter plot at right shows the (*actual weight, estimated weight*) data collected. The line drawn shows where an *estimate* is the same as the *actual* measurement.

Lucia's and Malcolm's Estimates

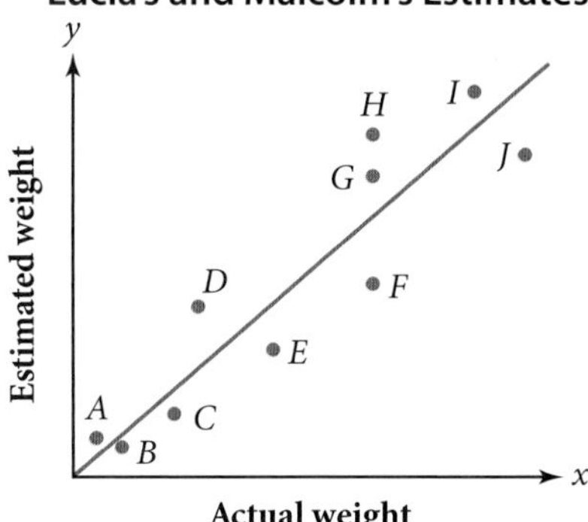

a. Which points represent Lucia's estimates?

b. What equation would model estimates that were exactly right?

c. Which points represent Malcolm's estimates?

d. Which inequality, $y > x$ or $y < x$, replaces the equal sign to describe the points identified in part c? Explain your choice.

2. Express as an interval.

a. 15 ± 3

b. 3.1 ± 0.4

3. Express using an error.

a. Between 13 and 17

b. Between 8.9 and 11.5

4. Find someone to help you complete this problem. Without showing them the chart ask them to estimate the year of these scientific advances in the 20th century. Record the estimates in a table next to the actual year.

20th Century Scientific Advances

Scientific advance	Actual year	Estimated year
First controlled split of the atom	1932	
First flight of the Wright brothers	1903	
First integrated circuit	1959	
First humans on the moon	1969	
First transistor	1947	
Discovery of penicillin	1928	
Structure of DNA described	1953	
First electronic computer (ENIAC)	1945	
Big Bang theory introduced	1927	
World Wide Web introduced	1991	

a. Graph a scatter plot so that each point (x, y) has the form (*actual year, estimated year*), and record the window used. Refer to the completed table.

b. If all the estimates were exactly right, what equation would they satisfy? Graph this equation on your scatter plot.

c. Are any points of the scatter plot above the line you graphed in 4b? What does this indicate?

d. Which inequality, $y > x$ or $y < x$, describes data points above the line? Explain.

5. These points represent student estimates of temperature in degrees Celsius for various samples of salt water. The data are recorded in the form (*actual temperature, estimated temperature*). Which points represent overestimates and which represent underestimates? ⓗ

$A(27, 20)$ $B(-4, 2)$ $C(18, 22)$ $D(0, 3)$ $E(47, 60)$

$F(36, 28)$ $G(-2, 0)$ $H(33, 31)$ $I(-1, -2)$

Reason and Apply

6. APPLICATION Xavier and Yolanda were both assigned to time the first eight runners in their P.E. class. The data in the table were plotted as an ordered pair for each runner in the form (*Xavier's time, Yolanda's time*).

a. What would it mean if many of the points fell on the line $y = x$?

b. What would it mean if the points consistently fell below the line $y = x$?

c. Plot these points and the line $y = x$. What does the graph tell you about Xavier's and Yolanda's times?

Runner	Adam	Bruno	Carla	Derrick	Eliza	Franco	German	Helen
Xavier's time (s)	306	306	302	289	284	316	305	301
Yolanda's time (s)	305	312	300	290	282	315	303	301

7. Copy the graph at right onto your paper.

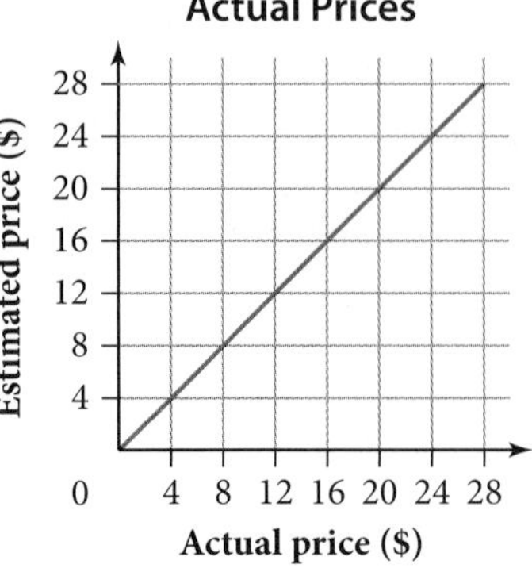

a. Plot a point that represents an overestimate of a \$12 item by \$4. Label it A. What are the coordinates of point A? @

b. Plot a point that represents an underestimate of an \$18 item by \$5. Label it B. What are the coordinates of point B? @

c. Plot and label the points $C(6, 8)$, $D(20, 25)$, and $E(26, 28)$. Describe each point as an overestimate or underestimate. How far off was each estimate?

d. Plot and label points F and G to represent two different estimates of an item priced at \$16. Point F should be an underestimate of \$3, and point G should be a perfect estimate. @

e. Where will all the points lie that represent an estimated price of \$16? Describe your answer in words and show it on the graph.

f. Where will all the points lie that represent an actual price of \$16? Describe your answer in words and show it on the graph.

g. If x represents the actual price and y represents the estimated price, where are all the points represented by the equation $y = x$? What do these points represent?

8. Graph the line $y = x$ on a coordinate grid with the x-axis labeled from -9 to 9 and the y-axis labeled from -6 to 6. Plot and label the points described.

a. Point A with x-coordinate -4 and y-coordinate 5 more than -4.

b. Point B with x-coordinate -2 and y-coordinate 3 less than -2.

c. Point C with x-coordinate 1 and y-coordinate 4 units above the line.

d. Now plot several points with coordinates that are opposites (*inverses*) of each other, for example, $(-5, 5)$ or $(5, -5)$. Describe the pattern these new points make. Write an equation to describe the pattern.

9. **APPLICATION** This graph shows the mean SAT verbal and mathematics scores for 50 states and the District of Columbia in 2008.

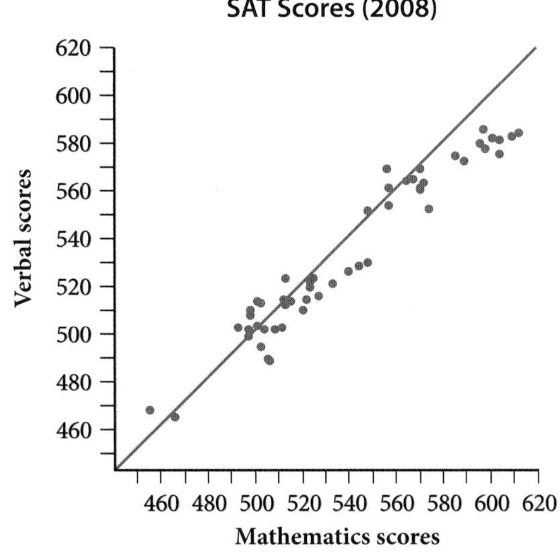

a. Explain what it means for a point to lie on the line $y = x$.

b. Locate the points that represent the states with the highest math scores. State two observations about their verbal scores. @

c. Which statement is true, "More states had students with higher mathematics scores than verbal scores" or "More states had students with higher verbal scores than mathematics scores"?

10. Using the data from Exercise 9, consider this second graph, where the line represents *verbal* = *math* − 18, as a model for predicting the average verbal score for a state.

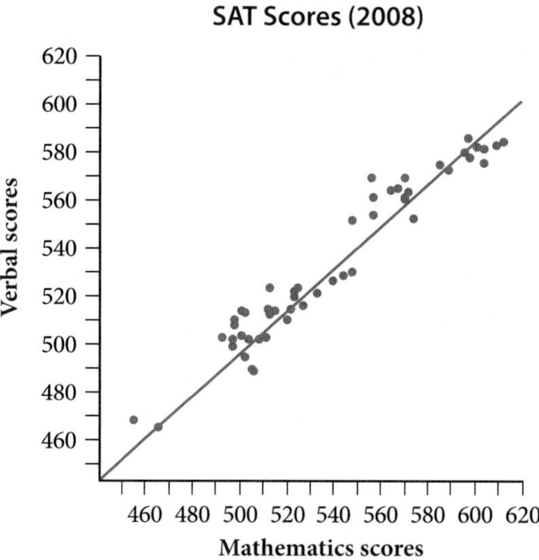

a. How well does this model predict the verbal score from the mathematics score? How often will the prediction be too high?

b. Which of these best describes the error of the prediction using this model: ±5 pts, ±10 pts, ±20 pts, ±40 pts, or ±80 pts?

c. If a state has an average mathematics score of 585, what interval would best predict the verbal score for this state?

11. APPLICATION A string and meterstick were passed around a class, and each student measured the length of the string in centimeters with precision 0.1 cm. Here are their results:

{126.5, 124.2, 124.8, 125.7, 123.3, 124.5, 125.4, 125.5, 123.7, 123.8, 126.4, 126.0, 124.6, 123.3, 124.7, 125.4, 126.1, 123.8, 125.7, 125.2, 126.0, 125.6}

a. What does the true length of the string probably equal? @

b. Why are there so many different values?

c. Create a measurement in the form *true length* ± *accuracy* (as in Step 10 of the investigation), which has an accuracy or error component, to describe the length of the string. @

Review

12. For each description, invent a seven-value data set such that all the values in the set are less than 10 and meet the conditions.

a. The box plot represents data with a median that is not inside the box. @

b. The box plot represents data with an interquartile range of zero.

c. The box plot represents data with one outlier on the left.

d. The box plot has no right whisker.

13. Rocky and his algebra classmates measured the circumference of their wrists in centimeters. Here are the data values:

{15.2, 14.7, 13.8, 17.3, 18.2, 17.6, 14.6, 13.5, 16.5, 15.8, 17.3, 16.8, 15.7, 16.2, 16.4, 18.4, 14.2, 16.4, 15.8, 16.2, 17.3, 15.7, 14.9, 15.5, 17.1}

Stem	Leaves
13	8 5
14	7 6 2 9
15	2 8 7 8 7 5
16	5 8 2 4 4 2
17	3 6 3 3 1
18	2 4

Key

10 | 4 means 10.4 cm

a. Rocky made the stem plot shown here. Unfortunately, he was not paying attention when these plots were discussed in class. Write a note to Rocky telling him what he did incorrectly.

b. Make a correct stem plot of this data set.

c. What is the range of this data set?

CHAPTER 1 REVIEW

In this chapter you learned how statistical measures and graphs can help you organize and make sense of **data.** You explored several different kinds of graphs—**bar graphs, pictographs, dot plots, box plots, histograms,** and **stem plots**—that can be used to represent **one-variable** data.

You analyzed the strengths and weaknesses of each kind of graph to select the most appropriate graph for a given situation. A bar graph displays data that can be grouped into **categories.** Numerical data can be shown individually with a dot plot. The **spread** of data is clearly displayed with a box plot built from a **five-number summary.** A histogram uses **bins** to show the **frequency** of data and is particularly useful for large sets of data. A stem plot also groups data into intervals but maintains the identity of each data value.

You can use **measures of center** to describe a typical data value. In addition to the **mean, median,** and **mode,** statistical measures such as **range, minimum, maximum, quartiles,** and **interquartile range** help you describe the spread of a data set and identify **outliers.** You learned to use the **mean absolute deviation** as a way to measure spread using all values. Another common measure of spread based on the mean is the **variance,** or the sum of squares of these distances to the mean. The square root of variance—the **standard deviation**—has the same units as the data and is less affected by outliers, so it is the most commonly used measure of spread.

You used the **coordinate plane** to compare estimates and actual values plotted on **two-variable** plots called **scatter plots.** Here, each variable is represented on a different axis, and an **ordered pair** shows the value of each variable for a single data item. You also analyzed scatter plots for situations involving the two variables *time* and *distance.* Scatter plots allowed you to find patterns in the data; sometimes these patterns could be written as an algebraic equation.

Lastly, you learned to construct relative frequency graphs. You learned to summarize categorical data for two categories in a two-way frequency table and to interpret relative frequencies in the context of the data. You found the **marginal relative frequency** by finding the ratio of the marginal totals to the table total. You used the ratio of the cell count to the table total to get the **joint relative frequency.** And you compared the data with respect to one specific condition through the **conditional relative frequencies.** You also looked for associations and trends in data to inform decision making.

Exercises

@ **Answers are provided for all exercises in this set.**

1. Seven students order onion rings. The mean number of onion rings they get is 16. The five-number summary is 9, 11, 16, 21, 22. How many onion rings might each student have been served?

2. This data set gives the number of hours of use before each of 14 batteries required recharging: 40, 36, 27, 44, 40, 34, 42, 58, 36, 46, 52, 52, 38, 36.

   a. Find the mean, median, and mode for the data set, and explain how you found each measure.

   b. Find the five-number summary for the data set, and make a box plot.

3. The table at right shows the mean monthly wages earned by individuals with various levels of education in the United States in 2008.

   a. Construct a bar graph for the data.

   b. Between which two consecutive levels of education is there the greatest difference in mean monthly wages? The smallest difference?

Mean Monthly Wages, 2008

Level of education	Amount ($)
Did not finish high school	1168
High school diploma only	1780
Two-year degree (AA/AS)	2702
Bachelor's degree (BA/BS)	3841
Master's degree (MA/MS)	4945
Doctorate degree	6938

(U.S. Bureau of the Census, *www.census.gov*)

4. The table below shows the top eleven scorers in the 2009 NCAA Women's Basketball Tournament.

   a. Construct a box plot for the data.

   b. Are there any outliers?

   c. Which measure of center would you use to describe a typical value?

Leading Scorers in 2009 NCAA Women's Basketball Tournament

Player	Points
Jayne Appel, Stanford	124
Maya Moore, Connecticut	124
Angel McCoughtry, Louisiana	124
Renee Montgomery, Connecticut	123
Tina Charles, Connecticut	110
Marissa Coleman, Maryland	87
Christina Wirth, Vanderbilt	75
Kristi Toliver, Maryland	75
Ashley Walker, Cal Berkeley	74
Shavonte Zellous, Pittsburgh	73
Epiphanny Prince, Rutgers	68

(National Collegiate Athletic Association, *www.ncaa.org*)

After an impressive college career, Angel McCoughtry went on to play professionally for the Atlanta Dream.

5. Twenty-three students were asked how many pages they had read in a book currently assigned for class. Here are their responses: 24, 87, 158, 227, 437, 79, 93, 121, 111, 118, 12, 25, 284, 332, 181, 34, 54, 167, 300, 103, 128, 132, 345. [Data set: **BKPGS**]

a. Find the measures of center.

b. Construct histograms for two different bin widths.

c. Construct a box plot.

d. What do the histograms and the box plot tell you about this data set? Make one or two observations.

6. Isabel made the estimates listed in the table at right for the year each item was invented.

a. Create a scatter plot of data points with coordinates having the form (*actual year, estimated year*).

b. Circle those points that picture an estimated year that is earlier than the actual year (underestimates).

c. Define your variables and write the equation of a line that would represent all estimates being the same as the actual years.

Invention Dates

Item	Actual year	Estimated year
Telephone	1876	1905
Color television	1928	1960
Video disk	1972	1980
Pacemaker	1952	1945
Motion picture	1893	1915
Ballpoint pen	1888	1935
Aspirin	1899	1917
Graphing calculator	1985	1980
Compact disc	1972	1990
Car radio	1929	1940

(*2009 World Almanac,* pp. 323–326)

7. This table shows the approximate populations of the five most populous countries in the world in 2000. The total world population at that time was 6,080,142,000.

Country	Population
China	1,261,832,000
India	1,014,004,000
United States	275,563,000
Indonesia	224,784,000
Brazil	172,860,000

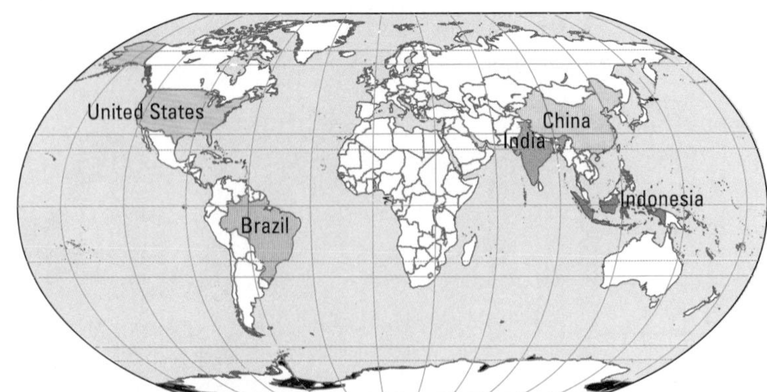

Create a relative frequency circle graph of this information with six categories—one for each country listed and one labeled "Other." Label your graph with category names and percents. List the degree measure of each sector.

8. The graph shows Kayo's distance over time as she jogs straight down the street in front of her home. Point A is Kayo's starting point (her home).

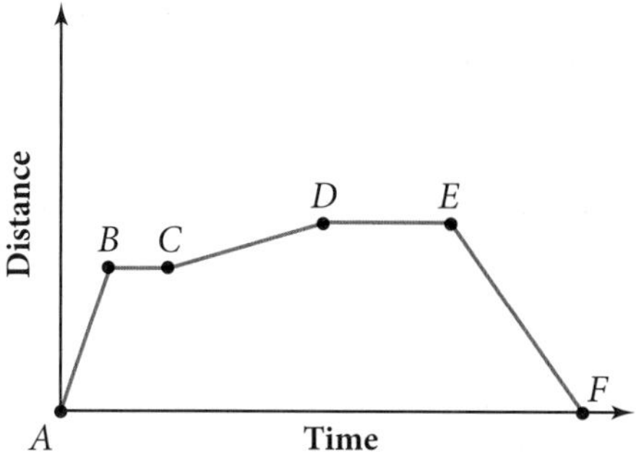

a. During which time period was Kayo jogging the fastest?

b. Explain what Kayo might have been doing during the time intervals between points B and C and between points D and E.

c. Write a brief story for this graph using all five segments.

9. The table at right shows the approximate 2008 populations of the ten most populated cities in the United States.

a. Write the approximate population of Chicago in 2008 as a whole number.

b. Create a bar graph of the data.

c. Create a stem plot of the data.

d. Create a box plot of the data.

e. Each of the graphs you have created highlights different characteristics of the data. Briefly describe what features are unique to each graph.

The Ten Most Populated U.S. Cities, 2008

City	Population (millions)
Chicago	2.85
Dallas	1.28
Houston	2.24
Los Angeles	3.83
New York	8.36
Philadelphia	1.45
Phoenix	1.57
San Antonio	1.35
San Diego	1.28
San Jose	0.95

(*census.gov*)

10. This stem-and-leaf plot shows the number of minutes of sleep for eight students. In this plot the dots indicate that the interval is divided in half at 50. Use the key to fully understand how to read this graph.

a. What is the mean?

b. What is the median?

c. What is the mode?

Minutes Sleeping

3	20
•	60 90
4	00
•	50 55 80 80

Key

3	20 means 320 minutes
•	60 means 360 minutes

11. This table reports the results of a survey of transportation used by students at Crystal High School.

	Male	Female	Totals
Walk	24	17	41
Car	35	38	73
Bus	58	45	103
Cycle	22	8	30
Totals	139	108	247

a. Identify one relative frequency from this table, and describe its meaning.

b. Identify one marginal frequency from this table, and describe its meaning.

c. Identify one conditional frequency from this table, and describe its meaning.

d. Write two conclusions you can make from this frequency table.

12. Members of the school mathematics club sold packages of hot chocolate mix to raise funds for their club activities. The numbers of packages sold by individual members are given below.

Hot Chocolate Packages Sold				
65	76	100	67	44
147	82	94	92	79
158	77	62	85	71
69	88	80	63	75
62	68	71	73	74

a. Find the median and interquartile range for this data set.

b. Find the mean and standard deviation.

c. Draw a box plot for this data set.

d. Remove the outliers from the data set and draw another box plot.

e. With the outliers removed, recalculate the median and interquartile range and the mean and standard deviation.

f. Which is more affected by outliers, the mean or the median? The standard deviation or the interquartile range? Explain why you think this is so.

Take Another Look

1. These two graphs display the same data set. The first graph is being presented by a citizen who argues that the city should use its budget surplus to buy land for a park. The second graph is being presented by another citizen who argues that a new park is not a high priority. State what position you would favor on this issue and what impact each graph had on your decision. Do you think either graph is deliberately misleading? If so, what other information would you want to know?

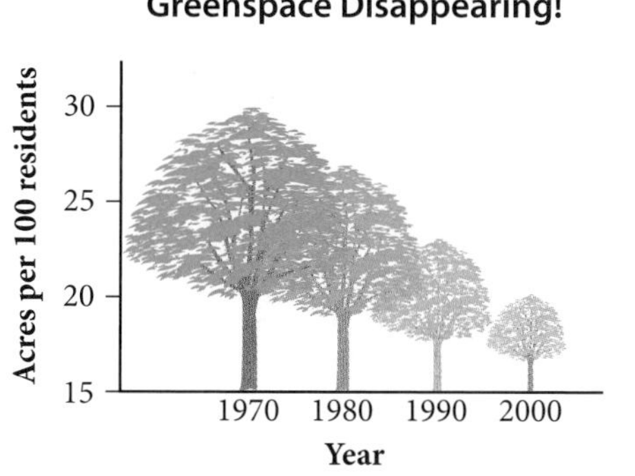

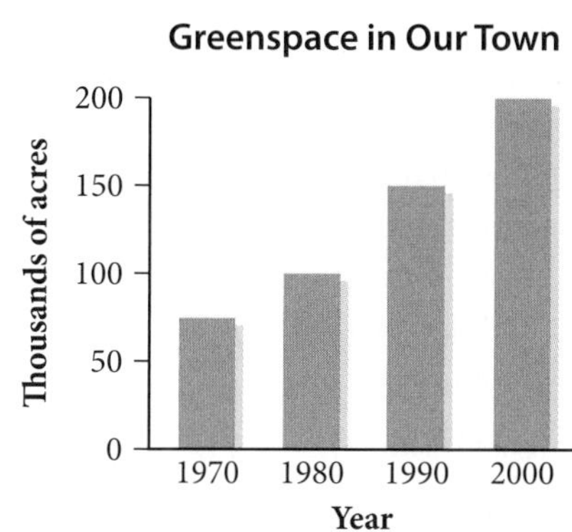

Find another graphic display in a newspaper, a magazine, or voter material that seems to be "engineered" to persuade the viewer to lean toward a particular point of view. Tell how the graph could be changed for a less biased presentation.

2. You have learned to construct several types of graphs, each with its own strengths and weaknesses. Add check marks to this table to identify the strengths of each type of graph. Categorical data count the number of items in given nonnumerical categories. Numerical data are values related to numbers or intervals of numbers.

	Bar graph	Dot plot	Box plot	Histogram	Stem plot
For categorical data					
For numerical data					
Shows individual data values					
Summarizes data					
Better for large data sets					
Better for bimodal data					

Assessing What You've Learned

WRITE IN YOUR JOURNAL Your course work in algebra will bring up many new ideas, and some are quite abstract. Sometimes you'll feel you have a good grip on these new ideas, but at other times, less so.

Regular reflection on your confidence level in mathematics generally, and your mastery of algebra skills in particular, will help you assess your strengths and weaknesses. Writing down these reflections will help you realize where you are having trouble, and perhaps you'll ask for help sooner. Likewise, realizing how much you know can boost your confidence. A good place to record these thoughts is in a journal—not a personal diary, but an informal collection of your feelings and observations about what you're learning. Like a travel journal that others would find interesting to read and that will help you recall the details of a trip, a mathematics journal is something your teacher will want to look at and something you'll look at again later.

Here are some questions to prompt your journal writing. Your teacher might give you other ideas, but you can write in your journal at any time.

- How is what you are learning an extension of your previous mathematics courses? How is it completely new?
- What are your goals for your work in algebra? What steps can you take to achieve them?
- Can you see ways to apply what you are learning to your everyday life? To a future career?
- What ideas have you found hard to understand?

UPDATE YOUR PORTFOLIO At the end of Chapter 0, you may have started a portfolio. Now would be a good time to add one or more pieces of significant work from Chapter 1. You could choose an investigation, a homework problem, or your work on Take Another Look. It might be a good idea to include a sample of every type of graph you've learned to interpret or create.

CHAPTER 2

Proportional Reasoning and Variation

Murals are just one of the many art forms around us that come to life with the help of ratios and proportions. To plan a mural like this one painted on a wall on South Street in Philadelphia, the artist draws sketches on paper, then uses a ratio to enlarge the image to the size of the final work.

OBJECTIVES

In this chapter you will

- review simplifying and ordering fractions
- use proportional reasoning to understand problem situations
- learn what rates are and use them to make predictions
- study how quantities vary directly and inversely
- use equations and graphs to represent variation
- solve real-world problems that involve variation
- review the rules for order of operations with algebraic expressions
- describe number tricks by using algebraic expressions
- solve equations by using the undoing method

Factors and Fractions

Your work with ratios and proportions in Chapter 2 will include a focus on fractions. To make working with fractions easier, you can simplify them by factoring numerators and denominators and dividing out common factors. When the numerator and denominator have no common factors, a fraction is said to be in *lowest terms.*

EXAMPLE A

Write each product as a single fraction in lowest terms.

a. $12 \cdot \frac{15}{28}$

b. $125 \cdot \frac{64}{100}$

Solution

a. One strategy is to factor each number into its prime factors and then divide out common factors.

$$\begin{aligned}12 \cdot \frac{15}{28} &= \frac{12}{1} \cdot \frac{15}{28} \\ &= \frac{\cancel{2} \cdot \cancel{2} \cdot 3}{1} \cdot \frac{3 \cdot 5}{\cancel{2} \cdot \cancel{2} \cdot 7} \\ &= \frac{3 \cdot 3 \cdot 5}{7} \\ &= \frac{45}{7}\end{aligned}$$

b. When the values are large, it is sometimes quicker to use their common factors rather than to go all the way to the prime factors.

$$\begin{aligned}125 \cdot \frac{64}{100} &= \frac{25 \cdot 5}{1} \cdot \frac{8 \cdot 4 \cdot 2}{25 \cdot 4} \\ &= \frac{\cancel{25} \cdot 5}{1} \cdot \frac{8 \cdot \cancel{4} \cdot 2}{\cancel{25} \cdot \cancel{4}} \\ &= \frac{80}{1} \\ &= 80\end{aligned}$$

To compare two fractions with the same denominator, just compare their numerators. For example, $\frac{7}{17} > \frac{6}{17}$ because $7 > 6$.

If one denominator is a multiple of the other, then you can use that knowledge to help you compare the fractions.

EXAMPLE B | Locate each of these values on the number line: $\frac{5}{12}$, $\frac{17}{36}$, $\frac{11}{24}$.

Solution

Each numerator is less than the denominator, so each fraction has a value between 0 and 1. Also, each numerator is not quite half the denominator, so each fraction is a bit less than $\frac{1}{2}$. How can you tell the order of these three values? Each denominator is a multiple of 12. So you can write equivalent fractions with a common denominator that is a multiple of 12.

$$\left.\begin{aligned}\frac{5}{12} &= \frac{5}{12}\\ \frac{17}{36} &= \frac{17}{12 \cdot 3}\\ \frac{11}{24} &= \frac{11}{12 \cdot 2}\end{aligned}\right\} \text{common denominator is } 12 \cdot 2 \cdot 3, \text{ so} \rightarrow \begin{aligned}\frac{5}{12} &= \frac{5 \cdot 2 \cdot 3}{12 \cdot 2 \cdot 3} = \frac{30}{72}\\ \frac{17}{36} &= \frac{17 \cdot 2}{12 \cdot 3 \cdot 2} = \frac{34}{72}\\ \frac{11}{24} &= \frac{11 \cdot 3}{12 \cdot 2 \cdot 3} = \frac{33}{72}\end{aligned}$$

Now you can put the values in order: $\frac{30}{72}$, $\frac{33}{72}$, $\frac{34}{72}$.

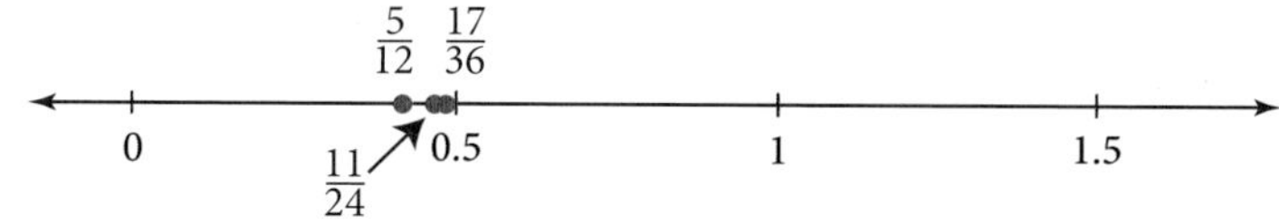

Another way to compare fractions is to write them as decimals.

EXAMPLE C | Use decimal representations to compare the fractions in Example B.

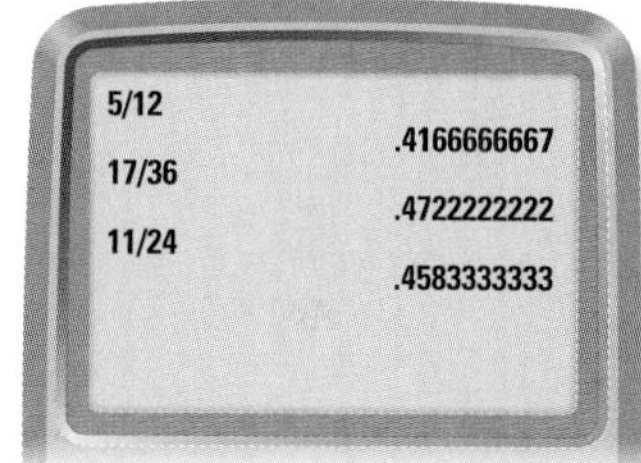

Solution

Using a calculator, you find $\frac{5}{12} \approx 0.417$, $\frac{17}{36} \approx 0.472$, and $\frac{11}{24} \approx 0.458$. Because each has the same digit in the tenths place, compare the digits in the hundredths place to see the order of these values. Placing the digits in order gives you 0.417, 0.458, 0.472, or $\frac{5}{12}$, $\frac{11}{24}$, $\frac{17}{36}$.

When you divide 1 by 2, the decimal form of the quotient ends, or **terminates.** The ratio $\frac{1}{2}$ equals 0.5 exactly. But when you divide 5 by 12, you get a **repeating decimal,** 0.416666666. . . . You can use a bar over the numerals that repeat to show a repeating $\frac{5}{12} = 0.41\overline{6}$. [▸ See **Calculator Note: Fractions** for more about converting fractions to decimals. ◂]

As you work through this chapter, try to look for the most efficient way to complete each calculation.

Exercises

1. List the common factors of each pair of numbers.

a. 24, 32

b. 15, 25

c. 60, 80

2. Complete the table. Note that there are many possible answers for 2c and 2e.

Fraction	Lowest-terms form	Decimal
$\frac{24}{32}$	**a.**	**b.**
c.	$\frac{4}{5}$	**d.**
e.	**f.**	0.6

3. Rewrite each product as a single fraction in lowest terms.

a. $12 \cdot \frac{7}{20}$

b. $45 \cdot \frac{30}{100}$

c. $24 \cdot \frac{15}{100}$

4. Without using your calculator, complete each statement with < or > to make it true. Explain your choice.

a. $\frac{3}{7} \square \frac{5}{7}$

b. $\frac{2}{15} \square \frac{2}{19}$

c. $\frac{5}{11} \square \frac{7}{13}$

5. Order each set of values on a number line.

a. $\frac{2}{3}, \frac{5}{12}, \frac{4}{9}, \frac{17}{36}$

b. $1.5, \frac{9}{8}, \frac{19}{12}, 1.74$

LESSON

2.1

Proportions

"Mathematics is not a way of hanging numbers on things so that quantitative answers to ordinary questions can be obtained. It is a language that allows one to think about extraordinary questions."

JAMES BULLOCK

When you say "I got 21 out of 24 questions correct on the last quiz," you are comparing two numbers. The **ratio** of your correct answers to the total number of questions is 21 to 24. You can write the ratio as 21:24 or as a fraction, $\frac{21}{24}$, or as a decimal, 0.875. The fraction bar means division, so these expressions are equivalent.

Ratio and Proportion

A ratio is a numerical comparison by relative size. Ratios are most usefully expressed as fractions.

For example:

$$\frac{\textit{number of questions correct}}{\textit{total number of questions}} = \frac{21}{24}$$

A proportion is an equation stating that two ratios are equal. For example:

Ratio of correct questions $\frac{21}{24} = \frac{87.5}{100}$ Ratio of points out of 100

EXAMPLE A

An O gauge model train is built on a $\frac{1}{48}$ scale. This means that 1 in. on the model corresponds to 48 in., or 4 ft, on a real train. A Yellowstone-type locomotive, one of the largest ever made, measured 128 ft in length. How long is an O gauge model of this locomotive?

Solution

Because 4 ft (48 in.) on the real locomotive corresponds to 1 in. on the model, you can write the ratio as $\frac{1 \text{ in.}}{4 \text{ ft}}$. To represent the locomotive, you need an equivalent fraction, $\frac{? \text{ in.}}{128 \text{ ft}}$. You can set up the proportion $\frac{1}{4} = \frac{?}{128}$. Because 4×32 is 128, you multiply the numerator and the denominator of the fraction on the left by 32 to get the same denominator as in the fraction on the right so the equivalent fraction is $\frac{32 \text{ in.}}{128 \text{ ft}}$. The model is 32 in. long.

Another example of a proportion is $\frac{2}{3} = \frac{8}{12}$. You can use the numbers 2, 3, 8, and 12 to write these true proportions:

$$\frac{2}{3} = \frac{8}{12} \qquad \frac{3}{2} = \frac{12}{8} \qquad \frac{3}{12} = \frac{2}{8} \qquad \frac{12}{3} = \frac{8}{2}$$

Do you agree that these are all true statements? One way to check that a proportion is true is by finding the decimal equivalent of each side. The statement $\frac{3}{8} = \frac{2}{12}$ is not true; 0.375 is not equal to $0.1\overline{6}$.

In algebra, a **variable** can stand for an unknown number or for a set of numbers. In the proportion $\frac{2}{3} = \frac{M}{6}$, you can replace the letter M with any number, but only one number will make the proportion true. That number is unknown until the proportion is solved.

INVESTIGATION

Multiply and Conquer

You can probably guess the value of M in the proportion $\frac{2}{3} = \frac{M}{6}$. In this investigation you'll examine ways to solve a proportion for an unknown number when guessing is more difficult. It would be hard to guess the value of M in the proportion $\frac{M}{19} = \frac{56}{133}$.

Step 1 Multiply both sides of the proportion $\frac{M}{19} = \frac{56}{133}$ by 19. Why can you do this? What does M equal?

Step 2 For each equation, choose a number to multiply both ratios by to solve the proportion for the unknown number. Then multiply and divide to find the missing value.

a. $\frac{p}{12} = \frac{132}{176}$ b. $\frac{21}{35} = \frac{Q}{20}$

c. $\frac{L}{30} = \frac{30}{200}$ d. $\frac{130}{78} = \frac{n}{15}$

Step 3 Check that each proportion in Step 2 is true by replacing the variable with your answer.

Step 4 In each equation in Step 2, the variable is in the numerator. Write a brief explanation of one way to solve a proportion when one of the numerators is a variable.

Step 5 The proportions you solved in Step 2 have been changed by switching the numerators and denominators. That is, the ratio on each side has been *inverted.* (You may recall that inverted fractions, like $\frac{p}{12}$ and $\frac{12}{p}$, are called **reciprocals.**) Do your solutions in Step 2 also make these new proportions true?

a. $\frac{12}{p} = \frac{176}{132}$ b. $\frac{35}{21} = \frac{20}{Q}$ c. $\frac{30}{L} = \frac{200}{30}$ d. $\frac{78}{130} = \frac{15}{n}$

Step 6 How can you use what you just discovered to help you solve a proportion that has the variable in the denominator, such as $\frac{20}{135} = \frac{12}{k}$? Why does this work? Solve the proportion.

Step 7 There are many ways to solve proportions. Here are three student papers, each answering the question "13 is 65% of what number?" What steps did each student follow? What other methods can you use to solve proportions?

a. **b.** **c.**

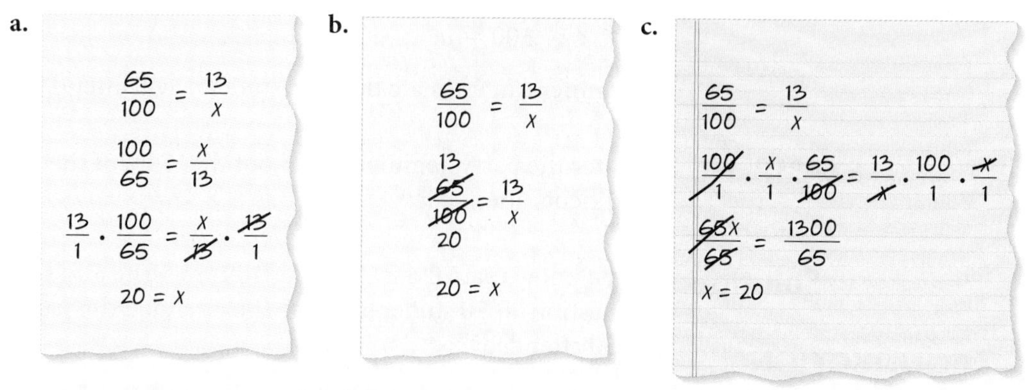

In the investigation, you discovered that you can solve for an unknown numerator in a proportion by multiplying both sides of the proportion by the denominator under the unknown value. You can also think of a proportion such as $\frac{M}{19} = \frac{56}{133}$ like this: "When a number is divided by 19, the result is $\frac{56}{133}$." To find the original number, you need to undo the division. Multiplying by 19 undoes the division.

EXAMPLE B

Jennifer estimates that two out of every three students will attend the class party. She knows there are 750 students in her class. Set up and solve a proportion to help her estimate how many people will attend.

Solution

To set up the proportion, be sure both ratios make the same comparison. Use a to represent the number of students who will attend.

Students who will attend → $\frac{2}{3} = \frac{a}{750}$ ← Students who will attend

Students who are invited → (denominators) ← Students who are invited

In the proportion, when a is divided by 750, the answer is $\frac{2}{3}$.

$$750 \cdot \frac{2}{3} = a \qquad \text{Multiply by 750 to undo the division.}$$

$$500 = a \qquad \text{Simplify.}$$

Jennifer can estimate that 500 students will attend the party.

EXAMPLE C

After the party, Jennifer found out that 70% of the class attended. How many students attended?

Solution

You know that 70% is 70 out of 100. So write and solve a proportion to answer the question "If 70 students out of 100 attended the party, how many students out of 750 attended?"

Let s represent the number of students who attended.

$$\frac{70}{100} = \frac{s}{750} \qquad \text{Write the proportion.}$$

$$750 \cdot \frac{70}{100} = s \qquad \text{Multiply by 750 to undo the division.}$$

$$525 = s \qquad \text{Simplify.}$$

525 out of 750 students attended the party.

The Pythagoreans, a group of philosophers begun by Pythagoras in about 520 B.C.E., realized that not all numbers are rational. For example, a square whose side is 1 unit in length has a diagonal with length $\sqrt{2}$, which is *irrational.* Another irrational number is pi, or π, the ratio of the circumference of a circle to its diameter.

You have worked with ratios and proportions in this lesson. Numbers that can be written as a ratio of two integers are called **rational numbers.**

Exercises

Practice Your Skills

1. Ms. Lenz collected information about the students in her class.

Eye Color

	Brown eyes	Blue eyes	Hazel eyes
9th graders	9	3	2
8th graders	11	4	1

Write these ratios as fractions.

a. ninth graders with brown eyes to ninth graders ⓐ

b. eighth graders with brown eyes to students with brown eyes

c. eighth graders with blue eyes to ninth graders with blue eyes ⓐ

d. all students with hazel eyes to students in both grades

2. Phrases such as *miles per gallon, parts per million (ppm),* and *accidents per 1000 people* indicate ratios. Write each ratio named here as a fraction. Use a number and a unit in both the numerator and the denominator. (h)

   a. In 2010, the SSC Ultimate Aero was the fastest car produced. Its top speed was recorded at 257 mi/h. (a)

   b. Pure capsaicin, a substance that makes hot peppers taste hot, is so strong that 10 ppm in water can make your tongue blister. (a)

   c. In 2000, women owned approximately 350 of every thousand firms in the United States. (a)

3. What number should you multiply by to solve for the unknown number in each proportion?

   a. $\frac{24}{40} = \frac{T}{30}$ (a) b. $\frac{49}{56} = \frac{R}{32}$ c. $\frac{M}{16} = \frac{87}{232}$ (a)

   d. $\frac{p}{100} = \frac{112}{28}$ e. $\frac{L}{28} = \frac{3}{2}$ f. $\frac{3.6}{18} = \frac{x}{5}$

4. Find the value of the unknown number in each proportion.

   a. $\frac{24}{40} = \frac{T}{30}$ (h) b. $\frac{49}{56} = \frac{R}{32}$ c. $\frac{52}{91} = \frac{42}{S}$ (a) d. $\frac{100}{30} = \frac{7}{x}$

   e. $\frac{M}{16} = \frac{87}{232}$ f. $\frac{6}{n} = \frac{62}{217}$ g. $\frac{36}{15} = \frac{c}{13}$ h. $\frac{220}{33} = \frac{60}{W}$

Reason and Apply

5. **APPLICATION** Write a proportion for each problem, and solve for the unknown number.

   a. Leaf-cutter ants that live in Central and South America weigh about 1.5 grams (g). One ant can carry a 4 g piece of leaf that is about the size of a dime. If a person could carry proportionally as much as the leaf-cutter ant, how much could a 55 kg algebra student carry? (h)

   b. The leaf-cutter ant is about 1.27 cm long and takes strides of length 0.84 cm. If a person could take proportionally equivalent strides, what length strides would a 1.65 m tall algebra student take?

   c. The 1.27 cm long ants travel up to 0.4 km from home each day. If a person could travel a proportional distance, how far would a 1.65 m tall person travel?

6. **APPLICATION** Jeremy has a job at the movie theater. His hourly wage is \$7.38. Suppose 15% of his income is withheld for taxes and Social Security.

   a. What percent does Jeremy get to keep?

   b. What is his hourly take-home wage? (h)

7. In a resort area during the summer months, only one out of eight people is a year-round resident. The others are there on vacation. If the year-round population of the area is 3000, how many people are in the area in the summer? (@)

8. **APPLICATION** To make three servings of Irish porridge, you need 4 cups of water and 1 cup of steel-cut oatmeal. How much of each ingredient will you need for two servings? For five servings?

9. **APPLICATION** When chemists write the formula for a chemical compound, they indicate how many atoms of each element combine to form a molecule of that compound. For instance, they write H_2O for water, which means there are two hydrogen atoms and one oxygen atom in each molecule of water. Acetone (or nail polish remover) has the formula C_3H_6O. The C stands for carbon.

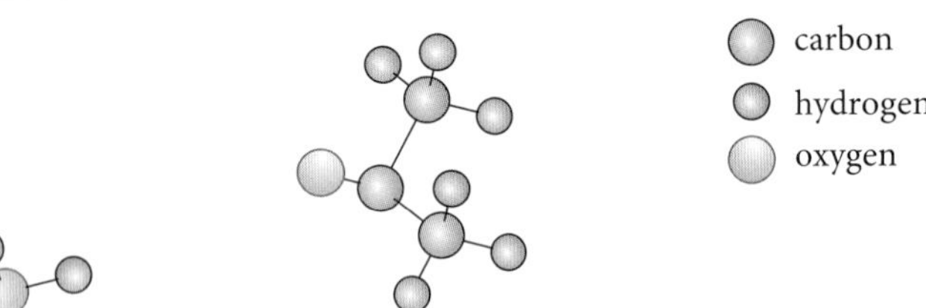

   a. How many of each atom are in one molecule of acetone? (@)

   b. How many atoms of carbon must combine with 470 atoms of oxygen to form acetone molecules? How many atoms of hydrogen are required? (@)

   c. How many acetone molecules can be formed from 3000 atoms of carbon, 3000 atoms of hydrogen, and 1000 atoms of oxygen? (@)

Review

10. List these fractions in increasing order by estimating their values. Then use your calculator to find the decimal value of each fraction to the nearest 0.01.

   a. $\frac{7}{8}$ b. $\frac{13}{20}$ c. $\frac{13}{5}$ d. $\frac{52}{25}$

   e. $\frac{25}{52}$ f. $\frac{5}{13}$ g. $\frac{20}{13}$ h. $\frac{8}{7}$

11. *The Forbes Celebrity 100* (*www.forbes.com/celebrities*) listed these ten people (and their incomes from June 2011 to June 2012 in millions) among the celebrities who got the most media attention. Find the three measures of center for their incomes, and explain why they are so different.

Angelina Jolie ($20)
Oprah Winfrey ($165)
Tyler Perry ($105)
Beyonce Knowles ($40)
Tiger Woods ($58)
Donald Trump ($63)
Steven Spielberg ($130)
Jennifer Lopez ($52)
Tom Cruise ($75)
Kobe Bryant ($50)

[Data set: **CELEB**]

12. Use the order of operations to evaluate these expressions. Check your results on your calculator.

a. $5 \cdot -4 + 8$

b. $-12 \div (7 - 4)$

c. $-3 - 6 \cdot 25 \div 30$

d. $18(-3) \div 81$

e. $\dfrac{-3[-12 + 2(-3)]}{-3 - 6}$

f. $\dfrac{2(-6) - 8 \div -2}{12 \div 3}$

13. The United States has many popular national parks. This table shows the number of visitors to ten of the national parks in 2012.

a. Find the mean number of visitors.

b. What is the five-number summary for the data?

c. Create a box plot for the data.

d. Identify any parks in the United States that are outliers in the numbers of visitors they had. Explain why they are outliers.

National Park	Visitors
Great Smoky Mountains	9,685,829
Grand Canyon	4,421,352
Yosemite	3,853,404
Yellowstone	3,447,729
Rocky Mountain	3,229,617
Zion	2,973,607
Olympic	2,824,908
Grand Teton	2,705,256
Acadia	2,431,052
Cuyahoga Valley	2,299,722

Kolob Terrace in Zion National Park, Utah

LESSON

2.2

Proportions with Percents

"The Universe is a grand book which cannot be read until one first learns to comprehend the language. . . . It is written in the language of mathematics."

GALILEO GALILEI

Wildlife biologists often want to estimate how many deer are in a national park or the size of the perch population in a large lake. To count each deer or fish would be impossible, so biologists use a method called *capture-recapture* that uses ratios to estimate the population. Biologists first capture some of the fish, for example, and put tags on them. The tagged fish are returned to the lake to mingle with the untagged fish. After allowing time for the fish to thoroughly mix, another sample is collected to see how many of the captured fish are tagged.

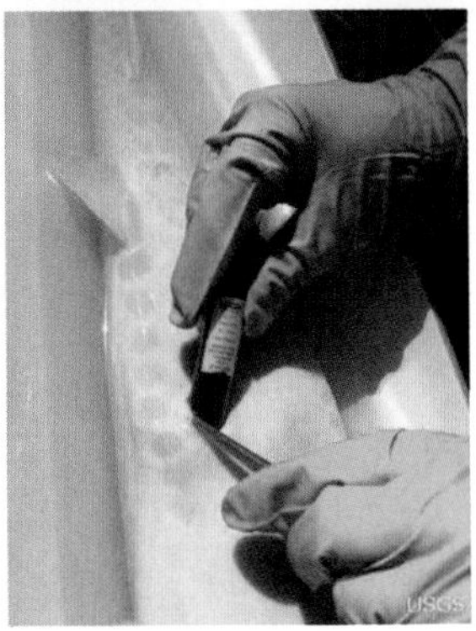

The **design** of an accurate capture-recapture study is important for getting useful results. Accurately estimating a fish population involves spreading out the capture and release of the tagged animals. The biologist must know the time it will take for the population to mix before taking the second **sample.**

INVESTIGATION

Fish in the Lake

YOU WILL NEED

- a paper bag
- white beans
- red beans

In this investigation you'll **simulate** the capture-recapture method and examine how it works.

The bag represents a lake, the white beans are the untagged fish in the lake, and the red beans will replace white beans to represent tagged fish. Your objective is to estimate the total number of fish in the lake.

Step 1 Reach into the lake and remove a handful of fish to tag. Count and record the number of fish you removed. Replace these fish (white beans) with an equal number of tagged fish (red beans). Return the tagged fish to the lake. Set aside the extra beans.

Step 2 Allow the fish to mingle (close the bag and shake it). Again remove a handful of fish, count them all, and count the number of tagged fish. In a table like this, record those counts and the ratio of tagged fish to total fish in the sample.

Tagging Simulation

Sample number	Number of tagged fish	Total number of fish	Ratio of tagged fish to total fish	Percent of fish tagged
1				
2				

You have taken one sample by randomly capturing some of the fish. You could use this sample to estimate the number of fish in the lake, but by taking several samples, you will get a better idea of the ratio of tagged fish to total fish in the lake. Replace the fish, mix them, and repeat the sampling process four times, filling in a row of your table each time.

Step 3 Choose a representative ratio for the five ratios. Explain how you decided this was a representative ratio.

Step 4 If you mixed the fish well, should the fraction of tagged fish in a sample be nearly the same as the fraction of tagged fish in the lake? Why or why not?

Step 5 Write and solve a proportion to estimate the number of fish in the lake. (About how many beans are in your bag?) Why is this method called capture-recapture? How accurate are predictions using this method? Why?

You know that your calculation in Step 5 is not exact. Estimates are more useful when you understand how accurate they are.

Step 6 Change your five ratios to percents. Divide your percents into two groups, large and small. Recalculate your population count by using a single high percent, and then recalculate by using a low percent. State your estimate as an accuracy interval that gives a high and a low population estimate.

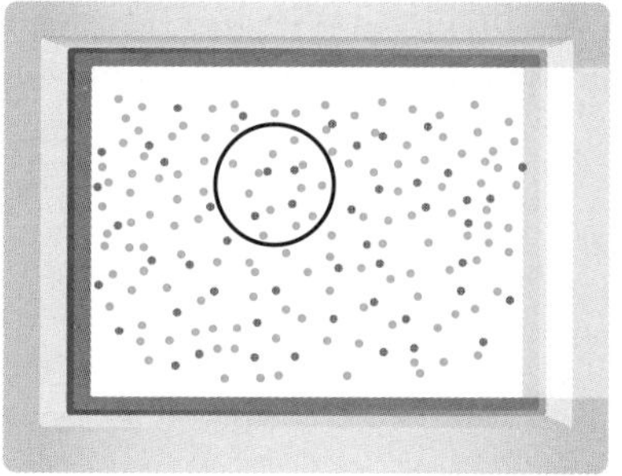

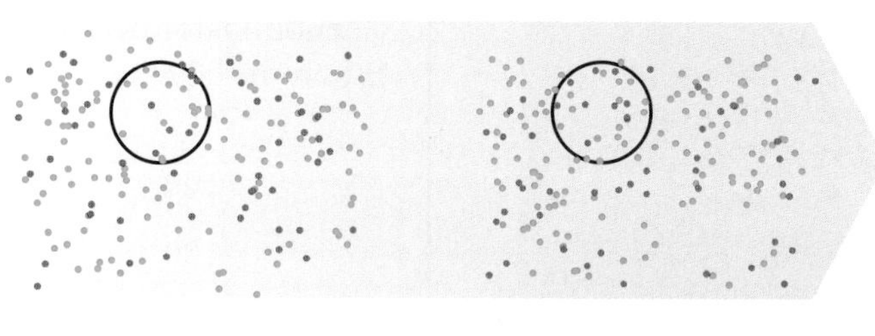

[▶ You can use the **Dynamic Algebra Exploration** found in your ebook to simulate a capture-recapture situation. You'll press a button to allow the fish to swim in the lake, and then you'll "capture" the fish in the circle and count the tagged and untagged fish. ◀]

You can describe the results of capture-recapture situations using percents, as in Step 6 of the investigation. These examples present three kinds of percent problems—finding an unknown percent, finding an unknown total, and finding an unknown part. In each case the percent equals the ratio of the part to the whole, or total.

EXAMPLE A

Finding an Unknown Percent

In a capture-recapture process, 200 fish were tagged. From the recapture results, the game warden estimates that the lake contains 2500 fish. What percent of the fish were tagged?

Solution

How does the police department know that only 80% of crimes are reported? How does the U.S. government know that only 97% of people responded to the census? Questions like these are answered using a process similar to the capture-recapture process.

You know that the ratio of tagged fish (the part) to total fish in the lake (the whole) is 200 to 2500. This ratio is equivalent to the percent p of tagged fish in the sample.

$\frac{p}{100} = \frac{200}{2500}$ Write the proportion.

$p = \frac{200}{2500} \cdot 100$ Multiply by 100 to undo the division.

$p = 8$ Simplify.

In the samples used for the estimate, 8% of the fish were tagged.

Percent means per 100. So 8% means that 8 fish out of 100 fish were tagged.

$$\frac{\textit{percent}}{100} = \frac{\textit{number of tagged fish}}{\textit{total number of fish}}$$

EXAMPLE B

Finding an Unknown Total

In a lake with 250 tagged fish, recapture results show that 11% of the fish are tagged. About how many fish are in the lake?

Solution

You can write 11% as the ratio $\frac{11}{100}$, or 11 parts to 100 (the whole). The variable is a denominator because the unknown quantity is the whole—the total number of fish in the lake.

$\frac{11}{100} = \frac{250}{f}$ Write the proportion.

$\frac{100}{11} = \frac{f}{250}$ Invert both ratios.

$250 \cdot \frac{100}{11} = f$ Multiply by 250 to undo the division.

$2273 \approx f$ Simplify.

There are about 2270 fish in the lake.

EXAMPLE C

Finding an Unknown Part

A lake is estimated to have 5000 fish after recapture experiments that showed 3% of the fish were tagged. How many fish were originally tagged?

Solution

You can write 3% as the ratio $\frac{3}{100}$, or 3 parts to 100 (the whole). The variable is a numerator because the unknown quantity is the number of tagged fish (the part).

$\frac{t}{5000} = \frac{3}{100}$ Write the proportion.

$t = \frac{3}{100} \cdot 5000$ Undo the division.

$t = 150$ Simplify.

About 150 fish were tagged.

Proportions can be used to estimate many types of quantities besides wildlife populations. In the exercises you will see some of these applications.

2.2 Exercises

Practice Your Skills

1. The proportion $\frac{320}{235} = \frac{g}{100}$ represents the question "320 is what percent of 235?" Write each proportion as a percent question.

a. $\frac{24}{w} = \frac{32}{100}$ ⓐ

b. $\frac{t}{450} = \frac{48}{100}$

c. $\frac{98}{117} = \frac{n}{100}$

2. Use the proportion $\frac{30}{120} = \frac{25}{100}$ to answer the questions.

a. What percent of 120 is 30?

b. What number is 25% of 120?

c. 25% of what number is 30?

3. You can write the question "What number is 15% of 120?" as the proportion $\frac{x}{120} = \frac{15}{100}$. Write each question as a proportion.

a. 125% of what number is 80? ⓐ

b. What number is 0.25% of 46?

c. What percent of 470 is 72?

4. Quintin knows that 17% of the 1582 students in his high school are twelfth graders. He argues that 10% of 1600 is 160, so 5% would be 80 and 20% would be 320.

a. Use these facts to estimate the number of twelfth graders.

b. Calculate the actual number of twelfth graders. By how many students did your estimate miss the actual number?

5. APPLICATION Write and solve a proportion for each situation.

a. A biologist tagged 250 fish. Then she collected another sample of 75 fish, of which 5 were tagged. How many fish would she estimate are in the lake? ⓗ

b. A biologist estimated that there were 5500 fish in a lake in which 250 fish had been tagged. A ranger collected a sample in which there were 15 tagged fish. Approximately how many fish were in the sample the ranger collected?

Reason and Apply

6. Marie and Richard played 47 games of backgammon last month. Marie's ratio of wins to losses was 28 to 19.

a. Estimate the number of games you expect Marie to win if she and Richard play 12 more games. Explain your thinking. ⓐ

b. Write a proportion, and solve for Marie's expected number of wins if she and Richard play 12 more games. ⓐ

c. Write a proportion, and solve it to determine how many games Marie and Richard will need to play before Richard can expect to win 30 games. ⓐ

7. Jon opened a package of candies and counted them. He found 60 candies in the 1.69 oz package.

a. Estimate the number of candies in a 1 lb (16 oz) bag. Explain your thinking in arriving at this estimate.

b. Write the proportion, and solve for the number of candies in a 1 lb package. Compare your approximation to your estimate in 7a.

c. What would 1 million candies weigh? Give your answer in pounds.

8. APPLICATION Fisherman Jack was hired to estimate fish populations in Long Lake. He and three friends fished for a week, and in that time they caught, tagged, and released 235 bass, 147 trout, and 151 perch. Later that summer they returned and spent two weeks fishing in different parts of the lake. Here are the results:

Fish Populations

	Bass	Trout	Perch
Tagged	24	15	16
Untagged	336	208	192

Use these data to estimate the population of each of the three fish species. Then use the first-row total and the second-row total to estimate the total population of the three species in the lake. Why don't you get the same total population when you add the three species populations?

Review

9. The ratio of ninth graders to eighth graders in the class is 5 to 3. Write these ratios as fractions.

a. ninth graders to eighth graders

b. ninth graders to students in the class @

c. eighth graders to students in the class

10. This histogram shows the ages of the first 44 presidents of the United States when they took office. (*New York Times Almanac 2009*, pp. iv, 110)

a. What is a good estimate of the median age?

b. How many presidents were younger than 50 when they took office? @

c. What ages were not represented among the presidents at inauguration? @

d. Redraw the histogram, changing the interval width from 2 to 4.

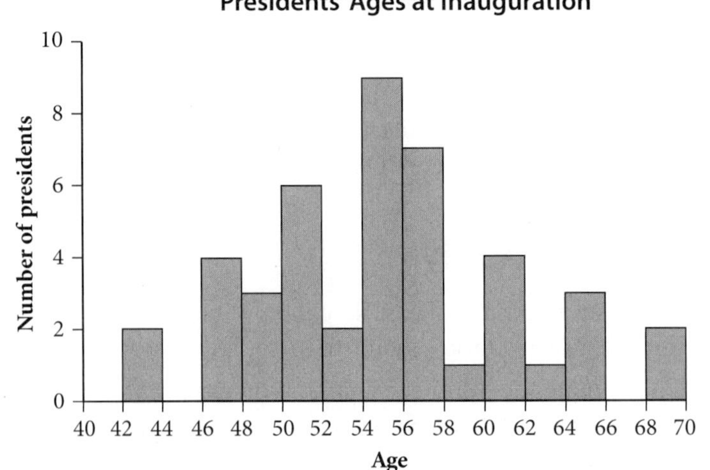

11. On a group quiz, your group needs to calculate the answer to $12 - 2 \cdot 6 - 3$. The three other group members came up with these answers:

Marta 57   Matt -3 Miguel 30

Who, if anyone, is correct? What would you say to the other group members to convince them?

LESSON

2.3

Conversion Factors and Unit Rates

Have you ever visited another country? If so, you needed to convert your money to that country's and perhaps convert some of your measurement units as well. For measurements many countries use the units of the Système Internationale, or SI, known in the United States as the metric system.

Instead of selling gasoline by the gallon, countries that use the metric system sell it by the liter. Distance signs are in kilometers rather than in miles, and vegetables are sold by the kilo (kilogram) rather than by the pound.

INVESTIGATION

Converting Centimeters to Inches

YOU WILL NEED

- a yardstick or tape measure
- a meterstick or metric tape measure

In this investigation you will find a ratio to help you convert inches to centimeters and centimeters to inches. Then you will use this ratio in a proportion to convert some measurements from the system that is standard in the United States to measurements in the metric system, and vice versa.

Step 1 Measure the length or width of each of six different-size objects, such as a pencil, a book, your desk, or your calculator. For each object, record the inch measurement and the centimeter measurement in a table like this:

Inches to Centimeters

Object	Measurement in inches	Measurement in centimeters

Step 2 Enter your measurements in inches and in centimeters into two separate calculator lists. Create a third list by dividing the centimeter values by the inch values: $\frac{\textit{centimeters} \text{ (second list)}}{\textit{inches} \text{ (first list)}}$. [▶ See **Calculator Note: Formula Generated Lists.** ◀]

Step 3 How do the ratios of centimeters to inches compare for the different measurements? If one of the ratios is much different from the others, recheck your measurements.

Step 4 Choose a single representative ratio of centimeters to inches. Write a sentence that explains the meaning of this ratio.

Step 5 Using your ratio, set up a proportion and convert each length.

a. 215 centimeters = x inches

b. 1 centimeter = x inches

c. 1 inch = x centimeters

d. How many centimeters high is a doorway that measures 80 inches?

Step 6 Using your ratio, set up a proportion and solve for the requested value.

a. y centimeters = x inches. Solve for y.

b. c centimeters = i inches. Solve for i.

In the investigation you found a common ratio, or **conversion factor,** between inches and centimeters. Once you've determined the conversion factor, you can convert from one system to the other by solving a proportion. If your measurements in the investigation were very accurate, the mean and median of the ratios were very close to the actual conversion factor, 2.54 centimeters to 1 inch.

EXAMPLE A

Jonas drove his car from Montana to Canada on vacation. While there, he needed to buy gasoline and noticed that it was sold by the liter rather than by the gallon. Use the conversion factor 1 gallon $\approx$ 3.79 liters to determine how many liters will fill his 12.5-gallon gas tank.

Solution

Using the conversion factor, you can write the proportion $\frac{3.79 \text{ liters}}{1 \text{ gallon}} = \frac{x \text{ liters}}{12.5 \text{ gallons}}$.

$$\frac{3.79}{1} = \frac{x}{12.5} \qquad \text{Original proportion.}$$

$$12.5 \cdot 3.79 = x \qquad \text{Undo the division.}$$

$$x = 47.375 \qquad \text{Simplify.}$$

Jonas's tank will hold about 47.4 liters of gasoline.

Some conversions require several steps. The next example offers a strategy called **dimensional analysis** for doing more complicated conversions.

EXAMPLE B

A radio-controlled car traveled 30 feet across the classroom in 1.6 seconds. How fast was it traveling in miles per hour?

Solution

Using the given information, you can write the speed as the ratio $\frac{30 \text{ feet}}{1.6 \text{ seconds}}$. Multiplying by 1 doesn't change the value of a number, so you can use conversion factors that you know $\left(\text{like } \frac{60 \text{ minutes}}{1 \text{ hour}}\right)$ to create fractions with a value of 1. Then multiply your original ratio by those fractions to change the units.

$$\frac{30 \cancel{\text{ft}}}{1.6 \cancel{\text{s}}} \cdot \frac{60 \cancel{\text{s}}}{1 \cancel{\text{min}}} \cdot \frac{60 \cancel{\text{min}}}{1 \text{ h}} \cdot \frac{1 \text{ mi}}{5{,}280 \cancel{\text{ft}}} = \frac{108{,}000 \text{ mi}}{8{,}448 \text{ h}}$$

$$\approx \frac{12.8 \text{ mi}}{1 \text{ h}}, \text{ or } 12.8 \text{ miles per hour}$$

Science **CONNECTION**

Medical experts have suggested that high school students should drink about eight 8 oz glasses of water a day. At that rate, how many gallons of water should you drink each year?

$\frac{8 \text{ oz}}{1 \text{ glass}} \cdot \frac{8 \text{ glasses}}{1 \text{ day}} \cdot \frac{365 \text{ days}}{1 \text{ yr}} \cdot \frac{1 \text{ gal}}{128 \text{ oz}}$
$= 182.5 \text{ gal/yr}$

That is the amount of water in a 6 ft long fish tank.

On the left side of the equation, each of the fractions after the first has the value 1 because the numerator and denominator of each fraction are equivalent: $60 \text{ s} = 1 \text{ min}$, $60 \text{ min} = 1 \text{ h}$, and $1 \text{ mi} = 5280 \text{ ft}$. The fractions equivalent to 1 are chosen so that when units cancel, the result is miles in the numerator and hours in the denominator.

Other fractions with 1 in the denominator might represent rates rather than conversion factors. A **rate** is a comparison between two quantities with different units. It is generally written as a **unit rate,** a comparison of one quantity to a single unit of another quantity, such as 12.8 miles per (1) hour, or 42 miles per (1) gallon.

In Example B, 12.8 miles per hour is a unit rate. A rate of travel (or speed) is just one example of a unit rate. Your weekly allowance, the cost per pound of shipping a package, and the number of cookies per box are also unit rates. Unit rates make calculations easier in many real-life situations. For instance, grocery stores price fruits and vegetables by the pound. Unit rates make comparisons easier in other situations, too. For instance, a baseball player's batting average is a unit rate of hits per times at bat. What other unit rates have you seen in this book?

2.3 Exercises

Practice Your Skills

1. Find the value of x in each proportion.

a. $\frac{1 \text{ meter}}{3.25 \text{ feet}} = \frac{15.2 \text{ meters}}{x \text{ feet}}$ @

b. $\frac{1.6 \text{ kilometers}}{1 \text{ mile}} = \frac{x \text{ kilometers}}{25 \text{ miles}}$

c. $\frac{0.926 \text{ meter}}{1 \text{ yard}} = \frac{200 \text{ meters}}{x \text{ yards}}$

d. $\frac{1 \text{ kilometer}}{0.6 \text{ mile}} = \frac{x \text{ kilometers}}{350 \text{ miles}}$

e. $\frac{2.54 \text{ centimeters}}{1 \text{ inch}} = \frac{x \text{ centimeters}}{12 \text{ inches}}$

f. $\frac{1000 \text{ meters}}{3281 \text{ feet}} = \frac{100 \text{ meters}}{x \text{ feet}}$

In Exercises 2–4, use the conversion factor 1 ounce $\approx$ 28.4 grams.

2. How many grams does an 8-ounce portion of prime rib weigh? @

3. If an ice-cream cone weighs 50 grams, how many ounces does it weigh? @

4. If a typical house cat weighs 160 ounces, how many grams does it weigh?

In Exercises 5–7, use the conversion factor 1 inch $\approx$ 2.54 centimeters.

5. A teacher is 62.5 inches tall. How many centimeters tall is she? @

6. A common ceiling height is 96 inches (8 feet). About how high is this in centimeters?

7. The diameter of a CD is 12 centimeters. What is its diameter in inches? @

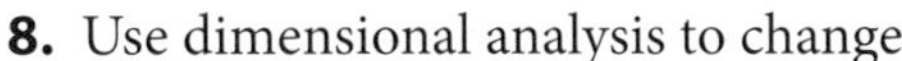

8. Use dimensional analysis to change

a. 60 miles per hour to miles per minute.

b. 4 miles per hour to feet per second.

c. 50 meters per second to kilometers per hour. (h)

d. 0.025 day to seconds.

e. 1200 ounces to tons (16 oz = 1 lb; 2000 lb = 1 ton).

9. In 2001, Alan Webb broke Jim Ryun's 36-year-old high school mile record by running 1 mile in 3 minutes 53.43 seconds. How fast was this in feet per second? (h)

Reason and Apply

10. Tab and Crystal both own cats.

a. Tab buys a 3-pound bag of cat food every 30 days. At what rate does his cat eat the food? @

b. Crystal buys a 5-pound bag of cat food every 45 days. At what rate does her cat eat the food?

c. Whose cat, Tab's or Crystal's, eats more food per day? (h)

11. A group of students measured several objects around their school in both yards and meters.

Measurements in Yards and Meters

Yards	7	3.5	7.5	4.25	6.25	11
Meters	6.3	3.2	6.8	3.8	5.6	9.9

a. Use their data, shown in the table, to find a conversion factor between yards and meters.

Use the conversion factor to answer these questions:

b. The length of a football field is 100 yards. How long is it in meters? @

c. If it is 200 meters to the next freeway exit, how far away is the exit in yards?

d. How many yards long is a 100-meter dash?

e. How many meters of fabric should you buy if you need 15 yards?

12. Which is longer: a 1-mile race or a 1500-meter race? Show your reasoning.

13. APPLICATION When mixed according to the directions, a 12-ounce can of lemonade concentrate becomes 64 ounces of lemonade.

a. How many 12-ounce cans of concentrate are needed to make 120 servings if each serving is 8 ounces? @

b. How many ounces of concentrate are needed to make 1 ounce of lemonade?

c. Write a proportion that you can use to find the number of ounces of concentrate, based on the number of ounces of lemonade you want. @

d. Use the proportion you wrote in 13c to find the number of ounces of lemonade that can be made from a 16-ounce can of the same concentrate.

Review

14. The students in the mathematics and chess clubs worked together to raise funds for their respective groups. Together the clubs raised \$480. There are 12 members in the mathematics club and only 8 members in the chess club. How should the funds be divided between the two clubs? Explain your answer. @

15. The box plot shows the length in centimeters of the members of the kingfisher family. The lengths of the five birds shown make up the five-number summary. Use the information below to match each kingfisher to its length.

- These kingfishers range in size from the tiny pygmy kingfisher to the laughing kookaburra.
- The best known kingfisher, the belted kingfisher, breeds from Alaska to Florida. It is only 2.6 centimeters longer than the mean kingfisher length.
- The ringed kingfisher, a tropical bird, is much closer to the median length than is the green kingfisher.

IMPROVING YOUR Visual Thinking SKILLS

The seven pieces of the ancient Chinese puzzle called a tangram are defined using a square *ABCD* and a set of midpoints. Points *E, F, G, H, I,* and J are the midpoints of segments *AB, BC, AC, AG, GC,* and *EF,* respectively. What is the ratio of the area of each of these tangram pieces to the area of the whole square?

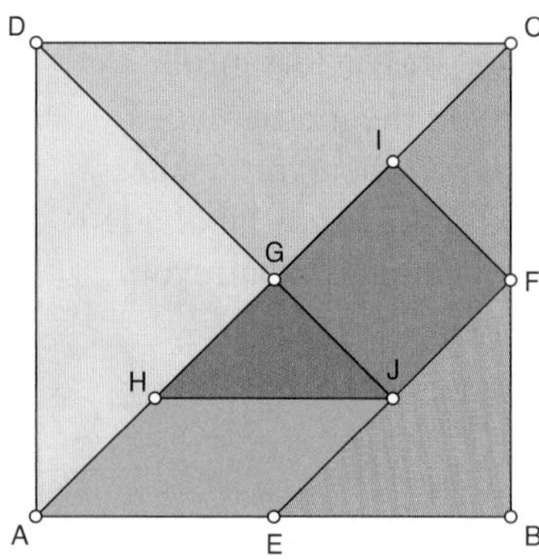

LESSON

2.4

Direct Variation

In Lesson 2.3 you worked with conversion factors to change from one unit of measure to another. You also worked with rates, such as *miles per hour,* and saw that a unit rate has 1 in the denominator. This makes rates convenient to calculate with. In this lesson you'll see patterns arise when you use rates to make tables or graphs. In the investigation you'll use algebra to understand these patterns better.

INVESTIGATION

YOU WILL NEED

- graph paper

Ship Canals

In this investigation you will use data about canals to draw a graph and write an equation to represent the relationship between miles and kilometers. You'll see several ways to find the information missing from this table.

Ship Canals

Canal	Length (mi)	Length (km)
Albert (Belgium)	80	129
Alphonse XIII (Spain)	53	85
Houston (Texas)	50	81
Kiel (Germany)	62	99
Main-Danube (Germany)	106	171
Moscow-Volga (Russia)	80	129
Panama (Panama)	51	82
St. Lawrence Seaway (Canada/U.S.)	189	304
Suez (Egypt)	101	
Trollhätte (Sweden)		87

(*The Top 10 of Everything 1998,* p. 57)

Step 1 Carefully draw and scale a pair of coordinate axes for the data in the table. Let x represent the length in miles and y represent the length in kilometers. Plot points for the first eight coordinate pairs.

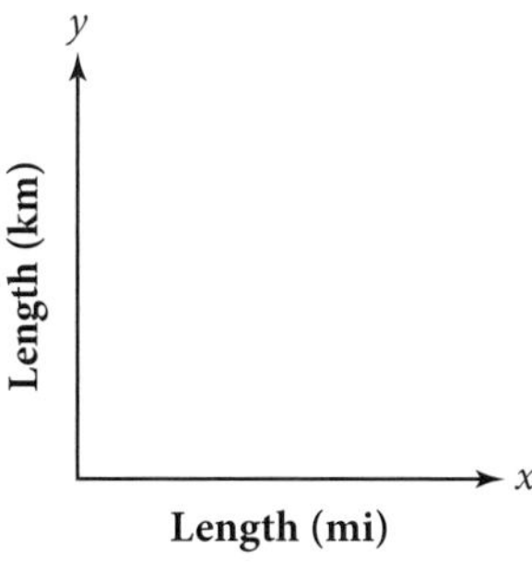

Step 2 What pattern or shape do you see in your graph? Connect the points to illustrate this pattern. Explain how you could use your graph to approximate the length *in kilometers* of the Suez Canal and the length *in miles* of the Trollhätte Canal.

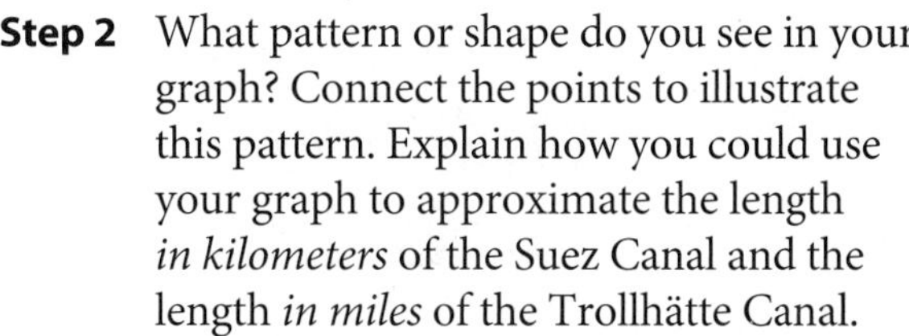

Step 3 On your calculator, make a plot of the same points, and compare it to your hand-drawn plot. [▶ See **Calculator Note: Scatter Plots** to review this type of plot. ◀]

Step 4 Calculate the ratio of your two lists to create a new list, $\frac{kilometers}{miles}$. [▶ See **Calculator Note: Formula Generated Lists** to review using lists to calculate values. ◀] Explain what the values in the third list represent. If you round each value in the third list to the nearest tenth, what do you get?

Step 5 Use the rounded value you got in Step 4 to find the length in kilometers of the Suez Canal. Could you also use your result to find the length in miles of the Trollhätte Canal?

The number of kilometers is the same in every mile, so the value you found is called a **constant.**

Step 6 Using the variables x miles and y kilometers, write an equation in the form $y = kx$ that shows how miles and kilometers are related.

Step 7 Use the equation you wrote in Step 6 to find the length in kilometers of the Suez Canal and the length in miles of the Trollhätte Canal. How is using this equation like using a rate?

Step 8 Graph your equation from Step 6 on your calculator. [▶ See **Calculator Note: Equations** to review graphing equations. ◀] Compare this graph to your hand-drawn graph. Why does the graph go through the origin?

Step 9 The Canal du Midi in France is 149 miles long. Use your equation from Step 6 or trace the graph to find this length in kilometers. [▶ See **Calculator Note: Equations** to review tracing equations. ◀]

Step 10 The Grand Canal in China is 1746 kilometers long. Find this length in miles, using any method you like.

Step 11 In this investigation you used several ways to find missing values—approximating with a graph, calculating with a rate, and solving an equation. Write several sentences explaining which of these methods you prefer and why.

History CONNECTION

The Panama Canal allows ships to cross the strip of land between the Atlantic and Pacific Oceans. Before the canal was completed in 1913, ships had to sail thousands of miles around the dangerous Cape Horn, even though only 50 mi separate the two oceans.

Ships passing through the Panama Canal.

Ratios, rates, and conversion factors are closely related. In this investigation you saw how to change the ratio $\frac{129\text{ km}}{80\text{ mi}}$ to a rate of approximately 1.6 kilometers per mile. You can also use that rate as a conversion factor between kilometers and miles. The numbers in the ratio vary, but the resulting rate remains the same, or constant. Kilometers and miles are **directly proportional**—there will always be the same number of kilometers in every mile. When two quantities vary in this way, they have a relationship called **direct variation.**

Direct Variation

An equation in the form $y = kx$ is a direct variation. The quantities represented by x and y are directly proportional, and k is the constant of variation. When the value of x is 0, the value of y is 0; therefore, the graph of a direct variation passes through the point (0, 0).

You can represent any ratio, rate, or conversion factor with a direct variation. Using a direct variation equation or graph is an alternative to solving proportions. A direct variation equation can also help you organize calculations with rates.

EXAMPLE

Sol is planning a camping and hiking trip in the Rockies. He wants to be sure he has enough water for the trip. The weekly ad for a local grocery store advertises four six-packs of bottled water for $6.00.

a. Write a rate for the cost per six-pack.

b. Write an equation showing the relationship between the number of six-packs purchased and the cost.

c. How much will 15 six-packs cost?

d. Sol bought $210 worth of bottled water. How many six-packs did he buy?

Solution

a. The ratio given is $\frac{\$6.00}{4\text{ six-packs}}$. This simplifies to a rate of $1.50 per six-pack.

b. Use x for the number of six-packs and y for the cost in dollars. Write a proportion.

$$\frac{y}{x} = \frac{1.50}{1}$$ y corresponds to 1.50 and x corresponds to 1.

$$y = \frac{1.50}{1} \cdot x$$ Multiply by x to undo the division.

$$y = 1.50x$$ Your result is a direct variation equation.

The constant of variation, k, is the rate \$1.50 per six-pack. Does every point on the graph of this equation make sense in this situation?

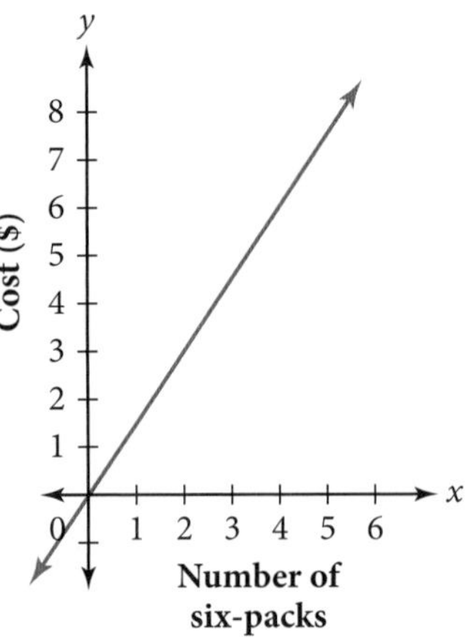

c. Using your calculator, you can trace the graph to find the point where $x = 15$, or you can substitute 15, the number of six-packs, for x in the equation.

$$y = 1.50(15) = 22.50$$

Fifteen six-packs will cost \$22.50.

d. You can search your calculator's table until you close in on the value of x that gives the y-value of 210. Or you can substitute 210, the cost in dollars, for y in the equation.

$210 = 1.50x$ Substitute 210 for y in the original equation.

$\frac{210}{1.50} = x$ Divide by 1.50 to undo the multiplication.

$140 = x$ Simplify.

Sol purchased 140 six-packs for \$210.

To emphasize that a particular ratio is constant, a direct variation is often written in the form $\frac{y}{x} = k$. Is the equation $\frac{y}{x} = 1$ a direct variation? What does its graph look like?

2.4 Exercises

You will need your graphing calculator for Exercises **1, 2, 3,** and **12.**

Practice Your Skills

Let x represent distance in miles and y represent distance in kilometers. Enter the equation $y = 1.6x$ into your calculator. Use it for Exercises 1–3.

1. Trace the graph of $y = 1.6x$ to find each missing quantity. Adjust the window settings as you proceed.

a. 25 miles ≈ ☐ kilometers @ b. 120 kilometers ≈ ☐ miles

2. Use the calculator table function to find the missing quantity.

a. 55 miles ≈ ☐ kilometers @ b. 450 kilometers ≈ ☐ miles

3. Find the missing values in this table. Round each value to the nearest tenth.

Distance (mi)	Distance (km)
@	4.5
7.8	
650.0	
	1500.0

4. Describe how to solve each equation for x. Then solve.

a. $14 = 3.5x$ @ b. $8x = 45(0.62)$ c. $\frac{x}{7} = 0.375$ d. $\frac{12}{x} = 0.8$

e. $\frac{3}{5} \cdot x = 1$ f. $\frac{5x}{7} = 20$ g. $\frac{20.8}{x} = \frac{2}{3}$ h. $0.6 = \frac{1}{x}$

5. Is the equation $\frac{y}{x} = -1$ a direct variation? Explain.

6. A car travels 116 miles in 2 hours. What is its unit rate?

7. APPLICATION The equation $c = 1.25f$ shows the direct variation relationship between the length of fabric and its cost. The variable f represents the length of the fabric in yards, and c represents the cost in dollars. Use the equation to answer these questions.
   a. How much does $2\frac{1}{2}$ yards of fabric cost?
   b. How much fabric can you buy for $5?
   c. What is the cost of each additional yard of fabric?

Christo (b 1935, Bulgaria) and Jeanne-Claude (1935–2009, Morocco) are environmental sculptors who have wrapped large objects and buildings in fabric. This is the German Reichstag in 1995.

Reason and Apply

8. Sketch a graph for each situation. Then answer the questions.
   a. Sid drove 54 miles in 1 hour. His friend Diego traveled 200 miles in 4 hours. Assume each drove at a constant rate. Sketch the graphs of both trips on the same set of axes. Who traveled at the faster rate? How can you tell?
   b. You stand with your back to a motion sensor and then walk at a constant rate away from it. What would you change to make the graph steeper?
   c. $\frac{y}{x} = -2$. How is this graph different from other direct variation graphs you have seen?
   d. $y \leq 0.75x$, and the points (x, y) are in Quadrant I. What would you need to do to the inequality to change the shading to the other side of the graph?

9. APPLICATION Market A sells 7 ears of corn for $1.25. Market B sells a baker's dozen (13 ears) for $2.75.
   a. Copy and complete these tables showing the cost of corn at each market.

Market A

Ears	7	14	21	28	35	42
Cost						

Market B

Ears	13	26	39	52	65	78
Cost						

   b. Let x represent the number of ears of corn and y represent the cost. Write equations for the cost of corn at each market. Graph the two equations on the same set of axes. Round the constants of variation to three decimal places. (h)
   c. If you wanted to buy only one ear of corn, how much would each market charge you? How are these prices related to the equations you found in 9b?
   d. How can you tell from the graphs which market is the cheaper place to buy corn?

Why is 13 called a baker's dozen? In the 13th century, bakers began to form guilds to prevent dishonesty. To avoid the penalty for selling a loaf of bread that was too small, bakers began giving 13 whenever a customer asked for a dozen.

10. Bernard Lavery, a resident of the United Kingdom, has held several world records for growing giant vegetables. The graph shows the relationship between weight in kilograms and weight in pounds.

a. Use the information in the graph to complete the table.

Bernard Lavery's Vegetables

Vegetable	Weight (kg)	Weight (lb)
Cabbage	56	
Summer squash		108
Zucchini		64
Kohlrabi	28	
Celery	21	
Radish		28
Cucumber	9	
Brussels sprout		18
Carrot	5	

(*The Top 10 of Everything 1998*, p. 98)

Relationship Between Kilograms and Pounds

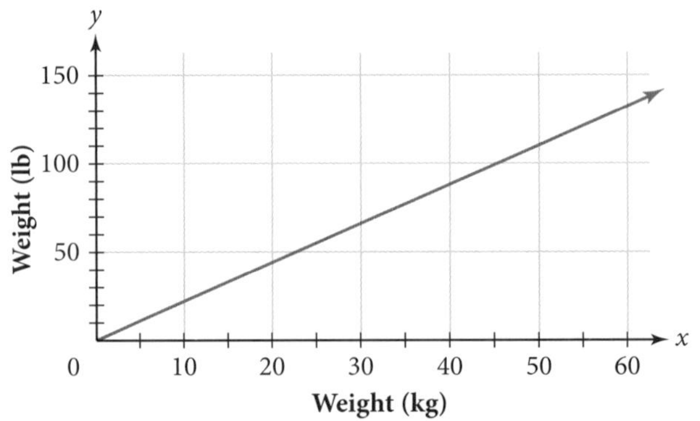

b. Calculate the rate of pounds per kilogram for each vegetable entry from the table. Use the rate you think best represents the data as the constant of variation. Explain why you think that rate best represents the data. Write an equation to represent the relationship between pounds and kilograms. ⓐ

c. Use the equation you wrote in 10b to find the weight in kilograms of a pumpkin that weighs 6.5 pounds. ⓐ

d. Use the equation you wrote in 10b to find the weight in pounds of an elephant that weighs 3600 kilograms. ⓐ

e. How many kilograms are in 100 pounds? How many pounds are in 100 kilograms? ⓐ

11. As part of their homework assignment, Thu and Sabrina each found equations from a table of data relating miles and kilometers. One entry in the table paired 150 kilometers and 93 miles. From this pair of data values, Thu and Sabrina wrote different equations.

a. Thu wrote the equation $y = 1.61x$. How did he get it? What does 1.61 represent? What do x and y represent? ⓗ

b. Sabrina wrote $y = 0.62x$ as her equation. How did she get it? What does 0.62 represent? What do x and y represent?

c. Whose equation would you use to convert miles to kilometers?

d. When would you use the other student's equation?

12. APPLICATION If you're planning to travel to another country, you will need to learn about its monetary system. This table gives some exchange rates that tell how many of each monetary unit are equivalent to one U.S. dollar.

International Monetary Units

Country	Monetary unit	Exchange rate (units per American dollar)
Brazil	real	2.31
Thailand	baht	31.26
Italy	euro	0.754
Japan	yen	98.12
Mexico	peso	12.73
India	rupee	61.43
United Kingdom	pound	0.645

(*www.xe.com*, August 2013)

a. Make a list of ten items and the price of each item in U.S. dollars. Enter these prices into the first list in your calculator.

b. Choose one of the countries in the table, and convert the U.S. dollar amounts in your list to that country's monetary unit. Use the second list to calculate these new values from the first list.

c. Using the third list, convert the values in the second list back to the values in the first list.

d. Describe how you would convert euros to pesos.

13. If you travel at a constant speed, the distance you travel is directly proportional to your travel time. Suppose you walk 3 mi in 1.5 h.

a. How far would you walk in 1 h? (h)

b. How far would you walk in 2 h?

c. How much time would it take you to walk 6 mi?

d. Represent this situation with a graph.

e. What is the constant of variation in this situation, and what does it represent? (@)

f. Define variables and write an equation that relates time to distance traveled. (@)

14. A bug is crawling horizontally along the wall at a constant rate of 5 inches per minute. You first notice the bug when it is in the corner of the room, behind your music stand.

a. Define variables and write an equation that relates time (in minutes) to distance traveled (in inches). (@)

b. What is the constant of variation of this direct variation relationship, and what does it represent?

c. How far will the bug crawl in 1 h?

d. How long would you have to practice playing your instrument before the bug completely "circled" the 14-ft-by-20-ft room? (@)

e. Draw a graph that represents this situation.

Review

15. Correct any errors you find in these calculations.

a. $\frac{\$19}{3\text{ ft}} \cdot 72\text{ ft} = \frac{\$456}{1\text{ ft}^2}$

b. $\frac{18\text{ ft}}{6\text{ s}} \cdot \frac{12\text{ in.}}{1\text{ ft}} \cdot \frac{2.54\text{ cm}}{1\text{ in.}} \cdot \frac{100\text{ m}}{1\text{ cm}} = \frac{9144\text{ m}}{1\text{ s}}$

16. U.S. speed limits are posted in miles per hour (mi/h). Germany's Autobahn has stretches where speed limits are posted at 130 kilometers per hour (km/h). (On most stretches of the German autobahn system, there is no posted speed limit.)

a. How many miles per hour is 130 km/h? @

b. How many kilometers per hour is 25 mi/h?

c. If the United States used the metric system, what speed limit do you think would be posted in place of 65 mi/h?

17. APPLICATION Marie and Tracy bought boxes of granola bars for their hiking trip. They noticed that the tags on the grocery-store shelf use rates.

a. Each tag shown uses two rates. Identify all four rates. @

b. A box of Crunchy Granola Bars contains 6 bars. Is the listed price per bar correct?

c. A box of Chewy Granola Bars contains 8 bars. Use the information on the tag to find the number of ounces per bar. @

d. A box of Crunchy Granola Bars weighs 10 ounces. What is the price per ounce?

e. If Marie and Tracy like Crunchy Granola Bars as much as they like Chewy Granola Bars, which should they buy? Explain your answer.

18. APPLICATION Amber makes $6 an hour at a sandwich shop. She wants to know how many hours she needs to work to save $500 in her bank account. On her first paycheck, she notices that her net pay is about 75% of her gross pay.

a. How many hours must she work to earn $500 in gross pay?

b. How many hours must she work to earn $500 in net pay?

LESSON

2.5

Inverse Variation

"One person's constant is another person's variable."
SUSAN GERHART

In each relationship you have worked with in this chapter, if one quantity increased, so did the other. If one quantity decreased, so did the other. If the working hours increase, so does the pay. The shorter the trip, the less gas the car needs. These are direct relationships. Do all relationships between quantities work this way? Can two quantities be related in such a way that increasing one causes the other to decrease?

Try opening your classroom door by pushing on it close to a hinge. Try it again farther from the hinge. Which way takes more force? As the distance from the hinge *increases,* the force needed to open the door *decreases.* This is an example of an *inverse* relationship.

INVESTIGATION

Text Boxes

YOU WILL NEED

- a computer with word-processing software

In this investigation you will explore the relationship between the width of a section of text and the number of lines it takes to display the same amount of text.

Step 1 Type the first paragraph of this lesson by using your word processor.

In each relationship you have worked with in this chapter, if one quantity increased . . .

Step 2 Using the ruler at the top of the document page, measure the width of the text. Count the number of lines of text. Record this information in the first row of a table like this one.

Width of text (in.)	Number of lines

In each relationship you have worked with in this chapter, if one quantity increased . . .

Step 3 Change the margins of the document. In the second row of the table, record the new width and number of lines.

Step 4 Repeat Step 3 until you have at least six data pairs, (*width, number of lines*).

Step 5 Enter the data into your calculator, and create a scatter plot that shows the data and both axes. [▶ See **Calculator Note: Entering Lists** and **Calculator Note: Scatter Plots.** ◀]

Step 6 Find an equation in the form $y = \frac{a}{x}$ that is a good model for the relationship between the width of the text and the number of lines. Experiment with different values of a until you find a curve that looks like a good fit for the data.

Step 7 What does your equation predict will happen if x is very large? Is this prediction realistic?

Step 8 What does your equation predict will happen if x is very small? Is this prediction realistic?

In the investigation, you dealt with the relationship between the number of lines of text and the width of the text box. You may have discovered that the product of these two variables was nearly constant. You could write the equation

first number of lines · *first text width* = *second number of lines* · *second text width*

You can also write this relationship as a proportion:

$$\frac{\textit{first number of lines}}{\textit{second number of lines}} = \frac{\textit{second text width}}{\textit{first text width}}$$

$$\frac{\textit{first number of lines}}{\textit{second text width}} = \frac{\textit{second number of lines}}{\textit{first text width}}$$

How can you show that all three of these equations are equivalent?

The proportions above differ from the proportions you wrote earlier in the chapter. When the values correspond in an opposite (or inverse) way, the proportions are called **inverse proportions.**

EXAMPLE A

Tyline measured the force needed as she opened a door by pushing at various distances from a hinge. She collected the data shown in the table. Find an equation to describe this relationship. (A newton, abbreviated N, is the metric unit of force.)

Distance (cm)	Force (N)
40.0	20.9
45.0	18.0
50.0	16.1
55.0	14.8
60.0	13.3
65.0	12.3
70.0	11.6
75.0	10.7

Solution

Enter the data into two calculator lists, and graph the points. The graph shows a curved pattern that is different from the graph of a direct relationship. If you study the values in the table, you can see that as distance increases, force decreases. The data pairs of this relationship might have a constant product like your data in the investigation.

Science CONNECTION

Scientists use precise machines to measure the amount of force needed to pull or push. Manufacturers use these tools to test the strength of products such as boxes. You can also measure force with simple tools such as a spring scale. This box shows a certificate that gives the results from several force tests.

The y-axis is being used for force (N).

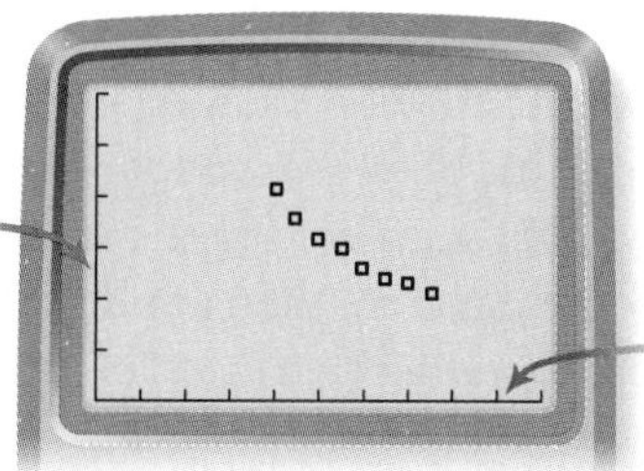

The x-axis is being used for distance from the hinge (cm).

[0, 100, 10, 0, 30, 5]

Calculate the products in another list. Their mean is approximately 810, so use that value to represent the product. Let x represent distance and y represent force.

Distance (cm)	Force (N)	Force · Distance (N-cm)
40	20.9	836.0
45	18.0	810.0
50	16.1	805.0
55	14.8	814.0
60	13.3	798.0
65	12.3	799.5
70	11.6	812.0
75	10.7	802.5

$xy = 810$ — The product of distance and force is 810.

$y = \frac{810}{x}$ — Divide by x to undo the multiplication.

Now you can enter this equation into your calculator. Graph the equation. Does it go through all the points? Why do you think the graph is not a perfect fit? It is a good practice to explore small changes to your equation's constant. A slightly different value might give an even better fit.

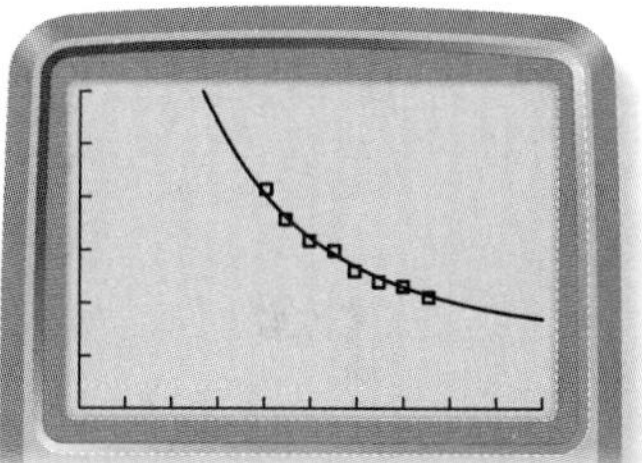

[0, 100, 10, 0, 30, 5]

The two variables in the inverse relationships you have seen have a constant product, so you can describe their relationship with an **inverse variation** equation. You can represent the constant product with k, just as you use k to represent the constant ratio of a direct variation. The graph of an inverse variation is always curved and will never cross the x- or y-axis. Why couldn't x or y be zero?

Inverse Variation

An equation in the form $y = \frac{k}{x}$ is an inverse variation. Quantities represented by x and y are inversely proportional, and k is the constant of variation.

EXAMPLE B

Lance noticed that it took him different amounts of time to get to school, depending on how fast he rode his bike. He wondered what the relationship was between his speed and the time, so he collected some data. He then applied that relationship to walking or riding in the car to get to school.

Speed (x)	Time (y)
20	8
15	11
18	9
12	13
22	7
10	16

a. What kind of relationship does his data show? How do you know?

b. Predict how long it would take Lance to walk to school at a rate of 4 mi/h.

c. Lance's mom occasionally drives him to school. What can his research help him predict about those trips?

Solution

a. The products of the data pairs, *speed* · *time*, are approximately the same. The mean product is 159.5, or about 160. So this is an inverse relationship.

Speed (x)	Time (y)	Product speed · time
20	8	160
15	11	165
18	9	162
12	13	156
22	7	154
10	16	160

b. With this relationship, 20 mi/h for 8 minutes must have the same product as 4 mi/h for x minutes.

$20 \cdot 8 = 4 \cdot x$ Original equation.

$\frac{20 \cdot 8}{4} = x$ Undo the multiplication.

$40 = x$ Simplify.

It will take Lance 40 minutes to walk to school at a rate of 4 mi/h.

c. If Lance can estimate his mother's average speed, he will know how long it will take to get to school when she drives him. He will then know when they have to leave the house so that he will get to school on time.

In a direct variation, the ratio $\frac{y}{x}$ is the same for all ordered pairs (x, y). In an inverse variation, the product xy is always the same.

2.5 Exercises

You will need your graphing calculator for Exercise **10.**

Practice Your Skills

1. Solve for y.

a. $xy = 15$ ⓐ b. $xy = 35$ c. $xy = 3$ d. $12.6 = xy$

2. Two quantities, x and y, are inversely proportional. When $x = 3$, $y = 4$. Find the missing coordinates for these points.

a. $(4, y)$ ⓗ b. $(x, 2)$ c. $(1, y)$ d. $(x, 24)$

3. Find five points that satisfy the inverse variation equation $y = \frac{20}{x}$. Graph the equation and the points to make sure the coordinates of your points are correct.

4. Henry noticed that the more television he watched, the less time he spent doing homework. One night he spent 1.5 h watching TV and 1.5 h doing homework. Another night he spent 2 h watching TV and only 1 h doing homework. To try to catch up, the next night he spent only a half hour watching TV and 2.5 h doing homework. Is this relationship an inverse variation? Explain why or why not.

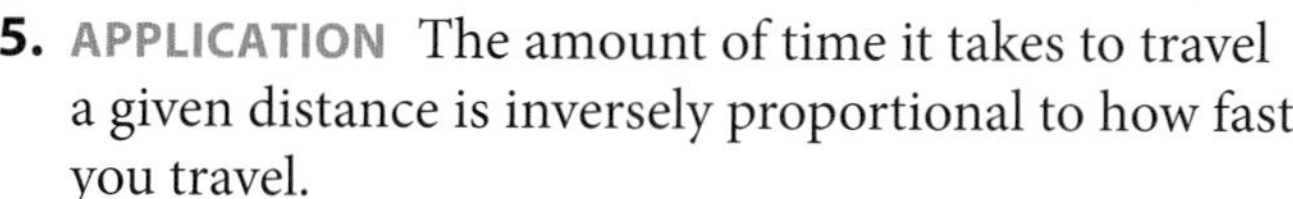

5. **APPLICATION** The amount of time it takes to travel a given distance is inversely proportional to how fast you travel.
   a. How long would it take to travel 90 mi at 30 mi/h? ⓐ
   b. How long would it take to travel 90 mi at 45 mi/h?
   c. How fast would you have to go to travel 90 mi in 1.5 h?

Reason and Apply

6. **APPLICATION** Emily and her little brother Sid are playing on a seesaw. Sid weighs 65 lb. The seesaw balances when Sid sits 4 ft from the center of the board and Emily sits $2\frac{1}{2}$ ft from the center.
   a. About how much does Emily weigh? ⓗ
   b. Sid's friend Seogwan sits with Sid at the same end of the seesaw. They weigh about the same. Can Emily balance the seesaw with both Sid and Seogwan on it? If so, where should she sit? If not, explain why not.

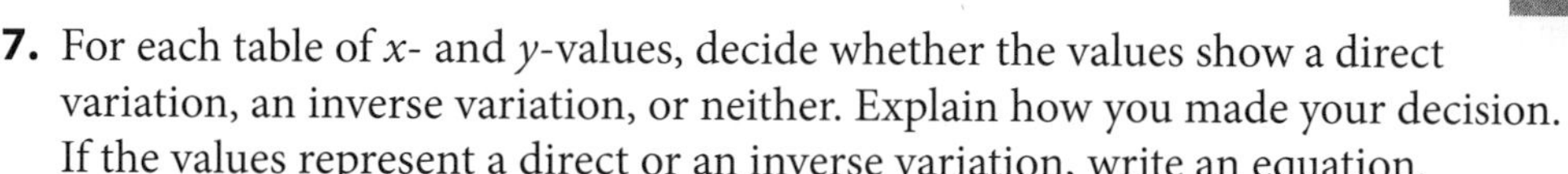

7. For each table of x- and y-values, decide whether the values show a direct variation, an inverse variation, or neither. Explain how you made your decision. If the values represent a direct or an inverse variation, write an equation.

a. ⓐ

x	y
2	12
8	3
4	6
3	8
6	4

b.

x	y
2	24
6	72
0	0
12	144
8	96

c.

x	y
4.5	2.0
0	9.0
3.0	3.0
9.0	0
6.0	1.5

d.

x	y
1.3	15.0
6.5	3.0
5.2	3.75
10.4	1.875
7.8	2.5

8. **APPLICATION** In Example A, you learned that the force in newtons needed to open a door is inversely proportional to the distance in centimeters from a hinge. For a heavy freezer door, the constant of variation is 935 N-cm.
   a. Find the force needed to open the freezer door by pushing at points 15 cm, 10 cm, and 5 cm from a hinge. ⓐ
   b. Describe what happens to the force needed to open the door as you push at points closer and closer to the hinge. How does the change in force needed compare as you go from 15 cm to 10 cm and from 10 cm to 5 cm?
   c. How is your answer to 8b shown on the graph of this equation?

9. To use a double-pan balance, you put the object to be weighed on one side and then put known weights on the other side until the pans balance.

   a. Explain why it is useful to have the balance point halfway between the two pans.

   b. Suppose the balance point is off-center, 15 cm from one pan and 20 cm from the other. An object is placed in the pan that is closer to the center. The pans balance when 7 kg is placed in the other pan. What is the weight of the unknown object? @

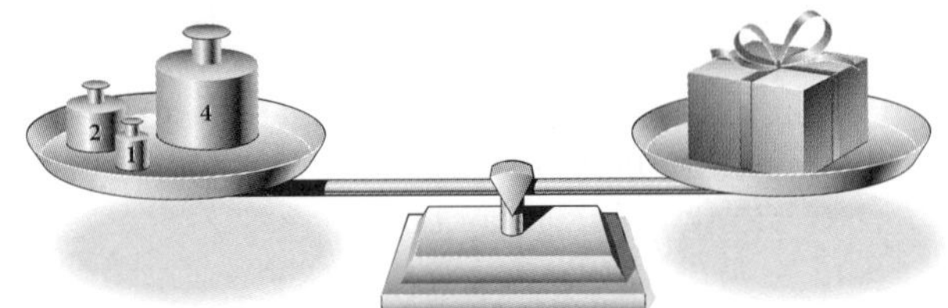

10. A tuning fork vibrates at a particular frequency to make the sound of a note in a musical scale. If you strike a tuning fork and place it over a hollow tube, the vibrating tuning fork will cause the air inside the tube to vibrate, and the sound will get louder. Skye found that if you put one end of the tube in water and raise and lower the tube, the loudness will vary. She used a set of tuning forks and, for each tuning fork, recorded the tube length that made the loudest sound.

Tuning Fork Experiment

Note	Frequency (hertz)	Tube length (cm)
A_4	440.0	84.6
C_5	523.3	71.1
D_5	587.3	63.4
F_5	698.5	53.3
G_5	784.0	47.5

   a. Graph the data on your calculator, and describe the relationship.

   b. Find an equation to fit the data. Explain how you did this and what your variables and constants represent.

   c. The last tuning fork in Skye's set is A_5, with frequency 880.0 hertz. What tube length should produce the loudest sound?

11. Match each equation with its graph.

   a. $xy = 2$ b. $xy = 4$ c. $xy = 8$

i.

ii.

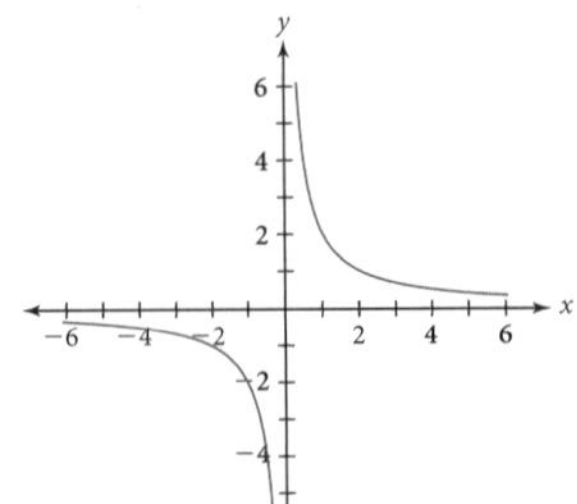

iii.

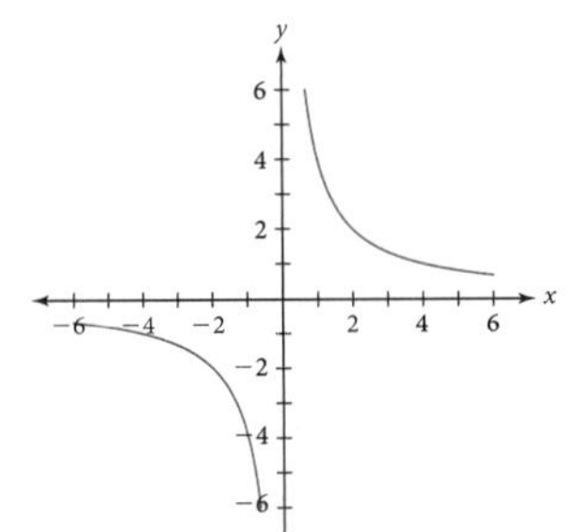

12. APPLICATION To squeeze a given amount of air into a smaller and smaller volume, you have to apply more and more pressure. Boyle's law describes the inverse variation between the volume of a gas and the pressure exerted on it. Suppose you start with a 1 L open container of air. If you position a plunger at the top of the container without applying any additional pressure, the pressure inside the container will be the same as the pressure outside the container, or 1 atmosphere (atm).

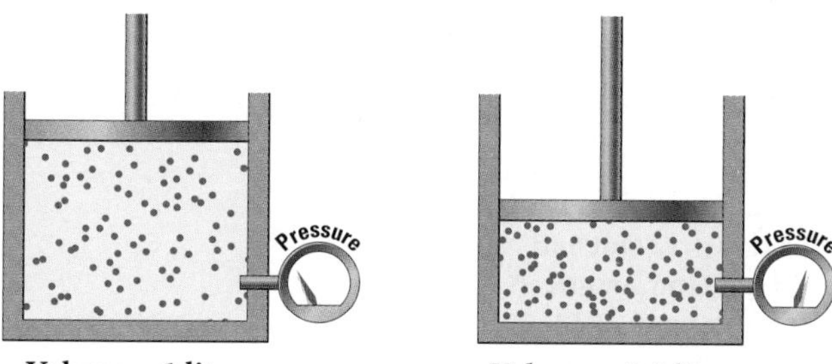

a. What will the pressure, in atmospheres, be if you push down the plunger until the volume of air is 0.5 L? @

b. What will the pressure, in atmospheres, be if you push down the plunger until the volume of air is 0.25 L?

c. Suppose you exert enough pressure so that the pressure in the container is 10 atm. What will the volume of air be? @

d. What would you have to do to make the pressure inside the container less than 1 atm?

e. Graph this relationship, with pressure (in atmospheres) on the horizontal axis and volume (in liters) on the vertical axis.

Review

13. APPLICATION A CD is on sale for 15% off its normal price of $13.95. What is its sale price? Write a direct variation equation to solve this problem.

14. Calcium and phosphorus play important roles in building human bones. A healthy ratio of calcium to phosphorus is 5 to 3.

a. If Mario's body contains 2.5 pounds of calcium, how much phosphorus should his body contain?

b. About 2% of an average woman's weight is calcium. Kyla weighs 130 pounds. How many pounds of calcium and phosphorus should her body contain?

15. APPLICATION Two dozen units in an apartment complex need to be painted. It takes 3 gallons of paint for each apartment.

a. How many apartments can be painted with 36 gallons?

b. How many gallons will it take to paint all 24 apartments?

16. Sulfuric acid, a highly corrosive substance, is used in the manufacture of dyes, fertilizer, and medicine. Sulfuric acid is also used by artists for metal etching and in aquatints. H_2SO_4 is the molecular formula for this substance. S stands for the sulfur atom. Use this information to answer each question.

a. How many atoms of sulfur, hydrogen, and oxygen are in one sulfuric acid molecule?

b. How many atoms of sulfur would it take to combine with 200 atoms of hydrogen? How many atoms of oxygen would it take to combine with 200 atoms of hydrogen?

c. If 500 atoms of sulfur, 400 atoms of hydrogen, and 400 atoms of oxygen are combined, how many sulfuric acid molecules could be formed?

This untitled drypoint and aquatint is by the American artist Mary Cassatt (1844–1926). Drypoint is a metal etching technique in which an image is incised into a plate with a hard-pointed "needle" of sharp metal or diamond point. Aquatint is a method of etching a copper plate in which the prints produced resemble watercolors.

17. Angie has some guests visiting from Italy, and they are planning to drive from her house to Washington, D.C. Angie wants her friends to understand how far they will need to drive.

a. Write a direct variation equation to convert miles to kilometers (1 mi $\approx$ 1.6 km).

b. Angie's house is about 250 miles from Washington, D.C. How many kilometers will her friends have to drive?

c. The hotel her friends are staying at says it is 2 miles from the Washington Monument. How far is that in kilometers?

d. The Washington Monument is taller than 555 feet. How tall is this in meters (1 m $\approx$ 3.3 ft)?

More on Proportions

To solve the proportion $\frac{x}{9} = \frac{10}{45}$, you've been taught to multiply each side of the equation by 9. Multiplying by 9 "undoes" the division of x by 9, which is indicated by the fraction bar. The multiplication gives $x = \frac{10}{45} \cdot 9$, or 2. Sometimes you can use mental arithmetic to solve proportions by thinking about equivalent fractions. You might notice that the right side of the proportion, $\frac{10}{45}$, reduces to an equivalent fraction with denominator 9. So $x = 2$.

$$\frac{x}{9} = \frac{10}{45}$$
$$\frac{x}{9} = \frac{2 \cdot \cancel{5}}{9 \cdot \cancel{5}}$$
$$\frac{x}{9} = \frac{2}{9}$$

EXAMPLE A | Solve for x: $\frac{2}{3} = \frac{4}{x+1}$

Solution | Solving the equation $\frac{2}{3} = \frac{4}{x+1}$ is not a one-step process. If you were asked to solve $\frac{2}{3} = \frac{4}{\square}$, you could do it quickly by looking for a relationship between the numerators. You know that $\frac{2}{3}$ and $\frac{4}{6}$ are equivalent fractions. If you relate this new fraction, $\frac{4}{\boxed{6}}$, to the right side of the proportion, $\frac{4}{x+1}$, you find that $6 = x + 1$. So $x = 5$.

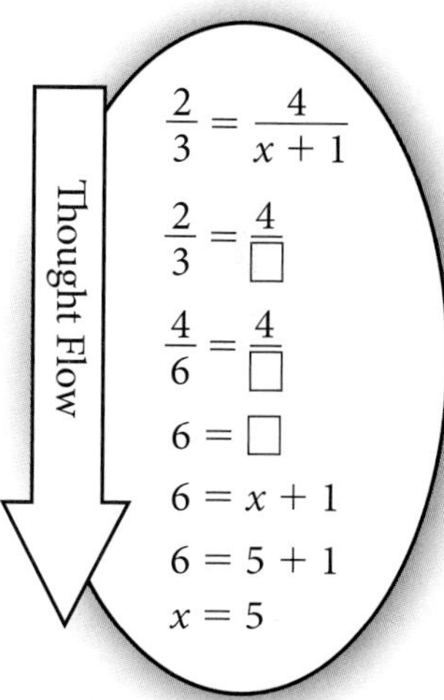

EXAMPLE B | Solve for x: $\frac{x}{4} + 2 = \frac{17}{3}$

Solution | Seeing this equation as $\square + 2 = \frac{17}{3}$, or $\square + \frac{6}{3} = \frac{17}{3}$, will tell you that $\square = \frac{11}{3}$.

Look back at the original equation. $\square$ represents $\frac{x}{4}$. So $\frac{x}{4} = \frac{11}{3}$.

Solving this equation gives you $4 \cdot \frac{x}{4} = \frac{11}{3} \cdot 4$, or $x = \frac{44}{3}$.

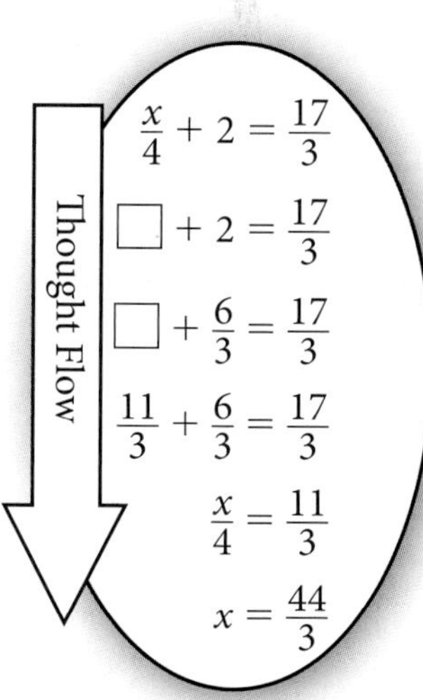

For each of the exercises, think about how equivalent fractions can be helpful. As you become more organized and skillful, look for ways to break down your problems into smaller parts.

Exercises

1. Solve each proportion mentally.

a. $\frac{x}{6} = \frac{12}{24}$ b. $\frac{x}{5} = \frac{15}{25}$ c. $\frac{6}{x} = \frac{12}{14}$ d. $\frac{4}{x} = \frac{24}{60}$

2. Solve each proportion by first finding a simpler equation.

i. Write the simpler equation.

ii. Write your solution to that equation.

iii. Check your solution by substituting it into the original equation.

a. $\frac{x+3}{48} = \frac{17}{12}$ b. $\frac{42}{x-1} = \frac{21}{11}$ c. $\frac{x+2}{12} = \frac{15}{6}$ d. $\frac{18}{x-9} = \frac{2}{11}$

3. Solve each equation by first finding a simpler equation.

i. Write the simple equation.

ii. Write your solution to that equation.

iii. Check your solution by substituting it into the original equation.

a. $\frac{6}{x} + \frac{3}{8} = \frac{7}{8}$ b. $\frac{x}{4} - 1 = \frac{3}{28}$ c. $\frac{5}{x} - \frac{3}{4} = 2$ d. $\frac{x}{3} + \frac{5}{11} = \frac{20}{22}$

4. Solve for x.

a. $\frac{x+1}{8} = \frac{5}{16}$ b. $\frac{4}{x} - \frac{1}{6} = \frac{2}{9}$ c. $\frac{5}{x-2} = 2$ d. $\frac{x+2}{5} + \frac{3}{4} = \frac{15}{4}$

LESSON 2.6

ACTIVITY DAY

Variation with a Bicycle

The Tour de France is a demanding bicycle race through France and several other countries. For 23 days cyclists ride approximately 3500 kilometers on steep mountain roads before crossing the finish line in Paris. The cyclists rely on their knowledge of gear shifting and bicycle speeds.

Many bicycles have several speeds or gears. In a low gear it's easier to pedal uphill. In a high gear it's harder to pedal, but you can go faster on flat surfaces and down hills. When you change gears, the chain shifts from one sprocket to another. In this activity you will discover the relationships among a bicycle's gears, the teeth on the sprockets, how fast you pedal, and how fast the bike goes.

ACTIVITY

The Wheels Go Round and Round

YOU WILL NEED

- a meterstick or metric tape measure
- a multispeed bicycle

In Steps 1–5, you'll analyze the effect of the rear sprockets.

Procedure Note

Changing Gears

You'll collect data with the bike upside down. You may be able to change gears in this position—rotate the pedals and the crank a few times. But if you have to turn the bike right side up to change gears, turn it upside down before you observe and record data.

Step 1 Shift the bicycle into its lowest gear (using the smallest front sprocket and largest rear sprocket).

Step 2 Count the number of teeth on the front and rear sprockets in use. Record your numbers in a table like this one:

Number of teeth on front sprocket	Number of teeth on rear sprocket	Number of revolutions of rear wheel for one revolution of pedals

Step 3 Line up the air valve, or a chalk mark on the tire of the rear wheel, with part of the bicycle frame. This will be the "starting point." Rotate the pedals through one complete revolution, and then stop the wheel immediately. Estimate the number of wheel revolutions to the nearest tenth, and enter it into the table.

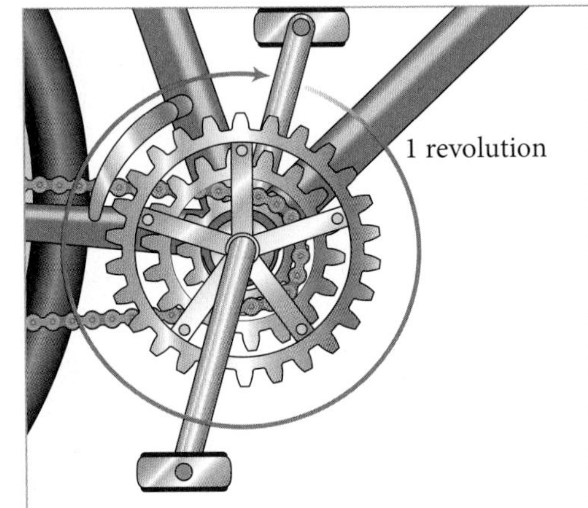

Step 4 Shift gears so that the chain moves onto the next rear sprocket. Do not change the front sprocket. Repeat Steps 2 and 3. Record your data in a new row of your table. Repeat this process for each rear sprocket.

Step 5 Describe how the number of teeth on the rear sprocket affects how many times the wheel turns. What kind of variation is this? Plotting the data on your calculator may help you see this relationship. Define variables and write an equation that relates the number of wheel revolutions to the number of teeth on the rear sprocket. Explain the meaning of the constant in this equation.

In Steps 6–10, you'll analyze the effect of the front sprockets.

Step 6 Shift the bicycle into its lowest gear again.

Step 7 In a second table, record the number of teeth on the sprockets in use.

Step 8 As you did in Step 3, record the number of wheel revolutions for one revolution of the pedals.

Step 9 Keep the chain on the same rear sprocket, and shift gears so that the chain moves onto the next front sprocket. Repeat Steps 7 and 8. The second table should have one row of data for each front sprocket.

Step 10 Describe how the number of teeth on the front sprocket affects the turning of the wheel. What kind of variation models this relationship? Plot the data on your calculator to verify your answer. Define variables and write an equation that relates the number of teeth on the front sprocket to the number of wheel revolutions. What is the meaning of the constant in this equation?

Now you'll see why gear shifting is such an important strategy in a bicycle race.

Step 11 Find a proportion relating the number of front teeth, rear teeth, wheel revolutions, and pedal revolutions. Use it to predict the number of wheel revolutions for a gear combination you have not tried yet. Test your prediction by doing the experiment with this gear combination.

Step 12 Explain why different gear ratios result in different numbers of rear wheel revolutions. Why is it possible to go faster in a higher gear?

Step 13 Find the circumference of the rear wheel in centimeters. How far will the bicycle travel when the wheel makes one revolution? How many revolutions will it take to travel 1 kilometer without coasting?

Step 14 For the lowest and highest gears, how many times do you need to rotate the pedals for the bike to travel 1 kilometer? (*Hint:* Write a proportion or other equation involving the gear ratio and the number of revolutions of the pedals and the rear wheel.)

The wheels on a cyclist's bicycle make roughly 1.6 million revolutions during the Tour de France. If the cyclist doesn't coast or change gears, he could pedal more than 1.5 million times.

LESSON

2.7

Evaluating Expressions

Melinda asked Tywan, "What's four plus six times three?" Do you think she meant $(4 + 6) \cdot 3$ or $4 + (6 \cdot 3)$? Is there a difference between these two expressions? What about $4 + 6 \cdot 3$? Is this the same as either of the previous expressions? As you learned when you worked with numerical expressions, there is a set of rules, called the **order of operations,** that is followed. The same rules apply to algebraic expressions so that a written mathematical expression is read and evaluated in the same way by everyone.

Order of Operations

1. **Evaluate expressions within parentheses or other grouping symbols.**
2. **Evaluate all exponents.**
3. **Multiply and divide from left to right.**
4. **Add and subtract from left to right.**

With these rules, the expression $4 + 6 \cdot 3$ equals $4 + 18$, or 22, because multiplication and division (Rule 3) happen before addition and subtraction (Rule 4). If Melinda meant $(4 + 6) \cdot 3$, she could say "First add four and six, and then multiply by three." In this lesson you will use the order of operations to write and evaluate expressions.

EXAMPLE A

Answer parts a–c using this statement:

Multiply 6 times a starting number, then add 15, divide this result by 3, and then subtract your answer from 80.

a. What is the result when you start with 5? With 14? With -3?

b. Write a mathematical expression that fits the statement, using x to represent the starting number.

c. Use your calculator to test your expression on the starting numbers in part a.

Solution

Apply the operations in the order they are given in the statement.

a. Starting with 5 — Starting with 14 — Starting with -3

6*5 30
Ans+15 45
Ans/3 15
80–Ans 65

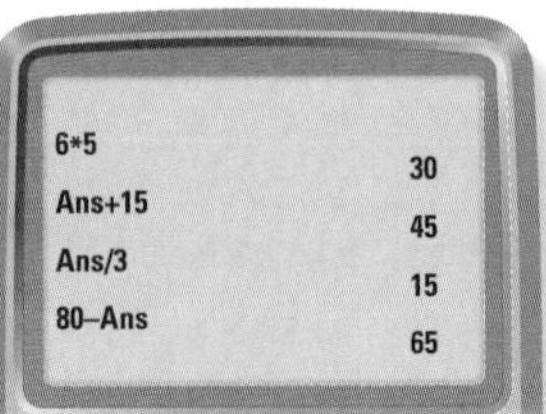

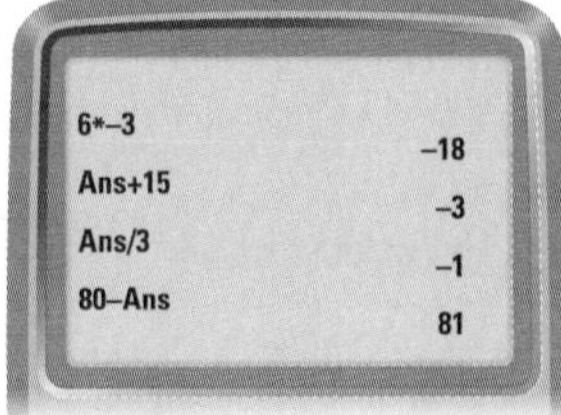

b. You can organize your work in a table.

Description	Expression
Starting value.	x
Multiply by 6.	$6x$
Add 15.	$6x + 15$
Divide this result by 3.	$\frac{6x + 15}{3}$
Subtract your answer from 80.	$80 - \frac{6x + 15}{3}$

The fraction bar is a grouping symbol meaning that the entire numerator is divided by 3.

c. You can evaluate expressions on your calculator as shown here.

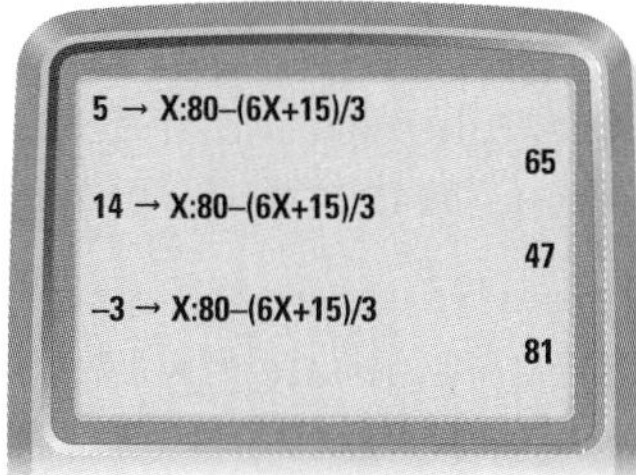

On the calculator, you need the parentheses to indicate the grouping of the numerator.

In the example the letter x was used to represent a starting number. In this instance the *variable* named x has no set value but instead can vary. So the value of an expression containing x will also vary. Sometimes you can get surprising results, as you will see in the investigation.

INVESTIGATION

Number Tricks

Try this trick: Each member of your group should think of a different number. Add 9 to it. Multiply the result by 3. Subtract 6 from the answer. Divide this answer by 3. Then subtract the original number. Compare your results.

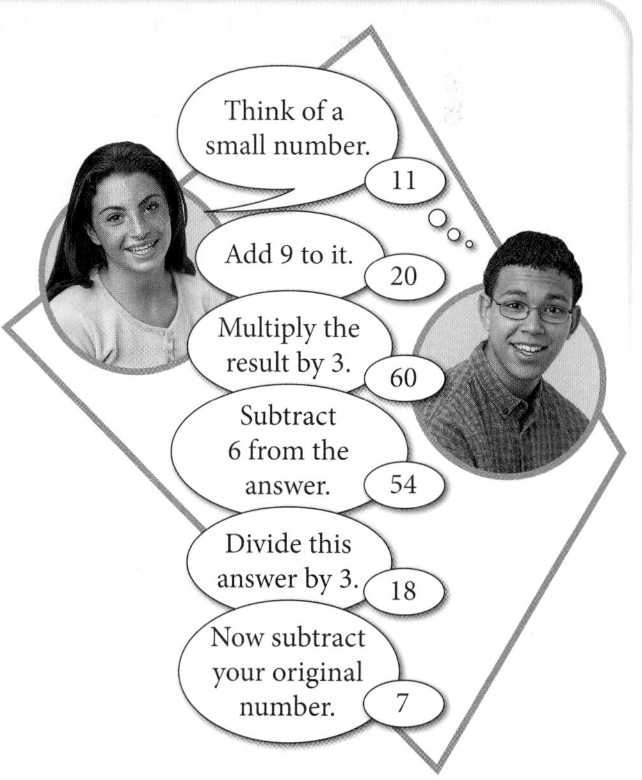

Do you think the result will be the same regardless of the number you start with? Do you think this would work if you chose a decimal number, a fraction, or a negative number? One way to answer these questions is to use a list of numbers instead of only a single starting value.

Step 1 Enter a list of at least four different numbers into the calculator home screen, and store this list. In the example at right, the list is {20, 1.2, -5, 4}, but you should try different numbers. Perform the operations on your own starting numbers. The last operation is to subtract your original number.

```
{20, 1.2, -5, 4} → L1
                  {20 1.2 -5 4}
Ans + 9
                  {29 10.2 4 13}
Ans * 3
                  {87 30.6 12 39}
Ans - 6
                  {81 24.6 6 33}
Ans / 3
                  {27 8.2 2 11}
Ans - L1
                  {7 7 7 7}
```

Step 2 Explain how the last operation is different from the others.

Step 3 Number tricks like this work because certain operations, such as multiplication and division, get "undone" in the course of the trick. Which step undoes Ans · 3?

Step 4 One way to analyze what is happening in a number trick is to translate the steps of the trick into an algebraic expression. Return to the description at the beginning of this investigation, and write an algebraic expression using x to represent your starting number.

Description	Expression
Starting value.	x
Add 9.	$x + 9$
⋮	⋮

Step 5 You can use the method in this table to help you figure out why any number trick works. The symbol +1 represents one positive unit. You can think of n as a variable or as a container for different unknown starting numbers. Complete the Description column by writing the steps in this new number trick.

Stage	Picture	Description	Expression
1	n	Pick a number.	
2	n +1 +1 +1		
3	n n +1 +1 +1 +1 +1 +1		
4	n n +1 +1		
5	n +1		
6	+1	Subtract the original number.	
7	+1 +1 +1		

Step 6 Complete the Expression column by writing an algebraic expression for each step in the trick.

Step 7 Evaluate the final expression in Step 6 using a list of starting numbers. What is the result? Explain why this happens.

Step 8 Invent your own number trick that has at least five stages. Test it on your calculator with a list of at least four different numbers to make sure all the results are the same. When you're convinced the number trick is working, try it on the other members of your group.

Experimenting with number tricks and writing them in different forms can help you understand the role that variables and expressions play in algebra. A single expression can represent an entire number trick.

EXAMPLE B

Consider this expression:

$$4\left(\frac{x+7}{4}+5\right)-x+13$$

a. Write in words the number trick that the expression describes.

b. Test the number trick to be sure you get the same result no matter what number you choose.

c. Which operations that undo previous operations make this number trick work?

Solution

a. Pick a number, x.
   Add 7.
   Divide the answer by 4.
   Add 5 to this result.
   Multiply the answer by 4.
   Subtract your original number.
   Then add 13.

b. One way to test the trick is to enter a list of numbers into your calculator and then enter the expression, using this list in place of the variable. Be sure to use parentheses to account for grouping symbols like the division bar. On some calculators: $4((L_1 + 7)/4 + 5) - L_1 + 13$.

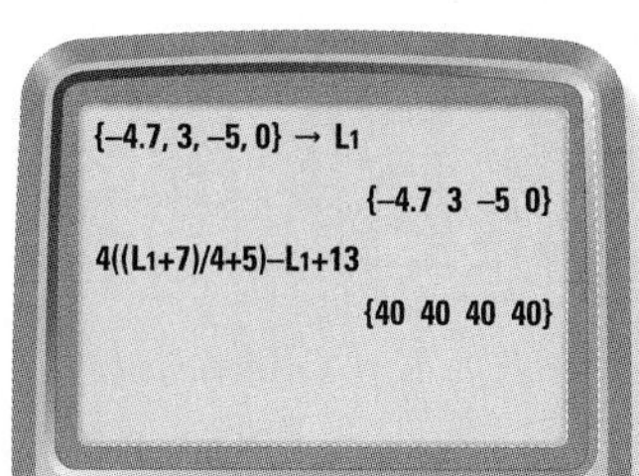

c. The multiplication by 4 undoes the division by 4. Because the original number, x, is subtracted, it doesn't matter what number you start with.

An **algebraic expression** is an expression that can involve both numbers and variables. The number tricks you have seen in this lesson can be represented as algebraic expressions whose values are determined by correctly applying the order of operations. Understanding this order is essential for success in your continuing study of algebra.

EXAMPLE C

Al and Cal both evaluated the expression $7 - 4 + 2$. Al said, "The answer is one because you can add in any order, so I did four plus two first." Cal said, "The answer is five because you have to go left to right." Who is right, and why?

Solution

Both Al and Cal have good ideas.

Al is correct that it doesn't matter in what order you add numbers. However, he needs to remember that $7 - 4 + 2$ is the same as $7 + -4 + 2$, so if he wants to change the order, he must add $-4 + 2$. Then he would get $7 + -2$, or 5, the same answer as Cal.

Cal is also correct in working from left to right. However, he may find it easier to evaluate some expressions if he thinks of subtraction as adding the opposite and then adds the numbers in the simplest combination, not necessarily always from left to right.

Thinking of subtraction as addition of negatives makes many calculations easier. Consider the number trick $\frac{5 - 3(x + 2)}{3} + x$. To describe the steps in a chart, it will be much easier to think of this as $\frac{5 + -3(x + 2)}{3} + x$ and then write

Pick a number.
Add 2.
Multiply by -3.
Add 5.
Divide by 3.
Add the original number.

Try to get in the habit of recognizing subtraction as simply a form of addition. It is also often convenient to change division to multiplication by a fraction, the reciprocal. (For example, dividing by 3 is the same as multiplying by $\frac{1}{3}$.) Although these procedures do not change the problem or the answer, they do sometimes prevent you from making errors when you are evaluating more complex expressions.

2.7 Exercises

You will need your graphing calculator for Exercises **1** and **5.**

Practice Your Skills

1. Use your calculator to evaluate each clue expression for the puzzle on the next page. Then write each answer in the puzzle. Enter the entire expression into your calculator so that you get the correct answer without having to calculate part of the expression first. [▶ See **Calculator Note: Instant Replay** to learn how to use the instant replay command. ◀] For answers that can be expressed as either decimal numbers or fractions, you should use the answer form indicated in the clue. Each negative sign, fraction bar, or decimal point occupies one square in the puzzle. Commas, however, are not entered as part of an answer. For instance, the answer 2,508.5 would require six squares. [▶ See **Calculator Note: Fractions to Decimals** for help in converting answers from decimal numbers to fractions and vice versa. ◀]

Across	Down
1. $\frac{2}{3}$ of 159,327	**1.** $9(-7 + 180)$
3. $\dfrac{-1 + 17^2}{4 + 2^2}$	**2.** $\left(\frac{9}{2}\right)\left(\frac{17}{5} + \frac{25}{4}\right)$ (fraction form)
4. $4835 - 541 + 1284$	**4.** $3 - 3(12 - 200)$
6. $\dfrac{3 + 140}{3 \cdot 14}$ (fraction form) @	**5.** $9 \cdot 10^2 - 9^2$
7. $8075 - 3(42)$	**8.** $15 + 47(922)$
9. $\sqrt{6^2 + 8^2}$	**10.** $25.9058 \cdot 20/4 - 89$ (decimal form) @
11. $\dfrac{740}{18.4 - 2.1 \cdot 9}$	**11.** $1284 - \dfrac{877}{0.2}$
12. 57^3	

Reason and Apply

2. Peter and Seija evaluated the expression $37 + 8 \cdot \frac{6}{2}$. Peter said the answer was 135. Seija said it was 61. Who is correct? What error did the other person make?

3. In what order would you perform the operations to evaluate each expression and get the correct answer?

a. $9 + 16 \cdot 4.5 = 81$ @

b. $18 \div 3 + 15 = 21$

c. $3 - 4(-5 + 6^2) = -121$

d. $\sqrt{5^2 + 12^2} = 13$

e. $16 - \dfrac{1}{16 - 3 \cdot 5} = 15$

f. $8 - \dfrac{24}{6} = 4$

4. Daxun, Lacy, Claudia, and Al are working on a number trick. Here are the number sequences their number trick generates:

Description	Daxun's sequence	Lacy's sequence	Claudia's sequence	Al's sequence
Pick the starting number.	14	−5	−8.6	x
	19	0		
	76	0		
	64	−12		
	16	−3		
	2	2		

a. Describe the stages of this number trick in the first column.

b. Complete Claudia's sequence.

c. Write a sequence of expressions for Al in the last column.

5. In this scheme the symbol $+1$ represents $+1$ and the symbol -1 represents -1. The symbol n represents the original number.

Stage	Picture	Description
1	n	
2	n -1 -1 -1	
3	n n -1 -1 -1 -1 -1 -1	
4	n n -1 -1	
5	n -1	
6	-1	Subtract the original number.
7	$+1$ $+1$ $+1$	

a. Explain what is happening as you move from one stage to the next. The explanation for Stage 6 is provided. @

b. At which stage will everyone's result be the same? Explain. @

c. To verify that this trick works, use a calculator list and an answer routine.

d. Represent this trick by writing an expression similar to that shown in the solution to part b of Example A. @

6. Jo asked Jack and Nina to try two number tricks that she had invented for homework. Jack's and Nina's number sequences are shown in the tables. Use words to describe each stage of the number tricks.

a. Number Trick 1: @

Description	Jack's sequence	Nina's sequence
Pick the starting number.	5	3
	10	6
	30	18
	36	24
	12	8
	7	5
	2	2

b. Number Trick 2:

Description	Jack's sequence	Nina's sequence
Pick the starting number.	-10	10
	-8	12
	-24	36
	-15	45
	-30	30
	-60	60
	-10	10

7. Insert operation signs, parentheses, or both into each string of numbers to create an expression equal to the answer given. Keep the numbers in the same order as shown. Write an explanation of your expression, including information on the order in which you performed the operations.

a. 3 2 5 7 = 18

b. 8 5 6 7 = 13

8. Marcella wrote an expression for a number trick.

Marcella's Trick
$\frac{4(x-5)+8}{2} - x + 6$

a. Describe Marcella's number trick in words.

b. Pick a starting number, and use it to do the trick. What answer do you get? Pick another starting number, and do the trick again. What is the "trick"?

9. Write your own number trick with at least six stages.

a. No matter what number you begin with, make the trick result in -4.

b. Describe the process you used to create the trick.

c. Write an expression to represent your trick.

10. In Example B of Sharpening Your Skills earlier in this chapter, you solved the equation $\frac{x}{4} + 2 = \frac{17}{3}$ using substitution. Graph the lines $y = \frac{x}{4} + 2$ and $y = \frac{17}{3}$, and describe the connections between the algebraic solution to the equation in the example and the intersection point of the graphs.

Review

11. APPLICATION Portia drove her new car 308 miles on 10.8 gallons of gasoline.

a. What is the car's rate of gasoline consumption in miles per gallon?

b. If this is the typical mileage for Portia's car, how much gas will it take for a 750-mile vacation trip?

c. If gas costs $4.25 per gallon, how much will Portia spend on gas on her vacation?

d. The manufacturer advertised that the car would get 30 to 35 miles per gallon. How does Portia's mileage compare to the advertised estimate?

12. You are helping design boxes for game balls that are 1 inch in diameter. Your supervisor wants the balls to be packaged in one rectangular layer of rows and columns.

a. Use a table to show all the ways to package 24 balls in rows and columns.

b. Plot these points on a graph.

c. Do the possible box dimensions represent direct or inverse variation? Explain how you know.

d. Represent the situation with an equation. Does the equation have any limitations? If so, what are they?

13. The table displays data for a bicyclist's distance from home during a four-hour bike ride.

a. Make a scatter plot of the data.

b. Find the bicyclist's average speed.

c. Find an equation that models the data, and graph it on the scatter plot.

d. At what times might the bicyclist be riding downhill or pedaling uphill? Explain.

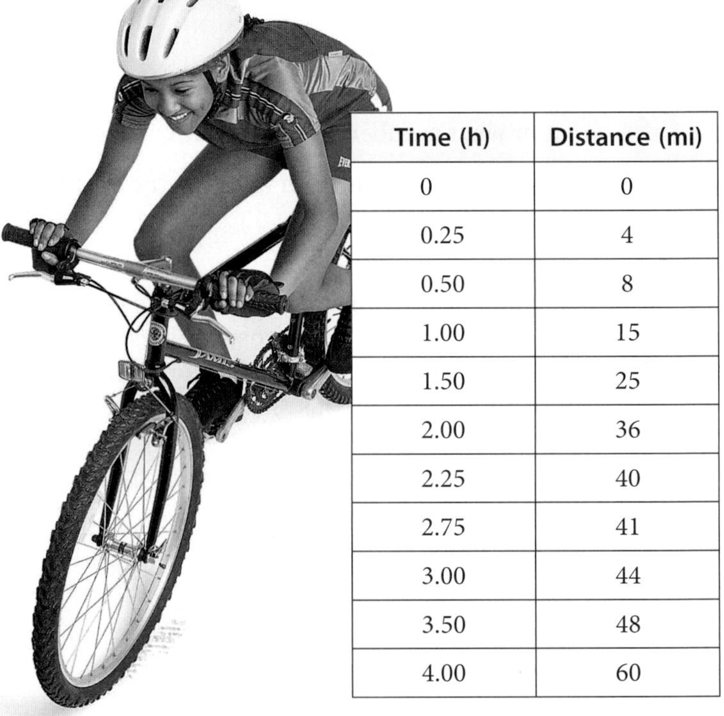

Time (h)	Distance (mi)
0	0
0.25	4
0.50	8
1.00	15
1.50	25
2.00	36
2.25	40
2.75	41
3.00	44
3.50	48
4.00	60

IMPROVING YOUR Reasoning SKILLS

Insert as few parentheses as necessary into each expression so that when you enter the expression into your calculator, you get the same result as $5 \cdot 13 - 5 \cdot 4$.

a. 5 · 13 − 4
b. 5 · 3^2
c. 5 · 13 + 5 · −4
d. 100 + 35 / 1 + 2
e. 6 + 3 · 5
f. 5 + 5 · 8
g. 5 · 1 + 8
h. 5 · 3^1 + 1
i. 65 − 5 · 3 + 1
j. 87 − 6 · 10 − 3
k. −3^2 + 54

LESSON

2.8

Undoing Operations

"All change is not growth; all movement is not forward."

ELLEN GLASGOW

After studying a lesson on number tricks, Virna came up with a new variation. She asked Killeen to pick a number and then do these operations in order: add 3, multiply by 7, subtract 4, divide by 2, and add 1. Killeen told her the final result was 13. Virna thought for a moment and then said, "Was your starting number 1?" It was, and Killeen was amazed! How did Virna figure that out? They tried the "trick" several more times, and each time Virna figured out Killeen's starting number.

In the investigation you will discover how Virna was using her understanding of the order of operations to solve an equation, and you'll see why the trick works.

INVESTIGATION

Just Undo It!

Step 1 Choose a secret number. Now choose four more nonzero numbers, and in any random order add one of them, multiply by another, subtract another, and divide by the final number. On a blank sheet of paper, record in words what you did and what your final result was. (For example, "I took my secret number, divided by 4, added 7, multiplied by 2, and subtracted 8. The result was 28.") Do not record your secret number. Trade papers with another student.

Step 2 Use the description on the paper given to you to complete a table like this one:

Description	Sequence	Expression		
Picked a number.	?	x		
Divided by 4.	Ans / 4	$\frac{x}{4}$		
Added 7.	Ans + 7	$\frac{x}{4}+7$		
Multiplied by 2.	Ans · 2	$2\left(\frac{x}{4}+7\right)$		
Subtracted 8.	Ans − 8	$2\left(\frac{x}{4}+7\right)-8$		

Step 3 Now add another column, listing the operation needed to undo each step.

Description	Sequence	Expression	Undo	
Picked a number.	?	x		
Divided by 4.	Ans / 4	$\frac{x}{4}$	·(4)	
Added 7.	Ans + 7	$\frac{x}{4}+7$	− (7)	
Multiplied by 2.	Ans · 2	$2\left(\frac{x}{4}+7\right)$	/ (2)	
Subtracted 8.	Ans − 8	$2\left(\frac{x}{4}+7\right)-8$	+ (8)	

Step 4 Add a fifth column to list results, and put the final result in the bottom right cell. Then work up the table from the bottom, undoing each operation as shown, to discover the original number. Was this the secret number? (In this example the final result was 28 and the original secret number was 44.)

Description	Sequence	Expression	Undo	Result
Picked a number.	?	x		44
Divided by 4.	Ans / 4	$\frac{x}{4}$	$\cdot(4)$	11
Added 7.	Ans + 7	$\frac{x}{4}+7$	$-(7)$	18
Multiplied by 2.	Ans • 2	$2\left(\frac{x}{4}+7\right)$	$/(2)$	36
Subtracted 8.	Ans − 8	$2\left(\frac{x}{4}+7\right)-8$	$+(8)$	28

Many equations can be solved using a table by undoing each operation in order, following these steps:

1. Complete the description column, using the order of operations.
2. Complete the undo column.
3. Finally, work up from the bottom of the table to solve the equation.

You can check your solution to an equation by substituting the solution into the original equation and evaluating to check that you get a true statement.

Study this example. Then you will create your own table to solve an equation.

Equation: $\frac{3+2(x-4)}{5}+6=11$		
Description	**Undo**	**Result**
Pick x.		15
$-(4)$	$+(4)$	11
$\cdot(2)$	$/(2)$	22
$+(3)$	$-(3)$	25
$/(5)$	$\cdot(5)$	5
$+(6)$	$-(6)$	11

Step 5 Solve this equation by using a table: $7+\frac{x-3}{4}=42$. Check your solution.

Step 6 Write a few sentences explaining why this method for solving an equation works.

An **equation** is a statement that says that the value of one expression is equal to the value of another expression. **Solving an equation** is the process you use to determine the value of the unknown that "works," or makes the equation true. This value is called the **solution.** Once you can identify all the steps that were done, starting with the unknown number, to come up with the result, you can simply **undo** them to find the solution. Remember, you have to undo the steps in the reverse order of the way they were done originally. That means you need to pay close attention to the order of operations in the original equation.

EXAMPLE A

To some number, add 3, multiply by -2, add 18, and finally divide by 6.

a. Find the starting number if the final result is 15.

b. Convert the description to an expression, and write an equation that states that this expression is equal to 15.

c. Test your solution to part a by using your equation from part b.

Solution

a. You can find the starting number by working backward, undoing each operation described. Perform the undo operations in reverse order, starting with the number 15.

Operation on x	Undo operation	Result
		$x = -39$
$+ (3)$	$- (3)$	-36
$\cdot (-2)$	$/ (-2)$	72
$+ (18)$	$- (18)$	90
$/ (6)$	$\cdot (6)$	15

b. One way to write this equation is $\frac{18 + -2(x + 3)}{6} = 15$.

c. Substitute -39 for x, and determine whether the equation is true.

$$\frac{18 + -2(-39 + 3)}{6} \stackrel{?}{=} 15$$

$$\frac{18 + -2(-36)}{6} \stackrel{?}{=} 15$$

$$\frac{18 + 72}{6} \stackrel{?}{=} 15$$

$$\frac{90}{6} \stackrel{?}{=} 15$$

$$15 = 15$$

This is a true statement, so the solution is correct.

Much of algebra involves translating a real-world situation into an equation and finding the solution to the equation. Once you understand the situation, you can write the equation that represents it algebraically. Then you can *undo* the operations to solve the equation. An organization table like the one you used in the investigation may be helpful.

EXAMPLE B

An online ticket agency adds a charge of c dollars to the price of each ticket it sells. Kent bought 4 tickets and paid with his debit card. His account had a balance of B dollars before he used the card and M dollars after. Find a formula for t, the price of one ticket.

Solution

An algebraic expression for the cost of the 4 tickets is $4(t + c)$. This cost was removed from Kent's original balance, B, leaving a final balance of M.

Equation: $B - 4(t + c) = M$

$B + -4(t + c) = M$		
Description	**Undo**	**Result**
Pick t		$\frac{M - B}{-4} - c$
$+ c$	$- c$	$\frac{M - B}{-4}$
$\cdot -4$	$/(-4)$	$M - B$
$+ B$	$- B$	M

The formula to find the price of one ticket, t, is $t = \frac{M - B}{-4} - c$.

2.8 Exercises

Practice Your Skills

1. The equation $\frac{5(F - 32)}{9} = C$ can be used to change temperatures in degrees Fahrenheit to the Celsius scale.

a. What is the first step when converting a temperature in degrees Fahrenheit to degrees Celsius? @

b. What is the last step when converting a temperature in degrees Fahrenheit to degrees Celsius?

c. What is the first step in undoing a temperature in degrees Celsius to find the temperature in degrees Fahrenheit?

d. What is the last step in undoing a temperature in degrees Celsius to find the temperature in degrees Fahrenheit?

2. Evaluate each expression without a calculator, using the given value of x. Then check your result with your calculator.

a. $(-3)(x) + (-2)$ for $x = 1.5$ b. $\frac{23 - 3(x - 9)}{5}$ for $x = 3$ c. $\frac{-4[7 + (-x)]}{5} - 6$ for $x = -13$

3. Evaluate each expression for $x = 6$.

a. $2x + 3$ b. $2(x + 3)$ c. $5x - 13$ d. $\frac{x + 9}{3}$

4. For each equation, identify the order of operations. Then work backward through the order of operations to find the value of x.

a. $\frac{x-3}{2} = 6$

b. $3x + 7 = 22$ @

c. $\frac{x}{6} - 20 = -19$

d. $\frac{x+9}{3} - 1 = 4$

e. $\frac{2(x-1)}{0.5} = 10$

f. $2.5 - 3(x - 4) = 16$

5. To change from miles per hour to feet per second, you can multiply by 5280, divide by 60, then divide by 60 again. Use the idea of undoing to explain how to convert feet per second to miles per hour.

6. Justine asked her group members to do this calculation: Pick a number, multiply by 5, and subtract 2. Quentin got 33 for an answer. Explain how Justine could determine what number Quentin picked. What number did Quentin pick?

Reason and Apply

7. The final answer in the sequence of calculations at right is 3. Starting with the final number, work backward, from the bottom to the top, undoing the operation at each step.

a. What is the original number? @

b. How can you check that your answer to 7a is correct? @

c. What is the original number if the final result is 15?

d. What makes this sequence of operations a number trick? @

x	____
Ans • 8	____
Ans + 9	____
Ans / 4	____
Ans + 5.75	14
Ans / 2	7
Ans − 4	3

8. The sequence of operations at right will always give you a different final answer depending on the number you start with.

a. What is the final answer if you start with 18?

b. What number did you start with if the final answer is 7.6?

c. Describe how you got your answer to 8b.

d. Let x represent the number you start with. Write an algebraic expression to represent this sequence of operations.

e. Set the expression you got in 8d equal to zero. Then solve the equation for x. Check that your solution is correct by using the value you got for x as the starting number. Do you get zero again?

Ans + 10	____
Ans • 2	____
Ans − 12	____
Ans / 5	____

9. Consider this expression:

$$\frac{5(x+7)}{3}$$

a. Find the value of the expression for $x = 8$. List the order in which you performed the operations.

b. Solve the equation $\frac{5(x+7)}{3} = -18$ by undoing the sequence of operations in 9a.

10. Solve each equation by using an undo table.

a. $3(x - 5) + 8 = -14.8$ Ⓐ

b. $3.5\left(\frac{x-8}{4}\right) = 2.8$

c. $\frac{4(x-5)-8}{-3} = 12$

d. $\frac{4-3(7+2x)}{5} + 18.5 = -74.9$ Ⓐ

11. Consider this expression:

$$\frac{2.5(x-4.2)}{5} - 4.3$$

a. Find the value of the expression if $x = 8$. Start with 8 and use the order of operations.

b. Solve the equation $\frac{2.5(x-4.2)}{5} - 4.3 = 5.4$ by undoing the operations in 11a.

12. The equation $D = 6 + 0.4(t - 5)$ represents the depth of water, in inches, in a swimming pool after t minutes of filling.

a. How deep is the water after 60 min? Ⓗ

b. How long does it take until the water is 36 in. deep?

c. Undo the sequence of operations on t to solve the original equation for t in terms of D.

13. Find the errors in this undo table and correct them.

Equation: $\frac{3(2-4x)}{4} - 7 = 14$		
Description	**Undo**	**Result**
Pick x.		52
$\cdot(-4)$	$\cdot(4)$	13
$-(2)$	$+(2)$	27
$+(3)$	$-(3)$	81
$/(4)$	$\cdot(4)$	21
$-(7)$	$+(7)$	14

Review

14. Evaluate each expression without a calculator. Then check your result with your calculator.

a. $-4 + (-8)$

b. $(-4)(-8)$

c. $-2(3 + 9)$

d. $5 + (-6)(-5)$ Ⓐ

e. $(-3)(-5) + (-2)$

f. $\frac{-15}{3} + 8$

g. $\frac{23 - 3(4-9)}{-2}$ Ⓐ

h. $\frac{-4[7+(-8)]}{8} - 6.5$

i. $\frac{6(2 \cdot 4 - 5) - 2}{-4}$

15. An electric slot car travels at a scale speed of 200 mi/h, meaning this would be its speed if it were full-size. If the car is $\frac{1}{87}$ of full size, find the car's actual speed in

a. Feet per minute.

b. Centimeters per second.

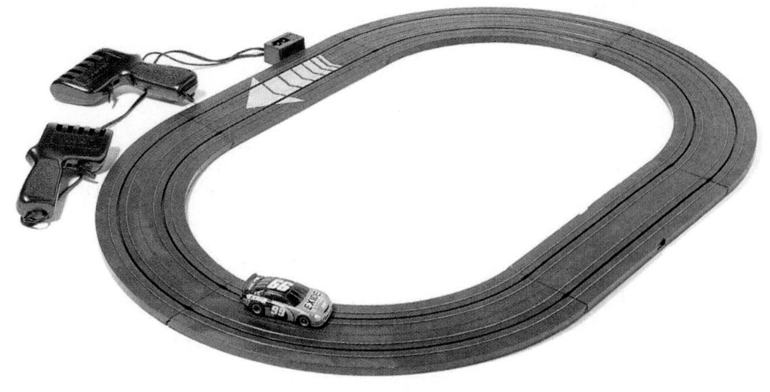

16. Find a rate for each situation. Then use the rate to answer the question.

a. Kerstin drove 350 mi last week and used 12.5 gal of gas. How many gallons of gas will he use if he drives 520 mi this week?

b. Angelo drove 225 mi last week and used 10.7 gal of gas. How far can he drive this week using 9 gal of gas?

IMPROVING YOUR Reasoning SKILLS

Three children went camping with their parents, a dog, and a tin of cookies just for the children. The children agreed to share the cookies equally.

The youngest child couldn't help thinking about the cookies, so alone she divided the cookies into three piles. There was one left over. She gave it to the dog, took her share, and left the rest of the cookies in the cookie tin.

A little later the middle child took the tin where he could be alone and divided the cookies into three piles. There was one left over. He gave it to the dog and took his share.

Not too long after that, the oldest child went alone to divide the cookies. When she made three piles, there was one left over, which the dog got. She took her share and put the rest back in the tin.

After dinner, the three children "officially" divided the contents of the cookie tin into three piles. There was one left over, which they gave to the dog.

What is the smallest number of cookies that the tin might have originally contained?

CHAPTER 2 REVIEW

In this chapter you explored and analyzed relationships among **ratios, proportions,** and percents. You used algebraic **variables** in equations and expressions, sometimes to represent specific unknown values and sometimes to represent any value. After you defined a proportion using a single variable, you solved the proportion to determine the unknown value of the variable. You learned that a **rational number** can be expressed as a ratio of two integers and that decimal representations of rational numbers either **terminate** or have a **repeating** pattern.

You also used ratios as **conversion factors** to change from one unit of measure to another. You used **dimensional analysis** to convert units such as miles per hour to meters per second. You learned that a rate is a comparison, or ratio, of two quantities with different units. And you saw that a **unit rate** is a ratio with denominator 1.

You learned that quantities are **directly proportional** when an increase in one value leads to a proportional increase in another. When you defined these proportions by using two variables, you established a relationship between pairs of values of the variables. These quantities form a **direct variation** when their *ratio* is constant. The constant ratio is called a **constant of variation.** Whenever you graphed a direct relationship, you discovered a straight line that passed through the origin.

For an **inverse variation,** the *product* of two quantities is constant. In this relationship an increase in one variable results in a decrease in the other. The graph of the relationship is curved rather than straight, and the graph does not touch either axis.

You studied the **order of operations,** which is used to ensure that everyone evaluates expressions in the same way. You explored number tricks and learned how to use an **undoing** process to find the original number. You also practiced writing **equations** to represent real-world situations and learned how to use the undoing process to find **solutions** to these equations.

Exercises

You will need your graphing calculator for Exercises **8** and **10.**

@ Answers are provided for all exercises in this set.

1. Solve each proportion for the variable.

a. $\frac{5}{12} = \frac{n}{21}$ b. $\frac{15}{47} = \frac{27}{w}$ c. $\frac{2.5}{3} = \frac{k}{6.2}$

2. Jeff can build 7 birdhouses in 5 hours. Write three different proportions that you could use to find out how long it would take him to build 30 birdhouses.

3. Plot the point (6, 3) on a graph.

a. List four other points where the y-coordinate is 50% of the x-coordinate. Plot these points on the same graph.

b. Describe the pattern formed by the points.

4. In a fairy tale written by the Brothers Grimm, Rapunzel has hair that is about 20 ells in length (1 ell = 3.75 ft) by the time she is 12 years old. In the story Rapunzel is held captive in a high tower with a locked door and only one window. From this window she lets down her hair so that people can climb up.

a. Approximately how long was Rapunzel's hair, in feet, when she was 12 years old?

b. If Rapunzel's hair grew at a constant rate from birth, approximately how many feet did her hair grow per month?

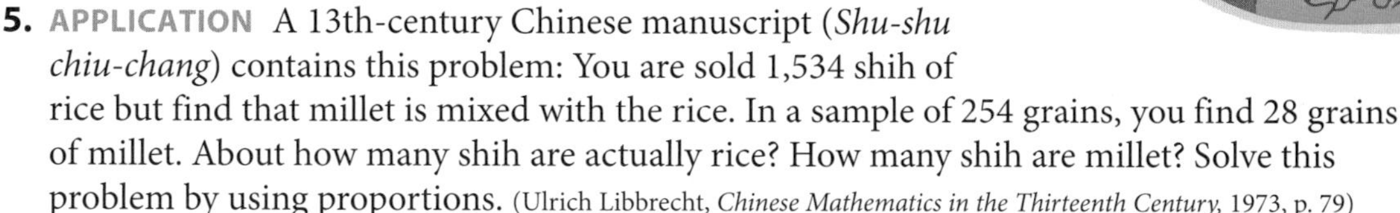

5. APPLICATION A 13th-century Chinese manuscript (*Shu-shu chiu-chang*) contains this problem: You are sold 1,534 shih of rice but find that millet is mixed with the rice. In a sample of 254 grains, you find 28 grains of millet. About how many shih are actually rice? How many shih are millet? Solve this problem by using proportions. (Ulrich Libbrecht, *Chinese Mathematics in the Thirteenth Century,* 1973, p. 79)

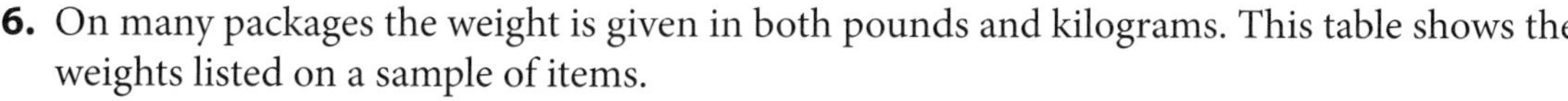

6. On many packages the weight is given in both pounds and kilograms. This table shows the weights listed on a sample of items.

Kilograms	1.5	0.7	2.25	11.3	3.2	18.1	5.4
Pounds	3.3	1.5	5	25	7	40	12

a. Use the information in the table to find an equation that relates weight in pounds to weight in kilograms. Explain what the variables represent in your equation.

b. Use your equation to calculate the number of kilograms in 30 lb.

c. Calculate the number of pounds in 25 kg.

7. Consider this graph of a sunflower's height above the ground.

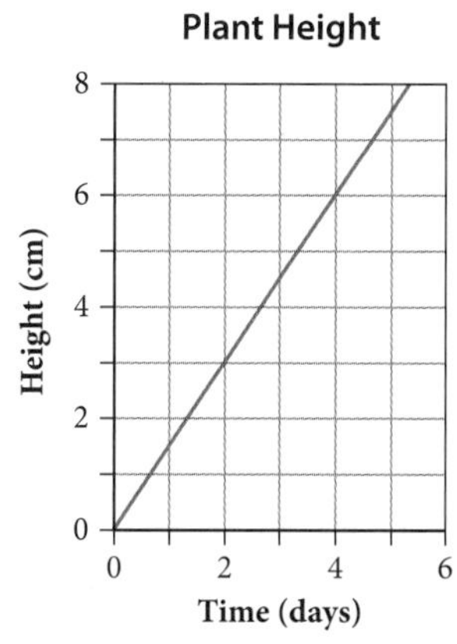

a. How tall was the sunflower after 5 days?

b. If the growth pattern continues, how many days will it take the plant to reach a height of 25 cm?

c. Write an equation to represent the height of the plant after any number of days.

x	y
12	4
5	9
16	3
22	2
9	5
43	1

8. Use the table of values at right to answer each question.

a. Are the data in the table related by a direct variation or an inverse variation? Explain.

b. Find an equation to fit the data. You can use your calculator to graph the equation and see how well the equation fits the data.

c. Use your equation to predict the value of y when x is 32.

9. In the formula $d = vt$, d represents distance in miles, v represents rate in miles per hour (mi/h), and t represents time in hours. Use the word *directly* or *inversely* to complete each statement. Then write an equation for each.

a. If you travel at a constant rate of 50 mi/h, the distance you travel is ____ proportional to the time you travel.

b. The distance you travel in exactly 1 h is ____ proportional to your rate.

c. The time it takes to travel 100 mi is ____ proportional to your rate.

10. APPLICATION Boyle's law describes the inverse variation between the volume of a gas and the pressure exerted on it. In the experiment shown, a balloon with volume 1.75 L is sealed in a bell jar with 1 atm of pressure. As air is pumped out of the jar, the pressure decreases, and the balloon expands to a larger volume.

Pressure = 1 atm

Pressure = 0.8 atm

a. Find the volume under 0.8 atm of pressure.

b. Find the pressure when the volume is 0.75 L.

c. Write an equation you can use to calculate the volume in liters from the pressure in atmospheres.

d. Graph this relationship on your calculator, and then sketch it on your own paper. Show on your graph the solutions to 10a and b.

11. The symbol -1 represents one negative unit. You can think of x as a variable or as a container for different unknown starting values. Consider this sequence of expressions:

Stage	Picture
1	x
2	x x
3	x x -1
4	x x -1 x x -1 x x -1
5	x x -1 x x -1 x x

a. Explain what is happening as you move from one stage to the next.

b. Write an algebraic expression describing each stage.

c. If the starting value is 4.5, what is the result at each stage?

d. If the result at the last stage is 22, what is the starting value?

12. Describe a process to evaluate the expression $\frac{12 - 3(x + 4)}{6} + 5$ when x equals 1.

13. Create an undo table and solve the given equation by undoing the order of operations.

Equation: $\frac{12 - 3(x + 4)}{6} + 5 = 4$		
Description	**Undo**	**Result**
Pick x.		
		4

IMPROVING YOUR Reasoning SKILLS

This problem is adapted from an ancient Chinese book, *The Nine Chapters on the Mathematical Art.*

A city official was monitoring water use when he saw a woman washing dishes in the river. He asked, "Why are there so many dishes here?" She replied, "There was a dinner party in the house." His next question was "How many guests attended the party?" The woman did not know but replied, "Every two guests shared one dish for rice. Every three guests used one dish for broth. Every four guests used one dish for meat. And altogether 65 dishes were used at the party." How many guests attended the party?

This is a detail from the 17th-century Chinese scroll painting *Landscapes of the Four Seasons* by Shen Shih-Ch'ing.

Take Another Look

The equation $y = kx$ is a *general equation* because it stands for a whole family of equations such as $y = 2x$, $y = \frac{1}{4}x$, and even $y = \pi x$. (Does $C = \pi d$ look more familiar?)

What might k be in the equation of each line graphed here? (If you're stumped, choose a point on the line, then divide its y-coordinate by its x-coordinate. Remember, $k = \frac{y}{x}$ is equivalent to $y = kx$.)

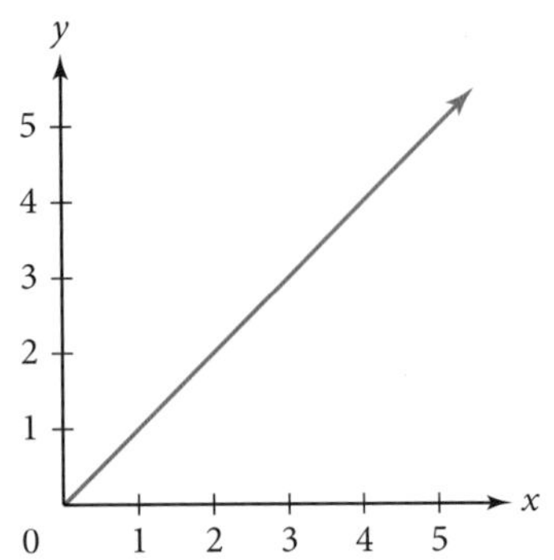

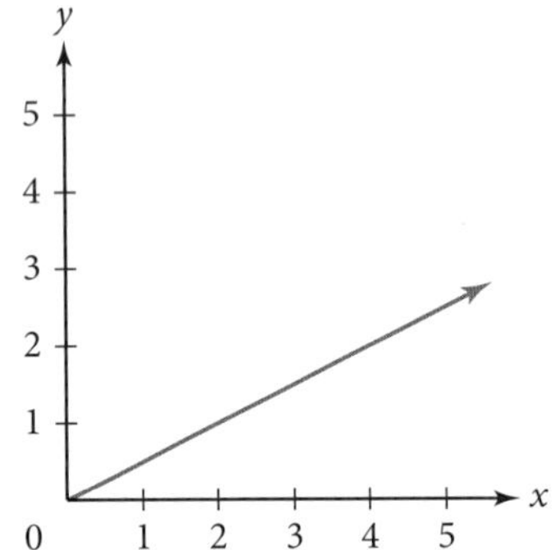

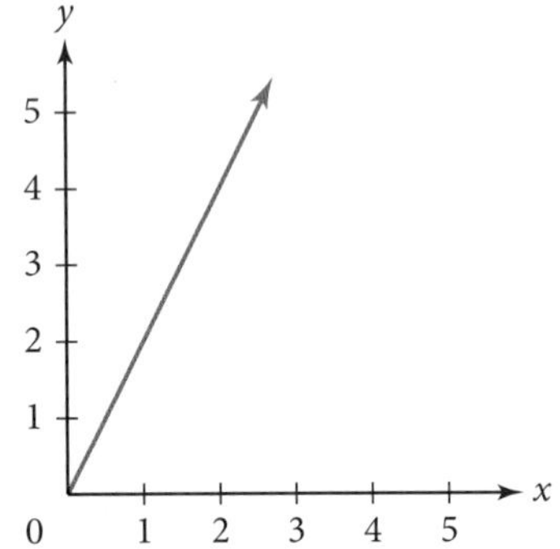

Most real-world quantities, such as time and distance, are measured or counted in positive numbers. If two positive quantities vary directly, their graph $y = kx$ is in Quadrant I, where both x and y are positive. Because the quotient $\frac{y}{x}$ of two positive numbers x and y must be positive, the constant k is positive.

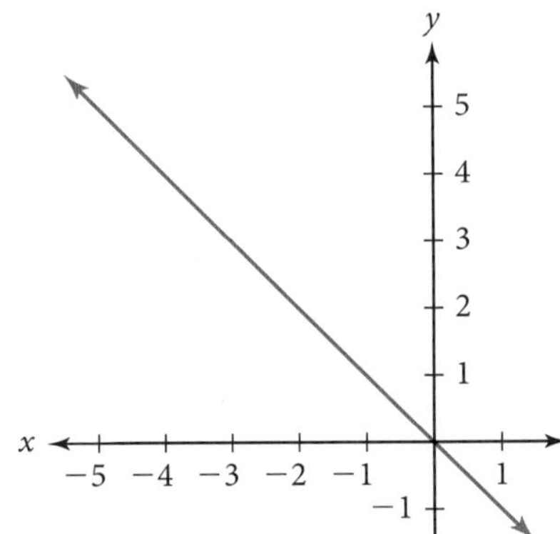

But the graph at right also shows a direct variation. What can you say about k for this graph?

What relationship do you see between the lines in each situation below? Between the k-values?

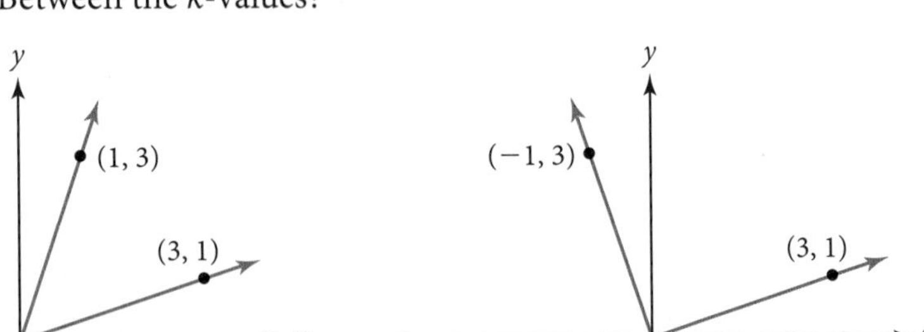

Finally, do you have a direct variation if $k = 0$? Why or why not?

Assessing What You've Learned

ORGANIZE YOUR NOTEBOOK You've created tables and answered questions as you've done the investigations. You've been working the exercises and taking quizzes and tests. You've made notes on things that you want to remember from class discussions. Are all those papers getting folded and stuffed into your book or mixed in with work from other classes? If so, it's not too late to get organized. Keeping a well-organized notebook is a habit that will improve your learning.

Your notebook should help you organize your work by lesson and chapter and should give you room to summarize. Look through your work for a chapter, and think about what you have learned. Write a short summary of the chapter. Include in the summary the new words you learned and things you learned about the graphing calculator. Write down questions you still have about the investigations, exercises, quizzes, or tests. Talk to classmates about your questions, or ask your teacher.

UPDATE YOUR PORTFOLIO Find the best work you have done in Chapter 2 to add to your portfolio. Choose at least one piece of work in which you used proportions to solve a problem and at least one investigation or exercise that involves algebraic expressions or the undoing method. Choose one direct or inverse variation graph you made. You might decide to put the graph with the graphs you selected for your Chapter 1 portfolio.

WRITE IN YOUR JOURNAL Add to your journal by expanding on a question from one of the investigations or exercises. Or use one of these prompts:

- Does graphing relationships help you understand how the quantities vary? Do you understand variation between quantities better when you look at a graph or when you read an equation?
- Tables of values, graphs, equations, and word descriptions are four ways to tell about a variation. What other mathematical ideas can you show in more than one way?
- Describe the progress you are making toward the goals you have set for yourself in this class. What things did you do and learn in this chapter that are helping you achieve those goals? What changes might you need to make to help keep you on track?

CHAPTER 3

Linear Equations

Weavers repeat steps when they make baskets and mats, creating patterns of repeating shapes. This process is not unlike recursion. In the top photo, a mat weaver in Myanmar creates a traditional design with palm fronds. The bottom photo shows bowls crafted by Native American artisans.

OBJECTIVES

In this chapter you will

- write recursive rules emphasizing start plus change
- study rate of change
- learn to write equations for lines using a starting value and a rate of change
- use equations and tables to graph lines
- solve linear equations
- estimate the margin of error of predictions
- define and calculate slope

Number Relationships and Estimation

In this chapter you'll work with integers like 5 and -3 and rational numbers like $\frac{-4}{7}$, $\frac{22}{7}$, and 6. Recall from Lesson 2.1 that a number is rational if it can be written as a ratio of two integers. The number 6 is rational because it can be written as $\frac{6}{1}$ or $\frac{-12}{-2}$. You also learned in Lesson 2.1 that terminal or repeating decimals can be rewritten as rational numbers. Every integer, decimal, and rational number is either positive, negative, or zero, and its location on the number line depends on its sign (+ or $-$) and relative size.

EXAMPLE A

Use estimation to match points A, B, C, and D on the number line with these numbers:

i. $1.\overline{41}$ ii. $\frac{-48}{20}$ iii. $\left(\frac{-2}{3}\right)^3$ iv. $\frac{17}{3}$

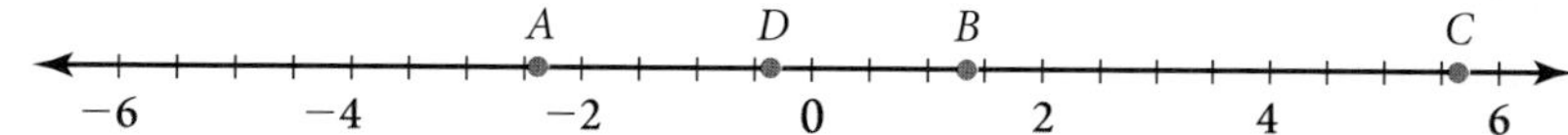

Solution

i. Point B, because $1.\overline{41}$ is slightly smaller than 1.5

ii. Point A, because $\frac{-48}{20}$ is between -2 and -3 (It is exactly -2.4.)

iii. Point D, because $\left(\frac{-2}{3}\right)^3 = \frac{-8}{27}$, which is between 0 and –0.5 (It is exactly $-0.\overline{296}$.)

iv. Point C, because $\frac{17}{3}$ is between 5 and 6 (It is exactly $5.\overline{6}$.)

In earlier courses you did arithmetic with signed numbers, such as $4(-3) = -12$. You learned that the product or quotient of a positive number and a negative number is negative and that the product or quotient of two negative numbers is positive. You can use your calculator to review the operations with negative and positive values. Remember to put parentheses around negative values and think about when to use the negation key or the subtraction key.

EXAMPLE B

For each calculation, state the color of the region(s) on this number line in which the result lies.

a. Multiply a number in the brown region by 0.5.

b. Divide a number in the brown region by -0.1.

c. Add a number in the brown region to a number in the blue region.

Solution

a. The product will lie in the brown or the blue region. A positive number (0.5) times a negative number (values less than -1) will give a negative result, and multiplying by 0.5 will produce a result closer to zero. Depending on where the starting number is in the brown region, the product might lie in either the brown region or the blue region.

b. The quotient will lie in the red region. The quotient of two negative numbers (-0.1 and values less than -1) is positive. Dividing by a value between 0 and 1 results in a value farther from zero.

c. The sum will be in the brown region. Adding one negative number to another negative number produces a result farther from zero than either value.

Getting the correct sign is important in any calculation, and it is always important to think about whether your calculations make sense.

Approximations can help you determine whether your answers are reasonable. In some cases, the approximate answer may be accurate enough. When you do computations, be sure to follow the order of operations.

EXAMPLE C

Estimate the value of each numerical expression by rounding all numbers to the nearest integer before you calculate. (Pay attention to the signs in your calculations.)

a. $-2 - 7.8(8.9 - 19.1)$

b. $\dfrac{6.5(-5.1)}{(-2)^3}$

Solution

Estimation simplifies the numbers and allows you to find an approximate answer without a calculator.

a. $-2 - 7.8(8.9 - 19.1) \approx -2 - 8(9 - 19)$

$-2 - 8(9 - 19) = -2 + 80 = 78$

The actual value is 77.56.

b. $\dfrac{6.5(-5.1)}{(-2)^3} \approx \dfrac{7(-5)}{-8}$

$\dfrac{7(-5)}{-8} = \dfrac{-35}{-8}$

$\dfrac{-35}{-8} \approx \dfrac{-32}{-8}$

$\dfrac{-32}{-8} = 4$

The actual value is 4.14375.

Exercises

1. Find these answers without a calculator. (Pay attention to the signs.)
   a. $-3 - (-3)$
   b. $-3 + (-3)$
   c. $3 - (-3)$
   d. $3 - (3)$

2. Estimate the color of the region(s) on this number line in which the result of each calculation lies.

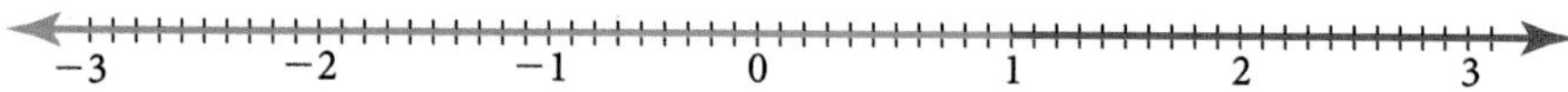

   a. Multiply a number in the blue region by 0.2.
   b. Divide a number in the red region by $-\frac{1}{3}$.
   c. Add -1.5 to a number in the green region.
   d. Multiply a number in the blue region by a number in the green region.

3. State whether each statement is always, sometimes, or never true. Give examples to justify your answer.
   a. You round values to the nearest integer. During a calculation, you will get the same sign ($+$ or $-$) as the exact answer.
   b. A number a is greater than its reciprocal, $\frac{1}{a}$.
   c. A number divided by its reciprocal will give a positive result.

4. Estimate the value of each numerical expression by rounding all numbers to the nearest integer before you calculate the result. Then find the exact answer using your calculator.
   a. $(-1.05)(4.15)(-8)$
   b. $11.9 - 1(-5 - 2.2)$
   c. $\frac{12 - 2.9^2}{-3}$
   d. $\frac{-2.3(4.2 + 8)}{2.2}$

LESSON

3.1

Recursively Defined Sequences

"A mathematician, like a painter or a poet, is a maker of patterns. If his patterns are more permanent than theirs, it is because they are made of ideas."

G. H. HARDY

The Empire State Building in New York City has 102 floors and is 1250 ft high. How high up are you when you reach the eightieth floor? You can answer this question using a recursive rule. In this lesson you will learn how to analyze geometric patterns, complete tables, and find missing values using numerical sequences.

A sequence is an ordered list of numbers. A **recursive rule** for a sequence gives the starting value for the sequence and a rule to get from each value in the sequence to the next.

EXAMPLE A

The table shows heights above and below ground at different floor levels in a 25-story building. Write a recursive rule for the sequence of heights $-4, 9, 22, 35, \ldots, 217, \ldots$ that corresponds to the building floor numbers $0, 1, 2, \ldots$. Use this rule to find each missing value in the table.

Floor number	Basement (0)	1	2	3	4	...	10	...		...	25
Height (ft)	−4	9	22	35		...		...	217	...	

Solution

The starting value is −4 because the basement is 4 ft below ground level. Each floor is 13 ft higher than the floor below it, so the rule for finding the next floor height is "add 13 to the current floor height."

The calculator screen shows how to enter this recursive rule into some calculators. [▸ See **Calculator Note: Recursion.** ◂] You can see that the fourth floor is at 48 ft.

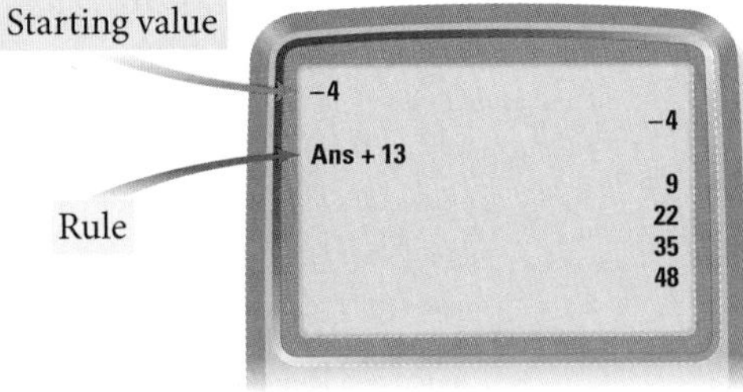

How high up is the tenth floor? Count the number of times you press ENTER. When you reach ten, you see that the tenth floor is 126 ft above ground level.

Which floor is at a height of 217 ft? Keep counting until you see that value on your calculator screen. When the calculator reads 217, you have pressed ENTER 17 times, so the seventeenth floor is at height 217 ft.

What's the height of the twenty-fifth floor? Keep applying the rule by pressing ENTER. When your count reaches 25, you find that the height of the twenty-fifth floor is 321 ft.

YOU WILL NEED

- a box of toothpicks

Recursive Toothpick Patterns

In this investigation you will learn to create and apply recursive rules to sequences modeled by patterns made with toothpicks.

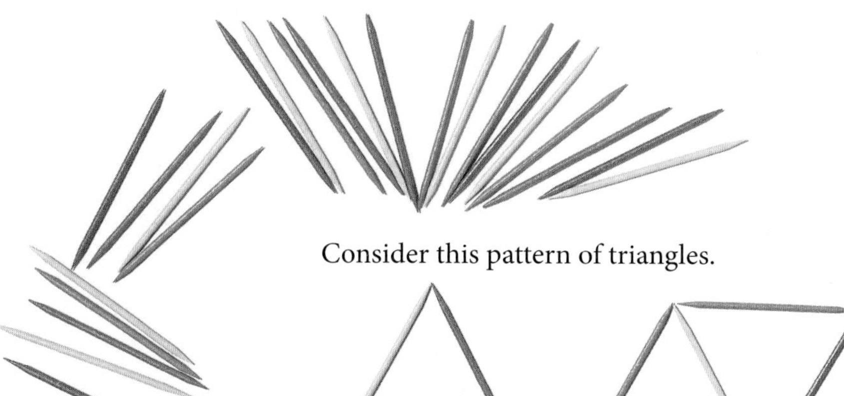

Consider this pattern of triangles.

Figure 1 **Figure 2** **Figure 3**

Step 1 Make Figures 1–6, following the pattern shown. How many toothpicks are used in each figure?

Step 2 Copy the table with enough rows for six figures of the pattern. Fill in the values only for the first column.

	Number of toothpicks	Perimeter
Figure 1		
Figure 2		

Step 3 What is the recursive rule for the number of toothpicks used in each figure? Explain your rule. Use a calculator routine to check your answer. (If you need a hint, see Example A.) Find the number of toothpicks that will be used in Figure 10.

Step 4 For Figures 1–6, count only the toothpicks on the perimeter of the figures. Write these values in the second column of your table.

Step 5 What is the recursive rule for finding the number of toothpicks on the perimeter of each figure? Explain your rule. Use a calculator routine to check your answers, and find the number of toothpicks on the perimeter of Figure 10.

Step 6 Create a toothpick pattern using a row of squares instead of triangles. Repeat Steps 1–5 and answer all the questions for the new design.

Step 7 Repeat Steps 1–5 again, but this time, start with a concave hexagon.

In the investigation you wrote number sequences in table columns. Remember that you can also display sequences as a list of numbers like this:

1, 3, 5, 7, . . .

Each number in the sequence is called a **term.** The three periods, or ellipsis, indicate that the numbers continue.

EXAMPLE B

Find the missing terms in each sequence.

a. 7, 12, 17, __, 27, __, __, 42, __, 52

b. 5, 1, −3, __, −11, −15, __, __, −27, __

c. −7, __, −29, __, −51, −62, __, −84, __

d. 2, −4, 8, −16, 32, __, 128, −256, __, __

How many hidden numbers can you find?

Solution

For each sequence, identify the starting value and the operation that must be performed to get the next term. The missing terms are shown in red.

a. The starting value is 7, and you add 5 each time to get the next term.

Starting value

+ 5 + 5 + 5 + 5 + 5 + 5 + 5 + 5 + 5

7, 12, 17, 22, 27, 32, 37, 42, 47, 52

b. The starting value is 5, and you subtract 4 each time to get the next term.

Starting value

− 4 − 4 − 4 − 4 − 4 − 4 − 4 − 4 − 4

5, 1, −3, −7, −11, −15, −19, −23, −27, −31

c. The starting value is −7. The difference between the fifth and sixth terms shows that you subtract 11 each time.

Starting value

− 11 − 11 − 11 − 11 − 11 − 11 − 11 − 11

−7, −18, −29, −40, −51, −62, −73, −84, −95

d. Adding or subtracting numbers does not generate this sequence. Notice that the numbers double each time. Also, they switch between positive and negative terms. So the rule is to multiply by −2. Multiply 32 by −2 to get the first missing term, −64. The last two missing terms are 512 and −1024.

Starting value

·(−2) ·(−2) ·(−2) ·(−2) ·(−2) ·(−2) ·(−2) ·(−2) ·(−2)

2, −4, 8, −16, 32, −64, 128, −256, 512, −1024

Before you move on to the exercises, make sure you can generate the sequences in Example B using your calculator.

Exercises

You will need your graphing calculator for Exercise **5.**

Practice Your Skills

1. Evaluate each expression without using your calculator. Then check your result with your calculator.

a. $-2(5-9)+7$

b. $\dfrac{(-4)(-8)}{-5+3}$

c. $\dfrac{5+(-6)(-5)}{-7}$

d. $\dfrac{-9-7}{-3-(-4)}$

2. First estimate the value of each expression by rounding all numbers to the nearest integer. Then find the answer using your calculator.

a. $\dfrac{10}{4-(2)(3.1)}$

b. $\dfrac{-3(6.2-8)}{5.1}$

c. $3.2+7(-2.4-1.6)$

d. $\dfrac{4(10.2-6)}{1.8^3}$

3. Find the first six values generated by the recursive rule.

-14.2 ENTER

Ans + 3.7 ENTER, ENTER, . . . @

4. Find the 7th term of each sequence.

a. Start with 2.3 and get from each term to the next by adding 0.9.

b. Start with 53.4 and get from each term to the next by adding -4.2.

c. Start with -3.5 and get from each term to the next by subtracting 6.4.

5. Consider the sequence of figures made from a row of pentagons.

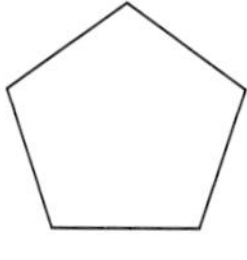

Figure 1

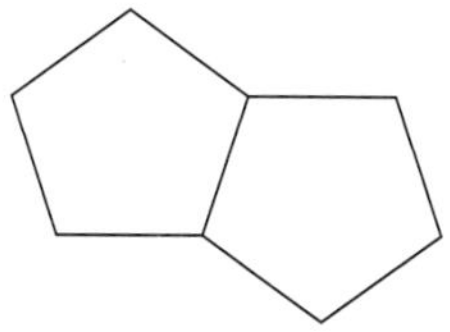

Figure 2

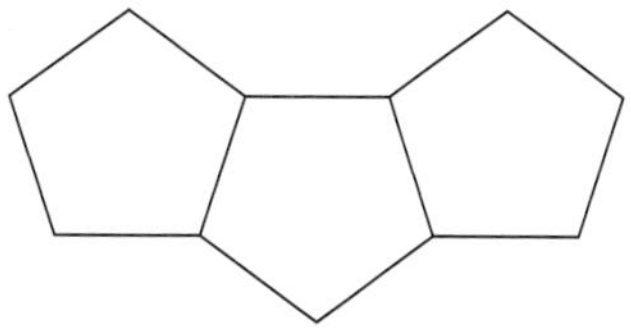

Figure 3

a. Copy and complete the table for five figures. @

b. Write a recursive rule to find the perimeter of each figure. Assume each side is 1 unit long.

c. Find the perimeter of Figure 10. @

d. Which figure has perimeter 47 units?

Figure number	Perimeter
1	5
2	8
3	

Reason and Apply

6. APPLICATION In the Empire State Building, the longest elevator shaft reaches the eighty-sixth floor, 1050 ft above ground level. Another elevator takes visitors from the eighty-sixth floor to the observation area on the one-hundred-second floor, 1224 ft above ground level. (*Hint:* Assume the first floor is at ground level and all of the first 86 floors are the same height.)

a. Write a recursive rule for the sequence of heights above ground level for the first 86 floors. What do the two parts of the rule represent?

b. Write a recursive rule for the sequence of heights of floors 86 through 102. What do the two parts of the rule represent?

c. When you are 531 ft above ground level, what floor are you on?

d. When you are on the ninetieth floor, how high up are you? When you are 1137 ft above ground level, what floor are you on?

7. The diagram at right shows a sequence of gray and white squares, each layered under the previous one.

a. Explain how the sequence 1, 3, 5, 7, . . . is related to the areas of these squares. @

b. Write a recursive rule that gives the sequence 1, 3, 5, 7, ... @

c. Use your rule to predict the number of additional unit squares you would need to enlarge this diagram by one additional row and column. Explain how you found your answer. @

1 3 5 7

d. What is the 20th term in the sequence 1, 3, 5, 7, . . . ?

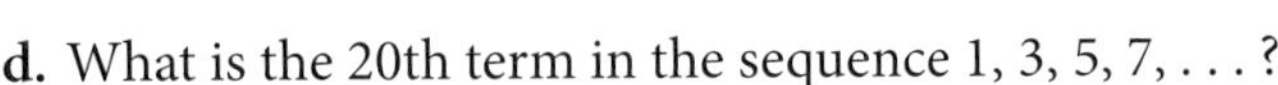

e. The first term in the sequence is 1, and the second is 3. Which term is the number 95? Explain how you found your answer.

8. The table shows a sequence. Find the missing table values, *a–e*, starting with *a*. Explain how you got your answers.

Description	Start	+(43.8)	+(43.8)	+(43.8)	+(43.8)	+(43.8)
Results	*e*	*d*	*c*	*b*	*a*	204.8

9. APPLICATION The table gives some floor heights in a building.

Floor	. . .	−1	0	1	2	. . .		. . .	25
Height (m)	. . .	−3	1	5	9	. . .	37	. . .	

a. How many meters are between the floors in this building?

b. Write a recursive rule that will give the sequence of floor heights if you start at the twenty-fifth floor and go to the basement (Floor 0). Which term in your sequence represents the height of the seventh floor? What is the height?

c. How many terms are in the sequence in 9b?

d. Floor "−1" corresponds to the first level of the parking substructure under the building. If there are five parking levels, how far underground is Level 5?

10. Consider the sequence __, −4, 8, __, 32, ...

a. Find two different recursive rules that could generate these numbers. (h)

b. For each rule, what are the missing terms? What are the next two terms?

c. If you want to generate this number sequence with exactly one rule, what more do you need?

11. Positive multiples of 7 are generally listed as 7, 14, 21, 28, ...

a. If 7 is the 1st multiple of 7 and 14 is the 2nd multiple, then what is the 17th multiple? (@)

b. How many multiples of 7 are between 100 and 200? (@)

c. Compare the number of multiples of 7 between 100 and 200 with the number between 200 and 300. Does the answer make sense? Do all intervals of 100 have this many multiples of 7? Explain. (@)

d. Describe two different ways to generate a list containing multiples of 7. (@)

12. Some babies gain an average of 1.5 lb per month during the first 6 months after birth.

a. Write a recursive rule that will generate a table of monthly weights for a baby weighing 6.8 lb at birth.

b. Write a recursive rule that will generate a table of monthly weights for a baby weighing 7.2 lb at birth.

c. How are the rules in 12a and b the same? How are they different?

d. Copy and complete the table of data for this situation.

Age (mo)	0	1	2	3	4	5	6
Weight of baby A (lb)	6.8						
Weight of baby B (lb)	7.2						

e. How are the table values for the two babies the same? How do they differ?

13. Write recursive rules to help you answer 13a–d.

a. Find the 9th term of the sequence 1, 3, 9, 27, ... (@)

b. Find the 123rd term of the sequence 5, −5, 5, −5, ... (@)

c. Find the missing terms in the sequence __, −0.5, 3.2, __, __, 14.3, __, 21.7, 25.4, 29.1, __.

d. Find the term number of the first positive term of the sequence −16.2, −14.8, −13.4, −12, ...

e. Which term is the first to be either greater than 100 or less than −100 in the sequence −1, 2, −4, 8, −16, . . . ?

Review

14. The table gives the normal monthly precipitation, in inches, for three cities in the United States.

    a. Display the data in three box plots, one for each city, and use them to compare the precipitation for the three cities.

    b. What information do you lose by displaying the data in a box plot? What type of graph might be more helpful for displaying the data?

Precipitation for Three Cities

	Precipitation (in.)		
Month	**Portland, Oregon**	**San Francisco, California**	**Seattle, Washington**
January	5.1	4.7	5.2
February	4.2	4.2	4.1
March	3.7	3.4	3.9
April	2.6	1.3	2.8
May	2.4	0.5	2.0
June	1.6	0.1	1.6
July	0.7	0.0	0.9
August	0.9	0.1	1.2
September	1.7	0.3	1.6
October	2.9	1.2	3.2
November	5.6	3.3	5.7
December	5.7	3.2	6.1

(*The New York Times Almanac 2009*, p. 482)

15. Create an undo table and solve the given equation by undoing the order of operations.

Equation: $8 + 3(x - 5) = -14.8$		
Description	**Undo**	**Result**
Pick x.		

LESSON

3.2

Linear Plots

Imagine a rabbit hopping down a path. If you know where it starts and the average length of each hop, you can generate a sequence of locations for all hops. When a recursive rule adds or subtracts a number, consecutive terms change by a constant amount. In this lesson you will learn that a recursive rule takes on special meaning in some real-world situations. Using your calculator, you will see how the starting value and rule let you generate data for tables quickly. You will also plot these data sets and learn that the starting value and rule relate to characteristics of the graph.

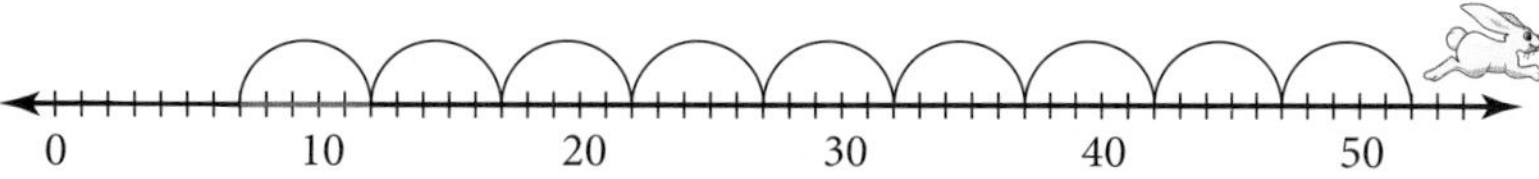

EXAMPLE

You walk into an elevator in the basement of a building. Its control panel displays "0" for the floor number. The table shows the floor numbers and their heights in relation to ground level.

Floor number	Height (ft)
0 (basement)	−4
1	9
2	22
3	35
4	48
...	...

a. Write recursive rules for the two number sequences in the table. Enter both rules into your calculator to generate the table values.

b. Define variables and plot the data in the table for the first few floors of the building. Does it make sense to connect the points on the graph?

c. What is the highest floor with a height less than 200 ft? Is there a floor that is exactly 200 ft high?

Solution

The starting value for the floor numbers is 0, and the rule is add 1. The starting value for the height is −4, and the rule is add 13. You can generate both number sequences on the calculator using lists.

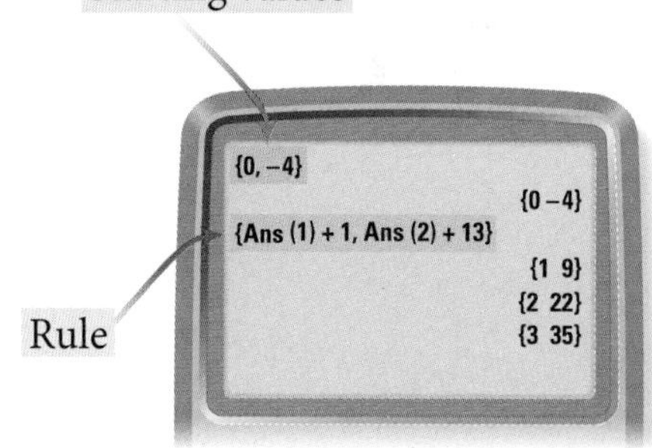

a. Press {0, −4} and press ENTER to input both starting values at the same time. To use the rules to get the next term in the sequence, press {Ans(1) + 1, Ans(2) + 13} ENTER. [▶ See **Calculator Note: Recursion on a List.** ◀]

These commands tell the calculator to add 1 to the first number in the list and to add 13 to the second number. Press ENTER again to compute the next floor number and its corresponding height as the elevator rises.

b. Let x represent the floor number and y represent the floor's height in feet. Mark a scale from 0 to 5 on the x-axis and from -10 to 50 on the y-axis. Plot the data from the table. The graph starts at $(0, -4)$ on the y-axis. The points appear to be in a line. It does not make sense to connect the points because it is not possible to have a decimal or fractional floor number.

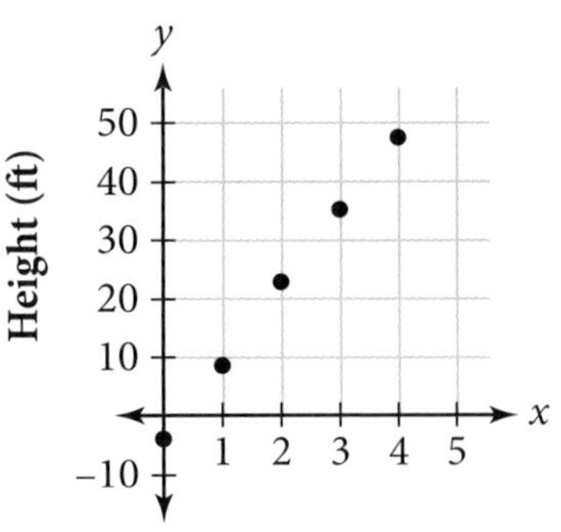

c. The recursive rule generates the points $(0, -4), (1, 9), (2, 22), \ldots, (15, 191), (16, 204), \ldots$. The height of the fifteenth floor is 191 ft. The height of the sixteenth floor is 204 ft. So the fifteenth floor is the highest floor with a height less than 200 ft. No floor is exactly 200 ft high.

Notice that to get to the next point on the graph from any given point, you move right 1 unit on the x-axis and up 13 units on the y-axis. The points you plotted in the example showed that the data are **linear**—that is, they form a line on the graph. We say that there is a linear relationship between floor numbers and their heights. In what other graphs have you seen linear relationships?

INVESTIGATION

YOU WILL NEED

- graph paper

On the Road Again

A green minivan starts at the Mackinac Bridge and travels south toward Flint on Highway 75. At the same time, a red sports car leaves Saginaw and a blue pickup truck leaves Flint. The car and the pickup are traveling toward the bridge. The minivan travels 72 mi/h. The pickup travels 66 mi/h. The sports car travels 48 mi/h.

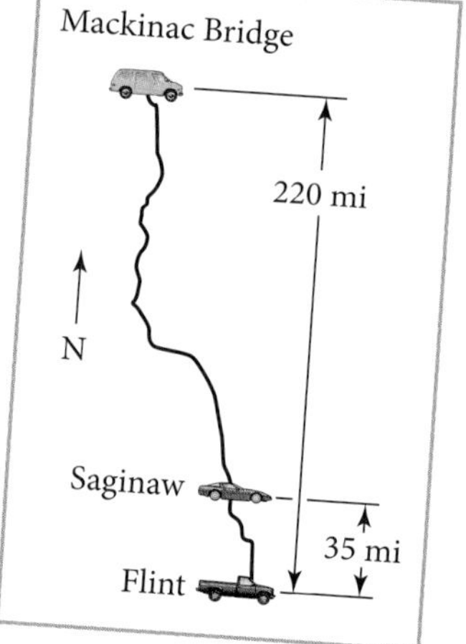

When and where will they pass each other on the highway? In this investigation you will learn how to use recursive rules to answer questions like these.

Step 1 What is the starting point for each vehicle? Write each as the number of miles from Flint.

Step 2 For each vehicle, write a recursive rule for the sequence of that vehicle's distance from Flint at each hour. How could you use the rule to determine the velocity of the vehicle?

Step 3 Make a table to record the highway distance from Flint for each vehicle each hour. Record values for up to 4 hours.

Highway Distance from Flint

Time (h)	Pickup (mi)	Sports car (mi)	Minivan (mi)
1			
2			
3			
4			

Step 4 Define variables and plot the information from the table onto a graph. Mark the axes as shown. Using a different color for each vehicle, plot its (*time, distance*) coordinates.

Step 5 On the graph, do the points for each vehicle seem to fall on a line? Does it make sense to connect each vehicle's points? If so, connect them. If not, explain why not.

Distance (mi): 20, 40, 60, 80, 100, 120, 140, 160, 180, 200, 220

Time (h): 1, 2, 3, 4

Use your graph and table to find the answers for Steps 6–10.

Step 6 Where does the starting value for each vehicle appear on the graph? How does each recursive rule relate to the points plotted?

Step 7 Which line represents the minivan? How can you tell?

Step 8 Estimate where all three vehicles are when the minivan meets the first northbound vehicle.

Step 9 How can you tell by looking at the graph whether the pickup or the sports car is traveling faster? Estimate when and where the pickup passes the sports car.

Step 10 Which vehicle arrives at its destination first? Estimate how much time passes before the second and third vehicles arrive at their destinations. How can you tell by looking at the graph?

Step 11 What assumptions about the vehicles are you making when you answer the questions in the previous steps?

Step 12 Consider how to model this situation more realistically. What if the vehicles are traveling at different speeds? What if one driver stops to get gas or a bite to eat? What if the vehicles' speeds are not constant? Discuss how these questions affect the recursive rules, the tables of data, and their graphs.

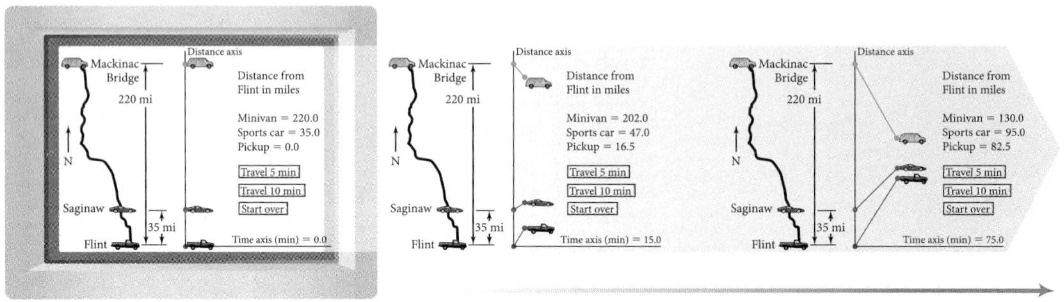

[▶ You can use the **Dynamic Algebra Exploration** found in your ebook to further explore the situation described in the investigation. ◀]

3.2 Exercises

You will need your graphing calculator for Exercise **7.**

Practice Your Skills

1. Percy the rabbit hops as shown on the number line.

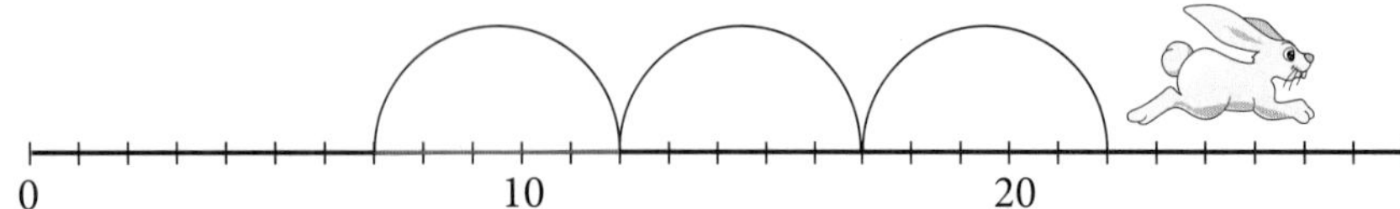

a. Write a recursive rule for the sequence of Percy's jump locations.

b. Find the missing values in the table.

Jump number	Location
0	
1	
2	
	37
12	

2. List the terms of each number sequence of y-coordinates for the points shown on each graph. Then write a recursive rule for each sequence.

a. 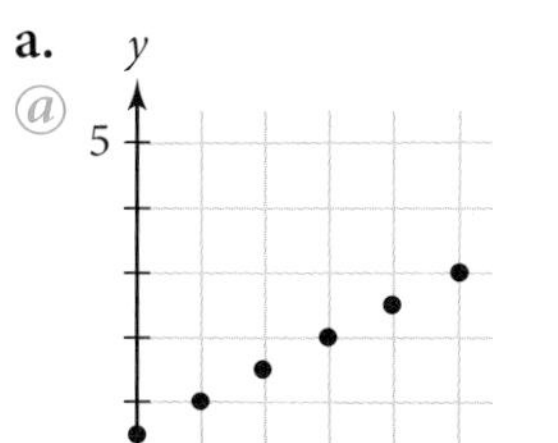

b. 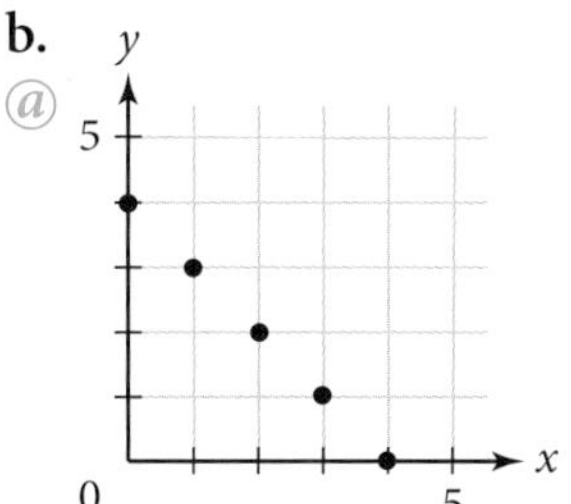

c. 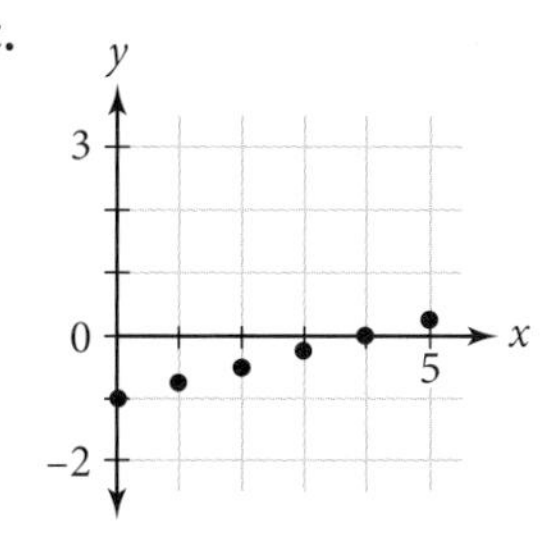

d. 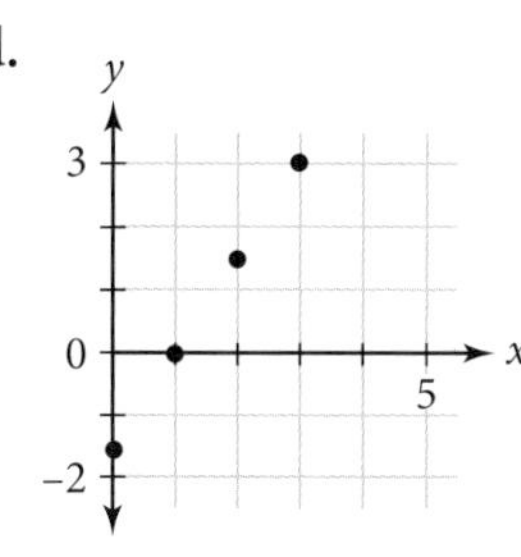

3. Make a table listing the coordinates of the points plotted in 2b and d.

4. Plot the first five points represented by each recursive routine in 4a and b on separate graphs. Then answer 4c and d.

a. $\{0, 5\}$ ENTER

$\{\text{Ans}(1) + 1, \text{Ans}(2) + 7\}$ ENTER, ENTER, . . .

b. $\{0, -3\}$ ENTER

$\{\text{Ans}(1) + 1, \text{Ans}(2) - 6\}$ ENTER, ENTER, . . .

c. On which axis does each starting point lie? What is the x-coordinate of each starting point?

d. As the x-value increases by 1, what happens to the y-coordinates of the points in each sequence in 4a and b? @

5. The direct variation $y = 2.54x$ describes the relationship between two standard units of measurement where y represents centimeters and x represents inches.

a. Write a recursive rule for a sequence of values for any whole number of inches.

b. Use your rule to complete the missing values in the table.

Inches	Centimeters
0	0
1	2.54
2	
	35.56
17	

Reason and Apply

6. APPLICATION A car is moving at a velocity of 68 mi/h from Dallas toward San Antonio. Dallas is about 272 mi from San Antonio.

a. Write a recursive rule for a sequence of table values relating time to distance from San Antonio for 0 h to 5 h in 1 h intervals.

b. Graph the information in your table.

c. What is the connection between your plot and the starting value in your recursive rule?

d. What is the connection between the coordinates of any two consecutive points in your plot and your recursive rule?

e. Draw a line through the points of your plot. Estimate when the car is within 100 mi of San Antonio. Explain how you got your answer.

f. How long does it take the car to reach San Antonio? Explain how you got your answer.

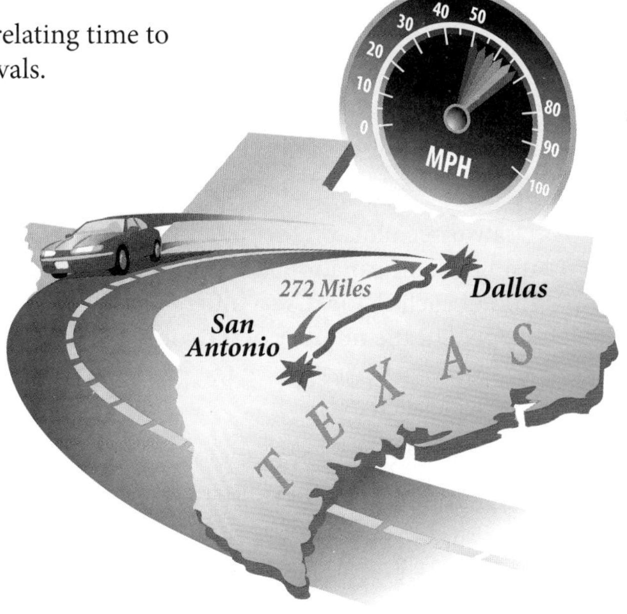

7. This table and graph show the changing depths of two submarines as they come to the surface.

USS *Alabama*

Time (s)	0	5	10	15	20	25	30
Depth (ft)	−38	−31	−24	−17	−10	−3	4

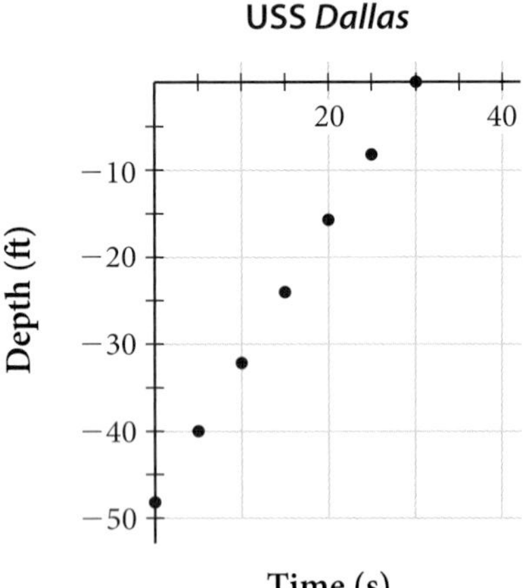

a. Which submarine starts at a greater depth? How do you know?

b. Which submarine is rising faster? How do you know?

c. What is the real-world meaning of the data value (30, 4) for the USS *Alabama?*

8. **MINI-INVESTIGATION** Each geometric design is made from tiles arranged in a row.

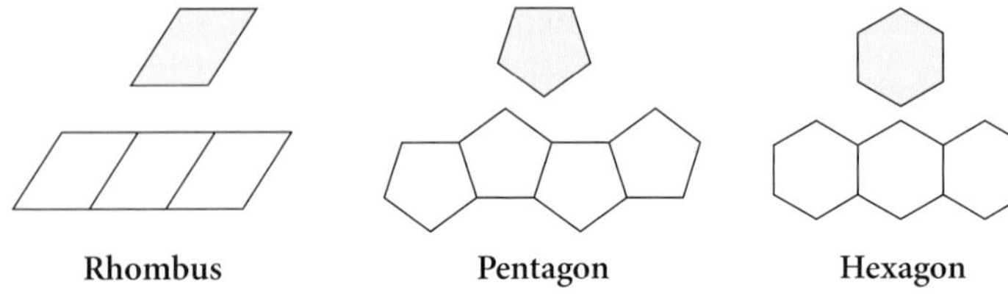

a. Make a table like the one shown. Find the number of tile edges on the perimeter of each design, and fill in five rows of the table. Look for patterns as you add more tiles. (h)

Tile Edges on the Perimeter

Number of tiles	Rhombus	Pentagon	Hexagon
1	4	5	6
2			
3			

b. Write a recursive rule for the sequence of values in each table column.

c. Find the number of tile edges on the perimeter of a 20-tile design for each shape.

d. Draw three plots on the same coordinate axes using the information for designs of one to five tiles of each shape. Use a different color for each shape. Put the number of tiles on the horizontal axis and the perimeter on the vertical axis. Label and scale each axis.

e. Compare the three scatter plots. How are they alike, and how are they different?

f. Would it make sense to draw a line through each set of points? Explain why or why not. (h)

9. APPLICATION A long-distance telephone carrier charges \$1.38 for international calls of 1 minute or less and \$0.36 for each additional minute.

a. Write a recursive rule for a calculator list to find the cost of a 7-minute phone call. @

b. Without graphing the sequence, give a verbal description of the graph showing the costs for calls that last whole numbers of minutes. Include in your description all the important values you need in order to draw the graph.

10. A bicyclist, 1 mi (5280 ft) away from you, pedals toward you at a rate of 600 ft/min for 3 min. The bicyclist then pedals at a rate of 1000 ft/min for the next 5 min.

a. Describe what you think the plot of (*time, distance from you*) will look like. @

b. Graph the data using 1 min intervals for your plot. @

c. Invent a question about the situation, and use your graph to answer the question.

Review

11. Decide whether each expression is positive or negative without using your calculator. Then check your answer with your calculator.

a. $-35(44) + 23$ b. $(-14)(-36) - 32$ c. $25 - \frac{152}{12}$

d. $50 - 23(-12)$ e. $\frac{-12 - 38}{15}$ f. $24(15 - 76)$

12. Consider the following expressions:

i. $\frac{14.2 - (x + 6)}{4}$ ii. $\frac{5.4 + 3.2(x - 2.8)}{1.2} - 2.3$

a. Use the order of operations to find the value of each expression for $x = 7.2$.

b. Set each expression equal to 3.8. Solve for x by undoing the sequence of operations you used in 12a.

13. Isaac learned a way to convert from degrees Celsius to Fahrenheit. He adds 40 to the Celsius temperature, multiplies by 9, divides by 5, and then subtracts 40.

a. Write an expression for Isaac's conversion method. @

b. Write the steps to convert from Fahrenheit to Celsius by undoing Isaac's method. @

c. Write an expression for the conversion in 13b.

14. Draw and label a coordinate plane with each axis scaled from -10 to 10.

a. Represent each point named with a dot, and label it using its letter name.

$A(3, -2)$ $B(-8, 1.5)$ $C(9, 0)$ $D(-9.5, -3)$ $E(7, -4)$

$F(1, -1)$ $G(0, -6.5)$ $H(2.5, 3)$ $I(-6, 7.5)$ $J(-5, -6)$

b. List the points in Quadrant I, Quadrant II, Quadrant III, and Quadrant IV. Which points are on the x-axis? Which points are on the y-axis?

c. Explain how to tell which quadrant a point will be in by looking at its coordinates. Explain how to tell if a point lies on one of the axes.

LESSON

3.3

Time-Distance Relationships

"In most sciences, one generation tears down what another has built, and what one has established, the next undoes. In mathematics alone, each generation builds a new story to the old structure."

HERMANN HANKEL

In this lesson you will learn how the starting position, speed, direction, and final position of a walker influence a graph and an equation.

This (*time, distance*) graph provides a lot of information about the "walk" it represents. The fact that the line is straight and increasing means that the walker is moving away from the motion sensor at a steady rate. The walker starts 1 m from the sensor at time 0 s. The graph represents a walker moving 3.5 − 1, or 2.5, m in 3 − 0, or 3, s, or 0.83 m/s.

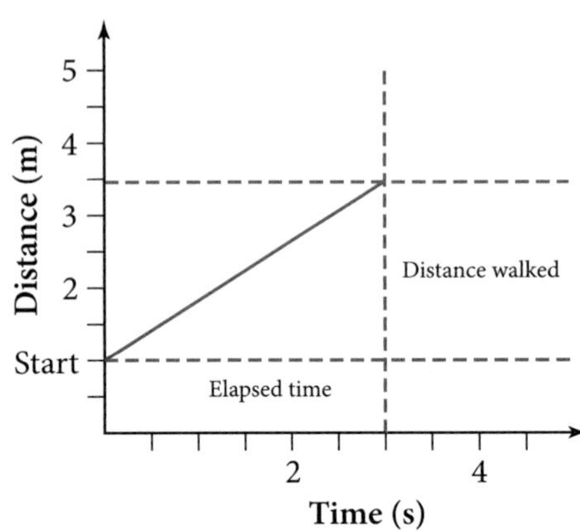

In this investigation you'll analyze time-distance graphs, and you'll use a motion sensor to create your own graphs.

INVESTIGATION

YOU WILL NEED

- a 4-meter measuring tape or four metersticks per group
- a motion sensor
- a stopwatch or watch that shows seconds

Walk the Line

Imagine that you have a 4-meter measuring tape positioned on the floor. A motion sensor measures your distance from the tape's 0-mark as you walk, and it graphs the information. On the calculator graphs shown here, the horizontal axis shows time from 0 to 6 seconds, and the vertical axis shows distance from 0 to 4 meters.

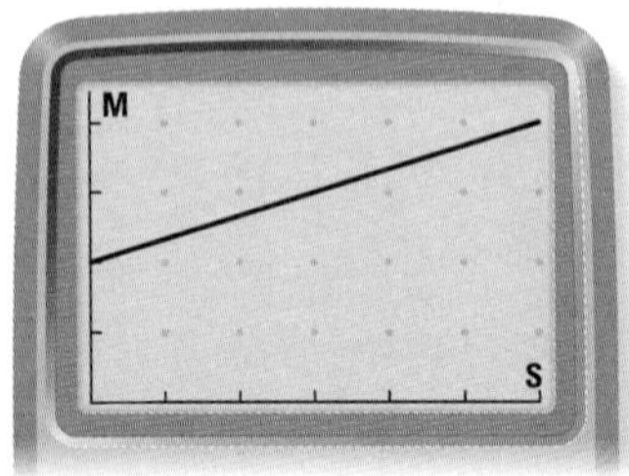

a.

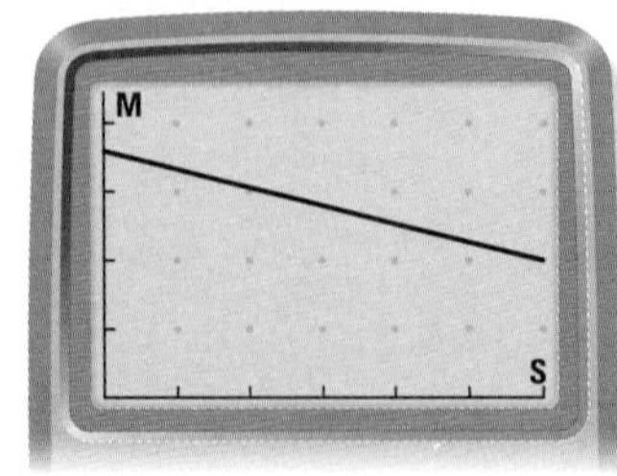

b.

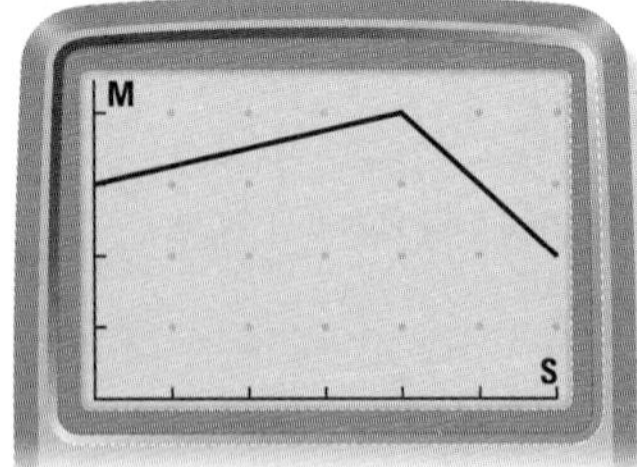

c.

Step 1 Write a set of walking instructions for each graph. Tell where the walk begins, how fast the person walks, and whether the person walks toward or away from the motion sensor located at the 0-mark.

a. In which of the graphs is the walker walking the fastest? How fast is that? How can you tell just by looking at the graph?

b. In which graph did the walker start closest to the sensor? Explain how you know this.

Step 2 Graph a 6-second walk based on each set of walking instructions or data.

a. Start at the 2.5-meter mark and stand still.

b. Start at the 3-meter mark and walk toward the sensor at a constant rate of 0.4 meter per second.

c.

Time (s)	0	1	2	3	4	5	6
Distance (m)	0.8	1.0	1.2	1.4	1.6	1.8	2.0

Step 3 Create a table for the walk in Step 2b. Then look at the tables for Steps 2b and 2c. How can you use the information in the table to determine which graph is steeper?

For the next part of the investigation, you will need a graphing calculator and a motion sensor. Your group will need a space about 4 m long and 1.5 m wide (13 ft by 5 ft). Tape to the floor a 4 m measuring tape or four metersticks end-to-end. Assign these tasks among your group members: walker, motion-sensor holder, coach, and timer.

Step 4 Your group will try to create graph a from Step 1. Remember that you wrote walking directions for this graph. Use your motion sensor to record the walker's motion. [► See **Calculator Note: EasyApp: Collecting Distance Data** for help using the motion sensor. ◄] After each walk, discuss what you could have done to better replicate the graph. Repeat the walk until you have a good match for graph a.

Step 5 Rotate jobs, and repeat Step 4 to model graphs b and c from Step 1 and the three descriptions from Step 2.

Using motion-sensor technology in the investigation, you were able to actually see how accurately you duplicated a given walk. The following examples will provide more practice with time-distance relationships.

EXAMPLE A

a. Graph a walk from the set of instructions "Start at the 0.5-meter mark and walk at a steady 0.25 meter per second for 6 seconds."

b. Write a set of walking instructions based on the table data, and then sketch a graph of the walk.

Time (s)	0	1	2	3	4	5	6
Distance (m)	4.0	3.6	3.2	2.8	2.4	2.0	1.6

Solution

Think about where the walker starts and how much distance he or she will cover in a given amount of time.

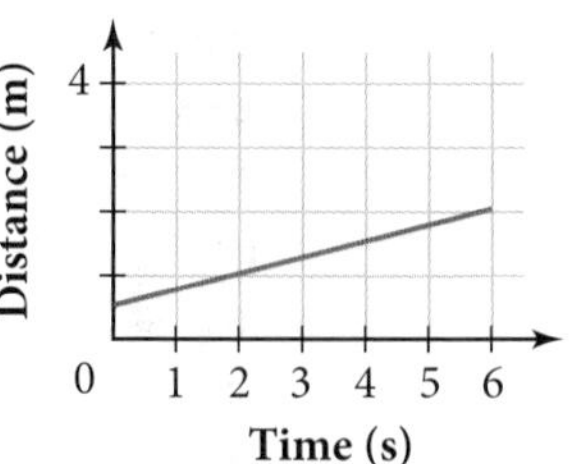

a. Walking at a steady rate of 0.25 meter per second for 6 seconds means the walker will move 0.25 m/s · 6 s, or1.5 m. The walker starts at 0.5 m and ends at 0.5 + 1.5 m, or 2 m.

b. Walking instructions: "Start at the 4-meter mark and walk toward the sensor at 0.4 meter per second." You can graph this walk by plotting the given data points.

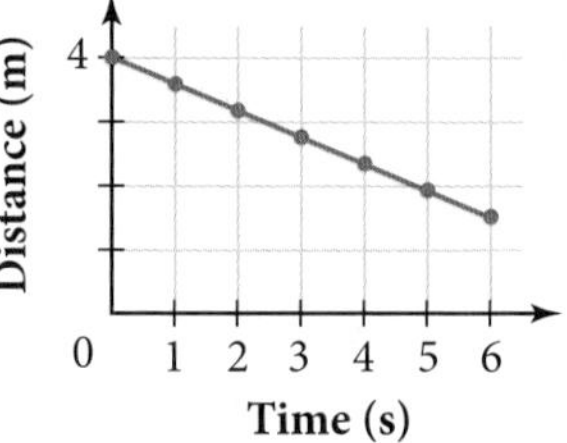

EXAMPLE B

Write a set of walking instructions for this graph.

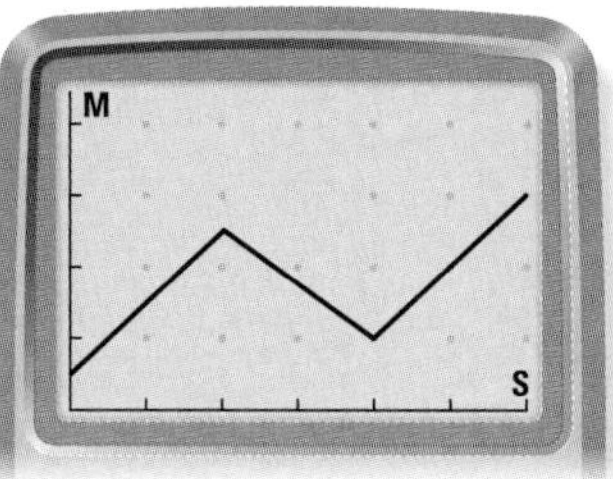

Solution

The graph starts at 0.5 on the y-axis, so the walker should start 0.5 m from the sensor. The graph goes up to the point (2, 2.5). This means the walker goes 2 m away from the sensor in 2 s, so she should walk at a rate of 1 m/s for 2 s.

The next section of the graph goes down, indicating that the walker is walking toward the sensor. The graph goes to the point (4, 1), meaning that the walker goes 1.5 m in 2 s. So she walks at a rate of 0.75 m/s for 2 s.

The final portion of the graph goes up to the point (6, 3), meaning that the walker goes 2 m away from the sensor in 2 s. So she walks at a rate of 1 m/s for 2 s.

3.3 Exercises

Practice Your Skills

1. Write a recursive rule for the second row of the table in Example A, part b. @

2. Sketch a graph of each walk.

a. Start at the 1-meter mark and walk away from the sensor at a constant rate of 0.5 meter per second.

b. Start at the 3.5-meter mark and do not move for 6 seconds.

c. Start at the 2-meter mark and walk in such a way that a graph of your walk contains the point (3, 3).

3. Write a set of walking instructions and sketch a graph of the walk described by {0, 0.8} and {Ans(1) + 1, Ans(2) + 0.2}. @

4. Each graph and table represent a walk.

i.

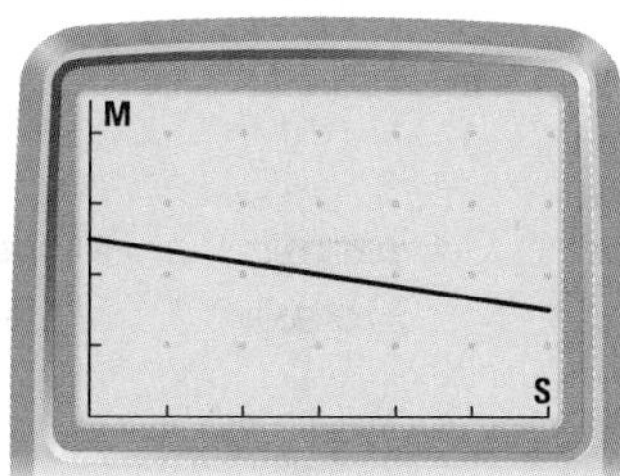

ii.

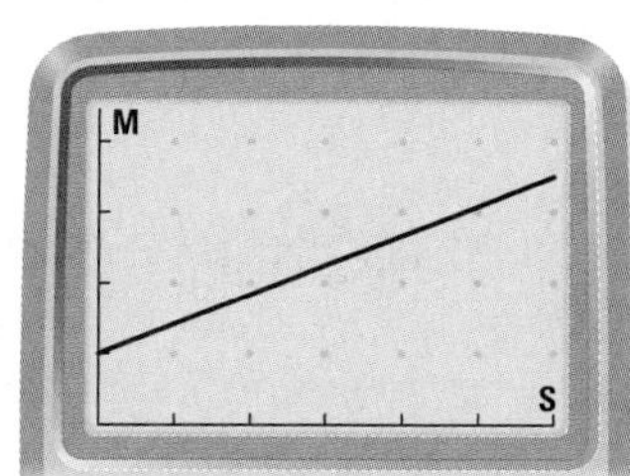

iii.

Time (s)	Distance (m)
0	6
1	5.8
2	5.6
3	5.4
4	5.2
5	5.0
6	4.8

iv.

Time (s)	Distance (m)
0	1.4
1	2.0
2	2.6
3	3.2
4	3.8
5	4.4
6	5.0

a. Arrange the four walks in order of starting distance from the sensor, from farthest away to closest. (@)

b. Arrange the four walks in order of speed, from slowest to fastest.

c. Identify which walks are moving toward the sensor and which are moving away from the sensor.

Reason and Apply

5. Which graph better represents a walk in which the walker starts 2 m from the motion sensor and walks away from it at a rate of 0.25 m/s for 6 s? Explain.

a.

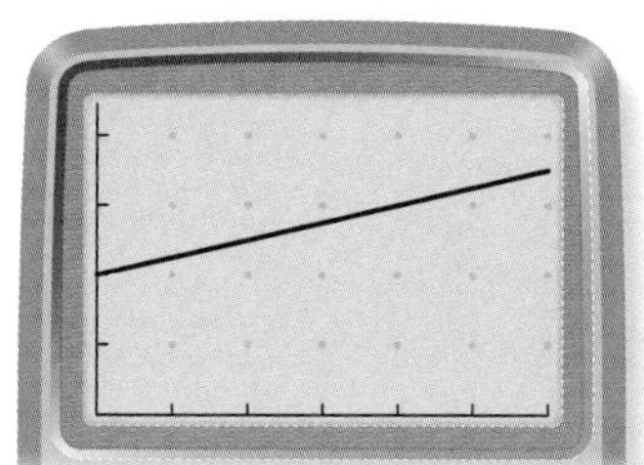

b.

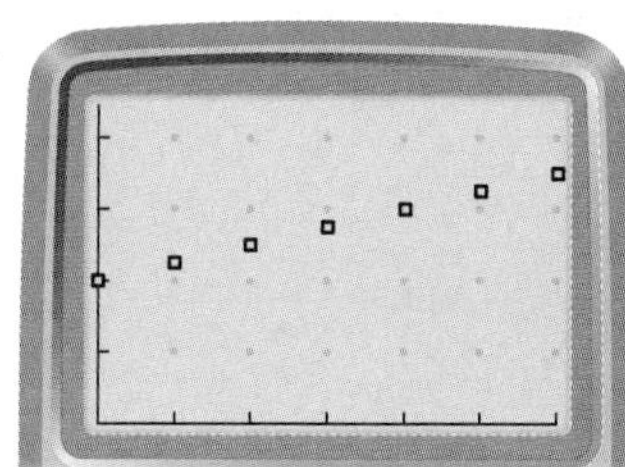

6. At what rate in feet per second would you walk so that you were moving at a constant speed of 1 mi/h? (h)

7. Describe how the rate affects the graph of each situation.

a. The graph of a person walking toward a motion sensor. (@)

b. The graph of a person standing still.

c. The graph of a person walking slowly.

8. The time-distance graph shows Carol walking at a steady rate. Her partner measures her distance from a motion sensor.

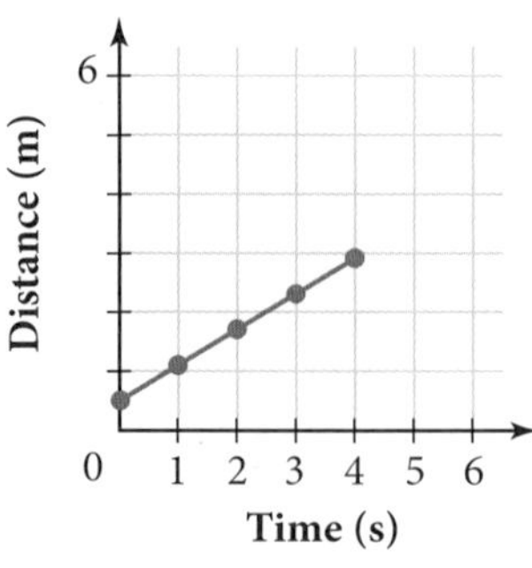

a. According to the graph, how much time did Carol spend walking?

b. Was Carol walking toward or away from the motion sensor? Explain your thinking.

c. Approximately how far away from the motion sensor was Carol when she started walking?

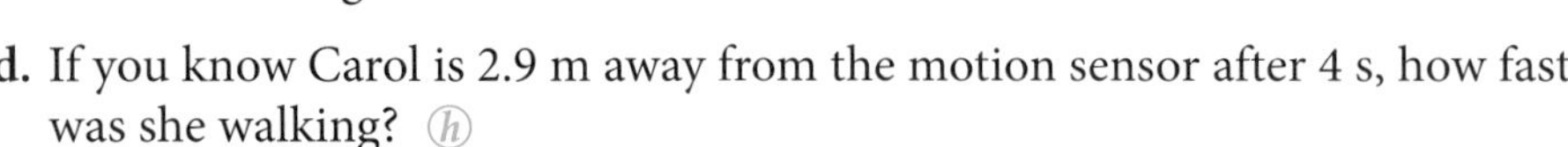

d. If you know Carol is 2.9 m away from the motion sensor after 4 s, how fast was she walking?

e. If the equipment will measure distances only up to 6 m, how many seconds of data can be collected if Carol continues walking at the same rate?

f. Looking only at the graph, how do you know that Carol was neither speeding up nor slowing down during her walk?

9. You start timing Carol's walk as she walks toward her partner, starting at a distance of 5.9 m while moving at a constant speed of 0.6 m/s. Draw a scatter plot of Carol's walk on your paper picturing (*time, distance*) at 1 s intervals.

10. Match each calculator Answer rule to a graph.

a. 2.5 ENTER

Ans + 0.5 ENTER, ENTER, . . .

b. 1.0 ENTER

Ans + 1.0 ENTER, ENTER, . . .

c. 2.0 ENTER

Ans + 1.0 ENTER, ENTER, . . .

d. 2.5 ENTER

Ans − 0.5 ENTER, ENTER, . . .

i.

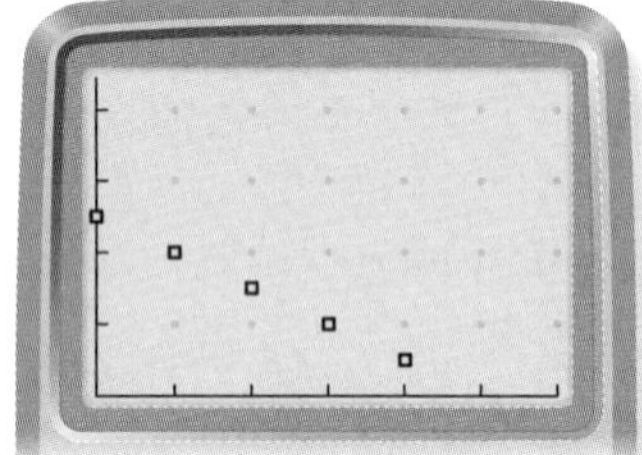

ii.

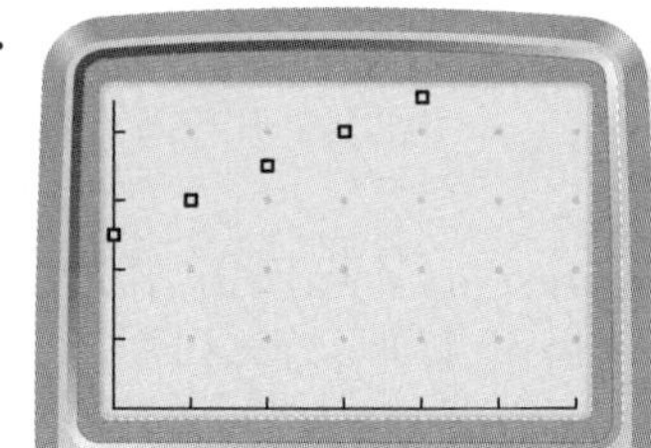

iii.

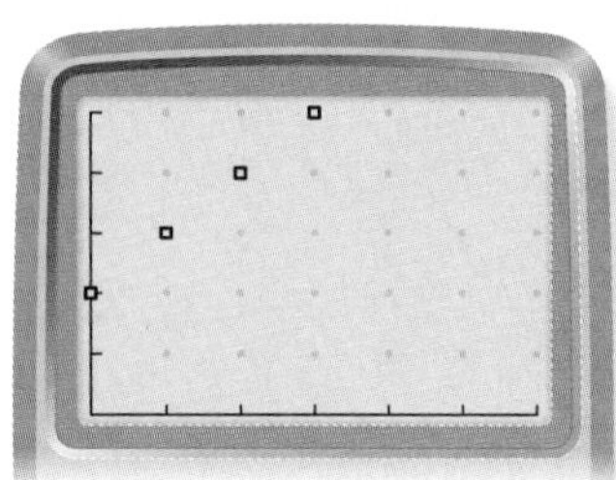

iv.

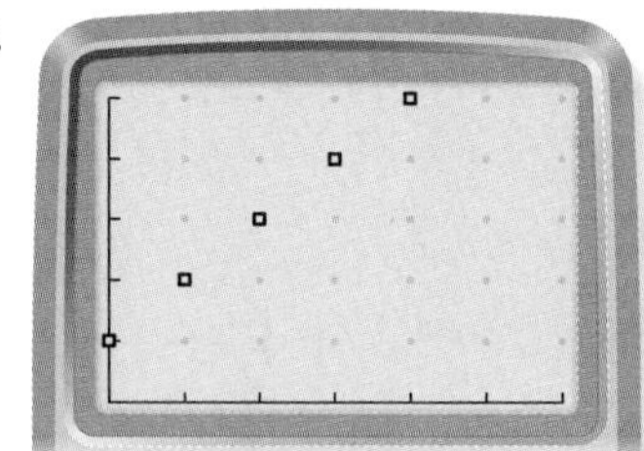

11. Compare the walks in the graphs from problem 10 by describing how the speeds, directions, and starting locations are related.

a. Graphs i and ii.

b. Graphs iii and iv.

12. Describe how you would instruct someone to walk the line $y = x$, where x is time measured in seconds and y is distance measured in feet. Then describe how to walk the line $y = x$, where x is time measured in seconds and y is distance measured in meters. Which line represents a faster rate? Explain.

13. For each situation, determine if it is possible to collect such walking data, and either describe how to collect it or explain why it is not possible.

a. ⓐ

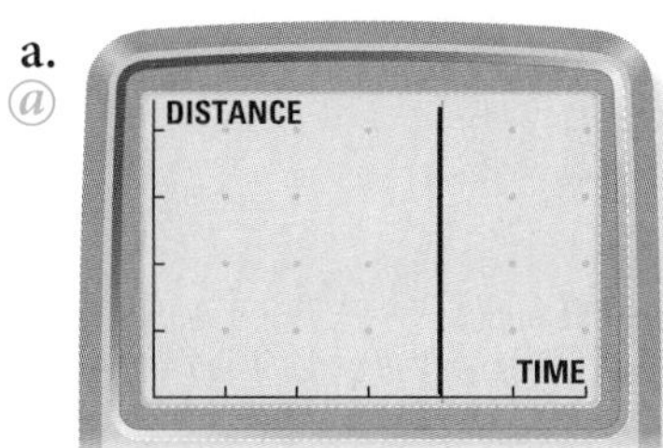

b.

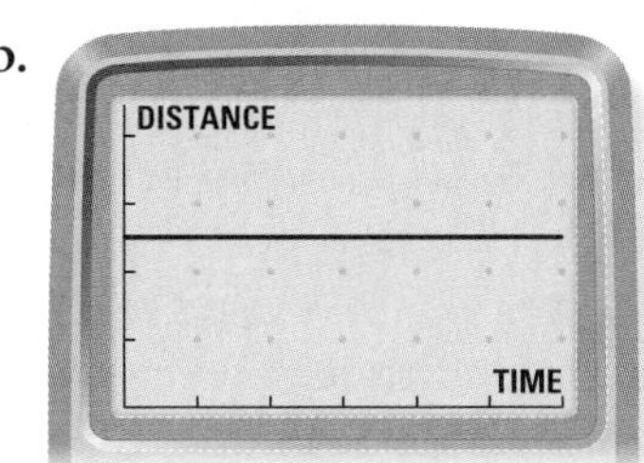

c.

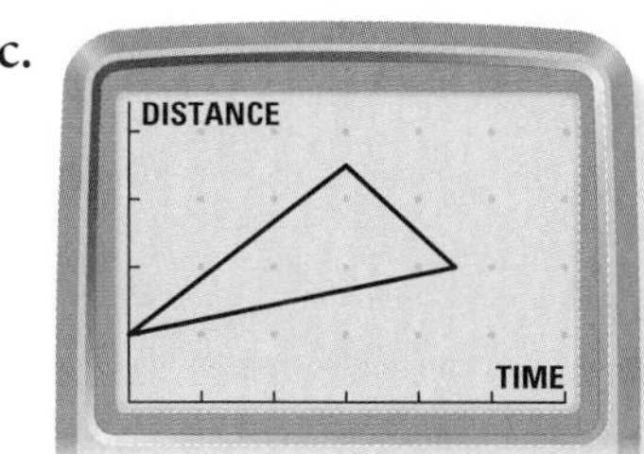

Review

14. Solve each proportion for x.

a. $\frac{x}{3} = \frac{7}{5}$

b. $\frac{2}{x} = \frac{9}{11}$ ⓐ

c. $\frac{x}{c} = \frac{d}{e}$

15. On his Man in Motion World Tour, starting in 1987, Canadian Rick Hansen wheeled himself 24,901.55 miles to support spinal cord injury research and rehabilitation, and wheelchair sport. He covered 4 continents and 34 countries in 2 years, 2 months, and 2 days. (*www.rickhansen.com*)

a. Find Rick's average rate of travel in miles per day. (Assume there are 365 days in a year and 30.4 days in a month.) ⓗ

b. How much farther would Rick have traveled if he had continued his journey for another $1\frac{1}{2}$ years?

c. If Rick continued at this same rate, how many days would it take him to travel 60,000 miles? How many years is that?

Photo courtesy of The Rick Hansen Foundation

China was one of the many countries through which Rick Hansen traveled during the Man in Motion World Tour.

16. APPLICATION Nicholai's car burns 13.5 gallons of gasoline every 175 miles.

a. What is the car's fuel consumption rate? ⓗ

b. At this rate, how far will the car go on 5 gallons of gas?

c. How many gallons of gas does Nicholai's car need to go 100 miles?

LESSON 3.4

Linear Equations and the Intercept Form

So far in this chapter you have used recursive rules, graphs, and tables to model linear relationships. In this lesson you will learn to write linear equations to model these relationships. You'll begin to see some common characteristics of linear equations and their graphs, starting with the relationship between exercise and calorie consumption.

Different physical activities cause people to burn calories at different rates depending on many factors such as body type, height, age, and metabolism. Coaches and trainers consider these factors when suggesting workouts for their athletes.

INVESTIGATION

Working Out with Equations

Manisha starts her exercise routine by jogging to the gym. Her trainer says this activity burns 215 calories. Her workout at the gym is to pedal a stationary bike. This activity burns 3.8 calories per minute.

First you'll model this scenario with your calculator.

Step 1 Write a recursive rule to generate the total number of calories Manisha has burned after each minute she pedals the bike. Include the 215 calories she burned on her jog to the gym.

Step 2 Copy and complete the table using your recursive rule.

Step 3 After Manisha has pedaled for 20 minutes, how many calories has she burned? How long did it take her to burn 443 total calories?

Manisha's Workout

Pedaling time (min) x	Total calories burned y
0	215
1	
2	
20	
30	
45	
60	

Next you'll learn to write an equation that gives the same values as the calculator routine.

Step 4 Write a numerical expression in the form *start value* + *rate* · *time* to find the total calories Manisha has burned after 20 minutes of pedaling. Check that your expression equals the value in the table.

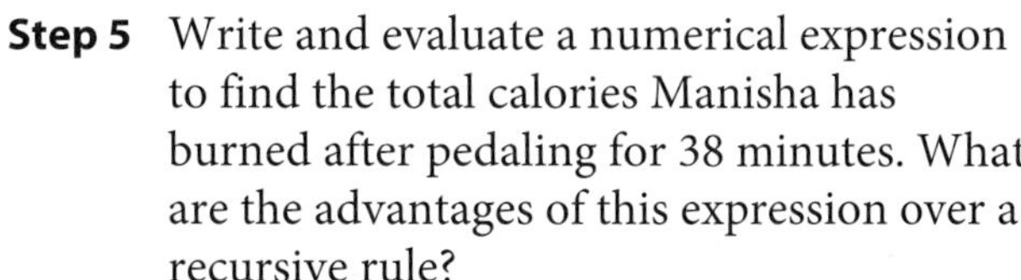

Step 5 Write and evaluate a numerical expression to find the total calories Manisha has burned after pedaling for 38 minutes. What are the advantages of this expression over a recursive rule?

Step 6 Let x represent the pedaling time in minutes. Write an algebraic expression representing the total number of calories Manisha burns for any given time.

Step 7 Let y represent the total number of calories Manisha burns. Write an equation relating time to total calories burned. Check that your equation produces all the values in the table.

Now you'll explore the connections between the equation and its graph.

Step 8 Plot the points from your table on your calculator. Then enter and graph your equation to check that it passes through the points. Give two reasons why drawing a line through the points realistically models this situation. [▶ See **Calculator Note: Equations** to review how to plot points and graph an equation. ◀]

Step 9 Substitute 538 for y in your equation to find the elapsed time required for Manisha to burn a total of 538 calories. Explain your solution process. Check your result.

Step 10 How do the starting value and your recursive rule show up in your equation? How do the starting value and the recursive rule show up in your graph? When is the starting value of the recursive rule also the value where the graph crosses the y-axis?

The equation for Manisha's workout shows a linear relationship between the total calories burned and the number of minutes pedaling on the bike. The graph of this equation is a line. Any equation that can be represented with a straight-line graph is a **linear equation.** You probably wrote this linear equation as

$$y = 215 + 3.8x \qquad \text{or} \qquad y = 3.8x + 215$$

Intercept Form

The form $y = a + bx$ is the intercept form.

y-intercept (points to a) **coefficient** (points to b)

The y-intercept is the value of y when x is zero. The intercept gives the location of the point $(0, a)$, where the graph crosses the y-axis. The number multiplied by x is the coefficient of x.

In the equation $y = 215 + 3.8x$, 215 is the value of a. It represents the 215 calories Manisha burned while jogging before her workout. The value of b is 3.8. It represents the rate at which her body burned calories while she was pedaling.

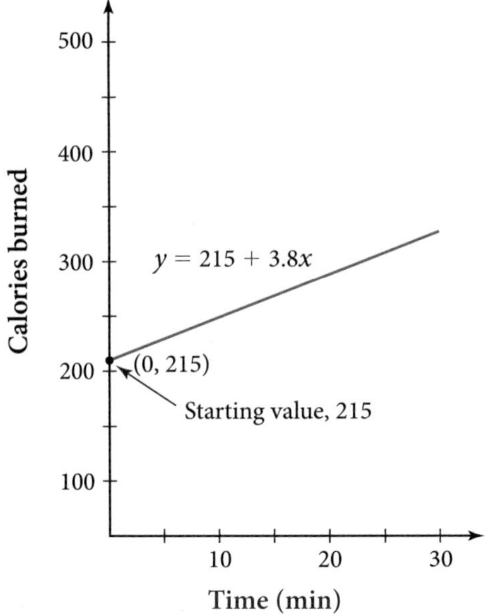

What would happen if Manisha chose a different physical activity before pedaling on the stationary bike?

You looked at direct variation in the form $y = kx$ in Chapter 2. Direct variation equations can also be seen as equations in intercept form. For instance, Sam's trainer tells him that swimming will burn 7.8 calories per minute. When the time spent swimming is zero, the number of calories burned is zero. In intercept form this is modeled by the equation $y = 0 + 7.8x$, or simply $y = 7.8x$. In Manisha's case, the number of calories burned is proportional to the time spent pedaling, or $y = 3.8x$. That is, there's a direct variation between x and y.

For Sam, the constant of variation k is 7.8, the rate at which his body burns calories while he is swimming. It plays the same role as b in $y = a + bx$. What does the a represent? Why is it zero?

EXAMPLE A

Suppose Sam has already burned 325 calories before he begins to swim for his workout. His swim will burn 7.8 calories per minute.

a. Create a table of values for the total calories Sam will burn by swimming for 60 minutes and the calories he will burn after each minute of swimming.

b. Define variables and write an equation in intercept form to describe this relationship.

c. On the same set of axes, graph the equation for total calories burned and the direct variation equation for calories burned by swimming.

d. How are your graphs from part c similar? How are they different?

Solution

a. The total calories burned appear in the third column of the table. Each entry is 325 plus the corresponding entry in the second column.

Sam's Swim

Swimming time (min)	Calories burned by swimming	Total calories burned
0	0	325
1	7.8	332.8
2	15.6	340.6
20	156	481
30	234	559
45	351	676
60	468	793

b. Let y represent the total number of calories burned, and let x represent the number of minutes Sam spends swimming.

$$y = 325 + 7.8x$$

c. The direct variation equation is $y = 7.8x$. Enter this equation and the equation $y = 325 + 7.8x$ into your calculator. Check to see that these equations give the same values as the table by looking at the calculator table.

d. The lower line shows the calories burned by swimming and is a direct variation. The upper line shows the total calories burned. It is 325 units above the first line because, at any particular time, Sam has burned 325 more calories. Both graphs have the same value for b, 7.8 calories per minute. The graphs have the same steepness but different y-intercepts.

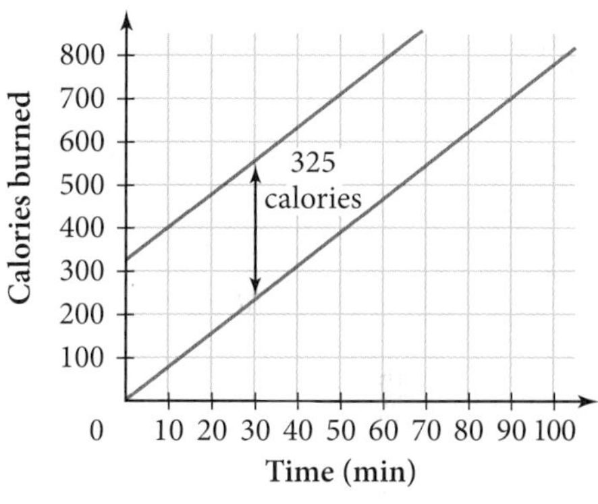

What will different values of a in the equation $y = a + bx$ do to the graph?

EXAMPLE B

A minivan is 220 mi from its destination, Flint. It begins traveling toward Flint at an average speed of 72 mi/h.

a. Define variables and write an equation in intercept form for this relationship.

b. Use your equation to calculate the location of the minivan after 2.5 h.

c. Use your equation to calculate when the minivan will be 130 mi from Flint.

d. Graph the relationship and locate the points that are the solutions to parts b and c.

e. What is the real-world meaning of the rate of change in this relationship? What does the sign of the rate of change indicate?

Solution

a. Let the input variable, x, represent the time in hours since the beginning of the trip. Let y represent the distance in miles between the minivan and Flint. The equation for the relationship is $y = 220 - 72x$.

b. Substitute the time, 2.5 h, for x.

$$y = 220 - 72 \cdot 2.5 = 40$$

So the minivan is 40 mi from Flint.

c. Substitute 130 mi for y and solve the equation $130 = 220 - 72x$. You might start with the equivalent equation $220 + (-72x) = 130$.

Equation: $220 - 72x = 130$			
Description	**Undo**	**Result**	**Equation**
Pick x.		1.25	$x = 1.25$
Multiply by -72.	$/(-72)$	-90	$-72x = -90$
Add 220.	$-(220)$	130	$220 + (-72x) = 130$

The minivan will be 130 mi from Flint after 1.25 h. You can change 0.25 h to minutes using dimensional analysis: $0.25 \text{ h} \cdot \frac{60 \text{ min}}{1 \text{ h}} = 15 \text{ min}$. So you can also write the answer as 1 h 15 min.

d. Set your calculator window to

$$[0, 3.5, 1, 0, 250, 50],$$

graph the equation, and press TRACE and the arrow keys to find the points where $x = 1.25$ and $x = 2.5$.

e. The rate of change indicates the velocity of the car. If it is negative, the minivan is getting closer to Flint. That is, as time increases, the distance decreases. A positive rate of change would mean that the vehicle was moving away from Flint.

In linear equations it is sometimes helpful to say which variable is the input variable and which is the output variable. The horizontal axis represents the input variable, and the vertical axis represents the output variable. In Example B, the input variable, x, represents time, so the x-axis is labeled time, and the output variable, y, represents distance, so the y-axis is labeled distance. What are the input and output variables in the investigation and in Example A?

3.4 Exercises

You will need your graphing calculator for Exercises **3, 6,** and **8.**

Practice Your Skills

1. Match the recursive rules a–d with the equations i–iv.

i. $y = 4 - 3x$ **ii.** $y = 3 + 4x$ **iii.** $y = -3 - 4x$ **iv.** $y = 4 + 3x$

a. 3 ENTER
Ans + 4 ENTER, ENTER, . . . @

b. 4 ENTER
Ans + 3 ENTER, ENTER, . . .

c. −3 ENTER
Ans − 4 ENTER, ENTER, . . .

d. 4 ENTER
Ans − 3 ENTER, ENTER, . . .

2. Write an equation in intercept form that will provide the data values (*jump number, position*) for any number of jumps for the rabbit Percy. Use x for the input variable and y for the output variable.

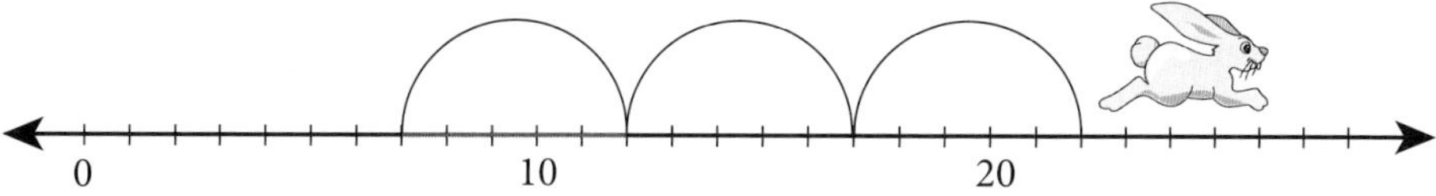

3. You can use the equation $d = 4.7 + 2.8t$ to model a walk in which the distance from a motion sensor, d, is measured in feet and the time, t, is measured in seconds. Graph the equation and use the trace function to find the approximate distance from a motion sensor for each time value given in 3a and b.

a. $t = 12$ s

b. $t = 7.4$ s

c. What is the real-world meaning of 4.7?

d. What is the real-world meaning of 2.8?

4. Undo the order of operations to find the x-value in each equation.

a. @

Equation: $3(x - 5.2) + 7.8 = 14$			
Description	**Undo**	**Result**	**Equation**
Pick x.			$x =$
			$3(x - 5.2) + 7.8 = 14$

b.

Equation: $3.5\left(\frac{x-8}{4}\right) = 2.8$			
Description	**Undo**	**Result**	**Equation**
Pick x.			$x =$
			$3.5\left(\frac{x-8}{4}\right) = 2.8$

5. The equation $y = 35 + 0.8x$ gives the distance a sports car is from Flint after x minutes.

a. How far is the sports car from Flint after 25 minutes?

b. How long will it take until the sports car is 75 miles from Flint? Show how to find the solution using two different methods.

Reason and Apply

6. You can use the equation $d = 24 - 45t$ to model the distance from a destination for someone driving on the highway. The input variable t, for *time*, is measured in hours, and the output variable d, for *distance*, is measured in miles. Graph the equation and use the trace function to find the approximate time for each distance given in 6a and b.

a. $d = 16$ mi ⓐ

b. $d = 3$ mi

c. What is the real-world meaning of 24? ⓐ

d. What is the real-world meaning of 45?

e. Solve the equation $24 - 45t = 16$.

7. The graphs below show the jumps of Percy and Quincy.

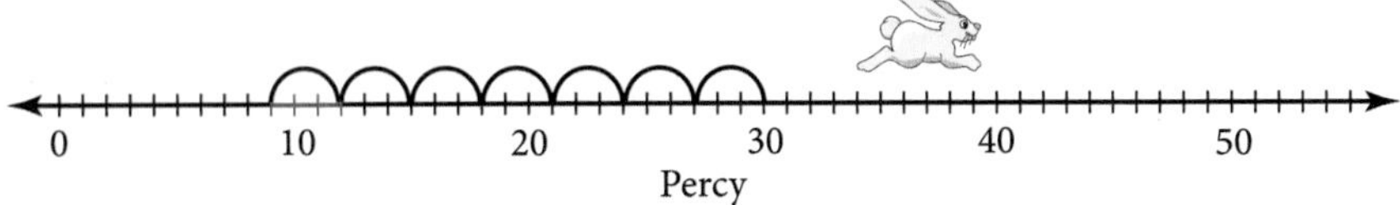

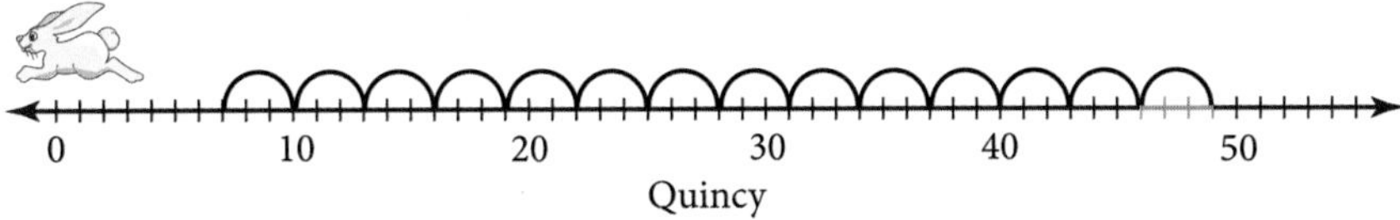

a. Write equations in intercept form that will provide the locations of Percy and Quincy at any jump number. For each rabbit, let x represent the number of jumps, and let y represent the rabbit's location.

b. What is the input variable? The output variable?

c. When do the rabbits pass each other?

8. APPLICATION Louis is beginning a new exercise workout. His trainer shows him a table with his workout time in minutes, the actual workout calories burned, and the target calories he wants to burn.

Time (min)	Actual workout calories burned	Target calories
0	400	700
1	420.7	700
2	441.4	700
3	462.1	700
4	482.8	700
5	503.5	700
6	524.2	700

a. Find how many calories Louis has burned before beginning to run, how many he burns per minute running, and the total calories he wants to burn. ⓗ

b. Write a recursive rule that generates the table values listed for actual workout calories burned. ⓐ

c. Use your recursive rule to write a linear equation in intercept form. Check that your equation generates the table values listed.

d. Write an equation that generates the table values listed for target calories. ⓐ

e. Graph the two equations on your calculator. Your window should show a time of up to 30 minutes. What is the real-world meaning of the y-intercept for the workout equation?

f. Use the trace function to find the approximate coordinates of the point where the lines meet. What is the real-world meaning of this point?

g. Write an equation whose solution gives the number of minutes Louis should run in order to reach his target. Solve your equation.

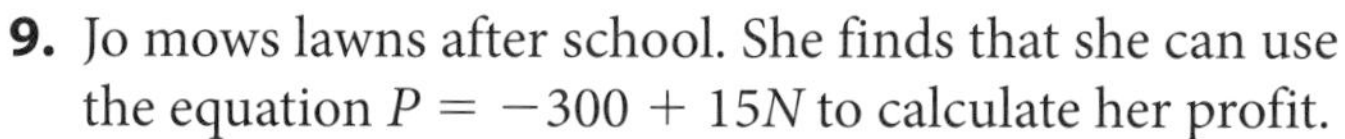

9. Jo mows lawns after school. She finds that she can use the equation $P = -300 + 15N$ to calculate her profit.

a. Give some possible real-world meanings for the numbers -300 and 15 and the variable N.

b. Invent two questions related to this situation and then answer them.

c. Solve the equation $P = -300 + 15N$ for the variable N.

d. What does the equation in 9c tell you?

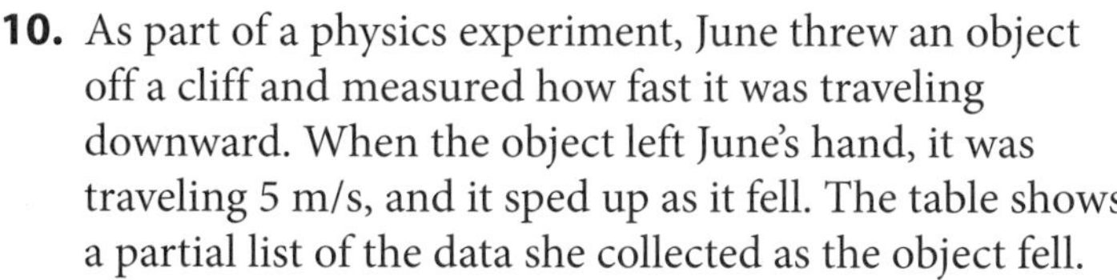

10. As part of a physics experiment, June threw an object off a cliff and measured how fast it was traveling downward. When the object left June's hand, it was traveling 5 m/s, and it sped up as it fell. The table shows a partial list of the data she collected as the object fell.

Time (s)	Speed (m/s)
0	5.0
0.5	9.9
1.0	14.8
1.5	19.7

a. Write an equation to represent the speed of the object. @

b. What was the object's speed after 3 s?

c. If it were possible for the object to fall long enough, how many seconds would pass before it reached a speed of 83.4 m/s? @

d. What limitations do you think this equation has in modeling this situation? @

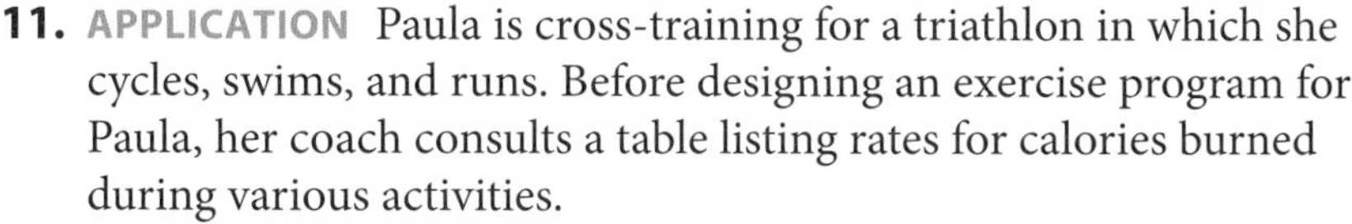

11. APPLICATION Paula is cross-training for a triathlon in which she cycles, swims, and runs. Before designing an exercise program for Paula, her coach consults a table listing rates for calories burned during various activities.

Cross-training activity	Calories burned (per minute)
Bicycling	3.8
Swimming	6.9
Jogging	7.3
Running	11.3

a. On Monday, Paula starts her workout by biking for 30 minutes and then swimming. Write an equation for the number of calories she burns on Monday in terms of the number of minutes she swims.

b. On Wednesday, Paula starts her workout by swimming for 30 minutes and then jogging. Write an equation for the number of calories she burns on Wednesday in terms of the number of minutes she jogs.

c. On Friday, Paula starts her workout by swimming 15 minutes, then biking for 15 minutes, and then running. Write an equation for the number of calories she burns on Friday in terms of the number of minutes she runs.

d. How many total calories does Paula burn on each day described in 11a–c if she does a 60-minute workout?

Review

12. A minivan starts driving toward a distant destination and travels at a constant velocity. The graph shows the time and distance from the destination.

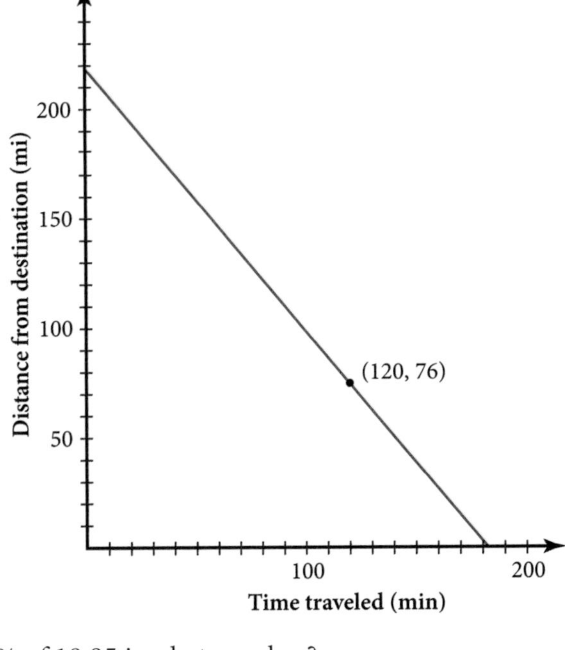

a. How far from its destination was the minivan when it started?

b. The point (120, 76) is on the graph. What is the real-world meaning of this point?

c. How fast is the minivan traveling, in miles per minute?

13. At a family picnic, your cousin tells you that he always has a hard time remembering how to compute percents. Write him a note explaining what *percent* means. Use these problems as examples of how to solve the different types of percent problems, with an answer for each.

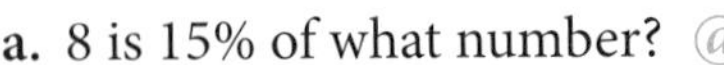

a. 8 is 15% of what number? @

b. 15% of 18.95 is what number?

c. What percent of 64 is 326?

d. 10% of what number is 40?

14. Bjarne is training for a bicycle race by riding on a stationary bicycle with a time-distance readout. He is riding at a constant speed. The graph shows his accumulated distance and the time as he rides.

a. How fast is Bjarne bicycling?

b. Copy and complete the table. @

c. Write a recursive rule for Bjarne's ride.

d. Looking at the graph, how do you know that Bjarne is neither slowing down nor speeding up during his ride?

e. If Bjarne keeps up the same pace, how far will he ride in one hour?

Distance Traveled

Bicyclists race through Sacramento, California.

Time (s)	Distance (m)
0	
1	
2	
3	
4	
5	
6	
7	
8	
9	
10	

15. Match each recursive rule to a graph. Explain how you made your decision and tell what assumptions you made.

i. 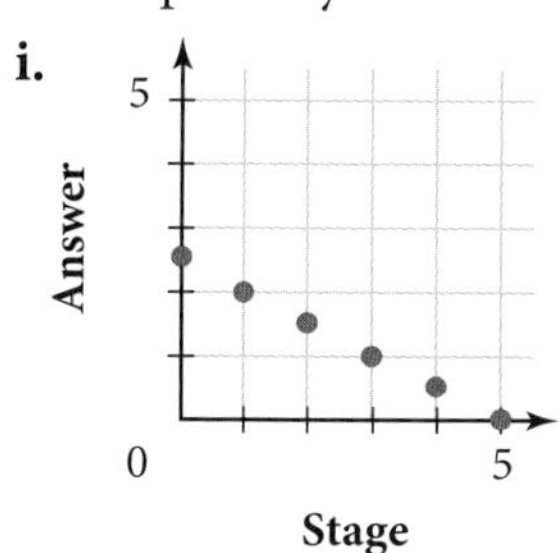

ii. 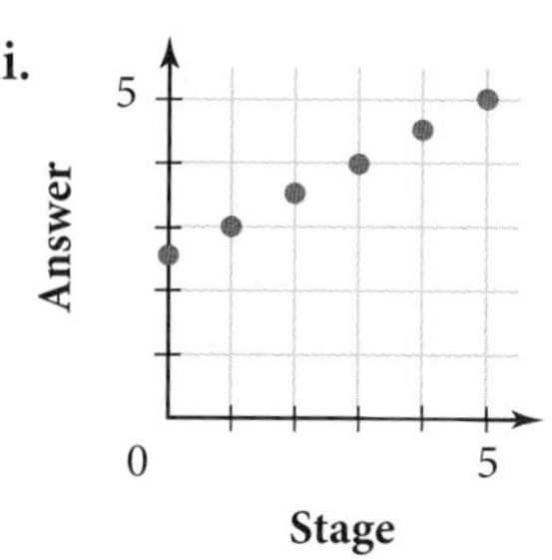

iii. 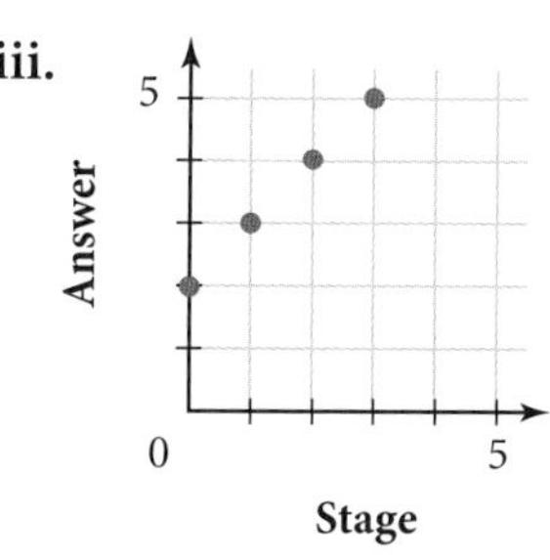

iv. 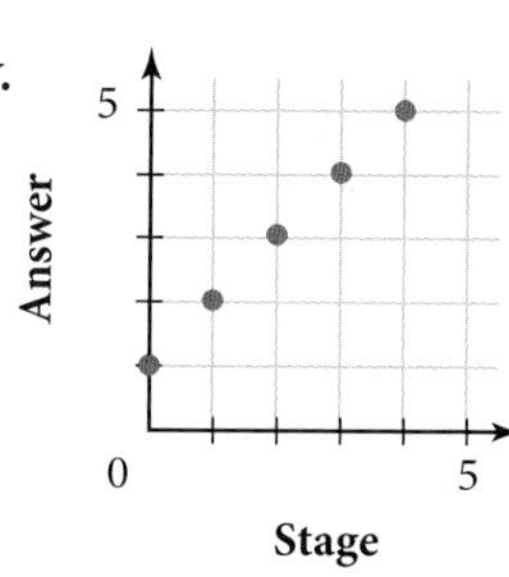

a. 2.5 (ENTER)
Ans + 0.5 (ENTER), (ENTER), . . .

b. 1.0 (ENTER)
Ans + 1.0 (ENTER), (ENTER), . . .

c. 2.0 (ENTER)
Ans + 1.0 (ENTER), (ENTER) . . .

d. 2.5 (ENTER)
Ans − 0.5 (ENTER), (ENTER), . . .

16. APPLICATION Carl has been keeping a record of his gas purchases for his new car. Each time he buys gas, he fills the tank completely. Then he records the number of gallons he bought and the miles since the last fill-up. Here is his record:

a. Copy and complete the table by calculating the ratio of miles per gallon for each purchase.

b. What is the average rate of miles per gallon so far?

c. The car's tank holds 17.1 gallons. To the nearest mile, how far should Carl be able to go without running out of gas?

d. Carl is planning a trip across the United States. He estimates that the trip will be 4230 miles. How many gallons of gas can Carl expect to buy?

Carl's Purchases

Miles traveled	Gallons	$\frac{\text{miles}}{\text{gallon}}$
363	16.2	
342	15.1	
285	12.9	

Many factors influence the rate at which cars use gas, including size, age, and driving conditions. Advertisements for new cars often give the average miles per gallon for city traffic (slow, congested) and highway traffic (fast, free-flowing). These rates help consumers make informed purchases.

17. Consider the expression $\frac{4(y-8)}{3}$.

a. Find the value of the expression for $y = 5$. Make a table to show the order of operations. ⓐ

b. Solve the equation $\frac{4(y-8)}{3} = 8$ by undoing the order of operations. ⓐ

IMPROVING YOUR Reasoning SKILLS

You have two containers of the same size; one contains juice and the other contains water. Remove 1 tablespoon of juice and put it into the water and stir. Then remove 1 tablespoon of the water and juice mixture and put it into the juice. Is there more water in the juice or more juice in the water?

LESSON

3.5

Linear Equations and Rate of Change

"How can it be that mathematics, being after all a product of human thought independent of experience, is so admirably adopted to the objects of reality?"

ALBERT EINSTEIN

In this lesson you will continue to develop your skills with equations, graphs, and tables of data by exploring in more depth the role that the value of b plays in this equation:

$$y = a + bx$$

You have already studied the intercept form of a linear equation in several real-world situations. You have used the intercept form to relate calories to minutes spent exercising, floor heights to floor numbers, and distances to time. So defining variables is an important part of writing equations. Depending on the context of an equation, its numbers take on different real-world meanings. Can you recall how these equations modeled each scenario?

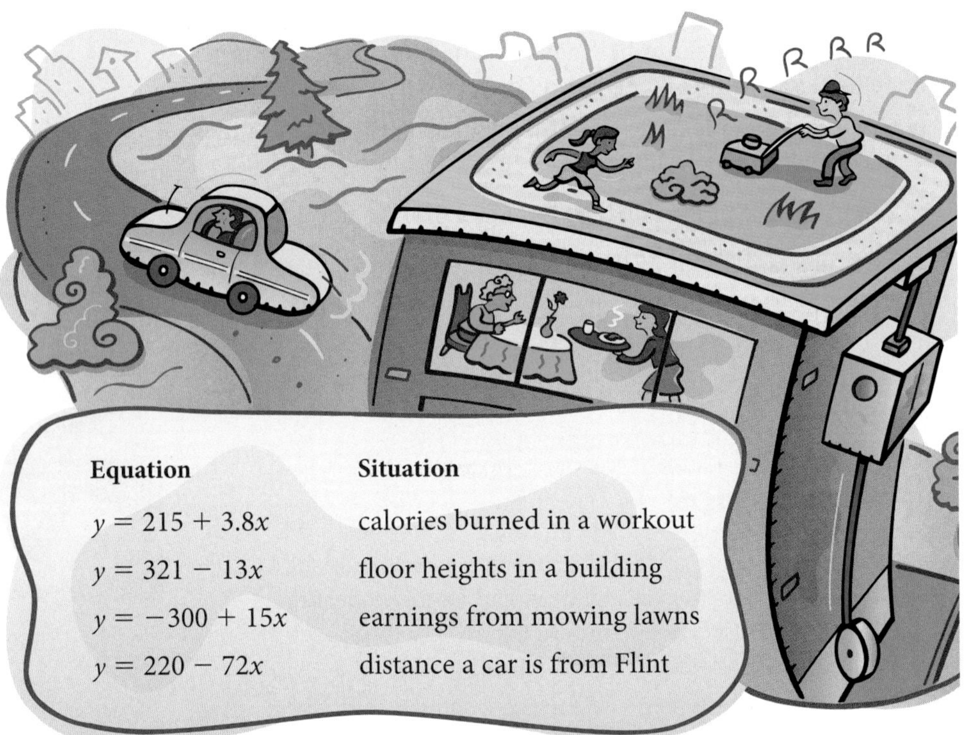

Equation	Situation
$y = 215 + 3.8x$	calories burned in a workout
$y = 321 - 13x$	floor heights in a building
$y = -300 + 15x$	earnings from mowing lawns
$y = 220 - 72x$	distance a car is from Flint

Winds of 40 mi/h blow on North Michigan Ave. in 1955 Chicago.

In most linear equations, there are different output values for different input values. This happens when the coefficient of x is not zero. You'll explore how this coefficient relates input and output values in the examples and the investigation.

In addition to giving the actual temperature, weather reports often indicate the temperature you *feel* as a result of the wind chill factor. The wind makes it feel colder than it actually is. In the next example you will use recursive rules to answer some questions about wind chill.

EXAMPLE A The table relates the approximate wind chills for different actual temperatures when the wind speed is 15 mi/h. Assume the wind chill is a linear relationship for temperatures between $-5°$ and $35°$.

Temperature (°F)	−5	0	5	10	15	20	25	30	35
Wind chill (°F)	−25.8	−19.4	−13			6.2		19	25.4

a. What are the input and output variables?

b. What is the change in temperature from one table entry to the next? What is the corresponding change in the wind chill?

c. Use calculator lists to write a recursive rule that generates the table values. What are the missing entries?

Solution

a. The input variable is the actual air temperature in degrees Fahrenheit. The output variable is the temperature you feel as a result of the wind chill factor.

b. For every 5° increase in temperature, the wind chill increases 6.4°.

c. For some calculators, the recursive rule to complete the missing table values is $\{-5, -25.8\}$ ENTER and $\{\text{Ans}(1) + 5, \text{Ans}(2) + 6.4\}$ ENTER. The calculator screen displays the missing entries.

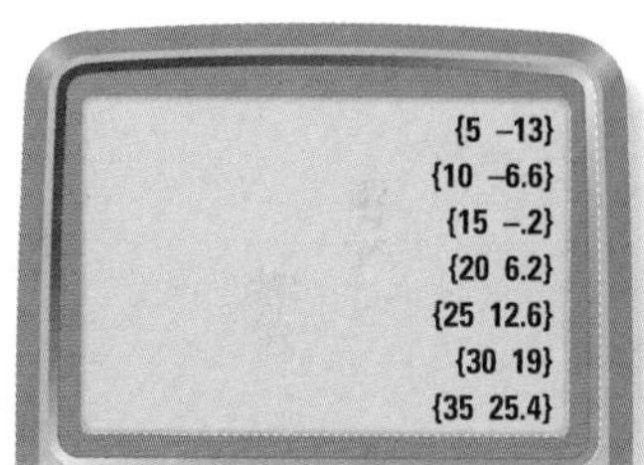

In Example A, the *rate* at which the wind chill drops can be calculated from the ratio $\frac{6.4}{5}$, or $\frac{1.28}{1}$. In other words, it feels 1.28° colder for every 1° drop in air temperature. This number is the rate of change for a wind speed of 15 mi/h.

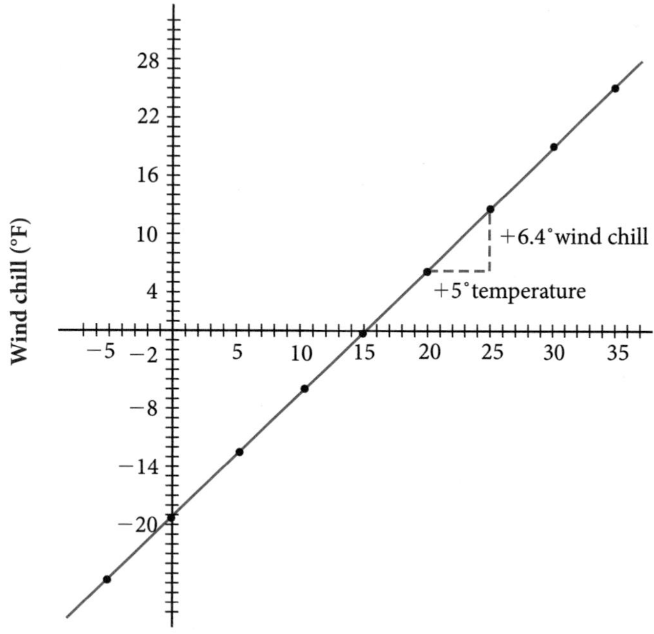

Do you think the rate of change differs with various wind speeds?

Rate of Change

The **rate of change** is equal to the change in output values as the input value increases by 1.

You can calculate the rate of change by dividing the change in output values by the change in input values.

$$b = \frac{\textit{change in output values}}{\textit{change in input values}}$$

In intercept form, the value of b is the rate of change.

$$y = a + bx$$

INVESTIGATION

Wind Chill

In this investigation you'll use the relationship between temperature and wind chill to explore the concept of rate of change and its connections to tables, scatter plots, recursive rules, equations, and graphs.

The data in the table represent the approximate wind chill temperatures in degrees Fahrenheit for a wind speed of 20 mi/h. Use this data set to complete each task.

Temperature (°F)	Wind chill (°F)
−5	−28.540
0	−21.980
1	−20.668
2	−19.356
5	−15.420
15	−2.300
35	23.940

[Data sets: **TMPWS, WNDCH**]

Step 1 Define the input and output variables for this relationship.

Step 2 Plot the points and describe the viewing window you used.

Step 3 Copy this table. Complete the third and fourth columns of the table by recording the changes between consecutive input and output values. Then find the rate of change.

Input	Output	Change in input values	Change in output values	Rate of change
−5	−28.540			
0	−21.980	5	6.56	$\frac{+6.56}{+5} =$
1	−20.668	1	1.312	
2	−19.356		1.312	$\frac{+1.312}{+1} =$
5	−15.420	3		
15	−2.300		13.12	$\frac{+13.12}{+10} =$
35	23.940			

High wind speeds drop temperatures below freezing.

Step 4 Write a recursive rule that gives the pairs of values listed in the table.

Step 5 Use your rule to write a linear equation in intercept form that relates wind chill to temperature. Note that the starting value, −28.540, is not the y-intercept. Where do the numbers in your rule appear in your equation?

Step 6 Graph the equation on the same set of axes as your scatter plot. Use the calculator table to check that your equation is correct. Does it make sense to draw a line through the points? Where does the y-intercept show up in your equation?

Step 7 What do you notice about the values for rate of change listed in your table? How does the rate of change show up in your equation? In your graph?

Step 8 Explain how to use the rate of change to find the actual temperature if the weather report indicates a wind chill of 9.5° with 20 mi/h winds.

EXAMPLE B

This table shows the temperature of the air outside an airplane at different altitudes.

Input	Output
Altitude (m)	Temperature (°C)
1000	7.7
1500	4.2
2200	−0.7
3000	−6.3
4700	−18.2
6000	−27.3

a. Add three columns to the table, and record the change in input values, the change in output values, and the corresponding rate of change.

b. Use the table and a recursive rule to write a linear equation in intercept form, $y = a + bx$.

c. What are the real-world meanings of the values of a and b in your equation?

Solution

a. Record the change in input values, the change in output values, and the rate of change in a table. Note the units of each value.

Input	Output			
Altitude (m)	Temperature (°C)	Changes in input values (m)	Changes in output values (°C)	Rate of change (°C/m)
1000	7.7			
1500	4.2	500	−3.5	$\frac{-3.5}{500} = -0.007$
2200	−0.7	700	−4.9	$\frac{-4.9}{700} = -0.007$
3000	−6.3	800	−5.6	$\frac{-5.6}{800} = -0.007$
4700	−18.2	1700	−11.9	$\frac{-11.9}{1700} = -0.007$
6000	−27.3	1300	−9.1	$\frac{-9.1}{1300} = -0.007$

b. Note that the rate of change is always -0.007, or $\frac{-7}{1000}$. You can also write the rate of change as $\frac{-0.7}{100}$, so this recursive rule models the relationship:

{1000, 7.7} ENTER

{Ans(1) + 100, Ans(2) − 0.7} ENTER

Working this rule backward, {Ans(1) − 100, Ans(2) + 0.7}, will eventually give the result {0, 14.7}. So the intercept form of the equation is $y = 14.7 - 0.007x$, where x represents the altitude in meters and y represents the air temperature in degrees Celsius.

Note that the starting value of the recursive rule is not the same as the value of the y-intercept in the equation.

c. The value of a, 14.7, is the temperature (in degrees Celsius) of the air at sea level. The value of b indicates that the temperature drops 0.007°C for each meter that a plane climbs.

3.5 Exercises

You will need your graphing calculator for Exercises **5d** and **10.**

Practice Your Skills

1. Copy and complete the table of input and output values for each equation.

a. $y = 50 + 2.5x$ @

Input x	Output y
20	
−30	
16	
15	
−12.5	

b. $y = -5.2 - 10x$

Input x	Output y
0	
−8	
24	
−35	
−5.2	

c. $y = 4.7 + 3x$

Input x	Output y
	−10
	−2
	4.7
	6.2
	21

2. Use the equation $w = -29 + 1.4t$, where t is temperature and w is wind chill—both in degrees Fahrenheit—to approximate the wind chill temperatures for a wind speed of 40 mi/h.

a. Find w for $t = 32°$.

b. Find t for $w = -8$. @

c. What is the real-world meaning of 1.4? @

d. What is the real-world meaning of -29?

3. Describe what the rate of change looks like in each graph.

a. The graph of a person walking at a steady rate toward a motion sensor @

b. The graph of a person standing still

c. The graph of a person walking at a steady rate away from a motion sensor

d. The graph of one person walking at a steady rate faster than another person

4. Using the input variable x and the output variable y, sketch a graph picturing Percy's location over time if he starts at 34 and moves 6 units to the left with each jump.

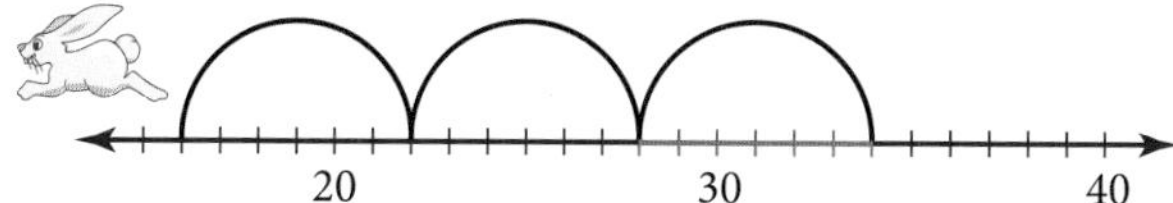

Reason and Apply

5. Each table shows a different input-output relationship.

i.

Input	Output
0	−6
1	−2.5
2	1
3	4.5
4	8

ii.

Input	Output
−1	−7
0	1
3	25
5	41
7	57

iii.

Input	Output
−8	34.2
−7	32.8
−3	27.2
2	20.2
8	11.8

a. Find the rate of change for the values in each table. Explain how you found this value.

b. For each table, find the output value that corresponds to the input value zero. What is this value called?

c. Use your results from 5a and 5b to write an equation in intercept form for each table.

d. Use a calculator list of input values to check that each equation actually produces the output values shown in the table.

6. Each table shows pairs of input and output values for some equation. Find the equation. Explain how you got your equation. For more practice, run the INOUT game on your calculator. [▸ Use the link in your ebook to download the program file INOUT. ◂]

a.

x	y
0	7
1	11
2	15
3	19
4	24

b.

x	y
0	28
1	17
2	6
3	−5
4	−16

c.

x	y
0	−4
1	4
2	12
3	20
4	28

7. The wind chill temperatures for a wind speed of 35 mi/h are given in the table.

Temperature (°F)	−5	5	10	20	35
Wind chill (°F)	−35	−21	−14	0	21

a. Define input and output variables. ⓐ

b. Find the rate of change. Explain how you got your answer. ⓐ

c. Write an equation in intercept form. ⓐ

d. Plot the points and graph the equation on the same set of axes. How are the graphs for the points and the equation similar? How are they different?

8. Samantha's and Darren's walks were recorded by a motion sensor. Each walk is represented here.

a. Write an equation for each walk in the form *distance from sensor* = *start distance* + *change*. ⓗ

b. If Samantha and Darren keep walking at the same rate, which of them will pass the sensor first?

Samantha's Walk

Time (s)	Distance (m)
0	4.0
2	3.4
6	2.2

Darren's Walk

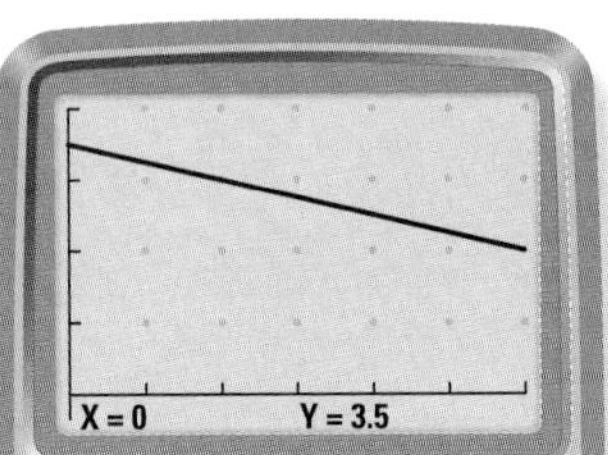

9. You can use the equation $7.3x = 200$ to describe a rectangle with area 200 square units, like the one shown. What are the real-world meanings of the numbers and the variable in the equation? Solve the equation for x, and explain the meaning of your solution. Is the rectangle drawn to scale? How can you tell?

200 square units

7.3 units

x units

10. Use the "Medium" setting of the INOUT game on your calculator to produce four data tables. Copy each table and write the equation you used to match the data values in the table. [▶ Use the link in your ebook to download the program file INOUT. ◀]

Review

11. Fill in the empty cells in each table to find the missing equation and its solution.

a.

Equation:			
Description	**Undo**	**Result**	**Equation**
Pick x.	//////		$x =$
Multiply by 0.8.			
Add 35.		153	

b.

Equation:			
Description	**Undo**	**Result**	**Equation**
Pick x.	//////		$x =$
Multiply by −1.2.			
Add 220.		35	

12. Show how you can solve these equations for x by using an undoing process. Check your results by substituting the solutions into the original equations.

a. $-15 = -52 + 1.6x$

b. $7 - 3x = 52$

c. $6x + 7y = 42$

d. $189 - 1.2(x - 26) = 0$

13. Evaluate each expression for the given value of x. Be sure to follow the order of operations.

a. $3 + 4x - 7, x = -2$ b. $3(x + 5) - 2(x - 8), x = 6$ c. $10 - 4(x + 9), x = -12$

14. Today while Don was swimming, he started wondering how many lengths he would have to swim in order to swim different distances. At one end of the pool, he stopped, gasping for breath, and asked the lifeguard. She told him that 1 length of the pool is 25 yards and that 72 lengths is 1 mile. As he continued swimming, he wondered:

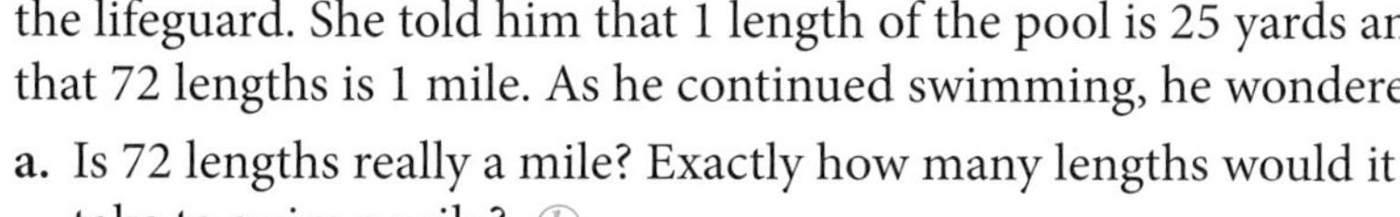

a. Is 72 lengths really a mile? Exactly how many lengths would it take to swim a mile?

b. If it took him a total of 40 minutes to swim a mile, what was his average speed in feet per second?

c. How many lengths would it take to swim a kilometer?

d. Last summer Don got to swim in a pool that was 25 meters long. How many lengths would it take to swim a kilometer there? How many for a mile?

15. APPLICATION Holly has joined a video rental club. After paying a membership fee of \$6 a year, she then has to pay only \$1.25 for each new release she rents.

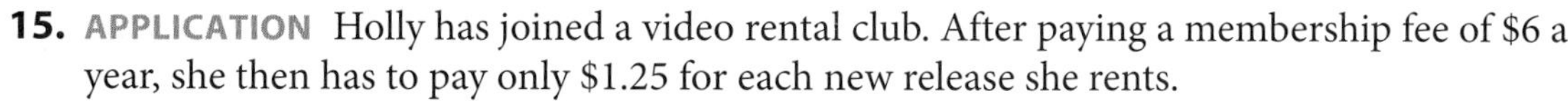

a. Write an equation in intercept form to represent Holly's cost for movie rentals.

b. Graph this situation for up to 60 movie rentals.

c. Video Unlimited charges \$60 for a year of unlimited movie rentals. How many movies would Holly have to rent for this to be a better deal?

16. APPLICATION To plan a trip downtown, you compare the costs of three different parking lots. ABC Parking charges \$5 for the first hour and \$2 for each additional hour or fraction of an hour. Cozy Car charges \$3 per hour or fraction of an hour, and The Corner Lot charges a \$15 flat rate for a whole day.

a. Make a table similar to the one shown. Write recursive rules to calculate the cost of parking up to 10 hours at each of the three lots.

b. Make three different scatter plots on the same pair of axes showing the parking rates at the three different lots. Use a different color for each parking lot. Put the hours on the horizontal axis and the cost on the vertical axis.

c. Compare the three scatter plots. Under what conditions is each parking lot the best deal for your trip? Use the graph to explain.

d. Would it make sense to draw a line through each set of points? Explain why or why not.

Hours parked	ABC Parking	Cozy Car	The Corner Lot
1			
2			
3			

LESSON

3.6

Solving Equations Using the Balancing Method

"Thinking in words slows you down and actually decreases comprehension in much the same way as walking a tightrope too slowly makes one lose one's balance."

LENORE FLEISCHER

In the previous two lessons, you learned about rate of change and the intercept form of a linear equation. In this lesson you'll learn symbolic methods to solve these equations. You've already seen the calculator methods of tracing on a graph and zooming in on a table. These methods usually give approximate solutions. Working backward to undo operations is a symbolic method that gives exact solutions. Another symbolic method that you can apply to solve equations is the **balancing method.** In this lesson you'll investigate how to use the balancing method to solve linear equations. You'll discover that it's closely related to the undoing method.

INVESTIGATION

YOU WILL NEED

- pennies
- three paper cups

Balancing Pennies

Here is a visual model of the equation $2x + 3 = 7$. A cup represents the variable x, and pennies represent numbers. Assume that each cup has the same number of pennies in it and that the containers themselves are weightless.

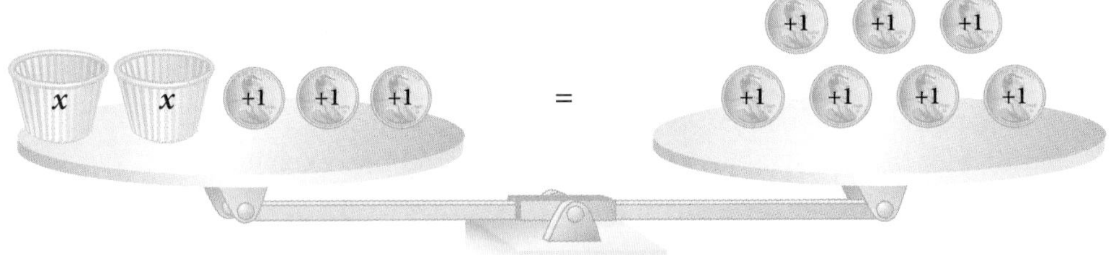

Step 1 How many pennies must be in each cup if the left side of the scale balances with the right side? Explain how you got your answer.

Your answer to Step 1 is the solution to the equation $2x + 3 = 7$. It's the number that can replace x to make the statement true. In Steps 2 and 3, you'll use pictures and equations to show stages that lead to the solution.

Step 2 Redraw the model, but with three pennies removed from each side of the scale. Write the equation that your picture represents.

Step 3 Redraw the model, this time showing half of what was on each side of the scale in Step 2. There should be just one cup on the left side of the scale and the correct number of pennies on the right side needed to balance it. Write the equation that this picture represents. This is the solution to the original equation.

Now your group will create a pennies-and-cups equation for another group to solve.

Step 4 Divide the pennies into two equal piles. If you have one penny left over, put it aside. Draw a large equal sign (or form one with two pencils), and place the penny stacks on opposite sides of it.

Step 5 From the pile on one side of your equal sign, make three identical stacks, leaving at least a few pennies out of the stacks. Hide each stack under a paper cup. You should now have three cups and some pennies on one side of your equal sign.

Step 6 On the other side you should have a pile of pennies. On both sides of the equal sign you have the same number of pennies, but on one side some of the pennies are hidden under cups. You can think of the two sides of the equal sign as being the two sides of a balance scale. Write an equation for this setup, using x to represent the number of pennies hidden under one cup.

Step 7 Move to another group's setup. Look at their arrangement of pennies and cups, and write an equation for it. Solve the equation; that is, find how many pennies are under one cup without looking. When you're sure you know how many pennies are under a group's cups, you can look to check your answer.

Step 8 Write a brief description of how you solved the equation.

You can do problems like those in the investigation using a balance scale as long as the weight of the cup is very small. But an actual balance scale can only model equations in which all the numbers involved are positive. The idea of balancing equations can also apply to equations involving negative numbers. Just remember, when you add any number to its opposite, you get 0. For this reason, the opposite of a number is called the **additive inverse.** Think of negative and positive numbers as having opposite effects on a balance scale. You can remove 0 from either side of a balance-scale picture without affecting the balance. These three figures all represent 0:

$1 + (-1) = 0$

$x\ x + (-x\ -x) = 0$

$-1\ -1\ -1 + +1\ +1\ +1 = 0$

Additive Inverses

Two numbers whose sum is zero are additive inverses. Multiply a value by -1 to determine its additive inverse. The additive inverse of a is $-a$, and the additive inverse of $-a$ is a, because $a + (-a) = 0$.

EXAMPLE A | Draw balance-scale pictures to solve the equation $6 = -2 + 4x$.

Solution | The goal is to end up with a single x-cup on one side of the balance scale. One way to get rid of something on one side is to add its opposite to both sides.

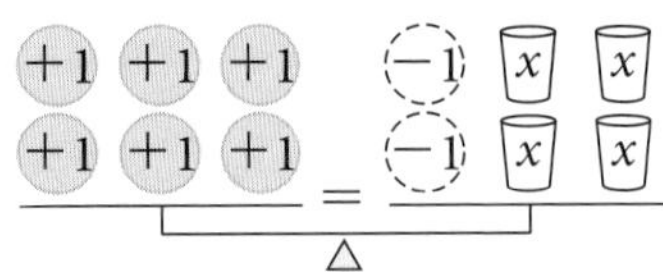

Here is the equation $6 = -2 + 4x$ solved by the balancing method:

Picture	Action taken	Equation
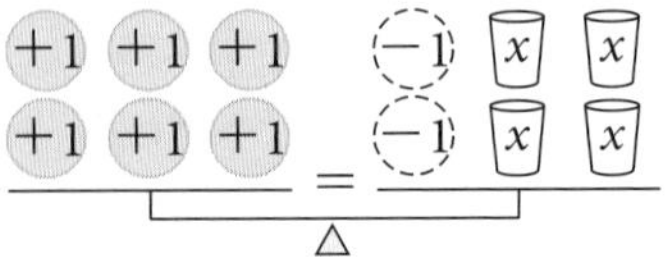	Original equation.	$6 = -2 + 4x$
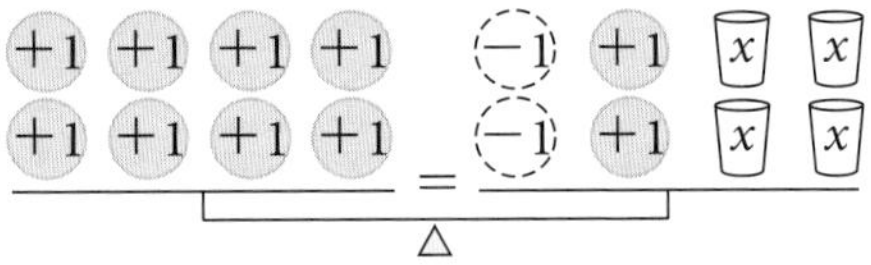	Add 2 to both sides.	$6 + 2 = -2 + 2 + 4x$
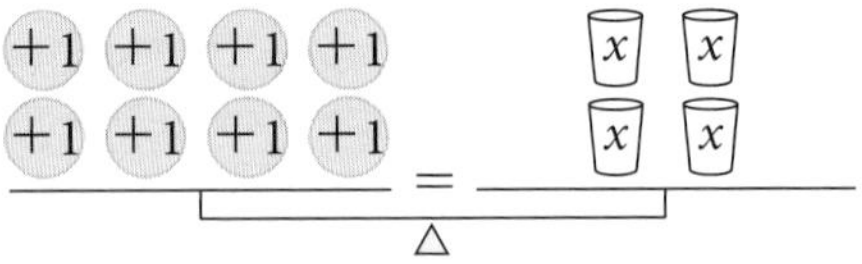	Remove the zero.	$8 = 4x$
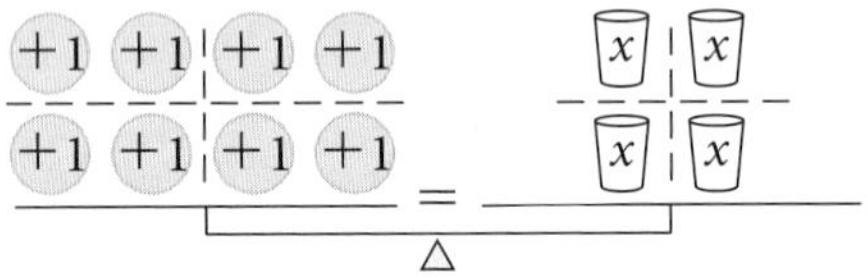	Divide both sides by 4.	$\frac{8}{4} = \frac{4x}{4}$
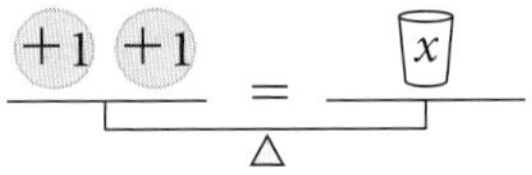	Simplify.	$2 = x$ or $x = 2$

In the second and third equations, you saw $6 + 2$ combine to 8 and $-2 + 2$ combine to 0. You can combine numbers because they are *like terms.* However, in the first equation, you could not combine -2 and $4x$, because they are *not* like terms.

Like Terms

Like terms are terms in which the variable and the exponent are the same. Their coefficients can differ, but their variables and exponents must match. Examples of pairs of like terms are $4y$ and $7y$, 6 and -2, and x^2 and $3x^2$.

Balance-scale pictures can help you see what to do to solve an equation by the balancing method. But you won't need the pictures once you get the idea of doing the same thing to both sides of an equation. And pictures are less useful if the numbers in the equation aren't "nice."

EXAMPLE B

Solve the equation $-31 = -50.25 + 1.55x$ using each method.

a. the balancing method

b. undoing operations

Solution

Both of these methods will give the same answer, but notice the differences between them. When might you prefer to use a particular method?

a. the balancing method

$-31 = -50.25 + 1.55x$	Original equation.
$-31 + 50.25 = -50.25 + 50.25 + 1.55x$	Add 50.25 to both sides.
$19.25 = 1.55x$	Combine like terms. (Evaluate and remove the 0.)
$\frac{19.25}{1.55} = \frac{1.55x}{1.55}$	Divide both sides by 1.55.
$12.42 \approx x$, or $x \approx 12.42$	Simplify.

b. undoing operations

This extended table shows the undoing method that you've been using and how it is related to balancing equations. In the last two columns, as you work up from the bottom, you can see how the equation changes as you apply the "undo" operation to both sides of the equation.

Equation: $-31 = -50.25 + 1.55x$			
Description	**Undo**	**Equation**	**Balance step**
Pick x.		$12.42 \approx x$	Divide both sides by 1.55.
Multiply by 1.55.	/ (1.55)	$19.25 = 1.55x$	Add 50.25 to both sides.
Subtract 50.25.	+ (50.25)	$-31 = -50.25 + 1.55x$	Original equation.

In parts a and b, if you convert the answer to a fraction, you get an exact solution, $\frac{385}{31}$.

You improve your equation-solving skills when you consider multiple approaches. Calculator graphs and tables provide approximate and sometimes exact solutions, and the "picture" provided by a graph can be valuable. The balancing and undoing methods use the same process of working backward to get an exact solution.

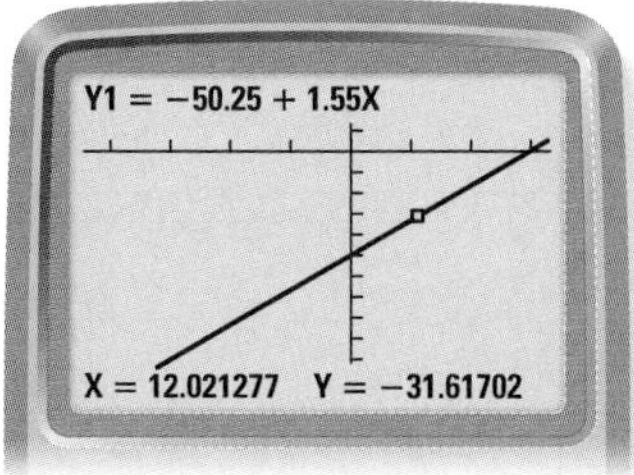

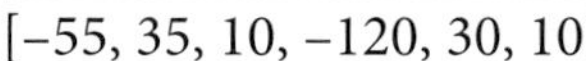

[−55, 35, 10, −120, 30, 10]

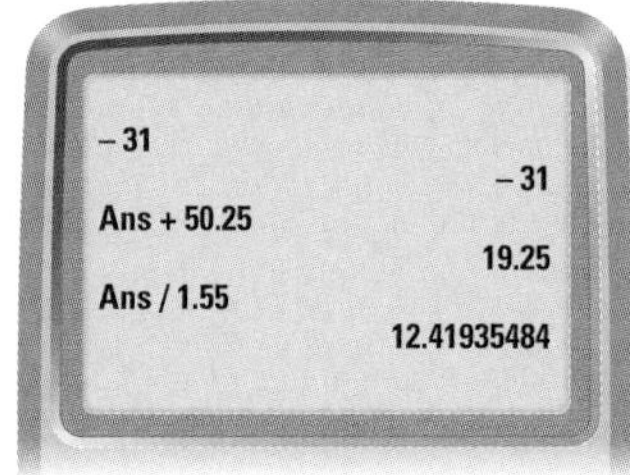

When the variable appears on both sides of the equation, the undoing method is tricky. In the next example, you'll see how the balancing method works in such a case.

EXAMPLE C

Use the balancing method to determine when the green minivan and the red sports car from Lesson 3.2 meet. Recall that the minivan starts at the Mackinac Bridge, 220 mi north of Flint, and travels south toward Flint at 72 mi/h. The red sports car leaves Saginaw, 35 mi north of Flint, and drives north toward the bridge at 48 mi/h.

Solution

The two vehicles will meet when they are the same distance from Flint. This means the expression representing the minivan's distance from Flint, $220 - 72x$, will be equal to the expression representing the sports car's distance from Flint, $35 + 48x$. You will need to get the variable terms on one side of the equation and the constant terms on the other side, and then simplify.

$220 - 72x = 35 + 48x$	Original equation.
$220 - 72x + 72x = 35 + 48x + 72x$	Add $72x$ to both sides.
$220 = 35 + 120x$	Combine like terms.
$220 - 35 = 35 - 35 + 120x$	Subtract 35 from both sides.
$185 = 120x$	Combine like terms.
$\frac{185}{120} = \frac{120x}{120}$	Divide both sides by 120.
$1.542 \approx x$	Simplify.

The vehicles meet after about 1.542 hours, or 92.5 minutes.

Whenever possible, outline the order of operations as you begin to solve an equation. If the variable appears more than once in your equation, find a way to maintain the balance or combine like terms so the variable appears only once

3.6 Exercises

You will need your graphing calculator for Exercises **8** and **14.**

Practice Your Skills

1. Give the equation that each picture models.

a. ⓐ

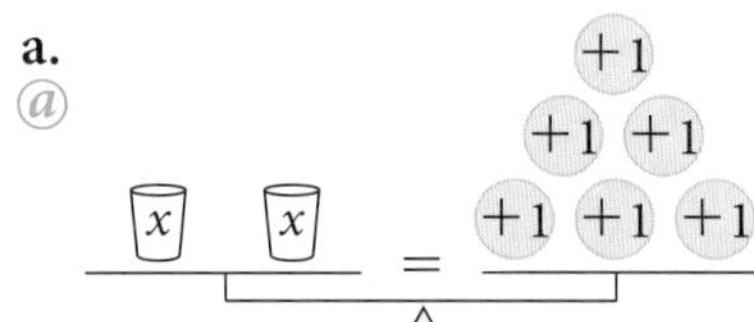

b.

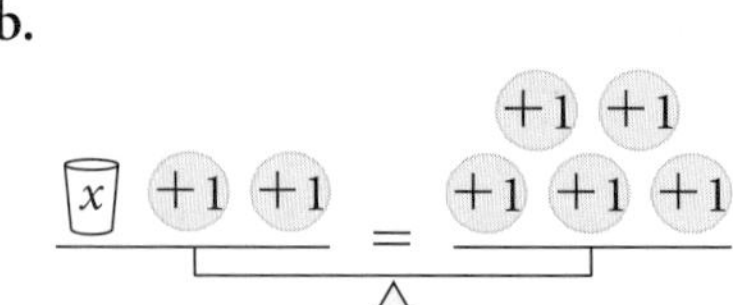

c.

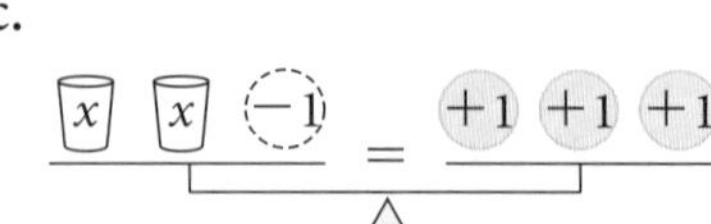

d.

2. Copy and fill in the table to solve the equation as in Example A.

Picture	Action taken	Equation
x x (−1) (−1) = (+1) (+1) (+1) (+1)	Original equation.	
	Add 2 to both sides.	
x x = (+1) (+1) (+1) (+1) (+1) (+1)		
	Divide both sides by 2.	$\frac{2x}{2} = \frac{6}{2}$
	Simplify.	

3. Give the next stages of the equation, matching the action taken, to reach the solution.

a. $0.1x + 12 = 2.2$ @

Original equation.
Subtract 12 from both sides.
Combine like terms.
Divide both sides by 0.1.
Simplify.

b. $\frac{12 + 3.12x}{3} = -100$

Original equation.
Multiply both sides by 3.
Subtract 12 from both sides.
Combine like terms.
Divide both sides by 3.12.
Simplify.

4. Solve these equations. Tell what action you take at each stage.

a. $144x = 12$

b. $\frac{1}{6}x + 2 = 8$

c. $\frac{1}{8}x + 5 = 15$

d. $7x - \frac{2}{3} = \frac{5}{6}$

e. $75 - 9x = 47$

f. $14 + 11x = -29$

5. Give the additive inverse of each number.

a. $\frac{1}{5}$ @

b. 17

c. -2.3

d. $-x$

Reason and Apply

6. A **multiplicative inverse** is a number or expression that you can multiply something by to get a value of 1. The multiplicative inverse of 4 is $\frac{1}{4}$ because $4 \cdot \frac{1}{4} = 1$. Give the multiplicative inverse of each number.

a. 12 @ b. $\frac{1}{6}$ c. 0.02 d. $-\frac{1}{2}$

7. You can solve an equation such as $a + bx = c$ for x with an undoing process. Subtract a and then divide the result by b. If b is a fraction, it might be easier to think of multiplying by its multiplicative inverse rather than dividing. Solve these equations and state what action you take at each stage.

a. $15 + 144x = 27$ b. $\frac{1}{5}x - 2 = 6$ c. $-5 + \frac{2}{3}x = 4$ d. $\frac{4}{3} - \frac{3}{2}x = \frac{2}{3}$

8. MINI-INVESTIGATION A solution to the equation $-10 + 3x = 5$ is shown.

$$-10 + 3x = 5$$
$$3x = 15$$
$$x = 5$$

a. Describe the steps that transform the original equation into the second equation and the second equation into the third (the solution).

b. Graph $y = -10 + 3x$ and $y = 5$ on your calculator, and trace to the lines' intersection. Write the coordinates of this point.

c. Graph $y = 3x$ and $y = 15$, and trace to the lines' intersection. Write the coordinates of this point.

d. Graph $y = x$ and $y = 5$, and trace to the lines' intersection. Write the coordinates of this point.

e. What do you notice about your answers to 8b–d? Explain what this illustrates.

9. Give the inequality represented by each unbalanced scale.

a.

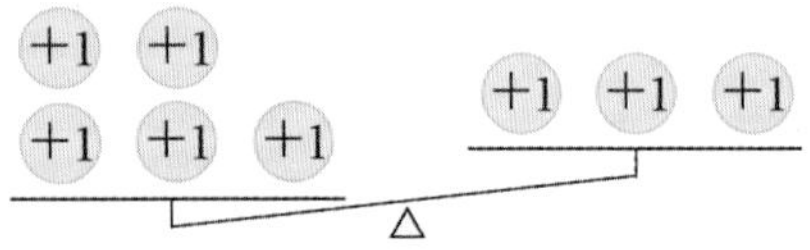

b.

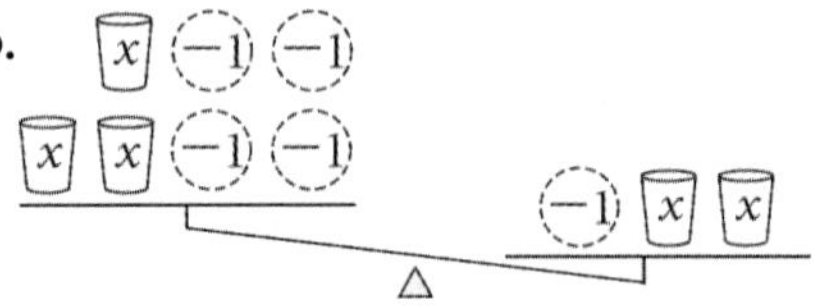

c.

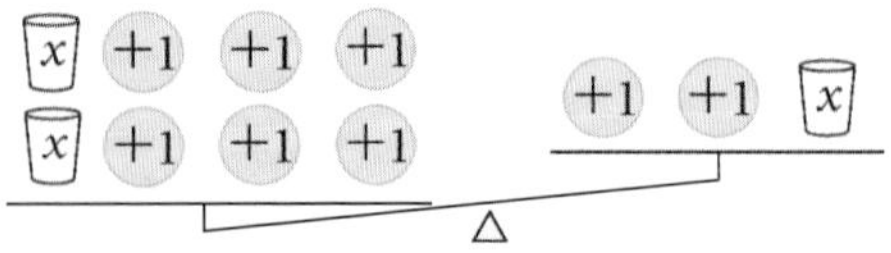

10. Solve the equation $4 + 1.2x = 12.4$ by using each method.

a. balancing b. undoing

11. Solve each equation symbolically using the balancing method.

a. $3 + 2x = 17$ @

b. $0.5x + 2.2 = 101.0$

c. $x + 307.2 = 2.1$

d. $2(2x + 2) = 7$

e. $\frac{4 + 0.01x}{6.2} - 6.2 = 0$ @

f. $5(x + 8) - 7 = 13$

g. $\frac{5 - 7x}{11} + \frac{2}{3} = \frac{5}{3}$

h. $\frac{2(3x + 1) - 4}{5} = 6$

i. $11 - 4(2x + 6) = 47$

12. You can solve familiar formulas for a specific variable. For example, solving $A = lw$ for l, you get

$A = lw$	Original equation.
$\frac{A}{w} = \frac{lw}{w}$	Divide both sides by w.
$\frac{A}{w} = l$	Simplify.

You can also write $l = \frac{A}{w}$. Try solving these formulas for the given variable.

a. $C = 2\pi r$ for r @

b. $A = \frac{1}{2}(hb)$ for h

c. $P = 2(l + w)$ for l @

d. $P = 4s$ for s

e. $d = rt$ for t

f. $A = \frac{1}{2}h(a + b)$ for h

13. An equation can have the variable on both sides. In these cases you can maintain the balance by eliminating the x's from one of the sides before you begin undoing.

a. Copy and complete this table to solve the equation. @

Picture	Action taken	Equation
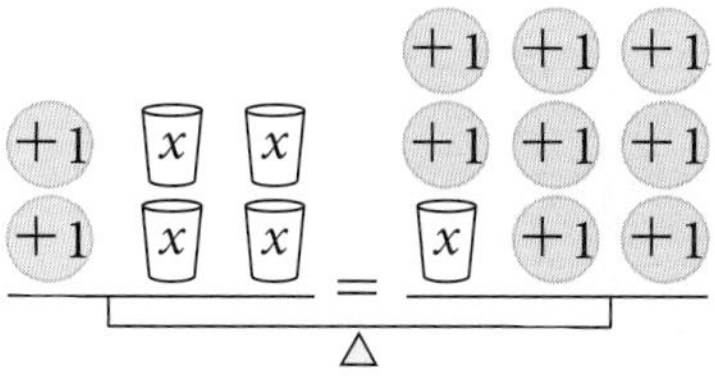	Original equation.	$2 + 4x = x + 8$
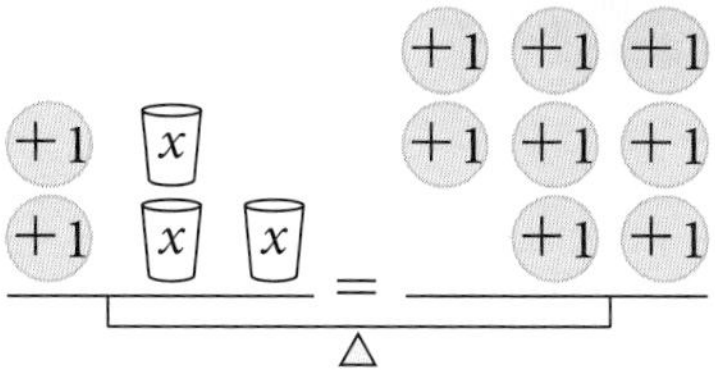		
		$3x = 6$
	Divide both sides by 3.	

b. Show the steps used to solve $5x - 4 = 2x + 5$ using the balancing method. Substitute your solution into the original equation to check your answer.

Review

14. Find the equation of a line through two points.

a. 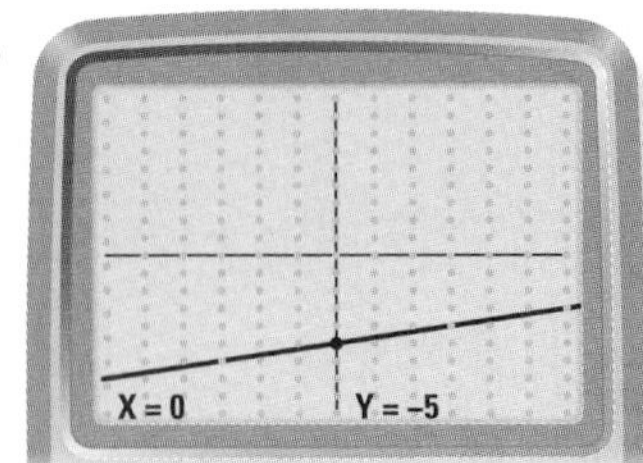

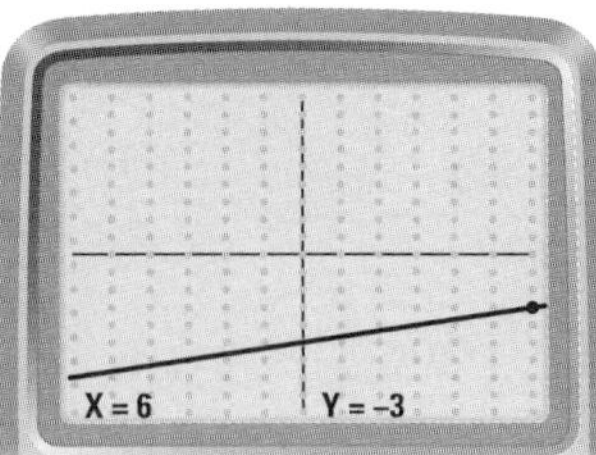

b. For more practice, run the easy level of the LINES program on your calculator. [▶ Use the link in your ebook to download the program file LINES. ◀]

15. The local bagel store sells a baker's dozen of bagels for \$6.49, while the grocery store down the street sells a bag of 6 bagels for \$2.50.

a. Copy and complete the tables showing the cost of bagels at the two stores.

Bagel Store

Bagels	13	26	39	52	65	78
Cost						

Grocery Store

Bagels	6	12	18	24	30	36	42	48	54	60
Cost										

b. Find equations to describe the cost of bagels at each store.

c. Graph the information for each market on the same coordinate axes. Put bagels on the horizontal axis and cost on the vertical axis.

d. Looking at the graphs, how can you tell which store is the cheaper place to buy bagels? How could you reach the same conclusion by looking only at the equations?

Evaluating Formulas

You will frequently encounter formulas in your life. You will need to use your algebra skills to evaluate formulas and solve them for different variables depending on your situation and purpose. As you do this, you'll need to remember the basic mathematical properties of equality and the order of operations.

EXAMPLE A

Use a formula to answer each question.

a. You are installing baseboard in your rectangular bedroom. The formula for the perimeter of a rectangle in terms of its width, w, and length, l, is $p = 2w + 2l$. Your bedroom has width 7 ft and length 9 ft. How much baseboard do you need to buy?

b. You are covering a square-based box with fabric. The formula for the surface area of a square prism in terms of its base length, b, and height, h, is $A = 2b^2 + 4bh$. Your box has base length 8 cm and height 10 cm. How much fabric should you purchase if you don't want any left over?

c. The formula for the distance between two points on a graph is $d = \sqrt{(x_2 - x_1)^2 + (y_2 - y_1)^2}$. If the first point, (x_1, y_1), is at (4, 8), and the second point, (x_2, y_2), is at (7, 12), what is the distance between the two points?

Solution

In each case, substitute the given values and evaluate. Pay close attention to the order of operations.

a.

$p = 2w + 2l$	Original equation.
$= 2(7) + 2(9)$	Substitute the given values.
$= 14 + 18$	Multiply.
$= 32$ ft	Add. Include the units.

b.

$A = 2b^2 + 4bh$	Original equation.
$= 2(8)^2 + 4(8)(10)$	Substitute the given values.
$= 2(64) + 320$	Multiply.
$= 128 + 320$	Simplify.
$= 448 \text{ cm}^2$	Add. Include the units.

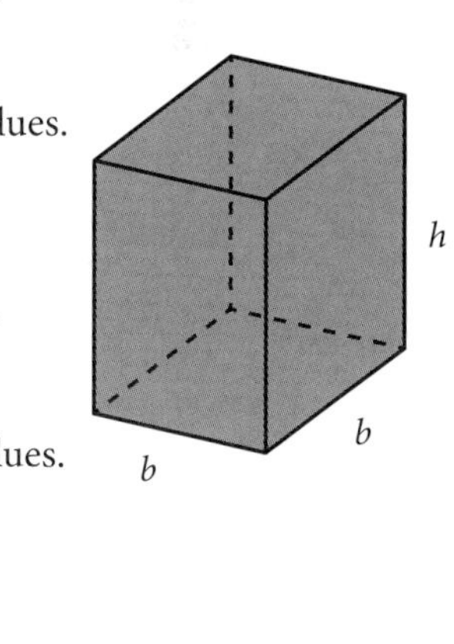

c.

$d = \sqrt{(x_2 - x_1)^2 + (y_2 - y_1)^2}$	Original equation.
$= \sqrt{(7 - 4)^2 + (12 - 8)^2}$	Substitute the given values.
$= \sqrt{3^2 + 4^2}$	Simplify both terms.
$= \sqrt{9 + 16}$	Square both terms.
$= \sqrt{25}$	Simplify.
$= 5$	Take the square root.

The order of operations was important in evaluating each formula correctly.

When you evaluate more complicated formulas, you have to be especially careful to use mathematical properties correctly.

EXAMPLE B

You will use some formulas routinely in your math classes and beyond. You have seen these formulas previously. Substitute the given values and solve for the missing variable.

a. $A = \frac{1}{2}(hb)$. Given $A = 12$ and $b = 4$, find h.

b. $b = \frac{(y_2 - y_1)}{(x_2 - x_1)}$. Given $b = 1.5$, $x_1 = 3$, $x_2 = 7$, and $y_2 = 5$, find y_1.

c. $A = (1 + r)^x$. Given $A = 27$ and $r = 2$, find x.

Solution

Substitute the given values and simplify to find the value of the requested variable.

a. $A = \frac{1}{2}(hb)$	Original equation.
$12 = \frac{1}{2}(h \cdot 4)$	Substitute 12 for A and 4 for b.
$24 = 4h$	Multiply both sides by 2. Simplify the right side.
$6 = h$	Divide both sides by 4.
b. $b = \frac{(y_2 - y_1)}{(x_2 - x_1)}$	Original equation.
$1.5 = \frac{(5 - y_1)}{(7 - 3)}$	Substitute 1.5 for b, 3 for x_1, 7 for x_2, and 5 for y_2.
$1.5 = \frac{5 - y_1}{4}$	Simplify.
$4 \cdot 1.5 = 5 - y_1$	Multiply both sides by 4 to undo the division.
$6 = 5 - y_1$	Simplify.
$1 = -y_1$	Subtract 5 from both sides.
$-1 = y_1$	Multiply both sides by -1.
c. $A = (1 + r)^x$	Original equation.
$27 = (1 + 2)^x$	Substitute 27 for A and 2 for r.
$27 = 3^x$	Simplify.
$3^3 = 3^x$	Substitute $3^3 = 27$.
$x = 3$	When the bases are the same, the exponents must be the same.

In Chapter 4 you will learn about a special notation used in some formulas.

Exercises

1. Substitute the given values into the given formula and solve to find the requested value.

a. The distance a rock falls when dropped: $d = \frac{1}{2}at^2$ where d is distance, a is acceleration due to gravity, and t is time. Find d given $a = 9.8$ m/s^2 and $t = 3$ s.

b. The value of an investment: $A = P(1 + r)^t$ where P is principal, r is interest rate, and t is time in years. Find A given $P = \$30{,}000$, $r = 0.065$, and $t = 4$ yr.

c. The population of rabbits on an island: $P = \frac{KA(2.7183)^{rt}}{K + A(2.7183^{rt} - 1)}$ where K is the carrying capacity in number of rabbits, A is the initial population, r is the growth rate, and t is the time in years. Carrying capacity is the total number of rabbits that can live sustainably on the island. Find P given $K = 10{,}000$, $A = 200$, $r = 0.03$, and $t = 7$ yr.

d. The area of a kite: $A = \frac{1}{2}dD$ where d is the length of the first diagonal and D is the length of the second diagonal. Find A given $d = 12$ cm and $D = 22$ cm.

2. Use the given values to evaluate each pair of formulas. Determine whether the two versions of the formula are equivalent. Explain your answer.

a. $g = \frac{GM}{r^2}$ and $g = G \cdot \frac{M}{r^2}$

$G = 6.672 \times 10^{-11}$, $M = 50{,}000$, $r = 10{,}000$

b. $v = \frac{a + b}{2}$ and $v = a + \frac{b}{2}$

$a = 47$, $b = 24$

c. $y = a^2 - b^2$ and $y = (a - b)^2$

$a = 10$, $b = 6$

d. $d = \frac{1}{2}n(n - 3)$ and $d = \frac{n^2 - 3n}{2}$

$n = 8$

3. Find the requested value in each formula.

a. $C = \frac{5}{9}(F - 32)$. Find F given $C = 45°$.

b. $P = 2s + b$. Find s given $P = 94$ in. and $b = 22$ in.

c. $A = \frac{1}{2}(b + B)h$. Find B given $A = 276$ cm^2, $b = 20$ cm, and $h = 12$ cm.

d. $W = \frac{1}{2}m(v_2{}^2 - v_1{}^2)$. Find v_2 given $W = 56$ J, $m = 7$ kg, and $v_1 = 3$ m/s.

LESSON

3.7

A Formula for Slope

"The nearest thing to nothing that anything can be and still be something is zero."

ANONYMOUS

You have seen that the steepness of a line can be a graphical representation of a real-world rate of change like a car's speed, the number of calories burned with exercise, or a constant relating two units of measure. Often you can estimate the rate of change of a linear relationship simply by looking at a graph of the line. Can you tell which line in the graph matches which equation?

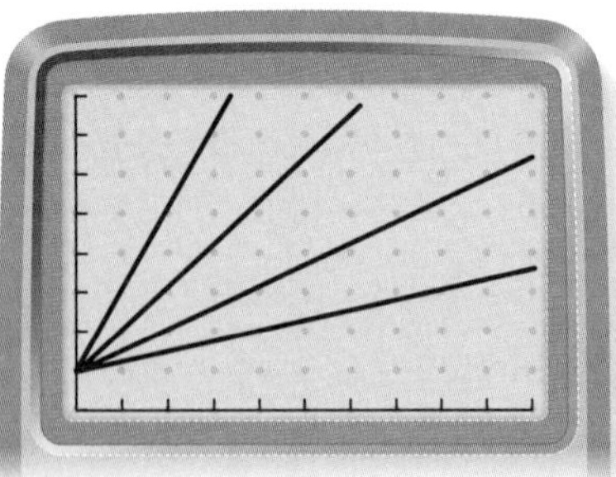

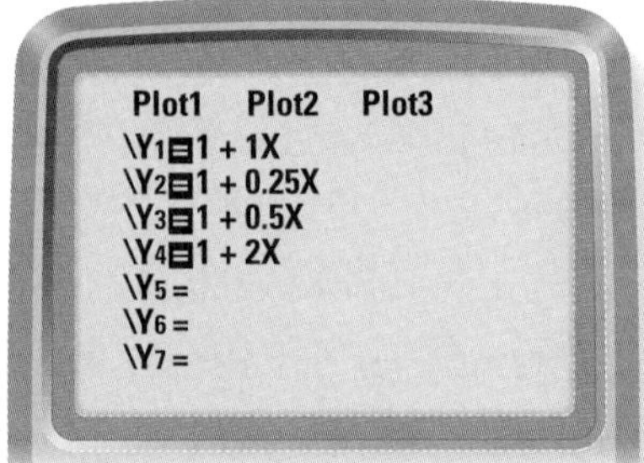

This term **slope** is used to describe the steepness of a line or the rate of change of a linear relationship. In this investigation you will explore how to find the slope of a line using two points on the line.

Ski slopes vary greatly depending on the steepness, difficulty and specific location. The steeper the slope the more experienced a skier must be.

INVESTIGATION

Points and Slope

YOU WILL NEED

- graph paper

Hector recently signed up with a limited-usage Internet provider. He pays a flat monthly fee and an hourly rate for the number of hours he is connected during the month. The table shows the amount of time he spent using the Internet for the first 3 months and the total fee he was charged.

Internet Use

Month	Time (h)	Total fee ($)
September	40	16.55
October	50	19.45
November	80	28.15

Step 1 Is there a linear relationship between the time in hours that Hector uses the Internet and his total fee in dollars? If so, why do you think such a relationship exists?

Step 2 Use the numbers in the table to find the hourly rate in dollars per hour. Explain how you calculated this rate.

Step 3 Draw a pair of coordinate axes on graph paper. Use the x-axis for time in hours and the y-axis for total fee in dollars. Plot and label the three points the table of data represents. Draw a line through the three points. Does this line support your answer in Step 1? Explain.

Step 4 Choose two points on your graph. Use arrows to show how you could move from one point to the other using only one vertical move and one horizontal move. How long is each arrow? What units do these values have?

Step 5 How do the arrow lengths relate to the hourly rate that you found in Step 2? Use the arrow lengths to find the amount of change each hour, or slope, for this situation. What units should you apply to the number?

In Step 4, you used arrows to show the vertical change and the horizontal change when you moved from one point to another. The right triangle you created is called a **slope triangle.**

Step 6 Choose a different pair of points on your graph. Create a slope triangle between them and use it to find the slope of the line. How does this slope compare to your answers in Step 2 and Step 5?

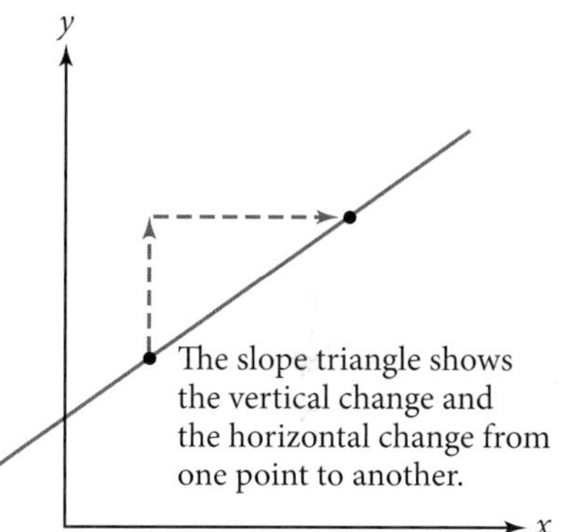

Step 7 Think about what you have done with your slope triangles. How could you use the coordinates of any two points to find the vertical change and the horizontal change represented by each arrow? Write a single numerical expression using the coordinates of two points to show how you can calculate slope.

Step 8 Write a symbolic algebraic rule for finding the slope of a line between any two points (x_1, y_1) and (x_2, y_2). The subscripts mean that these are two distinct points of the form (x, y).

[▶ Explore more about slope using the **Dynamic Algebra Exploration** in your ebook. ◀]

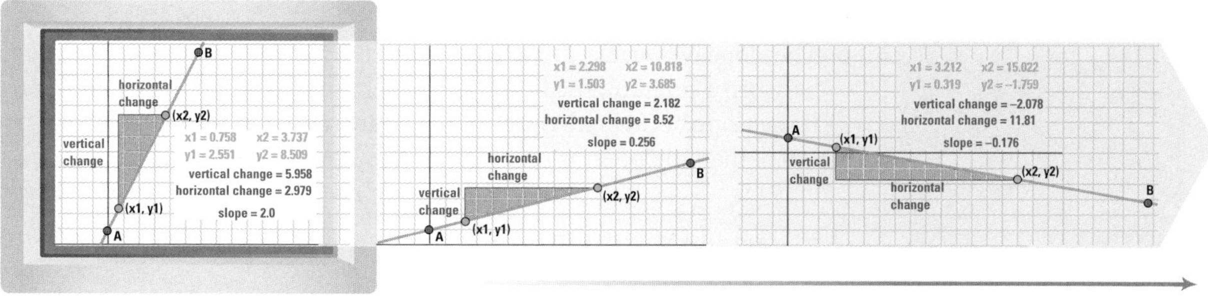

A slope triangle helps you visualize slope by showing you the vertical change and the horizontal change from one point to another. These changes are also called the "change in y" (vertical) and the "change in x" (horizontal). The example will help you see how to work with positive and negative numbers in slope calculations.

EXAMPLE

Consider the line through the points (1, 7) and (6, 4).

a. Find the slope of the line.

b. Without graphing, verify that the point (4, 5.2) is also on that line.

c. Find the coordinates of another point on the same line.

Solution

Plot the given points and draw the line between them.

a. There are two different slope triangles you could draw using these points.

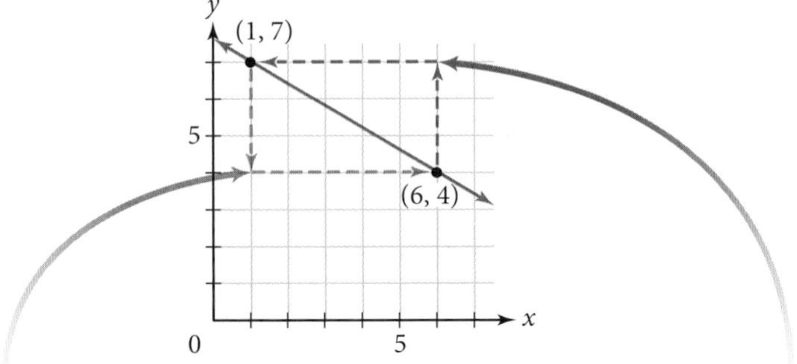

If you move from (1, 7) to (6, 4), the change in y is -3 (down 3) and the change in x is $+5$ (right 5). The slope is $\frac{-3}{+5}$.

If you move from (6, 4) to (1, 7), the change in y is $+3$ (up 3) and the change in x is -5 (left 5). The slope is $\frac{+3}{-5}$.

The fraction $\frac{-3}{+5}$ is equivalent to the fraction $\frac{+3}{-5}$. You get the same slope, $-\frac{3}{5}$ or -0.6, no matter which point you start from. The slope triangles help you see this relationship more clearly.

Move to (6, 4) from (1, 7).

$$\text{Slope} = \frac{4-7}{6-1} = \frac{-3}{5} = -\frac{3}{5} \quad \text{or}$$

Move to (1, 7) from (6, 4).

$$\text{Slope} = \frac{7-4}{1-6} = \frac{3}{-5} = -\frac{3}{5}$$

b. The slope between any two points on the line will be the same. (And the slope between a point on the line and a point not on the line will be different.) So, if the slope between the point (4, 5.2) and either of the original two points is -0.6, then the point is on the line. The slope between the points (4, 5.2) and (1, 7) is

$$\frac{7-5.2}{1-4} = \frac{1.8}{-3} = -\frac{1.8}{3} = -0.6$$

So the point (4, 5.2) is on the line.

c. You can find the coordinates of another point by adding the change in x and the change in y from any slope triangle on the line to the coordinates of a known point.

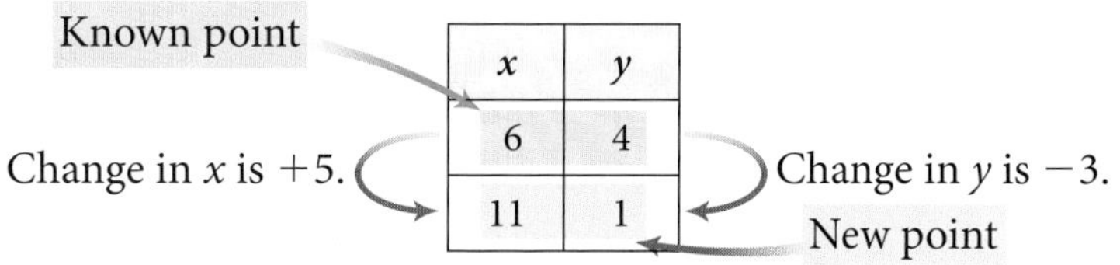

x	y
6	4
11	1

Starting with the point (6, 4) and using

$$\frac{\textit{change in } y}{\textit{change in } x} = \frac{-3}{5}$$

gives the new point $(6 + 5, 4 + (-3))$, or $(11, 1)$.

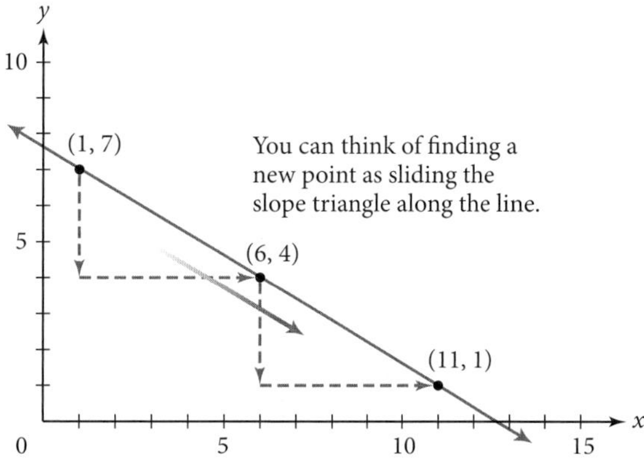

Try starting with the point (1, 7) and using

$$\frac{\textit{change in } y}{\textit{change in } x} = \frac{3}{-5}$$

to find another point. Try starting with either original point and using

$$\frac{\textit{change in } y}{\textit{change in } x} = \frac{-0.6}{1}$$

to find another point.

History CONNECTION

Slope is sometimes written $\frac{\Delta y}{\Delta x}$. The symbol Δ is the Greek capital letter delta. The use of Δ is linked to the history of calculus in the 18th century, when it was used to mean "difference."

Slope is an extremely important concept in mathematics and in applications that rely on mathematics, such as medicine and engineering. You may encounter different ways of describing slope—for example, "rise over run" or "vertical change over horizontal change." But you can always calculate the slope using this formula:

Slope Formula

The formula for the slope of the line passing through point 1 with coordinates (x_1, y_1) and point 2 with coordinates (x_2, y_2) is

$$\text{slope} = \frac{\textit{change in y}}{\textit{change in x}} = \frac{y_2 - y_1}{x_2 - x_1}$$

A line that goes up from left to right has a positive slope. A line that goes down from left to right has a negative slope.

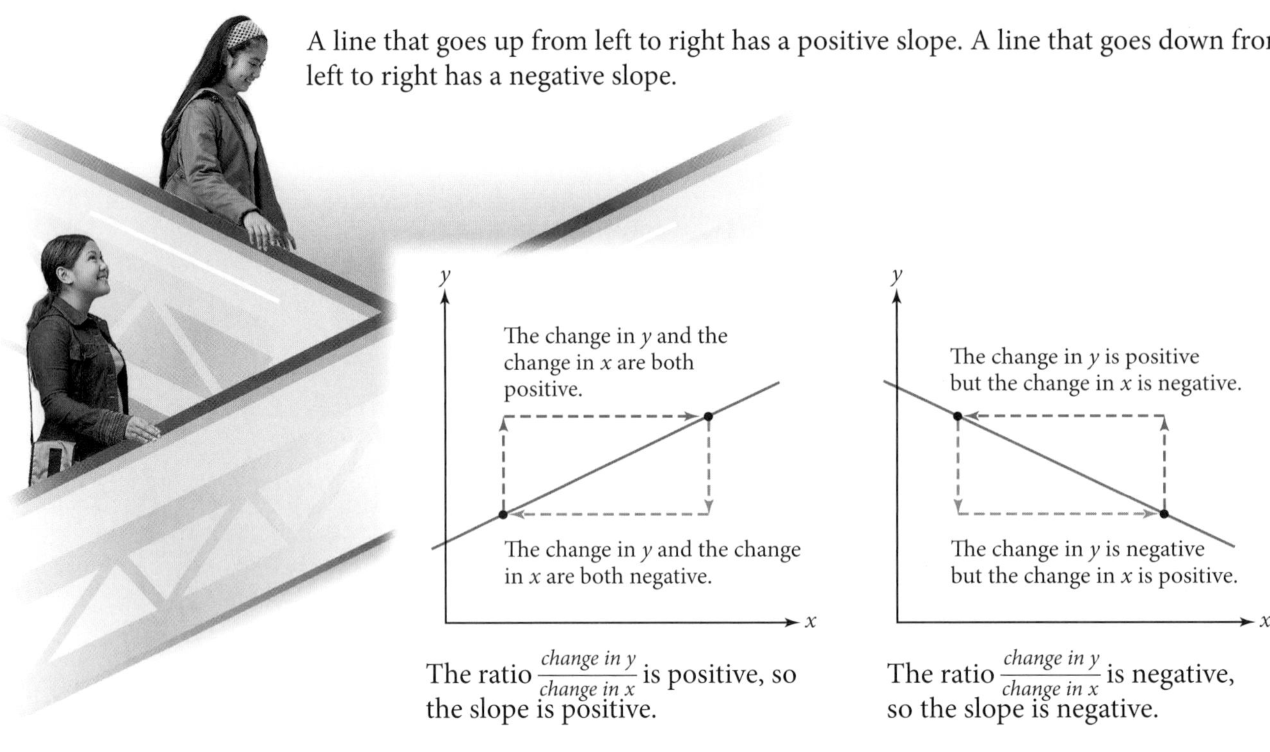

The ratio $\frac{change\ in\ y}{change\ in\ x}$ is positive, so the slope is positive.

The ratio $\frac{change\ in\ y}{change\ in\ x}$ is negative, so the slope is negative.

Horizontal lines have slope zero because they have no change in y. Vertical lines have no change in x. To calculate the slope of a vertical line, you would have to divide by zero, which is impossible. We say that the slope of a vertical line is undefined.

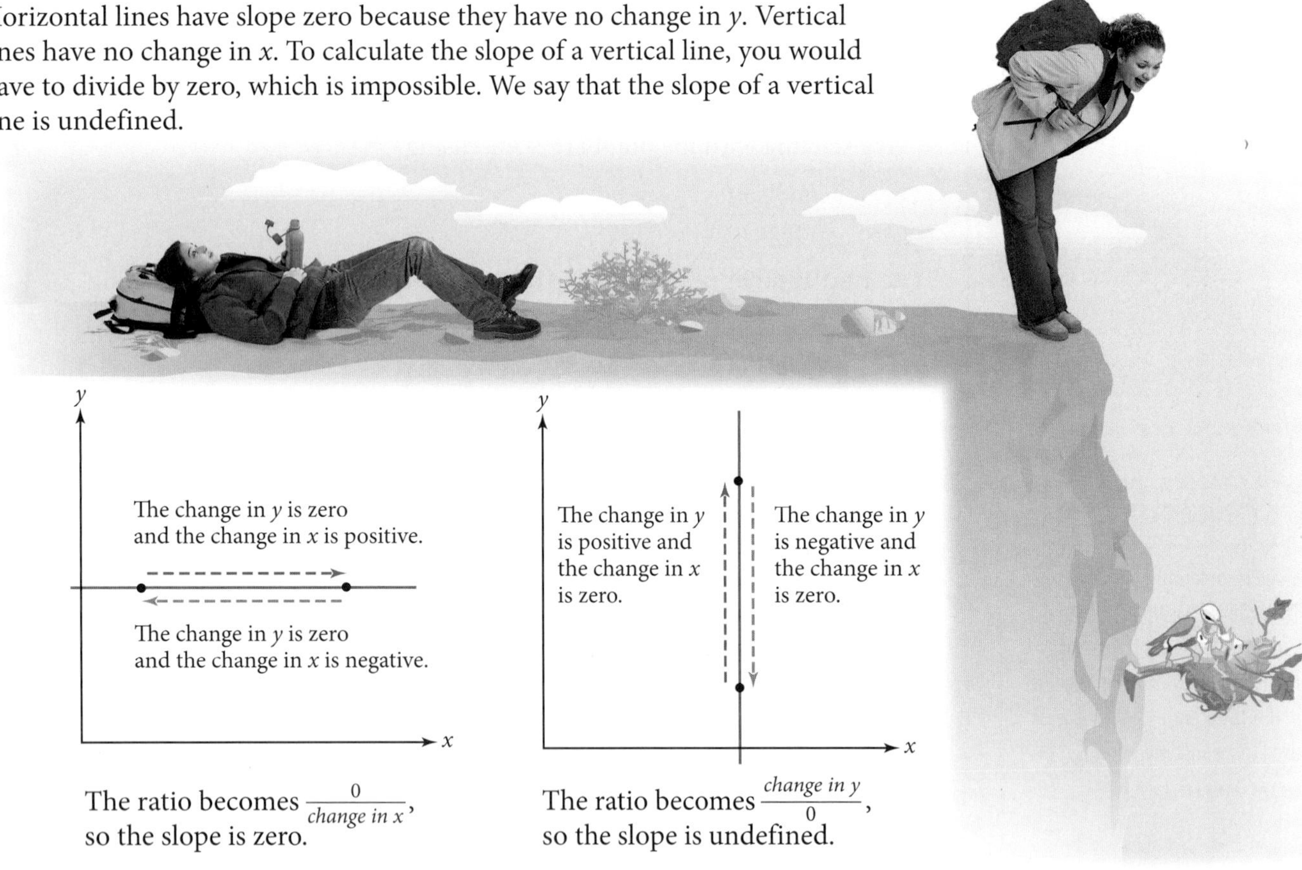

The ratio becomes $\frac{0}{change\ in\ x}$, so the slope is zero.

The ratio becomes $\frac{change\ in\ y}{0}$, so the slope is undefined.

As you work on the exercises, keep in mind that the slope of a line is the same as the rate of change of its equation. When a linear equation is written in intercept form, $y = a + bx$, which letter represents the slope?

Practice Your Skills

1. Find the slope of each line using a slope triangle or the slope formula.

a. @

b.

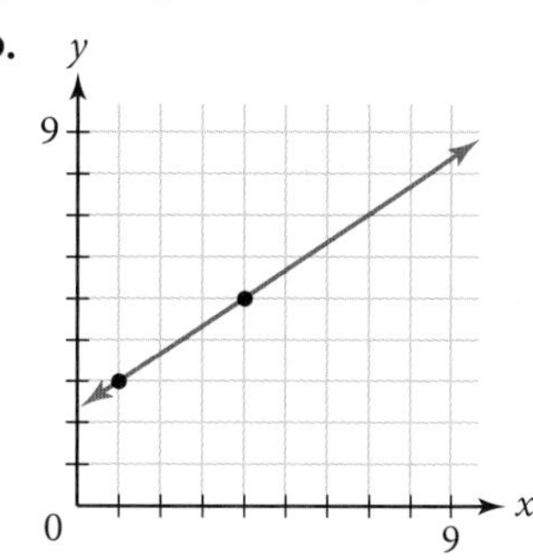

c.

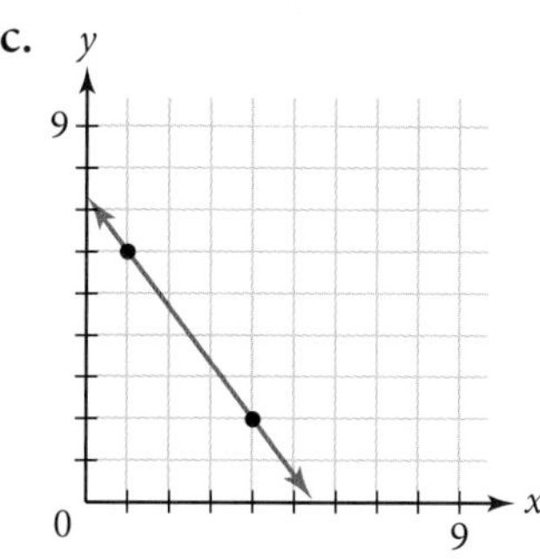

d.

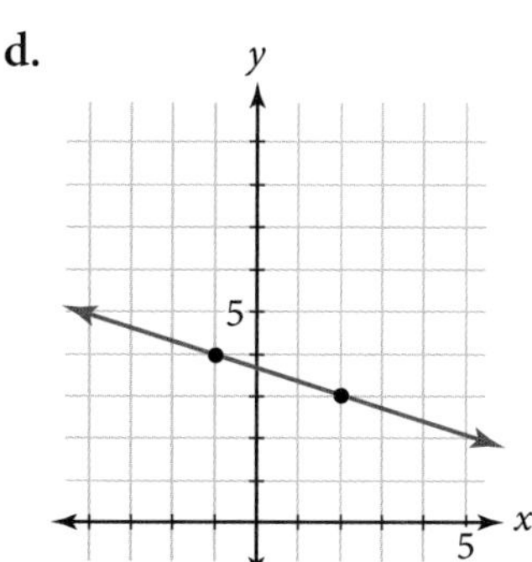

e.

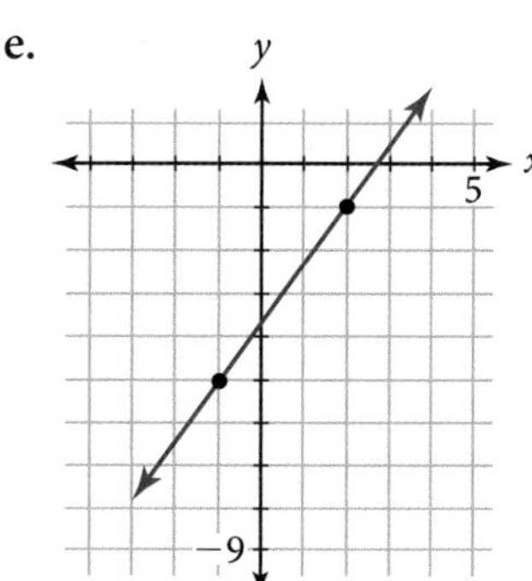

f.

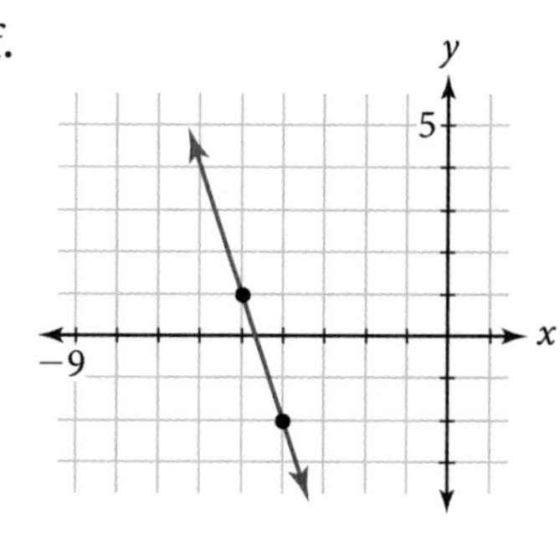

2. Find the slope of the line through each pair of points. Then give the coordinates of another point on the same line.

a. (2, 4), (4, 7) @

b. (6, −1), (2, 5)

c. (−1, −8), (3, −2)

d. (2, 4), (2, 7)

e.

x	y
−2	4
8	4

f.

x	y
1	−3
9	12

g.

x	y
3	1
−5	9

h.

x	y
−1	4
4	−2

3. Given the slope of a line and one point on the line, give the coordinates of two other points on the same line. Then use the slope formula to check that the slope between each of the two new points and the given point is the same as the given slope.

a. slope $\frac{3}{1}$; point (0, 4) @

b. slope −5; point (2, 8)

c. slope $-\frac{3}{4}$; point (8, 6)

d. slope 0.2; point (5, 7)

e. slope $\frac{1}{3}$; point (3, 0)

f. slope −0.5; point (2, 7)

4. Write the equation for each line using two points you can identify from the graph. Find the slope of the line by counting the change in y and the change in x on the graph. Use this slope as the rate of change in the equation $y = a + bx$. Then find the y-intercept. For more practice, run the LINES program on level "Easy." [▶ Use the link in your ebook to download the program file LINES. ◀]

a.

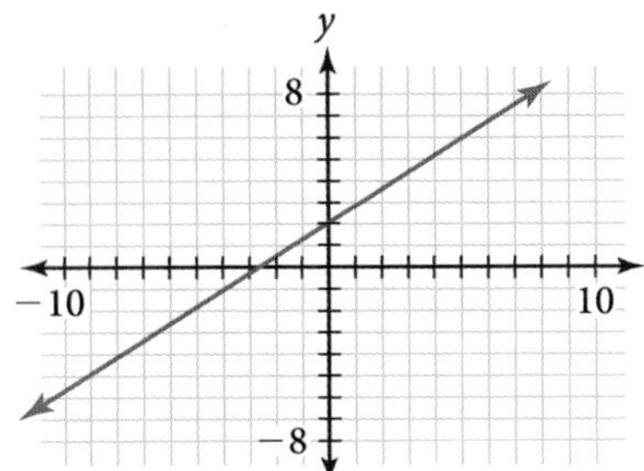

b.

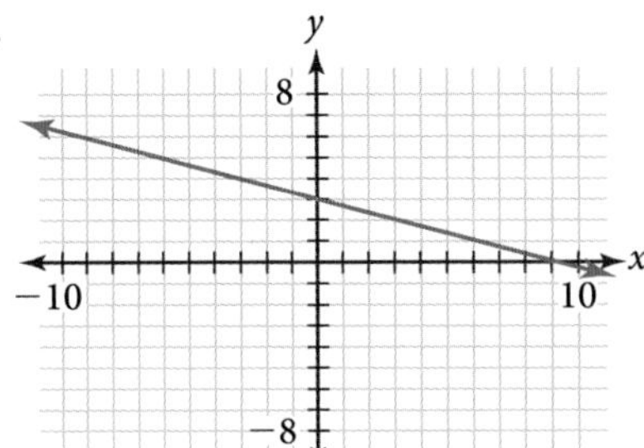

c.

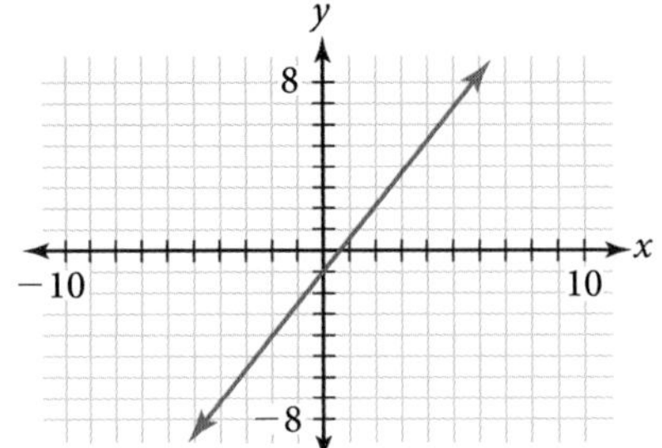

Reason and Apply

5. Each table or graph shows the coordinates of four points on a different line.

i. ⓐ

x	y
4	−8
4	0
4	3
4	20

ii.

x	y
0	5
1	3
3	−1
4	−3

iii.

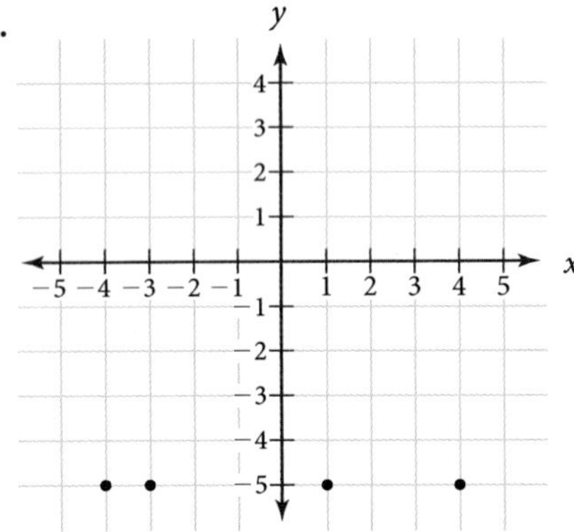

iv.

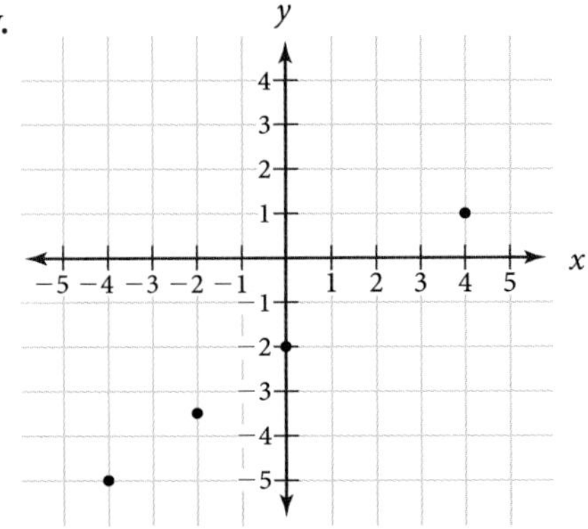

a. Without calculating, can you tell whether the slope of the line through each set of points is positive, negative, zero, or undefined? If so, explain how you can tell.

b. Choose two points from each table or graph and calculate the slope. Check that your answer is correct by calculating the slope using a different pair of points.

c. Write an equation for each table or graph.

6. Consider lines a and b shown in the graph at right.

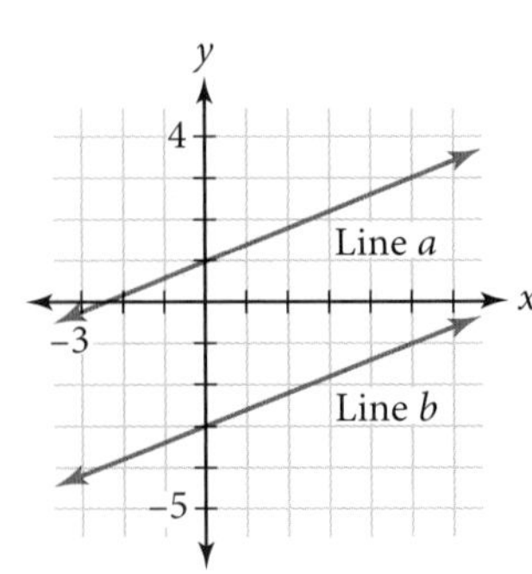

a. How are the lines in the graph alike? How are they different?

b. Which line represents the equation $y = -3 + \frac{2}{5}x$?

c. What is the equation of the other line?

d. How are the equations alike? How are they different?

7. APPLICATION Recall Hector's Internet use from the investigation. You probably found that his provider charges \$0.29 per hour of use—that was the slope of the line you graphed.

Internet Use

Month	Time (h)	Total fee (\$)
September	40	16.55
October	50	19.45
November	80	28.15

a. Use the rate of change and the data in the table to find the total fee for 30 h of use. How much is the total fee for 20 h? ⓐ

b. Repeat the process in 7a to find the total fee for 0 h of use. What is the real-world meaning of this number in this situation? (Look back at the investigation for help.) ⓐ

c. A mathematical model can be an equation, a graph, or a drawing that helps you better understand a real-world situation. Write a linear equation in intercept form that you can use to model this situation.

d. Use your linear equation to find the total fee for 280 h of use.

8. This line has slope 1. Graph it on your own paper.

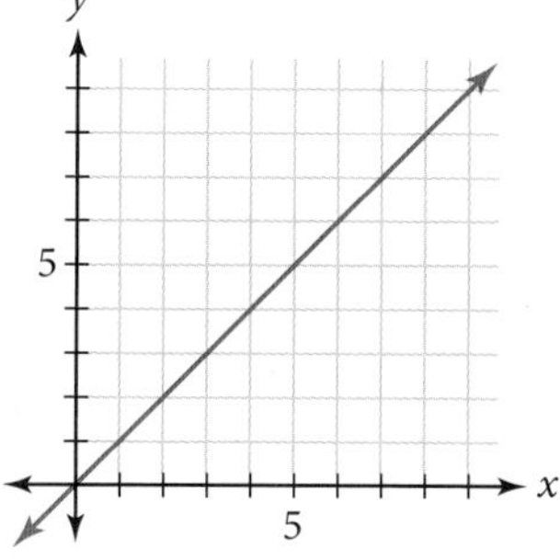

a. Draw a slope triangle on your line. How do the change in y and the change in x compare?

b. Draw a line that is steeper than the given line. How do the change in y and the change in x compare? How does the numerical slope compare to that of the original line?

c. Draw a line that is less steep than the given line, but still increasing. How do the change in y and the change in x compare? How does the numerical slope compare to that of the original line?

d. How would a line with slope -15 compare to your other lines? Explain your reasoning.

9. APPLICATION A hot-air balloonist gathered the data in this table.

Hot-Air Balloon Height

Time (min)	Height (m)
0	14
2.2	80
3.4	116
4	134
4.6	152

a. What is the slope of the line through these points?

b. What are the units of the slope? What is the real-world meaning of the slope? ⓐ

c. Write a linear equation in intercept form to model this situation.

d. What is the height of the balloon after 8 min? ⓐ

e. During what time interval is the height less than or equal to 500 m?

10. When you make a scatter plot of real-world data, the points may not be exactly linear but may have a linear pattern. Cal and Al each made a scatter plot of the same set of data and then added a line to the plot to identify the linear pattern. Explain why Cal's line is preferable to Al's.

i. 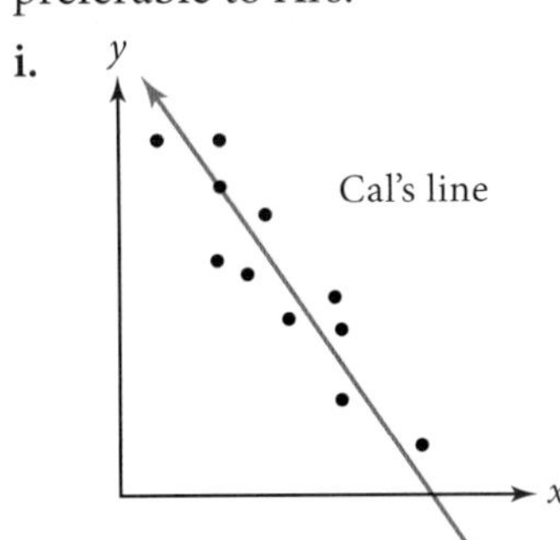

ii. 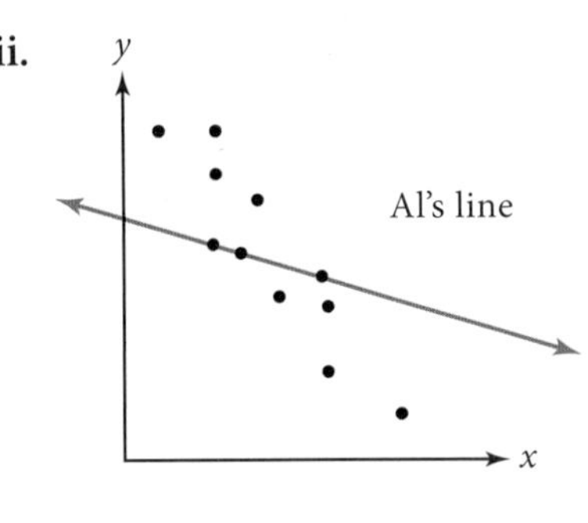

Review

11. Calista has five brothers. The mean of her brothers' ages is 10 years, and the median is 6 years. Create a data set that could represent the brothers' ages. Is this the only possible answer?

12. Convert each decimal number to a percent.

a. 0.85 **b.** 1.50

c. 0.065 **d.** 1.07

13. The equation $2x - 10 = 7x + 3$ is solved by balancing. Explain what happens in Steps 3, 4, and 6 of the balancing process.

$2x - 10 = 7x + 3$	1. Original equation.
$2x - 2x - 10 = 7x - 2x + 3$	2. Subtract $2x$ from both sides.
$-10 = 5x + 3$	3. __________
$-10 - 3 = 5x + 3 - 3$	4. __________
$-13 = 5x$	5. Combine like terms.
$\frac{-13}{5} = \frac{5x}{5}$	6. __________
$x = -2.6$	7. Simplify.
$2(-2.6) - 10 \stackrel{?}{=} 7(-2.6) + 3$	
$-5.2 - 10 \stackrel{?}{=} -18.2 + 3$	
$-15.2 = -15.2$	Solution checks.

LESSON

3.8

Precision and Accuracy

Whenever measuring is involved in collecting data, you can expect some variation in the pattern of data points. But when data can be closely approximated with an equation, you can begin to make predictions or draw conclusions. How much you can trust your approximation depends to some degree on how close to the actual data you have been able to get.

INVESTIGATION

Tying Knots

YOU WILL NEED

- one piece of rope for each pair of students
- a meterstick or a tape measure

In this investigation you'll explore the relationship between the number of knots in a rope and the length of the rope and write an equation to model the data.

Number of knots	Length of knotted rope (cm)
0	
1	
2	

Step 1 Record the length of your rope in a table like the one shown. Tie five or six knots, remeasuring the rope after you tie each knot.

Step 2 Graph your data, plotting the number of knots on the x-axis and the length of the knotted rope on the y-axis. What pattern does the data seem to form?

Step 3 What is the approximate rate of change for this data set? What is the real-world meaning of the rate of change? What factors have an effect on it?

Step 4 What is the y-intercept for the line that best models the data? What is its real-world meaning?

Step 5 Write an equation in intercept form of the line that you think best models the data. Graph your equation to check that it's a good fit. Adjust the coefficients in your equation to improve the fit if you can.

Step 6 Create a third column for your table and record the lengths predicted by your equation.

Number of knots	Length of knotted rope (cm)	Predicted length
0		
1		
2		

Step 7 If you began again with the same rope and tied the knots in the same way, do you think you would get exactly the same lengths the second time? Explain your answer.

Step 8 Create a fourth column for your table, and for each knot, find the positive difference between your measured length and the predicted length.

Step 9 Use your equation to predict the length of your rope with seven knots. Use the values in the fourth column of your table and the predicted length to suggest an interval of lengths, "between ___ cm and ___ cm," in which you would expect the actual length to lie.

Step 10 Tie the seventh knot and describe any difference between the measured length of your rope and the interval you suggested in Step 9.

The **margin of error** for an equation is a way of describing the precision of predictions made by the equation. In the rope investigation, a smaller margin of error means your measured lengths are closer to the predicted lengths and better to use for a model.

Prediction → 15 ± 0.7 ← Margin of error

Step 11 Looking at the fourth column again, what would you say is your margin of error?

Step 12 Use your equation to predict the length of the rope with five knots, if you started over again. Include your margin of error for this prediction ("___ ± ___"). Is the data value recorded for five knots within this predicted interval?

If all your measurements are 4 cm less than the actual length but with a small margin of error, they will be very precise but not accurate enough to be useful. Your goal is for your measurements to be accurate, or near the actual value, as well as precise—having a smaller margin of error.

EXAMPLE A

Chip walked for 6 s as his distance from a motion sensor was being recorded in meters. An equation modeling his walk is $d = (0.8 \pm 0.06) + 0.75t$.

a. What was the start location?

b. What was the walking rate?

c. When was Chip 4 m from the sensor?

Solution

Use the equation modeling Chip's walk to answer each question.

a. Because of the margin of error, we can't give an exact answer. At time $t = 0$ s, Chip was 0.8 m from the sensor with a margin of error of 0.06 m, so at the start he was between 0.74 m and 0.86 m (or between 74 cm and 86 cm) from the sensor.

b. Chip walked at an average rate of 0.75 m/s away from the sensor.

c. To find time t, we need to consider both ends of the interval described by the margin of error.

$4 = (0.8 + 0.06) + 0.75t$	$4 = (0.8 - 0.06) + 0.75t$	
$3.14 = 0.75t$	$3.26 = 0.75t$	Subtract 0.8 ± 0.06 from both sides.
$4.19 = t$	$4.35 = t$	Divide both sides by 0.75.

Chip was 4 m from the sensor at a time between 4.19 s and 4.35 s after the start.

Chip's distance from the motion sensor at any given second.

Chip's initial distance from the motion sensor.

Margin of error. This modifies Chip's distance at any given second.

Change in Chip's distance every second.

$d = (0.8 \pm 0.06) + 0.75t$

Do you see a difference between the walk in Example A and the knots data? The knots data consisted of discrete points. Values such as 4.7 or 8.5 knots don't make sense. But you can approximate a walker's location at *any* time between 0 s and 6 s, so a time of 4.19 s does make sense.

Margins of error make problems more complex. You often have to evaluate or solve twice to arrive at a solution. But real-life situations involve margins of error, for example, in which you can't predict the exact length of a rope or the exact position of a walker. Giving an interval with an answer provides information about the precision of the data and the answer.

EXAMPLE B

Two groups tied knots in their ropes and reported these equations, where x is the number of knots and y is the rope's length in centimeters.

Group 1: $y = (92.3 \pm 0.9) - 3.10x$

Group 2: $y = (88.5 \pm 1.3) - 4.72x$

a. Which group had the longer rope?

b. Which group had the thicker rope?

c. Which group had the stretchier rope?

Solution

Sample answers are given here. Do you agree with the reasoning?

a. Group 1 had the longer rope. The start value is the original length of the rope. Group 1 started with a rope with length 92.3 cm, although if you consider the margin of error, the actual length of the rope could be as little as 91.4 cm or as great as 93.2 cm. Taking the middle value, this is about 3.8 cm longer than Group 2's rope.

b. Group 2 had the thicker rope. With each knot, the thicker rope will get shorter more quickly than the thinner rope. The length of Group 2's rope is decreasing at a rate of 4.72 cm/knot, which is faster than the rate for Group 1, so Group 2 must have the thicker rope.

c. Group 2 had the stretchier rope. The larger margin of error for Group 2 indicates greater variation in the measures of length. This variation can be explained by trying to measure a stretchy rope.

In Example B, could a different margin of error change the answer to part a? In part c, could the larger margin of error also be due to less accurate measurements?

Exercises

Practice Your Skills

1. State the rate of change and the y-intercept for each equation.

a. $y = 3.2x$

b. $y = 1.7x + 3$

c. $y = 2.4$

d. $2x + y = 6$

2. Complete the table, using $y = (120 \pm 0.5) - 8.5x$ as a knot-tying model.

Number of knots	Length between maximum and minimum predictions (cm)	
0	119.5	
1		
2		
	51.5	52.5
	26	27

3. Use complete sentences to give the real-world meanings of the numbers in the equation from Exercise 2.

a. What is the real-world meaning of 120?

b. What is the real-world meaning of $-8.5x$?

c. What is the real-world meaning of ± 0.5? ⓐ

4. Write an equation that models these knot data. ⓐ

Rope A

Number of knots	Length (cm)
0	93.7
1	89.1
2	

Rope B

Number of knots	Length (cm)
0	
1	101.2
2	90.8

5. What are the predicted values for the missing table entries in Exercise 4?

Reason and Apply

6. Write an equation that models these knot data. Then fill in the missing table values.

Number of knots	Length (cm)
0	114
1	
2	
6	39

7. Madison walks toward a motion sensor. If d is distance in meters and t is time in seconds, an equation for her walk is $d = (5.47 \pm 0.04) - 0.58t$.

a. Predict her position after 3 s.

b. Predict when she will reach the motion sensor. ⓐ

8. When Sam swims, the number of calories burned after time x, in minutes, is given by the equation $y = (325 \pm 12) + 7.8x$.

a. How many calories has Sam burned after 45 min?

b. When will he have burned 1000 Cal?

9. Write an equation to model these data (including the margin of error).

a. 

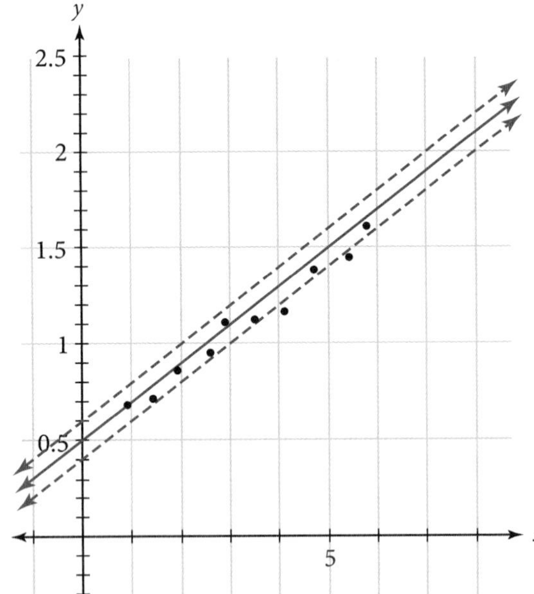

b.

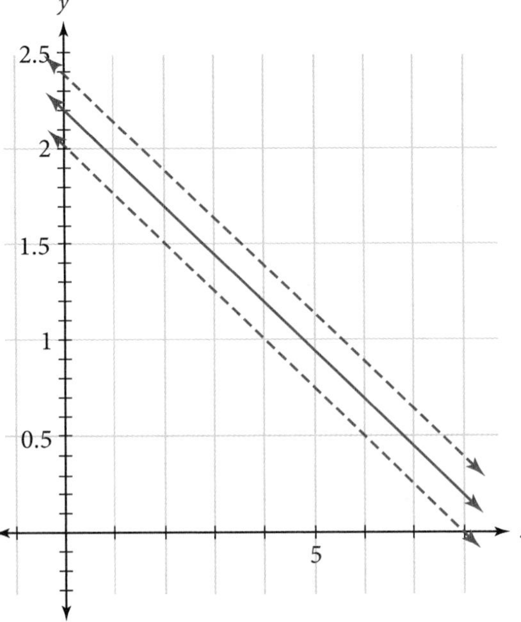

10. Georgia has written an equation to predict the length of a knotted rope. With three knots, she predicts a length between 68.4 cm and 69.0 cm. With four knots, she predicts a length between 61.2 cm and 61.8 cm. What is her equation?

11. Name three factors that might affect the margin of error when writing an equation that gives the length of a rope based on the number of knots tied in it.

Review

12. Chip and Madison's 6 s walks will be recorded simultaneously with two motion sensors. Describe what they should do so that the graphs depicting their walks are parallel lines.

13. The inequality $0.4 + 1.3x > 5$ describes a walk. Write a question that might be answered using this inequality.

14. Suppose the equation $y = 47.1 - 7.2x$ predicts the length of a rope after tying x knots. What length does the equation predict for 13 knots? Explain the problems you might have in making or believing this prediction. ⓐ

IMPROVING YOUR Reasoning SKILLS

There are 100 students and 100 lockers in a school hallway. All the lockers are closed. The first student walks down the hallway and opens every locker. The second student closes every even-numbered locker. The third student goes to every third locker and opens it if it is closed or closes it if it is open. This pattern repeats so that the nth student leaves every nth locker the opposite of how it was before. After all 100 students have opened or closed the lockers, how many lockers are left open?

Another Look at Solving Equations

You will encounter equations throughout your mathematical career. Some will be simple, such as $1.6 + 1.8x = 4$. Other equations can be complicated, such as this one used to model the population growth of fish in a lake.

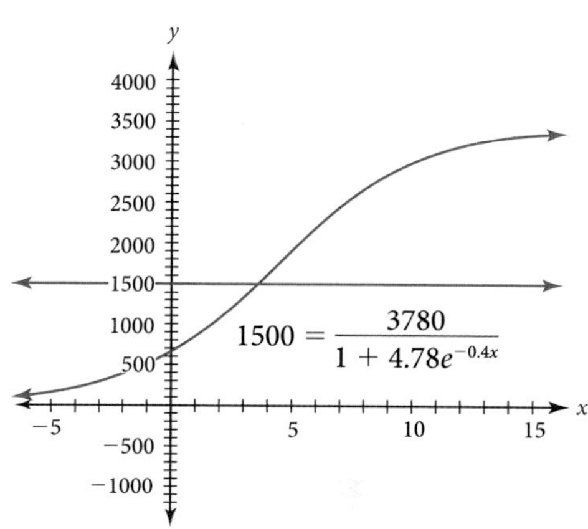

What you have learned about solving equations by undoing and by balancing will be useful in solving many equations. You should think about when each strategy will be most appropriate for a given situation.

EXAMPLE A

Determine whether you can solve each equation by undoing, by balancing, or by either technique. Solve each equation.

a. $3 - 5(x + 2) = 18$ **b.** $8x + 11 = 4x + 29$

Solution

Solving by undoing:

a.

Equation: $3 - 5(x + 2) = 18$ or $3 + (-5)(x + 2) = 18$			
Description	**Undo**	**Result**	**Equation**
Pick x.		-5	$x = -5$
Add 2.	$-(2)$	-3	$x + 2 = -3$
Multiply by -5.	$/(-5)$	15	$-5(x + 2) = 15$
Add 3.	$-(3)$	18	$3 - 5(x + 2) = 18$

Solving by balancing:

$3 - 5(x + 2) = 18$	Original equation.
$3 - 5(x + 2) - 3 = 18 - 3$	Subtract 3 from both sides.
$-5(x + 2) = 15$	Combine like terms.
$\frac{-5(x + 2)}{-5} = \frac{15}{-5}$	Divide both sides by -5.
$x + 2 = -3$	Simplify.
$x + 2 - 2 = -3 - 2$	Subtract 2 from both sides.
$x = -5$	Combine like terms.

Notice that the steps in the balancing method are the same as the steps in the undo table. The only difference is that you are working down from the top instead of up from the bottom.

b. There is a problem with "undoing" in this situation—x appears on both sides of the equation. You need to find an equivalent form of the equation in which the variable appears only once, and then proceed by either balancing or undoing.

$8x + 11 = 4x + 29$	Original equation.
$8x + 11 - 4x = 4x + 29 - 4x$	Subtract $4x$ from both sides.
$4x + 11 = 29$	Combine like terms. You could use undoing from this point.
$4x + 11 - 11 = 29 - 11$	Subtract 11 from both sides.
$4x = 18$	Combine like terms.
$\frac{4x}{4} = \frac{18}{4}$	Divide both sides by 4.
$x = \frac{9}{2}$, or $x = 4.5$	Simplify.

Solving by the balancing method is a powerful strategy. However, you always need to think about ways to undo the various operations and the order of your steps.

Have you ever been given a formula but needed to solve for a variable within the formula? It is very common in math, science, business, and engineering to have to rearrange a formula with several variables. For example, to find the rate of downhill skiers in the Olympics, since the distance is constant and times are recorded, it could be easier to solve the formula $d = rt$ for r, or $r = \frac{d}{t}$, and use that formula.

Formulas, or equations, are an example of *literal equations.* A literal equation is an equation which consists primarily of variables. The same methods you used to solve a linear equations are used to solve a literal equation. Instead of solving for a specific value for one variable, you are simply rearranging variables into a more convenient form so that you can plug in values for variables later.

EXAMPLE B

Solve the equation for the indicated variable.

$$A = \frac{(b_1 + b_2)h}{2} \text{ for } h$$

Solution

$A = \frac{(b_1 + b_2)h}{2}$	Original equation.
$2 \cdot A = \frac{(b_1 + b_2)h}{2} \cdot 2$	Multiply both sides by 2.
$2A = (b_1 + b_2)h$	Simplify.
$\frac{2A}{(b_1 + b_2)} = \frac{(b_1 + b_2)h}{(b_1 + b_2)}$	Divide both sides by $(b_1 + b_2)$.
$\frac{2A}{(b_1 + b_2)} = h$ or $h = \frac{2A}{(b_1 + b_2)}$	Simplify.

Exercises

1. Combine the like terms in each expression.

a. $3 + 4x - 7 + 8x$

b. $4 + 2x + 8x - 9$

c. $6x - 1 + x + 10$

d. $11x + 2 - 6x + 7 - 5x$

e. $4 + 7 - 3x + 2$

f. $4x - (-7x) + 3x$

g. $16 + 3x - 7 + 9x - 12x - 9$

h. $10x + 3x - 6 - x + 8$

2. Solve each equation.

a. $12 - 3(a - 1) = 17$

b. $-0.9b + 8 = 3.5$

c. $4(3c - 7) = 32$

d. $35 = 7d - 1 - d$

e. $8e + 7 = 4 + 3e$

f. $13 - 1(4f + 6) = 55$

g. $5g + 7 = 28 - 2g$

h. $14 + 8h - 9 = 6 - 5h$

i. $7i - 4 + 6i = 11 + 4i - 2$

3. Combine like terms on each side of each equation, and then solve.

a. $3 + 4x - 7 + 8x = 4 + 2x + 8x - 9$

b. $6x - 1 + x + 10 = 11x + 2 - 6x + 7 - 5x$

c. $4 + 7 - 3x + 2 = 4x - (-7x) + 3x$

d. $16 + 3x - 7 + 9x - 12x - 9 = 10x + 3x - 6 - x + 8$

4. What is the value of n if the equation $4x + n = 20$ has the solution $x = 6$?

5. What is the value of m if the equation $mx + 11 = 29$ has the solution $x = \frac{1}{2}$?

6. Solve these equations for the indicated variable.

a. $V = \pi r^2 h$ for h

b. $A = p + prt$ for t

c. $y = a + bx$ for x

d. $2ax - 5x = 2$ for a

e. $S = 3F - 24$ for F

CHAPTER 3 REVIEW

You started this chapter by investigating **recursive sequences**—using their starting values and **rates of change** to write **recursive rules.** You saw how rates of change and starting values appear in plots.

In a walking investigation you observed, interpreted, and analyzed graphical representations of relationships between time and distance. What does the graph look like when you stand still? When you move away from or move toward the motion sensor? If you speed up or slow down? You identified real-world meanings of the ***y*-intercept** and the rate of change of a **linear relationship,** and you used them to write a **linear equation** in the **intercept form,** $y = a + bx$. You learned the role of b, the coefficient of x. You explored relationships among verbal descriptions, tables, recursive rules, equations, and graphs. You created a **slope triangle** on a graph to show the vertical change and the horizontal change when you moved from one point to another. And you learned how to calculate **slope** using the slope formula, $b = \frac{y_2 - y_1}{x_2 - x_1}$.

Throughout the chapter you developed your equation-solving skills. You found solutions to equations by continuing to practice an undoing method and by using a **balancing** method. You found approximate solutions by tracing calculator graphs and by zooming in on calculator tables. Finally, you learned one way to model linear data that have some variation from the line and to express the accuracy of your model with a **margin of error.**

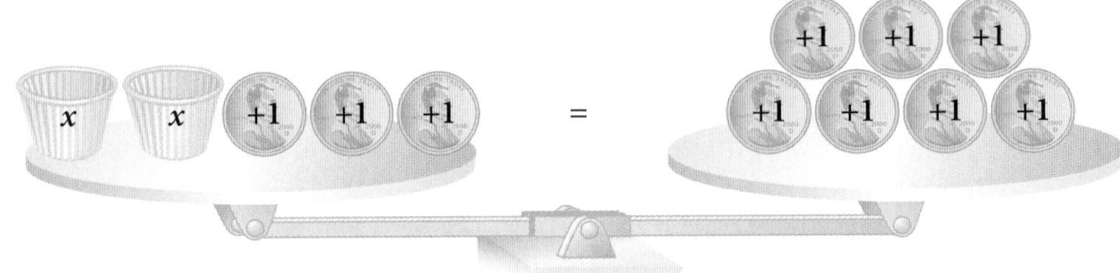

Exercises

You will need your graphing calculator for Exercise **4.**

@ **Answers are provided for all exercises in this set.**

1. Solve these equations. Give reasons for each step.

a. $-x = 7$

b. $4.2 = -2x - 42.6$

2. These tables represent linear relationships. For each relationship, give the rate of change, the y-intercept, the recursive rule, and the equation in intercept form.

a.

x	y
0	3
1	4
2	5

b.

x	y
1	0.01
2	0.02
3	0.03

c.

x	y
−2	1
0	5
3	11

d.

x	y
−4	5
12	−3
2	2

3. Match these walking instructions with their graph sketches.

i.

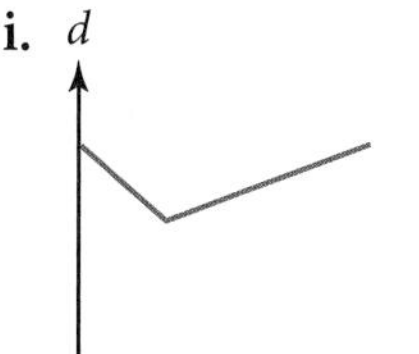

ii.

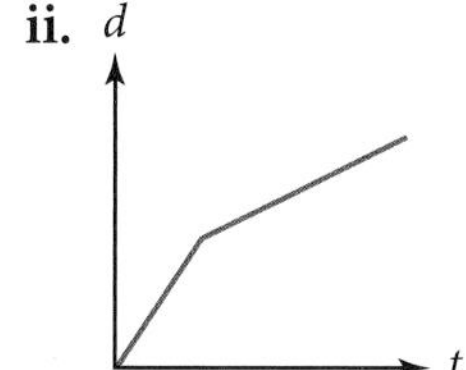

iii.

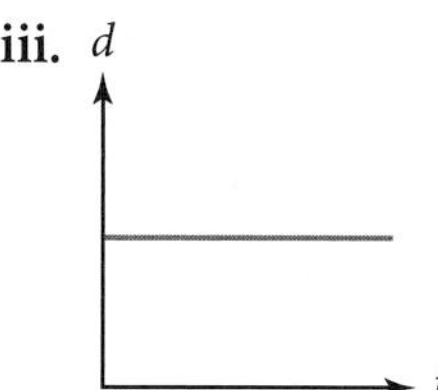

a. The walker stands still.

b. The walker takes a few steps toward the 0-mark and then walks away.

c. The walker steps away from the 0-mark and then abruptly changes speed, continuing more slowly in the same direction.

4. Graph each equation on your calculator, and trace to find the approximate y-value for the given x-value. Then substitute the x-value into the equation to find the exact y-value.

a. $y = 1.21 - x$ when $x = 70.2$

b. $y = 6.02 + 44.3x$ when $x = 96.7$

c. $y = -0.06 + 0.313x$ when $x = 0.64$

d. $y = 1183 - 2140x$ when $x = -111$

5. Write the equations for linear relationships that have these characteristics.

a. The output value is equal to the input value.

b. The output value is 3 less than the input value.

c. The rate of change is 2.3, and the y-intercept is -4.3.

d. The graph contains the points (1, 1), (2, 1), and (3, 1).

6. The profit for a small company depends on the number of bookcases it sells. One way to determine the profit is to use a recursive rule such as

$\{0, -850\}$ ENTER

$\{\text{Ans}(1) + 1, \text{Ans}(2) + 70\}$ ENTER, ENTER, . . .

a. Explain what the numbers and expressions 0, -850, Ans(1), Ans(1) + 1, Ans(2), and Ans(2) + 70 represent.

b. Make a plot of this situation.

c. When will the company begin to make a profit? Explain.

d. Explain the relationship between the values -850 and 70 and your graph.

e. Does it make sense to connect the points in the graph with a line? Explain.

7. Suppose a new small-business computer system costs $5,400. Every year, its value drops by $525.

a. Define variables and write an equation modeling the value of the computer in any given year.

b. What is the rate of change, and what does it mean in the context of the problem?

c. What is the y-intercept, and what does it mean in the context of the problem?

d. What is the x-intercept, and what does it mean in the context of the problem?

8. A single section and a double section of a log fence are shown.

a. How many additional logs are required each time the fence is increased by a single section?

b. Copy and fill in the missing values in this table.

Number of sections	1	2	3	4	...		...	50
Number of logs	4	7			...	91	...	

c. Describe a recursive rule that relates the number of logs required to the number of sections.

d. If each section is 3 m long, what is the longest fence you can build with 217 logs?

9. Andrei and his younger brother are having a race. Because the younger brother can't run as fast, Andrei lets him start out 5 m ahead. Andrei runs at a speed of 7.7 m/s. His younger brother runs at a speed of 6.5 m/s. The total length of the race is 50 m.

a. Write an equation to find how long it will take Andrei to finish the race. Solve the equation to find the time.

b. Write an equation to find how long it will take Andrei's younger brother to finish the race. Solve the equation to find the time.

c. Who wins the race? How far ahead was the winner at the time he crossed the finish line?

10. Solve each equation using the method of your choice. Then use a different method to verify your solution.

a. $14x = 63$

b. $-4.5x = 18.6$

c. $8 = 6 + 3x$

d. $5(x - 7) = 29$

e. $3(x - 5) + 8 = 12$

f. $2 + 7x = 15$

g. $4(x + 3) = -6x$

h. $-2(x - 1) = 3$

i. $2x + 4 = 3x - 5$

11. For each table, write an equation for y in terms of x.

a.

x	y
0	−5.7
1	−3.4
2	−1.1
3	1.2
4	3.5
5	5.8

b.

x	y
−3	19
−1	3
0	−5
2	−21
5	−45
6	−53

c.

x	y
3	13.5
−2	11
−9	7.5
0	12
6	15
−5	9.5

12. You can represent linear relationships with a graph, a table of values, an equation, or a rule stated in words. Here are two linear relationships. Show each relationship in all the other ways.

a.

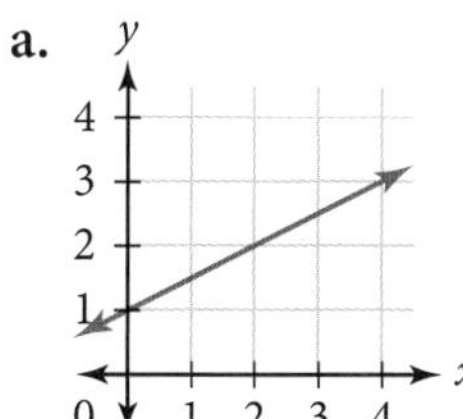

b.

x	y
−2	2
−1.5	1.5
0	0
3	−3

13. Find the slope of the line passing through the first two points given. Assume the third point is also on the line and find the missing coordinate.

a. (−1, 5) and (3, 1); (5, □)

b. (2, −5) and (2, −2); (□, 3)

c. (−10, 22) and (−2, 2); (□, −3)

d. (6, 3) and (1, 3); (□, 3)

14. The slope of the line passing through the points (2, 10) and $(x_2, 4)$ is −3. Find the value of x_2.

15. Plot the points (4, 2), (1, 3.5), and (10, −1) on graph paper. These points are **collinear,** or on the same line, so you can draw a line through them.

a. Draw a slope triangle between (4, 2) and (1, 3.5), and calculate the slope from the change in y and the change in x.

b. Draw another slope triangle between (10, −1) and (4, 2), and calculate the slope from the change in y and the change in x.

c. Compare the slope triangles and the slopes you calculated. What do you notice?

d. What would happen if you made a slope triangle between (10, −1) and (1, 3.5)?

16. The base of a triangle was recorded as 18.3 ± 0.1 cm, and the height was recorded as 7.4 ± 0.1 cm. These measurements indicate the measured value and a margin of error.

a. Use the formula $A = 0.5bh$ and the measured values for the base and height to calculate the area of the triangle.

b. Use the smallest possible lengths for base and height to calculate an area.

c. Use the largest possible lengths for base and height to calculate an area.

d. Use your answers to 11a–c to express the range of possible area values as a number $\pm$ a margin of error.

Take Another Look

1. The picture at right is a *contour map,* also called a *topographical map.* This type of map reveals the character of the terrain. All points on an *isometric line* are the same height in feet above sea level. The graph below shows how the hiker's walking speed changes as she covers the terrain on the dotted-line trail shown on the map.

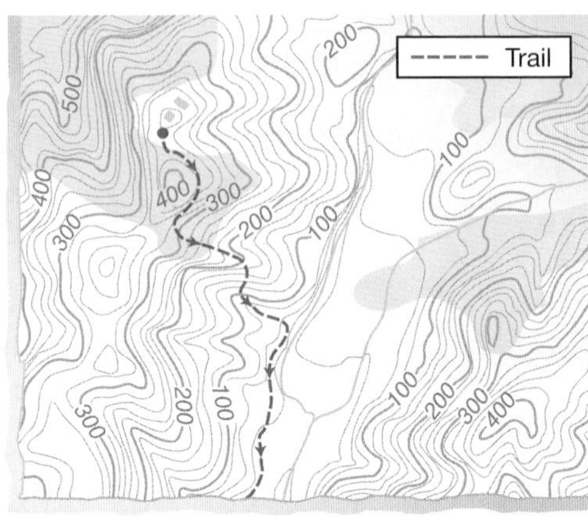

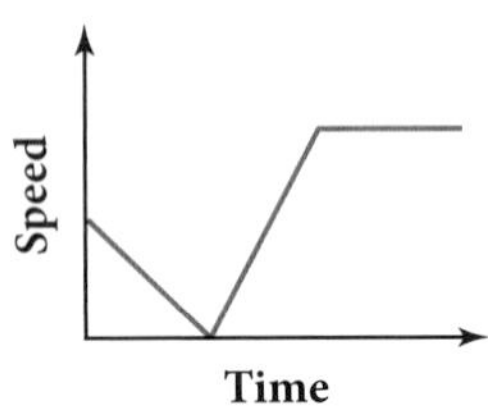

a. What quantities are changing in the graph and on the map?

b. How does each display reveal rate of change?

c. How could you measure distance on each display?

d. What would the graph sketch of this hike look like if distance were plotted on the vertical axis instead of speed?

e. What do these two displays tell you when you study them together?

Sediment layers form contour lines in the Grand Canyon.

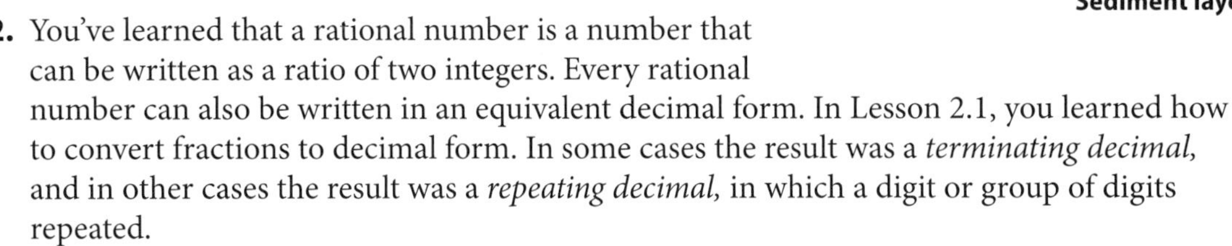

2. You've learned that a rational number is a number that can be written as a ratio of two integers. Every rational number can also be written in an equivalent decimal form. In Lesson 2.1, you learned how to convert fractions to decimal form. In some cases the result was a *terminating decimal,* and in other cases the result was a *repeating decimal,* in which a digit or group of digits repeated.

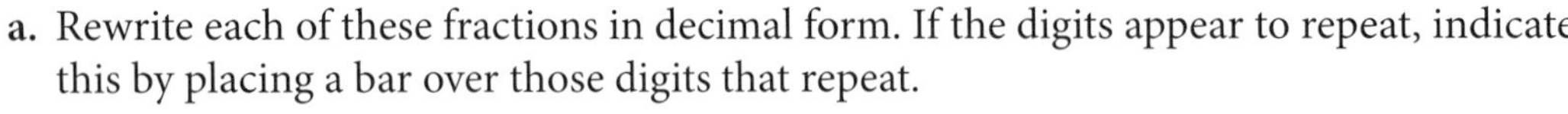

a. Rewrite each of these fractions in decimal form. If the digits appear to repeat, indicate this by placing a bar over those digits that repeat.

$\frac{1}{2}, \frac{7}{16}, \frac{11}{125}, \frac{7}{15}, \frac{9}{22}, \frac{11}{30}, \frac{7}{20}$

b. Describe how you can predict whether a fraction will convert to a terminating decimal or a repeating decimal.

Reversing the process—converting decimals to fractions

c. Write the decimals 0.25, 0.8, 0.13, and 0.412 as fractions.

You can use what you've learned in this chapter about solving equations to help you write an infinite repeating decimal, like $0.\overline{1}$, as a fraction. For example, to find a fraction equal to $0.\overline{1}$, you are looking for a fraction F such that $F = 0.11111\ldots$. Follow the steps shown.

$$F = 0.11111\ldots$$

$$10F = 1.11111\ldots$$

$$\text{So } 10F - F = 1.11111\ldots - 0.11111\ldots$$

$$9F = 1$$

$$F = \frac{1}{9}$$

Here, the trick was to multiply by 10 so that $10F$ and F had the same decimal part. Then, when you subtract $10F - F$, the decimal portion is eliminated.

d. Write the repeating decimal $0.\overline{18}$ as a fraction. (*Hint:* What can you multiply $F = 0.\overline{18}$ by so that you can subtract off the same decimal part?)

e. Write these repeating decimals as fractions.

i. $0.\overline{32}$ **ii.** $0.\overline{325}$ **iii.** $0.2\overline{325}$

IMPROVING YOUR Reasoning SKILLS

Did these plants grow at the same rate? If not, which plant was tallest on Day 4? Which plant took the most time to reach 8 cm? Redraw the graphs so that you can compare their growth rates more easily.

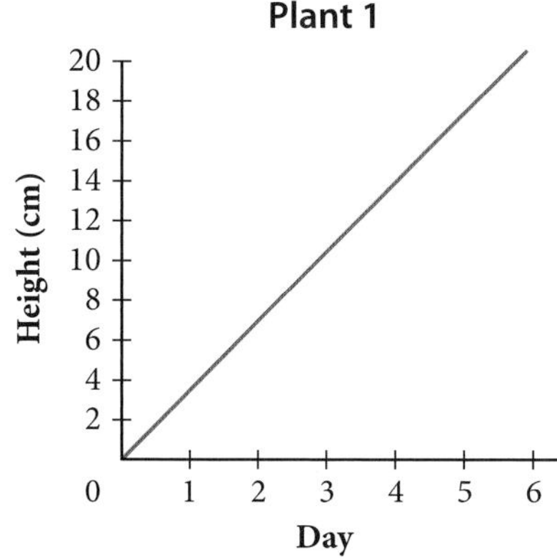

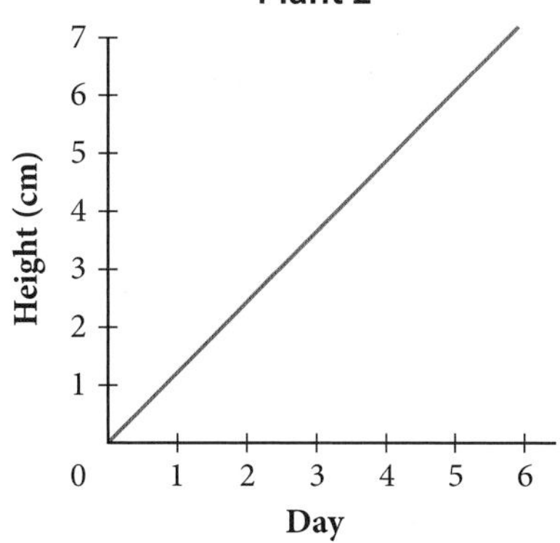

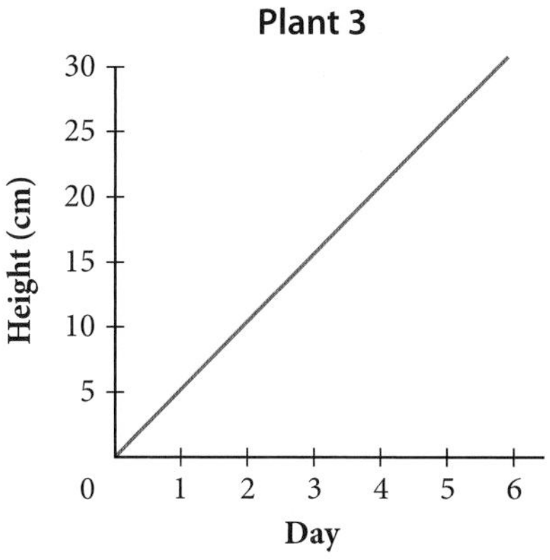

Assessing What You've Learned

GIVING A PRESENTATION Making presentations is an important career skill. Most jobs require workers to share information, to help orient new coworkers, or to represent the employer to clients. Making a presentation to the class is a good way to develop your skill at organizing and delivering your ideas clearly and in an interesting way. Most teachers will tell you that they have learned more by trying to teach something than they did simply by studying it in school.

Here are some suggestions to make your presentation go well:

- Work with a group. Acting as a panel member might make you less nervous than giving a talk on your own. Be sure the role of each panel member is clear so that the work and the credit are shared equally.
- Choose the topic carefully. You can summarize the results of an investigation, present what you've learned and how it connects to the chapter, or give your own thinking on Take Another Look or Improving Your Reasoning Skills.
- Prepare thoroughly. Outline your presentation and think about what you have to say on each point. Decide how much detail to give, but don't try to memorize whole sentences. Illustrate your presentation with models, a poster, a handout, or overhead transparencies. Prepare these visual aids ahead of time and decide when to introduce them.
- Speak clearly. Practice talking loudly and clearly. Show your interest in the subject. Don't hide behind a poster or the projector. Look at the listeners when you talk.

Here are other ways to assess what you've learned:

UPDATE YOUR PORTFOLIO Choose a piece of work you did in this chapter to add to your portfolio—your graph from the investigation On the Road Again (Lesson 3.2), or the most complicated equation you've solved.

WRITE IN YOUR JOURNAL What method for solving equations do you like best? Do you always remember to define variables before you graph or write an equation? How are you doing in algebra generally? What things don't you understand?

ORGANIZE YOUR NOTEBOOK You might need to update your notebook with examples of balancing to solve an equation, or with notes about how to trace a line or search a table to approximate the coordinates of the solution. Be sure you understand the meanings of important terms like *linear equation, rate of change,* and *intercept form.*

CHAPTER 4

Functions and Linear Modeling

The musician in *The Lute Player* by an unknown artist called the Master of the Half Figures plays her lute while reading sheet music. When music is composed or transcribed, it is written on a staff as notes in standard notation or as numbers in tablature. Playing music from notation and writing notation from music are very much like the relationships between input and output in mathematical functions.

OBJECTIVES

In this chapter you will

- explore the domain and range of a relation
- learn how to determine whether a relationship is a function
- graph functions of real world situations
- write an equation that fits a set of real-world data
- review the intercept form of a linear equation
- learn the slope-intercept form of a linear equation
- learn the point-slope form of a linear equation
- recognize equivalent equations written in different forms
- formalize algebraic properties

Algebraic Properties of Equality

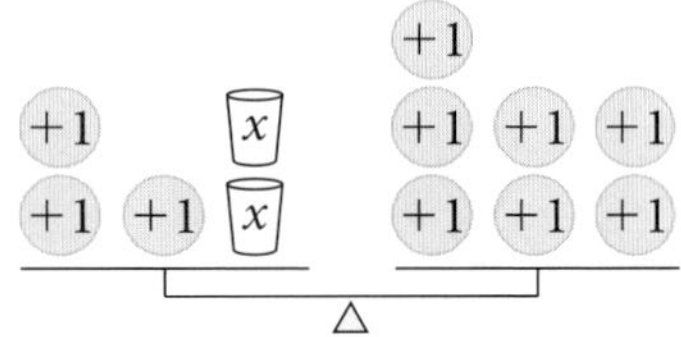

How you solve an equation depends on the equation and what approach you prefer. The equation $2x + 3 = 7$, represented on this balance scale, can be solved graphically by finding the intersection of the lines $y = 2x + 3$ and $y = 7$. You can also solve it by using the undoing method from Chapter 2 or the balancing method from Chapter 3. As you learn more about algebra, you will use all these strategies, and you will learn which strategy works best in a given situation.

EXAMPLE A Use the balancing method to find a value or values of x that satisfy the equation $2x + 3 = 7$, and give an appropriate reason for each step.

Solution

$2x + 3 = 7$	Original equation.
$2x + 3 - 3 = 7 - 3$	Subtract the same value from both sides of the equation.
$2x = 4$	Combine like terms.
$\frac{2x}{2} = \frac{4}{2}$	Divide both sides of the equation by the same value.
$x = 2$	Simplify.

A quick check verifies your answer: $2(2) + 3 = 7$ is a true statement.

Would you expect the two sides of an equation to remain balanced or equal if you subtracted 3 from only one side of the equation or if you subtracted 3 from one side and -3 from the other? If the same operation is applied to both sides of an equation, the resulting equation is equivalent to the original equation. This idea can be expressed as **properties of equality.** For example, the subtraction property of equality says that the two sides of an equation remain equal if the same number is subtracted from both sides. Symbolically, if $a = b$, then $a - c = b - c$. What property of equality was used in the fourth line of the solution in Example A?

Properties of Equality

Given $a = b$, for any number c,

$a + c = b + c$	**Addition property of equality.**
$a - c = b - c$	**Subtraction property of equality.**
$ac = bc$	**Multiplication property of equality.**
$\frac{a}{c} = \frac{b}{c}$ $(c \neq 0)$	**Division property of equality.**

Instead of subtracting, you could add the additive inverse. Recall that two numbers are additive inverses if their sum is zero. In Example A, instead of subtracting 3, you could add -3. Similarly, instead of dividing, you could multiply by the multiplicative inverse. Multiplicative inverses are two numbers whose product is 1. So, instead of dividing by 2, you could multiply by $\frac{1}{2}$.

EXAMPLE B

Give the additive inverse and the multiplicative inverse of each number.

a. 4

b. -2.5

c. $-\frac{2}{7}$

d. $\frac{13}{4}$

Solution

Number	Additive inverse (opposite)	Multiplicative inverse (reciprocal)
a. 4	-4, because $4 + (-4) = 0$	$\frac{1}{4}$, because $4 \cdot \frac{1}{4} = 1$
b. -2.5	2.5, because $-2.5 + 2.5 = 0$	$\frac{1}{-2.5}$, or -0.4, because $(-2.5) \cdot (-0.4) = 1$
c. $-\frac{2}{7}$	$\frac{2}{7}$, because $\left(-\frac{2}{7}\right) + \frac{2}{7} = 0$	$-\frac{7}{2}$, because $\left(-\frac{2}{7}\right) \cdot \left(-\frac{7}{2}\right) = 1$
d. $\frac{13}{4}$	$-\frac{13}{4}$, because $\frac{13}{4} + \left(-\frac{13}{4}\right) = 0$	$\frac{4}{13}$, because $\frac{13}{4} \cdot \frac{4}{13} = 1$

In this and following chapters, you will learn how to use properties of equality to solve equations such as $5x + 3 = 2 + x$ and $x^2 + 1 = 17$.

EXAMPLE C

Use a property of equality to find an equation equivalent to the equation $5x + 3 = 2 + x$ but with the variable appearing on only one side of the equal sign.

Solution

$5x + 3 = 2 + x$	Original equation.
$5x - x + 3 = 2 + x - x$	Subtraction property of equality (subtract x from both sides).
$4x + 3 = 2$	Combine like terms.

Alternatively, you might use the addition property of equality to add $-x$ to both sides of the equation.

Exercises

1. Complete each statement.

a. For the addition property of equality: "If the same number is ________ to both sides of an equation, the result is an equivalent equation."

b. For the multiplication property of equality: "If both sides of an equation are ________ by the same non-zero number, the result is an equivalent equation."

2. These eight values can be arranged into two pairs of additive inverses and two pairs of multiplicative inverses. List the pairs.

$\frac{2}{3}$ $\quad \frac{7}{22}$ $\quad 3\frac{1}{7}$ $\quad -\frac{1}{\sqrt{8}}$ $\quad -4.7$ $\quad \frac{47}{10}$ $\quad -\sqrt{8}$ $\quad -0.\overline{6}$

3. State the property used for each step of the solution.

a. $\frac{x-9}{14} = \frac{3}{7}$ Original equation.

$\frac{x-9}{14} \cdot 14 = \frac{3}{7} \cdot 14$ ________

$x - 9 = 6$ Simplify.

$x - 9 + 9 = 6 + 9$ ________

$x = 15$ Combine like terms.

b. $5x + 12 = 4$ Original equation.

$5x + 12 - 12 = 4 - 12$ ________

$5x = -8$ Combine like terms.

$5x \cdot \frac{1}{5} = -8 \cdot \frac{1}{5}$ ________

$x = -\frac{8}{5}$ Simplify.

4. Describe the number-line locations of these pairs.

a. The number n and its additive inverse.

b. The number n and its multiplicative inverse.

LESSON

4.1

Secret Codes

"Cryptography is an intellectual battle between the code-maker and the code-breaker."

SIMON SINGH

The study of secret codes is called *cryptography.* Early examples of codes go back 4000 years to Egypt. Writing messages in code plays an important role in history and in technology. Today you can find applications of codes at ATMs, in communications, and on the Internet.

The Rosetta Stone, found near Rashid, Egypt, in 1799, bears inscriptions in Greek, Egyptian hieroglyphics, and demotic (everyday) Egyptian. Having these three versions of the same text helped language researchers "break the code" of hieroglyphics.

In the investigation you will learn some of the mathematics behind secret codes.

INVESTIGATION

TFDSFU DPEFT

The table below shows that the letter A is coded into the letter Q, the letter B is coded into R, and so on. It also shows that the letter U is coded into the letter K. This code is an example of a *letter-shift code.* Can you see why? How would you use the code to write a message?

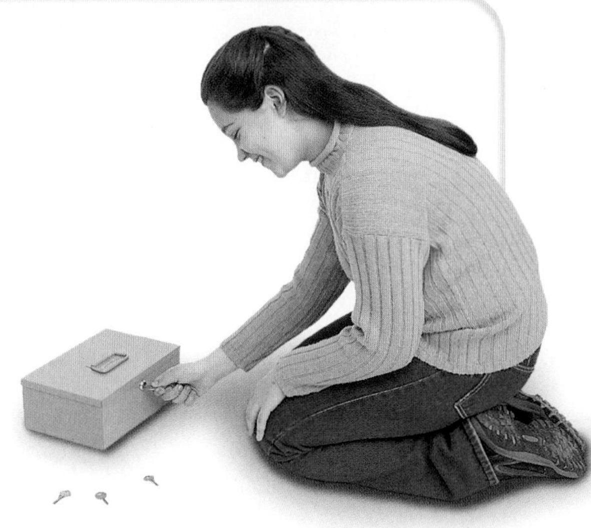

Original input	A	B	C	D	E	F	G	H	I	J	K	L	M	N	O	P	Q	R	S	T	U	V	W	X	Y	Z
Coded output	Q	R	S	T	U	V	W	X	Y	Z	A	B	C	D	E	F	G	H	I	J	K	L	M	N	O	P

You can also represent the code with a grid. Note that the input letters run across (horizontally). To code a letter, look for the colored square directly above it. Then find the coded output by looking across to the letters that run up (vertically).

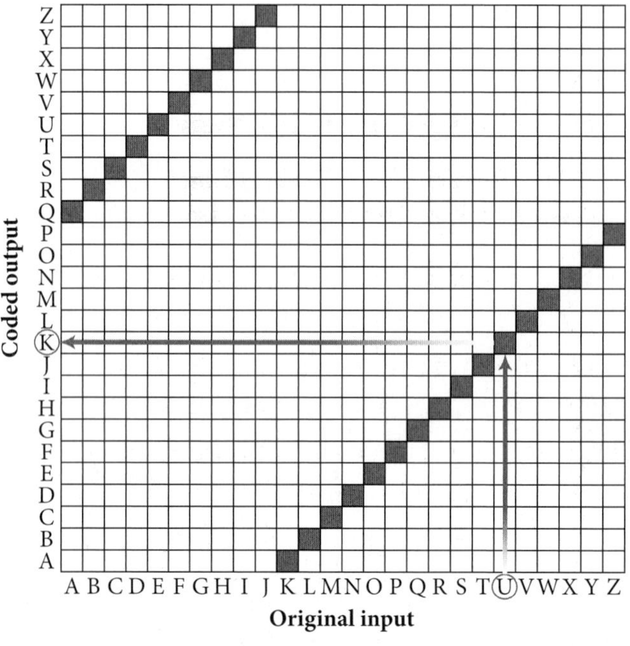

Step 1 Use the coding grid above to write a one-word or two-word message.

Step 2 Exchange your coded message with a partner. Use the grid to decode each other's messages.

Next you'll invent your own letter-shift code.

Step 3 Create a new code by writing a rule that shifts letters a certain specified number of places. Put the code on a grid like the one shown above. Do not allow your partner to see this grid.

Step 4 Use your new grid to code the same message you wrote in Step 1.

Step 5 Exchange your newly coded message with your partner. Use it along with the message in the first code to try to figure out each other's new codes. Write a rule or create a coding grid to represent your partner's new code.

Step 6 Compare your grid to your classmates' new grids. In what ways are the grids the same? How are they different? In any one grid, how many coded outputs are possible for one input letter? How many ways are there to decode any one letter in a coded message? Explain.

Step 7 Use the grid on the next page to send a new one-word or two-word message to your partner. Exchange and decode each other's messages.

Step 8 Did your partner successfully decode your message? Why or why not?

Use this code for Steps 7 to 10.

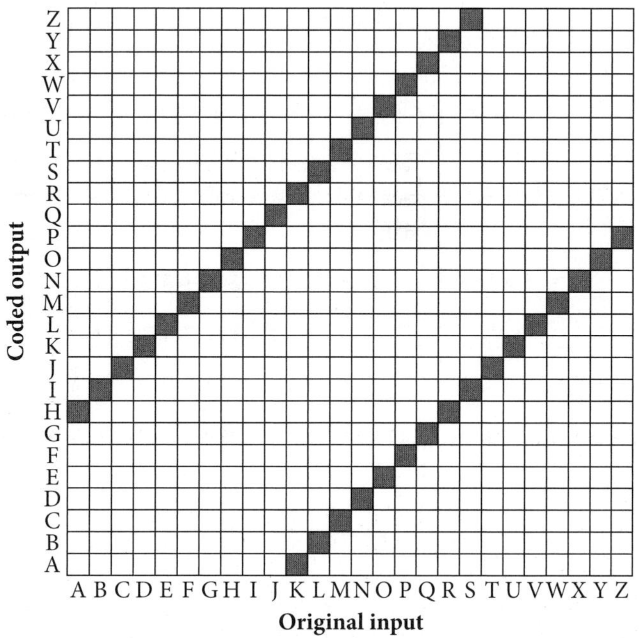

Step 9 How is the grid above different from the grid in Step 1? Code the word FUNCTION to help you answer this question.

Step 10 Which grid makes it easier to decode messages? Which coded output letters are difficult to decode into their original input letters?

You can think of a code as a set of ordered pairs (*input, output*). For example, in the first code in the investigation, the pairs were (A, Q), (B, R), . . . , (Z, P). A set of ordered pairs is called a **relation.** The set of inputs is the **domain** of the relation, and the set of outputs is the **range.**

As you saw in the investigation, a relation that serves as a code has a special property: No input can be paired with more than one output. When you had more than one choice of output for some inputs, it wasn't clear how to encode your message. A relation in which every input has only one output is called a **function.** A code must be a function.

Functions

Function: A relation in which every input has exactly one output.
Domain: The set of inputs in a relation.
Range: The set of outputs in a relation.

In the codes you've seen, the domain and range both consist of letters, but outputs can be different from inputs. Consider this code, in which the outputs are numbers.

Domain	A	B	C	D	E	F	G	H	I	J	K	L	M
Range	65	66	67	68	69	70	71	72	73	74	75	76	77

Domain	N	O	P	Q	R	S	T	U	V	W	Y	Y	Z
Range	78	79	80	81	82	83	84	85	86	87	88	89	90

Computers store letters as numbers. In the preceding code, the letter A is coded as the number 65, B is coded as 66, and so on. In this case, the domain is the letters of the alphabet, and the range is the set of whole numbers from 65 through 90. Notice that each letter in the domain matches no more than one number in the range. This is what makes the code a function.

EXAMPLE

State whether each table of values represents a function. Give the domain and range of each relation.

Table A

Input	Output
1	2
2	4
3	6

Table B

Input	1	0	1
Output	1	2	5

Table C

Input	1	2	3	4	5	6
Output	0	0	0	0	0	0

Solution

To be a function, each input must have exactly one output. It is helpful to use arrows to show which input value matches which output value.

Table A

Each input value matches one output value. So this relation is a function. The domain is {1, 2, 3}, and the range is {2, 4, 6}.

Input: 1 2 3

Output: 2 4 6

Alan Turing (1912–1954) was an English mathematician and a pioneer in computing theory. During World War II, he led the team that cracked the German codes of the notorious Enigma machine.

Table B

The input value 1 has two outputs, 1 and 5. This relation is not a function because there is an input value with more than one output value. The domain is {0, 1}, and the range is {1, 2, 5}.

Input: 0 1

Output: 1 2 5

Table C

Each input value has exactly one output value. So this relation is a function, even though all the inputs have the same output. The domain is {1, 2, 3, 4, 5, 6}, and the range is {0}.

Input: 1 2 3 4 5 6

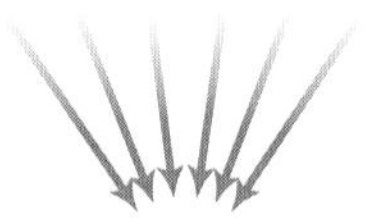

Output: 0

You can represent a relation with a table, a graph, an equation, symbols, a diagram, or even a written rule or description. Many of the relations you have studied in this text are functions. You will revisit some of them as you learn more about functions in this chapter and in Chapter 7.

4.1 Exercises

Practice Your Skills

1. Use this table to code each word.

Input	A	B	C	D	E	F	G	H	I	J	K	L	M	N	O	P	Q	R	S	T	U	V	W	X	Y	Z
Coded output	B	C	D	E	F	G	H	I	J	K	L	M	N	O	P	Q	R	S	T	U	V	W	X	Y	Z	A

a. RANGE @ b. DOMAIN c. TABLE d. GRAPH

2. Use the grid at right to decode each word.

a. SXZED

b. YEDZED

c. BOVKDSYXCRSZ @

d. BEVO

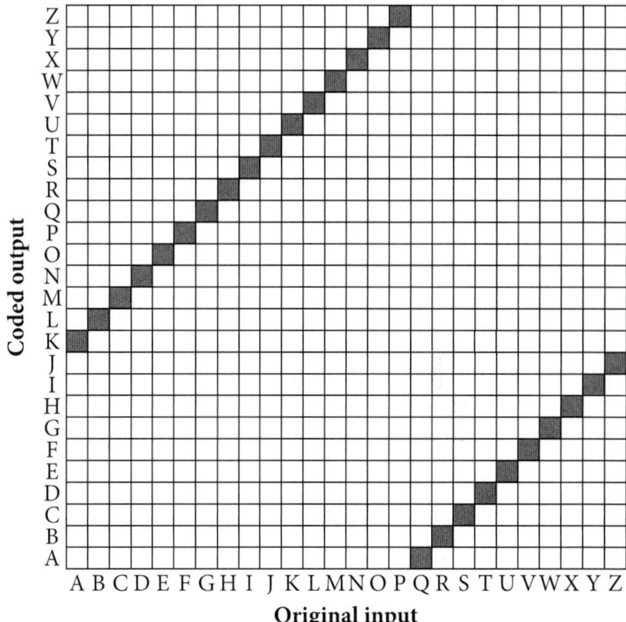

3. The title of the investigation, TFDSFU DPEFT, is the output of a one-letter-shift code.

a. Decode TFDSFU DPEFT. @

b. Write the rule or create the coding grid for the code.

4. Use the coding grid below to answer 4a–c.

a. What are the possible input values?

b. What are the possible output values?

c. Is this code a function? Explain why or why not.

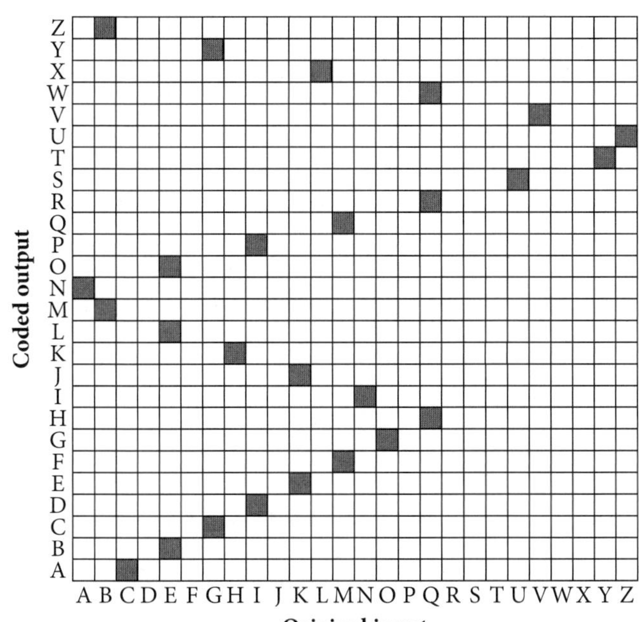

5. The table converts standard time to military time.

Standard time (A.M.)	12:00	1:00	2:00	3:00	4:00	5:00	6:00	7:00	8:00	9:00	10:00	11:00
Military time	0000	0100	0200	0300	0400	0500	0600	0700	0800	0900	1000	1100

Standard time (P.M.)	12:00	1:00	2:00	3:00	4:00	5:00	6:00	7:00	8:00	9:00	10:00	11:00
Military time	1200	1300	1400	1500	1600	1700	1800	1900	2000	2100	2200	2300

a. Describe the domain. @

b. Describe the range. @

c. Does the table represent a function? Explain why or why not. @

Reason and Apply

6. Use the letter-shift grid at right to

a. Find the output when the input is W.

b. Find the input when the output is W.

c. Code Q.

d. Decode K.

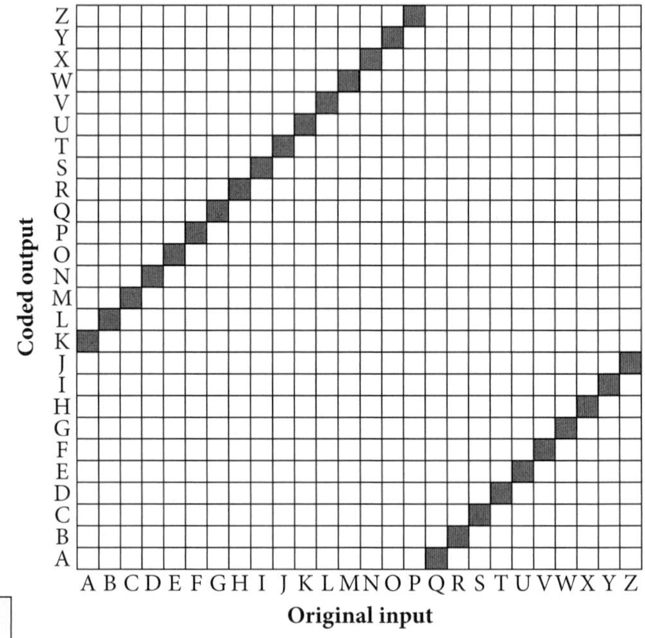

7. Each letter of the alphabet, from A to Z, can be represented by a number from 1 to 26. Using A = 1, B = 2, C = 3, and so on, the word CAT becomes 3, 1, 20.

a. Create a table for the word FUNCTION, like this one for CAT. Add 9 to each letter value, and then change the resulting value back to a letter.

Original letter	Original value	Value + 9	Coded value	Coded letter
C	3	12	12	L
A	1	10	10	J
T	20	29	3	C

b. In the CAT table, why is the coded value for the letter T not 29? Which letter values must be changed when you code the word FUNCTION using this rule?

c. In general, what numbers could you add to the original values so that the coded letters will be the same as the original letters?

8. Use the coding grid at right to decode CEOKEQC.

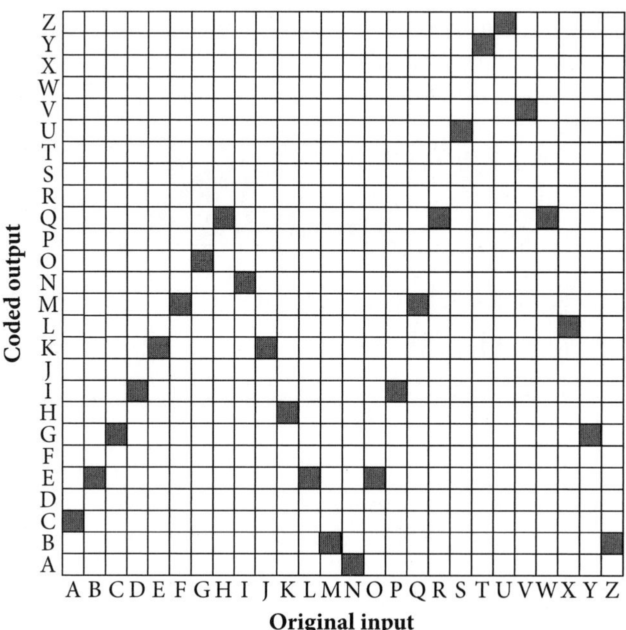

9. Here is a corner of a coding grid.

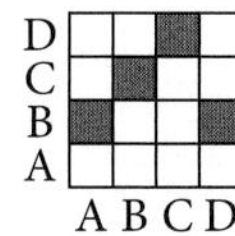

a. Does this grid represent a function? Why or why not? @

b. Does this grid represent a function that can be easily decoded? If not, how can you change the grid so that it does?

10. For each diagram, give the domain and range, and then tell whether each relation is a function. Explain how you know.

a. @

- 0 → 0
- 1 → 1
- −1 → 1
- 2 → 2
- −2 → 2

b.

- 1 → −1
- 1 → 1
- 4 → −2
- 4 → 2
- 9 → −3
- 9 → 3

11. For each table, give the domain and range, and state whether each relation is a function.

a.

Input	Output
1	1
2	3
3	1
4	3
5	1

b.

Input	Output
1	1
1	2
3	3
3	4

12. Does this set of ordered pairs represent a function? If so, what are its domain and range?
$(-2, 3), (3, -2), (1, 3), (0, -2)$ @

13. Is this set of ordered pairs a function? Explain your reasoning.
$(3, -2), (-2, 3), (3, 1), (-2, 0)$

14. The grid at right is based on an ancient Hebrew code called "atbash." (*A Short History of Cryptography,* Fred Cohen, *http://all.net/edu/curr/ip/Chap2-1.html*)

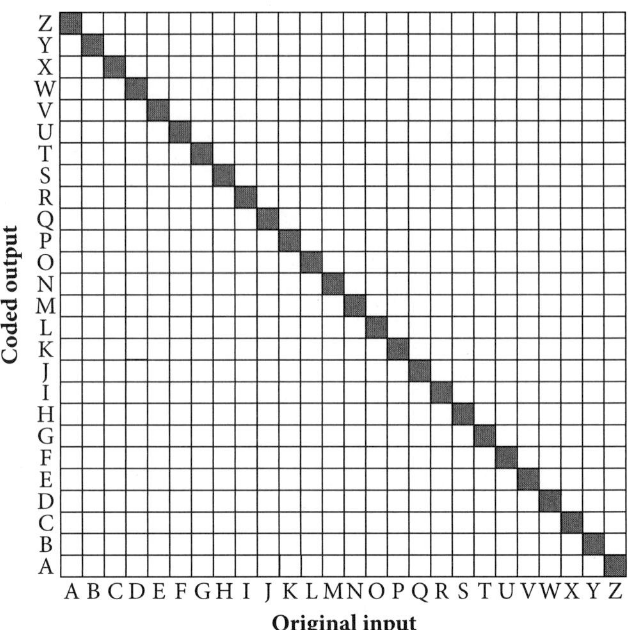

a. Create a rule for the atbash code. @

b. Is this code a function? Explain why or why not.

c. Use the atbash code to code your name.

15. If you know that TIPGKFXIRGYP is the study of coding and decoding, what is the rule for breaking this code? What is the original message?

Review

16. APPLICATION Zoe is an intern at Yellowstone National Park. One of her jobs is to estimate the chipmunk population in the campground areas. She starts by trapping 60 chipmunks, giving them a checkup, and banding their legs. A few weeks later, Zoe traps 84 chipmunks. Of these, 22 have bands on their legs. How many chipmunks should Zoe estimate are in the campgrounds?

17. If 1 calorie is 4.1868 joules, how many calories is 470 joules?

18. Tell whether the relationship between x and y is direct variation, inverse variation, or neither, and explain how you know. If the relationship is direct or inverse variation, write its equation.

a.

x	y
0.2	10
0.8	2.5
1	2
4	0.5
5	0.4

b.

x	y
0.3	6
0	3
1	13
3	33
10.0	103

c.

x	y
0.8	0.2
1	0.25
3	0.75
12	3
28.0	7

d.

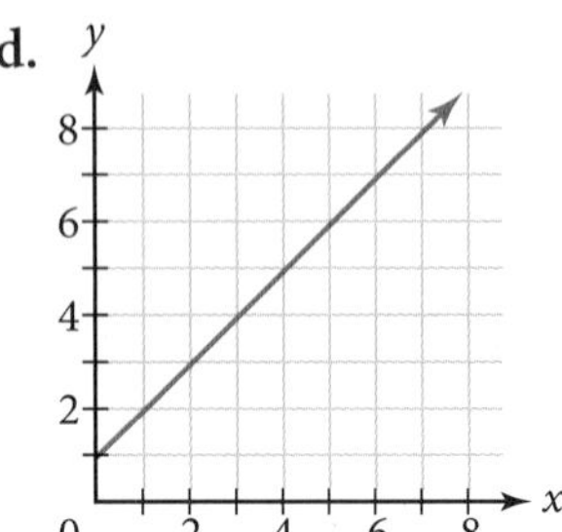

e.

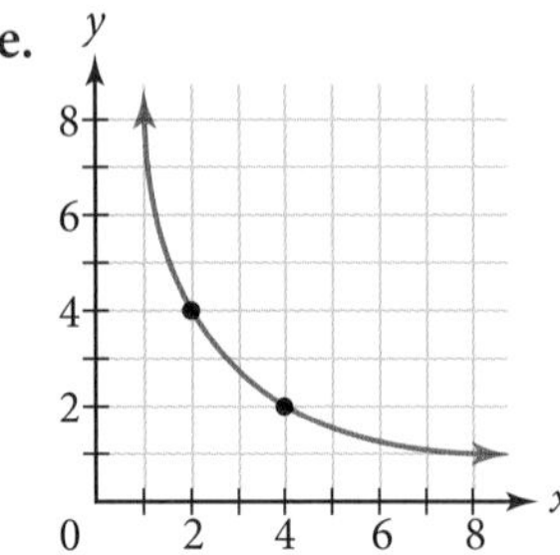

f.

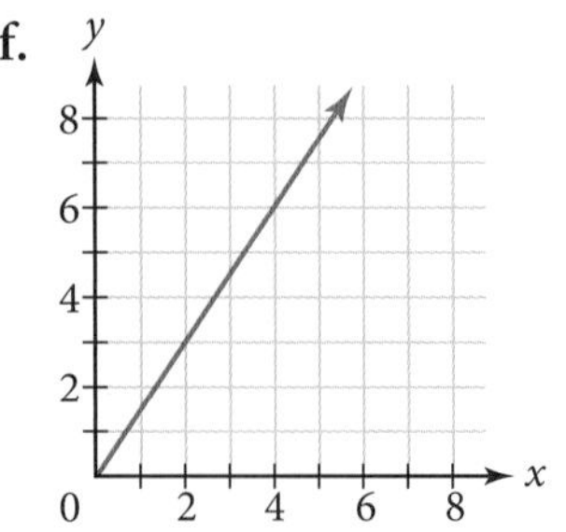

LESSON

4.2

Functions and Graphs

In Lesson 4.1, you learned that you can write rules for some coding grids. You can also write rules, often in the form of equations, to transform numbers into other numbers. One simple example is "Add 1 to each number." You can represent this relation with a table, an equation, a graph, or even a diagram.

Table

Input x	Output y
7	8
-47	-46
10.28	11.28
x	$x + 1$

Equation

$y = x + 1$

Graph

Diagram

Domain		Range
-47	→	-46
7	→	8
10.28	→	11.28

This rule turns 7 into 8, -47 into -46, 10.28 into 11.28, and x into $x + 1$.

When you explored relations in previous chapters, you used recursive rules, graphs, and equations to relate input and output data. To tell whether a relationship between input and output data is a function, you can apply a test to the relation's graph on the xy-plane.

The Spanish painter Pablo Picasso (1881–1973) was one of the originators of the art movement Cubism. Cubists were interested in creating a new visual language, transforming realism into a different way of seeing.

INVESTIGATION

Testing for Functions

In this investigation you will use various kinds of evidence to determine whether relations are functions.

Step 1 Each table represents a relation. Based on the tables, which relations are functions and which are not? Give reasons for your answers.

Table 1

Input x	Output y
−2	−3
−1	−1
0	1
1	3
2	5
3	7
4	9

Table 2

Input x	Output y
4	−2
1	−1
0	0
1	1
4	2
9	3
16	4

Table 3

Input x	Output y
−2	0.44
−1	0.67
0	1
1	1.5
2	2.25
3	3.37
4	5.06

Table 4

Input x	Output y
−2	−3
−1	−5
1	−1
1	−3
2	−10
3	−2
3	−8

Step 2 Each algebraic statement represents a relation. Which relations are functions and which are not? Give reasons for your answers.

Statement 1	Statement 2	Statement 3	Statement 4
$y = 1 + 2x$	$y^2 = x$	$y = 1.5$	$y < x + 2$

Step 3 Each graph represents a relation. Move a vertical line, such as the edge of a ruler, from side to side on the graph. Based on the graph and your vertical line, which relations are functions and which are not? Give reasons for your answers.

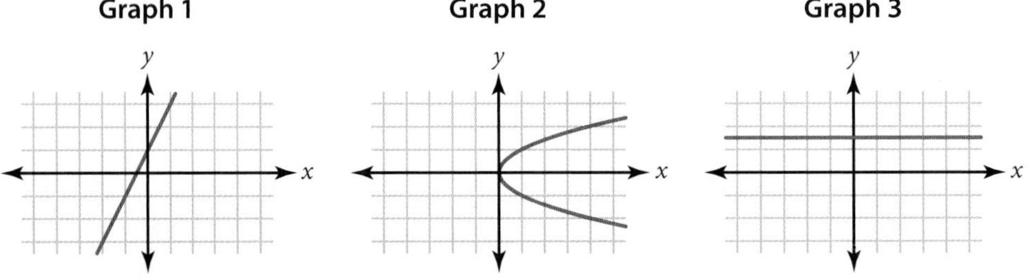

Step 4 Use your results in Step 3 to describe how you can determine whether a relation is a function, based only on its graph.

The **vertical line test** helps you determine whether a relation is a function. If all possible vertical lines cross the graph once or not at all, then the graph represents a function. The graph does not represent a function if you can draw even one vertical line that crosses the graph two or more times.

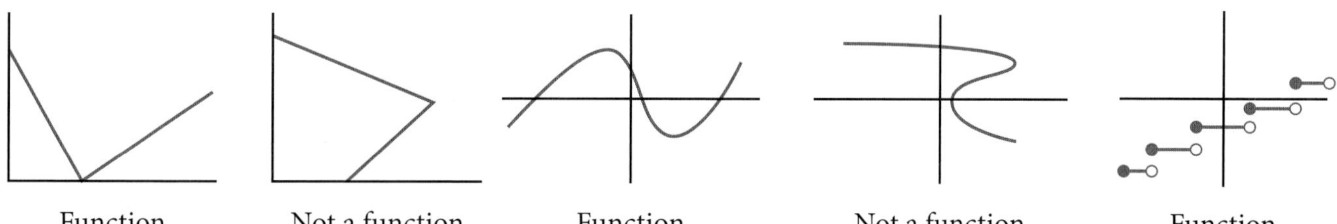

You have learned many forms of linear equations. In the example you will see whether all lines represent functions.

EXAMPLE

Graph each linear equation or inequality. Explain why each one is or is not a function.

a. $y = 0.5x + 2$ **b.** $y = \frac{3}{4}x$ **c.** $2x + 3y = 6$

d. $y = 5 + 2(x - 8)$ **e.** $y = 7$ **f.** $x = 9$

Solution

When you graph the equations, you can see that all except the graph of the equation in part f pass the vertical line test. So all the equations represent functions except for the one in part f.

a.

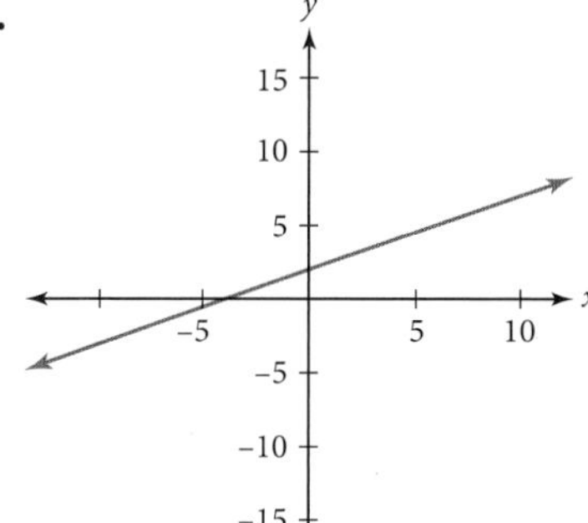

b.

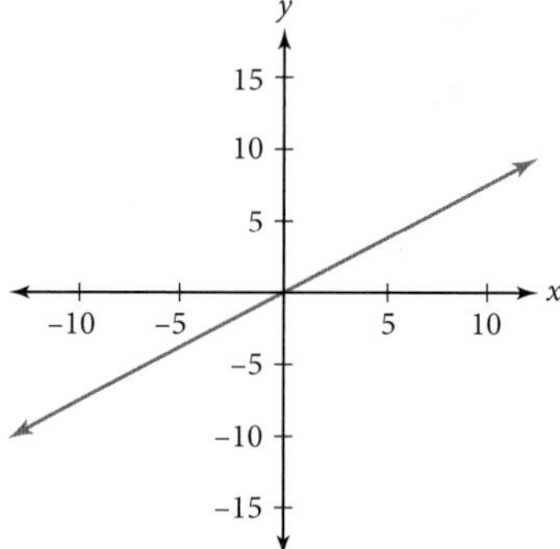

c.

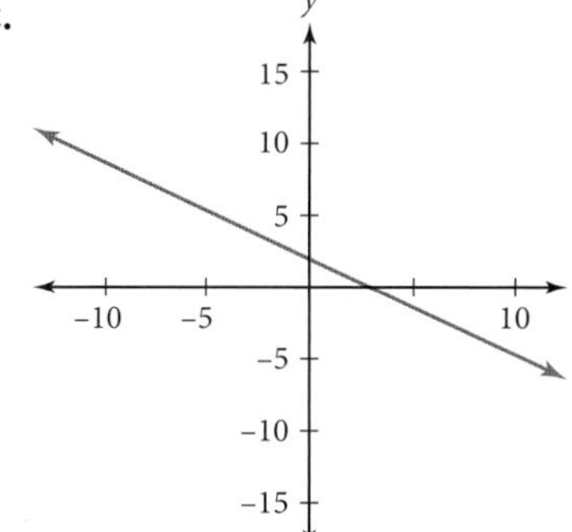

d.

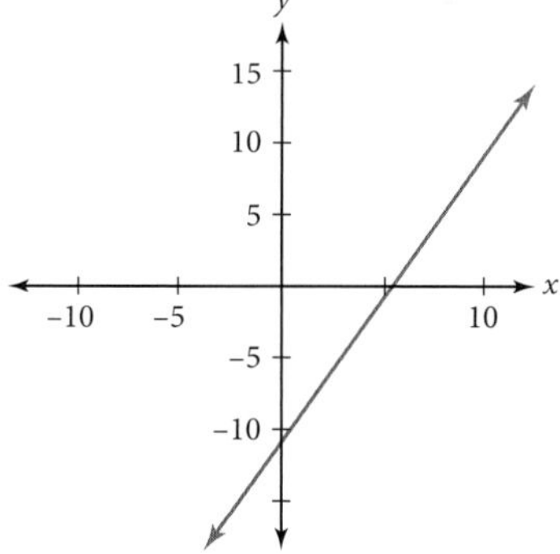

e.

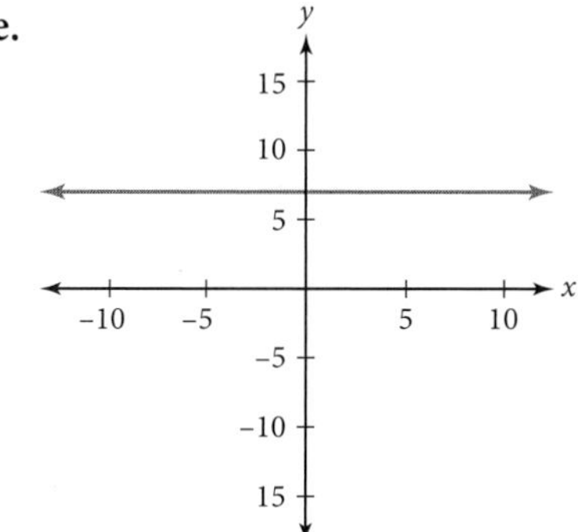

f.

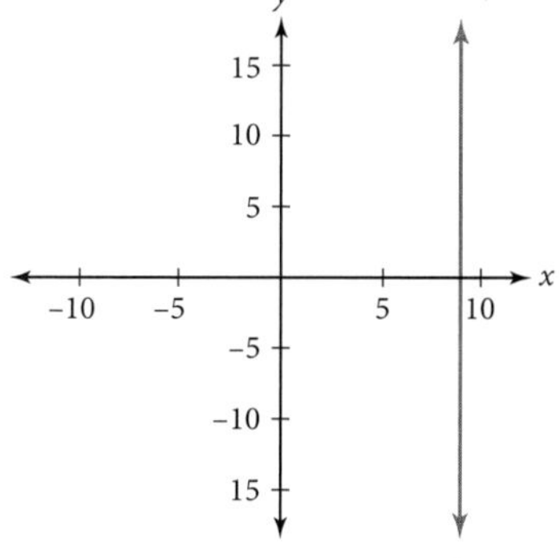

The graph of $x = 9$ fails the vertical line test because you can match more than one output value of y to a single input value of x. So, $x = 9$ does not represent a function. In fact, graphs of all vertical lines fail the vertical line test and therefore do not represent functions. All nonvertical lines represent functions.

As you work more with functions, you will be able to tell if a relation is a function without having to consider its graph on the xy-plane. If the graph is shown, use the vertical line test. Otherwise, see whether there is more than one output value for any single input value.

Carpenters use a tool called a *level* to determine if support beams are truly vertical.

4.2 Exercises

Practice Your Skills

1. Use the equations to find the missing entries in each table.

a. $y = 3 - x$

Input x	Output y
-3	
-1	
0	
2	
4	

b. $y = -4 + 2x$

Input x	Output y
-2	
0	
1	
	2
	6

c. $y = 4.2 + 0.8x$ @

Input x	Output y
-4	
-1	
1.5	
6.4	
9	

d. $y = 1.2 - 0.8x$

Domain x	Range y
-4	
-1	
2.4	
	-7.6
	-10

2. Plot the points in the table and graph the equation in Exercise 1a.

3. Plot the points in the tables and graph the equations in Exercise 1b–d.

4. Use the tables and graphs in Exercises 1–3 to tell whether the relations in Exercise 1 are functions. @

Reason and Apply

5. The graph at right describes another student's distance from you. What are the walking instructions for the graph? Does the graph represent a function? @

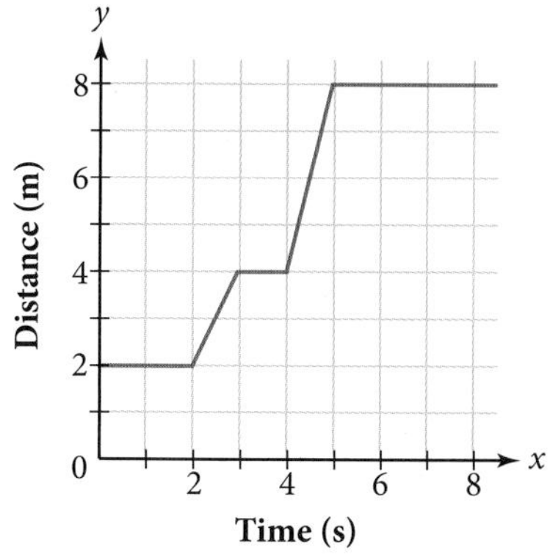

6. State whether each graph below represents a function. Does it pass the vertical line test?

a.

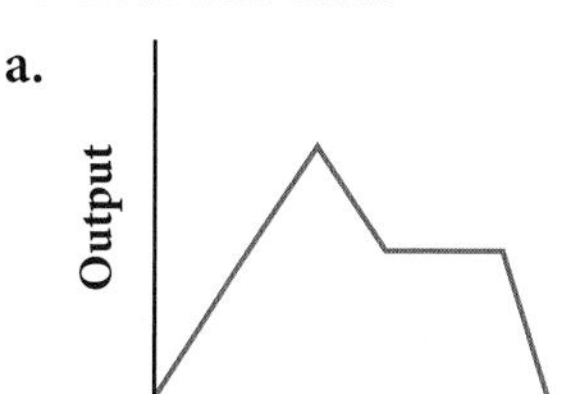

b.

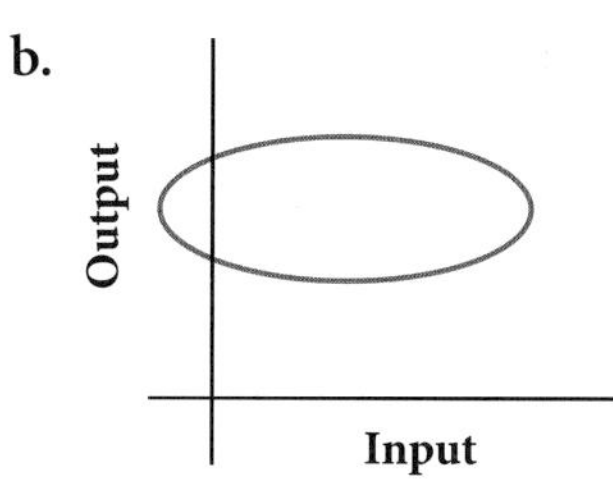

c. (h)

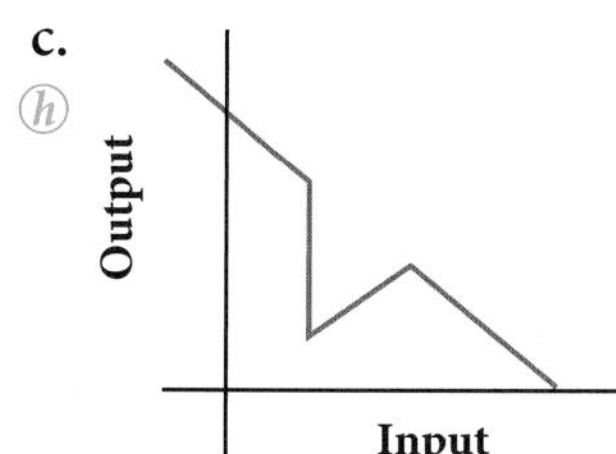

d.

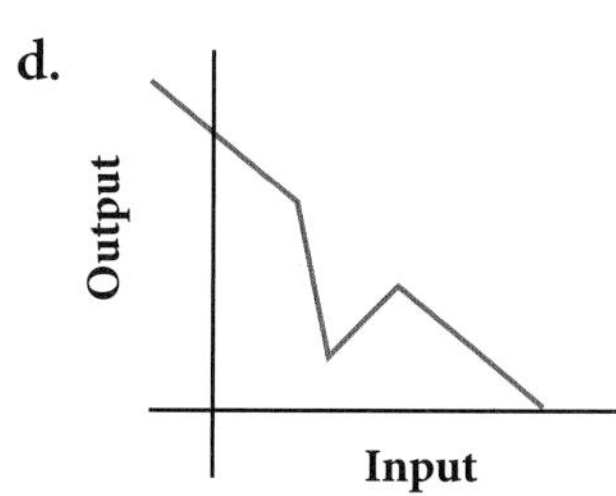

7. Does each relationship in the form (*input, output*) represent a function? If the relationship does not represent a function, find an example of one input that has two or more outputs. This is called a **counterexample.**

a. (*city, ZIP Code*) (h)

b. (*person, birth date*)

c. (*last name, first name*) @

d. (*state, capital*)

8. Consider these six graphs.

i.

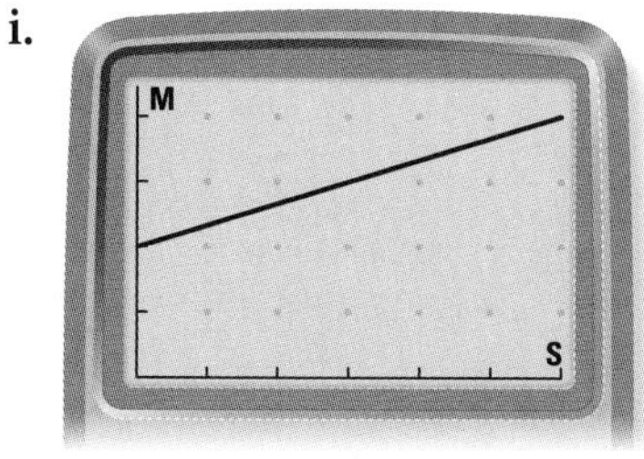

ii.

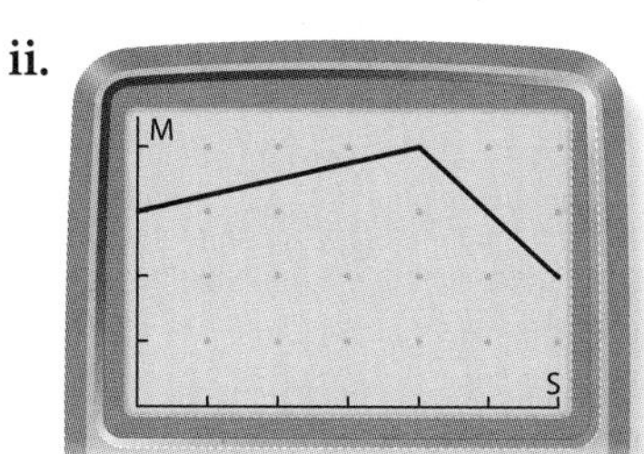

iii.

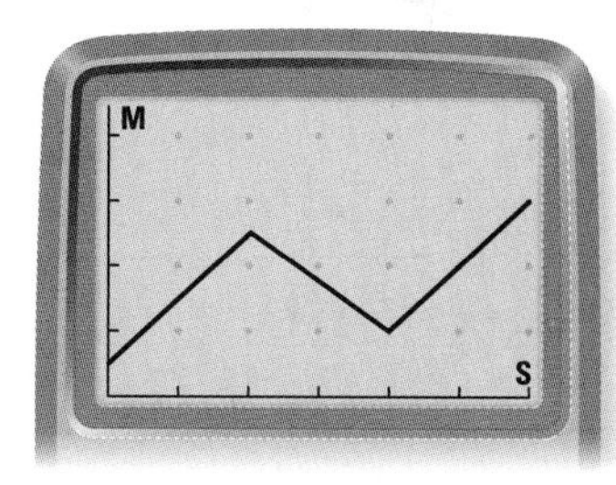

iv.

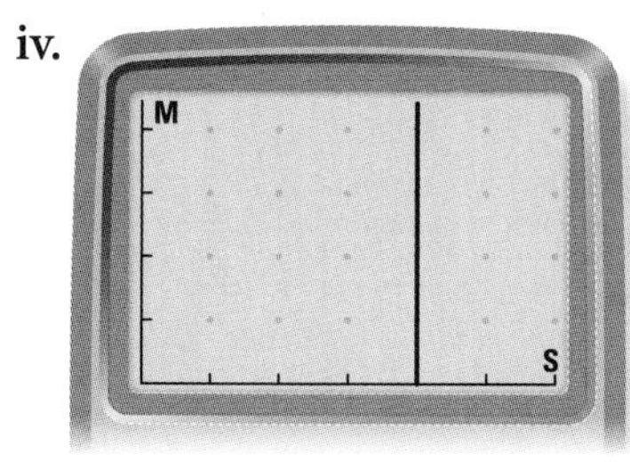

v.

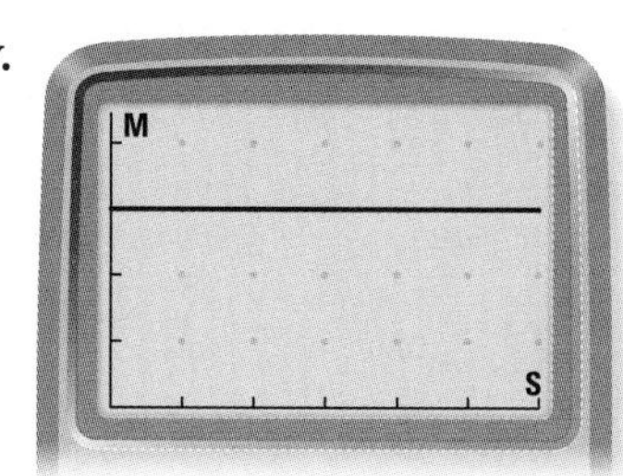

vi.

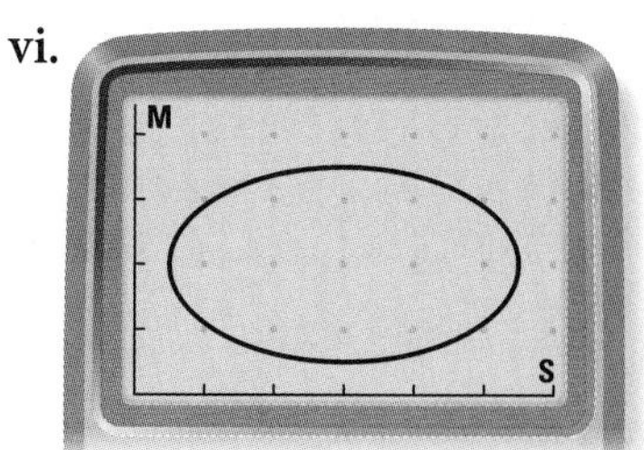

a. Which graphs represent functions?

b. Which graphs could represent walks recorded by a motion sensor?

c. What conclusion can you make?

9. State whether each table of x- and y-values represents a function. Explain your reasoning.

a.

Domain x	Range y
0	5
1	7
3	10
7	9
5	7
4	5
3	8

b.

Domain x	Range y
3	7
4	9
8	4
5	5
9	3
11	9
7	6

c.

Domain x	Range y
2	8
3	11
5	12
7	3
9	5
8	7
4	11

10. On graph paper, draw a graph that is a function and has these three properties:

- Domain of x-values satisfying $-3 \leq x \leq 5$
- Range of y-values satisfying $-4 \leq y \leq 4$
- Includes the points $(-2, 3)$ and $(3, -2)$ @

11. On graph paper, draw a graph that is *not* a function and has these three properties:

- Domain of x-values satisfying $-3 \leq x \leq 5$
- Range of y-values satisfying $-4 \leq y \leq 4$
- Includes the points $(-2, 3)$ and $(3, -2)$

12. Complete the table of values for each equation. Let x represent domain values, and let y represent range values. Determine whether each equation describes a function. Explain your reasoning.

a. $x - 3y = 5$ @

x	2		−4		0	
y		1		−2		0

b. $y = 2x^2 + 1$

x	−2	3	0	−3	−1	
y						9

c. $x + y^2 = 2$

x	−7				−2	2
y		1	−2	−3		

13. Identify all numbers in the domain and range of each graph.

a.

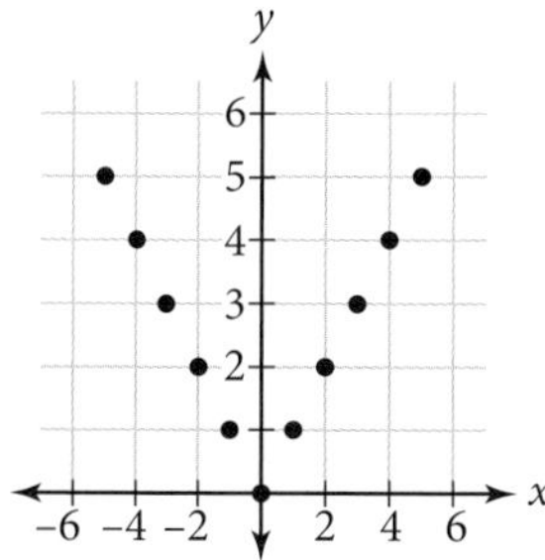

b. ⓐ

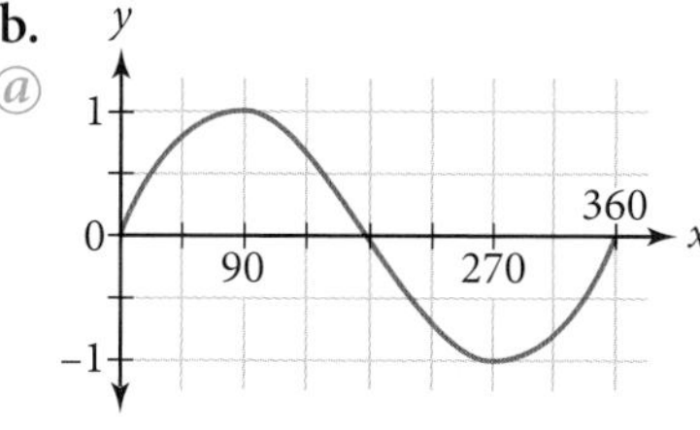

c.

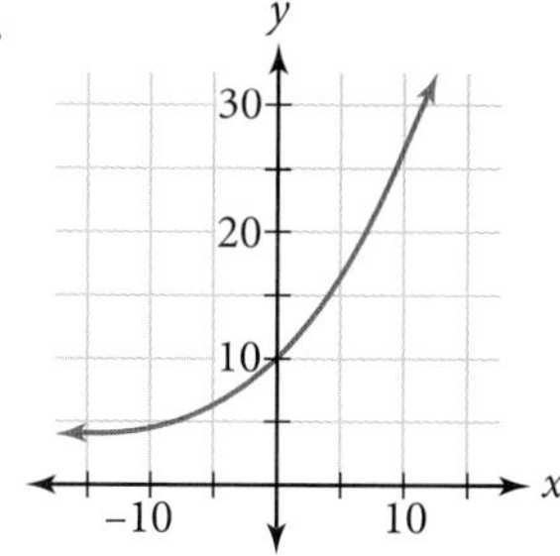

14. Consider the capital letters in our alphabet.

a. Draw two capital letters that do not represent the graph of a function. Explain. ⓗ

b. Draw two capital letters that do represent the graph of a function. Explain.

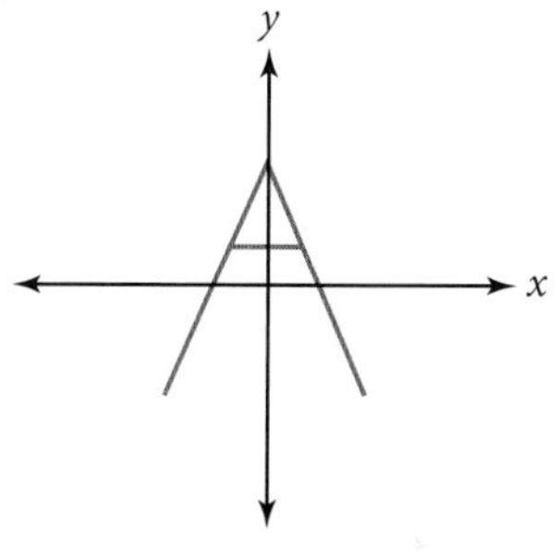

Graph of the letter A.

Review

15. This two-way frequency table shows activity preferences of a group of men and women. Use the information to answer the questions. Then state which frequency is reported by the answer.

	Dance	Sports	Movies	TOTAL
Men	11	21	18	50
Women	22	10	18	50
TOTAL	33	31	36	100

a. Which activity is the least preferred?

b. Which activity do women strongly prefer out of the total number of women surveyed?

c. Which activity do men strongly prefer?

16. Solve each equation.

a. $\frac{4(x-7)-8}{3} = 20$

b. $\frac{4.5}{x-3} = \frac{2}{3}$ ⓗ

LESSON

4.3

Graphs of Real-World Situations

"One picture is worth ten thousand words."

FRED R. BARNARD

Like pictures, graphs communicate a lot of information. You need to be able to interpret, draw, and communicate about graphs. In previous chapters you learned to use bar graphs, histograms, and box plots. You learned to graph data from recursive rules. Most graphs you've seen represent functions—some of these graphs were lines, or **linear,** and others were curves, or **nonlinear.**

In this lesson you will learn vocabulary for describing graphs (such as linear and nonlinear), and you will interpret the graphs of some real-world situations.

EXAMPLE A

This graph shows the depth of the water in a leaky swimming pool. State what quantities are varying and how they are related. Give possible real-world events in your explanation.

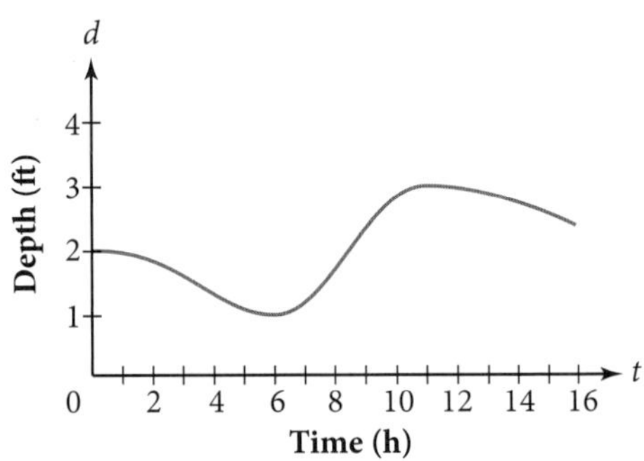

Solution

The graph shows that the water level, or depth, changes over a 16-hour time period. At the beginning, when no time has passed, $t = 0$, and the water in the pool is 2 feet deep, so $d = 2$. During the first 6-hour interval ($0 \leq t \leq 6$), the water level drops. The leak seems to get worse as time passes. When $t = 6$ and $d = 1$, it seems that someone starts to refill the pool. The water level rises for the next 5 hours, during the interval $6 \leq t \leq 11$. At $t = 11$, the water reaches its highest level at just about 3 feet, so $d = 3$. At the 11-hour mark, the in-flowing water is apparently turned off. The pool still has a leak, so the water level starts to drop again.

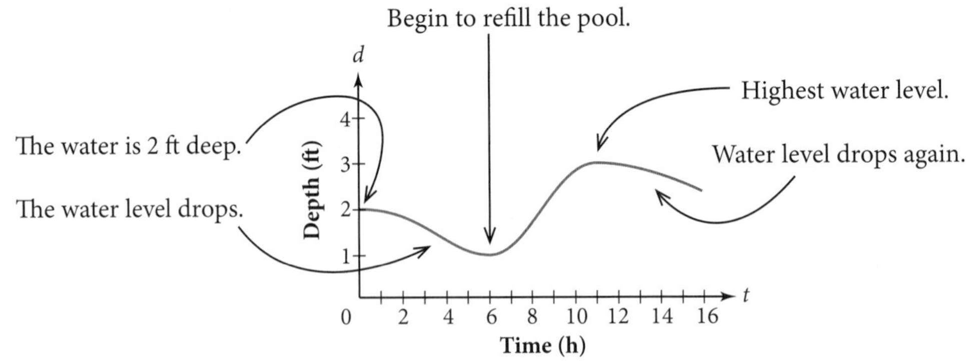

In the example the depth of the water is a function of time. That is, the depth depends on how much time has passed. So, in this case, the output—depth—is called the **dependent variable.** The input—time—is the **independent variable.** When you draw a graph, put the independent variable on the horizontal axis and the dependent variable on the vertical axis.

In the graph of the function in Example A, you can see the possible values of the independent variable. The domain consists of all times from 0 h through 16 h—that is, the time period represented by the function. You can express this interval as

$$0 \leq x \leq 16$$

where x is the independent variable, representing time.

You can also see the possible values of the dependent variable. The range appears to be all water depths from 1 ft to 3 ft—that is, all the water depths occurring during the 16 hours, from the least to the greatest. You can express this interval as

$$1 \leq y \leq 3$$

where y is the dependent variable, representing the depth of the water. Notice that the lowest possible value for the range is not necessarily the starting value, when x is zero.

While sections of the graph in Example A may appear linear, such as on the interval $8 \leq x \leq 10$, the function is nonlinear overall. This means that as x changes at a constant rate, the function values change at a varying rate. In the investigation that follows, Graphs A and D show linear functions—as x increases at a constant rate, the function values also change at a constant rate. In the investigation you'll discover another aspect of functions and use graphs of functions to describe real-world situations.

INVESTIGATION

Matching Up

First, you'll consider the concepts of increasing and decreasing functions.

Step 1 These are graphs of *increasing functions*. What do the three graphs have in common? How would you describe the rate of change in each?

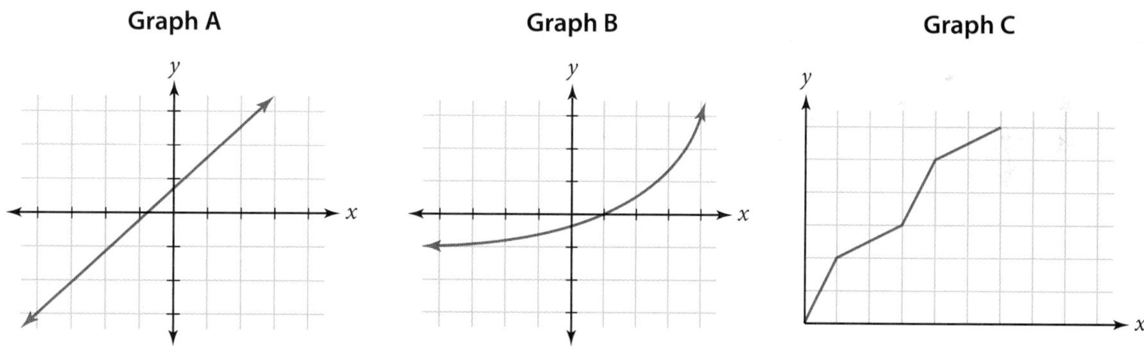

Step 2 These are graphs of *decreasing functions*. What do they have in common? How are they different from the graphs in Step 1? How would you describe the rate of change in these graphs?

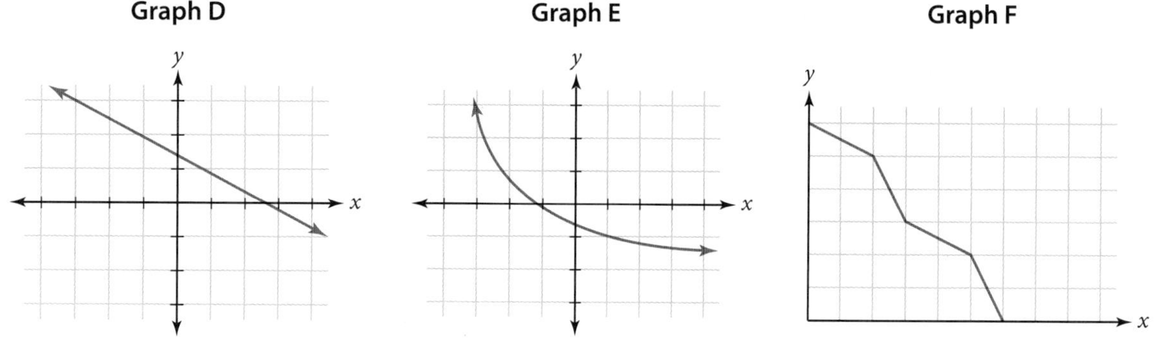

In Steps 3 to 5, you'll use this vocabulary to find and describe the graph that matches each of these real-world situations. Two of the graphs will not be used.

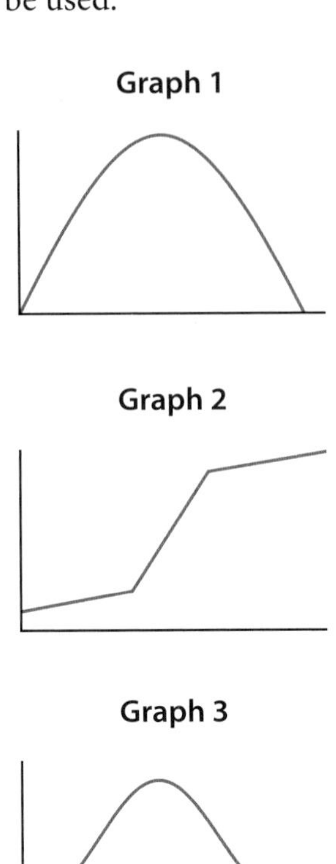

Situation A During the first few years, the number of deer on the island increased by a steady percentage. As food became less plentiful, the growth rate started slowing down. Now the number of births and deaths is about the same.

Situation B In the Northern Hemisphere, the amount of daylight increases slowly from January through February, faster until mid-May, and then slowly until the maximum in June. Then it decreases slowly through July, faster from August until mid-November, and then slowly until the year's end.

Situation C If you have a fixed amount of fencing, the width of your rectangular garden determines its area. If the width is very narrow, the garden won't have much area. As the width increases, the area also increases. The area increases more slowly until it reaches a maximum. As the width continues to increase, the area becomes smaller more quickly until it is zero.

Situation D Your cup of tea is very hot. The difference between the tea temperature and the room temperature decreases quickly at first as the tea starts to cool to room temperature. But when the two temperatures are close to each other, the cooling rate slows down. It actually takes a long time for the tea to finally reach room temperature.

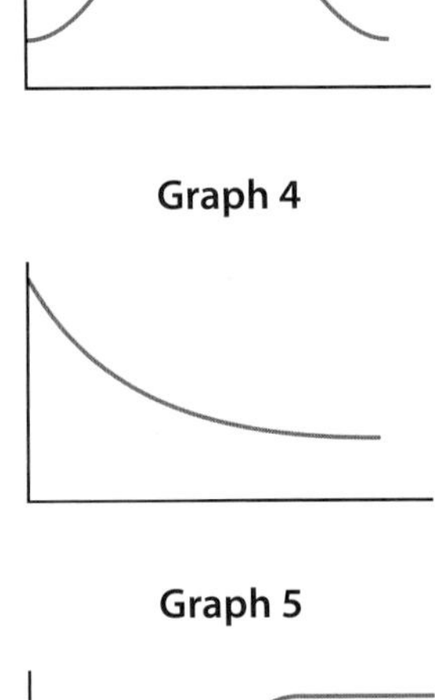

Step 3 In Situation A decide which quantities are varying. Also decide which variable is independent and which is dependent.

Step 4 Match and describe the graph that best fits Situation A. Write a description of the function and its graph using words such as *linear, nonlinear, increasing, decreasing, rate of change, maximum* or *greatest value,* and *minimum* or *least value.* Explain why you think the graph and your description match the situation.

Step 5 Repeat Steps 3 and 4 for the other three situations.

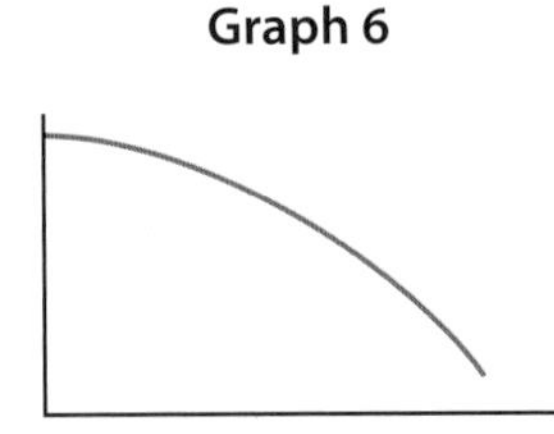

In the investigation you learned how to describe real-world situations with graphs and some function vocabulary. A function is **increasing** when the variables change in the same way—that is, the y-values *grow* when reading the graph from left to right. A function is **decreasing** when the variables change in different directions—that is, the y-values *drop* when reading the graph from left to right. It is easiest to see these patterns by looking at a graph of the function.

Increasing and Decreasing Functions

A function is increasing if the graph rises from left to right.
A function is decreasing if the graph falls from left to right.

Sometimes it is useful to name a part of the domain for which a function has a certain characteristic.

EXAMPLE B Describe this graph by telling how the variables in the graph are related to each other.

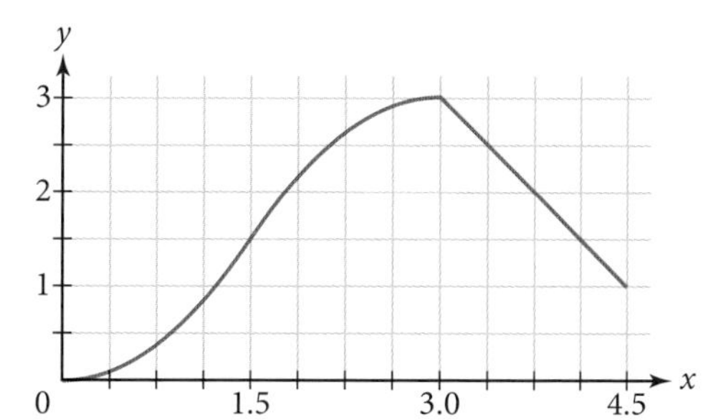

Solution Use the intervals marked on the x-axis to help you describe where the function is increasing or decreasing and where it is linear or nonlinear.

On the interval $0 \leq x < 3.0$, the function is nonlinear and increasing. As x increases steadily, y changes at a varying rate, so the graph is nonlinear. When read from left to right, the graph rises. So the y-values grow and the function is increasing.

On the interval $3.0 \leq x \leq 4.5$, the function appears linear and is decreasing. Because y appears to change at a constant rate on the graph, the function is linear. When read from left to right, the graph falls. So the y-values drop and the function is decreasing.

Situations C and D in the investigation are represented by **continuous** functions because there are no breaks in the domain or range. Situations A and B in the investigation are **discrete** functions because they involve quantities—number of deer and days—that are counted or measured only in whole numbers. When graphing the amount of daylight for every day of the year, the graph really should be a set of 365 points, as in the graph below. There is no value for day 47.35. Likewise, there may not be a day with exactly 11 hours 1 minute of daylight. But it's easier to draw this relationship as a smooth curve than to plot 365 points.

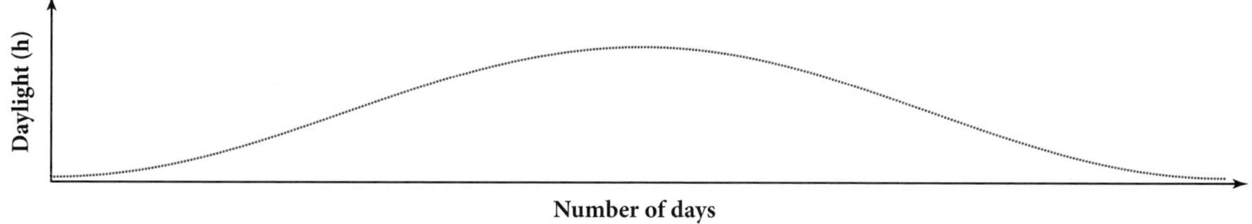

4.3 Exercises

Practice Your Skills

Traders on the floor of the New York Stock Exchange use graphs to show stock prices.

1. Sketch a reasonable graph and label the axes for each situation described. Write a few sentences explaining each graph.

a. The more students who help decorate for the homecoming dance, the less time it will take to decorate. @

b. The more you charge for T-shirts, the fewer T-shirts you will sell.

c. The more you spend on advertising, the more product you will sell.

2. Sketch a graph of a continuous function to fit each description.

a. always increasing with a faster and faster rate of change

b. decreasing with a slower and slower rate of change, then increasing with a faster and faster rate of change @

c. linear and decreasing

d. decreasing with a faster and faster rate of change @

3. Use the number line to write an inequality to represent each interval in 3a–e. Include the lowest value in each interval and exclude the highest value in each interval.

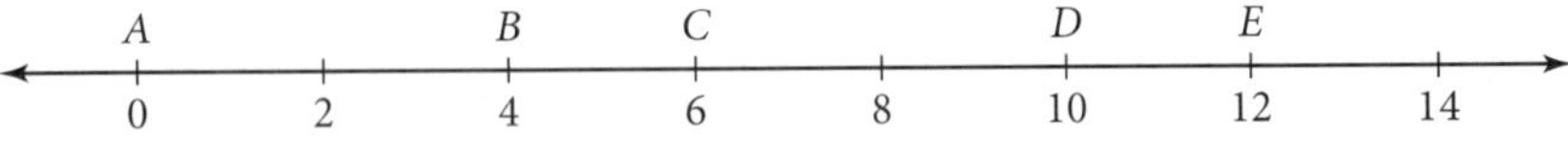

a. *A* to *B* @ b. *B* to *C* c. *B* to *D* d. *C* to *E* e. *A* to *E*

4. Sketch a discrete function graph to fit each description.

a. always increasing with a slower and slower rate of change @

b. linear with a constant rate of change equal to zero

c. linear and decreasing

d. decreasing with a faster and faster rate of change

5. For each relationship, identify the independent variable and the dependent variable.

a. the weight of your dog and the reading on the scale

b. the amount of time you spend in an airplane and the distance between your departure and your destination

c. the number of times you dip a wick into hot wax and the diameter of a handmade candle

Reason and Apply

6. The graph describes another student's distance from you.

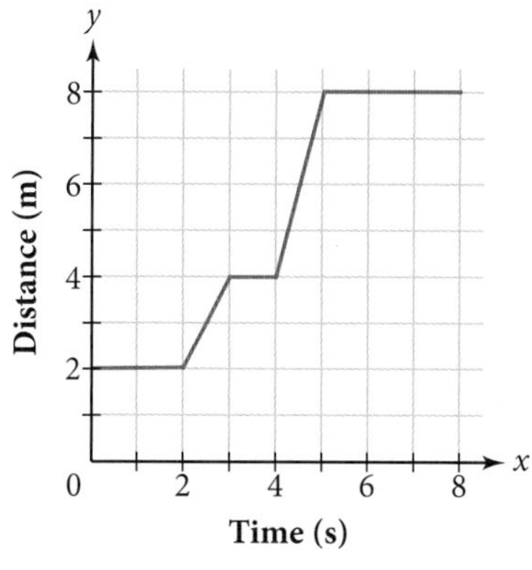

a. Is the relationship a function? Explain your reasoning.

b. What is the domain?

c. What is the range?

d. Explain what (0, 2) means in this situation.

e. Find the missing coordinate in each ordered pair.
$(3.5, y)$ $(5, y)$ $(x, 3)$

7. APPLICATION The diagram below shows a side view of a swimming pool that is being filled. The water enters the pool at a constant rate. Sketch a graph of your interpretation of the relationship between depth and time as the pool is being filled. Explain your graph. ⓗ

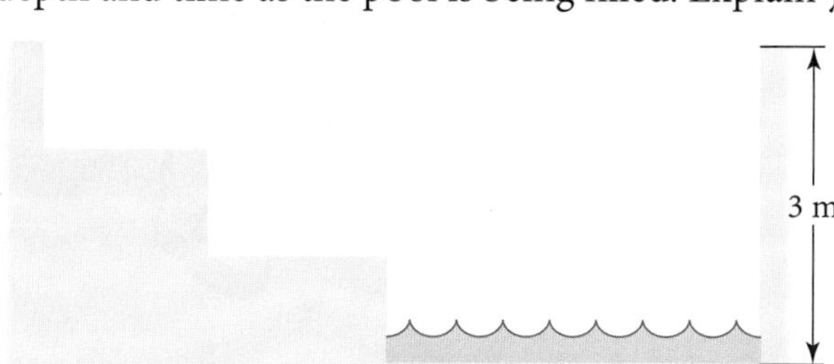
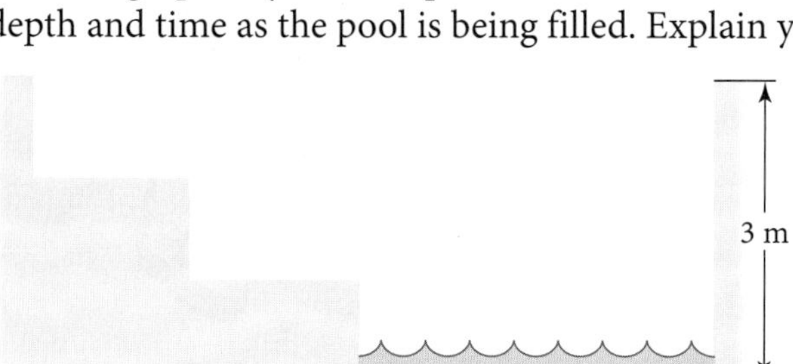

8. APPLICATION The graph at right shows Anne's blood sugar level during a morning at school. Give the points or intervals on the graph when her blood sugar matches each description.

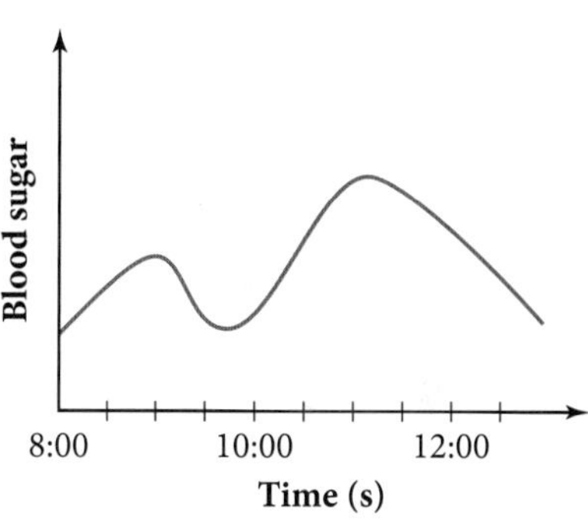

a. Reached its highest level.

b. Was rising fastest.

c. Was decreasing.

d. Give a possible explanation for the increases and decreases in the graph.

9. The graph at right shows the air temperature in a 24-hour period from midnight to midnight. Write a description of this graph, giving the intervals over which the graph changed in different ways.

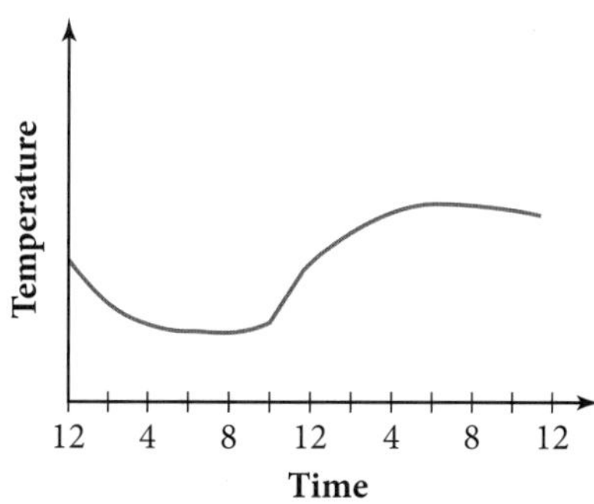

10. The graph represents the performance of Erica and Eileen in a 100-meter dash.

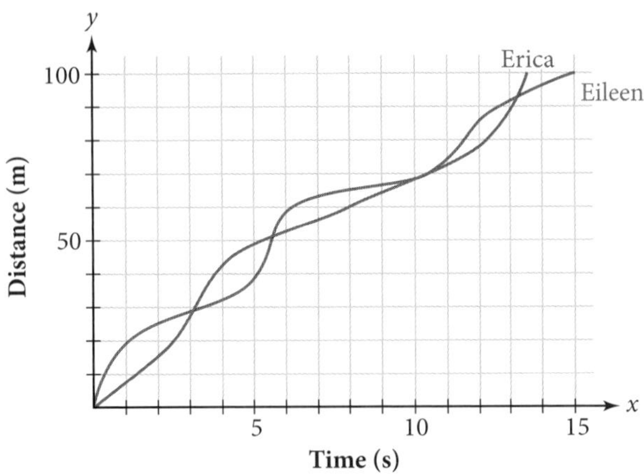

a. Who won the race and in how many seconds? Explain. @

b. Who was ahead at the 60-meter mark? @

c. At what approximate times were the runners even? @

d. When was Eileen in the lead? @

11. A turtle crawls steadily from its pond across the lawn. Then a small dog picks up the turtle and runs with it across the lawn. The dog slows down and finally drops the turtle. The turtle rests for a few minutes after this excitement. Then a young boy comes along, picks up the turtle, and slowly carries it back to the pond. Which graph describes the turtle's distance from the pond?

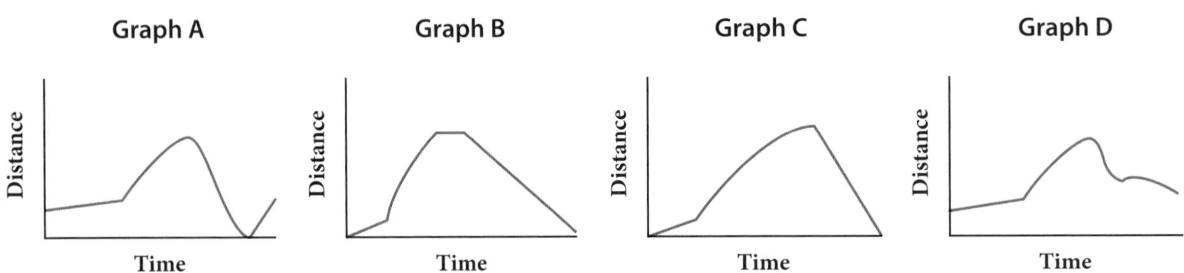

12. Sketch a graph and describe a reasonable scenario for each statement.

a. a domain for the independent variable, *time,* of 0 to 8 seconds and a range for the dependent variable, *velocity,* of 0, 2, and -2 meters per second @

b. your speed while you are riding or driving in a car following a school bus

c. the height of a basketball during a free throw shot

d. the height of the grass in a yard over the summer

e. the number of buses needed to take different numbers of students on a field trip

13. Each graph shows the distance of a person from a fixed point for a 4-second interval. Answer both questions for each graph.

i. Is the person moving toward or away from the point?

ii. Is the person speeding up, slowing down, or moving at a constant speed?

a. (@)

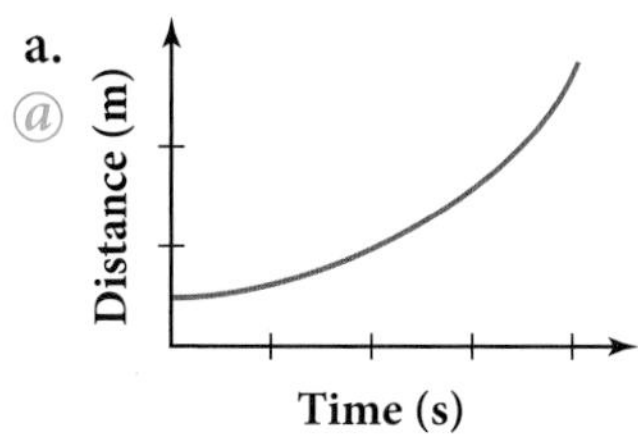

b.

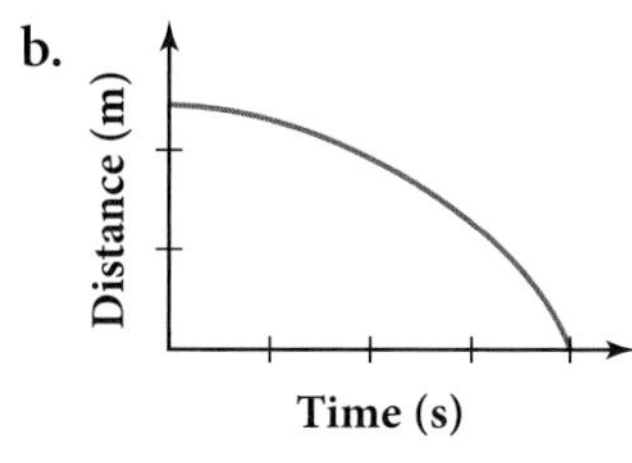

c.

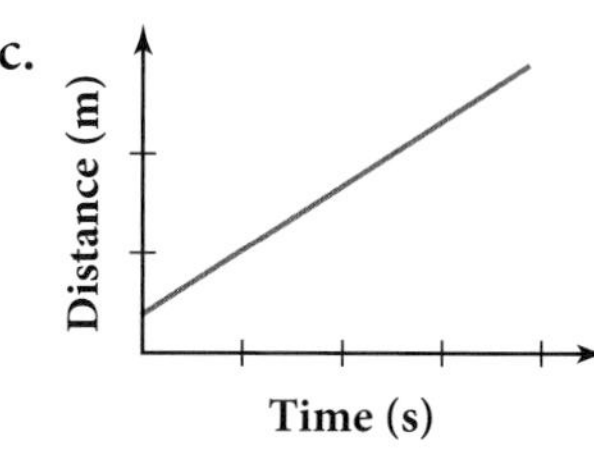

d.

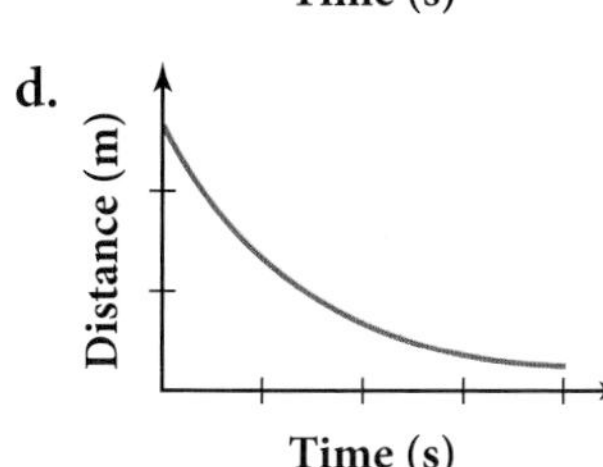

e.

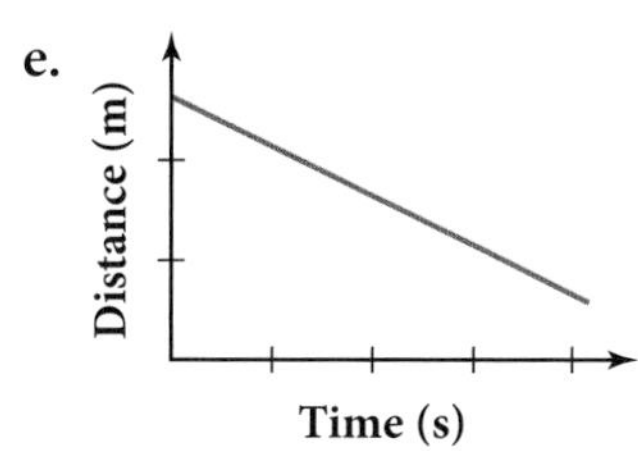

f.

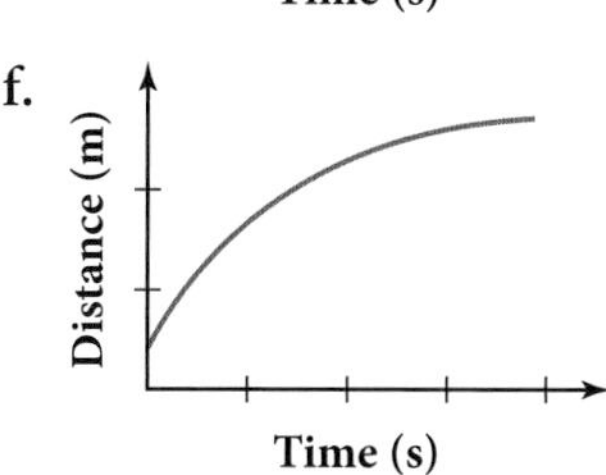

Review

14. Solve each equation for x using any method. Use another method to check your answer.

a. $\frac{2x - 4}{3} + 7 = 4$

b. $\frac{5(3 - x)}{-2} = -17.5$

c. $\frac{2}{x - 1} = 3$

15. In April 2004, the faculty at Princeton University voted that each department could give A grades to no more than 35% of their students. Japanese teacher Kyoko Loetscher felt that 11 of her 20 students deserved A's, as they had earned better than 90% in the course. However, she could give A's to only 35% of her students. How many students is this? Draw two relative frequency circle graphs: one that shows the grades (A's versus non-A's) that Loetscher would like to give and one that shows the grades she is allowed to give. (*Newsweek*, February 14, 2005, p. 8)

IMPROVING YOUR Geometry SKILLS

Use 16 toothpicks to make this pattern. Then remove 4 toothpicks so that you have 4 congruent triangles.

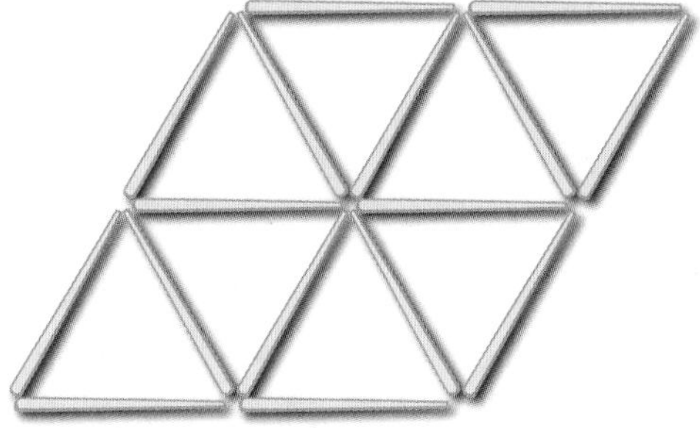

LESSON 4.4

Slope-Intercept Form of a Linear Equation

When you plot real-world data, you will often see a linear pattern. If you can find a line or an equation to model linear data, you can make predictions about unknown data values. However, data points rarely fall exactly on a line. How can you tell if a particular line is a good model for the data? One of the simplest ways is to ask yourself if the line shows the general direction of the data and if there are about the same number of points above the line as below the line. If so, then the line will appear to "fit" the data, and it is called a **line of fit.**

Can you visualize two lines that model this arrangement of geese?

EXAMPLE A

Papano's Pizza wants to offer an extra large pizza. To determine the price of the new 16-inch pizza they decide to use the pricing of their current four sizes to find a relationship between the diameter of the pizza and the price.

Size	Diameter (in.)	Price ($)
personal	7	3.75
small	10	6.99
medium	12	9.99
large	14	10.99

Solution

When you plot the points, you can see that they almost, but not quite, lie on a line. So you want to find the slope and y-intercept of a line of fit.

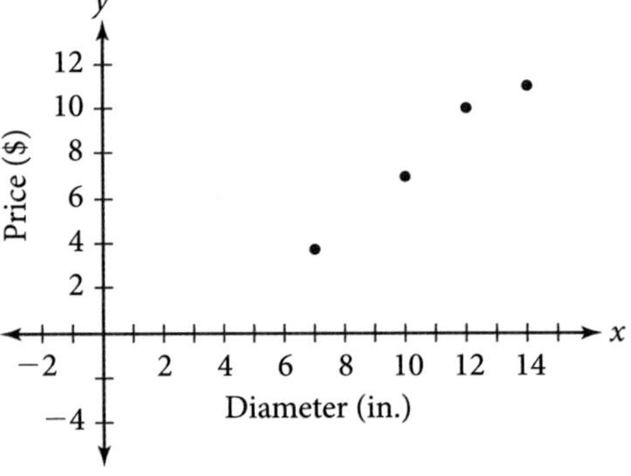

In Lesson 3.7, you connected the rate of change to the slope of a line. Using the personal and large pizza sizes, you might estimate the slope of the line of fit as $\frac{10.99 - 3.75}{14 - 7}$, or about $1.03 per inch. (Choosing different values would give you a slightly different slope.) To find a y-intercept, you might think about the start value. If you think a zero-inch pizza would cost zero dollars, you might try to use the model $price = 0 + 1.03 \cdot diameter$. But this line is not a good fit because all the points fall below the line.

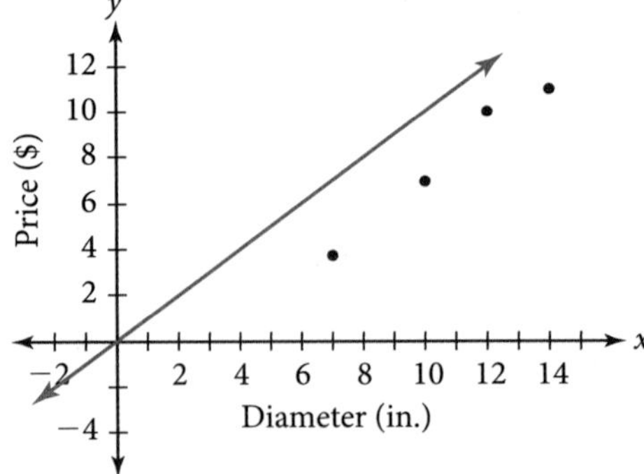

Intercepts are not always meaningful. In this case you can use guess-and-check to adjust the intercept value until you find that the model *price* = 1.03 · *diameter* − 3.3, or $y = 1.03x - 3.3$, is a good line of fit for these data. Using this equation, the 16-inch pizza should be priced at $13.18.

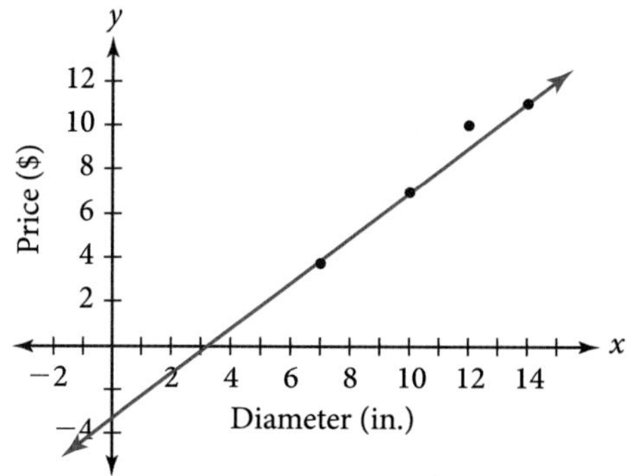

A linear equation written in the form $y = mx + b$, such as $y = 1.03x - 3.3$, is in **slope-intercept form.** How is this like the intercept form, $y = a + bx$, from Chapter 3? Does the constant, b, represent the same thing in both forms?

INVESTIGATION

Crosstown Traffic

YOU WILL NEED

- computer with Internet access
- uncooked linguine or another straight object

When you drive around in a big city, you might wonder how the distance between two locations is related to the time it takes to travel between them. Given varying speed limits, amounts of traffic, and so on, this might not be an easy relationship to model.

Step 1 Choose a large city, such as Chicago. Look up a map and driving directions on the Internet. Find a route between any two suburbs (e.g., from Oak Lawn to Skokie). Record the driving distance and time (in this example, 13.0 mi and 29 min).

Step 2 Repeat this procedure for six pairs of suburbs around the same city.

Step 3 Define the independent variable and the dependent variable. Plot your data on your calculator. Sketch the plot on your paper.

Step 4 Lay a piece of linguine on the plot to represent a line you think fits the data. Choose two points on that line. The points you choose do not need to be actual data points. Note the coordinates of these points, and calculate the slope of the line between them.

Step 5 Use the slope, m, that you found in Step 4 to graph the equation $y = mx$ on your calculator. Why is this line parallel to the line the points indicate? Is the line too low or too high to fit the data? [▶ See **Calculator Note: Equations** to review how to graph an equation on your calculator. ◀]

Step 6 With the linguine, estimate the y-intercept of your line from Step 5. Use this y-intercept to graph the equation $y = mx + b$ on your calculator. Adjust the value of b to get a better fit if needed. Sketch this line on your graph.

Step 7 In Step 4, everyone started with a visual model that went through two points. In your group, compare all final lines. Did everyone end up with the same line? Do you think a line of fit must go through at least two data points? Is any one line a better fit than the others? Why or why not?

Your line is a model for the relationship between the number of miles between suburbs and the time it takes to travel that distance in minutes.

Step 8 Explain the real-world meaning of the slope of your line.

Step 9 Use your linear model to predict the time it takes to travel 30 mi.

Step 10 Use your model to predict the distance you would travel in 30 min.

Step 11 Some of your data points may be very close to your line, while others could be described as outliers. What could cause these outliers?

Many variables impact the relationship between distance and time when traveling.

Writing a model to fit data can be useful in many situations that involve making predictions.

EXAMPLE B

This table shows how many grams of fat and how many calories there are in some hamburgers sold by national chain restaurants.

Nutrition Facts

Burger	Total fat (g)	Calories
Burger King Bacon Double Cheeseburger	24	440
Burger King Hamburger	8	240
Hardee's 1/3 lb Thickburger	52	810
Hardee's 2/3 lb Monster Thickburger	93	1300
Jack in the Box Bacon Ultimate Cheeseburger	56	910
Jack in the Box Jr. Jack	19	370
McDonald's Big Mac	29	550
McDonald's Quarter Pounder with Cheese	26	520
Wendy's 3/4 lb Triple	69	1120
Wendy's Classic 1/4 lb Single	31	580

(*www.bk.com, www.hardees.com, www.jackinthebox.com, www.mcdonalds.com, www.wendys.com*) as of 2013

Imagine how much total fat is in this burger!

a. Write a linear equation to model the data (*total fat, calories*).

b. Give the real-world meanings of the slope and y-intercept of your line.

c. Predict the calories in a burger with 80 g total fat.

d. Predict the total fat in a burger with 800 calories.

e. What is the x-**intercept,** and what does it represent in this situation?

Solution

Define the independent variable and the dependent variable. Draw a scatter plot of the data.

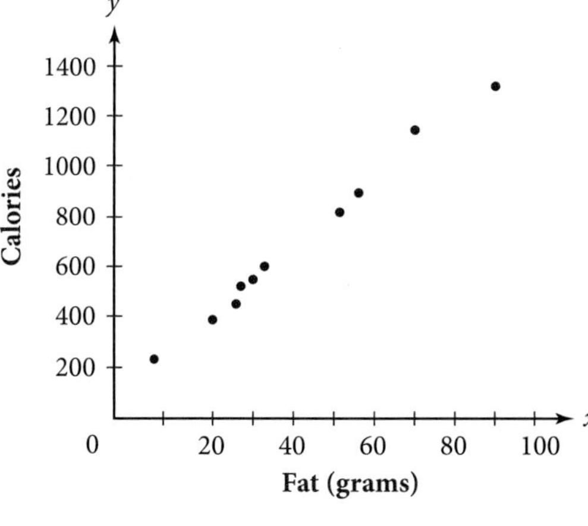

a. Let the independent variable, x, be the number of grams of total fat, and let the dependent variable, y, be the number of calories. The scatter plot shows a linear pattern in the data. A line through the points (26, 520) and (56, 910) seems to show the direction of the data. Calculate the slope, m, of the line between these two points.

$$m = \frac{(910 - 520)}{(56 - 26)} = \frac{390}{30} = 13$$

Substitute 13 for m in $y = mx$ to get

$$y = 13x$$

The equation $y = 13x$ shows the direction of the line, but almost all the points are above the line.

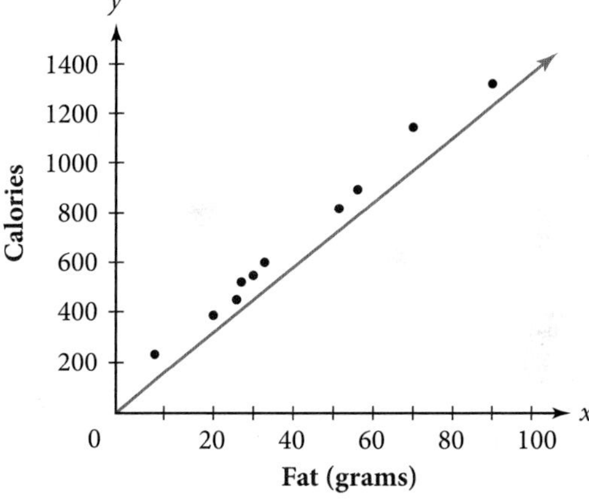

Adjust the y-intercept by tens until you find a line that appears to be a good fit for the data. You may find that the equation

$$y = 13x + 160$$

is a good model. Notice that the line of fit might miss some or all of the data points.

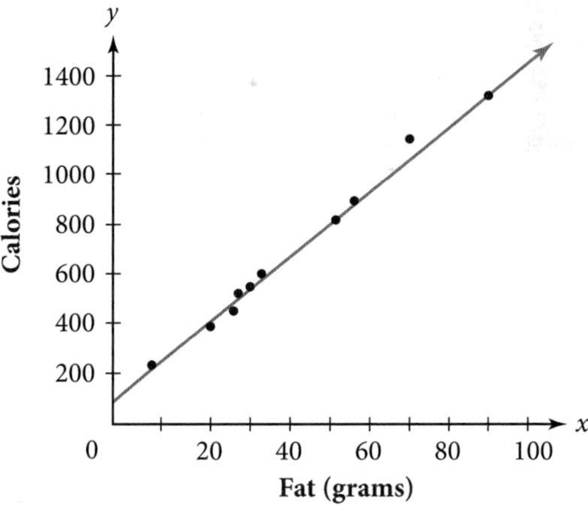

Science CONNECTION

Saturated and trans fats increase cholesterol and your risk of coronary heart disease. Trans fats, a result of hydrogenating or solidifying oil, have become increasingly common in processed foods—the U.S. Food and Drug Administration (FDA) required all foods to begin listing trans fat content beginning in January 2006. Since 2005, several U.S. cities, including New York City, Philadelphia, and San Francisco, have implemented bans of trans fats in restaurant food.

b. The y-intercept, 160, means that even without any fat, a burger has about 160 calories. The slope, 13, means that for each additional gram of fat there are an additional 13 calories.

c. Substitute 80 g fat for x in the equation.

$y = 13x + 160$	Original equation.
$y = 13(80) + 160$	Substitute 80 for x.
$y = 1200$	Simplify.

The model predicts that there would be 1200 calories in a burger with 80 g fat.

d. Substitute 800 calories for y in the equation.

$y = 13x + 160$	Original equation.
$800 = 13x + 160$	Substitute 800 for y.
$800 - 160 = 13x + 160 - 160$	Subtract 160 from both sides.
$640 = 13x$	Combine like terms.
$\frac{640}{13} = \frac{13x}{13}$	Divide both sides by 13.
$49.23 \approx x$	Simplify.

The model predicts that there would be about 49 g fat in a burger with 800 calories.

e. Substitute 0 calories for y in the equation.

$y = 13x + 160$	Original equation.
$0 = 13x + 160$	Substitute 0 for y.
$0 - 160 = 13x + 160 - 160$	Subtract 160 from both sides.
$-160 = 13x$	Combine like terms.
$\frac{-160}{13} = \frac{13x}{13}$	Divide both sides by 13.
$-12.3 \approx x$	Simplify.

The model predicts that a burger with 0 calories would have a negative amount of fat, which is impossible. This doesn't necessarily mean that the model is incorrect for realistic amounts of fat, but it does suggest that the model doesn't work at values very close to zero. Can you think of a situation in which the x-intercept is both possible and useful?

Slope-Intercept Form

The form $y = mx + b$ is the slope-intercept form. The value of b is the y-intercept. The coefficient of x, m, is the slope (rate of change).

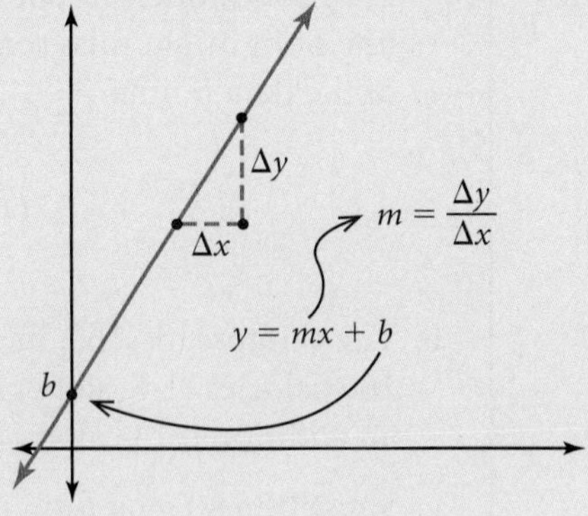

In the rest of this chapter, you will see how to find a line of fit for data using various forms of linear equations.

4.4 Exercises

Practice Your Skills

1. For each graph, tell whether you think the line drawn is a good representation of the data. Explain your reasoning.

a. 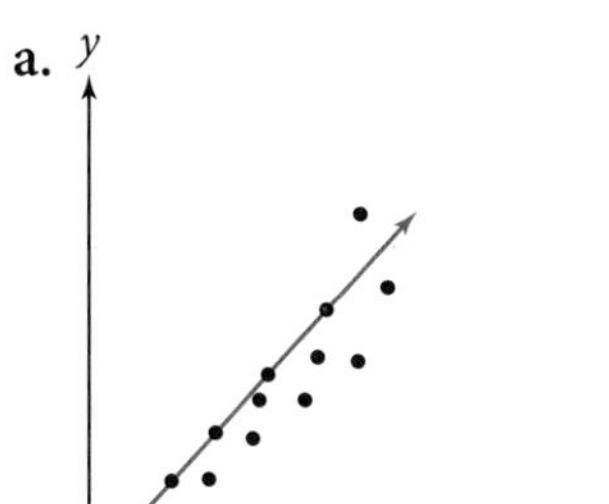

b. @ 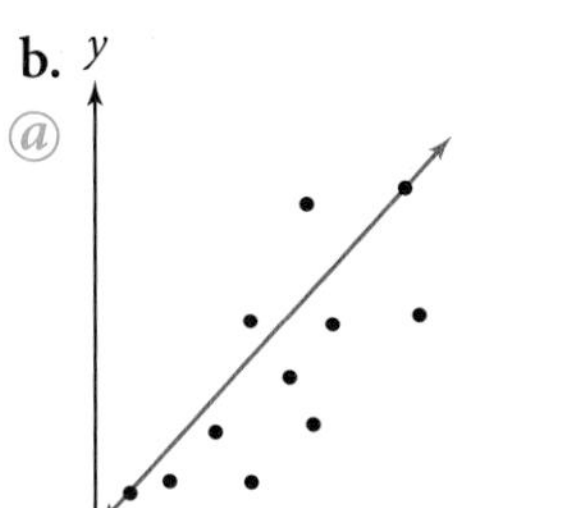

c. 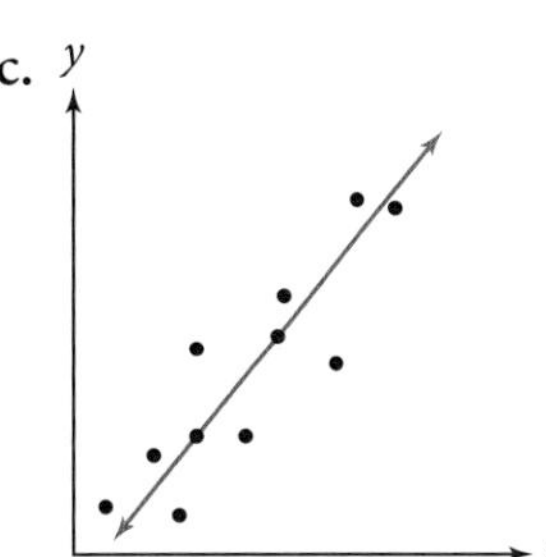

d. @ 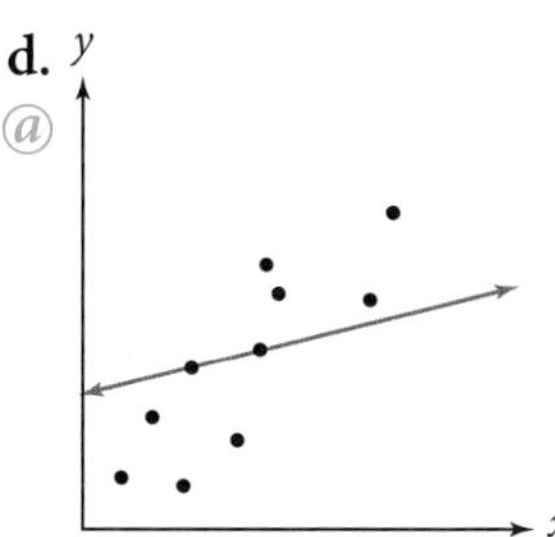

2. The line through the points (0, 5) and (4, 5) is horizontal. The equation of this line is $y = 5$, because the y-value of every point on it is 5. If a line goes through the points $(2, -6)$ and (2, 8), what kind of line is it? What is its equation?

3. Give the slope and y-intercept of each line.

a. $y = 3x + 2$

b. $y = 4 + 7x$

c. $y = \frac{1}{4} - \frac{4}{5}x$ @

d. $y = \frac{2}{3}x - \frac{5}{3}$

4. Write the equation of each line. For more practice, run the LINES program on level "Easy." [▶ Use the link in your ebook to download the program file LINES. ◀]

a.  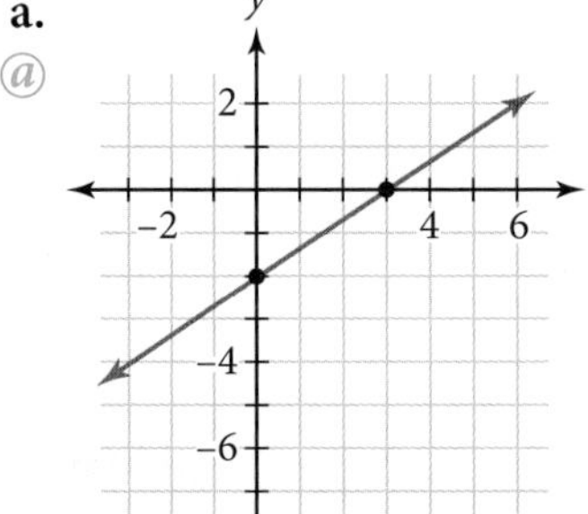

b. 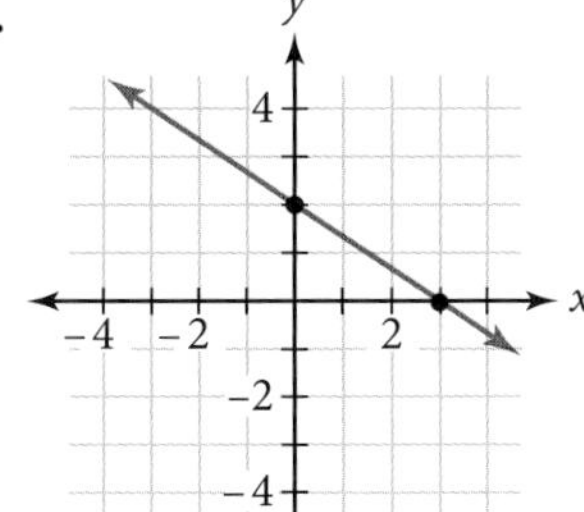

c. 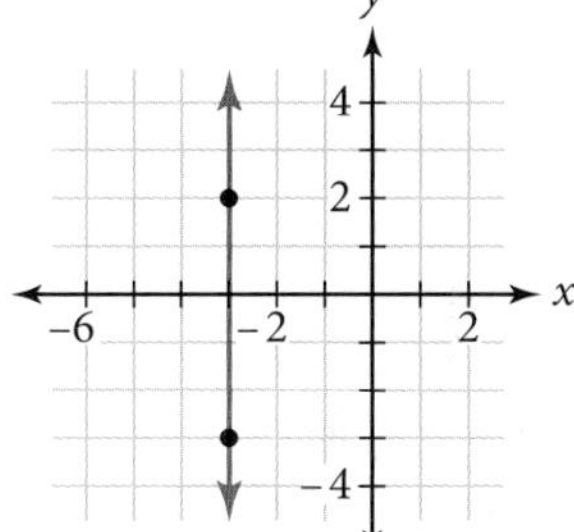

d. 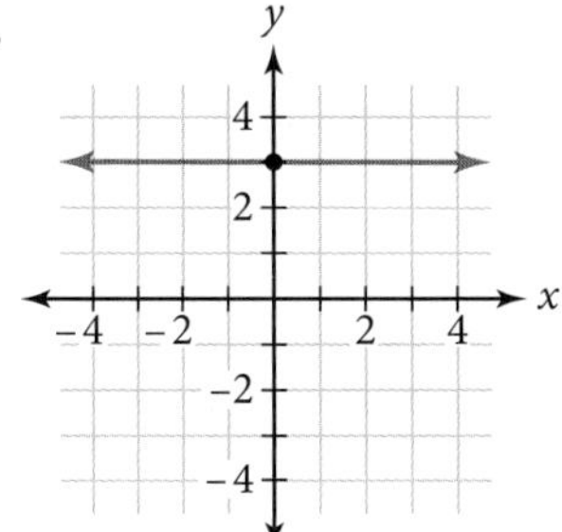

e. 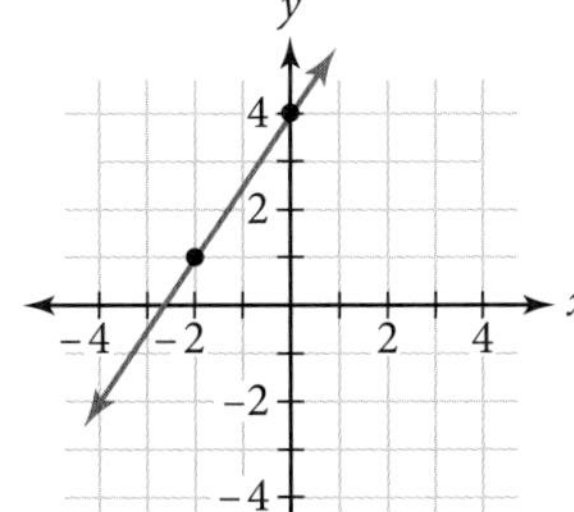

f. 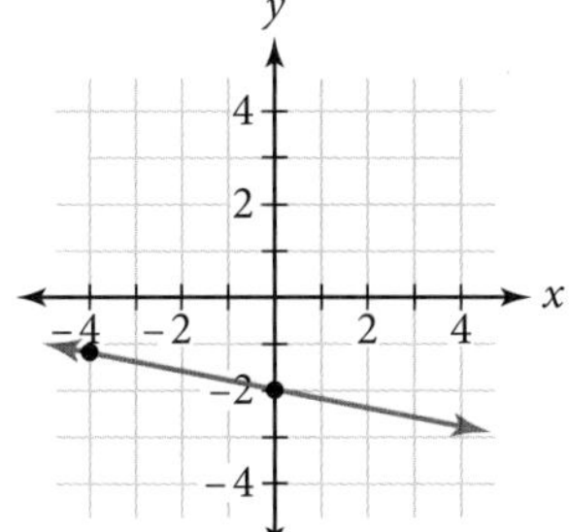

Reason and Apply

5. APPLICATION The U.S. Census is conducted every 10 years. One of the purposes of the census is to measure each state's population to determine how many members each state will have in the House of Representatives for the next decade. Use the table to look for a relationship between a state's population and the number of members in the House of Representatives from that state.

Statistics for Some States

State	Estimated population, 2010 (millions)	Number of members in House of Representatives, 2011–2020	Number of members in Senate, 2011–2020
Alabama	4.8	7	2
Indiana	6.5	9	2
Michigan	9.9	14	2
Mississippi	3.0	4	2
North Carolina	9.6	13	2
Oklahoma	3.8	5	2
Oregon	3.8	5	2
Tennessee	6.4	9	2
Utah	2.8	4	2
West Virginia	1.9	3	2

(U.S. Census Bureau, *www.census.gov*) [Data sets: **STPOP, HREPS**]

a. Which statement makes more sense: The population depends on the number of members in the House of Representatives, or the number of members in the House of Representatives depends on the population? @

b. Based on your answer to 5a, define the independent and the dependent variables and make a scatter plot of the data. @

c. Find the equation of a line of fit. What is the real-world meaning of the slope? What is the real-world meaning of the y-intercept? @

d. The 2010 census estimated California's population at 37.3 million. Use your equation to estimate the number of members California has in the House of Representatives.

e. Minnesota has eight members in the House of Representatives. Use your equation to estimate the population of Minnesota.

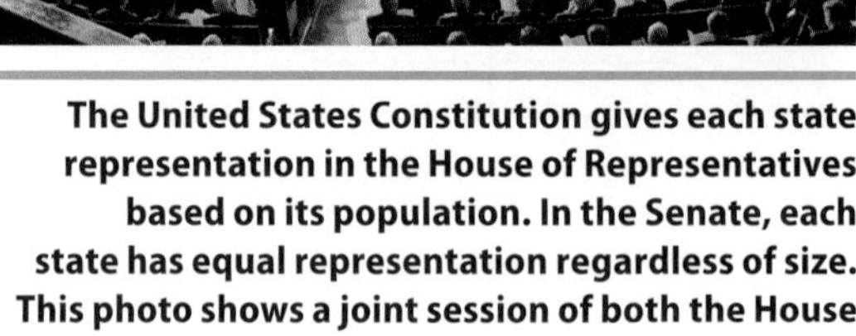

The United States Constitution gives each state representation in the House of Representatives based on its population. In the Senate, each state has equal representation regardless of size. This photo shows a joint session of both the House and the Senate.

f. You might find that a direct variation equation in the form $y = bx$ fits your data. Is this a reasonable model for the data? Explain why or why not.

6. Use the table in Exercise 5 to answer these questions.

a. Does the population of a state affect its number of members in the Senate?

b. Write an equation that models the number of senators from each state. Graph this equation on the same coordinate axes as 5b.

c. Describe the graph and explain why it looks this way.

7. Your friend walks steadily away from you at a constant rate such that her distance at 2 s is 3.4 m and her distance at 4.5 s is 4.4 m.

a. Define the independent variable and the dependent variable.

b. What is the slope of the line that models this situation? ⓗ

c. What is the y-intercept of this line? Explain how you found it.

d. Write a linear equation in intercept form that models your friend's walk.

e. Describe the domain and range of this function.

8. Find the equation of a line that

a. Has a positive slope and a negative y-intercept.

b. Has a negative slope and y-intercept 0.

c. Passes through the points (1, 7) and (4, 10).

d. Passes through the points (−2, 10) and (4, 10).

9. Each equation represents a family of lines. Describe what the lines in each family have in common.

a. $y = 3x + a$ ⓐ b. $y = bx + 5$ c. $y = a$ d. $x = c$

Review

10. For each table of x- and y-values, decide whether the values indicate a direct variation, an inverse variation, or neither. Explain how you made your decision. If the values represent a direct or an inverse variation, write an equation to model the relationship.

a.

x	y
−3	9
−1	1
−0.5	0.25
0.25	0.0625
7	49

b.

x	y
−20	−5
−8	−12.5
2	50
10	10
25	4

c.

x	y
0	0
−6	15
8	−20
−12	30
4	−10

d.

x	y
78	6
31.2	2.4
−145.6	−11.2
14.3	1.1
−44.2	−3.4

11. Show the steps to solve each equation. Then use your calculator to verify your solution.

a. $8 - 12m = 17$

b. $2r + 7 = -24$

c. $-6 - 3w = 42$

d. $3 - \frac{4}{5}t = 5$

e. $-2v - \frac{5}{3} = \frac{2}{3}$

f. $-4 + \frac{2}{3}y = -10$

12. Give the mean and median for each data set.

a. {1, 2, 4, 7, 18, 20, 21, 21, 26, 31, 37, 45, 45, 47, 48}

b. {30, 32, 33, 35, 39, 41, 42, 47, 72, 74}

c. {107, 116, 120, 120, 138, 140, 145, 146, 147, 152, 155, 156, 179}

d. {85, 91, 79, 86, 94, 90, 74, 87}

IMPROVING YOUR Visual Thinking SKILLS

The traditional Japanese abacus, or *soroban,* is still widely used today. Each column shows a different place value—1, 10, 100, 1000, and so on. The four lower beads are moved up to represent the digits from 1 to 4. The fifth bead is moved down to show the digit 5. The digits 6 to 9 are shown with a combination of lower and upper beads. The first abacus here shows the number 6053.

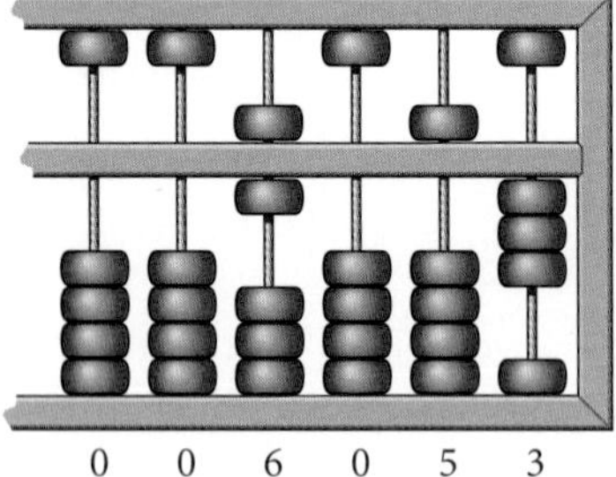

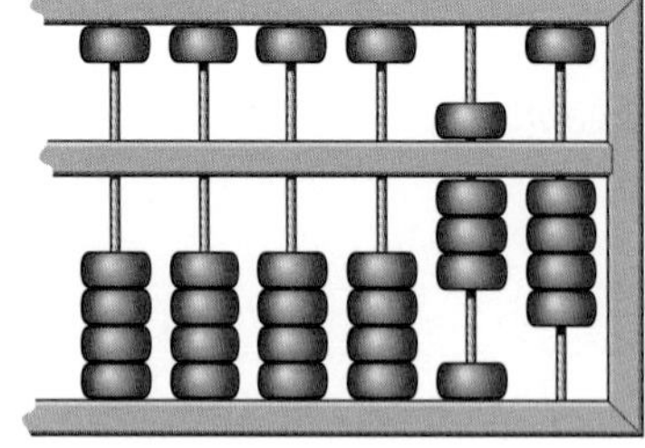

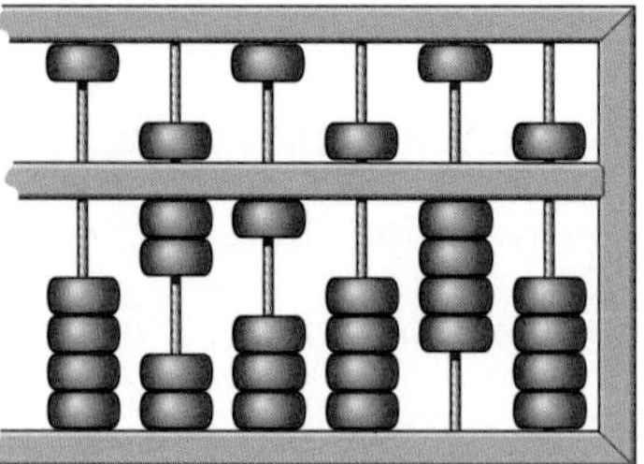

What numbers do the second and third abacuses show? Sketch an abacus to show the number 27,059.

LESSON

4.5

Point-Slope Form of a Linear Equation

"Success breeds confidence."

BERYL MARKHAM

So far you have worked with linear equations in intercept form, $y = a + bx$, and in slope-intercept form, $y = mx + b$. When you know a line's slope and y-intercept, you can write its equation directly in intercept or slope-intercept form. But what if you don't know the y-intercept? One method that you might remember from your homework is to work backward with the slope until you find the y-intercept. But you can also use the slope formula to find the equation of a line when you know the slope of the line and the coordinates of only one point on the line.

EXAMPLE

Since the time Beth was born, the population of her town has increased at a rate of approximately 850 people per year. On Beth's ninth birthday, the total population was nearly 307,650. If this rate of growth continues, what will be the population on Beth's sixteenth birthday?

Solution

Because the rate of change is approximately constant, a linear equation should model this population growth. First decide which variable is the independent variable and which is the dependent variable. Since population *depends* on time, let x represent time in years since Beth's birth, and let y represent the population.

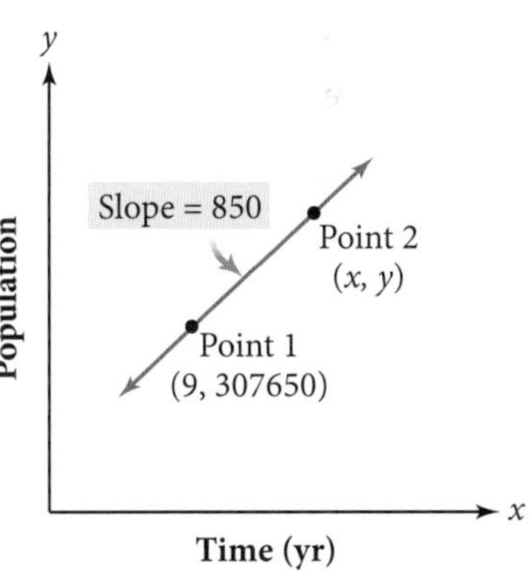

In the problem, you are given one point, (9, 307650). Any other point on the line will be in the form (x, y). So let (x, y) represent a second point on the line. You also know that the slope is 850. Now use the slope formula to find a linear equation.

$$\frac{y_2 - y_1}{x_2 - x_1} = b$$ Slope formula.

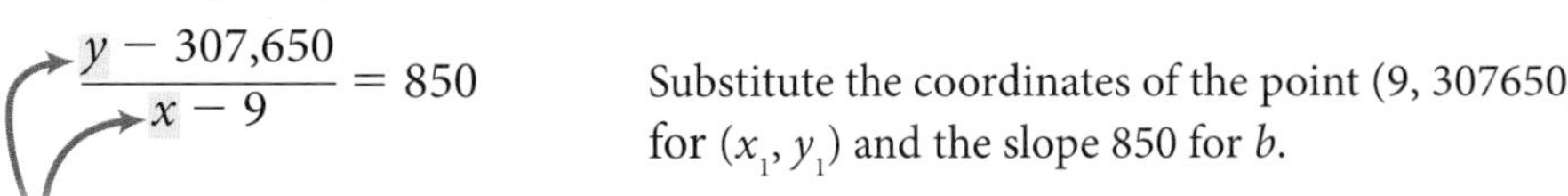

$$\frac{y - 307{,}650}{x - 9} = 850$$ Substitute the coordinates of the point (9, 307650) for (x_1, y_1) and the slope 850 for b.

Because we know only one point, we use (x, y) to represent any other point.

Now solve the equation for y by undoing the subtraction and division.

$y - 307{,}650 = 850(x - 9)$ — Multiply by $(x - 9)$ to undo the division.

$y = 307{,}650 + 850(x - 9)$ — Add 307,650 to undo the subtraction.

The equation $y = 307{,}650 + 850(x - 9)$ is a linear equation that models the population growth. To find the population on Beth's sixteenth birthday, substitute 16 for x.

$y = 307{,}650 + 850(x - 9)$ — Original equation.

$y = 307{,}650 + 850(16 - 9)$ — Substitute 16 for x.

$y = 313{,}600$ — Use order of operations.

The model equation predicts that the population on Beth's sixteenth birthday will be 313,600.

The equation $y = 307{,}650 + 850(x - 9)$ is a linear equation, but it is not in intercept or slope-intercept form. This equation has its advantages, too, because you can clearly identify the slope and one point on the line. Do you see the slope 850 and the point (9, 307650) within the equation? This form of a linear equation is appropriately called the **point-slope form.**

Point-Slope Form

If a line passes through the point (x_1, y_1) and has slope b, the point-slope form of the equation is

$$y = y_1 + b(x - x_1)$$

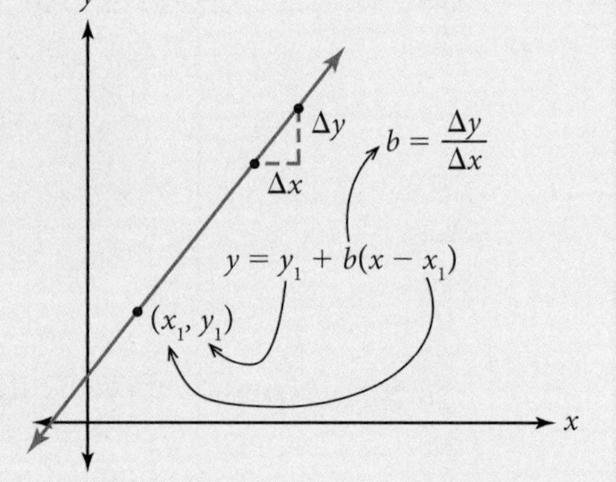

INVESTIGATION

The Point-Slope Form of Linear Equations

Silo and Jenny conducted an experiment in which Jenny walked at a constant rate. Unfortunately, Silo recorded only the data shown in this table.

Elapsed time (s) x	Distance to walker (m) y
3	4.6
6	2.8

Step 1 Find the slope of the line that represents this situation.

Step 2 Write a linear equation in point-slope form using the point (3, 4.6) and the slope you found in Step 1.

Step 3 Write another linear equation in point-slope form using the point (6, 2.8) and the slope you found in Step 1.

Step 4 Graph the equations from Steps 2 and 3 on your calculator. What do you notice?

Step 5 Look at the table of values for each equation. What do you notice? What do you think the results mean?

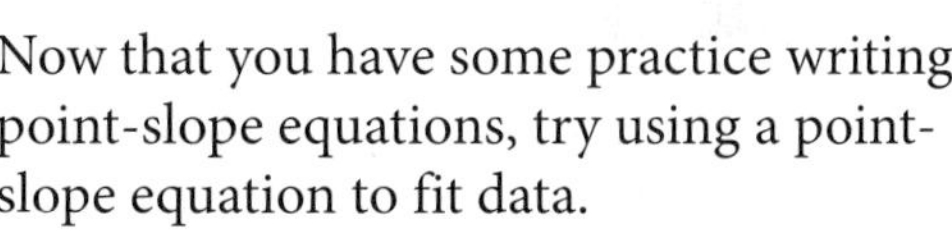

Now that you have some practice writing point-slope equations, try using a point-slope equation to fit data.

The table shows how the temperature of a pot of water changed over time as it was heated.

Water Temperature

Time (s) x	Temperature (°C) y
24	25
36	30
49	35
62	40
76	45
89	50

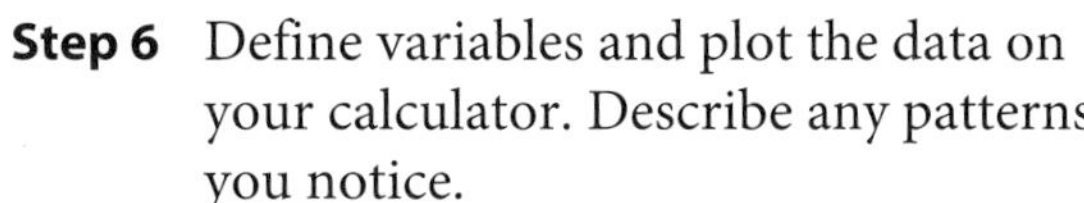

Step 6 Define variables and plot the data on your calculator. Describe any patterns you notice.

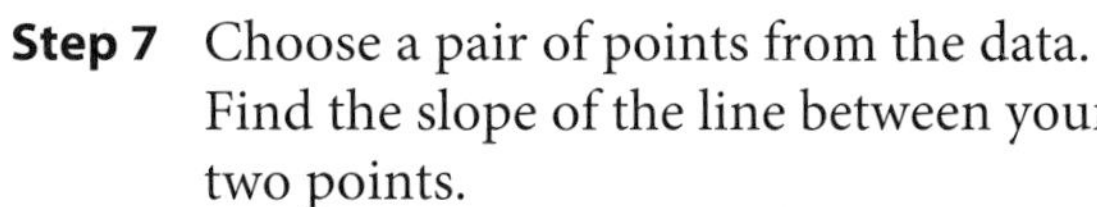

Step 7 Choose a pair of points from the data. Find the slope of the line between your two points.

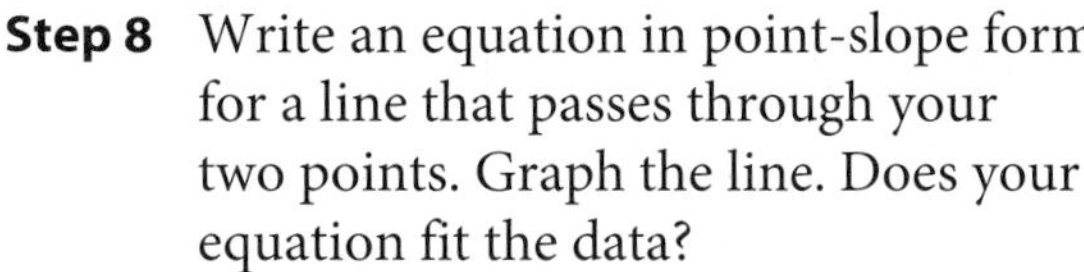

Step 8 Write an equation in point-slope form for a line that passes through your two points. Graph the line. Does your equation fit the data?

Step 9 Compare your graph to those of other members of your group. Does one graph show a line that is a better fit than the others? Explain.

If you look back at the investigation, you will notice that you found the point-slope form of a line even though you had only points (but not a slope) to start with. This was possible because you can still use the point-slope form when you only know two points on the line; there's just one additional step. What is it?

4.5 Exercises

You will need your graphing calculator for Exercises **3d, 4, 7a,** and **8d.**

Practice Your Skills

1. Name the slope and one point on the line that each point-slope equation represents.

a. $y = 3 + 4(x - 5)$ @
b. $y = 1.9 + 2(x + 3.1)$
c. $y = -3.47(x - 7) - 2$ @
d. $y = 5 - 1.38(x - 2.5)$
e. $y = 12.3(x + 4) - 7$
f. $y - 8 = -2.4(x - 3)$

2. Write an equation in point-slope form for a line, given its slope and one point that it passes through.

a. slope 3; point (2, 5)
b. slope -5; point $(1, -4)$
c. slope -1; point (3, 0)
d. slope 4.4; point $(-2, 3)$
e. slope 0; point (3, 7)
f. slope 1; point $(-3.1, -2.8)$

3. A line passes through the points $(-2, -1)$ and $(5, 13)$.

   a. Find the slope of this line. ⓐ

   b. Write an equation in point-slope form using the slope you found in 3a and the point $(-2, -1)$. ⓐ

   c. Write an equation in point-slope form using the slope you found in 3a and the point $(5, 13)$.

   d. Verify that the equations in 3b and c represent the same line. Enter the equations into your calculator, and compare their graphs and tables.

4. Write an equation in point-slope form for the line passing through both points. Check your equation by graphing it on your calculator and verifying that it includes the two points.

   a. $(3, 0)$ and $(0, 6)$

   b. $(1, 3)$ and $(5, 5)$

   c. $(-3, 1)$ and $(2, 4)$

   d. $(2.5, -3.1)$ and $(6.5, 4.9)$

5. Lauren rode her bicycle home from school. The equation $d = 3.6 - 0.15(t - 20)$ gives her distance from home, d, in miles after time spent riding, t, in minutes. Kaitlyn also rode her bike home from school. The table shows her distance from home after various times.

Kaitlyn's Distance from Home

t (min)	10	15	25
d (mi)	4.8	4.2	3.0

   a. Which girl is riding at a faster speed? Explain how you can tell.

   b. Which girl will reach home soonest? What feature on a graph gives you this information?

Reason and Apply

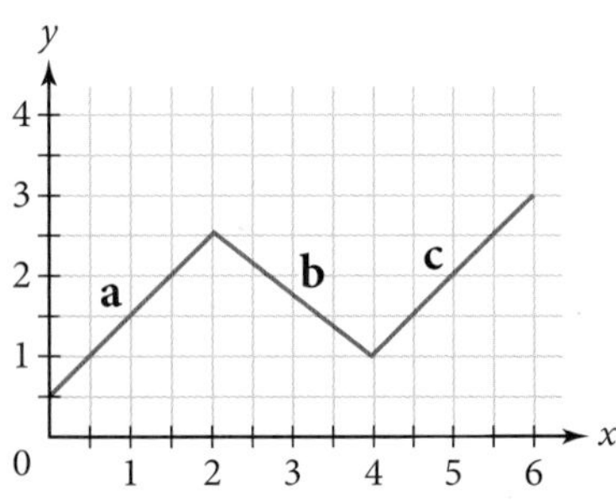

6. The graph at right is made up of linear segments **a, b,** and **c.** Write the equation of the line containing each line segment in the graph. Describe the domain and range of each segment. ⓗ

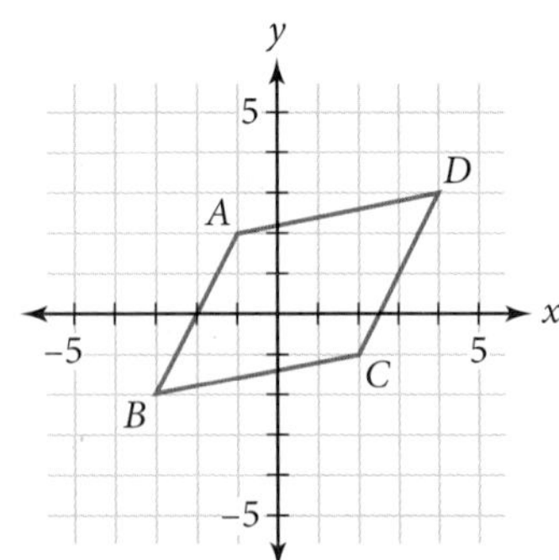

7. A **quadrilateral** is a polygon with four sides. Quadrilateral $ABCD$ is graphed at right.

   a. Write an equation in point-slope form for the line containing each segment in this quadrilateral. Check your equations by graphing them on your calculator.

   b. What is the same in the equations for the line through points A and D and the line through points B and C? What is different in these equations? ⓐ

   c. What kind of figure does $ABCD$ appear to be? Do the results from 7b have anything to do with this? ⓐ

   d. Describe the domain and range of each segment.

8. APPLICATION This table shows a linear relationship between actual temperature and approximate wind chill temperature when the wind speed is 20 mi/h.

Wind Chill with Wind Speed 20 mi/h

Temperature (°F) x	5	10	15	20	25
Wind chill (°F) y	-15.4	-8.9	-2.3	4.2	10.8

a. Find the rate of change of the data (the slope of the line).

b. Choose one point and write an equation in point-slope form to model the data.

c. Choose another point and write another equation in point-slope form to model the data.

d. Verify that the two equations in 8b and c represent the same line. Enter the equations into your calculator, and compare their graphs and tables.

e. What is the wind chill temperature when the actual temperature is 0°F? What does this represent in the graph?

9. APPLICATION The table shows U.S. postal rates for some first-class mail in the year 2010.

a. Make a scatter plot of the data. Describe any patterns you notice.

b. Find the slope of the line between any two points in the data. What is the real-world meaning of this slope? @

c. Write a linear equation in point-slope form that models the data. Graph the equation to check that it fits your data points.

d. Use the equation you wrote in 9c to find the cost of mailing a 10 oz package.

e. What would be the cost of mailing a 3.5 oz package? A 9.1 oz package? h

f. The equation you found in 9c is useful for modeling this situation. Is the graph of this equation, a continuous line, a correct model for the situation? Explain why or why not. @

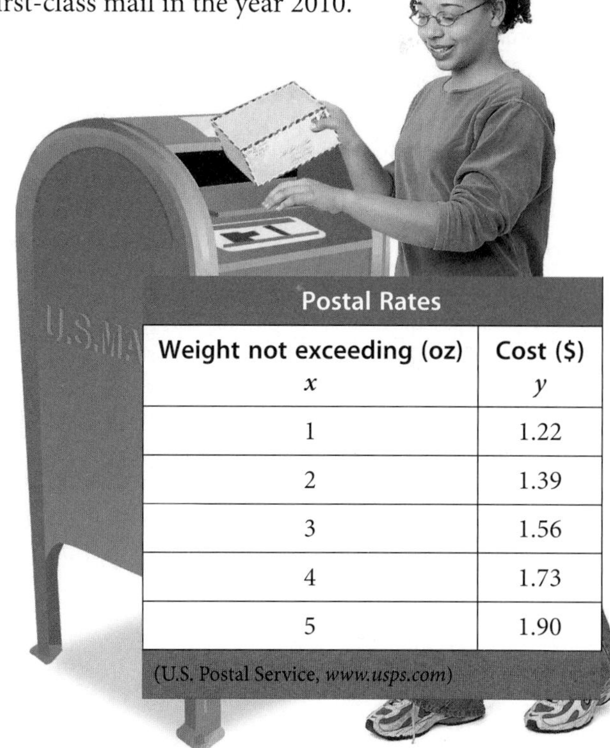

Postal Rates

Weight not exceeding (oz) x	Cost ($) y
1	1.22
2	1.39
3	1.56
4	1.73
5	1.90

(U.S. Postal Service, *www.usps.com*)

10. APPLICATION This table shows the amount of trash produced in the United States in 2000 and 2005.

a. Define the variables. Write an equation in point-slope form for the line passing through these two points. @

b. Plot the two data points, and graph the equation you found in 10a. @

c. In 2007, 254 million tons of trash were produced in the United States. Plot this data point on the same graph you made in 10b. Do you think the linear equation you found in 10a is a good model for these data? Explain why or why not. @

U.S. Trash Production

Year	Amount of trash (million tons)
2000	239
2005	250

(Environmental Protection Agency, *www.epa.gov*)

The table at right shows more data about the amount of trash produced in the United States.

d. Add these data points to your graph.

e. Do you think the linear equation you found in 10a is a good model for this larger data set? Explain why or why not.

f. Write the equation of a better-fitting line. ⓗ

g. Use your new equation from 10f to predict the amount of trash produced in 2020.

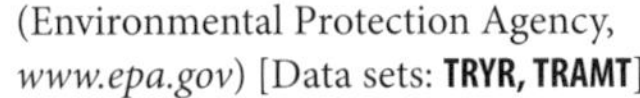

U.S. Trash Production

Year	Amount of trash (million tons)
1960	88
1970	121
1980	152
1990	205

(Environmental Protection Agency, *www.epa.gov*) [Data sets: **TRYR, TRAMT**]

Review

11. APPLICATION The volume of a gas is 3.50 L at 280 K. The volume of any gas is directly proportional to its temperature on the Kelvin scale (K).

a. Find the volume of this gas when the temperature is 330 K.

b. Find the temperature when the volume is 2.25 L.

12. Write the equation represented by this balance. Then solve the equation for x. ⓐ

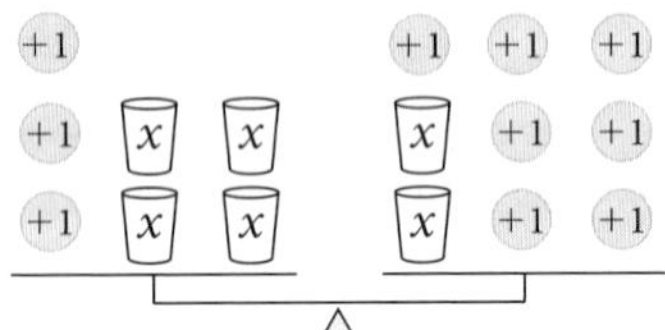

13. For each relationship, identify the independent and dependent variables. Then describe each relationship as *increasing* or *decreasing,* and *continuous* or *discrete.* Sketch a graph, with the independent variable on the horizontal axis and the dependent variable on the vertical axis.

a. The mass of a spherical lollipop and the number of times it has been licked

b. The number of scoops in an ice cream cone and the cost of the cone

c. The distance a rubber band will fly and the amount you stretch it before you release it

d. The number of coins you flip and the number of heads

LESSON

4.6

Equivalent Algebraic Equations

In Lesson 4.5, you learned how to find an equation of a line through a given point. But a line goes through many points, so if you choose a different point, you'll get a different equation! In this lesson you'll learn how to identify different equations that describe the same line.

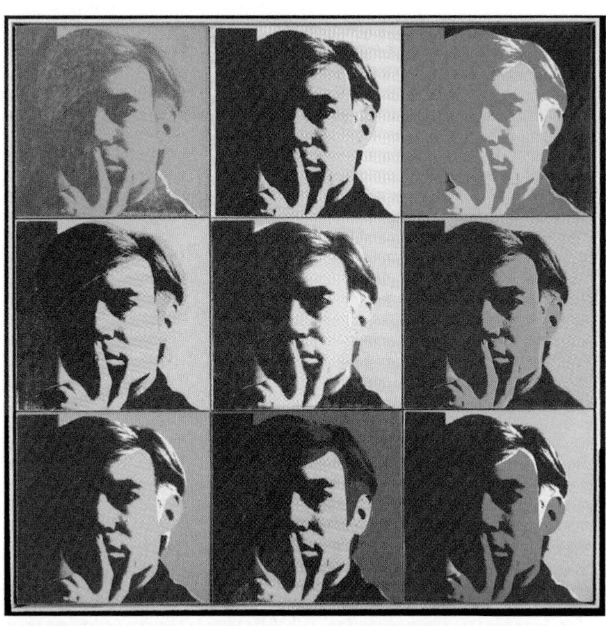

These self-portraits of the American pop artist Andy Warhol (1928–1987) are like equivalent equations. Each screen-printed image is the same as the next, but Warhol's choice of colorization makes each look different.

For example, the line with slope 2 that passes through the point $(-4, 3)$ can be described by the equation $y = 3 + 2(x + 4)$. This line also passes through the point $(1, 13)$, so it can also be described by the equation $y = 13 + 2(x - 1)$. You can test that these equations are equivalent by graphing them at the same time. The two equations graph the same line and give the same table values.

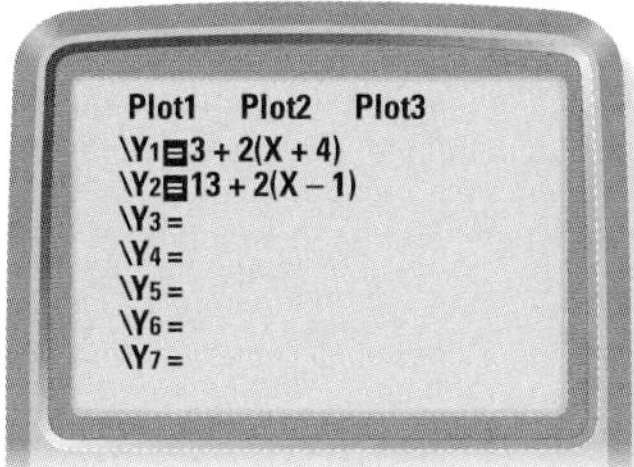

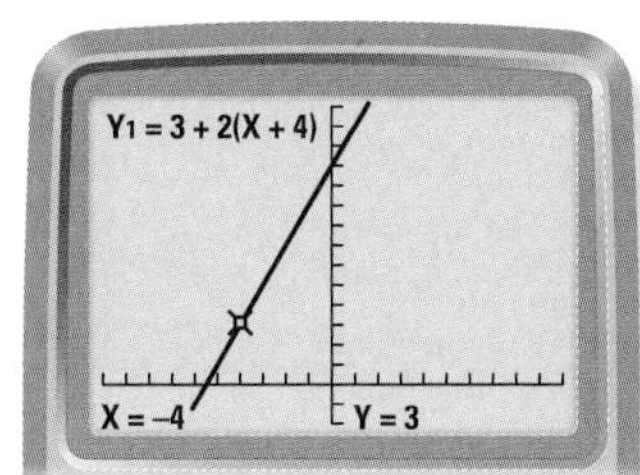

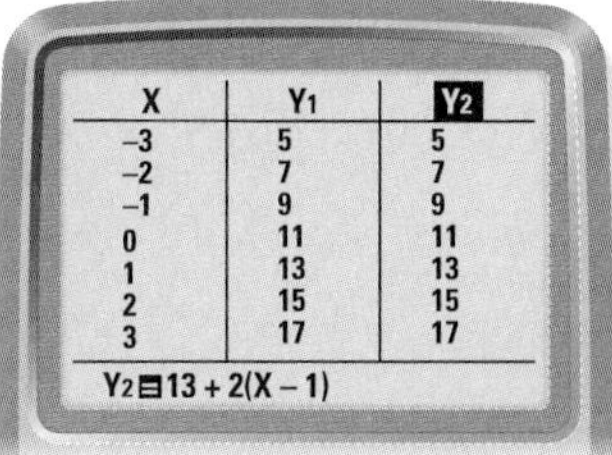

There are many different **equivalent equations** that can be used to describe any given line. In fact, both of the equations above can also be described in intercept form, $y = a + bx$, or in slope-intercept form, $y = mx + b$. In this lesson you'll learn how to change equations to equivalent equations in intercept form by using mathematical properties and the rules for order of operations.

The **distributive property** allows you to rewrite some expressions that contain parentheses. For an expression like $2(4 + 3)$, you can use the order of operations and add 4 and 3 and then multiply this value by 2 to get 14. Or you can "distribute" the number outside the parentheses to all the numbers inside: $2(4 + 3) = 2 \cdot 4 + 2 \cdot 3$ and then multiply twice and add 8 and 6 to get 14. The expressions $2(4 + 3)$ and $2 \cdot 4 + 2 \cdot 3$ are equivalent expressions. This figure shows a model of the expression $2(4 + 3)$. You can think of the large rectangle either as a 2×7 rectangle or as a 2×4 rectangle and a 2×3 rectangle. The area is 14 no matter which way you compute it.

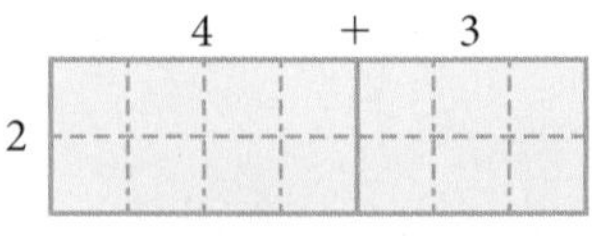

EXAMPLE A | Use the distributive property to write $y = 3 + 2(x + 4)$ without parentheses.

Solution | Before adding 3, distribute the 2 through the sum of x and 4.

x + 4
2 | $2x$ | 8

$y = 3 + 2(x + 4)$	Point-slope equation.
$y = 3 + 2 \cdot x + 2 \cdot 4$	Use the distributive property: Distribute 2 through $x + 4$.
$y = 3 + 2x + 8$	Simplify (Multiply $2 \cdot 4$).
$y = 11 + 2x$	Combine like terms (add $3 + 8$).

So $y = 3 + 2(x + 4)$ is equivalent to $y = 11 + 2x$. These equivalent equations, one in point-slope form and one in intercept form, represent the same line. What does each form tell you about the line it describes?

The distributive property can be generalized like this:

Distributive Property of Multiplication over Addition

For any values of a, b, and c, $a(b + c) = a \cdot b + a \cdot c$.

In the investigation you'll further explore how to identify equivalent equations.

INVESTIGATION

Equivalent Equations

Here are six different-looking equations in point-slope form.

a. $y = 3 - 2(x - 1)$ **b.** $y = -2(x - 5) - 5$

c. $y = 9 - 2(x + 2)$ **d.** $y = 0 - 2(x - 2.5)$

e. $7 - 2(x + 1) = y$ **f.** $y = -9 - 2(x - 7)$

Step 1 Do the six equations represent the same line or different lines? Explain.

Step 2 Divide these equations among the members of your group. Use the distributive property to rewrite the expression containing x in each equation. When you combine like terms, you should get an equation in intercept form.

Step 3 Enter both your point-slope equation and your intercept equation into your calculator. Check that the two equations have the same calculator graph or table. How does this show that the equations are equivalent?

Step 4 Now, as a group, compare your intercept equations. What do the results show about the six equations?

Step 5 As a group, explain how you can tell that an equation in point-slope form is equivalent to one in intercept form. Think about how you can do this graphically and symbolically.

Here are 15 equations. They represent only four different lines.

a. $y = 2(x - 2.5)$	**b.** $y = 18 + 2(x - 8)$
c. $y = 52 - 6(x + 8)$	**d.** $y = -6 + 2(x + 4)$
e. $21 + -6(x + 4) = y$	**f.** $y = -14 - 6(x - 3)$
g. $y = -10 + 2(x + 6)$	**h.** $6x + y = 4$
i. $y = 11 + 2(x - 8)$	**j.** $12x + 2y = -6$
k. $y = 2(x - 4) + 10$	**l.** $15 - 2(10 - x) = y$
m. $y = 7 + 2(x - 6)$	**n.** $y = -6(x + 0.5)$
o. $y = -6(x + 2) + 16$	

Step 6 Test your answer to Step 5 by finding the intercept form of each equation and then grouping equivalent equations.

Step 7 As a group, explain how you can tell that two equations in point-slope form are equivalent.

You have learned how to write linear equations in three different forms:

Intercept form	$y = a + bx$
Slope-intercept form	$y = mx + b$
Point-slope form	$y = y_1 + b(x - x_1)$

In the second part of the investigation, some of the equations had x and y on the same side, as in $12x + 2y = -6$. Equations in the form $ax + by = c$ are in **standard form.** What other equation in the investigation is in standard form?

Writing Linear Equations

Intercept form	$y = a + bx$
Slope-intercept form	$y = mx + b$
Point-slope form	$y = y_1 + b(x - x_1)$
Standard form	$ax + by = c$

Properties of Operations

For any values of a, b, and c, these properties are true:

Commutative Property of Addition	$a + b = b + a$
Commutative Property of Multiplication	$ab = ba$
Associative Property of Addition	$a + (b + c) = (a + b) + c$
Associative Property of Multiplication	$a(bc) = (ab)c$
Additive Identity Property of 0	$a + 0 = 0 + a = a$
Multiplicative Identity of 1	$a \cdot 1 = 1 \cdot a = a$
Distributive Property of Multiplication over Addition	$a\,(b + c) = a(b) + a(c)$

There are also the properties you have used to solve equations by balancing.

Properties of Equality

Given $a = b$, for any number c,

Addition Property of Equality	$a + c = b + c$
Subtraction Property of Equality	$a - c = b - c$
Multiplication Property of Equality	$ac = bc$
Division Property of Equality	$\frac{a}{c} = \frac{b}{c}$ $(c \neq 0)$
Reflexive Property of Equality	$a = a$
Symmetric Property of Equality	If $a = b$, then $b = a$
Transitive Property of Equality	If $a = b$ and $b = c$, then $a = c$

EXAMPLE B Is the equation $y = 2 + 3(x - 1)$ equivalent to $6x - 2y = 2$?

Solution Use the properties to rewrite each equation in intercept form.

$y = 2 + 3(x - 1)$	Original equation.
$y = 2 + 3x - 3$	Distributive property (distribute 3 over $x - 1$).
$y = -1 + 3x$	Combine like terms.

The intercept form of the first equation is $y = -1 + 3x$.

$6x - 2y = 2$	Original equation.
$-2y = 2 - 6x$	Subtraction property (subtract $6x$ from both sides).
$y = \dfrac{2 - 6x}{-2}$	Division property (divide both sides by -2).
$y = -1 + 3x$	Distributive property (divide each term by -2).

The intercept form of the second equation is also $y = -1 + 3x$.

So the equations are equivalent. You can also check that the intercept form and the point-slope form of the equation are equivalent by verifying that they produce the same line graph and have the same table of values. Unfortunately, you cannot enter the standard form into your calculator.

One of the authors, Jerald Murdock, works with two students.

EXAMPLE C Solve the equation $\frac{3x+4}{6} - 5 = 7$. Identify the property of equality used in each step.

Solution Make a list of the operations on x in order:

$\times 3$ $\quad +4$ $\quad \div 6$ $\quad -5$

To solve, undo these operations in reverse order.

	Undo	Equation	Property of equality
		$\frac{3x+4}{6} - 5 = 7$	Original equation
-5 →	$+5$	$\frac{3x+4}{6} = 12$	Addition property
$\div 6$ →	$\times 6$	$3x + 4 = 72$	Multiplication property
$+4$ →	-4	$3x = 68$	Subtraction property
$\times 3$ →	$\div 3$	$x = \frac{68}{3}$	Division property

4.6 Exercises

You will need your graphing calculator for Exercises **1** and **2.**

Practice Your Skills

1. Is each pair of expressions equivalent? If they are not, change the second expression so that they are equivalent. Check your work by comparing table values for both of the equivalent expressions on your calculator.

a. $3 - 3(x + 4)$ $\qquad 3x - 9$ @

b. $5 + 2(x - 2)$ $\qquad 2x + 1$

c. $5x - 3$ $\qquad 2 + 5(x - 1)$

d. $-2x - 8$ $\qquad -2(x - 4)$

2. Rewrite each equation in intercept form. Show your steps. Check your answer by using a calculator graph or table.

a. $y = 14 + 3(x - 5)$

b. $y = -5 - 2(x + 5)$ @

c. $6x + 2y = 24$

d. $3x - 3y = 12$

e. $y - 6 = -(x + 2)$

f. $y = 7(x + 3) + 4$

3. Solve each equation by balancing, and tell which property you used in each step.

a. $3x = 12$

b. $-x - 45 = 47$ @

c. $x + 15 = 8$

d. $\frac{x}{4} = 28$

e. $\frac{4}{7}x = 3$

f. $x + (-3) = 7$

4. Use the distributive property to rewrite each expression without parentheses.

a. $3(x - 2)$

b. $-4(x - 5)$

c. $-2(x + 8)$

d. $5(x - 1)$

e. $-3(x + 2)$

f. $2(x + 15) - 12$

5. In the expression $3x + 15$, the greatest common factor (GCF) of both $3x$ and 15 is 3. You can write the expression $3x + 15$ as $3(x + 5)$. This process, called **factoring,** is the reverse of distributing. Rewrite each expression by factoring out the GCF that will leave 1 as the coefficient of x. Use the distributive property to check your work.

a. $3x - 12$ @

b. $-5x + 20$ @

c. $32 + 4x$

d. $-7x - 28$

e. $9x - 27$

f. $-5x - 25$

g. $48 + 12x$

h. $8 - 8x$

i. $4x - 12$

j. $-6x + 6$

k. $10x + 15$

Reason and Apply

6. Solve each equation for the indicated variable.

a. $y = 3(x + 8)$ Solve for x.

b. $\frac{y - 3}{x - 4} = 10$ Solve for y.

c. $4(2y - 5) - 12 = x$ Solve for y.

7. MINI-INVESTIGATION Consider the equation $y = 10 + 5x$ in intercept form.

a. Factor the right side of the equation.

b. Use the commutative property of addition to swap the terms inside the parentheses.

c. Your result should look similar to the point-slope form of the equation. What's missing? What is the value of this missing piece? @

d. What point could you use to write the point-slope equation in 7c? What is special about this point? @

8. In each set of three equations, two equations are equivalent. Find them and explain how you know they are equivalent.

a. i. $y = 14 - 2(x - 5)$ @
ii. $y = 30 - 2(x + 3)$
iii. $y = -12 + 2(x - 5)$

b. i. $y = -13 + 4(x + 2)$
ii. $y = 10 + 3(x - 5)$
iii. $y = -25 + 4(x + 5)$

c. i. $y = 5 + 5(x - 8)$
ii. $y = 9 + 5(x + 8)$
iii. $y = 94 + 5(x - 9)$

d. i. $y = -16 + 6(x + 5)$
ii. $y = 8 + 6(x - 5)$
iii. $y = 44 + 6(x - 5)$

9. APPLICATION Dorine subscribes to a budget cell phone plan with a flat rate for up to 200 min of use each month. For each minute over the limit, there is an additional per-minute fee. The table shows data for Dorine's first two bills.

Cell Phone Use

Month	Talked (min)	Fee ($)
January	265	59.24
February	312	80.39

a. Define your variables and use the data in the table to write an equation in point-slope form that models Dorine's total monthly fee. @

b. For March Dorine was incorrectly charged $53 for using 250 min. What should her fee have been?

c. In April Dorine used 180 min. What was her total fee that month? Explain why you can't use your equation to answer this question.

d. How many minutes did Dorine use during a month when her fee was $87.59?

10. On Saturday morning Avery took a hike in the hills near her house. The table shows the cumulative number of calories she burned from the time she went to sleep Friday night until she finished her hike.

Avery's Hike

Time spent hiking (min)	Cumulative number of calories burned
5	568
10	591
15	614
20	637

a. Write a point-slope equation of a line that fits the data. @

b. Rewrite your equation from 10a in intercept form.

c. What are the real-world meanings of the slope and the y-intercept in this situation? (h)

d. Could you use the point-slope equation $y = 821 + 4.6(x - 60)$ to model this situation? Explain why or why not.

e. What is the real-world meaning of the point used to write the equation in 10d?

11. A line has the equation $y = 4 - 4.2x$.

a. Find the y-coordinate of the point on this line whose x-coordinate is 2.

b. Use the point you found in 11a to write an equation in point-slope form.

c. Find the x-coordinate of the point whose y-coordinate is 6.1.

d. Use the point you found in 11c to write a different point-slope equation.

e. Show that the point-slope equations you wrote in 11b and d are equivalent to the original equation in intercept form. Explain your procedure.

f. Is the point $(4, -12)$ on the line? What about the point $(-3, 16.6)$? Explain how you can determine whether a given point is on a line.

Review

12. The points $(1, 5)$ and $(2, 12)$ lie on a line.

a. How does the y-intercept of the line that passes through these two points compare to the y-intercept of the line $y = 1 + 8x$?

b. How does the slope of the line that passes through the points $(1, 5)$ and $(2, 12)$ compare to the slope of the line $y = 1 + 8x$?

13. Tamar has a new cell phone service that is billed at a base fee of \$15 per month plus 45¢ for each minute the phone is used. Consider the relationship between the time the phone is used and the total monthly cost. Let x represent time, in minutes, and let y represent cost, in dollars.

a. Give one point on the line, and state the slope of the line in dollars per minute. @

b. Write the equation of the line. Sketch its graph for the first 30 min.

c. How will the graph change if Tamar adds Call Forwarding, changing the base fee to \$20?

d. How will the graph change if Tamar drops Caller ID and Voice Mail so that there is no monthly base fee?

e. How will the graph change if instead Tamar adds the Text Messaging option, increasing the rate to 55¢ per minute?

14. Show how to solve the equation $3.8 = 0.2(z + 6.2) - 5.4$ by using an undoing process to write an expression for z. Check your answer by substituting it into the original equation.

Different Linear Forms

You have learned to find the equation of a line from the slope and the intercept, from the slope and a point, and from two points.

EXAMPLE A Find the equation of each line.

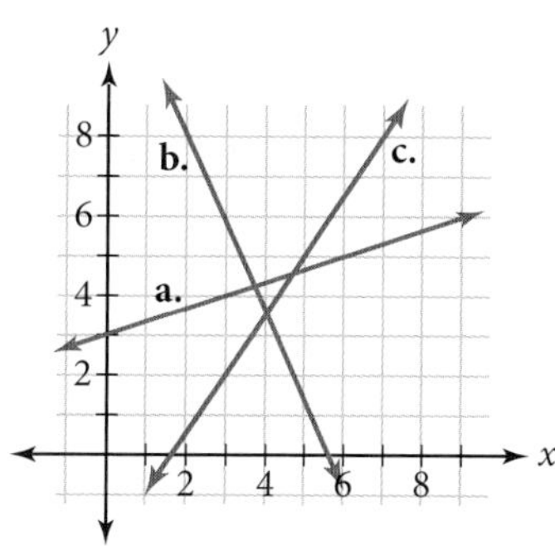

Solution Observe the graph to determine which form of the equation to use for each line.

a. This line has a clear y-intercept at the point (0, 3) and slope $\frac{1}{3}$. Use the intercept form to write its equation: $y = 3 + \frac{1}{3}x$.

b. This line has one point at (2, 8) and a slope of $\frac{-2}{0.9}$, or about -2.2. Use the point-slope form to write its equation: $y = 8 - 2.2(x - 2)$.

c. This line includes points at (3, 2) and (7, 8). First find its slope: $\frac{8-2}{7-3} = \frac{6}{4} = 1.5$. Then use the point-slope form to write its equation: $y = 2 + 1.5(x - 3)$.

EXAMPLE B Graph the two equations, and estimate the point of intersection of the two lines.

Line a: $y = 6 - \frac{2}{3}x$

Line b: $y = 1 + \frac{4}{3}(x - 1)$

Solution Line a has y-intercept 6 and slope $-\frac{2}{3}$. Plot the point (0, 6), and the point 2 units down and 3 units right, (3, 4). Then draw a line through these points.

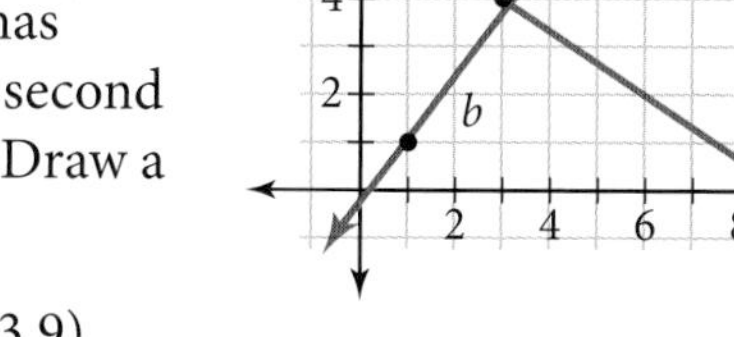

Line b passes through the point (1, 1) and has slope $\frac{4}{3}$. Plot the first point, and then plot a second point 4 units up and 3 units right, at (4, 5). Draw a line through these points.

The two lines intersect near the point (3.2, 3.9).

EXAMPLE C Solve both equations and explain how they are related to Example B.

$$6 - \frac{2}{3}x = \frac{35}{9}$$

$$1 + \frac{4}{3}(x - 1) = \frac{35}{9}$$

Solution

The process for solving each equation is almost the same.

$6 - \frac{2}{3}x = \frac{35}{9}$	Original equation.	$1 + \frac{4}{3}(x - 1) = \frac{35}{9}$
$6 - \frac{2}{3}x - 6 = \frac{35}{9} - 6$	Subtraction property.	$1 + \frac{4}{3}(x - 1) - 1 = \frac{35}{9} - 1$
$-\frac{2}{3}x = \frac{35}{9} - \frac{54}{9}$	Common denominators.	$\frac{4}{3}(x - 1) = \frac{35}{9} - \frac{9}{9}$
$-\frac{2}{3}x = -\frac{19}{9}$	Combine like terms.	$\frac{4}{3}(x - 1) = \frac{26}{9}$
$-\frac{2}{3}x \div \left(-\frac{2}{3}\right) = -\frac{19}{9} \div \left(-\frac{2}{3}\right)$	Division property.	$\frac{4}{3}(x - 1) \div \frac{4}{3} = \frac{26}{9} \div \frac{4}{3}$
$x = \frac{19}{6}$	Simplify.	$x - 1 = \frac{13}{6}$
	Addition property.	$x - 1 + 1 = \frac{13}{6} + 1$
	Combine like terms.	$x = \frac{13}{6} + \frac{6}{6} = \frac{19}{6}$

The equations in Example C are the equations from Example B with the y-value equal to $\frac{35}{9}$. Solving both equations gives $x = \frac{19}{6}$. So the graphs intersect at the point $\left(\frac{19}{6}, \frac{35}{9}\right)$, or (3.167, 3.889).

Exercises

1. Write an equation of each line in the most convenient form. If you cannot locate exact points, estimate points and slopes as accurately as possible.

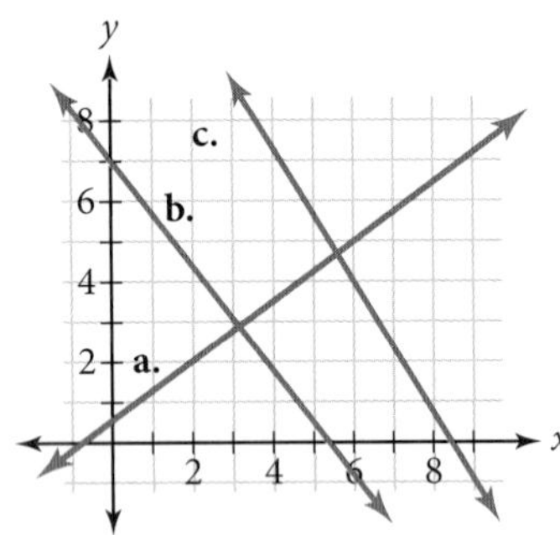

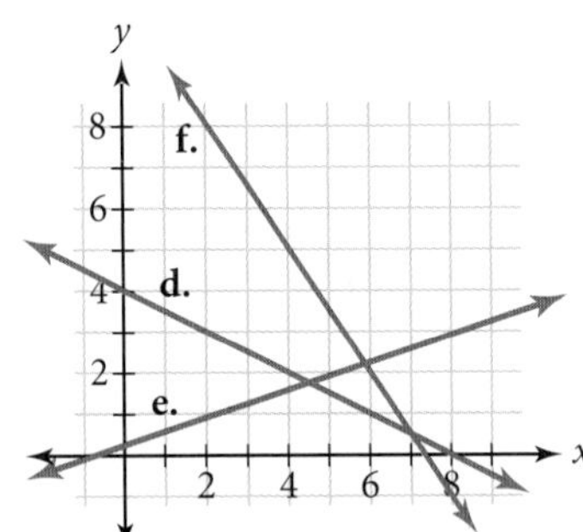

2. Graph each line.

a. $y = 2x + 3$ b. $y = 2 - 3(x + 1)$ c. $y = \frac{5}{2} + \frac{3}{2}x$

d. $y - 4 = -\frac{1}{2}(x - 3)$ e. $y = 2.1 + 1.6x$ f. $y = 5.2 - 2.5(x - 1.7)$

3. Solve each equation. Use a graph from Exercise 2 to check whether your answer is reasonable.

a. $y = 2x + 3$, when $y = -1$ b. $y = 2 - 3(x + 1)$, when $y = 5$

c. $y = \frac{5}{2} + \frac{3}{2}x$, when $y = \frac{7}{2}$ d. $y - 4 = -\frac{1}{2}(x - 3)$, when $y = -4$

e. $y = 2.1 + 1.6x$, when $y = 4.3$ f. $y = 5.2 - 2.5(x - 1.7)$, when $y = -6.3$

4. Explain how you used the graphs from Exercise 2 to check your answers in Exercise 3.

LESSON

4.7

Using Linear Equations

"To give an accurate description of what has never occurred is the proper occupation of the historian."

OSCAR WILDE

In this lesson you'll use the point-slope form of a linear equation to model linear data. You may find that using this form is more efficient than using the intercept form because you don't have to first write a direct variation equation and then adjust it for the intercept.

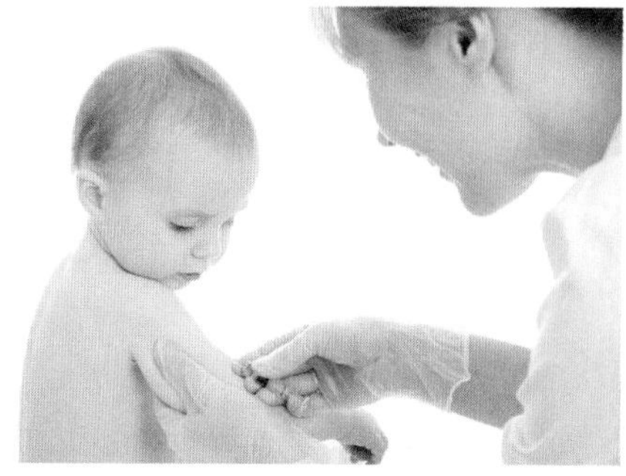

The development and improvement of vaccinations are factors that have increased life expectancy over the decades.

INVESTIGATION

YOU WILL NEED

- graph paper

Life Expectancy

This table shows the relationship between the number of years a person might be expected to live and the year he or she was born. Life expectancy is a prediction that is very useful in professions such as medicine and insurance.

U.S. Life Expectancy at Birth

Birth year	Female	Male	Combined
1940	65.2	60.8	62.9
1950	71.1	65.6	68.2
1960	73.1	66.6	69.7
1970	74.7	67.1	70.8
1980	77.5	70.0	73.7
1985	78.2	71.2	74.7
1990	78.8	71.8	75.4
1995	78.9	72.5	75.8
2000	79.5	74.1	76.9
2005	80.4	75.2	77.9

(National Center for Health Statistics, in *The World Almanac and Book of Facts 2009,* p. 217) [Data sets: **LEYR, LEFEM, LEMAL, LECOM**]

Step 1 Choose one column of life expectancy data—female, male, or combined. Define the independent variable, x, and the dependent variable, y. Graph the data points.

Step 2 Choose two points on your graph so that a line passing through them closely reflects the pattern of all the points on the graph. Use the two points to write the equation of this line in point-slope form.

Step 3 Graph the line with your data points. Does it fit the data? Explain.

Step 4 Use your equation to predict the life expectancy of a person who will be born in 2022.

Step 5 Compare your prediction from Step 4 to the prediction that another group made analyzing the same data. Are your predictions the same? Are they close? Explain why it's possible to make different predictions from the same data.

Step 6 Compare the slope of your line of fit to the slopes that other groups found working with different data sets. What does the slope for each data set tell you?

Step 7 As a class, select one line of fit that you think is the best model for each column of data—female, male, and combined. Graph all three lines on the same set of axes. Is it reasonable for the line representing the combined data to lie between the other two lines? Explain why or why not.

Step 8 How does the point-slope method of finding a line compare to the slope-intercept method you learned about in Lesson 4.4? What are the strengths and weaknesses of each method?

You will need your graphing calculator for Exercises **3** and **8.**

Practice Your Skills

1. Write the point-slope form of the equation for the line represented by each graph.

a. ⓐ

b.

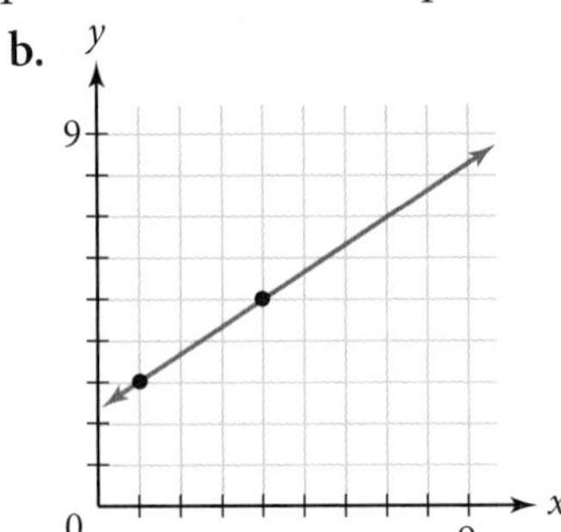

c.

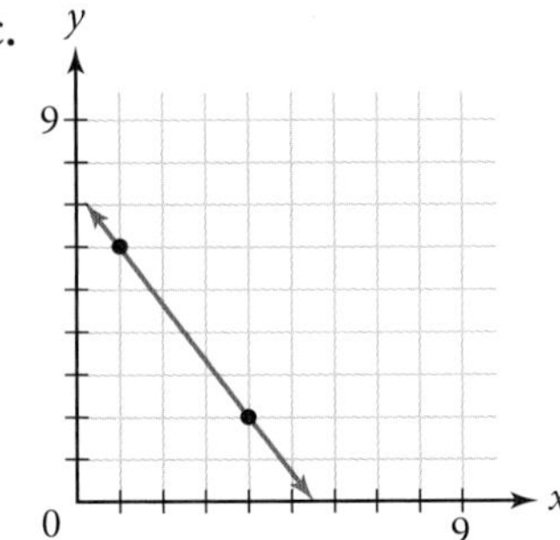

2. Look at each graph in Exercise 1 and estimate the y-intercept. Then convert your point-slope equations to intercept form. How close was your estimate? ⓗ

3. Graph each linear equation on your calculator and name the x-intercept. Make a conjecture about the x-intercept of any equation in the form $y = b(x - x_1)$.

a. $y = 2(x - 3)$ ⓐ

b. $y = \frac{1}{3}(x + 4)$

c. $y = -1.5(x - 6)$

4. APPLICATION Carbon dioxide (CO_2) is one of several greenhouse gases that is emitted into the atmosphere from a variety of sources, including automobiles. The table shows the concentration of CO_2 in the atmosphere measured from the top of Mauna Loa volcano in Hawaii each January. The concentration of CO_2 is measured in parts per million (ppm).

a. Define variables and write an equation in point-slope form that models the data.

b. Graph your equation to confirm that the line fits the data.

c. Use your equation to predict what the concentration of CO_2 will be in 2020.

d. What would be the x-intercept for the line modeled by your equation? Does its real-world meaning make sense? Explain why or why not.

e. According to your equation, what is the typical change in CO_2 concentration each year?

Mauna Loa is the largest and most active volcano on Earth. Research on Mauna Loa has revealed a great deal about global changes in the atmosphere.

CO_2 Concentration

Year	CO_2 (ppm)
1982	341
1984	344
1986	347
1988	351
1990	354
1992	356
1994	359
1996	363
1998	367
2000	369
2002	373
2004	377
2006	381
2008	385

(Carbon Dioxide Information Analysis Center, *cdiac.esd.ornl.gov*)
[Data sets: **CO2YR, CO2CN**]

Reason and Apply

5. APPLICATION Alex collected this table of data by using two thermometers simultaneously. Alex suspects that one or both of the thermometers are somewhat faulty.

a. Graph the data. @

b. Write an equation in point-slope form that models Alex's data. @

c. Graph your equation to confirm that the line fits the data.

d. The freezing point of water is 0°C, which is equivalent to 32°F. The boiling point of water is 100°C, which is equivalent to 212°F. Use this information to write another equation in point-slope form that models the true relationship between the Celsius and Fahrenheit temperature scales. @

e. Write the equations from 5b and d in intercept form. Are they equivalent? @

f. Do you think that Alex's thermometers are faulty? Explain why or why not.

Temperature Readings

Celsius (°C) x	Fahrenheit (°F) y
14.5	55.0
20.0	67.0
28.4	86.7
39.5	105.6
32.3	87.1
29.0	81.6
26.2	82.3
25.7	75.2
31.2	88.6

[Data sets: **TEMPC, TEMPF**]

6. MINI-INVESTIGATION Scoop has a rolling ice cream cart. He recorded his daily sales for the last seven days and the mean daytime temperature for each day.

Ice Cream Sales

Day	1	2	3	4	5	6	7
Temperature (°F)	83	79	75	70	71	67	62
Sales (cones)	66	47	51	23	33	30	21

[Data sets: **ICTMP, ISCAL**]

a. Find the equation of the line that passes through the points (79, 47) and (67, 30). (Use the second point as the point in the point-slope form.) ⓐ

b. Graph the data and your line from 6a on your calculator. Sketch the result.

You should have noticed in 6b that the line does not fit the data well. In fact, no two points from this data set make a good model. In 6c–e, you'll adjust the values of y_1 and b in the equation $y = y_1 + b(x - x_1)$ to find a better model.

c. Copy the table at right, and begin by changing the value of y_1. Write two new equations, one with a larger value for y_1 and one with a smaller value for y_1. Graph each equation, and describe how the graphs compare to that of your original equation. ⓐ

Value	**Increase**	**Decrease**
y_1		
b		

d. Now write two new equations that have the same values of x_1 and y_1 as the original but larger and smaller values of b. Graph each equation, and describe how the graphs compare to that of your original equation.

e. Continue to adjust your values for y_1 and b until you find a line that fits the data well. Record your final equation. Graph your equation with the data and sketch the result.

7. APPLICATION The table lists the concentration of dissolved oxygen (DO) in parts per million at various temperatures in degrees Celsius from a sample of lake water.

a. Graph the data.

b. Write an equation in point-slope form that models the data.

c. Graph your equation to confirm that the line fits the data.

d. Use your equation to predict the concentration of dissolved oxygen in parts per million when the water temperature is 2°C.

e. Use your equation to predict the water temperature in degrees Celsius when the concentration of dissolved oxygen is 12 ppm.

Dissolved Oxygen

Temperature (°C)	**DO (ppm)**
17	8
15	9
13	11
16	10
11	14
13	11
10	14
8	14
6	16
7	13
8	14
4	17
5	15
9	13
6	16

[Data sets: **DOTMP, DOPPM**]

8. Use the data and the equation you found in Exercise 7.

a. Write an equation with the same slope that passes through the point farthest above the line.

b. Write an equation with the same slope that passes through the point farthest below the line.

c. Rewrite all three equations in intercept form.

d. Based on your answer to 8c, how accurate are predictions made using your equation from Exercise 7 likely to be? ⓗ

Review

9. APPLICATION Bryan has bought a box of biscuits for his dog, Anchor. Anchor always gets three biscuits a day. At the start of the tenth day after opening the box, Bryan counts 106 biscuits left.

a. What are the independent and dependent variables for this situation?

b. In a graph of this situation, what is the slope? ⓗ

c. Write a point-slope equation that models the situation.

d. When will the box be empty?

e. What is the real-world meaning of the y-intercept?

f. Describe the domain and range of this situation.

10. Solve the equation $2x - 3(y + 1) = 12$ for y by copying and filling in this table. ⓐ

Description	Undo	Equation	Property
Pick y.		$y =$	

11. You've worked with various types of problems involving rates. A new kind of problem that uses rates is called a **work problem.** In a work problem, you usually know how long it would take someone or something to complete an entire job. You use the reciprocal of the complete time to find a rate of work. For example, if Mavis paints one entire room in 10 hours, she paints $\frac{1}{10}$ of the room each hour. These problems rely on the formula *rate of work · time = part of work.* Work problems also assume that a complete job is equivalent to 1.

Mavis and Claire work for a house painter. Mavis can paint a room in 10 h, and Claire can paint a room in 8 h. How long will it take them to paint a room if they work together?

Let t represent the number of hours that Mavis and Claire paint. Mavis paints $\frac{1}{10}$ of a room each hour, and Claire paints $\frac{1}{8}$ of a room each hour. So you can write the equation $\frac{1}{10}t + \frac{1}{8}t = 1$.

a. Solve this equation, check your answer, and state the solution.

b. Solve this problem using a similar procedure: When fully turned on, the faucet of a bathtub fills a tub in 30 min. When the tub is full of water and the drain is opened, the tub empties in 45 min. If the faucet is fully turned on *and* the drain is open at the same time, how long does it take to fill the tub?

LESSON

4.8

A Standard Linear Model

"When you can measure what you are talking about and express it in numbers, you know something about it."

LORD KELVIN

Several times in this chapter you have found the equation of a representative line to fit data. The process of making, analyzing, and using predictions based on equation models is important in the real world. For this reason it is often helpful and even important that different people arrive at the same model for a given set of data. For this to happen, each person must get the same slope and y-intercept. To do that, each has to follow the same systematic method.

Statisticians have developed many methods of finding a line or curve that fits a set of data well. In this lesson you'll learn a method that uses the quartiles you learned about in Chapter 1.

INVESTIGATION

YOU WILL NEED

- a stopwatch
- a bucket
- graph paper

Bucket Brigade

In this investigation you will use a systematic method of finding a particular line of fit for data.

Procedure Note

Select a class member as timer. Everyone should line up single file. Your line might wrap around the room. Spread out so that there is an arm's length between every two people.

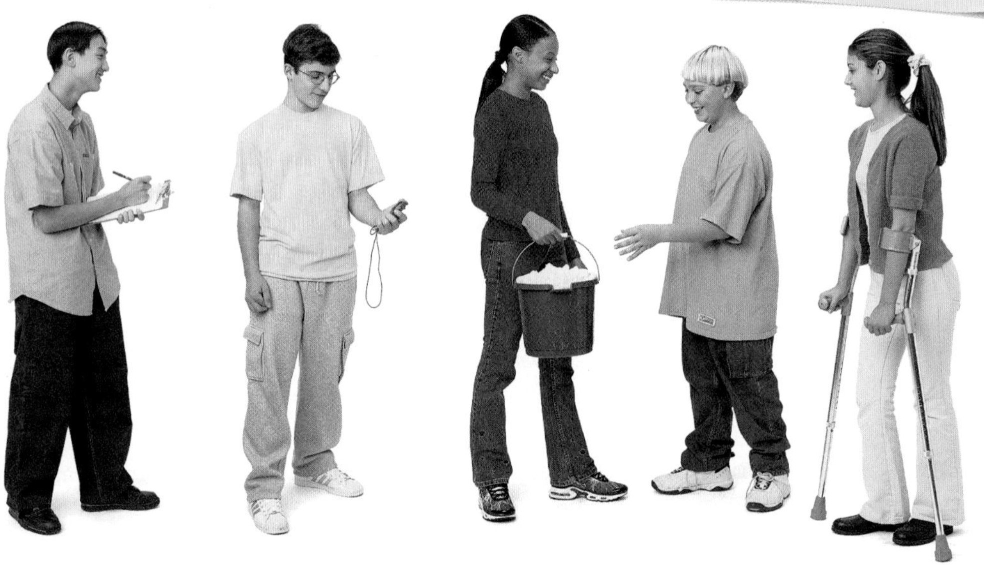

Step 1 Line up in a bucket brigade. (See the Procedure Note.) Record the number of people in the line. Starting at one end of the line, pass the bucket as quickly as you can to the other end. Record the total passing time from picking up the bucket to setting it down at the very end.

Step 2 Now have one or two people sit down, and close the gaps in the line. Repeat the bucket passing. Record the new number of people and the new passing time.

Step 3 Continue the bucket brigade until you have collected ten data points in the form (*number of people, passing time in seconds*).

Step 4 Let x represent the number of people, and let y represent time in seconds. Plot your data on graph paper.

Step 5 List the five-number summary for the x-values and the five-number summary for the y-values.

Step 6 What are the first-quartile (Q_1) and third-quartile (Q_3) values for the x-values in your data set? What are the Q_1- and Q_3-values for the y-values in your data set?

Step 7 On your graph, draw a horizontal box plot just below the x-axis using the five-number summary for the x-values. Draw a vertical box plot next to the y-axis using the five-number summary for the y-values. A sample graph is shown. Your data and graph will look different based on the data you collect.

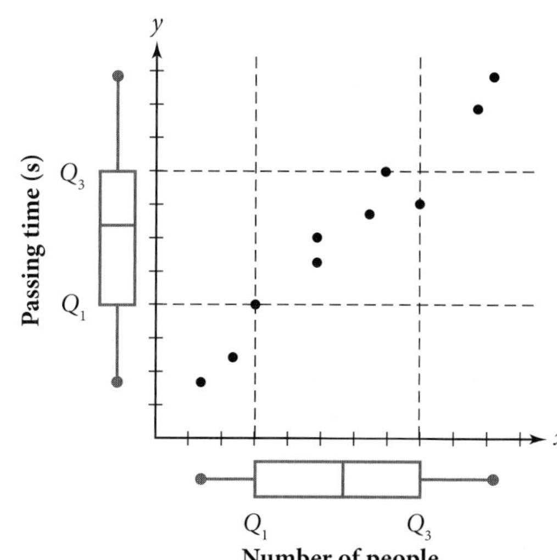

Step 8 Draw vertical lines from the Q_1- and Q_3-values on the x-axis box plot into the graph. Draw horizontal lines from the Q_1- and Q_3-values on the y-axis box plot into the graph. These lines should form a rectangle in the plot. The vertices of this rectangle are called **Q-points.** Do the Q-points have to be actual data points? Why or why not? Will everyone get the same Q-points?

Step 9 Draw the diagonal of this rectangle that shows the direction of the data. Extend this diagonal through the plot. Is the line a good fit for the data? Are any of the original data points on your line? If so, which ones?

Step 10 Find the coordinates of the two Q-points that the line passes through, and write a point-slope equation of the line.

Step 11 What are the real-world meanings of the slope and y-intercept of this model?

Step 12 What are the advantages and disadvantages of having a systematic procedure for finding a model for data?

The method of finding a line of fit based on Q-points is more direct than the methods you used in Lessons 4.4 and 4.7. It is also more systematic, because everyone will get the same points, and the points themselves relate to measures of center in the upper and lower halves of the data set.

[▸ For a **Dynamic Algebra Exploration** that investigates how moving one data point affects box plots and Q-points, see your ebook. ◂]

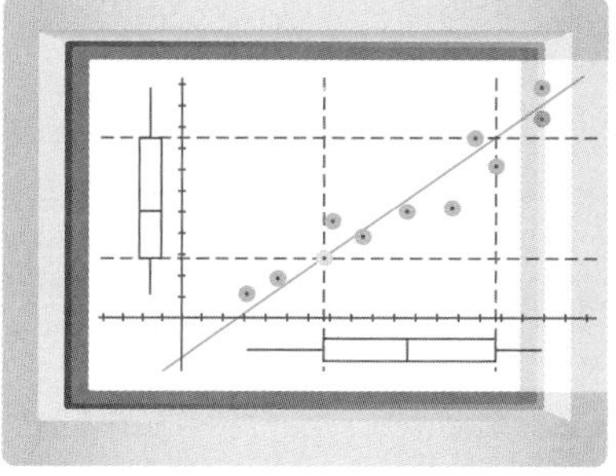

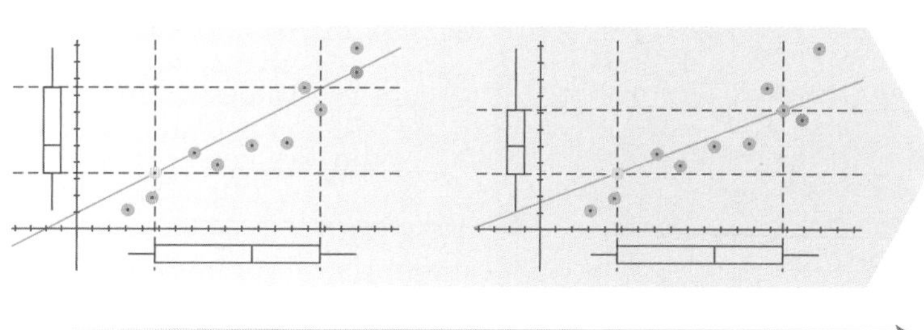

In the investigation you saw a change in the time based on the change in the number of people. This is an example of **causation,** where changes in one variable *cause* changes in another. A linear relationship does not always mean causation. In the next example, temperature and dissolved oxygen (DO) were measured. In this case the investigators did not control the temperature but simply measured it. Without deeper investigation, to say that changes in temperature "cause" changes in DO would be improper. You can, however, say that there is a **correlation** between temperature and DO—the two are related, but one does not necessarily cause the other.

These scientists are collecting water samples. Their samples can be analyzed for many things, including dissolved oxygen.

EXAMPLE

The table lists the concentration of DO in parts per million (ppm) at various temperatures in degrees Celsius from a series of samples of water from a lake. Find a line of fit for the data based on *Q*-points.

Dissolved Oxygen

Temperature (°C) x	DO (ppm) y	Temperature (°C) x	DO (ppm) y
17	8	8	14
16	10	8	14
15	9	7	13
13	11	6	16
13	11	6	16
11	14	5	15
10	14	4	17
9	13		

Solution

The five-number summaries are

For temperature (x-values):
4, 6, 9, 13, 17

For dissolved oxygen (y-values):
8, 11, 14, 15, 17

The first-quartile and third-quartile values are

For the x-values: $Q_1 = 6$, $Q_3 = 13$

For the y-values: $Q_1 = 11$, $Q_3 = 15$

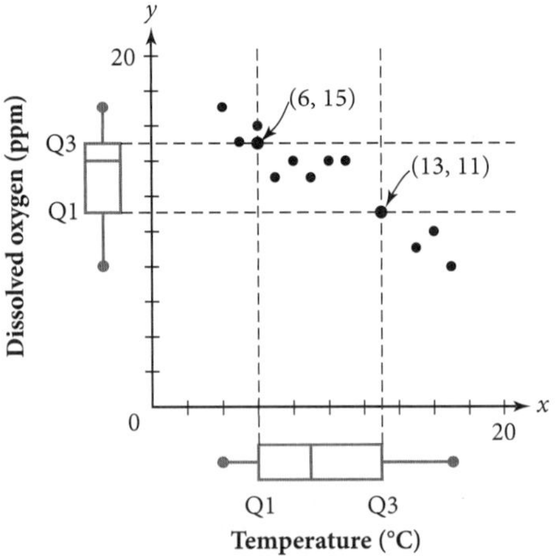

A sketch of the scatter plot shows that the appropriate *Q*-points are (6, 15) and (13, 11). Why are these the correct points rather than (6, 11) and (13, 15)? Note that (6, 15) is not actually one of the data points but (13, 11) is.

Calculating the slope between these two points, you get

$$b = \frac{y_2 - y_1}{x_2 - x_1} = \frac{(11 - 15)}{(13 - 6)} = \frac{-4}{7} \approx -0.57$$

This means that if the temperature of this lake *rises* 1°C, the dissolved oxygen concentration *decreases* by 0.57 ppm. It also means that if the temperature *drops* 1°C, the dissolved oxygen concentration *increases* by 0.57 ppm.

Using the slope −0.57 and the coordinates of the point (6, 15) in the point-slope form, $y = y_1 + b(x - x_1)$, gives

$$y = 15 - 0.57(x - 6)$$

The box summarizes the procedure for finding a line of fit based on *Q*-points.

Finding a Line of Fit Using *Q*-Points

To find a line of fit using *Q*-points:

1. **Separately put the *x*-values in order and the *y*-values in order.**
2. **Find the first and third quartiles for the *x*-values, and find the first and third quartiles for the *y*-values.**
3. **Look at your plot. You will need to pair the quartiles differently depending on whether the data are increasing or decreasing.**
4. **Based on your pairings, write the equation using the point-slope formula.**

4.8 Exercises

Practice Your Skills

1. Give the first and third quartile of each data set.

a. {12, 15, 16, 19, 20, 20, 22, 25, 29, 31}

b. {45, 48, 53, 57, 59, 60, 62, 62, 66} @

c. {33, 27, 41, 35, 24, 35, 44, 37, 29, 39, 42} @

d. {85, 88, 73, 62, 91, 80, 77, 93}

2. State whether the data values in each data set are increasing or decreasing.

a.

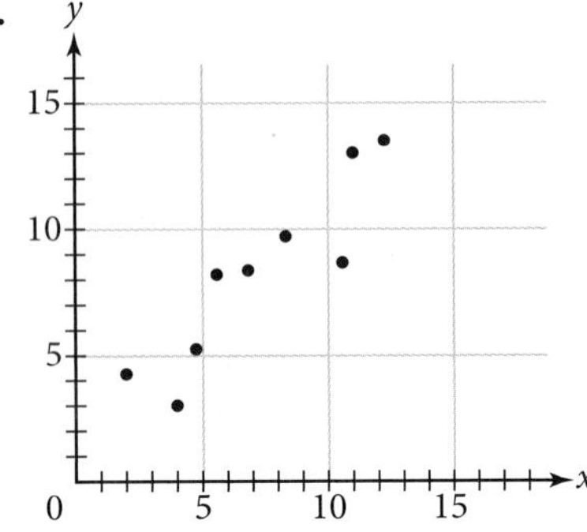

b.

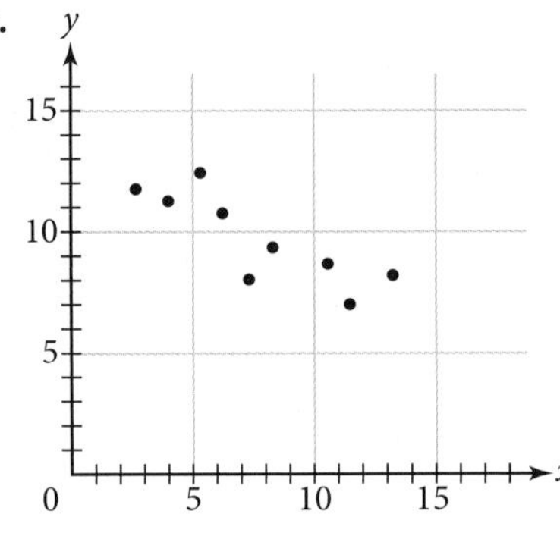

c.

x	y
3	9
5	10
7	4
8	6
11	3
12	3

d. @

x	y
22	19
30	26
25	20
33	30
28	28
23	22

3. Write an equation of the line that passes through each pair of points.

a. (5, 10) and (11, 4)

b. (23, 22) and (31, 26)

c. Q_1 and Q_3 are $x_1 = 40$, $x_2 = 60$, $y_1 = 19.2$, and $y_2 = 24.2$, and the line has positive slope. @

d. Q_1 and Q_3 are $x_1 = 40$, $x_2 = 60$, $y_1 = 19.2$, and $y_2 = 24.2$, and the line has negative slope.

4. APPLICATION Saturated fat in grams is a function of total fat in grams. Use the model $y = 10 + 0.5(x - 28)$ to predict the following.

a. The number of grams of saturated fat for a hamburger with 32 g total fat.

b. The total number of fat grams for a hamburger with 15 g of saturated fat.

5. Give the coordinates of the Q-points for each data set.

a. @

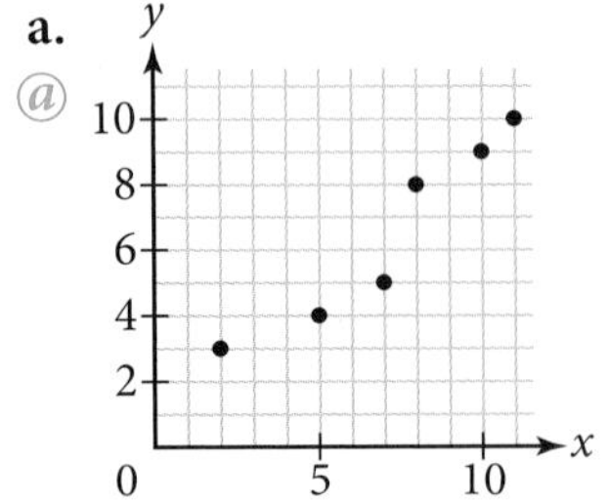

b.

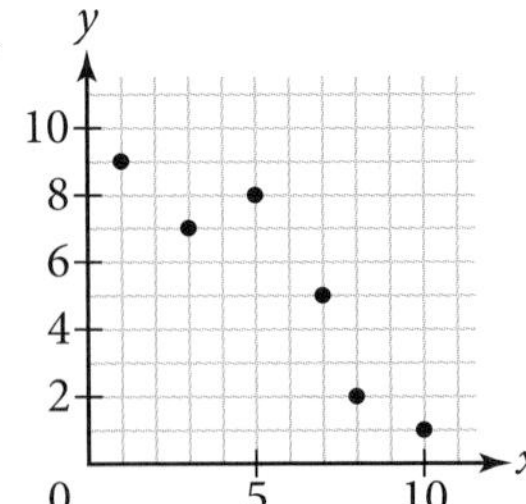

Reason and Apply

6. The table gives the winning times for the Olympic men's 10,000-m run.

a. Define variables and find the line of fit based on Q-points for the data.

b. Plot the data points and graph the equation of the model to verify that it is a good fit. ⓐ

c. What is the real-world meaning of the slope?

d. Mohamed Farah of Great Britain won this race in the 2012 Olympic Games. Compare his actual winning time, 27.50 min, with the winning time predicted by your model.

e. Can you make the strong statement "The change in year *causes* a change in winning time" or only the weaker statement "The change in year is correlated with a change in winning time"? Why?

Men's 10,000-Meter Run

Year	Champion	Time (min)
1956	Vladimir Kuts, USSR	28.76
1960	Pyotr Bolotnikov, USSR	28.54
1964	Billy Mills, United States	28.41
1968	Naftali Temu, Kenya	29.46
1972	Lasse Viren, Finland	27.64
1976	Lasse Viren, Finland	27.67
1980	Miruts Yifter, Ethiopia	27.71
1984	Alberto Cova, Italy	27.79
1988	Brahim Boutaib, Morocco	27.36
1992	Khalid Skah, Morocco	27.78
1996	Haile Gebrselassie, Ethiopia	27.12
2000	Haile Gebrselassie, Ethiopia	27.30
2004	Kenenisa Bekele, Ethiopia	27.08
2008	Kenenisa Bekele, Ethiopia	27.02

(International Olympic Committee, in *The World Almanac and Book of Facts 2009,* p. 851) [Data sets: **RUNYR, RUNTM**]

7. Create a data set that has Q-points at (4, 28) and (12, 47) so that only one of those two points is actually part of the data set. ⓗ

8. Which linear equation best fits the data in the table at right? Explain your reasoning.

i. $y = 1.3 + 0.18(x - 6)$

ii. $y = 2.2 + 0.18(x - 6)$

iii. $y = 1.3 - 0.18(x - 6)$

iv. $y = 2.2 - 0.18(x - 6)$

Time (s) x	Distance from motion sensor (m) y
2	2.8
6	2.2
8	1.7
9	1.5
11	1.3
14	0.9

9. At 2:00 P.M., elevator A passes the second floor of the Empire State Building going up. The table shows the floors and the times in seconds after 2:00 P.M.

Floor x	2	4	6	8	10	12	14
Time after 2:00 P.M. (s) y	0	1.3	2.5	3.8	5	6.3	7.5

a. What is the line of fit based on Q-points for the data? ⓐ

b. Give a real-world meaning of the slope. ⓐ

c. About what time will this elevator pass the sixtieth floor if it makes no stops? ⓐ

d. Where will this elevator be at 2:00:45 P.M. if it makes no stops? ⓐ

10. At 2:00 P.M., elevator B passes the ninety-fourth floor of the same building going down. The table shows the floors and the times in seconds after 2:00 P.M.

Floor x	94	92	90	88	86	84	80
Time after 2:00 P.M. (s) y	0	1.3	2.5	3.8	5	6.3	8.6

a. What is the line of fit based on Q-points for the data?

b. Give a real-world meaning of the slope.

c. About what time will this elevator pass the tenth floor if it makes no stops?

d. Where will this elevator be at 2:00:34 P.M. if it makes no stops?

11. Think about the elevators in Exercises 9 and 10.

a. Estimate when elevator A will pass elevator B if neither makes any stops.

b. Calculate the actual time.

Review

12. In Chapter 3, you worked with problems involving rate, often involving the equation $d = rt$. Here is another kind of **rate problem.**

Ellen and Eric meet on Saturday to train for a marathon. They live 7 miles apart and meet at the high-school track that is between their two homes. Ellen leaves at 8:00 A.M. and jogs south toward the school at 4 mi/h. Eric waits until 8:30 A.M. and jogs north toward the school at 6 mi/h. The two friends arrive at the school at exactly the same time. How much time did each person jog?

To solve this problem, let t represent Ellen's time in hours. Because Eric left a half hour after Ellen but arrived at the same time, he jogged for a half hour less. So let $t - \frac{1}{2}$ represent Eric's time in hours. You might now fill out a table like this to get expressions for distance. (Remember that *distance* = *rate* · *time*.)

	rate (mi/h)	time (h)	distance (mi)
Ellen	4	t	$4 \cdot t$
Eric	6	$t - \frac{1}{2}$	$6 \cdot \left(t - \frac{1}{2}\right)$
Combined			7

a. Write an equation that states that Ellen's distance and Eric's distance combine to 7 miles.

b. Solve the equation from 12a, check your answer, and state the solution.

c. Solve this problem using a similar procedure: A propeller airplane and a jet airplane leave the same airport at the same time, and both go in the same direction. The jet airplane's velocity is five times the propeller airplane's velocity. After 2.25 h, the jet airplane is 1170 km ahead of the propeller plane. What is the velocity of each plane in kilometers per hour?

13. A car is traveling from Sioux Falls, South Dakota, to Mt. Rushmore, which is near Rapid City, South Dakota. The car is traveling about 54 mi/h, and the distance from Sioux Falls to Mt. Rushmore is about 370 mi.

Wall Drug is a landmark in South Dakota. The store's fame began during the Great Depression, when it offered free ice water to travelers.

a. Write a recursive rule to create a table of values in the form (*time, distance from Mt. Rushmore*) for the relationship from 0 h to 6 h. ⓐ

b. Graph a scatter plot using 1 h time intervals.

c. Draw a line through the points of your scatter plot. What is the real-world meaning of this line? What does the line represent that the points alone do not?

d. What is the slope of the line? What is the real-world meaning of the slope?

e. When will the car be at the Wall Drug Store, which is 80 mi before the car gets to Mt. Rushmore? Explain how you know.

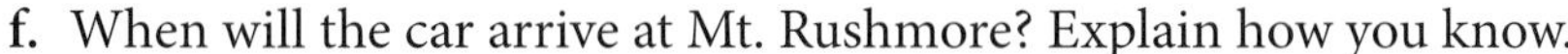

f. When will the car arrive at Mt. Rushmore? Explain how you know.

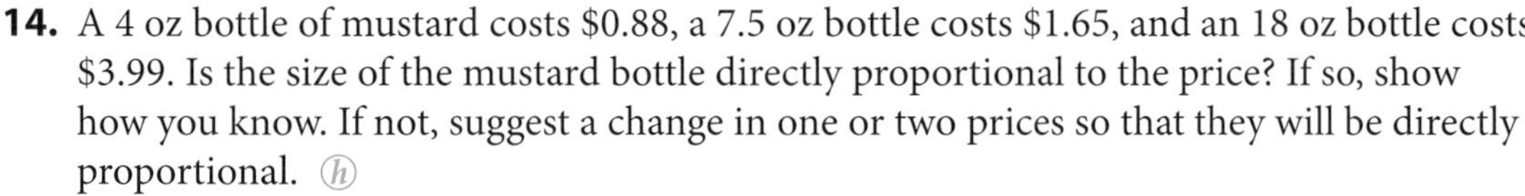

14. A 4 oz bottle of mustard costs \$0.88, a 7.5 oz bottle costs \$1.65, and an 18 oz bottle costs \$3.99. Is the size of the mustard bottle directly proportional to the price? If so, show how you know. If not, suggest a change in one or two prices so that they will be directly proportional. ⓗ

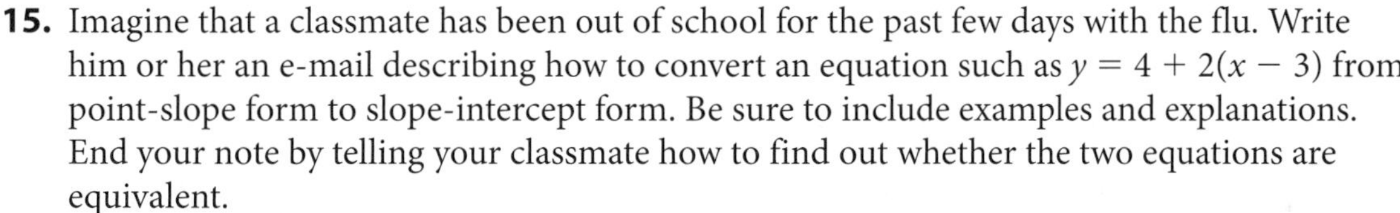

15. Imagine that a classmate has been out of school for the past few days with the flu. Write him or her an e-mail describing how to convert an equation such as $y = 4 + 2(x - 3)$ from point-slope form to slope-intercept form. Be sure to include examples and explanations. End your note by telling your classmate how to find out whether the two equations are equivalent.

16. At the Coffee Stop, you can buy a mug for \$25 and then pay only \$0.75 per hot drink.

a. What is the slope of the equation that models the total cost of refills? What is the real-world meaning of the slope?

b. Use the point (33, 49.75) to write an equation in point-slope form that models this situation.

c. Rewrite your equation in intercept form. What is the real-world meaning of the y-intercept?

LESSON 4.9

Correlation and Causation

You have been working with functions and linear models involving two variables. In the investigation and example in Lesson 4.8, you saw examples of causation, where changes in one variable cause changes in another, and correlation, where changes in the variables are related, but one does not necessarily cause the other. In this investigation you will explore all of the relationships that can be found in this data.

INVESTIGATION

Did It Really Cause That?

The linear relationship between *mean daily temperature* and *number of ice cream cones sold* data here comes from Lesson 4.7, Exercise 6. Scoop's daily ice cream sales for seven days and the mean daytime temperature for each day are recorded in the table.

Ice Cream Sales

Day	1	2	3	4	5	6	7
Temperature (°F)	83	79	75	70	71	67	62
Sales (cones)	66	47	51	23	33	30	21

Step 1 If any of these three variables are plotted on the horizontal, or x, axis and any are plotted on the vertical, or y, axis there are nine different graphs you can create. List them all.

Step 2 With the help of your team, plot all nine graphs.

Step 3 Summarize your work by ranking the graphs from the weakest relationship to the strongest. Also identify which graphs show a positive, or upward, association and which show a negative, or downward, association.

Step 4 Add a line of fit to each of your plots, and estimate the slope of each line.

Step 5 Write one sentence for each graph describing what the slope tells you.

Step 6 For which of the nine graphs can you say "A change in x *causes* a change in y"?

For the graph in the investigation that uses x to represent the *mean daily temperature* and y for the *number of ice cream cones sold,* you may have found a good line of fit with a slope of about $\frac{2\ cones}{1°F}$. You might interpret this slope as "in a typical day, for each degree warmer the vendor will sell two additional cones." This seems logical to those of us who eat ice cream. Therefore, on the graph that uses x for the *number of ice cream cones sold* and y for *mean daily temperature,* the slope of the line of fit is about $\frac{\frac{1}{2}\ °F}{1\ cone}$. Would you interpret this as "for each additional cone sold, the temperature warms by half a degree Fahrenheit"? If you think about the data, it probably seems foolish to imply that selling ice cream causes the temperature to go up!

Are you certain that an increasing temperature *causes* an increase in sales (or that a decrease in temperature *causes* a decrease in sales)? Do you know for certain that the reason sales dropped during the week was because the temperature was falling? Can you think of another reason why sales might show a downward trend over these seven days that has nothing to do with the temperature?

While it is easy to look at a graph to determine whether there is an association—or *correlation*—between two measures, it is a huge step to say there is *causation*. You must be extremely careful in saying that a change in one measure *causes* the change in another. In fact scientists and statisticians have a set of rules that must be followed about the data properties and the data collection methods to determine whether causation exists.

You should err on the side of caution by concluding that two variables are either well correlated or poorly correlated but avoid implying that one causes the other to change. It is often enough to simply say that the data correlate strongly or weakly, or that they correlate negatively or positively. To be more complete you might put some sort of number to this association. In Lesson 1.3, you learned to describe data using the mean absolute deviation, and in an investigation linked to that lesson you learned about variance of a single variable:

$$\text{Var}(x) = \frac{(x_1 - \bar{x})^2 + (x_2 - \bar{x})^2 + \ldots + (x_n - \bar{x})}{n - 1}$$

You can use a similar formula to measure the strength of the relationship between two variables, x and y. This measure is called the covariance:

$$\text{cov}(x, y) = \frac{(x_1 - \bar{x})(y_1 - \bar{y}) + (x_2 - \bar{x})(y_2 - \bar{y}) + \ldots + (x_n - \bar{x})(y_n - \bar{y})}{n - 1}$$

But knowing the covariance of these points to be *108.8°F · cones* still does not communicate how strong the relationship is. Statistician Karl Pearson noticed that the largest the covariance could ever be is when the points are perfectly in line, and that value is equal to the standard deviation of the x-values times the standard deviation of the y-values. So Pearson proposed the ratio of these values to measure the correlation. He called the resulting value r.

$$r = \frac{\text{cov}(x, y)}{s_x \cdot s_y}$$

Even with only seven data points there is a lot of subtracting, multiplying, adding, and dividing in this formula. Fortunately, all statistical software and calculators have this formula built in, so we don't have to hand calculate this formula.

EXAMPLE A

Consider the ice cream data collected by the vendor Scoop. Find and interpret the correlation of each of the nine scatter plots that can be created.

Ice Cream Sales

Day	1	2	3	4	5	6	7
Temperature (°F)	83	79	75	70	71	67	62
Sales (cones)	66	47	51	23	33	30	21

[Data set: **SCPIC**]

Solution

Because Pearson's formula is so complex, technology will be used to calculate this correlation measure. Enter all three lists into your calculator. Use the statistic calculation of the linear regression. [► See **Calculator Note: Statistical Calculation** to learn how to calculate Pearson's formula. ◄]

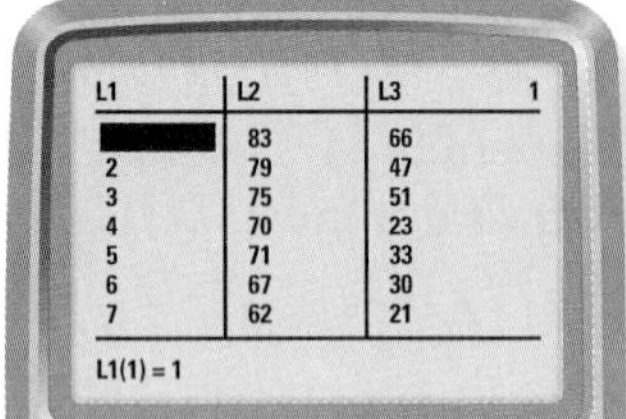

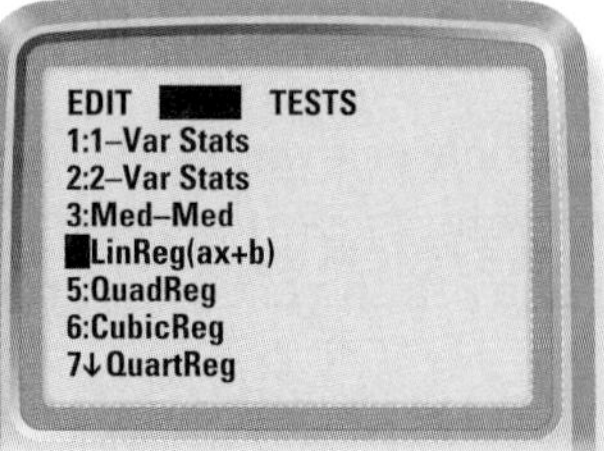

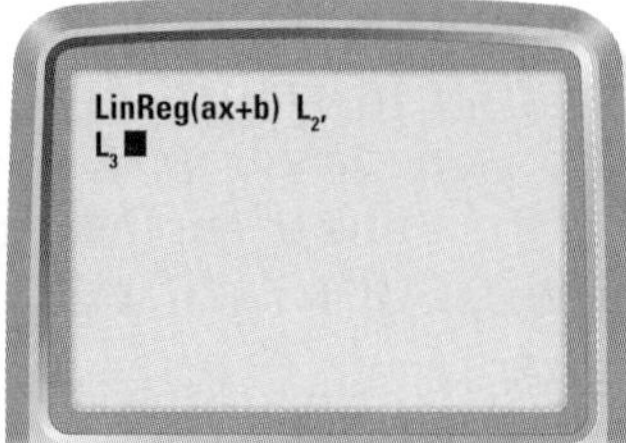

Of the values displayed, $r \approx 0.92086$ is the correlation for the sales vs. temperature data. This process can be repeated for each of the combinations. The table shows all nine of the pairings.

Ice Cream Sales

	Day	Temperature	Sales
Day	1	−0.98036669	−0.87440477
Temperature	−0.98036669	1	0.92086137
Sales	−0.87440477	0.92086137	1

S1 = correlation ( )

Though there are nine graphs, there are only four unique values in the table. Each variable correlates perfectly with itself, and the assignment of x and y do not affect the value of the correlation. Both temperature and sales have a negative association with the day, while temperature and sales are positively correlated. Although all variables show a significant association, the strongest correlation of different variables is the temperature and the day, and the weakest is the sales and the day.

By the way r is defined, its largest value is 1 and its smallest value is -1. A value of $r = 0$ indicates that there is no association between the variables, but a randomly collected set of data, even on things that are unrelated, will usually give some small value to r. You might collect data from your classmates on the time they woke up this morning and the length of their shoe and still find $r = 0.2$, so take care in your interpretations.

The measure of correlation can tell us how strong the linear association is between x and y (our two variables), but it doesn't tell us whether the best description is linear. When you learn about other types of models (quadratic, exponential, etc.) you will have the same question: Is this really the right equation to fit this data set? To answer this you must focus on the vertical difference between the data collected and the equation. The vertical distance is defined as the **residual.**

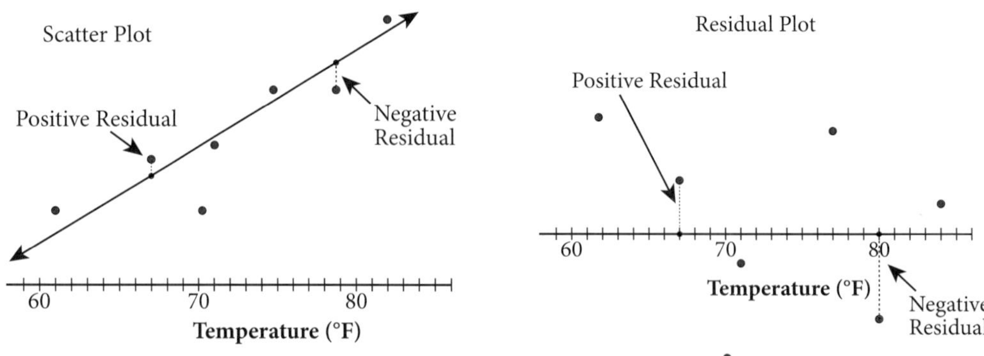

The next example uses these residuals to make a decision about modeling a data set.

EXAMPLE B

Rachel built a rubber band launcher that shoots a rubber band off the end of a ruler fixed at an angle of 30°. She varied the length of the stretch for each shot. The correlation for the length of the stretch and the flight distance is 0.9825, which indicates there is a strong association between these two measures. Using the *Q-points,* Rachel created a linear model, $y = 123 + 12.8(x - 27)$. Is this the best model?

Solution

Using her model Rachel predicted the flight distance for each of the ten stretches. These are the points on the line directly above or below the data points. The difference, $y_{data} - y_{model}$, is the residual. If the linear model is the best, then there should be no pattern to these values. You can create a new statistical graph called a **residual plot.** This is like the scatter plot except that you plot the residuals vs. the x-values instead. This is the plot that is below the scatter plot. [▶ See **Calculator Note: Finding Residual Values and Graph** to learn how to find Residual Values and graph them. ◀]

Length of stretch (cm)	Flight distance (in.)	Model distance (in.)	Residual (in.)
33	211	199.8	11.2
36	245	238.2	6.8
40	277	289.4	−12.4
21	26	46.2	−20.2
28	162	135.8	26.2
37	251	251	0
23	63	71.8	−8.8
27	123	123	0
39	256	276.6	−20.6
30	181	161.4	19.6

[Data set: **RBRES**]

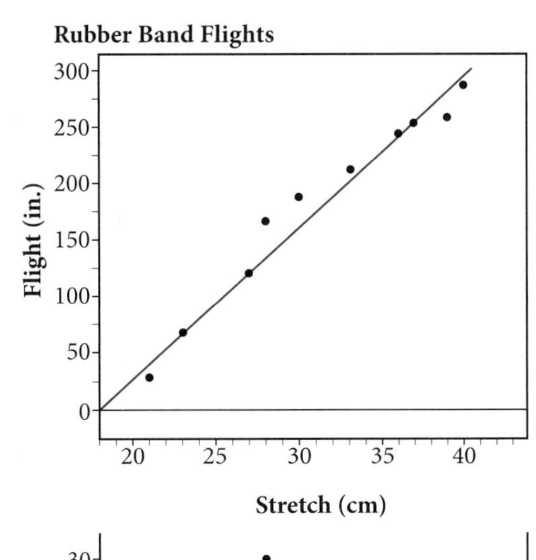

Residual (in.)

30 20 10 0 −10 −20 −30

20 25 30 35 40

Stretch (cm)

A residual plot with no pattern at all to the points would be evidence that you have found the correct model. The worst case is the one here, where there is a defined up or down curved pattern. So, while the linear equation can be used to estimate the flight distance, there is a better nonlinear model that would predict with greater accuracy.

4.9 Exercises

You will need your graphing calculator for Exercises **3, 4, 5, 6,** and **9.**

Practice Your Skills

1. Without using your calculator, match each plot of Olympic gold medal history to one of three r-values.

a. $r = 0.899$ @ **b.** $r = 0.747$ **c.** $r = -0.901$

i. Men's 100-Meter Dash

Time (s): 12.0, 11.5, 11.0, 10.5, 10.0; Year: 1880, 1920, 1960, 2000

ii.

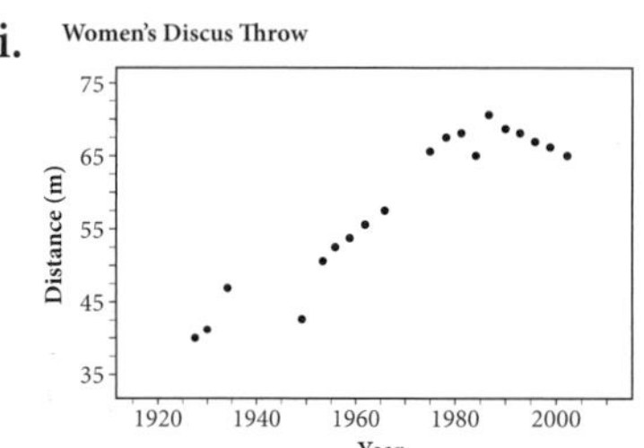

iii.

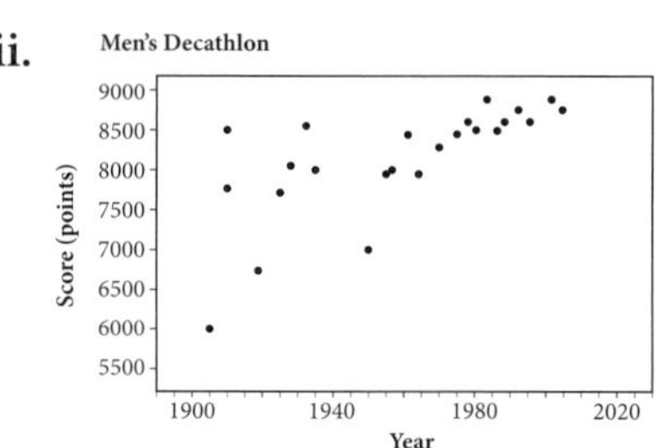

2. After a great deal of observation Jason has discovered that the people sitting in the middle of the lunchroom leave earlier than those sitting on the side. He found an equation that relates the distance from the center of the room (in feet) to the time of departure (in minutes) is $T = 18.51 + 0.05d$. Which of these is the best interpretation of the relationship?

i. Being a fast eater causes you to sit in the middle of the room.

ii. Sitting in the middle of the room causes you to eat faster.

iii. There is some association between where you sit and the time you take to complete the meal.

3. The school administration looked at the number of semesters of foreign language studied and the SAT scores of 19 college-bound students.

a. Find Q_1 and Q_3 for both the semesters and the SAT scores.

b. Use the two ordered pairs from 3a to create a model for this relationship.

c. Calculate the r-value.

d. What conclusion can you draw from this data? @

e. The administration wishes to make four semesters of foreign language a requirement for college-bound students in order to raise the average SAT score for the school. Will this work?

Semesters	SAT	Semesters	SAT
0	1440	4	1920
2	1590	4	1770
3	1800	2	1630
0	1510	0	1500
2	1860	1	1660
1	1600	4	2230
4	2020	0	1440
0	1390	3	1880
0	1500	2	1710
2	1750		

[Data set: **SATSCR**]

4. The model $y = 47 - 0.75(x - 12)$ is created for a set of data. Find the residual for each point.

a. (10, 50) @ b. (12, 45) c. (15, 44)

Reason and Apply

5. The data below show the percent of solid waste that is recycled each year.

	1985	1990	1995	2000	2005	2010
Percent recycled	10.1	16.0	25.7	28.6	31.6	34.1

http://www.epa.gov/osw/nonhaz/municipal/pubs/msw_2010_rev_factsheet.pdf

a. Plot the data on a graph.

b. Write the equation for a line of fit for these data, and add this line to your graph from 5a.

c. Using your equation from 5b, find the residual for the 1995 data point.

d. What is the real-world meaning of the residual from 5c?

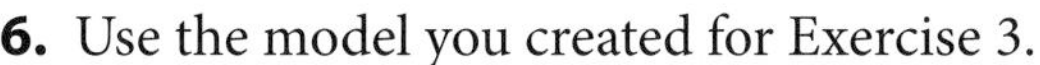

6. Use the model you created for Exercise 3.

a. Calculate the 19 residual values.

b. What is the average of these values, and what is the average of their absolute values? @

c. Which of these numbers is more meaningful about the model? Why?

d. Plot the residuals vs. semesters.

e. What does this plot tell you about the model?

7. Max has a variable-speed wind generator. He collected data at seven random times over the last two weeks. His model for energy production is $y = 35.1(x - 4)$, where x is the average wind speed in meters per second and y is the power in kilowatts. Below is a plot of his residuals.

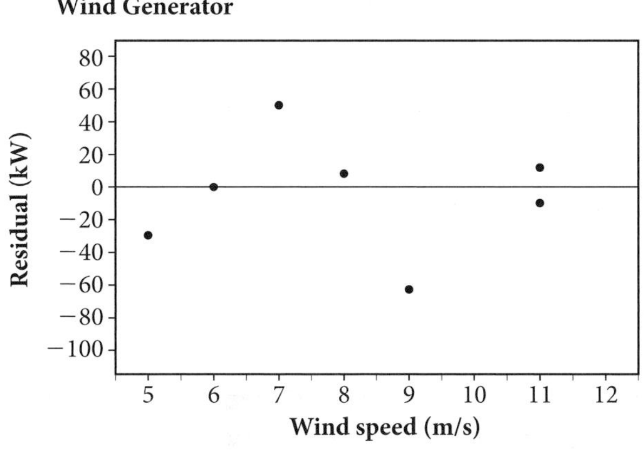

Wind speed (m/s)	Residual (kW)
6	2.1
9	−60.6
11	12.1
5	−29.4
7	49.3
11	−13.0
8	9.4

a. Based on the plot, would you consider a linear equation to be a good model? @

b. Using the equation and the residuals, find the actual power values that Max found.

c. Based on the equation, what would you predict for a wind speed of 14 m/s?

d. If the wind speed were 2 m/s, what power would you get? Explain your answer.

Review

8. Astrid works as an intern in a windmill park in Holland. She has learned that the anemometer, which measures wind speed, gives off electrical pulses and that the pulses are counted each second. The ratio of pulses per second to wind speed in meters per second is always 4.5 to 1.

a. If the wind speed is 40 meters per second, how many pulses per second should the anemometer be giving off?

b. If the anemometer is giving off 84 pulses per second, what is the wind speed?

9. This table shows the average diameter of the pupils of human eyes at different ages, in daylight and in darkness.

Age (yr)	Pupil diameter in daylight (mm)	Pupil diameter in darkness (mm)
20	4.7	8.0
30	4.3	7.0
40	3.9	6.0
50	3.5	5.0
60	3.1	4.1
70	2.7	3.2

a. Without graphing, what patterns do you observe in the data?

b. Plot data in the forms (*age, daylight diameter*) and (*age, darkness diameter*) on the same graph, with a different type of mark for each plot.

c. Write the equation of a line of fit, such as a line through the *Q*-points, for each of the data sets.

10. Here is a graph of a function f.

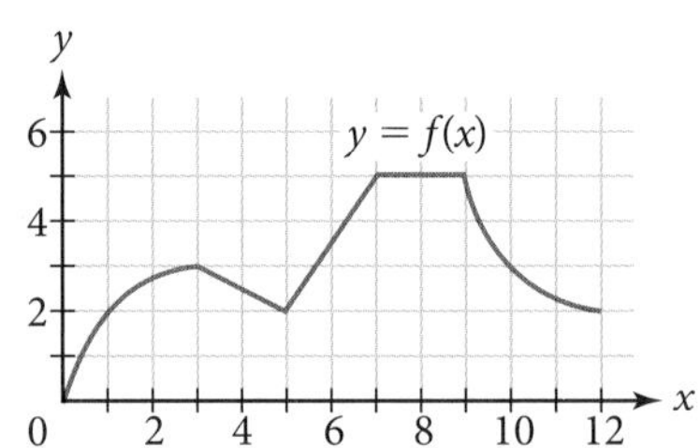

a. Use words such as *linear, nonlinear, increasing,* and *decreasing* to describe the behavior of the function.

b. What is the range of this function?

c. What is $f(3)$?

d. For what x-values does $f(x) = 2$?

e. For what x-values does $f(x) = 5$?

LESSON

4.10

ACTIVITY DAY

Data Collection and Modeling

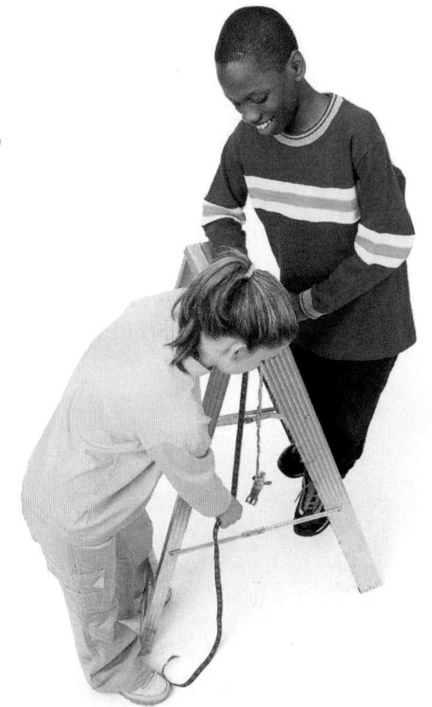

Here's your chance to take part in an extreme sport without the risk! In this activity you'll set up a bungee jump and collect data relating the distance a "jumper" falls and the number of rubber bands in the bungee cord. Then you'll model the data with an equation. Next you'll use your model to find the number of rubber bands you'd need in the cord for a near miss from a specific height.

ACTIVITY

YOU WILL NEED

- a toy to serve as "jumper"
- a supply of equal-size rubber bands
- a tape measure

The Toyland Bungee Jump

Step 1 Make a bungee cord by attaching two rubber bands to your "jumper." (You may first need to make a harness by twisting a rubber band around the toy.)

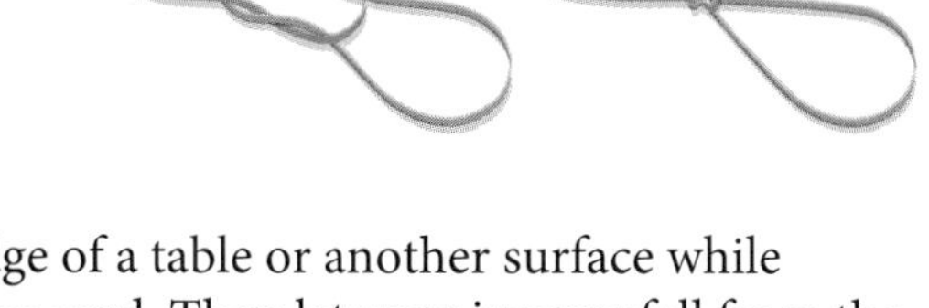

Step 2 Place your jumper on the edge of a table or another surface while holding the end of the bungee cord. Then let your jumper fall from the table. Use your tape measure to measure the maximum distance the jumper falls on the first plunge.

Step 3 Repeat this jump several times and find a mean value for the distance. Record the number of rubber bands (2) and the mean distance the jumper falls in a table like this one.

Number of rubber bands	2	4	5	6	
Distance fallen					

Step 4 Add one or two rubber bands to the bungee cord and repeat the experiment. Record this new information.

Step 5 Continue to make bungee cords of different lengths and measure the distance your jumper falls until you have at least seven pairs of data. When using long cords, you may need to move to a higher place to measure the falls.

Step 6 Define variables and make a scatter plot of the information from your table.

Step 7 Find the equation of a line of fit for your data. You may use any procedure, but you must be able to justify why your equation is a reasonable fit.

Step 8 The test! Decide on a good location for all the groups to conduct final bungee jumps from a particular height. Use your equation to determine the number of rubber bands you need in the cord to give your jumper the greatest thrill—falling as close as possible to the ground without touching it. When you have determined the number of rubber bands, make the bungee cord and wait your turn to test your prediction.

I like the "eyeballing" method because I can visualize the fit of the line before writing an equation.

Using two points and the point-slope method works best for me. It's nice to have definite points.

I prefer the certainty of using *Q*-points. I know my answer will be the same as anyone else's.

Step 9 Write a group report for this activity. Follow this outline to produce a neat, organized, thorough, and accurate report. Any reader of your report should not need to have watched the activity to know what is going on.

Report Outline

A. Overview	Tell what the investigation was about—its purpose or objective.
B. Data collection	Describe the data you collected and how the data were collected.
C. Data table	Use labels and units.
D. Graph	Show all data points. Use labels and units. Show the line of fit.
E. Model	Define your variables and give the equation. Describe how you found this equation and why you used this method.
F. Calculations	Show how you decided how many rubber bands to use in the final jump.
G. Results	Describe what happened on the final jump.
H. Conclusion	What problems did you have? What worked really well? If you could repeat the whole experiment, what would you do to improve it?

CHAPTER 4 REVIEW

In this chapter you used functions to describe real-world relationships. You began by designing and decoding secret messages. You discovered that the easiest way to code is to use a **function**—it codes each input into a single output.

You investigated functions represented by rules, equations, tables, and graphs. You learned to tell whether a relation is a function by applying the **vertical line test.** On a graph, this means that no vertical line can intersect the graph of a function at more than one point.

You learned new vocabulary—**independent variable, dependent variable, domain,** and **range.** You learned when a function is **increasing** or **decreasing** and when it is **linear** or **nonlinear,** as well as the difference between a **discrete graph** and a **continuous graph.**

In chapter 3, you learned how to write equations in intercept form, $y = a + bx$, and how to calculate slope using the slope formula, $b = \frac{y_2 - y_1}{x_2 - x_1}$. In this chapter, you learned to write equations in the similar slope-intercept form, $y = mx + b$. You also used the slope formula to derive another form of a linear equation—the **point-slope form.** The point-slope form, $y = y_1 + b(x - x_1)$, is the equation of the line through point (x_1, y_1) with slope b. You learned that this form is very useful in real-world situations when the starting value is not on the y-axis.

You investigated equivalent forms of expressions and equations using tables and graphs. You used the properties of operations—the **distributive property** of multiplication over addition and the **commutative** and **associative properties** of addition and multiplication—to write point-slope equations in intercept form.

You investigated several methods of finding a **line of fit,** and you discovered how to use the first and third quartiles from the five-number summaries of x- and y-values in a data set to write a linear model for data based on **Q-points.** You looked at whether there is an association—or **correlation**—between two measured variables and when actual **causation** exists. You also explored using the **residuals** to determine the right equation to fit a data set.

Exercises

You will need your graphing calculator for Exercises **8, 9,** and **14.**

@ **Answers are provided for all exercises in this set.**

1. Cody's code multiplies each letter's position by 2. Complete a table like the one shown. If a number is greater than 26, subtract 26 from it so that it represents a letter of the alphabet. Is the code a function? Is the rule for decoding a function?

A	B	C	D	E	
1	2	3	4	5	
2	4	6			

2. Answer each question for the graph of $f(x)$.

   a. What is the domain of the function?

   b. What is the range of the function?

   c. What is $f(3)$?

   d. For what values of x does $f(x) = 1$?

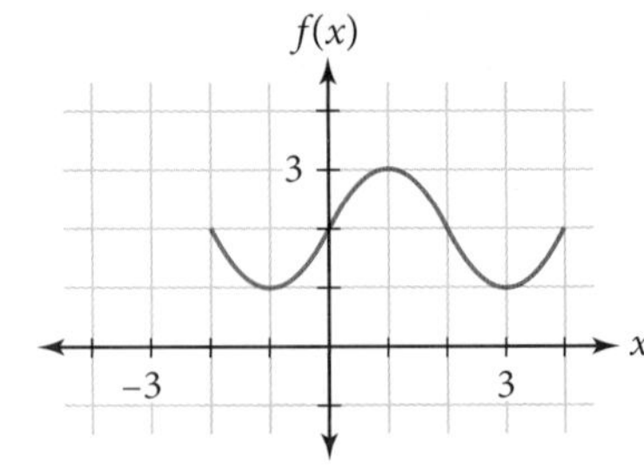

3. Which of these tables of x- and y-values represent functions? Explain your answers.

a.

x	y
0	5
1	7
3	10
7	9
5	7
4	5
2	8

b.

x	y
3	7
4	9
8	4
3	5
9	3
11	9
7	6

c.

x	y
2	8
3	11
5	12
7	3
9	5
8	7
4	11

4. The graph at right shows the relationship between time in seconds and an object's distance from a motion sensor in meters. Sketch a graph to represent the velocity of this object, dependent on time t.

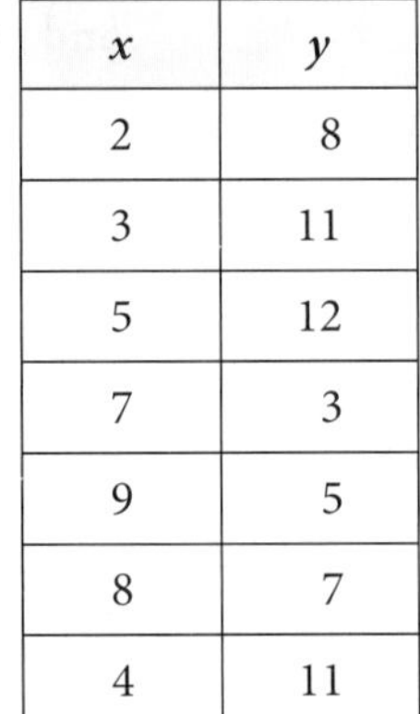

5. In a letter-shift code, ARCHIMEDES codes into ULWBCGYXYM. Use this information to decode the names of famous mathematicians in 5a–c.

   a. XYMWULNYM

   b. BSJUNCU

   c. YOWFCX

   d. Create a grid and state a rule for this code.

6. The graph below shows the velocities of three girls inline skating over a given time interval. Assume that they start at the same place at the same time.

   a. Create a story about these three girls that explains the graph.

   b. Are Caitlin and Bea ever in front of Abby? Explain.

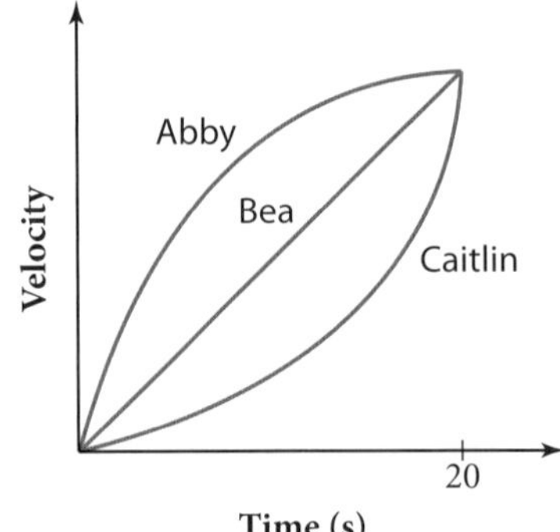
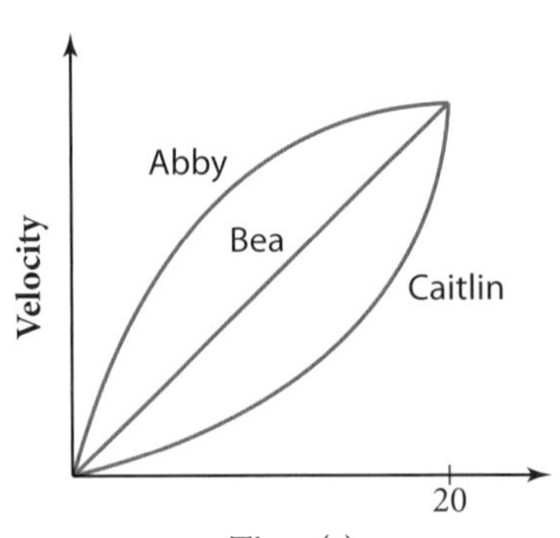

7. Give the slope and the y-intercept for each equation.

a. $y = -4 - 3x$ b. $2x + 7 = y$ c. $38x - 10y = 24$ d. $y = 5x + 7$

8. Line a and line b are shown on the graph at right. Name the slope and the y-intercept, and write the equation of each line. Check your equations by graphing on your calculator.

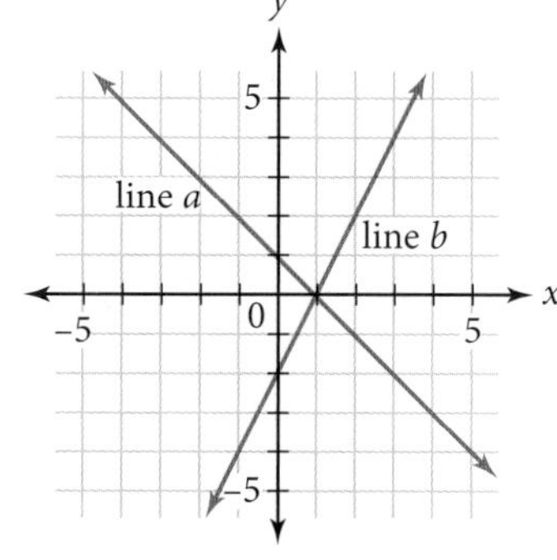

9. Write each equation in the form requested. Check your answers by graphing on your calculator.

a. Write $y = 13.6(x - 1902) + 158.2$ in intercept form.

b. Write $y = -5.2x + 15$ in point-slope form using $x = 10$ as the first coordinate of the point.

c. Write $y - 2 = \frac{1}{2}(x + 4)$ in slope-intercept form.

10. Consider the point-slope equation $y = -3.5 + 2(x + 4.5)$.

a. Name the point used to write this equation.

b. Write an equivalent equation in intercept form.

c. Factor your equation from 10b and name the x-intercept.

d. A point on the line has y-coordinate 16.5. Find the x-coordinate of this point and use this point to write an equivalent equation in point-slope form.

e. Explain how you can verify that all four equations are equivalent.

11. Show all the steps in a symbolic solution to each problem.

a. $4 + 2.8x = 51$ b. $38 - 0.35x = 27$

c. $11 + 3(x - 8) = 41$ d. $220 - 12.5(x - 6) = 470$

12. APPLICATION Suppose Karl bought a used car for \$12,600. Each year its value is expected to decrease by \$1,350.

a. Define your variables. Write an equation modeling the value of the car as a function of time.

b. What is the slope, and what does it mean in the context of the problem?

c. What is the y-intercept, and what does it mean in the context of the problem?

d. What is the x-intercept, and what does it mean in the context of the problem?

13. Recall the data about heating a pot of water from the investigation in Lesson 4.5. A possible linear model of the temperature in degrees Celsius as a function of time in seconds is $y = 30 + 0.375(x - 36)$.

a. What equation could you solve to find how long it would take before the pot of water reaches 43°C?

b. Using a table or graph, find the approximate time indicated in 13a.

c. Show a symbolic solution to your equation in 13a.

14. APPLICATION The table gives the winning heights for the Olympic women's high jump.

a. Find the five-number summary values for the year and height data.

Tia Hellebaut of Belgium competes at the 2012 Olympic Games.

Women's High Jump

Year	Champion	Height (m)
1960	Iolanda Balas, Romania	1.85
1964	Iolanda Balas, Romania	1.90
1968	Miloslava Rezková, Czechoslovakia	1.82
1972	Ulrike Meyfarth, West Germany	1.92
1976	Rosemarie Ackerman, East Germany	1.93
1980	Sara Simeoni, Italy	1.97
1984	Ulrike Meyfarth, West Germany	2.02
1988	Louise Ritter, United States	2.03
1992	Heike Henkel, Germany	2.02
1996	Stefka Kostadinova, Bulgaria	2.05
2000	Yelena Yelesina, Russia	2.01
2004	Yelena Slesarenko, Russia	2.06
2008	Tia Hellebaut, Belgium	2.05

(*http://trackandfield.about.com/od/highjump/qt/olymhijumpwomen.htm*)
[Data sets: **JMPYR, JMPHT**]

b. Name the Q-points for this data set.

c. Write an equation of the line that passes through the Q-points.

d. Graph the line and the data, and explain whether you think this line is a good model for the data pattern.

e. Predict the winning height for the year 2012. How does your predicted height compare to the actual winning height of 2.05 m by Russia's Anna Chicherova.

15. APPLICATION This table shows the federal minimum hourly wage for 1975 through 2007.

a. Find the line of fit based on Q-points.

b. Give the real-world meaning of the slope.

c. Use your model to predict the minimum hourly wage for 2015.

d. Estimate when the minimum hourly wage was $1.00.

United States Minimum Wage

Year x	Hourly minimum y	Year x	Hourly minimum y
1975	$2.00	1981	$3.35
1976	$2.20	1990	$3.80
1977	$2.30	1991	$4.25
1978	$2.65	1996	$4.75
1979	$2.90	1997	$5.15
1980	$3.10	2007	$7.25

(Bureau of Labor Statisitics, *www.bls.gov*)

16. Explain how to find the equation of a line when you know

a. The slope and the y-intercept.

b. Two points on that line.

Take Another Look

1. Is rate of change the same as slope? For linear equations, you've seen that it is. But what about curves? You've studied inverse variations, whose equations have the form $y = \frac{k}{x}$. Let's look at the equation $y = \frac{12}{x}$ and its graph.

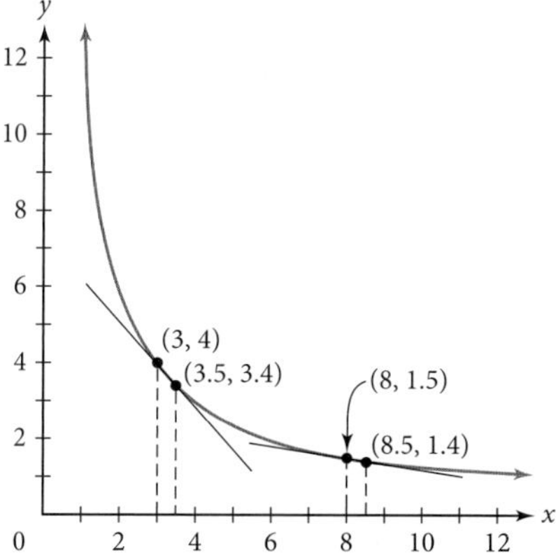

The point (3, 4) is on the curve. Let's choose another nearby point. Substituting 3.5 for x in the equation, you get $y \approx 3.4$. Using the points (3, 4) and (3.5, 3.4) in the formula for slope gives

$$b = \frac{y_2 - y_1}{x_2 - x_1} = \frac{3.4 - 4}{3.5 - 3} = \frac{-0.6}{0.5} = -1.2$$

We can say that the *average* rate of change for $y = \frac{12}{x}$ on the interval $x = 3$ to $x = 3.5$ is -1.2. But -1.2 is not the "slope" of $y = \frac{12}{x}$. Instead, it is the slope of the *straight* line that passes through the two points (3, 4) and (3.5, 3.4). Is the average rate of change on the x-interval from 3 to 3.25 the same as that from 3.25 to 3.5?

Try points on the "wings" of the curve. For instance, the point (8, 1.5) is on the curve and so is the point (8.5, 1.4). Again, the y-coordinate is approximate. What is the average rate of change between these points? The x-interval is the same as for the points (3, 4) and (3.5, 3.4), but is the rate of change the same? What does this tell you? What *straight* line that passes through the point (8, 1.5) has slope equal to the average rate of change on the interval $x = 8$ to $x = 8.5$?

2. You learned to solve linear equations by "undoing" the order of operations in them. You learned to code and decode secret messages. Both are examples of reversing the order of a process, or finding an **inverse.**

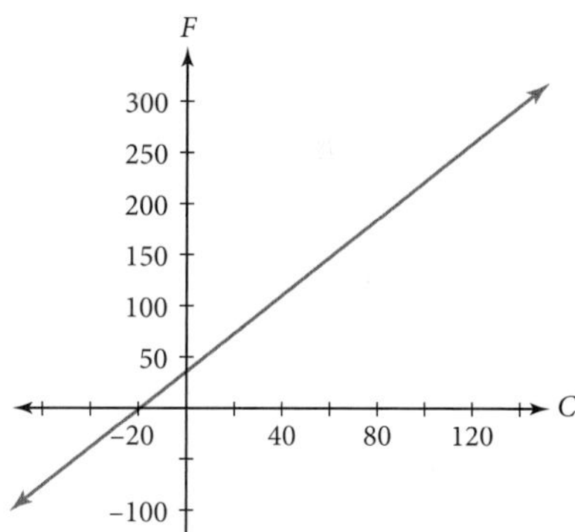

How do you find the inverse of a function? The equation $y = \frac{9}{5}x + 32$ converts temperatures from x in degrees Celsius to y in degrees Fahrenheit.

If you want to write an equation that converts temperature from degrees Fahrenheit to degrees Celsius, you can swap the two variables in the equation and solve for y.

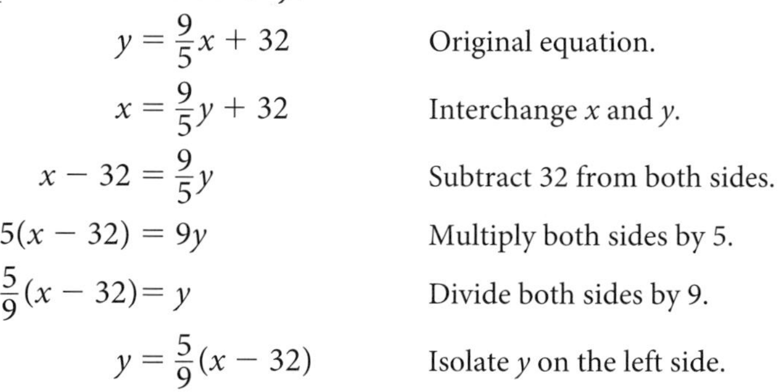

$y = \frac{9}{5}x + 32$	Original equation.
$x = \frac{9}{5}y + 32$	Interchange x and y.
$x - 32 = \frac{9}{5}y$	Subtract 32 from both sides.
$5(x - 32) = 9y$	Multiply both sides by 5.
$\frac{5}{9}(x - 32) = y$	Divide both sides by 9.
$y = \frac{5}{9}(x - 32)$	Isolate y on the left side.

Note that after the switch x represents degrees in Fahrenheit and y represents degrees in Celsius. The domain of the inverse is the range of the original function, and vice versa. Is this a function? Does each input in °F give exactly one output in °C?

How can you tell from the graph of a function whether it has an inverse that's a function? Does every linear function in the form $y = a + bx$ have an inverse function? Look for patterns in the graphs of these functions and others. Can you restrict the values on the domain of a function so that the inverse is a function?

Assessing What You've Learned

PERFORMANCE ASSESSMENT This chapter has been about writing equations for lines, recognizing equivalent equations written in different forms, and fitting lines to data. So assessing what you've learned really means checking to see if you can write the equation of a given line in one or more forms, if you can find an equivalent equation for the one you've already written, and if you can write an equation of a line that looks like a good fit of a given set of data. Can you do one of the investigations in this chapter on your own? Can you verify whether two equations are equivalent? Showing that you can do tasks like these is sometimes called "performance assessment."

UPDATE YOUR PORTFOLIO Choose a piece of work from this chapter to add to your portfolio. Describe the work in a cover sheet, giving the objective, the result, and what you might have done differently.

WRITE IN YOUR JOURNAL Add to your journal by answering one of these prompts:

- You have seen many forms of equations—direct and indirect variation, and linear relationships expressed in many different forms. Do you think all equations represent functions? Can you represent all functions as equations?
- What have you enjoyed more in studying algebra—the numbers, symbols, graphs, and other abstract ways of describing relationships, or the concrete applications and examples that show how people use these ideas in the real world?

GIVE A PRESENTATION Create your own code for making secret messages. Explain the rule for your code with a grid or with an equation or with both. Is your code a function? Is it simple to code? Is it hard to decode? How does the concept of functions apply to code making and code breaking?

CHAPTER 5

Systems of Equations and Inequalities

Handmade Asian paper umbrellas are beautifully decorated with great attention to detail. The sticks in their frames form intersecting lines like the graphs of linear equations. Where do you see only two lines intersecting at a point? Where do several lines intersect?

OBJECTIVES

In this chapter you will

- learn to solve systems of linear equations
- learn to use slope to identify parallel and perpendicular lines
- solve systems using the substitution method
- solve systems using the elimination method
- graph inequalities in one and two variables
- solve systems of linear inequalities

CHAPTER 5 REFRESHING YOUR SKILLS

Standard Form of a Line

The marching band hopes to raise \$1,000 for new uniforms by having several car washes. They plan on charging \$5 for every small vehicle, like a car or pickup truck, washed and \$8 for every large vehicle, like a van or RV, washed. Let x be the number of large vehicles washed and let y be the number of small vehicles washed. There are many ways to earn a profit of \$1,000.

\$8 for one large vehicle times x (number of large vehicles washed) $= 8x$

\$5 for one small vehicle times y (number of small vehicles washed) $= 5y$

The total profit is $8x + 5y$.

Number of large vehicles washed	Number of small vehicles washed	Total profit
x	y	$8x + 5y$

The ordered pairs (x, y) that satisfy the equation $8x + 5y = 1000$ represent the possible numbers of large and small vehicles the band can wash to earn exactly \$1,000. Each term on the left side of the equation shows the part of the total earned for each type of vehicle. Recall from Chapter 4 that this form of a linear equation is called the standard form. To graph a linear equation written in standard form, you could solve for y and identify the slope and intercept (or a point on the line). You could also find the two intercepts, $(x, 0)$ and $(0, y)$, giving you two points needed to draw the line as well as values to set an appropriate window if you are graphing on a calculator.

EXAMPLE A | Graph the equation $8x + 5y = 1000$ by finding the intercepts.

Solution

The x-intercept has $y = 0$.

$$8x + 5(0) = 1000$$
$$8x = 1000$$
$$x = \frac{1000}{8}$$
$$x = 125$$

The y-intercept has $x = 0$.

$$8(0) + 5y = 1000$$
$$5y = 1000$$
$$y = \frac{1000}{5}$$
$$y = 200$$

Plot the points (125, 0) and (0, 200) and connect them to draw the line.

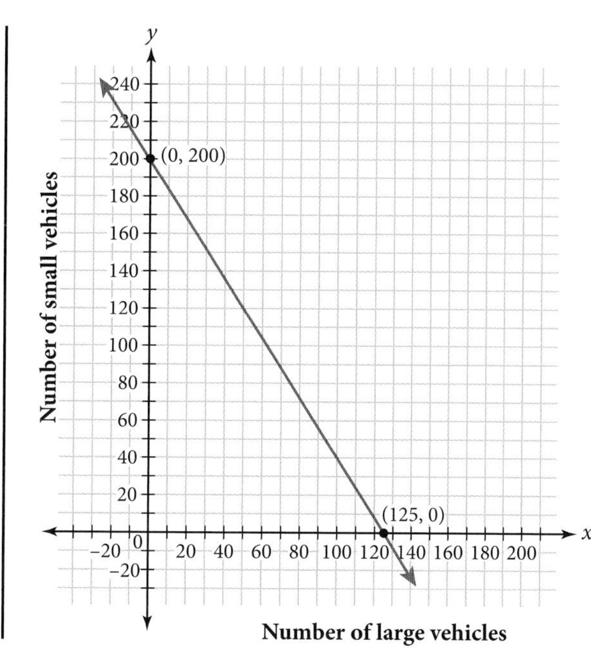

They will only get paid for washing whole vehicles. So only the points with whole number coordinates on the line graphed in Example A represent a possible number of vehicles that can be washed to earn exactly $1,000. Points not on the line represent possible numbers of vehicles washed that earn other amounts of profit.

EXAMPLE B

What is the profit earned by washing these combinations of vehicles?

a. 50 large vehicles and 100 small vehicles

b. 100 large vehicles and 80 small vehicles

Solution

Evaluate the profit expression, $8x + 5y$, for each possibility.

a. $8(50) + 5(100) = 400 + 500 = 900$, so the profit is $900.

b. $8(100) + 5(80) = 800 + 400 = 1200$, so the profit is $1,200.

If you plot the points in Example B on the graph in Example A, you see that the point (50, 100) lies below the line and the point (100, 80) lies above the line. This shows that the ordered pair (50, 100) earns less than $1,000 and the ordered pair (100, 80) earns more than $1,000.

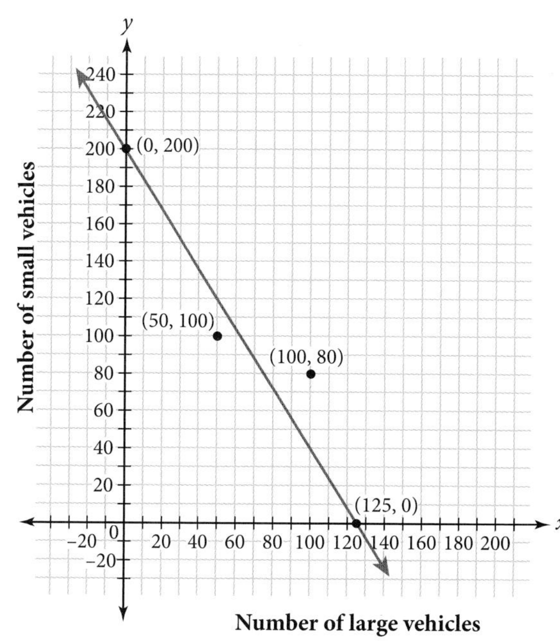

Exercises

1. Graph each equation and label both intercepts.

   a. $3x + 4y = 12$ b. $2x - y = 30$ c. $12x + 5y = 120$

   d. $40x + 10y = 30$ e. $1.2x + 3.5y = 84$ f. $0.15x - 0.02y = 30$

2. Denise does a 15 mi workout each day of training. She bicycles part of the distance and runs the other part. Her average cycling speed is 20 mi/h, and her average running speed is 5 mi/h. Let x represent the time spent cycling, and let y represent the time spent running.

   a. Copy this table and fill in each cell with an expression for the distance described. Then write an equation to represent Denise's workout.

Distance Denise cycles	Distance Denise runs	Total distance

   b. Which of these possible combinations of cycling time and running time results in a 15 mi workout?

      i. $\frac{1}{2}$ h cycling and 3 h running

      ii. $\frac{3}{4}$ h cycling and 1 h running

      iii. $\frac{1}{4}$ h cycling and 2 h running

   c. Graph your equation from 2a. and plot the three points from 2b.

3. To be accepted by the college of his choice, Alejandro must earn at least 100 points on an entrance exam. Each correct answer earns 4 points, and each incorrect answer earns -1 point. (Unanswered questions earn 0 points.) Let x represent the number of correct answers, and let y represent the number of incorrect answers.

   a. Copy this table and fill in each cell with an expression for the points described. Then write an equation to represent how Alejandro could earn exactly 100 points.

Correct answer points	Incorrect answer points	Total points

   b. How many points will Alejandro earn for each possibility listed? Which combinations will earn him the points he needs to be accepted by his preferred college?

      i. 26 correct and 10 incorrect

      ii. 32 correct and 25 incorrect

      iii. 28 correct and 12 incorrect

   c. Graph your equation from 3a. and plot the three points from 3b.

LESSON

5.1

Solving Systems of Equations

A statement like "There are twice as many girls in the math club as boys" does not tell you the number of either boys or girls, but it does give you a relationship. The statement "There are 27 members in the math club" gives you a second relationship. Again, this statement alone does not tell you how many of each gender are in the club. A **system of equations** defines two or more relationships for the same variables.

When solving a system of equations, you look for a solution that makes both equations true. There are several strategies you can use. In this lesson you will use tables and graphs to solve systems of equations.

INVESTIGATION

Where Will They Meet?

YOU WILL NEED

- one motion sensor
- a tape measure or chalk to make a 6-meter line segment

In this investigation you'll solve a system of simultaneous equations to find the time and distance at which two walkers meet.

Suppose two people begin walking in the same direction at different average speeds. The faster walker starts behind the slower walker. When and where will the faster walker overtake the slower walker?

Distance

Time

Step 1 Sketch a graph showing two people walking away from you at constant but different speeds. The faster walker starts closer to you than the slower walker. Label the lines representing both the faster walker and the slower walker, and mark the point where the faster walker overtakes the slower walker.

Now act out the walk.

Procedure Note

The timekeeper counts each second out loud. The walkers walk at the given speeds by noting their positions on the marked segment. The recorder uses a motion sensor to measure the time and position of each walker.

Step 2 On the floor, mark a 6 m segment at 1 m intervals. In your group, designate Walkers A and B, a timekeeper, and a recorder.

Step 3 Practice these walks: Walker A starts at the 0.5 m mark and walks quickly along the segment toward the 6 m mark. At the same time, Walker B starts at the 2 m mark and walks very slowly toward the 6 m mark. Be sure that Walker A is directly behind Walker B until passing him or her. This passing should occur before either walker reaches the 6 m mark.

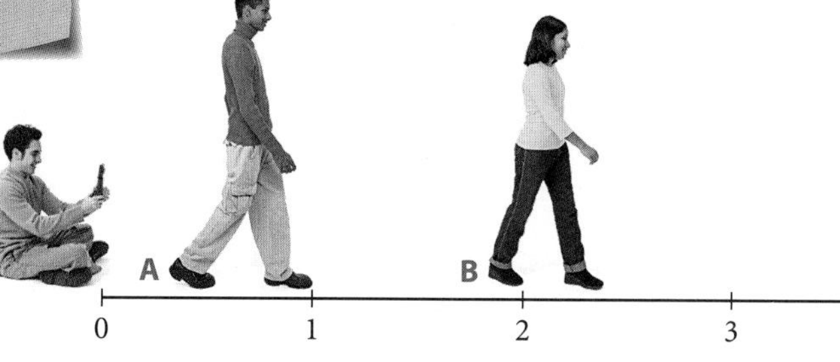

Step 4 When the walkers can follow the walk instructions accurately, record and download the motion of each walker as a separate event. First record Walker A's motion with the motion sensor. Download Walker A's data to a graphing calculator and move it to other lists. [▶ See **Calculator Note: Collecting Distance Data Using the EasyData App** and **Calculator Note: Transferring Programs or Lists.** ◀] Then record Walker B's motion, and download these data to the same graphing calculator.

Next you'll model the walks with a system of equations.

Step 5 Sketch a graph of the two walks, and label which line represents Walker A and which line represents Walker B.

Step 6 Use the graph to determine the rate for each walker, and write an equation to model each walk. To write the equations, you will need to use what you know about the walkers' starting locations.

Step 7 Estimate the coordinates of the point at which the two lines intersect. Explain the meaning of this point.

Step 8 Do the coordinates of the point of intersection make both equations true statements? Why or why not?

Next you'll consider what happens under different conditions.

Step 9 Suppose that Walker A walks faster than 1 m/s. How is the graph different? What happens to the point of intersection?

Step 10 Suppose that two people walk at the same speed in the same direction from different starting marks. What does this graph look like? What happens to the solution point?

Step 11 Suppose that two people walk at the same speed in the same direction from the same starting mark. What does this graph look like? How many points satisfy this system of equations?

In the investigation you were asked to find the point of intersection of two lines. In this example you'll see how you can find or confirm a point of intersection using a graph, a table of values, and some calculations.

EXAMPLE

Edna leaves the trailhead at dawn to hike 12 mi toward the lake, where her friend Maria is camping. At the same time, Maria starts her hike toward the trailhead. Edna is walking uphill so she averages only 1.5 mi/h, while Maria averages 2.5 mi/h walking downhill. When and where will they meet?

a. Define variables for time and for distance from the trailhead.

b. Write a system of two equations to model this situation.

c. Solve this system by creating a table and finding the values of the variables that make both equations true. Then locate this solution on a graph.

d. Check your solution and explain its real-world meaning.

Solution

Both women hike the same amount of time. When Edna and Maria meet, they will both be the same distance from the trailhead, although they will have hiked different distances.

a. Let x represent the time in hours, and let y represent the distance in miles from the trailhead.

b. The system of equations that models this situation is grouped in a brace:

$$\begin{cases} y = 1.5x & \text{Edna's hike.} \\ y = 12 - 2.5x & \text{Maria's hike.} \end{cases}$$

Edna starts at the trailhead, so she increases her distance from it as she hikes 1.5 mi/h for x hours. Maria starts 12 mi from the trailhead and reduces her distance from it as she hikes 2.5 mi/h for x hours.

c. Create a table and graph from the equations. Fill in the times and calculate each distance. The table shows the x-value that gives equal y-values for both equations. When $x = 3$, both y-values are 4.5. So the solution is the ordered pair (3, 4.5). We say that these values "satisfy" both equations.

Hiking Times and Distances

x	$y = 1.5x$	$y = 12 - 2.5x$
0	0	12
1	1.5	9.5
2	3	7
3	4.5	4.5
4	6	2
5	7.5	−0.5

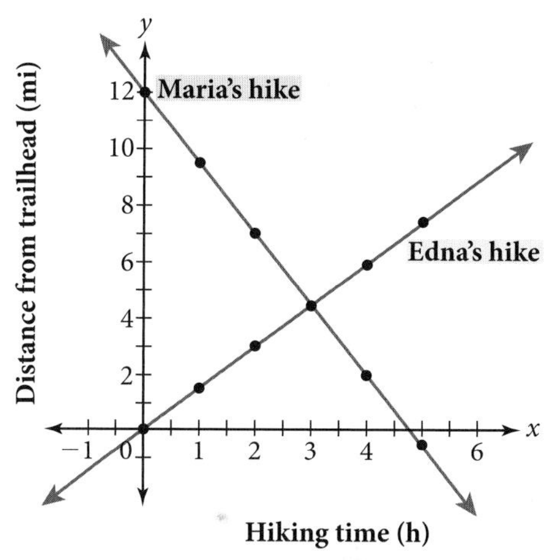

On the graph this solution is the point at which the two lines intersect. You can use the trace function on your calculator to approximate the coordinates of the solution point, although sometimes you'll get an exact answer.

d. The coordinates (3, 4.5) must satisfy both equations.

Edna	**Maria**	
$y = 1.5x$	$y = 12 - 2.5x$	Original equations.
$4.5 \stackrel{?}{=} 1.5(3)$	$4.5 \stackrel{?}{=} 12 - 2.5(3)$	Substitute 3 for the time x and 4.5 for the distance y into both equations.
$4.5 = 4.5$	$4.5 = 4.5$	These are true statements, so (3, 4.5) is a solution for both equations.

After hiking for 3 h, Edna and Maria meet on the trail 4.5 mi from the trailhead.

Is it possible to draw two lines that intersect in two points? How many possible solutions do you think a linear system of two equations in two variables can have?

System of Equations

A **system of equations** is a set of two or more equations that have the same variables. A solution to a system of equations satisfies both equations (that is, it makes both equations true).

When you solve a system of two equations, you're finding a solution in the form (x, y) that makes both equations true. When you have a graph of two distinct linear equations, the solution of the system is the point at which the two lines intersect, if they cross at all. You can estimate these coordinates by tracing on the graph. To find the solution more precisely, zoom in on a table. In Lesson 5.3, you'll learn how to find the *exact* coordinates of the solution by working with the equations.

5.1 Exercises

You will need your graphing calculator for Exercises **2, 6, 7,** and **9.**

Practice Your Skills

1. Verify whether the given ordered pair is a solution to the system. If it is not a solution, explain why not.

a. $(-15.6, 0.2)$
$\begin{cases} y = 47 + 3x \\ y = 8 + 0.5x \end{cases}$

b. $(-4, 23)$
$\begin{cases} y = 15 - 2x \\ y = 12 + x \end{cases}$

c. $(2, 12.3)$
$\begin{cases} y = 4.5 + 5x \\ y = 2.3 + 5x \end{cases}$ @

d. $(2, -11)$
$\begin{cases} y = 12x - 35 \\ y = 5 - 8x \end{cases}$

e. $(3, -8)$
$\begin{cases} y = 8 + 2(x - 11) \\ y = 1 - 3x \end{cases}$

f. $(4, 0)$
$\begin{cases} y = 12 + 3(x - 8) \\ y = 24 - 3(x + 4) \end{cases}$

2. Graph each system on your calculator using the window given. Use the TRACE function to find the point of intersection. Does the calculator give you approximate or exact solutions?

a. $[-18.8, 18.8, 5, -12.4, 12.4, 5]$
$\begin{cases} y = 3 + 0.5x \\ y = -9 + 2x \end{cases}$ @

b. $[-4.7, 4.7, 1, -3.1, 3.1, 1]$
$\begin{cases} y = 4x - 5.5 \\ y = -3x + 5 \end{cases}$

3. Estimate the coordinates of the point of intersection of each pair of lines.

a. Lines k and l

b. Lines m and n @

c. Lines k and m

d. Lines l and m

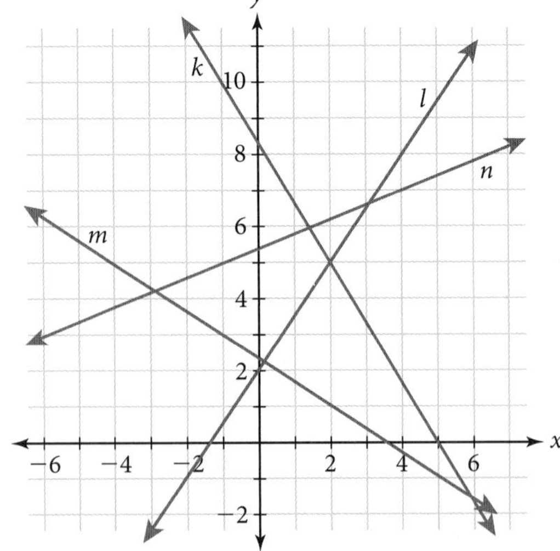

4. Match each graph of a system of equations to its corresponding table values. The tick marks on each graph are 1 unit apart.

Graph of system

a.

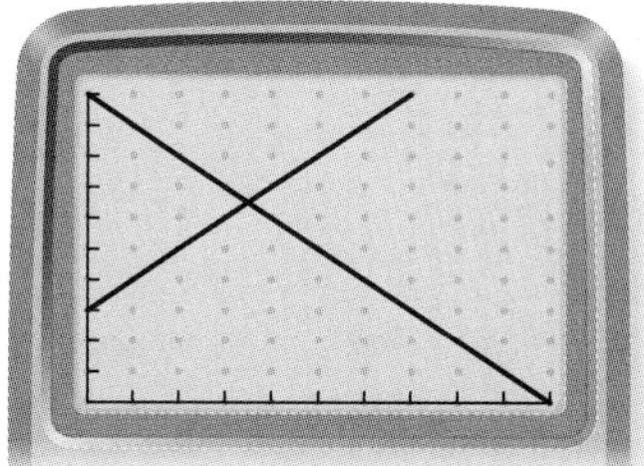

b.

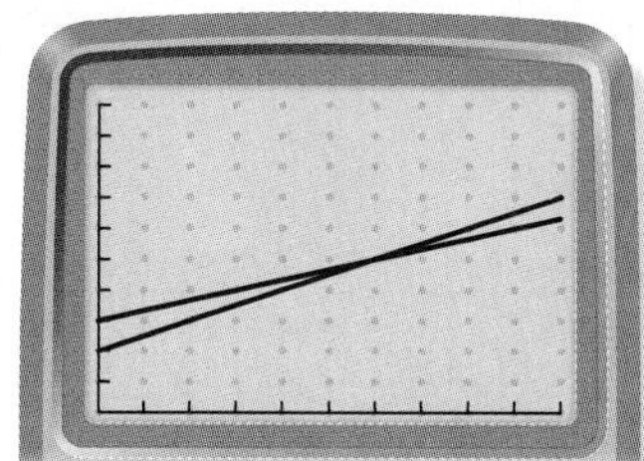

c.

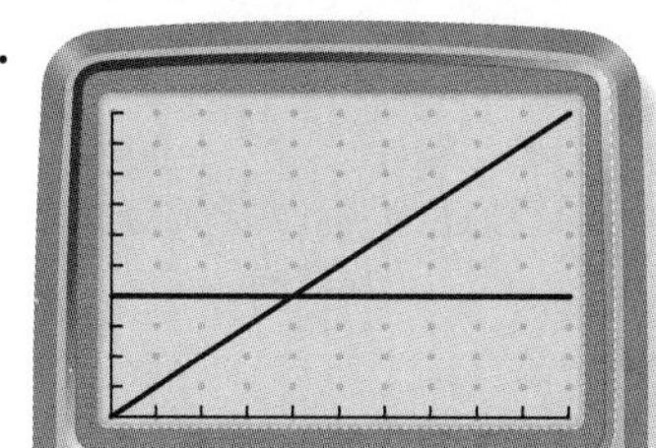

d.

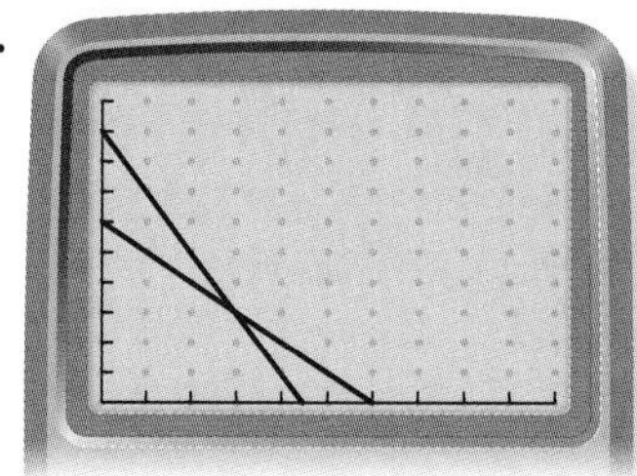

Table values of system

i.

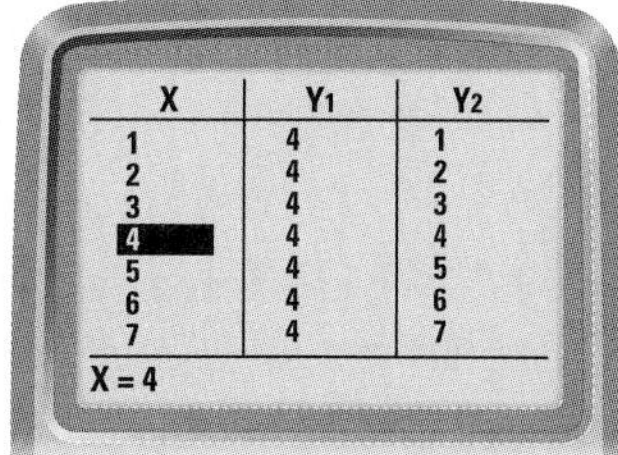

X	Y1	Y2
1	4	1
2	4	2
3	4	3
4	4	4
5	4	5
6	4	6
7	4	7

X = 4

ii.

X	Y1	Y2
−2	13	8
−1	11	7
0	9	6
1	7	5
2	5	4
3	3	3
4	1	2

X = 3

iii.

X	Y1	Y2
3	3.5	4
4	4	4.3333
5	4.5	4.6667
6	5	5
7	5.5	5.3333
8	6	5.6667
9	6.5	6

X = 6

iv.

X	Y1	Y2
2	8	5
2.5	7.5	5.5
3	7	6
3.5	6.5	6.5
4	6	7
4.5	5.5	7.5
5	5	8

X = 3.5

5. Write a system of equations representing the lines graphed here. ⓐ

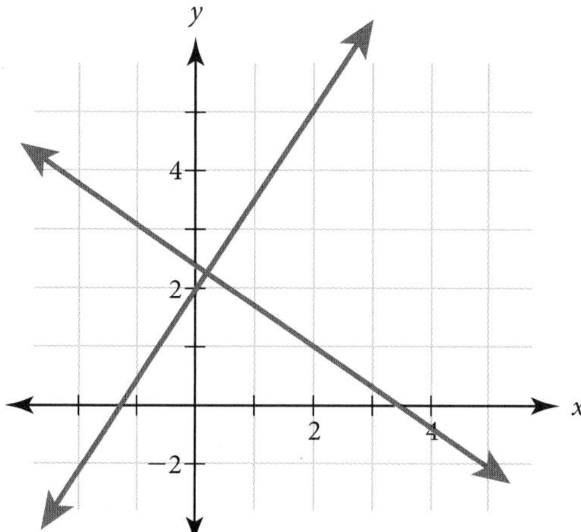

Reason and Apply

6. APPLICATION Two friends start rival Internet companies in their homes. It costs Gizmo.kom \$12,000 to set up the computers and buy the necessary office supplies. Advertisers pay Gizmo.kom \$2.50 for each hit (each visit to the website).

a. Define variables and write an equation to represent profit as a function of number of hits for Gizmo.kom. ⓐ

b. The profit equation for the rival company, Widget.kom, is $P = -5000 + 1.6N$. Explain possible real-world meanings of the numbers and variables in this equation, and tell why they're different from those in 6a. ⓐ

c. Use a calculator table to find the N-value that gives approximately equal P-values for both equations. ⓐ

d. Use your answer to 6c to select a viewing window, and graph both equations to display their intersection and all x- and y-intercepts.

e. What are the coordinates of the point of intersection of the two graphs? Explain how you found this point and how accurate you think it is.

f. What is the real-world meaning of these coordinates?

7. APPLICATION After seeing her friends profit from their websites in Exercise 6, Sally wants to start a third company, Gadget.kom, with the start-up costs of Widget.kom and the advertising rate of Gizmo.kom.

a. What is Sally's profit equation?

b. Graph profit as a function of number of hits for Gadget.kom and Gizmo.kom.

c. What does the graph tell you about Sally's profits compared to Gizmo.kom's? ⓗ

d. What is the x-intercept for the graph of Sally's equation? What is its real-world meaning?

8. APPLICATION The total tuition for students at University College and State College consists of student fees plus costs per credit. Some classes have different credit values. The table shows the total tuition for programs with different numbers of credits at each college.

a. Write a system of equations that represents the relationship between credit hours and total tuition for each college. ⓐ

b. Find the solution to this system of equations and check it. ⓐ

c. Which method did you use to solve this system? Why?

d. What is the real-world meaning of the solution? ⓐ

e. When is it cheaper to attend University College? State College?

Total Tuition

Credits	University College (\$)	State College (\$)
1	55	47
3	115	111
6	205	207
9	295	303
10	325	335
12	385	399

9. The equations $y = 28.65 - 0.0411(x - 1962)$ and $y = 27.5 - 0.0411(x - 1990)$ both model the data for the winning times for the Olympic men's 10,000-meter race. The variable x represents the year, and y represents the winning time in minutes.

a. Find the approximate winning time given by each equation for the year 1972. What is the difference between the values?

b. Find the approximate winning time given by each equation for the year 2016. What is the difference between the values?

c. Select an appropriate window and graph the two equations.

d. Do you think these equations represent the same line? Explain your reasoning. @

10. MINI-INVESTIGATION You have seen systems of two linear equations that have one solution. Do all systems have exactly one solution?

a. Draw two lines that never intersect. What is the same about these lines?

b. If the lines $y = 2 + 3x$ and $y = 1 + bx$ never intersect, what do you know about the value of b? How many solutions does this system have?

c. Draw two lines that intersect more than once. (Remember, lines are straight.) What is the same about these lines?

d. If the lines $y = 2 + 3x$ and $y = a + bx$ intersect more than once, what do you know about the values of a and b? How many solutions does this system have?

e. If the lines $y = 2 + 3x$ and $y = a + bx$ intersect in exactly one point, what do you know about the values of a and b?

Review

11. APPLICATION Hydroplanes are boats that move so fast they skim the top of the water. The hydroplane *Miss Albert Lee* qualified for the 2008 Columbia Cup race with a speed of 147.545 mi/h. The hydroplane *Miss Ellstrom Elam* qualified with a speed of 162.722 mi/h. (Northwest Hydro Racing, *www.hydroracing.com*)

a. How long will it take each hydroplane to run a five-lap race if one lap is 2.5 miles?

b. These boats limit the amount of fuel the motor burns to 4.3 gallons per minute. How much fuel will each boat use to run a five-lap race?

c. Hydroplanes have a 50-gallon tank, although generally only about 43 gallons are put in. The rest of the tank is filled with foam to prevent sloshing. How many miles can each hydroplane go on one 43-gallon tank of fuel?

d. Find each boat's fuel efficiency rate in miles per gallon.

Hydroplanes are frequently powered by surplus engines from military aircraft. The fastest hydroplane ever, the *Spirit of Australia*, was powered by a jet engine and traveled at a speed of more than 300 mi/h.

12. Solve each equation using the method you prefer. Then substitute your value for x back into the equation to check your solution.

a. $0.75x = 63.75$

b. $6 = 12 - 2x$

c. $9 = 6(x - 2)$

d. $8x + 7 = 5x + 28$

e. $4(x + 5) - 8 = 18$

13. Write the equation represented by this balance. Then solve the equation for x using the balancing method. ⓐ

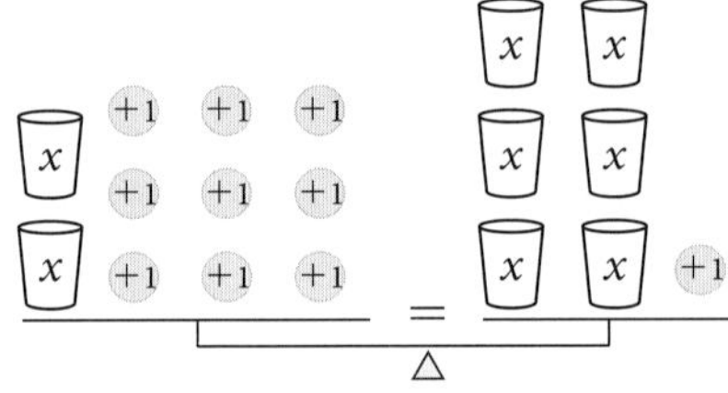

14. Solve each equation for y.

a. $y + 2 = 5x$

b. $5y = 4 - 7x$

c. $2y - 6x = 3$

d. $3x + y = 18$

e. $4x - 2y = 12$

f. $7x = 8 - y$

IMPROVING YOUR Geometry SKILLS

On graph paper, draw a triangle that satisfies each of these sets of conditions. If it's not possible, explain why not.

1. a triangle with all three sides having positive slope

2. an equilateral triangle (three equal sides) with one side having slope 0

3. an isosceles triangle (two equal sides) with all three sides having positive slope

4. a right triangle with one side having undefined slope, one side having slope 0, and one side having slope 1

5. a triangle with two sides having the same slope

LESSON

5.2

Parallel and Perpendicular Lines

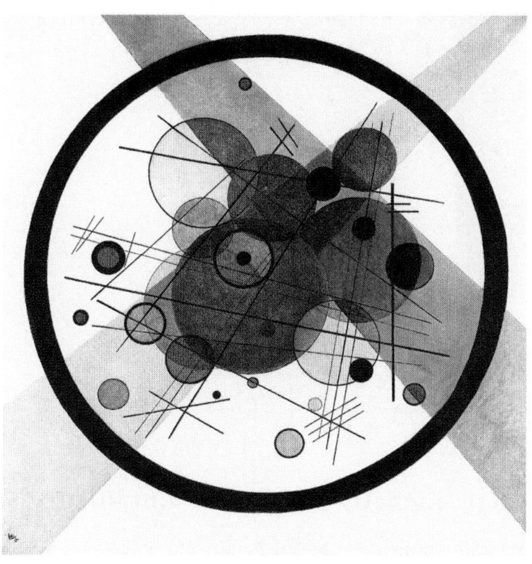

The Russian artist Wassily Kandinsky (1866–1944) used parallel and perpendicular line segments in his 1923 work titled *Circles in a Circle.*

In Lesson 5.1, you looked at the graphs of systems of two linear equations. You found that the solution to the system is the point at which the lines intersect. In Exercise 10, you saw that some lines don't intersect. **Parallel lines** are lines in the same plane that never intersect. They are always the same distance apart. What do you think is the relationship between the slopes of parallel lines?

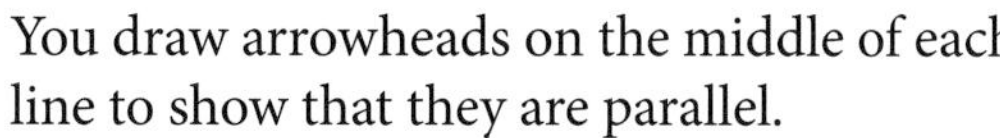

You draw arrowheads on the middle of each line to show that they are parallel.

Some lines intersect in a special way, forming **right angles;** that is, they form 90° angles where they meet. Such lines are called **perpendicular lines.** What do you think is the relationship between the slopes of perpendicular lines?

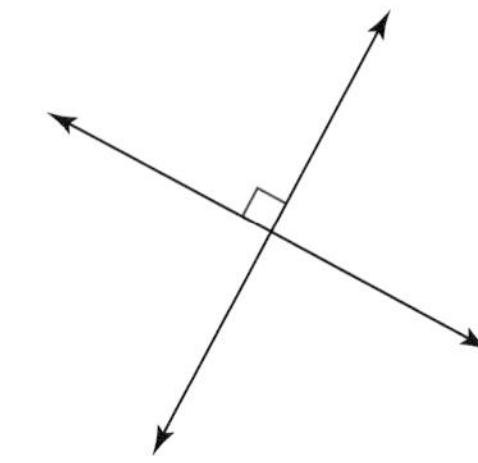

You draw a small box in one of the angles to show that the lines are perpendicular.

INVESTIGATION

YOU WILL NEED

- graph paper
- a straightedge

Slopes

A rectangle has two pairs of parallel line segments and four right angles. When you draw a rectangle on the coordinate plane and notice the slopes of its sides, you will discover how the slopes of parallel and perpendicular lines are related.

Step 1 Draw coordinate axes centered on graph paper. Each member of your group should choose one of the following sets of points. Plot the points and connect them, in order, to form a closed figure. You should have formed a rectangle.

a. $A(6, 20)$, $B(13, 11)$, $C(-5, -3)$, $D(-12, 6)$

b. $A(3, -1)$, $B(-3, 7)$, $C(9, 16)$, $D(15, 8)$

c. $A(-11, 21)$, $B(17, 11)$, $C(12, -3)$, $D(-16, 7)$

d. $A(3, -10)$, $B(-5, 22)$, $C(7, 25)$, $D(15, -7)$

The slope of a line segment is the same as the slope of the line containing the segment. You can write the segment between points A and D as $\overline{AD}$.

Step 2 Find the slopes of parallel sides $\overline{AD}$ and $\overline{BC}$.

Step 3 Find the slopes of parallel sides $\overline{AB}$ and $\overline{DC}$.

Step 4 What conjecture can you make about the slopes of parallel lines based on your answers to Steps 2 and 3?

The ties underneath these railroad tracks are a real-world example of parallel segments.

Step 5 Express the slope values of perpendicular sides $\overline{AB}$ and $\overline{BC}$ as simplified fractions.

Step 6 Express the slope values of perpendicular sides $\overline{AD}$ and $\overline{DC}$ as simplified fractions.

Step 7 What conjecture can you make about the slopes of perpendicular lines? What is their product? Check your conjecture by finding the slopes of any other pair of perpendicular sides in your rectangle.

These street intersections are a real-world example of perpendicular line segments.

To find the **reciprocal** of a number, you write the number as a fraction and then invert it (exchange the numerator and denominator). For example, the reciprocal of $\frac{2}{3}$ is $\frac{3}{2}$. The product of reciprocals is 1.

The relationships you found in investigating the slopes of the sides of a rectangle can be applied to parallel and perpendicular lines.

Slopes of Parallel and Perpendicular Lines

Lines with equal slopes are parallel.
Lines with opposite reciprocal slopes are perpendicular.

EXAMPLE A Without graphing, identify pairs of lines that are parallel and pairs of lines that are perpendicular.

i. $y = 3 + 2x$ **ii.** $y = 3 - 2x$ **iii.** $y = 3 + \frac{1}{2}x$

iv. $y = 4 + 2x$ **v.** $y = 4 - \frac{1}{2}x$

Solution Identify the slopes of the lines.

i. $y = 3 + 2x$ Slope is 2.

ii. $y = 3 - 2x$ Slope is -2.

iii. $y = 3 + \frac{1}{2}x$ Slope is $\frac{1}{2}$.

iv. $y = 4 + 2x$ Slope is 2.

v. $y = 4 - \frac{1}{2}x$ Slope is $-\frac{1}{2}$.

Parallel lines have the same slope, so lines **i.** and **iv.** are parallel.

Perpendicular lines have opposite reciprocal slopes, and 2 and $-\frac{1}{2}$ are opposite reciprocals; so lines **i.** and **iv.** are perpendicular to line **v.** The slopes -2 and $\frac{1}{2}$ are also opposite reciprocals; so lines **ii.** and **iii.** are perpendicular.

When lines are parallel, they don't intersect. A system of two equations that each represent a parallel line has no solution. The solution set for such a system is the empty set or **null set.**

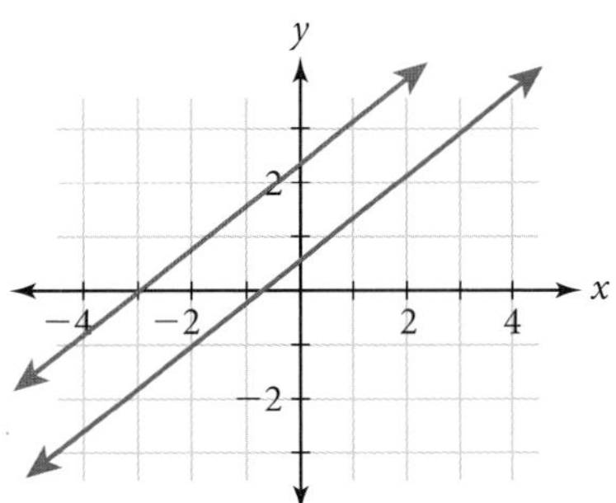

A system with no solution

Perpendicular lines are a special case of lines that intersect at only one point. Any system of two equations that represent lines that intersect at exactly one point has a **unique solution.**

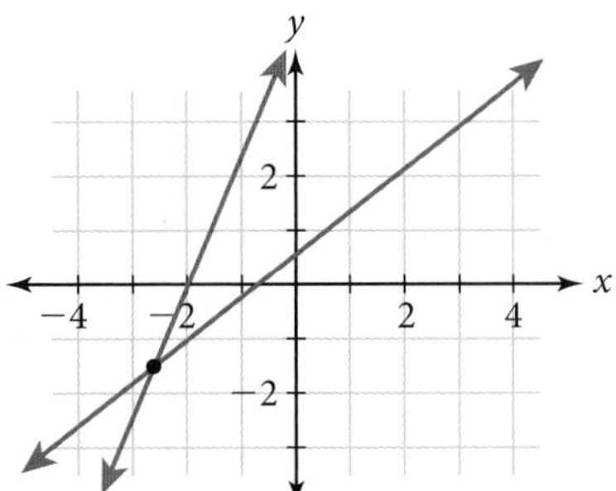

A system with a unique solution

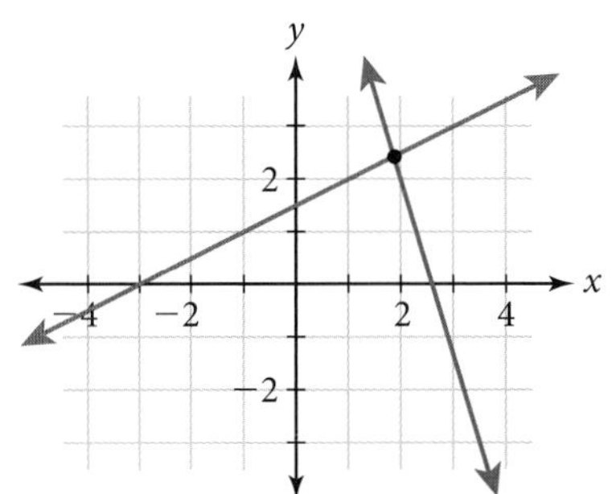

A system with a unique solution

If the two equations in a system represent the same line, then the system has **infinitely many solutions.**

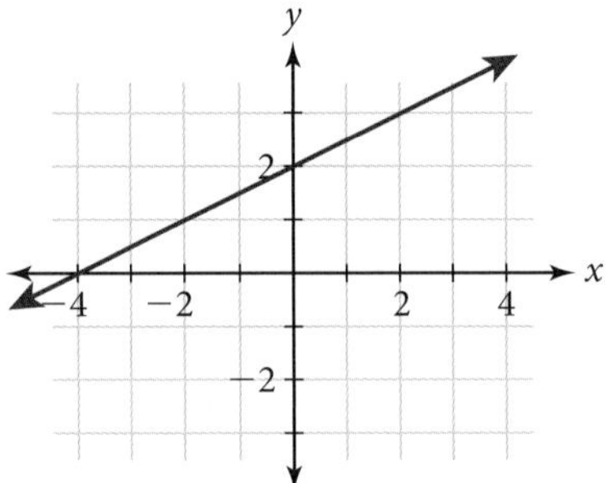

A system with infinite solutions
(two identical lines)

In this chapter you will most often consider systems that have unique solutions. Occasionally, though, you will see a system with no solution or infinitely many solutions. A quick check of the slopes can help you identify these cases.

You can also use what you know about the slopes of parallel and perpendicular lines to write equations.

EXAMPLE B

Write an equation to model each line described.

a. The line parallel to $y = 3 - 5x$ passing through the point $(1, 7)$

b. The line perpendicular to $y = 3 - 5x$ passing through the point $(1, 7)$

Solution

You might find it easiest to use the point-slope form to write the equations.

a. Parallel lines have the same slope, so the line must have slope -5. Using the point-slope form, with the point $(1, 7)$ gives the equation $y = 7 - 5(x - 1)$.

b. Perpendicular lines have opposite reciprocal slopes, so the line must have slope $\frac{1}{5}$. The point-slope form of the equation of the line through point $(1, 7)$ is $y = 7 + \frac{1}{5}(x - 1)$.

In Steps 4 and 7 of the investigation, you made conjectures based on studying examples. When you do this, you are using **inductive reasoning.** You used inductive reasoning every time you made a conjecture—for example, when you observed that $3^4 \cdot 3^2 = 3^6$ and $x^3 \cdot x^6 = x^9$, you concluded that $b^m \cdot b^n = b^{m+n}$.

The process of showing that certain statements or conclusions follow logically from an initial assumption or fact is called **deductive reasoning.** When you solved an equation and justified each step, you were doing deductive reasoning. For example, you started with the equation $\frac{3x + 4}{6} - 5 = 7$ and followed steps to show that this was equivalent to $x = 22\frac{2}{3}$. In this case, you solved an equation by using deductive reasoning to prove that two equations are equivalent. A deductive argument starts with a general statement that is assumed to be true, called the **hypothesis,** and shows how that statement leads to a specific result, called the **conclusion.** Each step of the argument is supported by a **premise**—a definition, property, or proven fact.

Inductive and deductive reasoning are used extensively in mathematics and in life. You have been doing both forms of reasoning throughout this course.

Exercises

You will need your graphing calculator for Exercise **2.**

Practice Your Skills

1. Find the slope of each line.

a. $y = 0.8(x - 4) + 7$ **b.** $y = 5 - 2x$ **c.** $y = -1.25(x - 3) + 1$ (@) **d.** $y = -4 + 2x$

e. $6x - 4y = 11$ (@) **f.** $3x + 2y = 12$ **g.** $-9x + 6y = -4$ (@) **h.** $10x - 15y = 7$

2. Determine whether each pair of lines is parallel, perpendicular, or neither. Verify by graphing on your calculator using a square window. [▶ See **Calculator Note: Square Windows.** ◀] (h)

a. $y = 0.8(x - 4) + 7$
$y = -1.25(x - 3) + 1$

b. $y = 5 - 2x$
$y = -4 + 2x$

c. $6x - 4y = 11$
$-9x + 6y = -4$

d. $3x + 2y = 12$
$10x - 15y = 7$

3. Line ℓ has slope 1.2. What is the slope of line p that is parallel to line ℓ?

4. Line ℓ has slope 1.2. Line m is perpendicular to line ℓ.

a. What is the slope of line m? (@)

b. What is the product of the slopes of line ℓ and line m? (@)

5. Find the equation in point-slope form of the line that passes through the point $(8, -2)$ and is perpendicular to the line $y = 3x + 7$.

Reason and Apply

6. Identify whether each system has no solution, a unique solution, or infinitely many solutions. You may first need to solve some of the equations for y.

a. (@) $\begin{cases} y = 7 - 3x \\ y = 3x - 7 \end{cases}$

b. $\begin{cases} 2x + y = 7 \\ y = 7 - 2x \end{cases}$

c. $\begin{cases} y = 4 + \left(\frac{1}{5}\right)x \\ y = 8 - 5x \end{cases}$

d. $\begin{cases} 4x + 4y = 8 \\ y = 6 - x \end{cases}$

7. Two different but simultaneous walks are to be recorded by two different motion sensors. Describe what the walkers must do to create each situation.

a. The lines containing their recorded graphs will never intersect.

b. The lines containing their recorded graphs are perpendicular.

8. Write equations of the line segments containing the sides of this rectangle. Describe the domain and range of each equation.

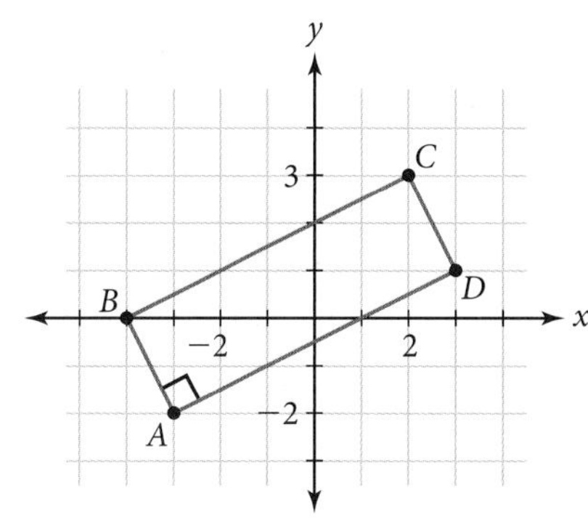

9. To write the equation of a diagonal in the rectangle in Exercise 7, you must indicate that you will use only part of the line. An equation modeling diagonal $\overline{AC}$ is $y = -2 + (x + 3)$ with $-3 \leq x \leq 2$. Write a similar equation to model the other diagonal. (@)

10. If this system has infinitely many solutions, give possible values of a, b, and c.

$$\begin{cases} y = 5 - 6x \\ ax + by = c \end{cases}$$

11. Write equations for a system of perpendicular lines with the unique solution (2, 3).

12. One side of a rectangle has slope $\frac{3}{4}$ and a vertex at the point $(2, -1)$.

a. Write an equation of the line containing this side of the rectangle.

b. What is the slope of the other side of the rectangle that also has an endpoint at the point $(2, -1)$?

c. Write an equation of the line containing this second side of the rectangle.

13. One side of a square is contained in the line $y = 2 - 3x$. The opposite side passes through the point (4, 7). Write an equation of the line containing this opposite side.

14. For each situation, identify whether inductive or deductive reasoning is used. Then state the hypothesis and conclusion.

a. The dinosaur *Tyrannosaurus rex* had sharp teeth. Animals with sharp teeth eat meat. Meat-eating animals are called carnivores. Therefore, *Tyrannosaurus rex* was a carnivore.

b. Krystal adds $5 + 6$ and gets 11. Then she adds $13 + 14$ and gets 27. Then she adds $92 + 93$ and gets 185. Krystal concludes that the sum of any two consecutive integers is odd.

c. Kendra uses the properties of numbers to show that $2(x - 3) = 10$ is equivalent to $x = 8$.

Review

15. Solve each equation for y.

a. $3x + y = 7$

b. $4 + y = 2x$

c. $x + 2y = 5x - 6$

16. Suppose a chicken sandwich costs \$2.99 and a hamburger costs \$1.99. If x represents the number of chicken sandwiches ordered by the members of a band when they stop for lunch and y represents the number of hamburgers ordered, what does the expression $2.99x + 1.99y$ represent?

17. State whether the ordered pair (2, 5) is a solution to each equation.

a. $y = 2x + 1$

b. $3x - y = 1$

c. $2x - y = 1$

LESSON

5.3

Solving Systems of Equations Using Substitution

Graphing systems and comparing their table values are good ways to see solutions. However, it's not always easy to find a good graphing window or the right settings for a table. Also, the solutions you find are often only approximations. To find exact solutions, you need to work algebraically with the equations themselves. One way to do this is to use the **substitution method.**

EXAMPLE A

On a rural highway, a police officer sees a motorist run a red light at 50 mi/h and begins pursuit. At the instant the police officer passes through the intersection at 60 mi/h, the motorist is 1 mi down the road. If both drivers maintain a constant speed, when and where will the officer catch up to the motorist?

a. Identify the dependent and independent variables. Write a system of equations in two variables to model this situation.

b. Solve this system by the substitution method, and check the solution.

c. Explain the real-world meaning of the solution.

Solution

Let the independent variable, t, represent the time in hours, with $t = 0$ being the instant the officer passes through the intersection. Let the dependent variable, d, represent the distance in miles from the intersection.

a. The system of equations is

$$\begin{cases} d = 1 + 50t & \text{motorist's distance from the intersection} \\ d = 60t & \text{officer's distance from the intersection} \end{cases}$$

b. When the officer catches up to the motorist, they will both be the same distance from the intersection. At this time, both equations will have the same d-value. So you can replace d in one equation with an equivalent expression for d that you find from the other equation. Substituting $60t$ for d in the equation $d = 1 + 50t$ gives the new equation:

$$\begin{cases} d = 1 + 50t \\ d = 60t \end{cases} \longrightarrow 60t = 1 + 50t$$

There is now one equation to solve. Notice that the variable t occurs on both sides of the equal sign and that the variable d has dropped out. Now you use the balancing method to find the solution.

$60t = 1 + 50t$	New equation.
$60t - 50t = 1 + 50t - 50t$	Subtract $50t$ from both sides of the equation.
$10t = 1$	Combine like terms.
$t = 0.1$	Divide both sides of the equation by 10 and simplify.

At time $t = 0.1$ the officer will catch up to the motorist, so they should be the same distance from the intersection. To find the d-value of the solution, substitute 0.1 for t in one of the original equations.

$$t = (0.1)$$

$$\begin{aligned} d &= 1 + 50t \\ d &= 1 + 50(0.1) \\ d &= 6 \end{aligned} \quad \text{and} \quad \begin{aligned} d &= 60t \\ d &= 60(0.1) \\ d &= 6 \end{aligned}$$

If both equations give the same d-value, 6 in this case, then you have the correct solution.

c. The solution is the only ordered pair of values, (0.1, 6), that works in both equations. The police officer will catch up to the motorist 6 mi from the intersection in 0.1 h, which is 6 min after passing through the intersection.

The calculator screen shows the system of equations from Example A in the window [0, 0.15, 0.01, 0, 10, 1]. It is difficult to guess the solution at these window settings because the two lines have very similar slopes and close y-intercepts. But the substitution method helps you find the exact solution no matter how difficult it is to set windows or tables. Once you have the exact solution, it is much easier to find a good window to display it.

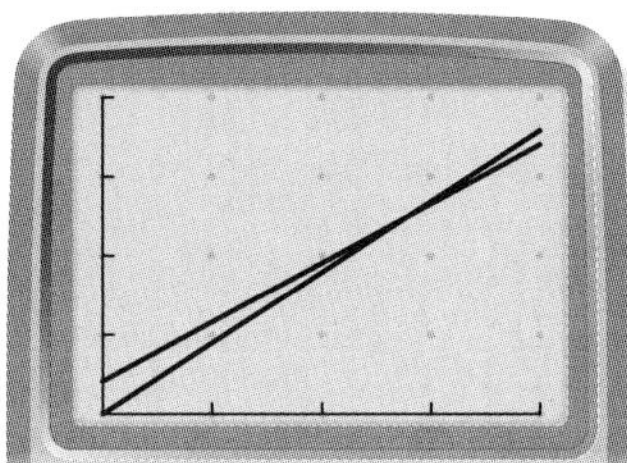

INVESTIGATION

All Tied Up

YOU WILL NEED

- two ropes of different thickness, both about 1 meter long
- a meterstick or tape measure
- a 9-meter-long thin rope (optional)
- a 10-meter-long thick rope (optional)

In this investigation you'll work with rope lengths and predict how many knots it would take in each rope to make a thicker rope the same length as a thinner one.

First you'll collect data and write equations.

Step 1 Measure the length of the thinner rope without any knots. Then tie a knot and measure the length of the rope again. Continue tying knots until no more can be tied. Knots should be of the same kind, size, and tightness. Record the data for number of knots and length of rope in a table.

Step 2 Define variables and write an equation in intercept form of rope length as a function of the number of knots to model the data you collected in Step 1. What are the slope and y-intercept, and how are they related to the rope?

Step 3 Repeat Steps 1 and 2 for the thicker rope.

Step 4 Suppose you have a 9-meter-long thin rope and a 10-meter-long thick rope. Write a system of equations of rope length as a function of the number of knots.

Next you'll analyze the system to find a meaningful solution.

Step 5 Solve this system of equations using the substitution method.

Step 6 Select an appropriate window setting and graph this system of equations. Estimate coordinates for the point of intersection to check your solution. Compare this solution to the one from Step 5.

Step 7 Explain the real-world meaning of the solution to the system of equations.

Step 8 What happens to the graph of the system if the two ropes have the same thickness? The same length? Justify your answers.

The systems you solved in this chapter have had equations expressed as y in terms of x. In other words, they are already solved for the output variable, y. This form makes it easy to use the substitution method: You can simply set the two expressions in x equal to each other because both are equal to y. When you do this, you are using the **transitive property of equality.**

Transitive Property of Equality

For any values of a, b, and c, if $a = b$ and $b = c$, then $a = c$.

Because both a and c are equal to b, they are equal to each other. When two equations in a system are both written so that the part containing x is equal to y, the expressions containing x are equal to each other. You used this property in Example A and in the investigation.

Another type of substitution occurs when you substitute an expression for one variable into another equation, as you'll do in the next example.

EXAMPLE B

A pharmacist has 5% saline (salt) solution and 20% saline solution. How much of each solution should be combined to create a bottle of 90 mL of 10% saline solution?

a. Write a system of equations that models this situation.

b. Solve one equation for x or y, and substitute into the other equation to find a solution.

c. Check your solution.

Solution

First decide what your variables are. You are trying to find how much of 5% and how much of 20% saline solution to use. Let x represent the amount of 5% saline solution, and let y represent the amount of 20% saline solution, in milliliters.

a. The total amount of saline solution needed is 90 mL, so write the equation

$$x + y = 90$$

The amount of salt in x milliliters of 5% saline solution is $0.05x$, and the amount of salt in y milliliters of 20% saline solution is $0.2y$. The total combined salt must be 10% of 90 mL, or $0.1(90)$. So write the equation

$$0.05x + 0.2y = 0.1(90)$$

The system of equations that models this situation is

$$\begin{cases} x + y = 90 \\ 0.05x + 0.2y = 9 \end{cases}$$

b. To use the substitution method, one of the equations must be solved for one of the variables. It will be easier to solve the first equation for one of the variables. You can solve for either x or y, using the balancing method.

$x + y = 90$	Original equation.
$x + y - y = 90 - y$	Subtract y from both sides.
$x = 90 - y$	Combine like terms.

Substitute $90 - y$ for x in the second equation, and solve for y.

$0.05x + 0.2y = 9$	Original equation.
$0.05(90 - y) + 0.2y = 9$	Substitute $90 - y$ for x.
$4.5 - 0.05y + 0.2y = 9$	Distributive Property: distribute 0.05 through $(90 - y)$.
$4.5 + 0.15y = 9$	Combine like terms.
$0.15y = 4.5$	Subtract 4.5 from both sides.
$y = 30$	Divide both sides by 0.15 and simplify.

To find the corresponding x-value, substitute 30 for y in one of the equations.

$x = 90 - y$	The first equation, in intercept form.
$x = 90 - 30 = 60$	Substitute 30 for y and evaluate.

c. To check your solution, substitute 60 for x and 30 for y in the original equations.

$x + y = 90$	$0.05x + 0.2y = 9$
$30 + 60 \stackrel{?}{=} 90$	$0.05(60) + 0.2(30) \stackrel{?}{=} 9$
$90 = 90$	$3 + 6 \stackrel{?}{=} 9$
	$9 = 9$

Both equations result in true statements, so the solution is correct. The pharmacist must combine 60 mL of 5% saline solution and 30 mL of 20% saline solution.

Problems like the one in Example B are called **mixture problems.** This type of problem often involves a system of equations.

To solve a system with the substitution method, as in Example B, first solve one equation for one of the variables.

$$\begin{cases} x + y = 90 \\ 0.05x + 0.2y = 9 \end{cases} \longrightarrow \begin{cases} x = 90 - y \\ 0.05x + 0.2y = 9 \end{cases}$$

Then substitute the resulting expression for the variable *in the other equation* to get a single equation with only one variable.

$$\begin{cases} x = 90 - y \\ 0.05x + 0.2y = 9 \end{cases} \longrightarrow 0.05(90 - y) + 0.2y = 9$$

Next solve for the remaining variable.

$$0.05(90 - y) + 0.2y = 9 \quad \longrightarrow \quad y = 30$$

Finally substitute the resulting value into one of the original equations, and solve for the other variable.

$$x = 90 - y \quad \longrightarrow \quad x = 90 - 30 \quad \longrightarrow \quad x = 60$$

These solutions involve several steps, with each step requiring skill in **symbolic manipulation.** This simply means working with the properties you have used in the balancing and "undoing" methods to keep both sides of the equation equal.

5.3 Exercises

You will need your graphing calculator for Exercises **12** and **17.**

Practice Your Skills

1. The system of equations

$$\begin{cases} d = 1.5t \\ d = 12 - 2.5t \end{cases}$$

describes the distance traveled by two hikers, Edna and Maria, from the example in Lesson 5.1. By setting the expressions of the right sides of the equations equal to each other, you can find the time when Edna and Maria meet. Explain what happens in Steps 3 and 5 of the substitution process.

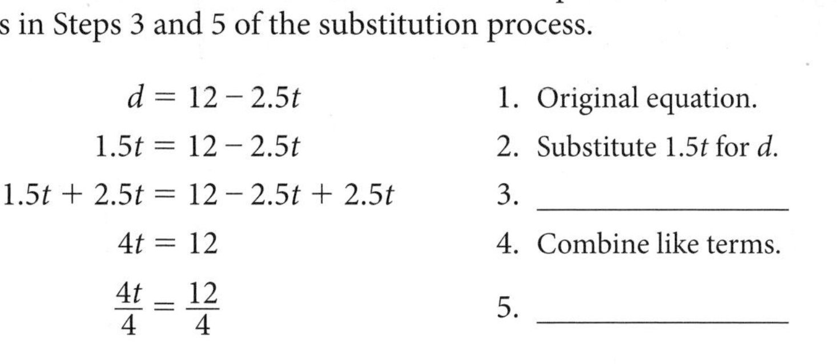

$d = 12 - 2.5t$	1. Original equation.
$1.5t = 12 - 2.5t$	2. Substitute $1.5t$ for d.
$1.5t + 2.5t = 12 - 2.5t + 2.5t$	3. ________________
$4t = 12$	4. Combine like terms.
$\frac{4t}{4} = \frac{12}{4}$	5. ________________
$t = 3$	6. Simplify.

2. Check whether each ordered pair is a solution to each system. If the pair is not a solution point, explain why not. ⓗ

a. $(-2, 34)$ $\begin{cases} y = 38 + 2x \\ y = -21 - 0.5x \end{cases}$

b. $(4.25, 19.25)$ $\begin{cases} y = 32 - 3x \\ y = 15 + x \end{cases}$

c. $(2, 12.3)$ $\begin{cases} y = 2.3 + 3.2x \\ y = 5.9 + 3.2x \end{cases}$

d. $(3, 0.5)$ $\begin{cases} 3x - 2y = 10 \\ 2x + 4y = 8 \end{cases}$

3. Solve each equation by symbolic manipulation.

a. $14 + 2x = 4 - 3x$ ⓐ b. $7 - 2y = -3 - y$ ⓐ c. $5d = 9 + 2d$ d. $12 + t = 4t$

4. Solve each system of equations using the substitution method, and check your solution. ⓗ

a. $\begin{cases} y = 25 + 30x \\ y = 15 + 32x \end{cases}$

b. $\begin{cases} y = 20 + 10x \\ y = 44 - 5x \end{cases}$

c. $\begin{cases} y = 14 + 7x \\ y = 11 + 4x \end{cases}$

5. Substitute $4 - 3x$ for y. Then rewrite each expression in terms of one variable.

a. $5x + 2y$

b. $7x - 2y$ @

6. Solve each system of equations by substitution, and check your solution.

a. $\begin{cases} y = 4 - 3x \\ 5x + 2y = -7 \end{cases}$

b. $\begin{cases} y - 4 = -3x \\ 7x - 2y = 18 \end{cases}$

c. $\begin{cases} y = 4 - 3x \\ y = 2x - 1 \end{cases}$

d. $\begin{cases} 2x - 2y = 4 \\ x + 3y = 1 \end{cases}$

Reason and Apply

7. **APPLICATION** This system of equations models the profits of two home-based Internet companies.

$$\begin{cases} P = -12{,}000 + 2.5N \\ P = -5{,}000 + 1.6N \end{cases}$$

The variable P represents profit in dollars, and N represents hits to the company's website.

a. Use the substitution method to find an exact solution. @

b. Is an approximate or an exact solution more meaningful in this model? @

8. **APPLICATION** The students in the International Club collected nickels and dimes for hunger relief in developing countries. Altogether they collected 1026 coins worth a total of \$78.90.

a. Let N represent the number of nickels collected, and let D represent the number of dimes collected. Write an equation to model the total number of coins collected.

b. Write an equation to model the amount of money collected.

c. Use your equations from 8a and b to write a system of equations. Then solve the system to find how many nickels and how many dimes were collected.

9. **APPLICATION** The manager of a movie theater wants to know the number of adults and children who go to the movies. The theater charges \$8 for each adult ticket and \$4 for each child ticket. At a showing where 200 tickets were sold, the theater collected \$1,304.

a. Let the variable A represent the number of adult tickets, and let C represent the number of child tickets. Write an equation for the total number of tickets sold. @

b. Write an equation for the total cost of the tickets. @

c. Use your equations from 9a and b to write a system of equations whose solution represents the number of adult and child tickets sold. Solve this system by symbolic manipulation.

10. The table at right gives equations that model the three vehicles' distances in the Investigation On the Road Again from Lesson 3.2.

The variable d represents the distance in miles from Flint, and t represents time in minutes, with $t = 0$ being the instant all three vehicles start traveling.

For each event described in 10a–c, write a system of equations, solve by the substitution method, and explain the real-world meaning of your solution.

Distance from Flint

Equation	Vehicle
$d = 220 - 1.2t$	minivan
$d = 35 + 0.8t$	sports car
$d = 1.1t$	pickup truck

a. The pickup truck passes the sports car. ⓐ

b. The minivan meets the pickup truck.

c. The minivan meets the sports car.

d. Write and solve an equation to find when the minivan is twice as far from Flint as the sports car. ⓗ

11. APPLICATION This table shows the winning times for the Olympic women's and men's 100-meter breaststroke. The times are given in minutes and seconds. For example, 1:15.80 means 1 min 15.80 s.

Women's and Men's 100-Meter Breaststroke

Year	Women's champion and country	Time	Men's champion and country	Time
1968	Djurdjica Bjedov, Yugoslavia	1:15.80	Donald McKenzie, United States	1:07.79
1972	Catherine Carr, United States	1:13.58	Nobutaka Taguchi, Japan	1:04.94
1976	Hannelore Anke, East Germany	1:11.16	John Hencken, United States	1:03.11
1980	Ute Geweniger, East Germany	1:10.22	Duncan Goodhew, Great Britain	1:03.44
1984	Petra Van Staveren, Netherlands	1:09.88	Steve Lundquist, United States	1:01.65
1988	Tanya Dangalakova, Bulgaria	1:07.95	Adrian Moorhouse, Great Britain	1:02.04
1992	Elena Roudkovskaia, Unified Team	1:08.00	Nelson Diebel, United States	1:01.50
1996	Penny Heyns, South Africa	1:07.73	Frédéric Deburghgraeve, Belgium	1:00.60
2000	Megan Quann, United States	1:07.05	Domenico Fioravanti, Italy	1:00.46
2004	Xuejuan Luo, China	1:06.64	Kosuke Kitajima, Japan	1:00.08
2008	Leisel Jones, Australia	1:05.17	Kosuke Kitajima, Japan	0:58.10

(International Olympics Committee, in *The World Almanac and Book of Facts 2009,* pp. 846, 848) [Data sets: **SWMYR, SWMWM, SWMMN**]

a. Find a line of fit based on Q-points for the women's and the men's data sets. (*Hint:* You'll probably want to change the times to seconds. For example, 1:15.80 is 75.80 s.) ⓐ

b. Solve a system of equations whose solution tells you when the men and women will have equal winning times for this Olympic event. ⓐ

c. Select an appropriate window and graph this system and its solution.

d. Discuss the reasonableness of this model and the solution. ⓐ

Japan's Kosuke Kitajima swims to win the men's 100-meter breaststroke final at the Beijing 2008 Olympic Games.

12. Students in an algebra class did an experiment similar to the Investigation Where Will They Meet? from Lesson 5.1. They wrote the system

$$\begin{cases} d = 0.5 + 0.75t \\ d = 2.5 + 0.75t \end{cases}$$

a. What real-world information does the system provide?

b. Use the substitution method to solve this system.

c. What is the real-world meaning of the solution you found in 12b?

13. A candy store manager is making a sour candy mix by combining sour cherry worms, which cost her \$2.50 per pound, and sour lime bugs, which cost her \$3.50 per pound. How much of each candy should she include if she wants 20 pounds of a mix that costs her a total of \$65? @

14. Mrs. Abdul mixes bottled fruit juice with natural orange soda to make fruit punch for a party. The bottled fruit juice is 65% real juice, and the natural orange soda is 5% real juice. How many liters of each are combined to make 10 liters of punch that is 33% real juice?

Review

15. A system of two linear equations has the solution (3, −4.5). Write the equations of the lines described.

a. A horizontal line through the solution point.

b. A vertical line through the solution point.

16. You and your family are visiting Seattle and take the elevator to the observation deck of the Space Needle. The observation deck is 520 ft high, while the needle itself is 605 ft high. The elevator travels at a constant speed, and it takes 43 s to travel from the base, at 0 ft, to the observation deck.

a. What is the slope of the graph of this situation? @

b. If the elevator could go all the way to the top, how long would it take to get there? @

c. If a rider gets on the elevator at the restaurant at the 100 ft level, what equation models her ride to the observation deck? @

The Space Needle, shown here in the city skyline, was built for the 1962 Seattle World's Fair.

17. Do each calculation by hand, and then check your results with a calculator. Express your answers as fractions.

a. $3 - \frac{5}{6}$

b. $\frac{1}{4} + \frac{5}{12}$

c. $\frac{3}{4} \cdot \frac{2}{9}$

d. $\frac{1}{5} + \frac{2}{3} + \frac{3}{4}$

LESSON

5.4

Solving Systems of Equations Using Elimination

"I happen to feel that the degree of a person's intelligence is directly reflected by the number of conflicting attitudes she can bring to bear on the same topic."

LISA ALTHER

You have seen how to approximate the solution to a system of equations using a table or graph, and you've seen how to calculate the exact solution to a system of equations using the substitution method. In this lesson you'll learn another method for finding an exact solution, which will have advantages for certain systems.

You know that when you add equal quantities to both sides of an equation, the resulting equation is equivalent and has the same solution as the original.

$y - 7 = 12$	Original equations.	$3x - 5y = 9$
$+ \quad 7 = 7$	Add equal quantities to both sides.	$+ \quad 5y = 5y$
$y \quad = 19$	The resulting equations are true and have the same solutions as the originals.	$3x \quad = 9 + 5y$

In the same way, when you add two quantities that are equal, c and d, to two other quantities that are equal, a and b, the resulting expressions are equal.

$a = b$	Original equation.
$+ c = d$	Add equal quantities.
$a + c = b + d$	The resulting equation is true and has the same solutions as the original equations.

The **elimination method** makes use of this fact to solve systems of linear equations.

EXAMPLE A

J. P. is thinking of two numbers, but he won't say what they are. He tells you that the sum of the two numbers is 163 and that their difference is 33. Find the two numbers.

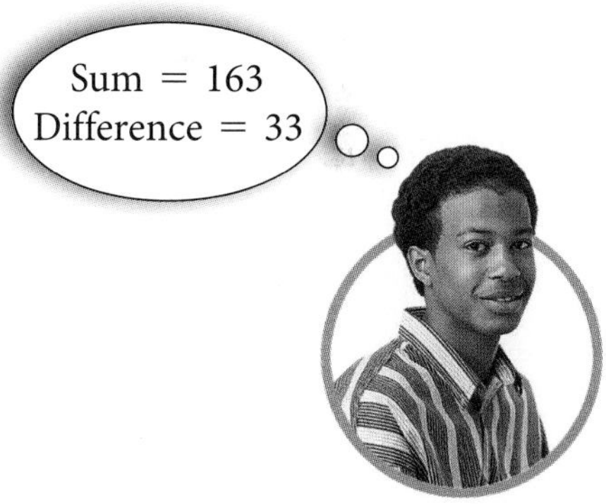

a. Write a system of equations for the sum and difference of these numbers.

b. Use the elimination method to solve this system.

Solution

a. Let f and s represent the first and second numbers, respectively. Then the system is

$$\begin{cases} f + s = 163 \\ f - s = 33 \end{cases}$$

The first equation describes the sum, and the second describes the difference.

b. Note that adding the equations eliminates the variable s. Then solve for f.

$f + s = 163$	Original equations.
$+ f - s = 33$	
$2f = 196$	Add.
$f = 98$	Divide both sides by 2.

So the first number is 98. Now you need to find the second number.

To find s, substitute 98 for f in one of the original equations:

$$98 + s = 163 \qquad \text{or} \qquad 98 - s = 33$$

Either way, the second number is 65. Check that your solutions are correct.

$$\begin{aligned} f + s &= 163 \\ 98 + 65 &\stackrel{?}{=} 163 \\ 163 &= 163 \end{aligned} \qquad \begin{aligned} f - s &= 33 \\ 98 - 65 &\stackrel{?}{=} 33 \\ 33 &= 33 \end{aligned}$$

Adding the two equations quickly leads to a solution because the resulting equation has only one variable. The other variable was eliminated! However, you won't always have coefficients that add to 0. In these cases you'll need another strategy for the elimination method to work.

INVESTIGATION

Paper Clips and Pennies

YOU WILL NEED

- three paper clips
- several pennies
- an 8.5-by-11-inch sheet of paper

In this investigation you'll create a system of equations by using paper clips and pennies as variables.

Step 1 Lay one paper clip along the long side of the paper. Then add enough pennies to complete the 11-inch length.

Step 2 Use C for the length of one paper clip and P for the diameter of one penny. Write an equation in standard form showing your results.

Step 3 Now you'll write the other equation for the system. Lay two paper clips along the shorter edge of your paper, and then add pennies to complete the 8.5-inch length.

Step 4 Using the same variables as in Step 2, write an equation to represent your results for the shorter side.

Step 5 In this system the equations from Steps 2 and 4 have different coefficients for each variable. What can you do to one equation so that the variable C is eliminated when you add both equations?

Step 6 Use your answer to Step 5 to set up the addition of two equations. Once you eliminate the variable C, use the balancing method to solve for P.

Step 7 Substitute the value of P into one of the original equations to find C.

Step 8 Check that your solution satisfies both equations.

Step 9 Describe at least one other way to solve this system by elimination.

Step 10 Explain the real-world meaning of the solution. Describe other experiments in measuring that you can solve using a system of equations.

The goal of the elimination method is to get one of the variables to have coefficient 0 when you add the two equations. If you start with additive inverses, such as s and $-s$ in Example A, then you can simply add the equations. But often you must first multiply one or both of the equations by some convenient number before you add them.

EXAMPLE B

The Montague family and their neighbors the Capulets attended the school play together. The Montagues bought two adult tickets and three student tickets for \$16. The Capulets purchased three adult tickets and two student tickets for \$19.

a. Define variables and write a system of linear equations in standard form for this situation.

b. Use elimination to solve this system.

c. Check your solution by substituting it into the original equations.

Solution

a. Let A represent the cost of an adult ticket, and let S represent the cost of a student ticket. Write a system of linear equations in the standard form $ax + by = c$ for the cost of the tickets.

$$\begin{cases} 2A + 3S = 16 & \text{Cost of the Montagues' tickets.} \\ 3A + 2S = 19 & \text{Cost of the Capulets' tickets.} \end{cases}$$

b. To eliminate A when you add the equations, you must turn the coefficients of A in the two equations into additive inverses—that is, the same number with opposite signs. If you multiply the Montague equation by 3 and the Capulet equation by -2, you will get two new equations on which to use the elimination method.

$3(2A + 3S) = 16(3)$	→	$6A + 9S = 48$	Multiply both sides by 3.
$-2(3A + 2S) = 19(-2)$	→	$\underline{-6A - 4S = -38}$	Multiply both sides by -2.
		$5S = 10$	Add the equations.
		$S = 2$	Solve for S.

To find the value of A, you could substitute 2 for S in one of your original equations and solve for A as in Lesson 5.3. Or you could go back to the original equations and eliminate the variable S. To do this, multiply the Montague equation by -2 and the Capulet equation by 3.

$-2(2A + 3S) = 16(-2)$	→	$-4A - 6S = -32$	Multiply both sides by -2.
$3(3A + 2S) = 19(3)$	→	$\underline{9A + 6S = 57}$	Multiply both sides by 3.
		$5A = 25$	Add the equations.
		$A = 5$	Solve for A.

The solution to the system is (5, 2). So the adult tickets cost \$5 each and the student tickets cost \$2 each.

c. Check your answers by substituting them into the original equations.

$$2(5) + 3(2) \stackrel{?}{=} 16 \qquad 3(5) + 2(2) \stackrel{?}{=} 19$$
$$10 + 6 \stackrel{?}{=} 16 \qquad 15 + 4 \stackrel{?}{=} 19$$
$$16 = 16 \qquad 19 = 19$$

You get true statements for both equations, so the solution checks.

There is no single correct order to the steps used in solving a system of equations, so you can start by choosing a variable that's easy to eliminate. You can use both elimination and substitution if that's easiest. Always check your solution by substituting it into the original equations in the system.

5.4 Exercises

You will need your graphing calculator for Exercises **9** and **12.**

Practice Your Skills

1. Consider the equation $5x + 2y = 10$.

a. What are the x- and y-intercepts of the line represented by this equation? ⓐ

b. Multiply both sides of the equation $5x + 2y = 10$ by 3, and then find the x- and y-intercepts of the line represented by the new equation. How does the graph of this equation compare with the graph of the original equation? Explain your answer. ⓐ

2. Use the equation $5x - 2y = 10$ to find the missing coordinate of each point.

a. $(6, a)$ ⓗ
b. $(-4, b)$ ⓐ
c. $(c, 25)$
d. $(d, -5)$
e. $(e, 0)$
f. $(10, f)$

3. Solve each system of equations by elimination. Show your work.

a. $\begin{cases} 6x + 5y = -20 \\ -6x - 10y = 25 \end{cases}$

b. $\begin{cases} 5x - 4y = 23 \\ 7x + 8y = 5 \end{cases}$

4. Anisha tured in this quiz in her algebra class.

a. What method did she use?

b. What is missing from her solution?

c. Complete Anisha's solution.

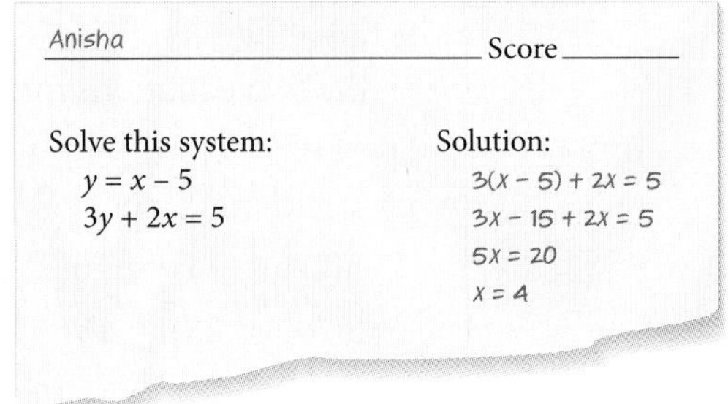
Anisha ____________ Score ______

Solve this system:
$y = x - 5$
$3y + 2x = 5$

Solution:
$3(x - 5) + 2x = 5$
$3x - 15 + 2x = 5$
$5x = 20$
$x = 4$

5. Consider this system of equations:

$$\begin{cases} 3x + 7y = -8 \\ 5x + 8y = -6 \end{cases}$$

a. Explain how you can eliminate the x-term when you combine the equations by addition. ⓐ

b. Explain how you can eliminate the y-term when you combine the equations by addition.

Reason and Apply

6. List the different ways you have learned to solve the system of equations. Then choose one method and find the solution. ⓐ

$$\begin{cases} 3x + 7y = -8 \\ 5x + 8y = -6 \end{cases}$$

7. Solve each system of equations using the elimination method.

a. $\begin{cases} 2x + y = 10 \\ 5x - y = 18 \end{cases}$

b. $\begin{cases} 3x + 5y = 4 \\ 3x + 7y = 2 \end{cases}$

c. $\begin{cases} 2x + 9y = -15 \\ 5x + 9y = -24 \end{cases}$

d. $\begin{cases} 2x + 5y = 31 \\ 6x - 2y = -26 \end{cases}$

e. $\begin{cases} 3x - 8y = -15 \\ 10x - 5y = 80 \end{cases}$

f. $\begin{cases} -7x + 12y = 62 \\ 14x - 6y = -52 \end{cases}$

8. In 8a–c, use the intercepts to graph each equation on the same set of axes.

a. $x - 2y = 6$ ⓐ

b. $3x + 4y = 8$ ⓐ

c. The equation you get from adding the two equations in 8a and b ⓐ

d. What is interesting about the graph of the line in 8c? ⓐ

9. Refer to this system from Example A to answer each question.

$$\begin{cases} x + y = 163 \\ x - y = 33 \end{cases}$$

a. Solve each equation for y, and enter these new equations into your calculator. What window did you use to graph this system? Why?

b. Use the elimination method to find the y-value of the solution. Enter the resulting equation into your calculator and add its graph to your graph from 9a. ⓐ

c. Use elimination to find the x-value of the solution. Draw a vertical line on the graph in 9b to represent the resulting equation.

d. Describe what you notice about the four lines on your screen, and explain why this happens.

10. Part of Adam's homework paper is missing. If the ordered pair (5, 2) is the only solution to the system shown, write a possible equation that completes the system. ⓗ

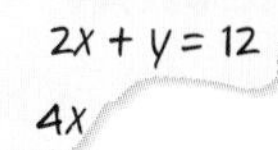

11. Consider this system of equations:

$$\begin{cases} 2x - 5y = 12 \\ 6x - 15y = 36 \end{cases}$$

a. By what number can you multiply which equation to eliminate the x-term when you combine the equations by addition? Do this multiplication.

b. What is the sum of these equations?

c. What is the solution to the system?

d. How can you predict this result by examining the original equations?

12. MINI-INVESTIGATION Consider this system:

$$\begin{cases} 3x + 2y = 7 \\ 2x - y = 4 \end{cases}$$

a. Solve each equation for y, and graph the result on your calculator. Sketch the graph on your paper.

b. Add the two original equations, and solve the resulting equation for y. Add this graph to your graph from 12a. What do you notice?

c. Multiply the second original equation by 2, and then add this new equation to the first equation. Solve the resulting equation for x, and add its graph to your graph from 12a. What do you notice?

d. Multiply the first original equation by 2 and the second by -3, and then add the equations. Solve the resulting equation for y, and add its graph to your graph from 12a. What do you notice?

e. What is the solution to this system of equations? How is this point related to the graphs you drew in 12a–d?

f. Write a few sentences summarizing any conjectures you can make based on this exercise. [▶ You can explore this property of lines further using the **Dynamic Algebra Exploration** in your ebook. ◀]

13. APPLICATION The school photographer took pictures of couples at this year's prom. She charged \$3.25 for wallet-size pictures and \$10.50 for portrait-size pictures.

a. Write a system of equations representing the fact that LaKesha and Wali bought a total of ten pictures for \$61.50. ⓐ

b. Solve this system and explain what your solution means.

14. APPLICATION Automobile companies advertise two rates for fuel mileage. City mileage is the rate of fuel consumption for driving in stop-and-go traffic. Highway mileage is the rate for driving at higher speeds for long periods of time. Cynthia's new car gets 17 mi/gal in the city and 25 mi/gal on the highway. She drove 220 miles on 11 gallons of gas.

a. Define variables and write a system of equations for the number of gallons burned at each mileage rate. @

b. Solve this system and explain the meaning of the solution. @

c. Find the number of city miles and the number of highway miles Cynthia drove. @

d. Check your answers. @

Review

15. For each pair of fractions, name a fraction that lies between them.

a. $\frac{1}{2}$ and $\frac{3}{4}$ b. $\frac{2}{3}$ and $\frac{7}{8}$ c. $-\frac{1}{4}$ and $-\frac{1}{5}$ d. $\frac{7}{11}$ and $\frac{5}{6}$

e. Describe a strategy for naming a fraction between any two fractions.

16. APPLICATION When you go up a mountain, the temperature drops about 4 degrees Fahrenheit for every 1000 feet you ascend.

Mt. McKinley in Denali National Park, Alaska

a. While climbing a trail on Mt. McKinley in Alaska, Marsha intended to record the elevation and temperature at three locations. Complete the table for her.

Marsha's Climb

	Elevation (ft)	Temperature (°F)
Start	4,300	78
Rest station		64
Highest point	11,900	

b. Write an equation to model temperature as a function of elevation. Explain the meanings of the slope and the y-intercept.

c. Mt. McKinley is 20,320 feet high. On the day Marsha was climbing, how cold was it at the summit?

17. Write an equation in point-slope form using the given information.

a. A line that passes through the point $(5, -3)$ and has slope -2

b. A line that passes through the point $(-3, 7)$ and has slope 2.5

18. The graph at right represents distances from a motion sensor for two walkers. (Walker A starts at 0.5 ft and walks at 1 ft/s. Walker B waits at 10.5 ft until 1 s has passed and then walks at a rate of 0.5 ft/s.)

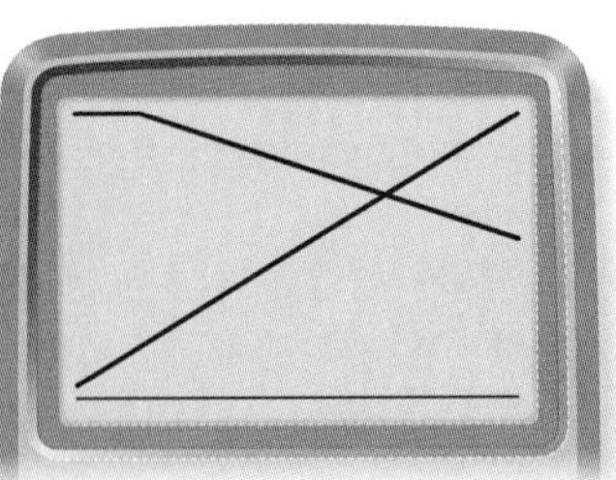

a. Write an equation to model each walk. (*Hint:* Walker B's distance can be recorded in two segments. The first is $y = 10.5$ when $x \leq 1$.)

b. When and where do the walkers meet?

c. When is Walker B farther from the sensor than Walker A?

More on Solving Systems

You have learned to solve systems of linear equations using the substitution method and the elimination method, as well as by using graphs and tables. You can now consider which is the most efficient method for solving a given system.

EXAMPLE A

Which method is the most efficient for solving each of these systems? Why?

a. $\begin{cases} 2x + 3y = 7 \\ 5x - 3y = 14 \end{cases}$ b. $\begin{cases} y = 2 - 3x \\ 5x + 4y = 11 \end{cases}$ c. $\begin{cases} y = 4 + 6x \\ y = 12 - 8x \end{cases}$

Solution

Look at the form and coefficients of the two equations to determine which method to use.

a. The two equations are written in standard form, and adding them eliminates the y-terms. So the elimination method is the most efficient option.

b. One of the equations is solved for y. The other is in standard form. Substituting for y in the second equation is the most efficient option.

c. Both equations are solved for y. You could graph the equations by hand to find an approximate solution or use your calculator to find a more precise solution. If you want an exact solution, you should use substitution: Use the transitive property to set the expressions containing x equal to each other.

Some systems are not initially set up for either substitution or elimination. You will have to do some work to get one or both of the equations in the next example into a more convenient form.

EXAMPLE B

Solve this system:

$$\begin{cases} 13x - 3 + 2y = -14 + 7x + 9y \\ -5x + y = 12 - 11x \end{cases}$$

Solution

The second equation has only one occurrence of the variable y. You can solve this equation for y and then substitute the expression for y in the first equation.

$$-5x + y = 12 - 11x \quad \text{Original equation.}$$

$$y = 12 - 6x \quad \text{Add } 5x \text{ to both sides.}$$

The system can now be written as $\begin{cases} 13x - 3 + 2y = -14 + 7x + 9y \\ y = 12 - 6x \end{cases}$

You can either combine like terms in the first equation before substituting or simply substitute for y in the original equation.

$$13x - 3 + 2(12 - 6x) = -14 + 7x + 9(12 - 6x) \quad \text{Substitute } (12 - 6x) \text{ for } y.$$

$$13x - 3 + 24 - 12x = -14 + 7x + 108 - 54x \quad \text{Distributive property.}$$

$$x + 21 = 94 - 47x \quad \text{Combine like terms.}$$

$$48x + 21 = 94$$ Add $47x$ to both sides.

$$48x = 73$$ Subtract 21 from both sides.

$$x = \frac{73}{48}$$ Divide both sides by 48 and simplify.

You can use any earlier equation containing both x and y and solve to find the y-value. In this case, it's easiest to use the equation $y = 12 - 6x$.

$$y = 12 - 6x$$ Original equation.

$$y = 12 - 6\left(\frac{73}{48}\right)$$ Substitute $\frac{73}{48}$ for x.

$$y = 12 - \frac{73}{8}$$ Multiply.

$$y = \frac{96}{8} - \frac{73}{8}$$ The common denominator is 8, so multiply 12 by 1 in the form $\frac{8}{8}$.

$$y = \frac{23}{8}$$ Combine like terms.

The solution is $\left(\frac{73}{48}, \frac{23}{8}\right)$.

You also could have rewritten each original equation in standard form and used the elimination method. Try it!

Exercises

1. State whether substitution or elimination is a more efficient method for solving each system. Explain your answer. Then solve the system.

a. $\begin{cases} 3x + 4y = 7 \\ 5x - 2y = 16 \end{cases}$ **b.** $\begin{cases} 7x - 3y = 18 \\ y = 6x + 5 \end{cases}$ **c.** $\begin{cases} 6x + 4y = 7 \\ 8x + 5y = 11 \end{cases}$

d. $\begin{cases} 10x + 3y = 15 \\ 3y = 4x + 1 \end{cases}$ **e.** $\begin{cases} 15x - 8y = 18 \\ 5x + 2y = 6 \end{cases}$ **f.** $\begin{cases} 9x + 4y = 21 \\ 4y - 1 = 6x \end{cases}$

2. Solve each system of equations.

a. $\begin{cases} 5x + 2y = 14 \\ 3x - 6 = y - x \end{cases}$ **b.** $\begin{cases} 3x - 6 = 3 - y \\ 5x + 7 - 4y = 8 + 3x - 5y \end{cases}$ **c.** $\begin{cases} 8x = 5x - y + 10 \\ 7 - y = 2x \end{cases}$

d. $\begin{cases} 4x - 3y - 5 = 0 \\ 2x - 1 = 9y \end{cases}$ **e.** $\begin{cases} 4x - 5y + 1 = 4(2 - y) \\ 4(x + y) - 5 = 7 \end{cases}$ **f.** $\begin{cases} 5 + 3(3x - 1) = 16 - 7y \\ 6x + 2(y - 5) = -3y \end{cases}$

3. Find the point of intersection of each pair of lines.

a. Line m has slope 3 and y-intercept -10. Line n has slope $\frac{-1}{2}$ and passes through the point $(-1, 8)$.

b. Line s passes through the points $(2, 5)$ and $(7, 12)$. Line t passes through the points $(-1, 3)$ and $(1, 8)$.

c. Line v has x-intercept 20 and y-intercept 30. Line w is perpendicular to line v and passes through the point $(1, 9)$.

LESSON

5.5

Inequalities in One Variable

"Some material may be inappropriate for children under 13."

DESCRIPTION OF PG-13 RATING, MOTION PICTURE ASSOCIATION OF AMERICA

Drink at least six glasses of water a day. Store milk at temperatures below 40°F. Eat snacks with fewer than 20 calories. Spend at most $10 for a gift. These are a few examples of inequalities in everyday life. Before now, you have looked at situations where an expression needed to be equal to a particular value. In this and future lessons, you will use many of the same solving methods in situations where a particular value represents an upper or lower limit. In this lesson you will analyze situations involving inequalities in one variable and learn how to find and graph their solutions.

An **inequality** is a statement that one quantity is less than or greater than another. You write inequalities using these symbols:

less than	$<$	less than or equal to	$\leq$
greater than	$>$	greater than or equal to	$\geq$

Sometimes you need to translate everyday language into the phrases you see in the table above. Here are some examples.

Everyday phrase	Translation	Inequality
at least six glasses	The number of glasses is greater than or equal to 6.	$g \geq 6$
below 40°F	The temperature is less than 40°F.	$t < 40$
fewer than 20 calories	The number of calories is less than 20.	$c < 20$
at most $10	The price of the gift is less than or equal to $10.	$p \leq 10$
between 35°F and 120°F	35°F is less than the temperature and the temperature is less than 120°F.	$35 < t < 120$

History CONNECTION

Thomas Harriot (1560–1621) introduced the symbols of inequality $<$ and $>$. Pierre Bouguer (1698–1758) first used the symbols $\leq$ and $\geq$ about a century later.
(Florian Cajori, *A History of Mathematics,* 1985)

You solve inequalities very much like you solve equations. You use the same strategies—adding or subtracting the same quantity to both sides, multiplying both sides by the same number or expression, and so on. However, there is one exception you need to remember when solving inequalities. You will explore this exception in the investigation.

INVESTIGATION

Toe the Line

YOU WILL NEED

- chalk or a tape measure to mark a segment

Procedure Note

The announcer calls out operations for Walkers A and B. The walkers perform operations on their numbers by walking to the resulting values on the number line. The recorder logs the position of each walker after each operation.

In this investigation you will analyze properties of inequalities and discover some interesting results.

First you'll act out operations on a number line.

Step 1 In your group, choose an announcer, a recorder, and two walkers. The two walkers make a number line on the floor with marks from −10 to 10. The announcer and recorder make a table with these column headings and twelve rows. The operations to use as row headings are Starting number, Add 2, Subtract 3, Add −2, Subtract −4, Multiply by 2, Subtract 7, Multiply by −3, Add 5, Divide by −4, Subtract 2, and Multiply by −1.

Operation	Walker A's position	Inequality symbol	Walker B's position
Starting number	2		4
Add 2			

Step 2 Read the Procedure Note. As a trial, act out the first operation in the table: Walker A simply stands at 2 on the number line, and Walker B stands at 4.

In your table, enter the inequality symbol that describes the relative position of Walkers A and B on the number line. Be sure you have written a true inequality.

Step 3 Call out the operations. After the walkers calculate their new numbers, record the operation and the walkers' positions in the next row.

Step 4 As a group, discuss which inequality symbol to enter into each cell of the third column. Justify your choice.

Next you'll analyze what each operation does to the inequality.

Step 5 What happens to the walkers' relative positions on the number line when the operation adds or subtracts a positive number? A negative number? Does anything happen to the direction of the inequality symbol? Explain.

Step 6 What happens to the walkers' relative positions on the number line when the operation multiplies or divides by a positive number? Does anything happen to the inequality symbol? Explain.

Step 7 What happens to the walkers' relative positions on the number line when the operation multiplies or divides by a negative number? Does the inequality symbol change directions? Explain.

Step 8 Which operations on an inequality reverse the inequality symbol? Does it make any difference which numbers you use? Consider fractions and decimals as well as integers. Explain your answers.

Step 9 Check your findings about the effects of adding, subtracting, multiplying, and dividing by the same number on both sides of an inequality by creating your own table of operations and walkers' positions.

In square dancing, a caller tells the dancers which steps to take. Their maneuvers depend on their relative positions.

This example will show you how to graph solutions to inequalities.

EXAMPLE A

Graph each inequality on a number line.

a. $t > 5$

b. $x \leq -1$

c. $-2 \leq x < 4$

Solution

a. Any number greater than 5 satisfies the inequality $t > 5$. So $5.0001 > 5$, $7\frac{1}{2} > 5$, and $1{,}000{,}000 > 5$ are all true statements. You show this by drawing an arrow through the values that are greater than 5.

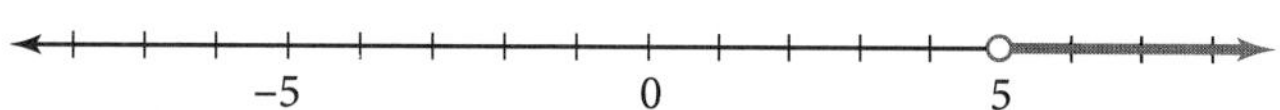

The open circle at 5 excludes 5 from the solutions because $5 > 5$ is not a true statement.

b. The inequality $x \leq -1$ reads "x is less than or equal to -1." The solid circle at -1 includes the value -1 among the solutions because $-1 \leq -1$ is a true statement.

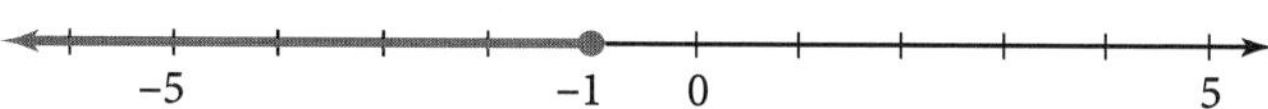

c. This statement is a **compound inequality.** It says that -2 is less than or equal to x and that x is less than 4. So the graph includes all values that are greater than or equal to -2 but less than 4. The solid circle at -2 includes -2 among the solutions because $-2 \leq -2$ is true. The open circle at 4 excludes 4 from the solutions because $4 < 4$ is not true.

When you graph inequalities, always label 0 on the number line as a point of reference.

EXAMPLE B

Erin says, "I lose 15 minutes of sleep every time the dog barks. Last night I got less than 5 hours of sleep. I usually sleep 8 hours." Find the number of times Erin woke up.

To solve the problem, let x represent the number of times Erin woke up, and write an inequality.

Solve the inequality and graph your solutions.

Solution

The number of hours Erin slept is 8 hours minus $\frac{1}{4}$ hour times x, the number of times she woke up. The total is less than 5 hours. So the inequality is $8 - 0.25x < 5$.

Solve the inequality for x. Remember to reverse the inequality symbol if you multiply or divide by a negative number.

$8 - 0.25x < 5$	Original inequality.
$8 - 0.25x - 8 < 5 - 8$	Subtract 8 from both sides of the inequality.
$-0.25x < -3$	Evaluate.
$\dfrac{-0.25x}{-0.25} > \dfrac{-3}{-0.25}$	Divide both sides by -0.25, and reverse the inequality symbol.
$x > 12$	Divide.

The dog woke Erin up more than 12 times. However, she can wake up only a whole number of times, so the solution might be more accurately written as "$x > 12$, where x is a whole number." The solution graph of this statement looks like this:

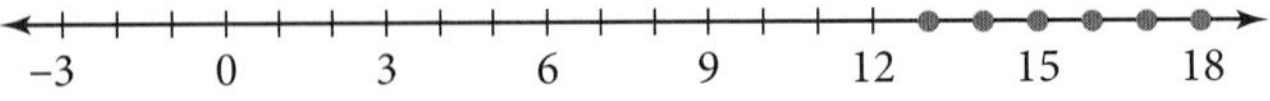

Is there a maximum number of times that Erin can be woken up during the night? You'll explore this question in Exercise 15.

Working with inequalities is very much like working with equations. An equation shows a balance between two quantities, but an inequality shows an imbalance. The important thing to remember is that multiplying or dividing both sides of an inequality by a negative number tips the scales in the opposite direction.

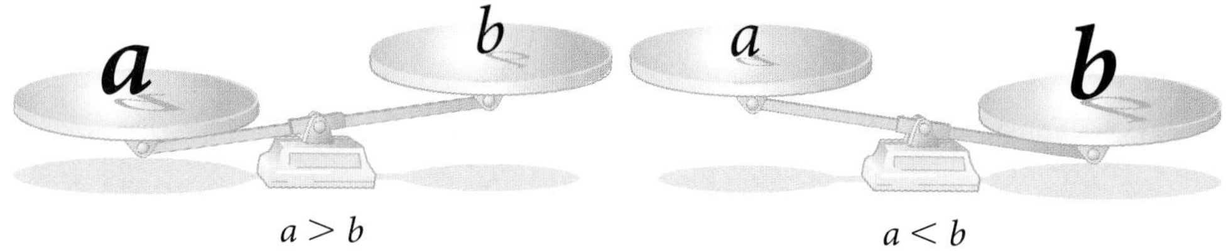

$a > b$ $a < b$

Exercises

Practice Your Skills

1. Tell what operation on the first inequality gives the second one, and give the result using the correct inequality symbol.

a. $3 < 7$
$4 \cdot 3 \square 7 \cdot 4$ @

b. $5 \leq 12$
$-3 \cdot 5 \square 12 \cdot (-3)$

c. $-4 \geq x$
$-4 + (-10) \square x + (-10)$ @

d. $b + 3 > 15$
$b + 3 - 8 \square 15 - 8$

e. $24d < 32$
$\frac{24d}{3} \square \frac{32}{3}$ @

f. $24x \leq 32$
$\frac{24x}{-3} \square \frac{32}{-3}$

2. Find three values of the variable that satisfy each inequality.

a. $5 + 2a > 21$ @

b. $7 - 3b < 28$

c. $-11.6 + 2.5c < 8.2$

d. $4.7 - 3.25d > -25.3$

3. Give the inequality graphed on each number line.

a. 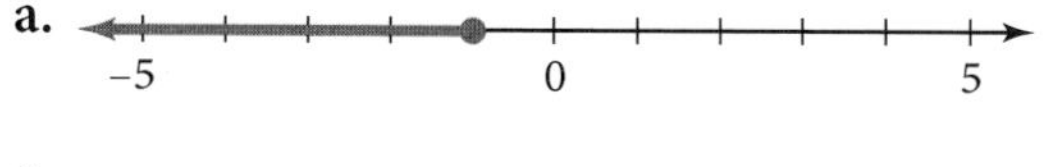

@

b. 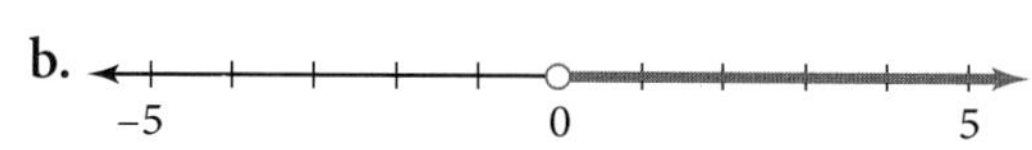

c. 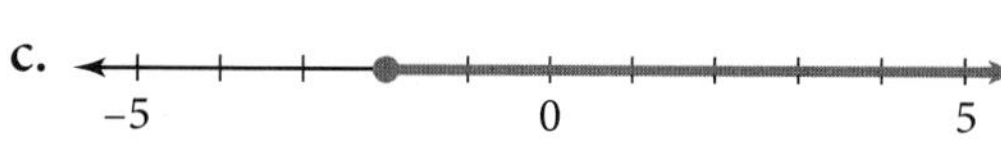

d. 

@

e. 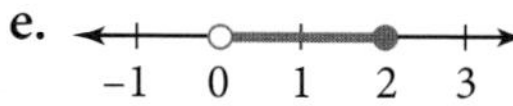

4. Express each statement in symbols.

a. 3 is more than x.

b. y is at least −2. @

c. z is no more than 12.

d. n is not greater than 7.

5. Graph each inequality on a number line.

a. $x > 3$

b. $x < -1$

c. $x < 2$

d. $x \geq 0$

Reason and Apply

6. Solve each inequality. Show your work.

a. $4.1 + 3.2x > 18$ ⓐ

b. $7.2 - 2.1b < 4.4$

c. $7 - 2(x - 3) \geq 25$

d. $11.5 + 4.5(x + 1.8) \leq x$

e. $4 + 3(x + 1) \geq x - 5$

f. $2x + 3 < 5(x + 1) - 2$

7. Solve each inequality and graph the solutions on a number line.

a. $3x - 2 \leq 7$

b. $4 - x > 6$ ⓐ

c. $3 + 2x \geq -3$

d. $10 \leq 2(5 - 3x)$

e. $4x + 7 > 23$

f. $6 - 2x \geq 14$

8. Ezra received \$50 from his grandparents for his birthday. He makes \$7.50 each week for odd jobs he does around the neighborhood. Since his birthday, he has saved more than enough to buy the \$120 gift he wants to buy for his parents' twentieth wedding anniversary. How many weeks ago was his birthday? ⓗ

9. For each graph, tell what operation moves the two points in the inequality to their new positions. Write the new inequality, stating the position of the red dot first.

a. $1 < 2$ ⓐ

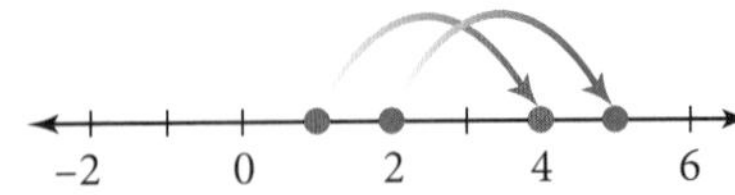

b. $6 > 2$

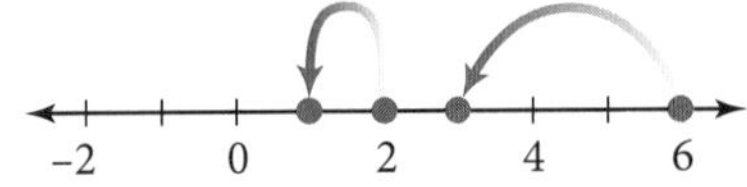

c. $-1 < 1$

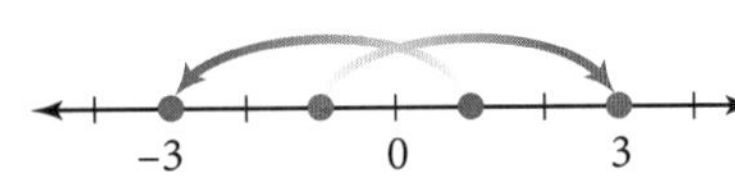

d. $0 < 3$

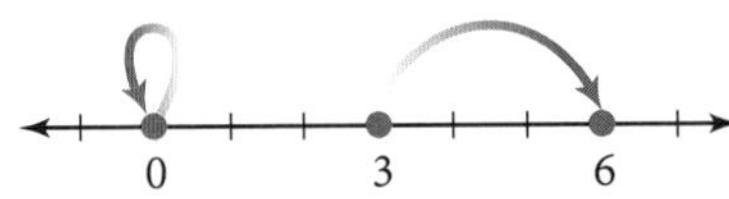

10. State whether each inequality is true or false for the given value.

a. $x - 14 < 9, x = 5$

b. $3x \geq 51, x = 7$

c. $2x - 3 < 7, x = 5$

d. $4(x - 6) \geq 18, x = 12$

11. Solve each inequality. Explain the meaning of the result. On a number line, graph the values of x that make the original inequality true.

a. $2x - 3 > 5x - 3x + 3$ ⓐ

b. $-2.2(5x + 3) \geq -11x - 15$

12. Data collected by a motion sensor will vary slightly in accuracy. A given sensor has a known accuracy of ± 2 mm (0.002 m), and a distance is measured as 2.834 m. State this distance and accuracy as an inequality statement.

13. You read the inequality symbols, $<$, $\leq$, $>$, and $\geq$, as "is less than," "is less than or equal to," "is greater than," and "is greater than or equal to," respectively. But you describe everyday situations with different expressions. Identify the variable in each statement, and write the inequality to describe each situation. ⓗ

a. I'll spend no more than $30 on CDs this month.

b. You must be at least 48 inches tall to go on this ride.

c. Three or more people make a carpool.

d. No one under age 17 will be admitted without a parent or guardian.

14. The table gives equations that model the three vehicles' distances in the Investigation On the Road Again from Lesson 3.2. The variable x represents the time in minutes since all three vehicles began traveling, and y represents the distance in miles from Flint.

Equation	Vehicle
$y = 220 - 1.2x$	minivan
$y = 35 + 0.8x$	sports car
$y = 1.1x$	pickup truck

a. What question is represented by the statement $35 + 0.8x \geq 131$?

b. What is the solution to the inequality $35 + 0.8x \geq 131$?

c. What question is represented by the statement $220 - 1.2x < 35 + 0.8x$?

d. What is the solution to the inequality $220 - 1.2x < 35 + 0.8x$?

15. In Example B, the inequality $8 - 0.25x < 5$ was written to represent the situation in which Erin slept less than 5 h and her sleep time was 8 h minus 0.25 h for each time the dog barked. However, Erin can't sleep less than 0 h, so a more accurate statement would be the compound inequality $0 \leq 8 - 0.25x < 5$. You can solve a compound inequality in the same way you've solved other inequalities; you just need to make sure you apply the same operation to all *three* parts. Solve this compound inequality for x and graph the solution.

Review

16. List the order in which you would perform the operations to get the correct answer.

a. $72 - 12 \cdot 3.2 = 33.6$ b. $2 + 1.5(3 - 5^2) = -31$ c. $21 \div 7 - 6 \div 2 = 0$

17. Solve each equation for y.

a. $3x + 4y = 5.2$ b. $3(y - 5) = 2x$

c. $2x - 5y = 14$ d. $8 + 2(y + 1) = 4x$

18. Use the distributive property to rewrite each expression without parentheses.

a. $-2(x + 8)$ b. $4(0.75 - y)$ c. $-(z - 5)$

LESSON 5.6

Graphing Inequalities in Two Variables

In Lesson 5.5, you learned to graph inequalities in one variable on a number line. However, in some situations, such as the number of points a football team scores by touchdowns and field goals, you might want to keep track of more than one variable. In this lesson you will learn to graph inequalities in two variables on a coordinate plane.

You have graphed equations like $y = 1 + 0.5x$. In the investigation you will learn how to graph inequalities such as $y < 1 + 0.5x$ and $y > 1 + 0.5x$.

INVESTIGATION

Graphing Inequalities

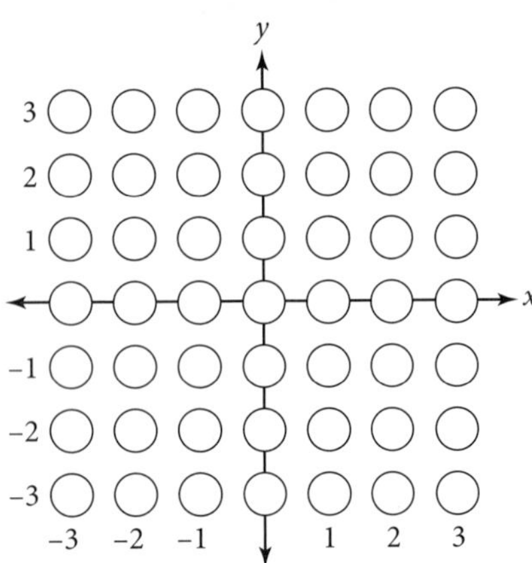

First you'll make a graph from one of four statements.

i. $y \square 1 + 0.5x$ ii. $y \square -1 - 2x$

iii. $y \square 1 - 0.5x$ iv. $y \square 1 - 2x$

Step 1 Each member of the group should choose a different statement from above.

Step 2 Evaluate the right side of your statement for $x = -3$. For each circle in the first column on the graph, fill in $>$ if the y-value of the point is greater than your value, $=$ if the values are equal, and $<$ if the y-value is less than your value.

Step 3 Repeat Step 2 for $x = -2, -1, 0, 1, 2,$ and 3.

Next you'll analyze the results of your graph.

Step 4 What do you notice about the circles filled with the equal sign? Describe any other patterns you see.

Step 5 Use a straightedge to draw a line connecting all the circles containing =. What do you observe about all the circles containing $<$?

Step 6 Copy this statement, with the correct choices: "If I were to graph

$y < x$-expression, then I would include all the points _____ the line _____ include the line."

Step 7 Complete the statement from Step 6 three more times, using $\leq$, $>$, and $\geq$.

Step 8 Compare the four statements you wrote in Steps 6 and 7 with the statements written by others in your group. Explore and discuss any differences until you all agree.

Step 9 Describe how to use one point to check the graph of an inequality.

The graph of the solutions to a single inequality is called a **half-plane** because it includes half of the plane, that is, all the points in the coordinate plane that fall on one side of the boundary line. When the solution includes the line, draw a solid line; when it does not include the line, draw a dashed line.

EXAMPLE A

Check to see whether each point is part of the solution to the inequality $2x - 3y > 3$. Then graph the inequality.

i. $(3, -2)$

ii. $(3, 1)$

iii. $(-1, 2)$

iv. $(-2, -3)$

Solution

To check a point, substitute the x- and y-coordinates into the inequality $2x - 3y > 3$ and evaluate whether the resulting statement is true or false.

Point	Substitution into $2x - 3y > 3$	True or false?
i. $(3, -2)$	$2(3) - 3(-2) > 3$ $12 > 3$	true
ii. $(3, 1)$	$2(3) - 3(1) > 3$ $3 > 3$	false
iii. $(-1, 2)$	$2(-1) - 3(2) > 3$ $-8 > 3$	false
iv. $(-2, -3)$	$2(-2) - 3(-3) > 3$ $5 > 3$	true

These results show that points $(3, -2)$ and $(-2, -3)$ are part of the solution to $2x - 3y > 3$, while points $(3, 1)$ and $(-1, 2)$ are not.

To graph the inequality, first consider the equation you get by changing the inequality symbol to an equal sign. This is the boundary of the half-plane. You could solve this equation for y or use the intercepts to graph the line.

$$2x - 3y = 3$$

If $x = 0$, then $-3y = 3$.	If $y = 0$, then $2x = 3$.
$y = -1$ Divide each side by -3.	$x = 1.5$ Divide each side by 2.
The y-intercept is -1.	The x-intercept is 1.5.

Plot the two intercepts. You are actually graphing an inequality rather than an equation, and in this case the inequality does not include the boundary line. Draw a dashed line to indicate that points on the line are not part of the solution to the inequality.

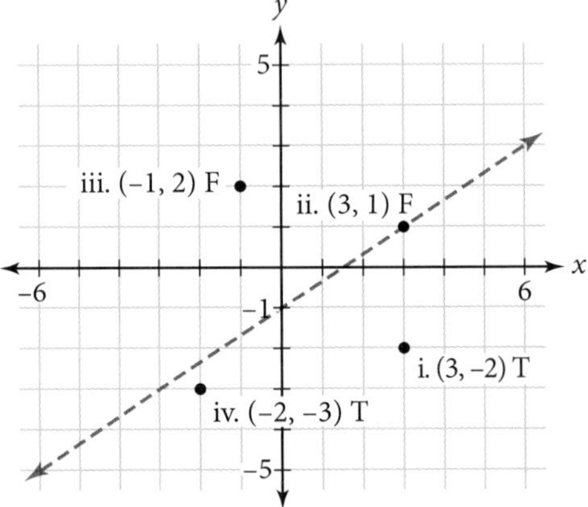

To complete the graph, shade the region on one side of the dashed line. Notice that the two points below the boundary line did satisfy the inequality, and the points above and on the boundary line did not. Shade the region on the side of the line where the "true" points lie.

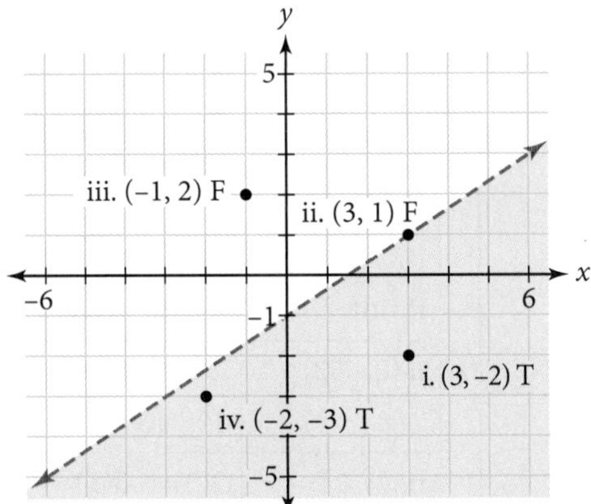

Graphing Inequalities

- ▸ Draw a broken or dashed line on the boundary for inequalities with $>$ or $<$.
- ▸ Draw a solid line on the boundary for inequalities with $\geq$ or $\leq$.
- ▸ Select a point not on the line and test it to find which side of the line to shade.

You could determine the shaded region on the graph by choosing only one point not on the boundary line and testing whether it satisfies the inequality. If it does, shade that side of the boundary line. If it does not, shade the other side. When the point (0, 0) does not lie on the boundary line, it is a convenient point to test. [▶ See **Calculator Notes: Graphing Inequalities in Two Variables** and **Graphing Inequalities Using the Inequalz App** to graph inequalities in two variables on your calculator. ◀]

EXAMPLE B Graph each inequality. Test whether the point (0, 0) satisfies the inequality to determine which side of the boundary line to shade.

a. $x > -2$

b. $3y \leq 1$

c. $-2x \geq 5$

d. $3 - y < 7$

Solution Solve for the variable in each inequality. Don't forget to switch the direction of the inequality when multiplying or dividing by a negative!

a. $x > -2$

Test point (0, 0):
$0 > -2$ True.

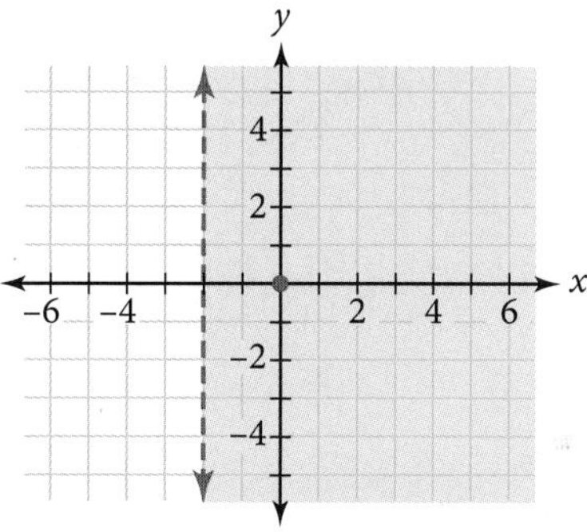

b. $3y \leq 1$ Divide each side by 3.

$y \leq \frac{1}{3}$

Test point (0, 0):
$3(0) \leq 1$
$0 \leq 1$ True.

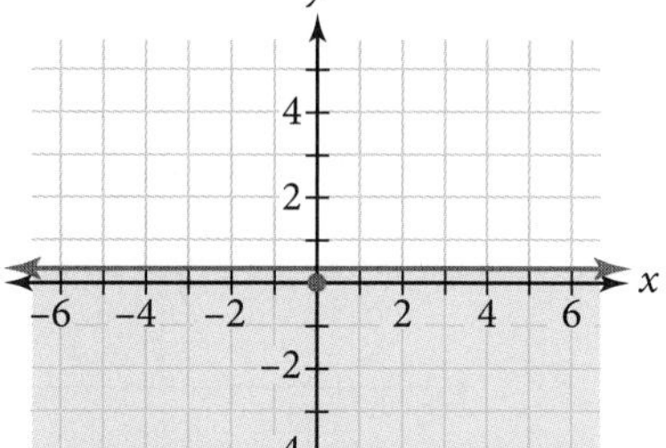

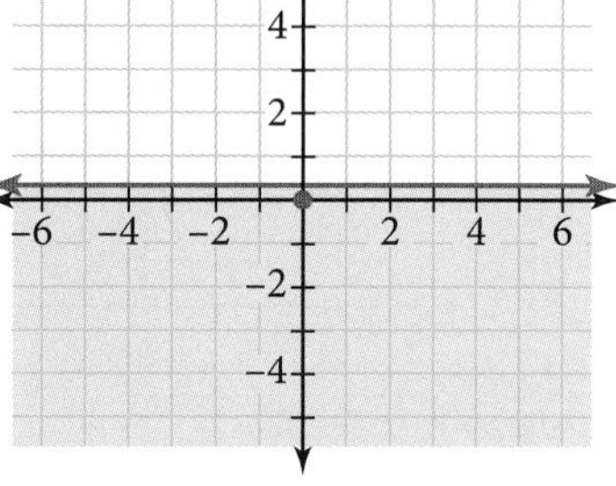

c. $-2x \geq 5$ Divide each side by -2.

$x \leq -\frac{5}{2}$ or -2.5

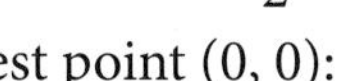

Test point (0, 0):
$-2(0) \geq 5$
$0 \geq 5$ False.

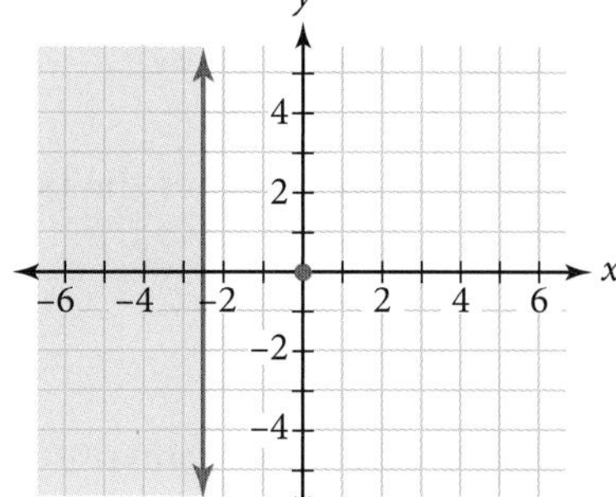

d. $3 - y < 7$	Subtract 3 from each side.	
$-y < 4$	Multiply each side by -1.	
$y > -4$		
Test point (0, 0): $3 - 0 < 7$		
$3 < 7$	True.	

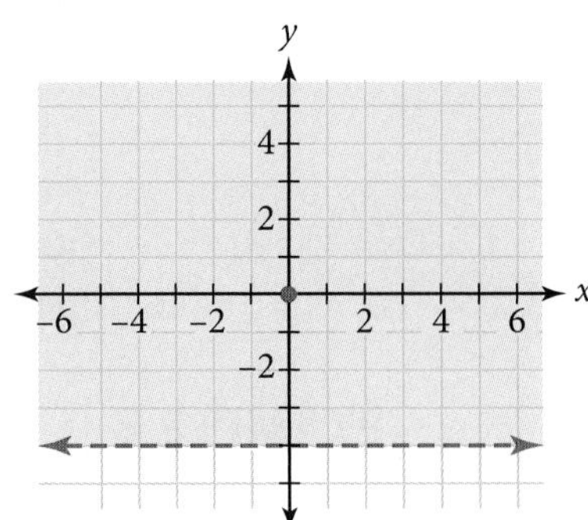

Exercises

You will need your graphing calculator for Exercise **11.**

Practice Your Skills

1. Match each graph to an inequality.

a. $y \leq 3 + 2x$ b. $y \leq 2 + 3x$ c. $2x + 3y \leq 6$ @ d. $2x + 3y \geq 6$

i.

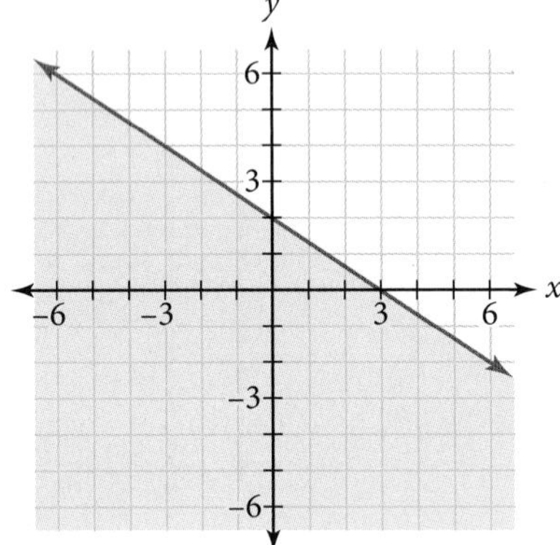

ii.

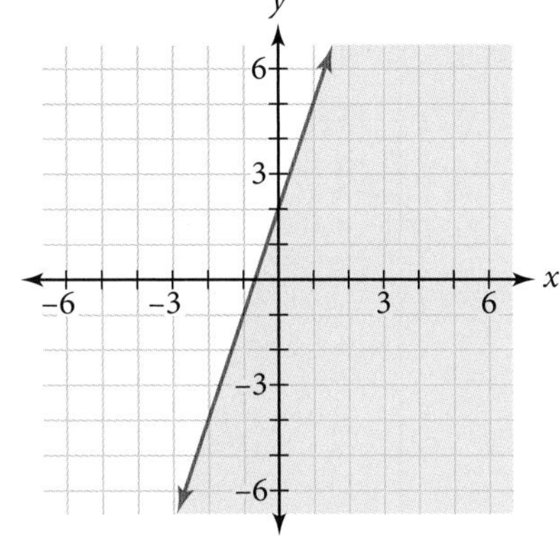

iii.

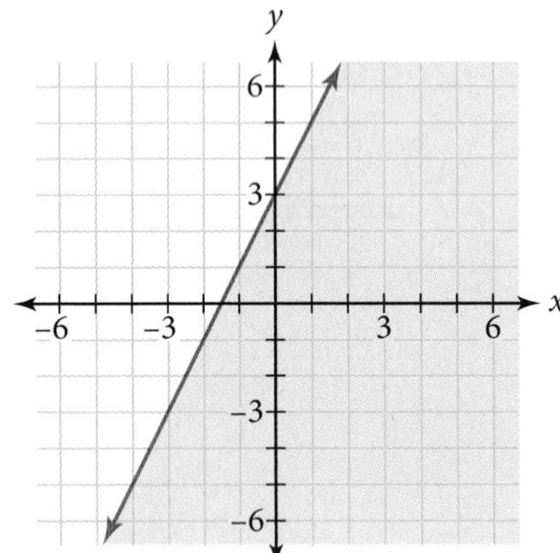

iv.

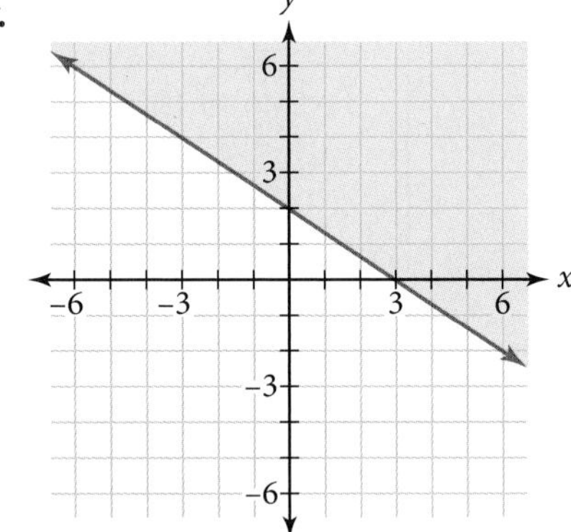

2. Determine whether the point (0, 0) is in the solution set of each inequality.

a. $84x + 7y \geq 70$ @ b. $4.8x - 0.12y < 7.2$

c. $15x + 3y \leq 75$ d. $2.5x - 1.5y > 3$

3. Sketch each inequality on a number line.

a. $x \leq -5$ b. $x > 2.5$ c. $-3 \leq x \leq 3$ @ d. $-1 \leq x < 2$

4. Consider the inequality $y < 2 - 0.5x$.

a. Graph the boundary line for the inequality on axes scaled from -6 to 6. ⓐ

b. Determine whether each given point satisfies the inequality $y < 2 - 0.5x$. Plot the point on the graph you drew in 4a. Label the point T (true) if it is included in the solution or F (false) if it is not included in the solution. ⓐ

i. $(1, 2)$ ii. $(4, 0)$ iii. $(2, -3)$ iv. $(-2, -1)$

c. Use your results from 4b to shade the half-plane that represents the inequality. ⓐ

5. Consider the inequality $y \geq 1 + 2x$.

a. Graph the boundary line for the inequality on axes scaled from -6 to 6.

b. Determine whether each given point satisfies the inequality $y \geq 1 + 2x$. Plot the point on the graph you drew in 5a, and label the point T (true) if it is included in the solution or F (false) if it is not included in the solution.

i. $(-2, 2)$ ii. $(3, 2)$ iii. $(-1, -1)$ iv. $(-4, -3)$

c. Use your results from 5b to shade the half-plane that represents the inequality.

Reason and Apply

6. Sketch each inequality.

a. $y \leq -3 + x$ ⓐ b. $y > -2 - 1.5x$ c. $2x - y \geq 4$

d. $x + y < 4$ e. $3x - 4y \geq 12$ f. $5x + 6y > 12$

7. Write the inequality represented by each graph. ⓗ

a. 

(0.5, 0)

b. 

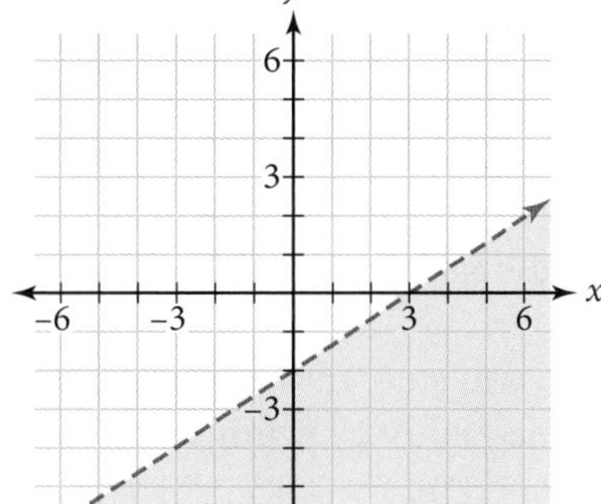

c. 

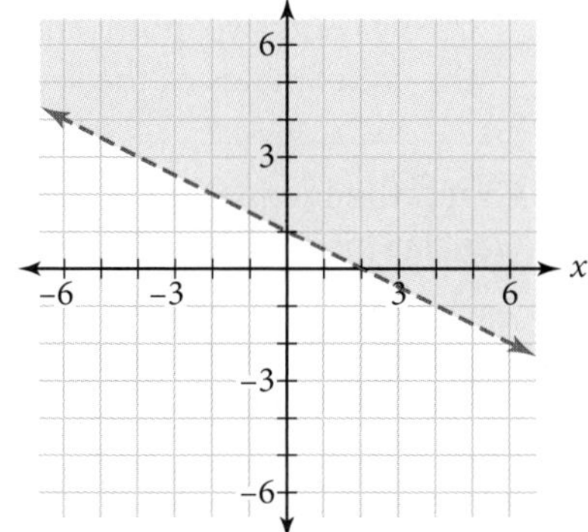

d.

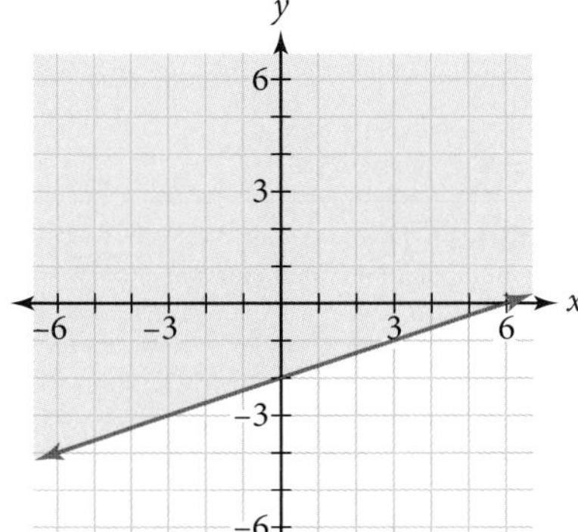

e. ⓐ

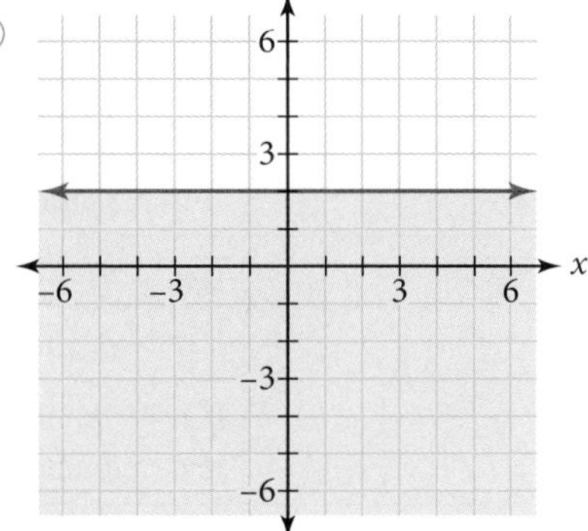

f.

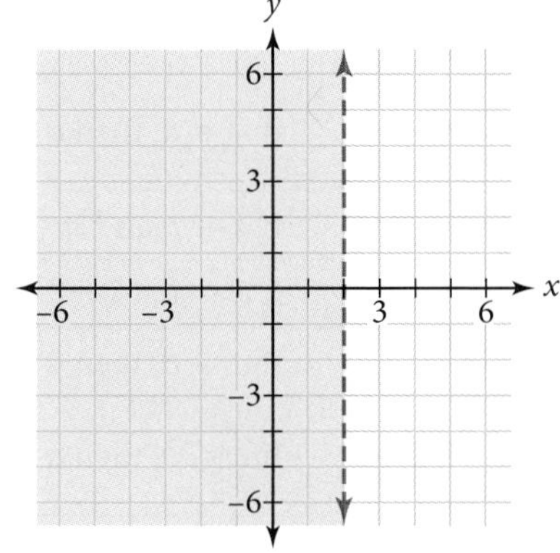

8. MINI-INVESTIGATION Consider linear inequalities written in standard form.

a. Use intercepts to graph the boundary of each inequality's graph, and use the point (0, 0) to determine which side of the boundary to shade.

i. $3x - 2y \leq 6$

ii. $3x + 2y \leq 6$

iii. $3x - 2y \leq -6$

iv. $-3x - 2y \leq 6$

v. $-3x + 2y \leq -6$

vi. $-3x + 2y \leq 6$

b. When a linear inequality with $\leq$ is written in standard form, how might you know whether to shade above or below the boundary line without testing a point?

9. Sketch each inequality on coordinate axes.

a. $y < 4$ @ b. $x \leq -3$ c. $y \geq -1$ d. $x > 3$

10. APPLICATION The total number of points from a combination of one-point free throws, F, and two-point shots, S, is less than 84 points.

a. Write an inequality to represent this situation. @

b. Write the equation of the boundary line for this situation. @

c. Graph this inequality with S on the horizontal axis and F on the vertical axis. Show the scale on the axes.

d. On your graph, indicate three possible combinations of free throws and two-point shots that give the point total 50. Label the coordinates of these points.

Alan Lewis shoots a free throw during the 2012 National Veterans Wheelchair Games.

11. Graph the inequalities in Exercises 4 and 5 on your calculator. [▸ See **Calculator Notes: Graphing Inequalities in Two Variables** and **Graphing Inequalities Using the Inequalz App.** ◂]

12. MINI-INVESTIGATION In Lesson 4.6, you studied the Properties of Equality. Complete the statements of the Properties of Inequality by filling in the boxes with <, =, or >. (*Hint:* Try numbers in place of a, b, and c.)

	Properties of Equality	Properties of Inequality @
Reflexive :	$a = a$	Exactly one of the following is true: $a \square b$, $a \square b$, or $a \square b$.
Symmetric:	If $a = b$, then $b = a$	If $a > b$, then $b \square a$ If $a > b$, then $-a \square -b$
Transitive:	If $a = b$ and $b = c$, then $a = c$	If $a > b$ and $b > c$, then $a \square c$
Addition:	If $a = b$, then $a + c = b + c$	If $a > b$, then $a + c \square b + c$
Subtraction:	If $a = b$, then $a - c = b - c$	If $a > b$, then $a - c \square b - c$
Multiplication:	If $a = b$, then $a \times c = b \times c$	If $a > b$ and $c > 0$, then $a \times c \square b \times c$ If $a > b$ and $c < 0$, then $a \times c \square b \times c$
Division:	If $a = b$, then $a \div c = b \div c$	If $a > b$ and $c > 0$, then $a \div c \square b \div c$ If $a > b$ and $c < 0$, then $a \div c \square b \div c$

Review

13. APPLICATION This table shows that the traveling distances between some cities depend on how you travel.

Traveling Distances

From	To	Flying distance (mi)	Driving distance (mi)
Detroit, MI	Memphis, TN	623	756
St. Louis, MO	Minneapolis, MN	466	559
Dallas, TX	San Francisco, CA	1483	1765
Seattle, WA	Los Angeles, CA	959	1150
Washington, DC	Pittsburgh, PA	192	241
Philadelphia, PA	Indianapolis, IN	585	647
New Orleans, LA	Chicago, IL	833	947
Cleveland, OH	New York, NY	405	514
Birmingham, AL	Boston, MA	1052	1194
Denver, CO	Buffalo, NY	1370	1991
Kansas City, MO	Omaha, NE	166	204

[Data sets: **FLYDS, DRVDS**]

a. Graph the data. Put the flying distances on the x-axis.

b. Find a line of fit based on the Q-points for the data.

c. The flying distance from Louisville, Kentucky, to Miami, Florida, is 919 mi. Predict the driving distance from Louisville to Miami.

d. The driving distance from Phoenix, Arizona, to Salt Lake City, Utah, is 651 mi. Predict the flying distance from Phoenix to Salt Lake City.

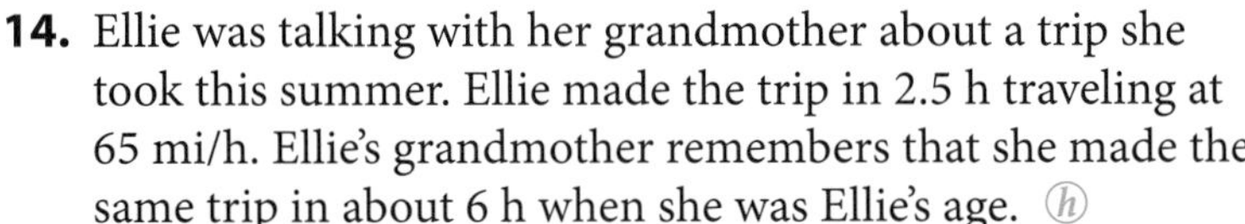

14. Ellie was talking with her grandmother about a trip she took this summer. Ellie made the trip in 2.5 h traveling at 65 mi/h. Ellie's grandmother remembers that she made the same trip in about 6 h when she was Ellie's age. ⓗ

a. What speed was Ellie's grandmother traveling when she made the trip?

b. Explain how this situation is an application of inverse variation.

15. Solve each equation for y.

a. $7x - 3y = 22$

b. $5x + 4y = -12$

IMPROVING YOUR Visual Thinking SKILLS

In this chapter you have seen three possible outcomes for a system of two equations in two variables. If one solution exists, it is the point of intersection. If no solution exists, the lines are parallel and there is no point of intersection. If infinitely many solutions exist, the two lines overlap.

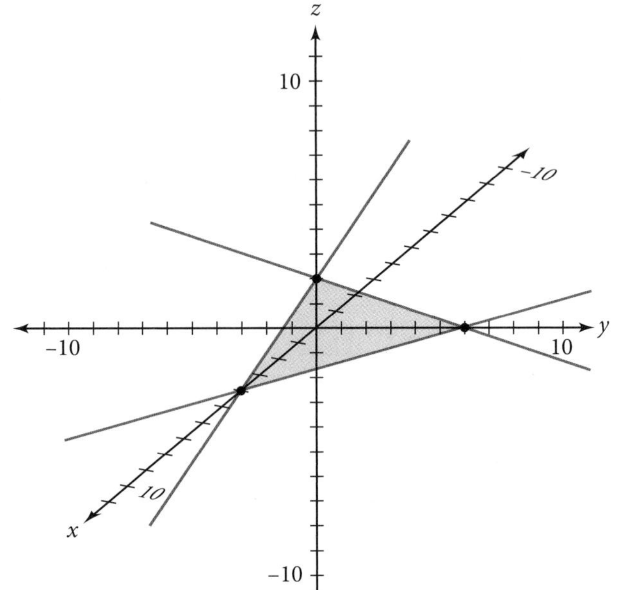

What do the solutions look like in a system of three linear equations in three unknowns? An equation like $3x + 2y = 12$ is a line, but an equation in three variables is a plane. Consider the graph of $3x + 2y + 6z = 12$. Imagine the x-axis coming out of the page. The shaded triangle indicates the part of the solution plane whose coordinates are all positive. The complete plane is infinite.

If you have two more planar equations, you have a system of three equations in three variables. There will be three planes on the graph. The solutions to this system are where the planes intersect, if they do so at all. Visualize how three planes could intersect to answer these questions.

- Can three planes intersect in one point? If so, how many solutions will this system have?
- If a system has infinitely many solutions, must all three equations be the same plane?
- If the system has no solutions, must the planes be parallel?

LESSON

5.7

Systems of Inequalities

"All mathematical truths are relative, conditional."

CHARLES PROTEUS STEINMETZ

You learned that the solution to a system of two linear equations, if there is exactly one solution, is the coordinates of the point at which the two lines intersect. In this lesson you'll learn about **systems of inequalities** and their solutions. Many real-world situations can be described by a system of inequalities. When solving these problems, you'll need to write inequalities, often called **constraints,** and graph them. You'll then find a region, rather than a single point, that represents all solutions.

Translucent sheets of blue, red, and yellow intersect to form overlapping regions of new colors—orange, green, and purple.

INVESTIGATION

A "Typical" Envelope

The U.S. Postal Service imposes several constraints on acceptable sizes for an envelope. One constraint is that the ratio of length to width must be less than or equal to 2.5, and another is that this ratio must be greater than or equal to 1.3.

Step 1 Define variables and write an inequality for each constraint.

Step 2 Solve each inequality for the variable representing length. Decide whether you have to reverse the direction of the inequality symbols. Then write a system of inequalities to describe the Postal Service's constraints on envelope sizes.

Step 3 Decide on appropriate scales for each axis, and label a set of axes. Decide whether you should draw the boundaries of the system with solid or dashed lines. Graph each inequality on the same set of axes. Shade each half-plane with a different color or pattern.

Step 4 Where on the graph are the solutions to the system of inequalities? Discuss how to check that your answer is correct.

Step 5 Decide whether each envelope satisfies the constraints by locating the corresponding point on your graph.

a. 5 in. by 8 in.

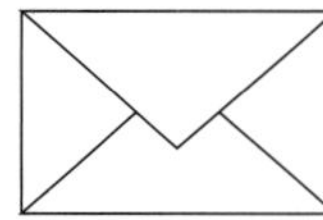

b. 3 in. by 3 in.

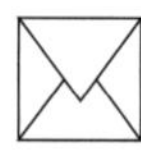

c. 2.5 in. by 7.5 in.

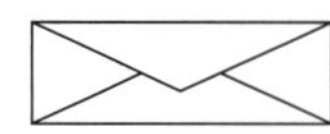

d. 5.5 in. by 7.5 in.

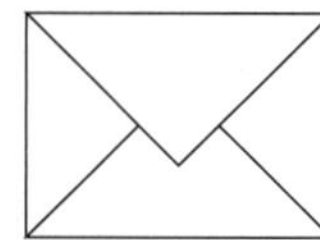

Step 6 Do the coordinates of the origin satisfy this system of inequalities? Explain the real-world meaning of this point. What constraints can you add to more realistically model the Postal Service's acceptable envelope sizes? How do these additions affect the graph?

EXAMPLE A

Graph the system of inequalities

$$\begin{cases} y \leq -2 + \frac{3}{2}x \\ y > 1 - x \end{cases}$$

Graph the boundary lines and shade the half-planes. Indicate the solution area as the darkest region.

Solution

First determine whether the boundary lines are solid or dashed. Graph $y = -2 + \frac{3}{2}x$ with a solid line, because points on the line satisfy the inequality. Graph $y = 1 - x$ with a dotted line, because its points do not satisfy the inequality.

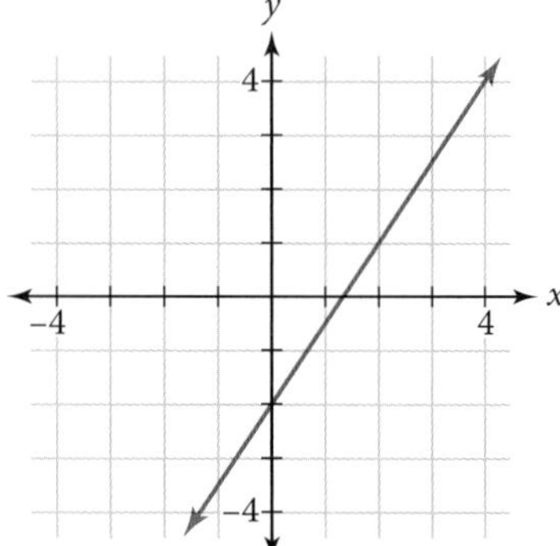

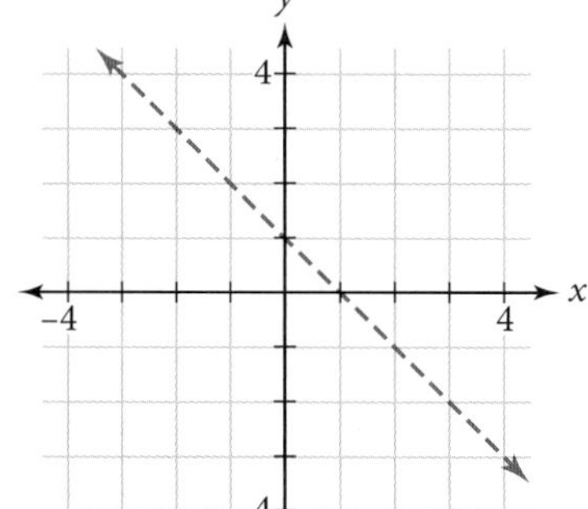

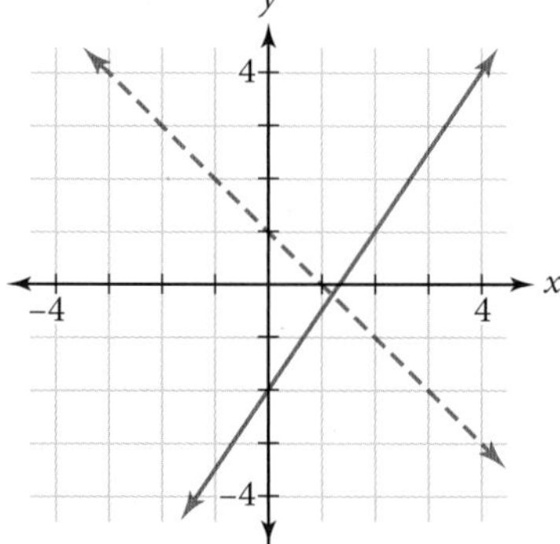

Shade the half-plane below the solid line $y = -2 + \frac{3}{2}x$, because its inequality has the "less than or equal to" symbol, $\leq$. Shade above the dotted line $y = 1 - x$, because its inequality has the "greater than" symbol, $>$. Use different colors or patterns to distinguish each shaded area.

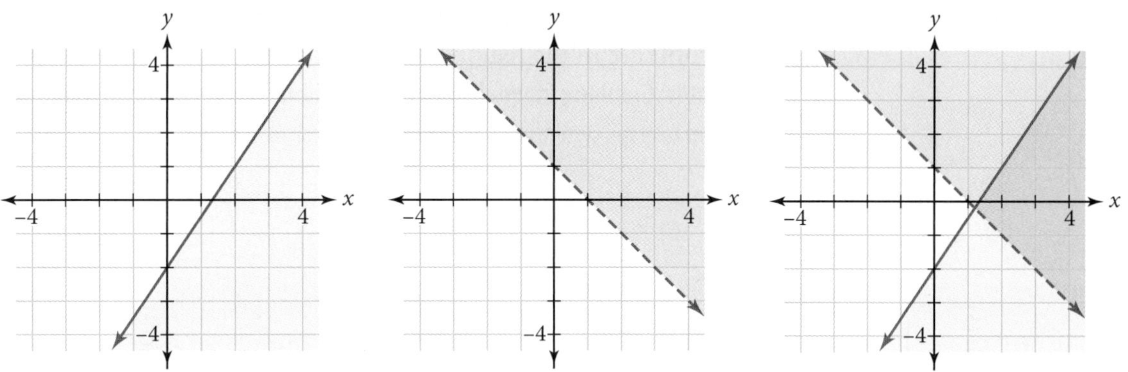

Each shaded area indicates the region of points that satisfy each inequality. The overlapping area bounded by $y \leq -2 + \frac{3}{2}x$ and $y > 1 - x$ satisfies both. Only the points that lie in both half-planes are solutions to the system of inequalities.

EXAMPLE B

A cereal company is including a chance to win a \$1,000 scholarship in each box of cereal. In this promotional campaign, it will give away one scholarship each month, regardless of the number of boxes sold. The cereal is priced differently at various locations, so the profit from a single box is between \$0.47 and \$1.10.

a. Write a system of inequalities to model profit as a function of the number of boxes sold.

b. Graph the system of inequalities.

c. Is it possible to sell 3000 boxes and make a profit of \$1,000?

Solution

a. Let x represent the number of boxes sold, and let y represent the profit. The lowest profit per box is \$0.47. So $0.47x$ is the minimum profit when x boxes are sold. Subtract \$1,000 for the scholarship given each month. So the profit y is at least $0.47x - 1000$ dollars for x boxes sold. This is given by the inequality

$$y \geq -1000 + 0.47x$$

Likewise, if the maximum profit is \$1.10 per box, then the profit is at most $1.1x - 1000$ dollars. So the second inequality is

$$y \leq -1000 + 1.1x$$

The profit during each month is given by the system

$$\begin{cases} y \geq -1000 + 0.47x \\ y \leq -1000 + 1.1x \end{cases}$$

b. Each inequality is graphed for up to 5000 boxes on separate axes. The possible profits are in the region where the two half-planes overlap. [▶ See **Calculator Notes: Graphing Inequalities in Two Variables** and **Graphing Inequalities Using the Inequalz App** to graph systems of inequalities on your calculator. ◀]

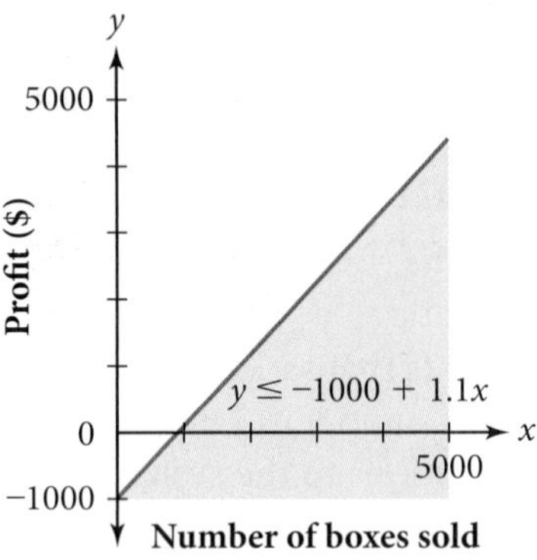

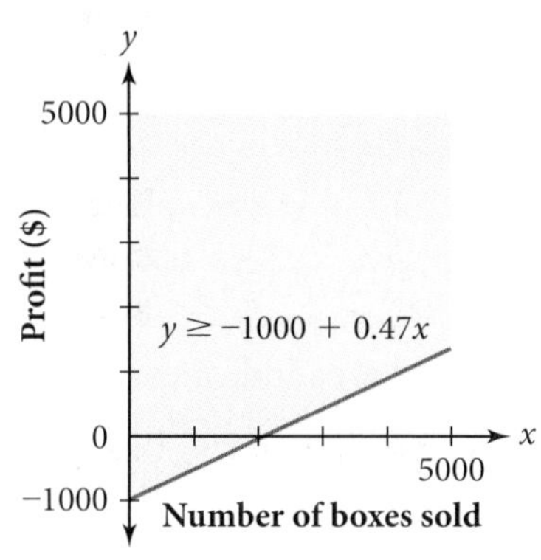

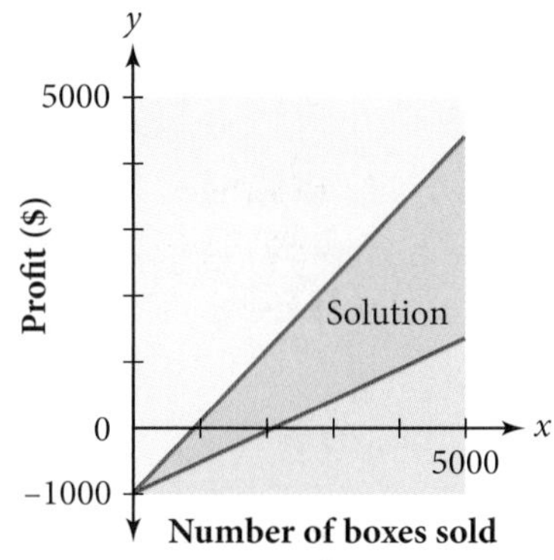

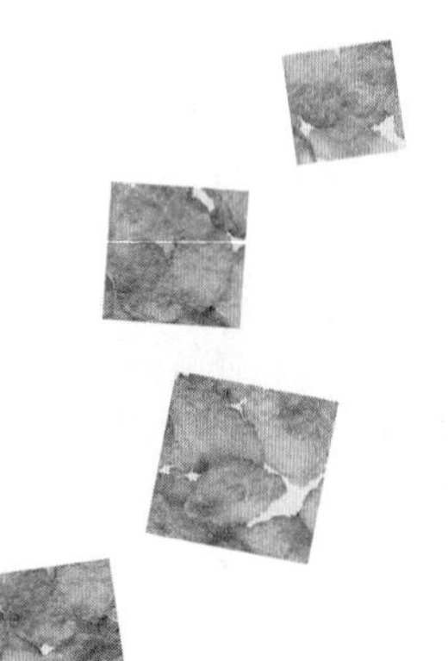

c. To see if it is possible to make a profit of \$1,000 when 3000 boxes are sold, plot the point (3000, 1000) on the graph in part b. The point is in the solution region, so the coordinates satisfy both inequalities.

You can also substitute 3000 for x and 1000 for y in the inequalities and see if you get true statements.

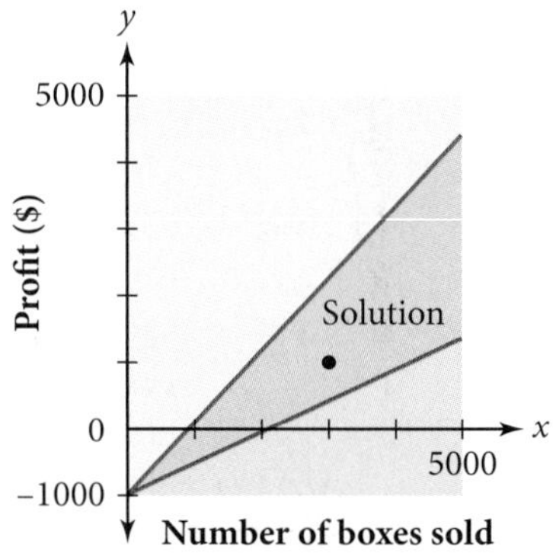

$$y \geq -1000 + 0.47x \qquad y \leq -1000 + 1.1x$$
$$1000 \geq -1000 + 0.47(3000) \quad \text{and} \quad 1000 \leq -1000 + 1.1(3000)$$
$$1000 \geq 410 \qquad 1000 \leq 2300$$

Both inequalities are true, so it is possible to sell 3000 boxes and make \$1,000.

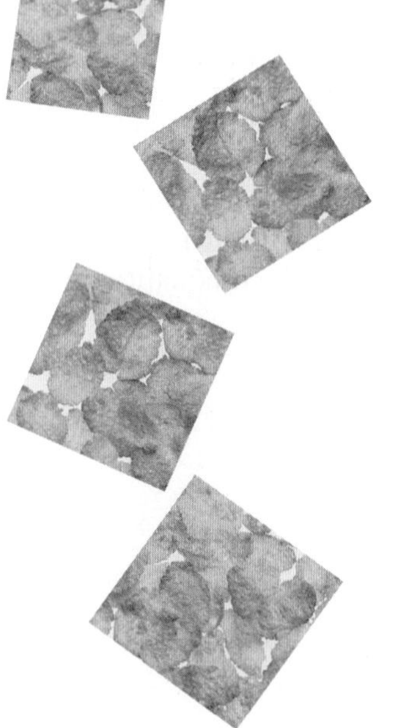

With enough constraints the solution to a system of inequalities might resemble a geometric shape or polygon. No matter how small the region, there are infinitely many points that satisfy the system. However, in some situations, only **discrete solutions** are possible. In Example B, it is not possible to sell partial boxes of cereal, so the solution is actually all points in the region with whole-number x-coordinates. In every situation, think carefully about what values in the solution make sense.

5.7 Exercises

You will need your graphing calculator for Exercise **11.**

Practice Your Skills

1. Match each system of inequalities to its graph.

a. $\begin{cases} y < 3 \\ x \geq 2 \end{cases}$

b. $\begin{cases} y > 2 + x \\ y > 1 - x \end{cases}$

c. $\begin{cases} 2x - y \leq 6 \\ 3x + 2y \geq 12 \end{cases}$

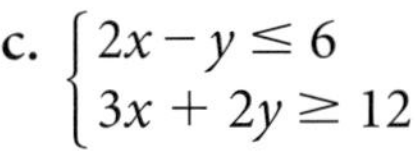

i.

ii.

iii.

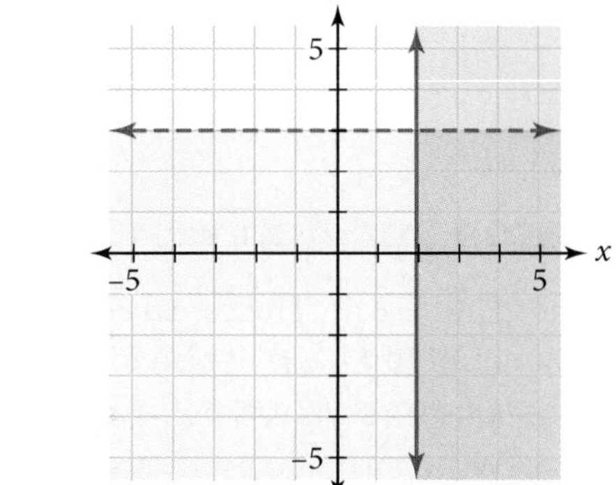

2. Here is the graph of this system of inequalities:

$$\begin{cases} y > x \\ y > 2 - \frac{1}{2}x \end{cases}$$

Is each point listed a solution to the system? Explain why or why not.

a. (1, 2) @

b. (3, 2)

c. $\left(\frac{4}{3}, \frac{4}{3}\right)$

d. (5, −3)

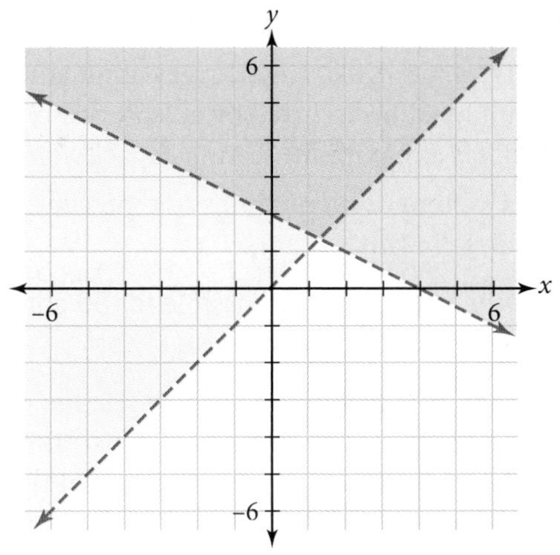

3. Consider these two inequalities together as a system.

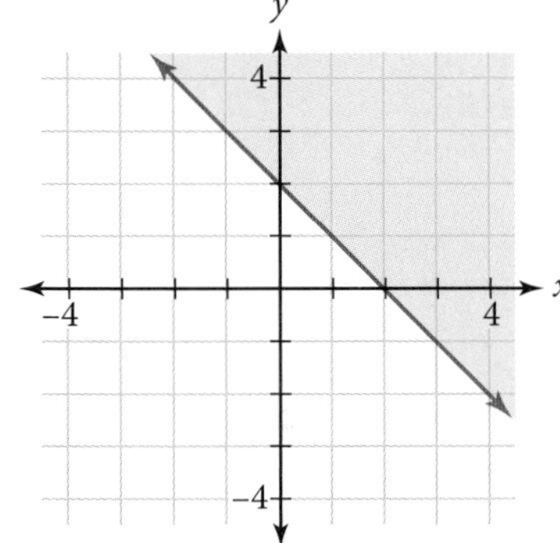

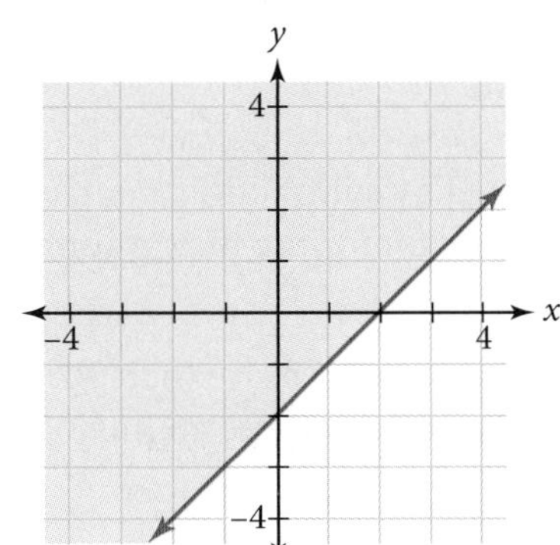

a. Name the inequality represented in each graph. @

b. Sketch a graph showing the solution to this system.

4. Graph each system of inequalities.

a. $\begin{cases} y \leq 2 \\ x < 2 \end{cases}$ b. $\begin{cases} x + y \leq 4 \\ x - y \leq 4 \end{cases}$ c. $\begin{cases} y < 3 \\ y \geq -1 \end{cases}$ d. $\begin{cases} x + y > 2 \\ x - y > 2 \end{cases}$

5. Write a system of inequalities for the solution shown on the graph. ⓗ

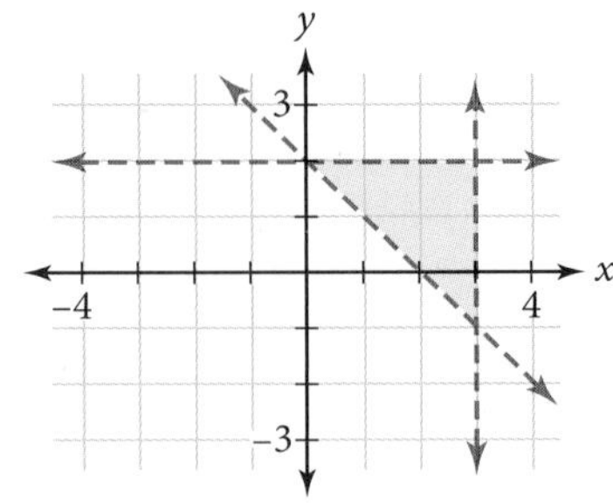

Reason and Apply

6. APPLICATION The cereal company from Example B decides to raise the scholarship amount to $1,250. It also lowers the cereal's pricing so that the expected profit from a single box is between $0.40 and $1.00.

a. Write inequalities to represent this new situation. ⓐ

b. Graph the expected profit for up to 5000 boxes sold in a month. ⓐ

7. APPLICATION On Kids' Night, every adult admitted into a restaurant must be escorted by at least one child. The restaurant has a maximum seating capacity of 75 people.

a. Write a system of inequalities to represent the constraints in this situation. ⓐ

b. Graph the solution. Is it possible for 50 children to escort 10 adults into the restaurant?

c. Why might the restaurant reconsider the rules for Kids' Night? Add a new constraint to address these concerns. Draw a graph of the new solution.

8. APPLICATION The American College of Sports Medicine considers age as one factor when it recommends low and high heart rates during workout sessions.

a. The safest maximum heart rate is calculated by subtracting a person's age from 220 beats per minute. Write an expression for the maximum heart rate in terms of age, a.

b. The heart rate during a workout, r, should reach no more than 90% of the maximum rate. Use your expression from 8a to write an inequality expressing this statement.

Heart rate

Age

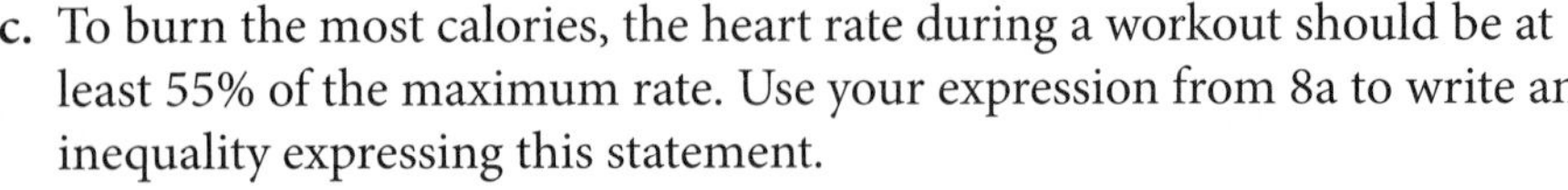

c. To burn the most calories, the heart rate during a workout should be at least 55% of the maximum rate. Use your expression from 8a to write an inequality expressing this statement.

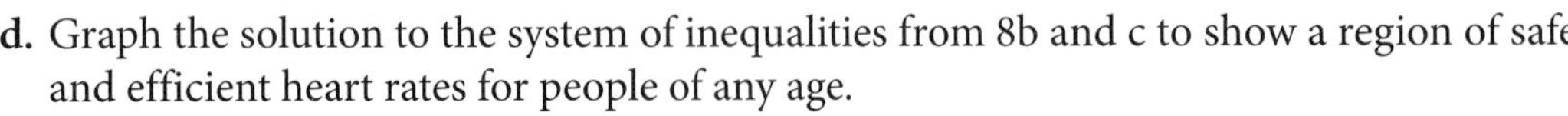

d. Graph the solution to the system of inequalities from 8b and c to show a region of safe and efficient heart rates for people of any age.

e. If you are 20 years old, is a heart rate of 185 recommended?

9. Write two inequalities that describe the shaded area below. Assume that the boundaries are solid lines and that each grid mark represents 1 unit.

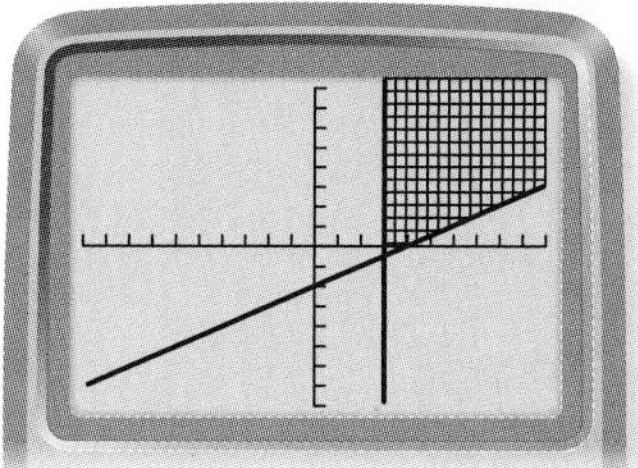

10. Write a system of inequalities to describe the shaded area on the graph. Write each slope as a fraction. (h)

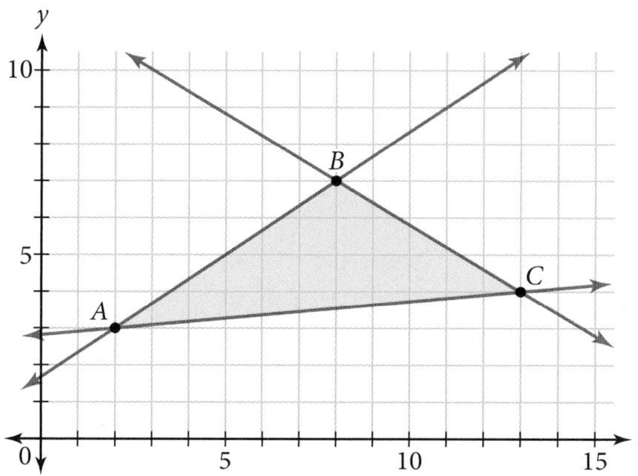

11. Graph this system of inequalities on the same set of axes. Describe the shape of the solution region.

$$\begin{cases} y \leq 4 + \frac{2}{3}(x-1) \\ y \leq 6 - \frac{2}{3}(x-4) \\ y \geq -17 + 3x \\ y \geq 1 \\ y \geq 7 - 3x \end{cases}$$

12. Write a system of inequalities that defines each shaded region of parallelogram *ABCD* in the graph. (h)

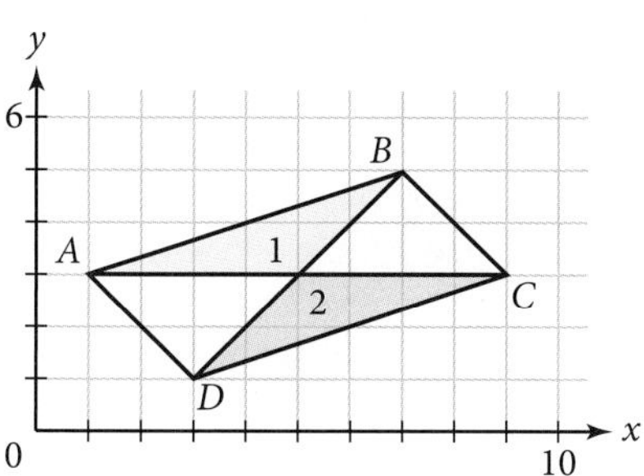

Review

13. APPLICATION Manuel has a sales job at a local furniture store. Once a year, on Founders' Day, every item in the store is 15% off regular price. In addition, salespeople earn a 25% commission on the items they sell as a bonus.

a. A loft bed with a built-in desk and closet usually costs $839. What will it cost on Founders' Day?

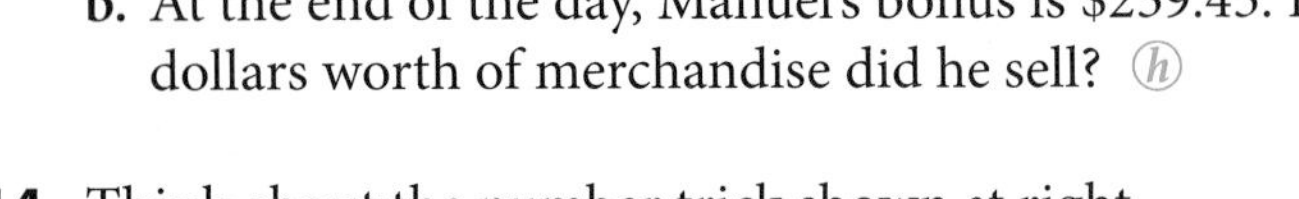

b. At the end of the day, Manuel's bonus is $239.45. How many dollars worth of merchandise did he sell?

14. Think about the number trick shown at right.

a. Layla got the final number 4. What was her original number?

b. Robert got the final answer 10. What was his original number?

c. Let x represent the starting number. Write an algebraic expression to represent this sequence of operations. Then simplify the expression as much as possible.

x	______
Ans · 3	______
Ans + 12	______
Ans / 5	______
Ans − 1.4	______
Ans · 10	______
Ans − 10	______
Ans / 6	______

15. Solve each system of equations by using a symbolic method. Check that your solution is correct.

a. $\begin{cases} f(x) = 4x - 3 \\ f(x) = 2x + 9 \end{cases}$

b. $\begin{cases} 3x - 4y = -2 \\ -2x + 3y = 1 \end{cases}$

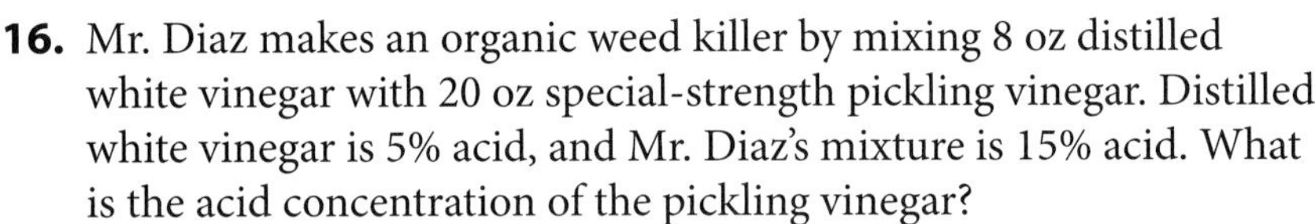

16. Mr. Diaz makes an organic weed killer by mixing 8 oz distilled white vinegar with 20 oz special-strength pickling vinegar. Distilled white vinegar is 5% acid, and Mr. Diaz's mixture is 15% acid. What is the acid concentration of the pickling vinegar?

IMPROVING YOUR Reasoning SKILLS

Suppose 9 crows each make 9 caws 9 times throughout the day. How many total caws are there?

Suppose 99 crows make 99 caws 99 separate times in one day. Now how many caws are there?

Answer the question again for 999 crows making 999 caws 999 times. If you continue this pattern of problems, at what number does your calculator round the answer? What is the exact number of caws in this case?

Write the answers to the first three questions and look for a pattern. Use the pattern to find how many caws there are when the number is 99,999.

CHAPTER  5 REVIEW

In this chapter you learned to model many situations with a **system of equations** in two variables. You learned that systems of linear equations can have zero, one, or infinitely many solutions. You used tables, used graphs, and solved symbolically to find the solutions to systems. You discovered that the methods of **elimination** and **substitution** allow you to find exact solutions to problems, not just the approximations given by graphs and tables. You also learned how to identify **parallel lines** and **perpendicular lines** from the relationship between their slopes.

Then you analyzed situations involving **inequalities** and discovered how to find their solutions using graphs, tables, and symbolic manipulation. The graph of an inequality in one variable is a part of a number line, and the graph of a linear inequality in two variables is a shaded **half-plane** that contains points whose coordinates make the inequality true. A **compound inequality** is the combination of two inequalities.

You discovered how to use inequalities to define **constraints** that limit the solution possibilities in real-world applications. You learned how to graph a **system of inequalities.**

Exercises

@ **Answers are provided for all exercises in this set.**

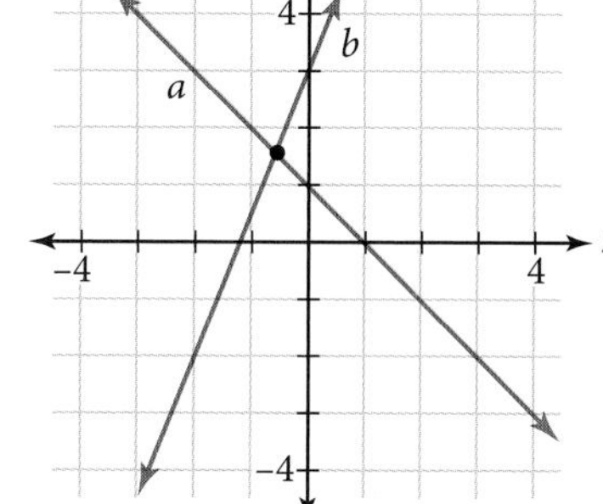

1. Lines a and b at right form a system of equations. Write the equations of the lines and find the exact point of intersection.

2. Find the point where the graphs of the equations intersect. Check your answer.

$$\begin{cases} 3x - 2y = 10 \\ x + 2y = 6 \end{cases}$$

3. Graph this system of equations, and find the solution point.

$$\begin{cases} y = 5 - 0.5(x - 3) \\ y = -4 + 1.5(x + 2) \end{cases}$$

4. Show the steps involved in solving this system symbolically by the substitution method. Justify each step.

$$\begin{cases} y = 16 + 4.3(x - 5) \\ y = -7 + 4.2x \end{cases}$$

5. Complete each sentence.

a. A system of two linear equations has no solution if . . .

b. A system of two linear equations has infinitely many solutions if . . .

c. A system of two linear equations has exactly one solution if . . .

6. Write the inequality that each graph represents.

a. 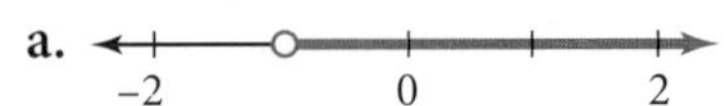

b. 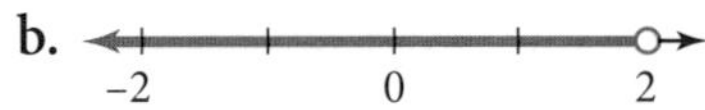

c. 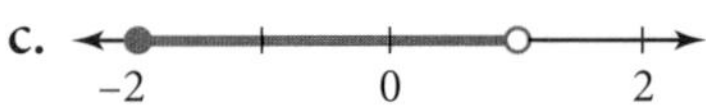

7. Solve the inequality $5 \leq 2 - 3x$ for x, and graph the solution on a number line.

8. Write a system of inequalities to describe the shaded area on the graph.

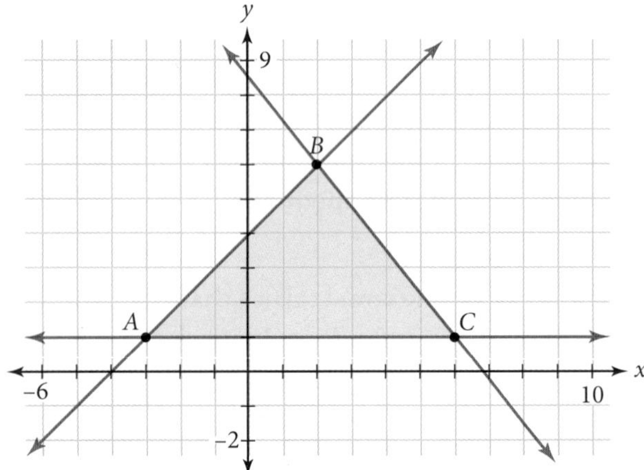

9. APPLICATION Harold cuts lawns after school. He has a problem on Wednesdays when he cuts Mr. Fleming's lawn. His lawn mower has two speeds—at the higher speed he can get the job done quickly, but he always runs out of gas; at the lower speed he has plenty of gas, but it seems to take forever to get the job done. So he has collected this information.

- On Monday he cut a 15-meter-by-12-meter lawn at the higher speed in 18 minutes. He used a half tank of gas, or 0.6 liter.
- On Tuesday he cut a 20-meter-by-14-meter lawn at the lower speed in 40 minutes. He used a half tank of gas.
- Mr. Fleming's lawn measures 22 meters by 18 meters.

a. How many square meters of lawn can Harold cut per minute at the higher speed? At the lower speed?

b. If Harold decides to cut Mr. Fleming's lawn using the higher speed for 10 minutes and the lower speed for 8 minutes, will he finish the job?

c. Let h represent the number of minutes cutting at higher speed, and let l represent the number of minutes cutting at lower speed. Write an equation that models completion of Mr. Fleming's lawn.

d. How much gas does the lawn mower use in liters per minute at the higher speed? At the lower speed?

e. Write an equation in terms of h and l that has Harold use all of his gas.

f. Using the equations from 9c and e, solve the system and give a real-world meaning of the solution.

10. Use these three equations to answer the questions.

i. $2x - 3y = 8$ ii. $3x + 2y = 7$ iii. $y = \frac{2}{3}x - 6$

a. Which lines are parallel?

b. Which lines are perpendicular?

c. Write an equation of the line parallel to line **iii.** through the point (4, 7).

d. Write an equation of the line perpendicular to line **iii.** through the point (7, 11).

Take Another Look

Businesses use systems of equations and inequalities to determine how to maximize profits. A process called **linear programming** applies the concepts of constraints, points of intersection, and algebraic expressions to solve this very real application problem. Here is one example.

A company manufactures scooters and skateboards. The factory has the capacity to make at most 6000 scooters in one day, and the factory can make at most 8000 skateboards in one day. However, the factory can produce a combination of no more than 10,000 scooters and skateboards together. Define variables and write a system of three inequalities to describe these constraints. Label a set of axes and graph the solution. This is called a **feasible region.** What do the points in this shaded region represent? Find the points of intersection at the corners of this region.

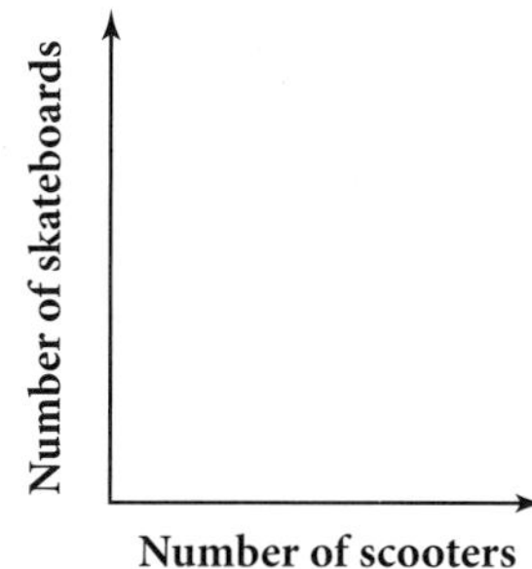

The company makes a profit of \$15 per scooter and \$10 per skateboard. How many of each should the company make to maximize its profits? To answer this question, use the variables defined earlier to write an expression representing the total profit the company makes from scooters and skateboards. Then substitute the coordinates of several points from the feasible region into this expression, including the points of intersection. For example, if the company makes 5000 scooters and 5000 skateboards, substitute 5000 for x and 5000 for y in your expression to find the profit. Which point gives the greatest profit?

Assessing What You've Learned

In each of the five chapters from Chapter 0 to Chapter 4, you were introduced to a different way to assess what you learned. Maybe you have tried all five ways—keeping a portfolio, writing in your journal, organizing your notebook, giving a presentation, and doing a performance assessment. Maybe you have tried just a couple of these methods. Your teacher has probably adapted these ideas to suit the needs of your class.

By now you should realize that assessment is not just giving and taking tests. In the working world, performance in some occupations can be measured in tests, but in all occupations there is a need to communicate what you know to coworkers. In all jobs, workers demonstrate to their employer or to their clients, patients, or customers that they are skilled in their field. They need to show they are creative and flexible enough to apply what they've learned in new situations. Assessing your own understanding and letting others assess what you know gives you practice in this important life skill. It also helps you develop good study habits, and that, in turn, will help you advance in school and give you the best possible opportunities in your work life. Keep that in mind as you try one or more of these suggestions.

UPDATE YOUR PORTFOLIO Choose your best graph of a system of inequalities from this chapter to add to your portfolio. Redraw the graph with a clearly labeled set of axes. Use color to highlight each inequality and its half-plane. Indicate the solution region with a visually pleasing design or pattern.

WRITE IN YOUR JOURNAL Add to your journal by answering one of these prompts:

- You have learned five methods to find a solution to a system of equations. Which method do you like best? Which one is the most challenging to you? What are the advantages and disadvantages of each method?
- Describe in writing the difference between an inequality in one variable and an inequality in two variables. How do the graphs of the solutions differ? Compare these to the graph of a system of inequalities.

ORGANIZE YOUR NOTEBOOK Update your notebook with an example, investigation, or exercise that demonstrates each solution method for a system of equations. Add one problem that demonstrates each of these concepts: inequalities in one variable, inequalities in two variables, and systems of inequalities.

GIVE A PRESENTATION Write your own word problem for a system of equations or inequalities. Choose a setting that is meaningful to you or that you wish to know more about, and write a problem to model the situation. It can be about winning times for Olympic events, the point where two objects meet while traveling, percent mixture, or something new you create. Solve the problem using one of the methods you learned in this chapter. Make a poster of the problem and its solution, and present it to the class. Work with a partner or in a group.

PERFORMANCE ASSESSMENT As a classmate, family member, or teacher watches, solve a system of equations using at least two different methods. Explain your process, and show how to check your solution.

CHAPTER 6

Exponents and Exponential Models

This "Chinese Horse" is part of a prehistoric cave painting in Lascaux, France. Scientific methods that use equations with exponents have determined that parts of the Lascaux cave paintings are more than 15,000 years old. For archaeologists, dating ancient artifacts helps them understand how civilizations evolved. Drawings and pieces of art help them understand what existed at that time and what was important to the civilization. You will see that exponents are useful in many other real-world settings too.

OBJECTIVES

In this chapter you will

- write recursive rules for nonlinear sequences
- learn an equation for exponential growth or decrease
- use properties of exponents to rewrite expressions
- write numbers in scientific notation
- model real-world data with exponential equations

CHAPTER 6 REFRESHING YOUR SKILLS

Percents and Decimals

"Fifty-eight percent of the students in our school have their own computer." "Sales of cell phones in our town increased by 18% this year." "Everything in the store is 40% off the regular price." Statements like these using percents are very common. But how do you calculate with percents? In many cases, when you are solving a problem that involves percents, you'll find that the calculations are easier if you express a percent in the equivalent decimal form.

EXAMPLE A

Express each percent in decimal form.

a. 58%

b. 2.5%

c. $\frac{1}{4}\%$

d. 118%

e. 40%

Solution

The word *percent* means per hundred, so every percent can be written as a fraction with denominator 100: $n\% = \frac{n}{100}$. In other words, to change a percent to a decimal, you divide by 100. A quick way to divide by 100 is to move the decimal point two places to the left.

a. $58\% = \frac{58}{100} = 0.58$

b. $2.5\% = \frac{2.5}{100} = 0.025$

c. It is often easiest to first change the fraction to a decimal:

$$\frac{1}{4}\% = 0.25\% = \frac{0.25}{100} = 0.0025$$

d. Percents greater than 100 are equivalent to decimal values greater than 1.

$$118\% = \frac{118}{100} = 1.18$$

e. $40\% = \frac{40}{100} = 0.40$

In Lesson 2.2, you learned how to use a proportion with percents to find an unknown percent, an unknown total, or an unknown part. There is a different way to do the calculations. For example:

What is 27% of 80?

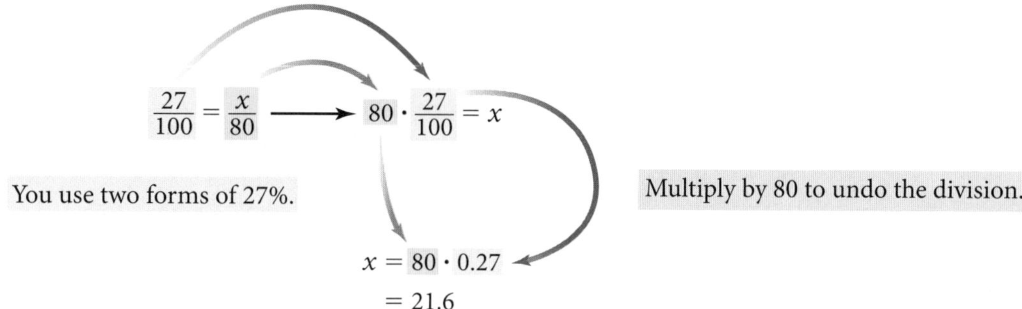

Calculating 27% of 80 is the same as multiplying the percent, in decimal form, by 80.

EXAMPLE B

There are 657 students in a school, and 58% of them have their own computer. How many students in the school have their own computer?

Solution

Using a proportion	Without writing a proportion
$\frac{58}{100} = \frac{x}{657}$	$x = 0.58 \cdot 657$
$x = \frac{58}{100} \cdot 657$	$x = 381.06$
$x \approx 381$ students	$x \approx 381$ students

You can summarize this process as follows: To find p% of a number, first express the percent as a decimal and then multiply by the number.

In this chapter you will use percent increases and decreases to help you discover and understand how to work with exponents.

EXAMPLE C

Express each percent change as a decimal.

a. 18% increase

b. 40% decrease

Solution

a. In each part, you start with 100% of something, or 1. Increasing by 18% is the same as adding 18% to what you started with. You can express the result as

$$1 + \frac{18}{100} = \frac{100}{100} + \frac{18}{100} = \frac{118}{100} = 1.18.$$

You can write this number as $(1 + 0.18)$ to emphasize that the 18% is an increase.

b. Decreasing by 40% is the same as subtracting 40% from what you started with. You can express the result as

$$1 - \frac{40}{100} = \frac{100}{100} - \frac{40}{100} = \frac{60}{100} = 0.60.$$

Again, you can write this number as $(1 - 0.40)$ to emphasize that the 40% is a decrease.

Exercises

1. Express each percent as a decimal.

a. 79%

b. 3.15%

c. $2\frac{3}{4}\%$

d. 283%

2. The table gives some information about the 850 students at City High School.

Percent who study French	Percent who ride the bus to school	Percent who are sophomores
12%	88%	27%

a. How many students study French?

b. How many students ride the bus to school?

c. How many students are *not* sophomores?

3. Express each percent change as an expression in the form $(1 + p)$ or $(1 - p)$, such as $(1 + 0.18)$ or $(1 - 0.40)$. Then simplify to get a decimal such as 1.18 or 0.60.

a. Unemployment increased by 25%.

b. The price of a car decreased by 7%.

c. The population of a city increased by 4%.

d. The value of a boat decreased by 29%.

LESSON

6.1

Multiplicative Recursion

"Slow buds the pink
dawn like a rose
From out night's gray
and cloudy sheath
Softly and still it
grows and grows
Petal by petal, leaf
by leaf"
SUSAN COOLIDGE

Have you ever noticed that it doesn't take very long for a cup of steaming hot chocolate to cool to sipping temperature? If so, then you may have also noticed that it stays about the same temperature for a long time. Have you ever left food in your locker? It might look fine for several days, and then suddenly some mold appears and a few days later it's covered with mold. The same mathematical principle describes both of these situations. Yet these patterns are different from the linear patterns you saw in rising elevators and shortening ropes—situations you modeled with repeated addition or subtraction. Now you'll investigate a different type of pattern, a pattern seen in a population that increases very rapidly.

INVESTIGATION

YOU WILL NEED
- graph paper

Bugs, Bugs, Everywhere Bugs

Imagine that a bug population has invaded your classroom. One day you notice 16 bugs. Every day new bugs hatch, increasing the population by 50% each week. So in the first week the population increases by 8 bugs.

Step 1 In a table like this one, record the total number of bugs at the end of each week for 4 weeks.

Bug Invasion

Weeks elapsed	Total number of bugs	Increase in number of bugs (rate of change per week)	Ratio of this week's total to last week's total
Start (0)	16		
1	24	8	$\frac{24}{16} = \frac{3}{2} = 1.5$
2			

Step 2 The increase in the number of bugs each week is the population's rate of change per week. Calculate each rate of change, and record it in your table. Does the rate of change show a linear pattern? Why or why not?

Step 3 Let x represent the number of weeks elapsed, and let y represent the total number of bugs. Graph the data using (0, 16) for the first point. Connect the points with line segments, and describe how the slope changes from point to point.

Step 4 Calculate the ratio of the number of bugs each week to the number of bugs the previous week, and record it in the table. See the entry in the last column for week 1. Repeat this process to complete your table. How do these ratios compare? Explain what the ratios tell you about the bug population growth.

Step 5 What is the **constant multiplier** for the bug population? How can you use this number to calculate the population when 5 weeks have elapsed?

Step 6 Model the population growth by writing a recursive rule that shows the growing number of bugs. [► See **Calculator Note: Recursion on a List** to review recursive rules. ◄] Describe what each part of this calculator command does.

Step 7 By pressing ENTER a few times, check that your recursive rule gives the sequence of values in your table (in the column "Total number of bugs"). Use the rule to find the bug population at the end of weeks 5 to 8.

Step 8 What is the bug population after 20 weeks have elapsed? After 30 weeks have elapsed? What happens in the long run?

In the investigation you found that repeated multiplication is the key to the growth of the bug population. Populations of people, animals, and even bacteria have similar growth patterns. Many decreasing patterns, such as cooling liquids and decay of substances, can also be described with repeated multiplication.

EXAMPLE A

Maria has saved $10,000 and wants to invest it for her daughter's college tuition. She is considering two options. Plan A guarantees a payment, or return, of $550 each year. Plan B grows by 5% each year. With each plan, what would Maria's new balance be after 5 years? After 10 years?

Solution

With plan A, Maria's investment would grow by $550 each year.

next balance = *current balance* + $550

With plan B, her investment grows by 5% each year. It grows because her money earns 5% *interest* each year.

next balance = *current balance* + *current balance* · 0.05

The next year's balance will be 105% of the current balance. The constant multiplier is 1.05, (1 + 0.05).

next balance = *current balance* · 1.05

You can use a table to compare the balance generated by each plan over time.

Year	Plan A (balance A + 550)	Balance A	Plan B (balance B · 1.05)	Balance B
0		\$10,000		\$10,000
1	10,000 + 550	10,550	10,000 · 1.05	10,500
2	10,550 + 550	11,100	10,500 · 1.05	11,025
3	11,100 + 550	11,650	11,025 · 1.05	11,576.25
⋮	⋮	⋮	⋮	⋮
5	12,200 + 550	12,750	12,155.06 · 1.05	≈ 12,762.82
⋮	⋮	⋮	⋮	⋮
10	14,950 + 550	15,500	15,513.28 · 1.05	≈ 16,288.95

Although initially the amounts for plan B (fifth column) are less than those for plan A (third column), eventually the growth involving a constant multiplier or percent is much greater than the growth achieved by adding a constant amount because each year you're finding a percent of a larger current balance than in the previous year.

You can generate the sequence of balances from year to year on some calculators using this recursive rule:

{0, 10000} ENTER

{Ans(1)+1, Ans(2) · (1.05)} ENTER

ENTER, ENTER, . . .

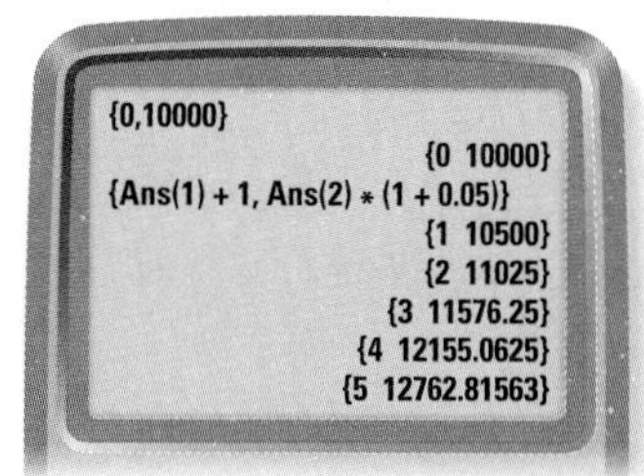

A graph illustrates how the investment plans compare. Given enough time, the balance from plan B, which is growing by a constant percent, will always outgrow the balance from plan A, which has only a constant amount added to it. After 20 years you see an even more significant difference: \$26,533 compared to \$21,000.

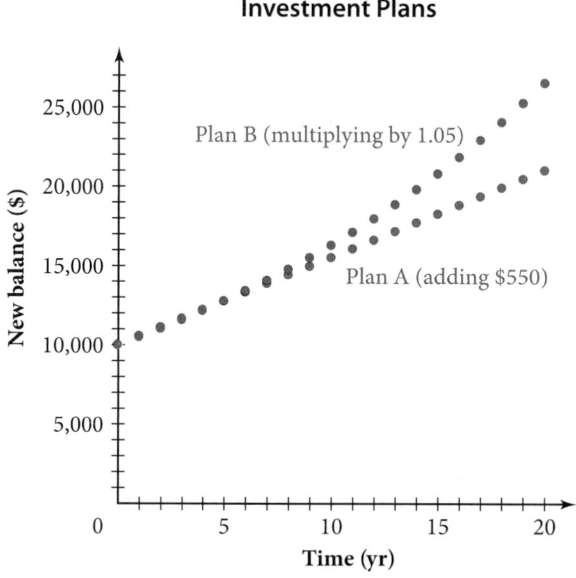

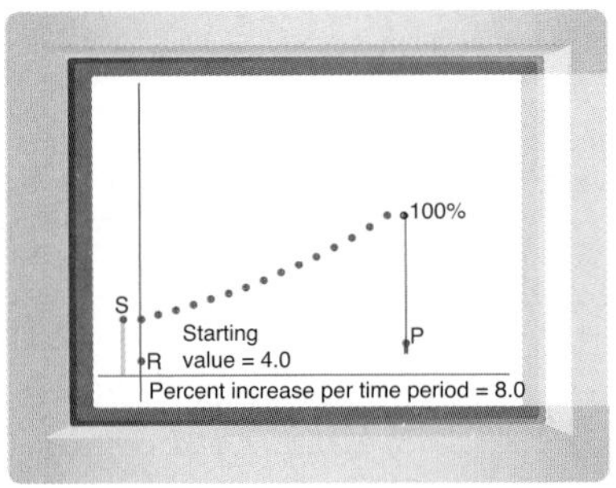

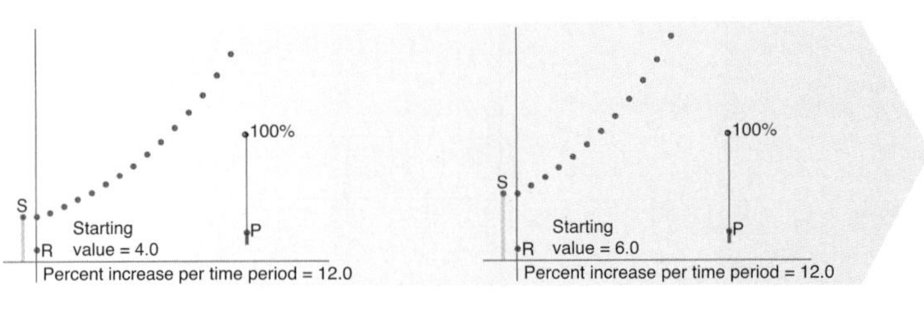

[► The graphs of growth defined by repeated multiplication share certain characteristics. You can use the **Dynamic Algebra Exploration** in your ebook to explore these graphs and to solve some of the exercises in this lesson. ◄]

It is helpful to think of a constant multiplier, like 1.05 in Example A, as a sum. The plus sign in $1 + 0.05$ shows that the pattern increases and 0.05 is the percent growth per year, written as a decimal. When a balance or population decreases, say by 15% during a given time period, you write the constant multiplier as a difference, for example, $1 - 0.15$. The subtraction sign shows that the pattern decreases and 0.15 is the percent decrease per time period, written as a decimal.

Example B uses a constant multiplier to calculate a marked-down price.

EXAMPLE B

Birdbaths at the Feathered Friends store are marked down 35%. What is the cost of a birdbath that was originally priced at $39.99? What is the cost if the birdbath is marked down 35% a second time?

Solution

If an item is marked down 35%, then it must retain $(100 - 35)$ percent of its original price. So you can solve this problem by using the constant multiplier $(1 - 0.35)$.

Starting value is $39.99.

$$39.99(1 - 0.35) \approx 25.99$$

$$25.99(1 - 0.35) \approx 16.90$$

So the cost after two successive markdowns is $16.90. Is this a different cost than if the birdbath had been marked down 70% one time?

EXAMPLE C

Give the starting value and constant multiplier for this sequence. Then find the 10th term of the sequence.

$$3, -4.5, 6.75, -10.125, 15.1875, \ldots$$

Solution

The first term, or starting value, is 3.

Find the ratio between successive terms to find the constant multiplier.

$$\frac{-4.5}{3} = -1.5 \qquad \frac{6.75}{-4.5} = -1.5 \qquad \frac{-10.125}{6.75} = -1.5 \qquad \frac{15.1875}{-10.125} = -1.5$$

You can use a recursive rule to find the 10th term.

3 ENTER

Ans · (−1.5) ENTER

ENTER, ENTER . . .

The 10th term is approximately −115.33.

Constant Multipliers

To increase a value by $n\%$:

$$\textit{next value} = \textit{current value} \cdot \left(1 + \frac{n}{100}\right)$$

To decrease a value by $n\%$:

$$\textit{next value} = \textit{current value} \cdot \left(1 - \frac{n}{100}\right)$$

6.1 Exercises

You will need your graphing calculator for Exercises **7** and **9.**

Practice Your Skills

1. Give the starting value and constant multiplier for each sequence. Then find the 7th term of the sequence.

a. 16, 20, 25, 31.25, . . . (@)

b. 27, 18, 12, 8, . . .

c. 1, 2, 4, 8, . . .

d. 1, 0.1, 0.01, 0.001, . . .

e. 4.2, −14.7, 51.45, −180.075, . . .

f. ______, 2187, 729, 243, 81, . . .

2. Use a recursive rule to find the first six terms of each sequence.

a. Starts with 100 and has constant multiplier −1.6

b. Starts with 620 and has constant multiplier $\frac{1}{2}$

3. Write each percent change as a ratio comparing the result to the original quantity. For example, a 3% increase is $\frac{103}{100}$. Then write it as a constant multiplier, for example, $1 + 0.03$.

a. 8% increase

b. 11% decrease

c. 12.5% growth (@)

d. $6\frac{1}{4}\%$ loss (@)

e. $x\%$ increase

f. $y\%$ decrease

4. Use the distributive property to rewrite each expression in an equivalent form. For example, you can write $500(1 + 0.05)$ as $500 + 500(0.05)$.

a. $75 + 75(0.02)$

b. $1000 - 1000(0.18)$ (@)

c. $P + Pr$ (@)

d. $75(1 - 0.02)$

e. $80(1 - 0.24)$

f. $A(1 - r)$

5. You may remember from Chapter 0 that the geometric pattern shown is the beginning of a fractal called the *Sierpiński triangle*. Write a recursive rule that generates the sequence of shaded areas. Then use your rule to find the shaded area in Stage 5. (h)

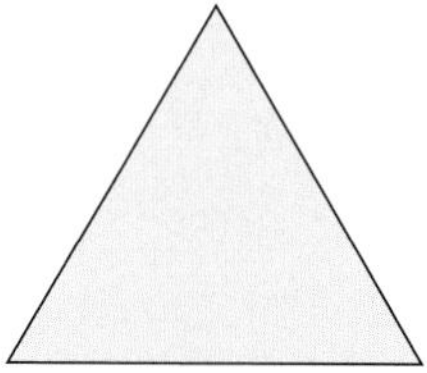

Stage 0
Area = 32 square units

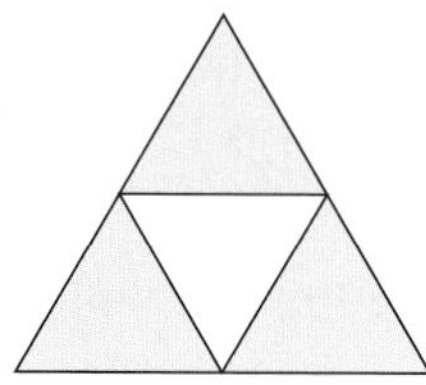

Stage 1
Area = 24 square units

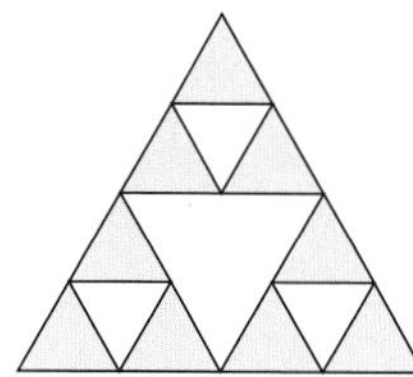

Stage 2
Area = 18 square units

Reason and Apply

6. APPLICATION Toward the end of the year, to make room for next year's models, a car dealer may decide to drop prices on this year's models. Imagine a car that has a sticker price of $20,000. The dealer lowers the price by 4% each week until the car sells.

a. Write a recursive rule to generate the sequence of decreasing prices. @

b. Find the 5th term and explain what your answer means in this situation. @

c. If the dealer paid $10,000 for the car, how many weeks would pass before the car's sale price would produce no profit for the dealer?

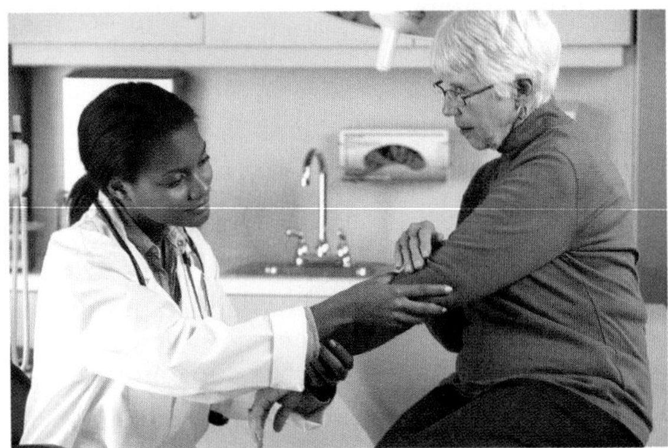

7. APPLICATION Health care expenditures in the United States exceeded $1 trillion in the mid-1990s and exceeded $2 trillion in 2005. Many elderly and disabled persons rely on Medicare benefits to help cover health care costs. According to the Centers for Medicare and Medicaid *2005 Annual Report,* Medicare expenditures were $7.1 billion in 1970.

a. Assume Medicare spending has increased by 11.7% per year since 1970. Write a recursive rule to generate the sequence of increasing Medicare spending. @

b. Use your recursive rule to find the missing table values. Round to the nearest $0.1 billion.

Medicare Spending

Year	1970	1975	1980	1985	1990	1995	2000	2005
Elapsed time (yr) x	0	5	10	15	20	25	30	35
Spending ($ billion) y	7.1							

c. Plot the data points from your table and draw a smooth curve through them.

d. What does the shape of the curve suggest about Medicare spending? Do you think this is a realistic model?

8. APPLICATION Ima Shivring took a cup of hot cocoa outdoors where the temperature was 0°F. When she stepped outside, the temperature of the cocoa was 115°F. The temperature in the cup dropped by 3% each minute.

a. Write a recursive rule to generate the sequence representing the temperature of the cocoa each minute.

b. How many minutes does it take for the cocoa to cool to less than 80°F?

9. APPLICATION The advertisement for a Super-Duper Bouncing Ball says it rebounds to 85% of the height from which it is dropped.

a. If the ball is dropped from a starting height of 2 m, how high should it rebound on the first bounce? ⓐ

b. Write a recursive rule to generate the sequence of heights for the ball when it is dropped from a height of 2 m. ⓐ

c. How high should the ball rebound on the sixth bounce?

d. If the ball is dropped from a height of 10 ft, how high should it rebound on the tenth bounce? ⓗ

e. When the ball is dropped from a height of 10 ft, how many times will it bounce before the rebound height is less than 0.5 ft?

f. A collection of Super-Duper Bouncing Balls was tested. Each ball was dropped from a height of 2 m. The table shows the height of the first rebound for eight different balls. Do you think the advertisement's claim that the ball rebounds to 85% of its original height is accurate? Explain your thinking.

Balls Dropped from 2 m

Ball number	1	2	3	4	5	6	7	8
Height of rebound (m)	1.68	1.67	1.69	1.78	1.64	1.68	1.66	1.8

10. Look back at the six expressions in Exercise 4. Imagine that each expression represents the value of an antique that is increasing or decreasing in value each year. For each expression, identify whether it represents an increasing or decreasing situation, give the starting value, and give the percent increase or decrease per year. ⓗ

11. Grace manages a local charity. A wealthy benefactor has offered two options for making a donation over the next year. One option is to give $50 now and $25 each month after that. The second option is to give $1 now and twice that amount next month; each month afterward the benefactor would give twice the amount given the month before.

a. Determine how much Grace's charity would receive each month under each option. Use a table to show the values over the course of one year. ⓐ

b. Use another table to record the total amount Grace's charity will have received after each month.

c. Let x represent the number of the month (1 to 12), and let y represent the total amount Grace will have received after each month. On the same coordinate axes, graph the data for both options. How do the graphs compare?

d. Which option should Grace choose? Why?

12. APPLICATION Tamara works at a bookstore, where she earns \$7.50 per hour.

a. Her employer is pleased with her work and gives her a 3.5% raise. What is her new hourly rate?

b. A few weeks later business drops off dramatically. The employer must reduce wages. He decreases Tamara's latest wage by 3.5%. What is her hourly rate now?

c. What is the final result of the two pay changes? Explain. (h)

Review

13. Write an equation in point-slope form for a line with slope -1.2 that passes through the point $(600, 0)$. Find the y-intercept.

14. Find the equation of the line that passes through $(2.2, 4.7)$ and $(6.8, -3.9)$.

15. Match the recursive rule to the equation.

a. $y = 3x + 7$	i. Start with 7, and then apply the rule Ans + 3.
b. $y = -3x + 7$	ii. Start with 3, and then apply the rule Ans + 7.
c. $y = 7x + 3$	iii. Start with 7, and then apply the rule Ans − 3.
d. $y = -7x + 3$	iv. Start with 3, and then apply the rule Ans − 7.

16. APPLICATION A wireless phone service provider offers two calling plans. The first plan costs \$50 per month and offers 500 minutes free per month; additional minutes cost 35¢ per minute. The second plan costs only \$45 a month and offers 600 minutes free per month; but additional minutes cost more—55¢ per minute.

a. Define variables and write an equation for the first plan if you use it for 500 minutes or less. (a)

b. Write an equation for the first plan if you use it for more than 500 minutes. (a)

c. Write two equations for the second plan similar to those you wrote in 15a and b. Explain what each equation represents.

d. Sydney generally talks on her phone about 550 minutes per month. How much would each plan cost her? Which plan should she choose? (a)

e. Louis averages 850 minutes of phone use per month. How much would each plan cost him? Which plan should he choose?

f. For how many minutes of use will the cost of the plans be the same? How can you decide which of these two wireless plans is better for a new subscriber? (a)

LESSON

6.2

Exponential Equations

Recursive rules are useful for seeing how a sequence develops and for generating the first few terms. But, as you learned in Chapter 3, if you're looking for the 50th term you'll have to do many calculations to find your answer. For most of the sequences in Chapter 3, you found that the graphs of the points formed a linear pattern, so you learned how to write the equation of a line.

Recursive rules with a constant multiplier create a different type of increasing or decreasing pattern. In this lesson you'll discover a connection between these recursive rules and exponents. Then, with a new type of equation, you'll be able to find any term in a sequence generated by a constant multiplier without having to find all the terms before it.

The exponential growth pattern of the chambers in a chambered nautilus was first described by French philosopher and mathematician René Descartes in the early 1600s and later extensively investigated by Swiss mathematician Jacob Bernoulli.

INVESTIGATION

Growth of the Koch Curve

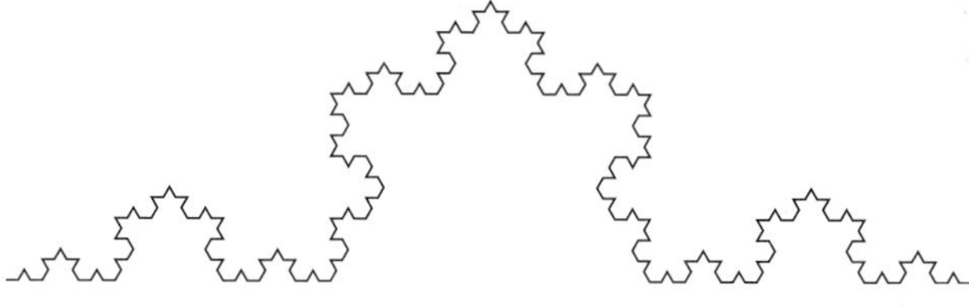

In this investigation you will look for patterns in the growth of a fractal. You may remember the *Koch curve* from Chapter 0. Here you will think about the relationship between the length of the Koch curve and the repeated multiplication you studied in Lesson 6.1. Stage 0 of the Koch curve is already drawn on the Investigation Worksheet. It is a segment 27 units long.

Step 1 Draw the Stage 1 figure below the Stage 0 figure. The first segment is drawn for you on the worksheet. As shown here, the Stage 1 figure has four segments, each $\frac{1}{3}$ the length of the Stage 0 segment.

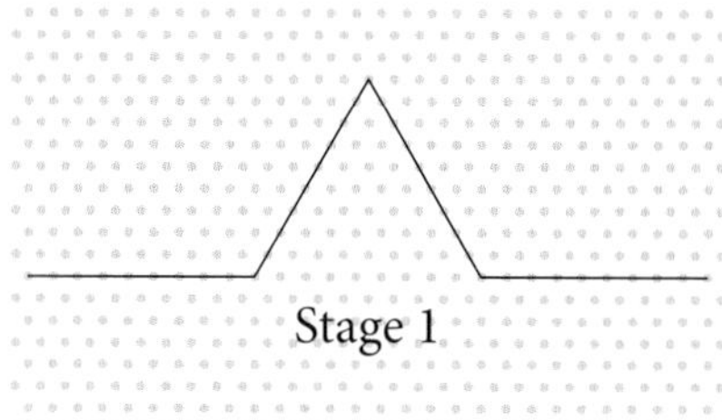

Step 2 Determine the total length at Stage 1, and record it in a table like this:

Stage number	Total length (units)
0	27
1	
2	
3	

Step 3 Draw the Stage 2 and Stage 3 figures of the fractal. Again, the first segment for each stage is drawn for you. Record the total length at each stage.

Step 4 Find the ratio of the total length at any stage to the total length at the previous stage. What is the constant multiplier?

Step 5 Use your constant multiplier from Step 4 to predict the total length of this fractal at Stages 4 and 5.

Step 6 How many times do you multiply the original length at Stage 0 by the constant multiplier to get the length at Stage 2? Write an expression that represents the length at Stage 2.

Step 7 How many times do you multiply the length at Stage 0 by the constant multiplier to get the length at Stage 3? Write an expression that represents the length at Stage 3.

Step 8 If your expressions in Steps 6 and 7 do not use exponents, rewrite them so that they do.

Step 9 Use an exponent to write an expression that predicts the total length of the Stage 5 figure. Evaluate this expression using your calculator. Is the result the same as you predicted in Step 5?

Step 10 Write an equation to model the total length of this fractal as a function of the stage number. Graph your equation and check that the calculator table contains the same values as your table.

Step 11 What does the graph tell you about the growth of the Koch curve?

A recursive rule that uses a constant multiplier represents a pattern that increases or decreases by a constant ratio or a constant percent. Because exponents are another way of writing repeated multiplication, you can use exponents to model these patterns. In the investigation you discovered how to calculate the length of the Koch curve at any stage by using this equation. Your equation probably looked like the one at the top of the next page.

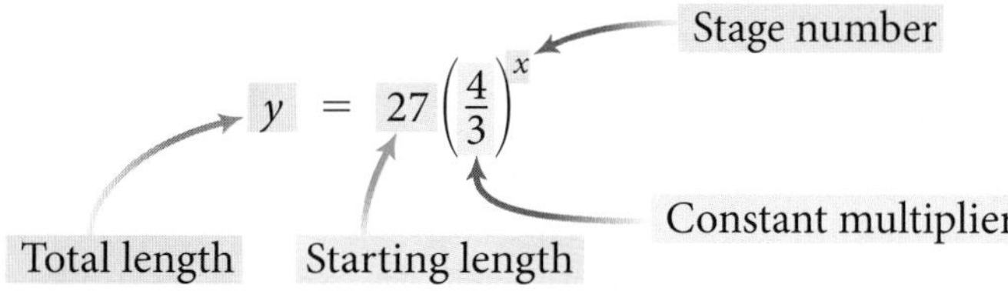

Equations like this are called **exponential equations** because a variable, in this case x, appears in the exponent. The standard form of an exponential equation is $y = a \cdot b^x$.

When you write out a repeated multiplication expression to show each factor, the expression is written in **expanded form.** When you show a repeated multiplication expression using an exponent, it is in **exponential form** and the factor being multiplied is called the **base.**

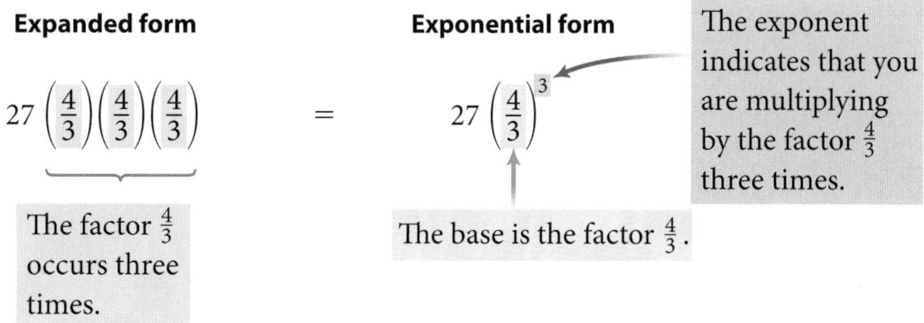

EXAMPLE A

Write each expression in exponential form.

a. (5)(5)(5)(5)(5)(5)

b. 3(3)(2)(2)(2)(2)(2)(2)(2)(2)(2)

c. the current balance of a savings account that was opened 7 years ago with \$200 earning 2.5% interest per year

Solution

The exponent tells how many times each base is used as a factor.

a. 5^6

b. The factor 3 occurs twice, and the factor 2 occurs nine times, so you write

$$3^2 \cdot 2^9$$

You can't combine 3^2 and 2^9 any further because the terms have different bases.

c. The factor $(1 + 0.025)$ will be multiplied seven times and will be multiplied by the starting value of \$200, so you write

$$200(1 + 0.025)^7$$

EXAMPLE B

Seth deposits \$200 in a savings account. The account pays 5% annual interest. Assuming that he makes no more deposits and no withdrawals, calculate Seth's account balance after 10 years.

Solution

The interest represents a 5% rate of growth per year, so the constant multiplier is $(1 + 0.05)$. Now find an equation that you can use to determine the new balance after any number of years by considering these yearly calculations and results:

	Expanded form	**Exponential form**	**New balance**
Starting balance:	\$200		$= \$200.00$
After 1 year:	$\$200(1 + 0.05)$	$= \$200(1 + 0.05)^1$	$= \$210.00$
After 2 years:	$\$200(1 + 0.05)(1 + 0.05)$	$= \$200(1 + 0.05)^2$	$= \$220.50$
After 3 years:	$\$200(1 + 0.05)(1 + 0.05)(1 + 0.05)$	$= \$200(1 + 0.05)^3$	$\approx \$231.53$
After x years:	$\$200(1 + 0.05)(1 + 0.05)\ldots(1 + 0.05)$	$= \$200(1 + 0.05)^x$	

You can now use the equation $y = 200(1 + 0.05)^x$, where x represents time in years and y represents the balance in dollars, to find the balance after 10 years.

$y = 200(1 + 0.5)^x$ Original equation.

$y = 200(1 + 0.05)^{10}$ Substitute 10 for x.

$y \approx 325.78$ Use your calculator to evaluate the exponential expression.

The balance after 10 years will be \$325.78.

Amounts that increase by a constant percent, like the savings account in the example, have **exponential growth.**

Exponential Growth

Any constant percent growth can be modeled by the exponential equation

$$y = A(1 + r)^x$$

where A is the starting value, r is the rate of growth written as a positive decimal or fraction, x is the number of time periods elapsed, and y is the final value.

You can model amounts that decrease by a constant percent with a similar equation. What would need to change in the exponential equation to show a constant percent decrease?

6.2 Exercises

You will need your graphing calculator for Exercises **5, 7, 9,** and **13.**

Practice Your Skills

1. Rewrite each expression using exponents.

a. (7)(7)(7)(7)(7)(7)(7)(7)

b. (3)(3)(3)(3)(5)(5)(5)(5)(5)

c. $(1 + 0.12)(1 + 0.12)(1 + 0.12)(1 + 0.12)$ @

2. A bacteria culture grows at a rate of 20% each day. There are 450 bacteria today.

a. How many will there be tomorrow? @

b. How many will there be one week from now?

To study the growth of bacteria over time, technicians put the bacteria in petri dishes of agar. Agar is a gelatin-like substance made from algae. The agar holds the bacteria in place on the petri dish and provides nutrients for growth of the bacteria.

3. Match each equation with a table of values.

a. $y = 4x^2$ b. $y = 4(0.5)^x$ c. $y = 2(4)^x$ d. $y = 2(0.25)^x$

i.

x	y
0	2
1	0.5
2	0.125
3	0.03

ii.

x	y
0	0
1	4
2	16
3	36

iii.

x	y
0	4
1	2
2	1
3	0.5

iv.

x	y
0	2
1	8
2	32
3	128

4. Match each recursive rule with the equation that gives the same values.

a. 1.05 ENTER
Ans · (0.95) ENTER

b. 1.05 ENTER
Ans + Ans · 0.05 ENTER

c. 0.95 ENTER
Ans · (1+0.05) ENTER

d. 0.95 ENTER
Ans · (1−0.05) ENTER

i. $y = 0.95(1.05)^x$

ii. $y = 1.05(1 + 0.05)^x$

iii. $y = 0.95(0.95)^x$

iv. $y = 1.05(1 - 0.05)^x$

5. For each table, find the value of the constants a and b such that $y = a \cdot b^x$. (*Hint:* To check your answer, enter your equation into your calculator. Then see if a table of values matches the table in the book.)

a.

x	y
0	1.2
1	2.4
2	4.8
3	9.6
4	19.2

b. @

x	y
0	500
2	20
3	4
5	0.16
7	0.0064

c.

x	y
3	8
1	50
5	1.28
2	20
7	0.2048

d. For more practice, play the INOUTEXP game on your calculator. Start with the Easy setting. [▶ Use the link in your ebook to download the program file INOUTEXP. ◀] You might want to team up with another student and use one calculator to run the program while using another calculator to find the constant multiplier.

6. The equation $y = 500(1 + 0.04)^x$ models the amount of money in a savings account that earns annual interest. Explain what each number and variable in this expression means.

7. The equation, table, and graph represent three different equations.

i. $y = 2 \cdot 3^x$

ii.

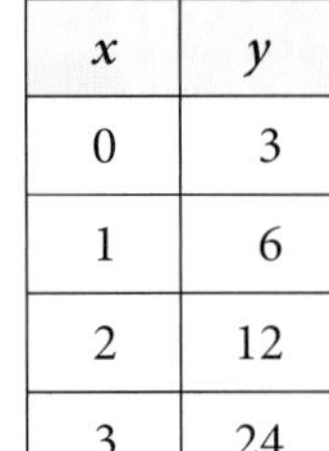

x	y
0	3
1	6
2	12
3	24

iii.

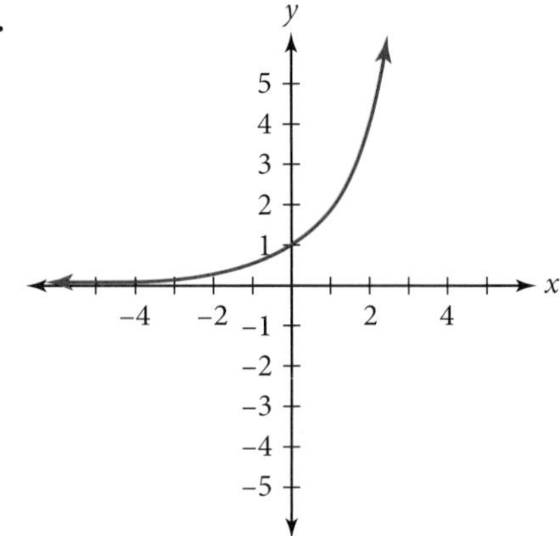

a. List in order of increasing y-intercept.

b. Which two represent situations with the same pattern of growth?

c. Which will have the greatest y-value when x equals 10? Why?

Reason and Apply

8. **APPLICATION** A credit card account is essentially a loan. A constant percent interest is added to the balance. Stanley buys $100 worth of groceries with his credit card. The balance then grows by 1.75% interest each month. How much will Stanley owe if he makes no payments for 4 months? Write the expression you used to make this calculation in expanded form and also in exponential form. @

9. APPLICATION Phil purchases a used truck for \$11,500. The value of the truck is expected to decrease by 20% each year. (A decrease in monetary value over time is sometimes called *depreciation.*)

a. Find the truck's value after 1 year.

b. Write a recursive rule that generates the value of the truck after each year.

c. Create a table showing the value of the truck when Phil purchases it and after each of the next 4 years.

d. Write an equation in the form $y = A(1 - r)^x$ to calculate the value, y, of the truck after x years.

e. Graph the equation from 9d, showing the value of the truck up through 10 years after Phil purchases it.

10. Draw a "starting" line segment with length 2 cm on a sheet of paper.

a. Draw a segment 3 times as long as the starting segment. How long is this segment?

b. Draw a segment 3 times as long as the segment in 10a. How long is this segment?

c. Use the starting length and an exponent to write an expression that gives the length, in centimeters, of the next segment you would draw. @

d. Use the starting length and an exponent to write an expression that gives the length, in centimeters, of the longest segment you could draw on a 100 m soccer field.

11. Kinsie and Majena open savings accounts. Kinsie deposits \$300 in an account that pays 2% annual interest. The equation $y = 400(1 + 0.01)^x$ gives the balance in Majena's account after x years.

a. Which person deposited the most money in her account initially?

b. Whose account is earning a higher annual interest rate?

c. Whose account will have more money in the long run? Why?

12. Fold a sheet of paper in half. You should have two layers. Fold it in half again so that there are four layers. Do this as many times as you can. Make a table and record the number of folds and number of layers.

a. As you fold the paper in half each time, what happens to the number of layers?

b. Estimate the number of folds you would have to make before you have about the same number of layers as the number of pages in this textbook.

c. Calculate the answer for 12b. You may use a recursive rule, the graph or table of an equation, or a trial-and-error method.

Origami is the Japanese art of paper folding.

13. APPLICATION Phil's friend Shawna buys an antique car for \$5,000. She estimates that it will increase in value (*appreciate*) by 5% each year.

a. Write an equation to calculate the value, y, of Shawna's car after x years. @

b. On the same set of axes graph the equation in 13a and the equation you found in 9d. Where do the two graphs intersect? What is the meaning of this point of intersection? @

14. Invent a situation that could be modeled by each equation below. Sketch a graph of each equation, and describe similarities and differences between the two models.

$y = 400 + 20x$

$y = 400(1 + 0.05)^x$

15. Consider this recursive rule:

Starting value: 100

Rule: *next value* = *current value* · (1 − 0.035)

a. Invent a situation that this rule could model.

b. Create a problem related to your situation. Carefully describe the meaning of the numbers in your problem.

c. Use an exponential equation to solve your problem.

Review

16. Look at this "step" pattern. In the first figure, which has one step, each side of the block has length 1 cm.

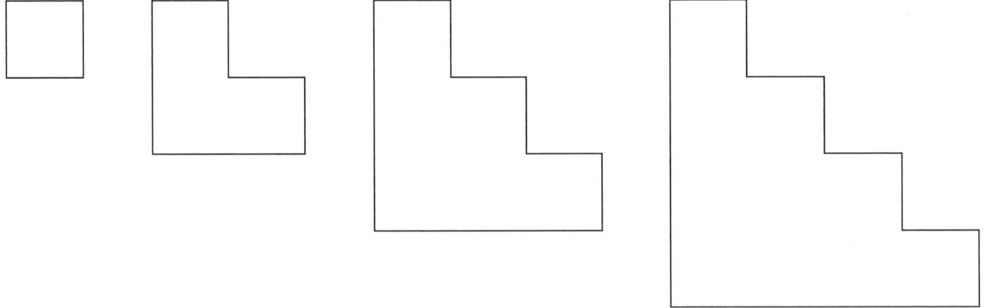

a. Make a table showing the number of steps (x) and the perimeter (y) of each figure. @

b. On a graph, plot the coordinates your table represents.

c. Write an equation that relates the perimeter of these figures to the number of steps.

d. Use your equation from 16c to predict the perimeter of a figure with 47 steps.

e. Is there a figure with perimeter 74 cm? If so, how many steps does it have? If not, why not?

LESSON

6.3

Multiplication and Exponents

"Growth for the sake of growth is the ideology of the cancer cell."

EDWARD ABBEY

In Lesson 6.2, you learned that the exponential expression $200(1 + 0.05)^3$ can model a situation with a starting value of 200 and a rate of growth of 5% over three time periods. How would you change the expression to model five time periods, seven time periods, or more? In this lesson you will explore that question and discover how the answer is related to a rule for showing multiplication with exponents.

Every year the population of the United States increases. This photo shows Grand Central Station in New York City, which is the most populated U.S. city.

Social Science CONNECTION

The U.S. Bureau of the Census only collects population information every 10 years. It uses mathematical models, such as exponential equations, to make population predictions between census years.

Suppose the population of a town is 12,800. The table shows calculations for a population growth rate of 2.5% each year.

Years elapsed	Expanded form	Exponential form
0		12,800
1	$12{,}800 \cdot (1 + 0.025)$	$12{,}800(1 + 0.025)^1$
2	$12{,}800 \cdot (1 + 0.025) \cdot (1 + 0.025)$	$12{,}800(1 + 0.025)^2$
3	$12{,}800 \cdot (1 + 0.025) \cdot (1 + 0.025) \cdot (1 + 0.025)$	$12{,}800(1 + 0.025)^3$

You can also think about the growth from one year to the next recursively.

$$\textit{next population} = \textit{current population} \cdot (1 + 0.025)$$

For example, for the population 4 years from now

$$\begin{aligned}\textit{4th-year population} &= \textit{3rd year population} \cdot (1 + 0.025)\\ &= 12{,}800(1 + 0.025)^3 \cdot (1 + 0.025)\end{aligned}$$

You can see from the third column that the 4th-year population should be $12{,}800(1 + 0.025)^4$.

This means that

$$12{,}800(1 + 0.025)^3 \cdot (1 + 0.025) = \underbrace{12{,}800}_{\text{Start amount}}(1 + \underbrace{0.025}_{\text{Base}})^{\overbrace{4}^{\text{Exponent}}}$$

Both methods make sense, and both give the same result.

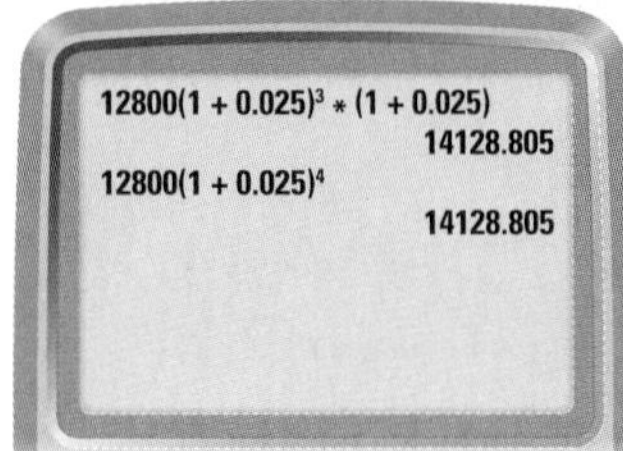

So you can advance exponential growth one time period either by multiplying the previous amount by the base (the constant multiplier) or by increasing the exponent by 1. Every time you increase by one the number of times the base is used as a factor, the exponent increases by one. But what happens when you want to advance the growth by more than one time period? In the next investigation you will discover a shortcut for multiplying exponential expressions.

INVESTIGATION

Moving Ahead

Step 1 Rewrite each product in expanded form, and then rewrite it in exponential form with a single base. Use your calculator to check your answers.

a. $3^4 \cdot 3^2$

b. $x^3 \cdot x^5$

c. $(1 + 0.05)^2 \cdot (1 + 0.05)^4$

d. $10^3 \cdot 10^6$

Step 2 Compare the exponents in each final expression you got in Step 1 to the exponents in the original product. Describe a way to find the exponents in the final expression without writing the expanded form.

Step 3 Generalize your observations in Step 2 by filling in the blank.

$b^m \cdot b^n = b^{\square}$

Step 4 Apply what you have discovered about multiplying expressions with exponents.

a. The number of ants in a colony after 5 weeks is $16(1 + 0.5)^5$. What does the expression $16(1 + 0.5)^5 \cdot (1 + 0.5)^3$ mean in this situation? Rewrite the expression with a single exponent.

All ants live in colonies.

b. The depreciating value of a truck after 7 years is $11{,}500(1 - 0.2)^7$. What does the expression $11{,}500(1 - 0.2)^7 \cdot (1 - 0.2)^2$ mean in this situation? Rewrite the expression with a single exponent.

c. The expression $A(1 + r)^n$ can model n time periods of exponential growth. What does the expression $A(1 + r)^{n+m}$ model?

Step 5 How is looking ahead in time with an exponential model related to multiplying expressions with exponents?

In the investigation you discovered the **multiplication property of exponents.**

Multiplication Property of Exponents

For any nonzero value of b and any integer values of m and n,

$$b^m \cdot b^n = b^{m+n}$$

This property is very handy for rewriting exponential expressions. However, you can add exponents to multiply numbers only when the bases are the same.

EXAMPLE A

Cal and Al got different answers when asked to write $3^4 \cdot 2^2$ in simplified exponential form. Who was right and why?

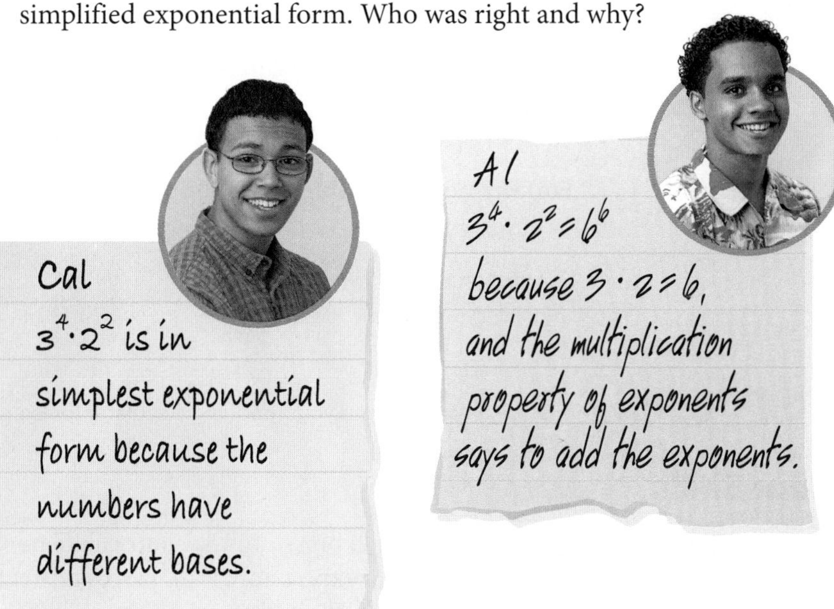

Solution

Rewrite the original expression in expanded form.

$$3 \cdot 3 \cdot 3 \cdot 3 \cdot 2 \cdot 2 \quad = \quad 3^4 \cdot 2^2$$

The factor 3 occurs 4 times. The factor 2 occurs 2 times.

The factors are not all the same, so the multiplication property of exponents does not allow you to write this expression with a single exponent. Cal was right. Use your calculator to check that $3^4 \cdot 2^2$ and 6^6 are not equivalent.

EXAMPLE B Rewrite each expression without parentheses.

a. $(4^5)^2$ b. $(x^3)^4$ c. $(5^m)^n$ d. $(xy)^3$

Solution

a. Here, a number with an exponent has another exponent. You can say that 4^5 is **raised to the power** 2. Begin by writing $(4^5)^2$ as the factor 4^5 twice.

$$(4^5)^2 = 4^5 \cdot 4^5 = 4^{5+5} = 4^{10}$$

The factor 4 occurs a total of $5 \cdot 2$, or 10, times.

b. $(x^3)^4 = x^3 \cdot x^3 \cdot x^3 \cdot x^3 = x^{3+3+3+3} = x^{12}$

The factor x occurs a total of $3 \cdot 4$, or 12, times.

c. Based on parts a and b, when you raise an exponential expression to a power, you multiply the exponents.

$(5^m)^n = 5^{mn}$

d. Here, a product is raised to a power. Begin by writing $(xy)^3$ as the factor xy three times.

$(xy)^3 = xy \cdot xy \cdot xy = x \cdot x \cdot x \cdot y \cdot y \cdot y = x^3y^3$

Do you remember which property allows you to write $xy \cdot xy \cdot xy$ as $x \cdot x \cdot x \cdot y \cdot y \cdot y$?

The example has illustrated two more properties of exponents

Power Properties of Exponents

For any nonzero values of a and b and any integer values of m and n,

$(b^m)^n = b^{mn}$

$(ab)^n = a^nb^n$

You will need your graphing calculator for Exercises **1, 8, 9,** and **13.**

Practice Your Skills

1. Use the properties of exponents to rewrite each expression. Use your calculator to check that your expression is equivalent to the original expression. [▶ See **Calculator Note: Equivalent Expressions** to learn how to check equivalent expressions. ◀]

a. $(5)(x)(x)(x)(x)$ @ b. $(x \cdot x)(3 \cdot x \cdot x)$ c. $2 \cdot x \cdot 3 \cdot x \cdot x \cdot 4 \cdot x \cdot x \cdot x$

d. $3x^4 \cdot 5x^6$ e. $4x^7 \cdot 2x^3$ f. $3x \cdot x \cdot x^2$ @

2. Write each expression in expanded form. Then rewrite the product in exponential form.

a. $3^5 \cdot 3^8$ b. $7^3 \cdot 7^4$ @ c. $x^6 \cdot x^2$

d. y^8y^5 e. $(1 - 0.07)^2 \cdot (1 - 0.07)$ f. $\left(\frac{1}{2}\right)^3 \cdot \left(\frac{1}{2}\right)^3$

g. $4x^2 \cdot x^5$ h. $4x^2 \cdot 2x^5$ i. $x^2y^4 \cdot xy^3$

3. Rewrite each expression with a single exponent.

a. $(3^5)^8$ b. $(7^3)^4$ c. $(x^6)^2$ d. $(y^8)^5$

e. $(3^8)^5$ f. $(7^4)^3$ g. $(y^2)^6$ h. $(y^1)^1$

4. Use the properties of exponents to rewrite each expression.

a. $(rt)^2$ b. $(x^2y)^3$ c. $(4x)^5$ d. $(2x^4y^2z^5)^3$

e. $(10ab)^2$ f. $(10a^2b)^2$ g. $\left(\frac{3}{4}a^3b\right)^4$ h. $(x^ay^b)^c$

Reason and Apply

5. An algebra class had this problem on a quiz: "Find the value of $2x^2$ when $x = 3$."
Two students reasoned differently.

Student 1 Two times three is six. Six squared is thirty-six.

Student 2 Three squared is nine. Two times nine is eighteen.

Who was correct? Explain why. ⓗ

6. Match expressions from this list that are equivalent but written in different exponential forms. There can be multiple matches.

i. $(4x^4)(3x)$ ii. $(8x^2)(3x^2)$ iii. $(12x)(4x)$ iv. $(6x^3)(2x^2)$

v. $12x^6$ vi. $24x^4$ vii. $12x^5$ viii. $48x^2$

7. Evaluate each expression in Exercise 6 using the x-value 4.7.

8. Use the properties of exponents to rewrite each expression. Use your calculator to check that your expression is equivalent to the original expression. [▶ See **Calculator Note: Equivalent Expressions** to learn how to check equivalent expressions. ◀]

a. $3x^2 \cdot 2x^4$ b. $5x^2y^3 \cdot 4x^4y^5$ c. $2x^2 \cdot 3x^3y^4$

d. $x^3 \cdot 4x^4$ e. $3^x \cdot 3^{4x}$ f. $2^x \cdot 2^3$

9. Cal and Al's teacher asked them, "What do you get when you square negative five?" Al said, "Negative five times negative five is positive twenty-five." Cal replied, "My calculator says negative twenty-five. Doesn't my calculator know how to do exponents?" Experiment with your calculator to see if you can find a way for Cal to get the correct answer.

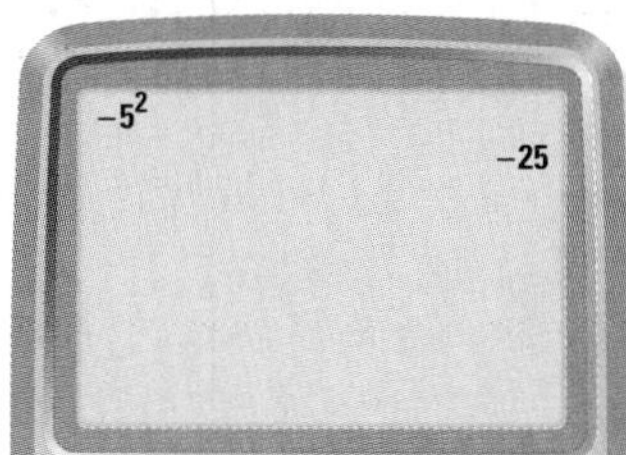

10. Evaluate $2x^2 + 3x + 1$ for each x-value.

a. $x = 3$ ⓐ b. $x = 5$ c. $x = -2$ d. $x = 0$

11. The properties you learned in this section involve adding and multiplying exponents and applying an exponent to more than one factor.

a. Write and solve a problem that requires adding exponents.

b. Write and solve a problem that requires multiplying exponents.

c. Write and solve a problem that requires applying an exponent to two factors.

d. Write a few sentences describing when to add exponents, when to multiply exponents, and when to apply an exponent to more than one factor.

12. APPLICATION Lara buys a \$500 sofa at a furniture store. She buys the sofa with a new credit card that charges 1.5% interest per month, with an offer of "no payments for a year."

a. What balance will Lara's credit card bill show after 6 months? Write an exponential expression and evaluate it. ⓐ

b. How much total interest will be added after 6 months? ⓐ

c. What balance will Lara's credit card bill show after 12 months? Write an exponential expression and evaluate it.

d. How much more interest will be added between 6 and 12 months?

e. Explain why more interest builds up between 6 and 12 months than between 0 and 6 months.

13. Use the distributive property and the properties of exponents to write an equivalent expression without parentheses. Use your calculator to check your answers, as you did in Exercise 1.

a. $x(x^3 + x^4)$ b. $(-2x^2)(x^2 + x^4)$ c. $2.5x^4(6.8x^3 + 3.4x^4)$

d. $x(x + x)$ e. $3x^3(2x + 3x^2)$ f. $4y^5(2y^2 - 2y)$

14. Write an equivalent expression in the form $a \cdot b^n$. ⓗ

a. $3x \cdot 5x^3$ b. $x \cdot x^5$ c. $2x^3 \cdot 2x^3$

d. $3.5(x + 0.15)^4 \cdot (x + 0.15)^2$ e. $(2x^3)^3$ f. $[3(x + 0.05)^3]^2$

Review

15. An equation of a line is $y = 25 - 2(x + 5)$.

a. Name the point used to write the point-slope equation. ⓗ

b. Find x when y is 15.

16. A sample labeled "50 grains" weighs 3.24 grams on a balance. What is the conversion factor for grams to grains?

17. Solve each system.

a. $\begin{cases} y = 7.3 + 2.5(x - 8) \\ y = 4.4 - 1.5(x - 2.9) \end{cases}$ b. $\begin{cases} 2x + 5y = 10 \\ 3x - 3y = 7 \end{cases}$ ⓐ

IMPROVING YOUR Visual Thinking SKILLS

A pentomino is made up of five squares joined along complete sides. The first pentomino can be folded into an open box. The second pentomino can't.

Draw all 12 unique pentominoes, and then identify those that can be folded into open boxes.

LESSON

6.4

Scientific Notation for Large Numbers

"In fact, everything that can be known has number, for it is not possible to conceive of or to know anything that has not."

PHILOLAUS

Did you know that there are approximately 75 thousand genes in each human cell and more than 50 trillion cells in the human body? This means that $75{,}000 \cdot 50{,}000{,}000{,}000{,}000$ is a low estimate of the number of genes in your body!

Whether you use paper and pencil, an old-fashioned slide rule, or your calculator, exponents are useful when you work with very large numbers. For example, instead of writing 3,750,000,000,000,000,000 genes, scientists write this number more compactly as 3.75×10^{18}. This compact method of writing numbers is called **scientific notation.** You will learn how to use this notation for large numbers—numbers far from 0 on a number line. The properties of exponents you've learned will help you work with numbers in scientific notation.

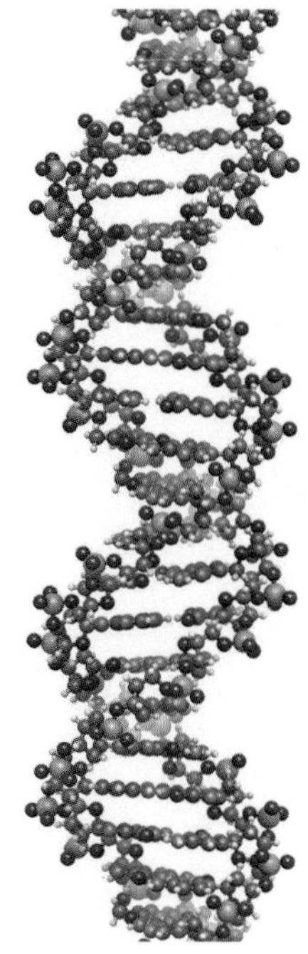

This is a computer model of a DNA strand. Many strands of DNA combine to form the genetic information in each cell.

INVESTIGATION

A Scientific Quandary

Consider these two lists of numbers:

In scientific notation	Not in scientific notation
3.4×10^5	27×10^4
7.04×10^3	120,000,000
6.023×10^{17}	42.682×10^{29}
8×10^1	4.2×12^6
1.6×10^2	42×10^2

Step 1 Classify each of these numbers as in scientific notation or not in scientific notation. If a number is not in scientific notation, tell why not.

a. 4.7×10^3 **b.** 32×10^5 **c.** 24×10^6

d. 1.107×10^{13} **e.** 0.28×10^{11}

Step 2 Define what it means for a number to be in scientific notation.

Use your calculator's Scientific Notation mode to help you figure out how to convert standard notation to scientific notation and vice versa.

Step 3 Set your calculator to Scientific Notation mode. [▶ See **Calculator Note: Scientific Notation.** ◀]

Step 4 Enter the number 5000 and press ENTER. Your calculator will display its version, 5×10^3. Use a table to record the standard notation for this number, 5000, and the equivalent scientific notation.

Step 5 Repeat Step 4 for these numbers:

a. 250 **b.** $-5{,}530$

c. 14,000 **d.** 7,000,000

e. 18 **f.** $-470{,}000$

Technicians perform maintenance at Fermi National Accelerator Lab in Batavia, Illinois. When working with the physics of atomic particles, physicists need scientific notation to write quantities such as 2 trillion electron volts.

Step 6 In scientific notation, how is the exponent on the 10 related to the number in standard notation? How are the digits before the 10 related to the number in standard notation? If the number in standard notation is negative, how does that show up in scientific notation?

Step 7 Write a set of instructions for converting 415,000,000 from standard notation to scientific notation.

Step 8 Write a set of instructions for converting 6.4×10^5 from scientific notation to standard notation.

Scientific Notation

A number in scientific notation has the form $a \times 10^n$, where either $1 \le a < 10$ or $-10 < a \le -1$ and n is an integer.

In other words, the number is rewritten in scientific notation as a number with one nonzero digit to the left of the decimal point multiplied by a power of 10. The number of digits to the right of the decimal point in the number depends on the degree of precision you want to show.

Maria Mitchell (1818–1889) was the first female professional astronomer in the United States.

EXAMPLE

Meredith is doing a report on stars and wants an estimate for the total number of stars in the universe. She reads that astronomers estimate there are at least

125 billion galaxies in the universe. An encyclopedia says that the Milky Way, Earth's galaxy, is estimated to contain more than 100 billion stars. Estimate the total number of stars in the universe. Give your answer in scientific notation.

Solution

One billion is 1,000,000,000, or 10^9. Write the numbers in the example using powers of 10 and multiply them.

$(125 \times 10^9)(100 \times 10^9)$	125 billion (galaxies) times 100 billion (stars per galaxy).
$125 \times 100 \times 10^9 \times 10^9$	Regroup using the associative and commutative properties of multiplication.
$125 \times 10^2 \times 10^9 \times 10^9$	Express 100 as 10^2.
125×10^{20}	Use the multiplication property of exponents.

Because 125 is greater than 10, the answer is not yet in scientific notation.

$1.25 \times 10^2 \times 10^{20}$	Convert 125 to scientific notation.
1.25×10^{22}	Use the multiplication property of exponents.

So the universe contains more than 1.25×10^{22} stars.

A slide rule is a mechanical device that uses a scale related to exponential notation. Slide rules were used widely for calculating with large numbers until electronic calculators became readily available in the 1970s.

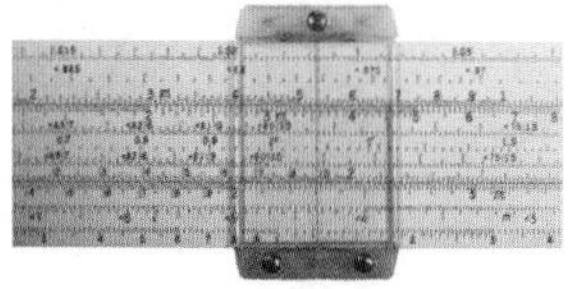

Notice in the example that you used exponential expressions that were not in scientific notation. Numbers like 125 billion, 100×10^{18}, or 0.03×10^{12} can come up in calculations, and sometimes these numbers make comparisons easier. Scientific notation is one of several ways to write large numbers.

Exercises

You will need your graphing calculator for Exercises **7, 9, 13,** and **16.**

Practice Your Skills

1. Write each number in scientific notation.

a. 34,000,000,000 @ b. −2,100,000 c. 10,060

d. 2,500 e. −15,200,000 f. $25{,}000^2$

2. Write each number in standard notation.

a. 7.4×10^4 @ b. -2.134×10^6 c. 4.01×10^3

d. -7.05×10^5 e. 1×10^9 f. -1.084×10^2

3. Owen insists on reading his calculator's display as "three point five to the seventh." Bethany tells him that he should read it as "three point five times ten to the seventh." He says, "They are the same thing. Why say all those extra words?" Write Owen's and Bethany's expressions in expanded form, and evaluate each to show Owen why they are not the same thing.

Reason and Apply

4. There are approximately 5.58×10^{21} atoms in a gram of silver. How many atoms are there in 3 kilograms of silver? Express your answer in scientific notation. ⓐ

5. The speed of light is approximately 3×10^8 m/s, and the Sun is approximately 1.5×10^{11} m from Earth. Select the best choice for the number of seconds it takes light from the Sun to reach Earth.

a. 4.5×10^3 b. 4.5×10^{19} c. 2×10^3 d. 500

6. Because the number of molecules in a given amount of a compound is usually a very large number, scientists often work with a quantity called a *mole.* One mole is about 6.02×10^{23} molecules.

a. A liter of water has about 55.5 moles of H_2O. How many molecules is this? Write your answer in scientific notation.

b. How many molecules are there in 6.02×10^{23} moles of a compound? Write your answer in scientific notation.

The number of molecules in one mole is called *Avogadro's number.* The number is named after the Italian chemist and physicist Amadeo Avogadro (1776–1856).

7. Write each number in scientific notation. How does your calculator show each answer?

a. 250

b. 7,420,000,000,000

c. -18

8. Cal and Al were assigned this multiplication problem for homework:

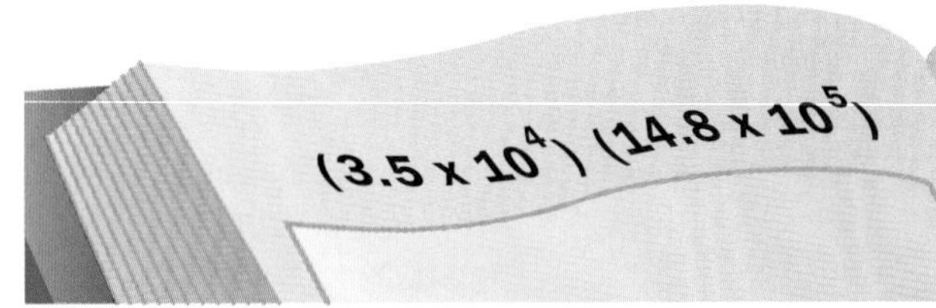

Cal got the answer 51.8×10^9, and Al got 5.18×10^{10}.

a. Are Cal's and Al's answers equivalent? Explain why or why not. ⓐ

b. Whose answer is in scientific notation? ⓐ

c. Write another exponential expression equivalent to Cal's and Al's answers. ⓐ

d. Explain how you can rewrite a number such as 432.5×10^3 in scientific notation. ⓐ

9. Consider these multiplication expressions:

i. $(2 \times 10^5)(3 \times 10^8)$ ii. $(6.5 \times 10^3)(2.0 \times 10^5)$

a. Set your calculator to Scientific Notation mode, and multiply each expression.

b. Explain how you could do the multiplication in 9a without using a calculator. ⓗ

c. Without using your calculator, find the product $(4 \times 10^5)(6 \times 10^7)$ and write it in scientific notation.

10. Pew Internet Life project suggested that approximately 65% of the nearly 7 billion people in the world were using cell phones at the end of 2012. (*www.mobiledia.com*)

a. Write the estimate of the world population in scientific notation.

b. Write the estimated number of cell phone users at the end of 2012 in scientific notation.

11. On average a person sheds 1 million dead skin cells every 40 minutes. (*The World in One Day,* 1997, p. 16)

a. How many dead skin cells does a person shed in 1 hour? Write your answer in scientific notation. ⓗ

b. How many dead skin cells does a person shed in 1 year? (Assume that there are 365 days in a year.) Write your answer in scientific notation.

Dead skin cells are one of the components of dust.

12. A *light-year* is the distance light can travel in 1 year. This distance is approximately 9,460 billion kilometers. The Milky Way galaxy is estimated to be about 100,000 light-years in diameter.

a. Write both distances in scientific notation.

b. Find the diameter of the Milky Way in kilometers. Use scientific notation.

c. Scientists estimate the diameter of Earth to be greater than 1.27×10^4 km. How many times larger is the diameter of the Milky Way?

Review

13. Enter the equations $y = 9 \cdot 6^x$ and $y = 8 + x^7$ into your calculator.

a. Create a table of values for each equation for x-values 0, 1, 2, 3, 4, and 5.

b. Which equation has the larger y-value when $x = 1$? When $x = 5$? When $x = 30$?

c. Which equation will have the larger y-value when x gets very large? Why do you think this happens?

d. Do you think the result will be the same if x^7 is replaced by an expression with a larger exponent? Why?

14. Use the properties of exponents to rewrite each expression.

a. $3x^5(4x)$ b. $y^8(7y^8)$ ⓐ

c. $b^4(2b^2 + b)$ d. $2x(5x^3 - 3x)$

15. Use the properties of exponents to rewrite each expression.

a. $3x^2 \cdot 4x^3$ b. $(3y^3)^4$ ⓐ

c. $2x^3(5x^4)^2$ d. $(3m^2n^3)^3$

16. APPLICATION The exponential equation $P = 3.8(1 + 0.017)^t$ approximates Australia's annual population (in millions) since 1900.

a. Explain the real-world meaning of each number and variable in the equation. ⓐ

b. What interval of t-values will give information up to the current year? ⓐ

c. Graph $P = 3.8(1 + 0.017)^t$ over the time interval you named in 16b.

d. What population does the model predict for the year 1950? ⓐ

e. Use the equation to predict today's population. ⓗ

17. Graph the inequality $y \leq -2(x - 5)$.

IMPROVING YOUR Reasoning SKILLS

The *Jinkōki* (Wasan Institute, 2000, p. 146) poses this ancient Japanese problem:

> A breeding pair of rats produced 12 baby rats (6 female and 6 male) in January. There were 14 rats at that time. In February, each female-male pair of rats again bred 12 baby rats. The total number of rats was then 98. In this way, each month, the parents, their children, their grandchildren, and so forth, breed 12 baby rats each. How many rats would there be at the end of one year?

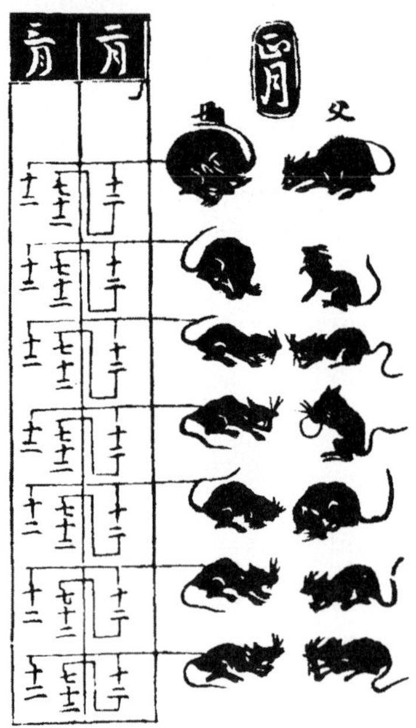

Solve this problem using an exponential model. If you use your calculator, you will get an answer in scientific notation that doesn't show all the digits of the answer. Devise a way to find the "missing" digits.

LESSON

6.5

Looking Back with Exponents

"The eye that directs a needle in the delicate meshes of embroidery, will equally well bisect a star with the spider web of the micrometer."

MARIA MITCHELL

You've learned that looking ahead in time to predict future growth with an exponential model is related to the multiplication property of exponents. In this lesson you'll discover a rule for dividing expressions with exponents. Then you'll see how dividing expressions with exponents is like looking *back* in time.

INVESTIGATION

The Division Property of Exponents

Step 1 Write the numerator and the denominator of each quotient in expanded form. Then pair common factors in the numerator and denominator that can be simplified to 1. Rewrite the remaining factors in exponential form. Use your calculator to check your answers.

a. $\frac{5^9}{5^6}$ **b.** $\frac{3^3 \cdot 5^3}{3 \cdot 5^2}$ **c.** $\frac{4^4x^6}{4^2x^3}$

Step 2 Compare the exponents in each final expression you got in Step 1 to the exponents in the original quotient. Describe a way to find the exponents in the final expression without rewriting in expanded form.

Step 3 Use your method from Step 2 to rewrite this expression so that it is not a fraction. You can leave $\frac{0.08}{12}$ as a fraction.

$$\frac{5^{15}\left(1+\frac{0.08}{12}\right)^{24}}{5^{11}\left(1+\frac{0.08}{12}\right)^{18}}$$

Recall that exponential growth is related to repeated multiplication. When you look ahead in time, you multiply by repeated constant multipliers, or increase the exponent. To look back in time, you need to undo some of the constant multipliers, or divide.

Step 4 Apply what you have discovered about dividing expressions with exponents.

a. After 7 years the balance in a savings account is $500(1 + 0.04)^7$. What does the expression $\frac{500(1+0.04)^7}{(1+0.04)^3}$ mean in this situation? Rewrite this expression with a single exponent.

b. After 9 years of depreciation, the value of a car is $21{,}300(1-0.12)^9$. What does the expression $\frac{21{,}300(1-0.12)^9}{(1-0.12)^5}$ mean in this situation? Rewrite this expression with a single exponent.

c. After 5 weeks the population of a bug colony is $32(1+0.50)^5$. Write a division expression to show the population 2 weeks earlier. Rewrite your expression with a single exponent.

d. The expression $A(1+r)^n$ can model n time periods of exponential growth. What expression models the growth m time periods earlier?

Step 5 How is looking back in time with an exponential model related to dividing expressions with exponents?

Expanded form helps you understand many properties of exponents. It also helps you understand how the properties work together.

EXAMPLE A

Use the properties of exponents to rewrite each expression.

a. $\frac{6x^9}{5x^4}$ b. $\frac{(3x^2)(8x^4)}{-4x^3}$ c. $\frac{4^5a^3b^4}{(4ab)^2}$ d. $\frac{7.5\times10^8}{1.5\times10^3}$

Solution

a.

Use expanded form and simplify.

$$\frac{6x^9}{5x^4}=\frac{6\cdot x\cdot x\cdot x\cdot x\cdot x\cdot x\cdot x\cdot x\cdot x}{5\cdot x\cdot x\cdot x\cdot x}$$

$$\frac{6}{5}\cdot\frac{x}{x}\cdot\frac{x}{x}\cdot\frac{x}{x}\cdot\frac{x}{x}\cdot\frac{x}{1}\cdot\frac{x}{1}\cdot\frac{x}{1}\cdot\frac{x}{1}\cdot\frac{x}{1}$$

$$\frac{6}{5}\cdot1\cdot1\cdot1\cdot1\cdot\frac{x}{1}\cdot\frac{x}{1}\cdot\frac{x}{1}\cdot\frac{x}{1}\cdot\frac{x}{1}=\frac{6x^5}{5},\text{ or }1.2x^5$$

$$\frac{6\cdot x\cdot x\cdot x\cdot x\cdot x}{5}$$

$$\frac{6x^{9-4}}{5}$$

In expanded form, 4 factors of x can be simplified from the numerator and denominator. That leaves 9 – 4, or 5, factors of x in the numerator.

b.

Use expanded form and simplify.

$$\frac{(3x^2)(8x^4)}{-4x^3}=\frac{3\cdot8}{-4}\cdot\frac{x\cdot x\cdot x\cdot x\cdot x\cdot x}{x\cdot x\cdot x}$$

$$\frac{3\cdot8\cdot x^2\cdot x^4}{-4\cdot x^3}$$

$$\frac{3\cdot8}{-4}\cdot\frac{x\cdot x\cdot x}{x\cdot x\cdot x}\cdot\frac{x\cdot x\cdot x}{1}=-6x^3$$

$$\frac{3\cdot8}{-4}\cdot1\cdot\frac{x\cdot x\cdot x}{1}$$

$$\frac{3\cdot8}{-4}\cdot x^{(2+4)-3}$$

In expanded form, 2 factors of x are combined with 4 factors of x in the numerator. Then 3 factors of x can be simplified from the numerator and denominator. That leaves $(2+4)-3$, or 3, factors of x in the numerator.

c. Use expanded form and simplify.

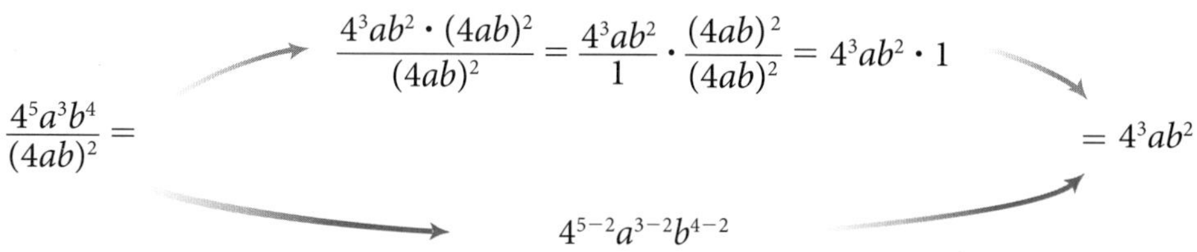

$$\frac{4^3ab^2 \cdot (4ab)^2}{(4ab)^2} = \frac{4^3ab^2}{1} \cdot \frac{(4ab)^2}{(4ab)^2} = 4^3ab^2 \cdot 1$$

$$\frac{4^5a^3b^4}{(4ab)^2} = \qquad = 4^3ab^2$$

$$4^{5-2}a^{3-2}b^{4-2}$$

In expanded form, 2 factors of 4, a, and b appear in the denominator. All factors of 4, a, and b in the denominator can be paired with the same factors in the numerator and simplified to 1. That leaves in the numerator $5 - 2$, or 3, factors of 4; $3 - 2$, or 1, factor of a; and $4 - 2$, or 2, factors of b.

d.

$$\frac{7.5 \times 10^8}{1.5 \times 10^3} = \qquad \frac{7.5}{1.5} \times \frac{10^3 \cdot 10^5}{10^3} \qquad = 5.0 \times 10^5$$

$$\frac{7.5}{1.5} \times 10^{8-3}$$

So division involving scientific notation can be done just like division of any other expression with exponents.

The investigation and example have introduced the **division property of exponents.**

Division Property of Exponents

For any nonzero value of b and any integer values of m and n,

$$\frac{b^n}{b^m} = b^{n-m}$$

The division property of exponents lets you divide expressions with exponents simply by subtracting the exponents if the expressions have the same base.

EXAMPLE B

Six years ago, Anne bought a van for \$18,500 for her flower delivery service. Based on the prices of similar used vans, she estimates a rate of depreciation of 9% per year.

a. How much is the van worth now?

b. How much was it worth last year?

c. How much was it worth 2 years ago?

Solution

The original price was \$18,500, and the rate of depreciation as a decimal is 0.09. Use the expression $A(1 - r)^x$.

a. Right now the value of the van has been decreasing for 6 years.

$$A(1 - r)^x = 18{,}500(1 - 0.09)^6 \approx 10{,}505.58$$

The van is currently worth \$10,505.58.

b. A year ago, the van was 5 years old. One approach is to use 5 as the exponent.

$$18{,}500(1 - 0.09)^5 \approx 11{,}544.59$$

Another approach is to undo the multiplication in part a by using division.

$$\frac{18{,}500(1-0.09)^6}{(1-0.09)} = 18{,}500(1-0.09)^5$$

The numerator on the left side of this equation represents the starting value multiplied by 6 factors of the constant multiplier $(1 - 0.09)$. Dividing by the constant multiplier once leaves an expression representing 5 years of exponential depreciation. Either way, the exponent is decreased by 1. The van was worth $11,544.59 last year.

c. To find the value 2 years ago, decrease the exponent in part a by 2.

$$18{,}500(1-0.09)^{6-2} = 18{,}500(1-0.09)^4 \approx 12{,}686.37$$

Subtracting 2 from the exponent gives the same result as undoing two multiplications. The van was worth $12,686.37 two years ago.

6.5 Exercises

Practice Your Skills

1. Eliminate factors equivalent to 1, and rewrite the right side of this equation in simplified exponential form.

$$\frac{x^5y^4}{x^2y^3} = \frac{x \cdot x \cdot x \cdot x \cdot x \cdot y \cdot y \cdot y \cdot y}{x \cdot x \cdot y \cdot y \cdot y}$$

2. Use the properties of exponents to rewrite each expression.

a. $\dfrac{7^{12}}{7^4}$ ⓐ

b. $\dfrac{x^{11}}{x^5}$

c. $\dfrac{12x^5}{3x^2}$ ⓐ

d. $\dfrac{7x^6y^3}{14x^3y}$

e. $\dfrac{3.2 \times 10^7}{8 \times 10^4}$

f. $\dfrac{5^3a^6b^3}{5ab^2}$

g. $\dfrac{6(5)^{x+7}}{2(5)^4}$

h. $\dfrac{x^{2b}}{x^b}$

3. Cal says that $\frac{3^6}{3^2}$ equals 1^4 because you divide the 3's and subtract the exponents. Al knows Cal is incorrect, but he doesn't know how to explain it. Write an explanation so that Cal will understand why he is wrong and how he can get the correct answer. ⓗ

4. APPLICATION Webster owns a set of antique dining-room furniture that has been in his family for many years. The historical society tells him that furniture similar to his has been appreciating in value at 10% per year for the last 20 years and that his furniture could be worth $10,000 now.

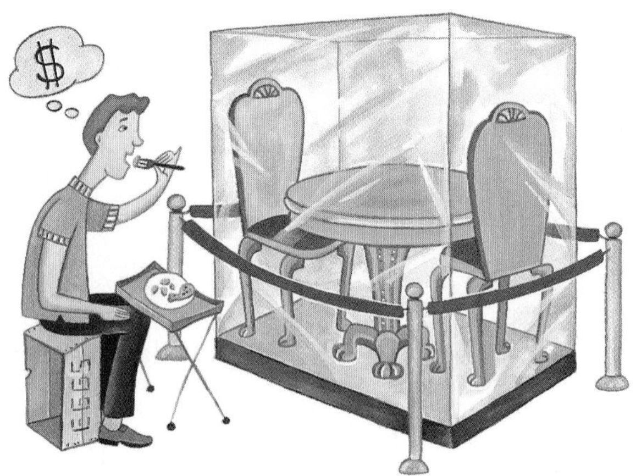

a. Which letter in the equation $y = A(1 + r)^x$ could represent the value of the furniture 20 years ago, when it started appreciating? ⓐ

b. Substitute the other given information into the equation $y = A(1 + r)^x$. ⓐ

c. Solve your equation in 4b to find how much Webster's furniture was worth 20 years ago. Show your work. ⓐ

5. Use the properties of exponents to rewrite each expression.

a. $(2x)^3 \cdot (3x^2)^4$

b. $\dfrac{(5x)^7}{(5x)^5}$

c. $\dfrac{(2x)^5}{-8x^3}$ ⓐ

d. $(4x^2y^5) \cdot (-3xy^3)^3$

e. $\dfrac{(12x^2)^3}{144x^3}$

f. $\left(\dfrac{4a^3}{5a}\right)^3$

g. $(2x^3) \cdot \dfrac{15x}{2x^2}$

h. $(-4a^3b^5) \cdot (-2a)^2$

Reason and Apply

6. APPLICATION **Population density** is the number of people per square mile. If the population of a country were spread out evenly across an entire nation, the population density would be the number of people in each square mile.

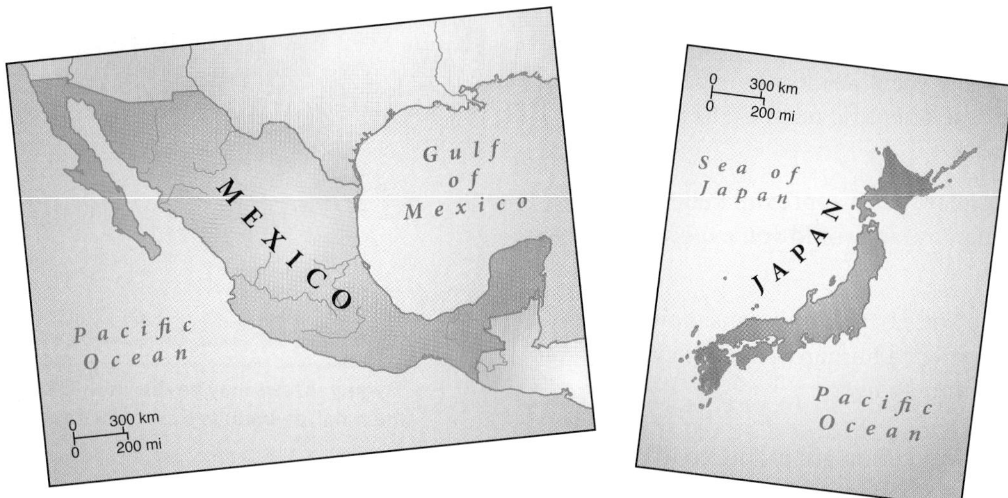

a. In 2009, the population of Mexico was about 1.11×10^8. Mexico has a land area of about 7.6×10^5 square miles. What was the population density of Mexico in 2009? (Central Intelligence Agency, *www.cia.gov*) ⓐ

b. In 2009, the population of Japan was about 1.27×10^8. Japan has a land area of about 1.5×10^5 square miles. What was the population density of Japan in 2009? (Central Intelligence Agency, *www.cia.gov*)

c. How did the population densities of Mexico and Japan compare in 2009?

7. APPLICATION Eight months ago, Tori's parents put $5,000 into a savings account that earns 3% annual interest. Now, her dentist has suggested that she get braces.

a. If the interest is calculated each month, what is the monthly interest rate? ⓐ

b. Tori's parents want to use the money in their savings account to pay for the braces. How much do they have now?

c. If Tori's dentist had suggested braces 3 months ago, how much money would have been in Tori's parents' savings account then?

d. Tori's dentist says that Tori can probably wait up to 2 months before having the braces fitted. How much will be in Tori's parents' savings account if she waits?

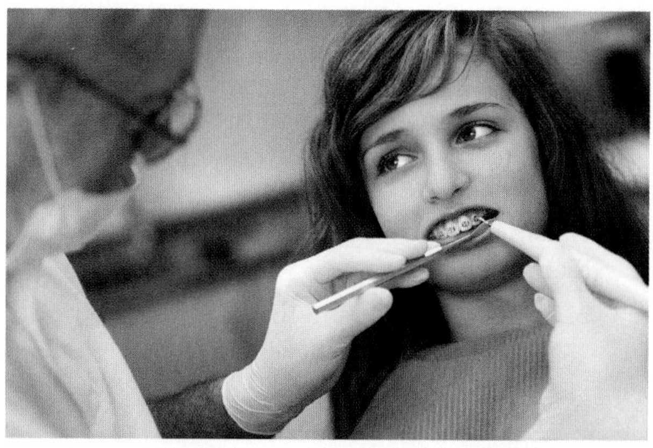

Orthodontic treatment can cost between $4,000 and $6,000 depending on the extent of the procedure. An estimated 5 million people were treated by orthodontists in the United States in 2000.

8. APPLICATION During its early stages, a disease can spread exponentially as those already infected come in contact with others. Assume that the number of people infected by a disease approximately triples every day. At one point in time, 864 people are infected. How many days earlier had fewer than 20 people been infected? Show two different methods for solving this problem. ⓗ

9. The population of a city has been growing at a rate of 2% for the last 5 years. The population is now 120,000. Find the population 5 years ago.

10. APPLICATION In the course of a mammal's lifetime, its heart beats about 1 billion times, regardless of the mammal's size or weight. (This excludes humans.)

a. An elephant's heart beats approximately 25 times a minute. How many years would you expect an elephant to live? Use scientific notation to calculate your answer. ⓐ

b. A pygmy shrew's heart beats approximately 1150 times a minute. How many years would you expect a pygmy shrew to live?

c. If this relationship were true for humans, how many years would you expect a human being with a heart rate of 60 beats per minute to live?

Pygmy shrews may be the world's smallest mammal, as small as 5 cm from nose to tail.

11. More than 57,000 tons of cotton are produced in the world each day. It takes about 8 ounces of cotton to make a T-shirt. The population of the United States in 2000 was estimated to be more than 275 million. If all the available cotton were used to make T-shirts, how many T-shirts could have been manufactured every day for each person in the United States in 2000? Write your answer in scientific notation. (*www.cotton.net*)

12. Each day, bees sip the nectar from approximately 3 trillion flowers to make 3300 tons of honey. How many flowers does it take to make 8 ounces of honey? Write your answer in scientific notation. (*The World in One Day*, 1997, p. 21) ⓗ

Review

13. On his birthday Jon figured out that he was 441,504,000 seconds old. Find Jon's age in years. (Assume that there are 365 days per year.)

14. Halley is doing a report on the solar system and wants to make models of the Sun and the planets showing relative size. She decides that Pluto, now classified as a dwarf planet, should have a model diameter of 2 cm.

a. Using the table, find the diameters of the other models she would have to make. ⓗ

b. What advice would you give Halley on her project?

Size of Objects in the Solar System

Object	Diameter (mi)
Mercury	3.1×10^3
Venus	7.5×10^3
Earth	7.9×10^3
Mars	4.2×10^3
Jupiter	8.8×10^4
Saturn	7.1×10^4
Uranus	5.2×10^4
Neptune	3.1×10^4
Pluto	1.5×10^3
Sun	8.64×10^5

Science CONNECTION

Pluto was discovered in 1930 and was classified as a planet, named after the Roman god of the dead. However, it didn't fit the definition of a planet very well. It was smaller than the other planets, and its orbit was so noncircular that sometimes it was nearer to the Sun than Neptune and sometimes it was farther away. In 2006, scientists voted to reclassify Pluto as a dwarf planet, like 44 other small bodies that orbit the Sun. (*www.nasa.gov*)

LESSON

6.6

Zero and Negative Exponents

"It is not knowledge which is dangerous, but the poor use of it."

HROTSWITHA

Have you noticed that so far in this chapter the exponents have been positive integers? In this lesson you will learn what a zero or a negative integer means as an exponent.

INVESTIGATION

More Exponents

Step 1 Use the division property of exponents, $\frac{b^n}{b^m} = b^{n-m}$, to rewrite each of these expressions with a single exponent. Use your calculator to check your answers.

a. $\frac{y^7}{y^2}$ **b.** $\frac{3^2}{3^4}$ **c.** $\frac{7^4}{7^4}$ **d.** $\frac{2}{2^5}$ **e.** $\frac{x^3}{x^6}$

f. $\frac{z^8}{z}$ **g.** $\frac{2^3}{2^3}$ **h.** $\frac{x^5}{x^5}$ **i.** $\frac{m^6}{m^3}$ **j.** $\frac{5^3}{5^5}$

Some of your answers in Step 1 should have a positive exponent, some should have a negative exponent, and some should have a zero exponent.

Step 2 How can you tell what type of exponent will result simply by looking at the original expression?

Step 3 Go back to the expressions in Step 1 that resulted in a negative exponent. Write each in expanded form. Then simplify them.

Step 4 Compare your answers from Step 3 and Step 1. Explain what a base raised to a negative exponent means.

Step 5 Go back to the expressions in Step 1 that resulted in a zero exponent. Write each in expanded form. Then simplify them.

Step 6 Compare your answers from Step 5 and Step 1. Explain what a base raised to a zero exponent means.

Step 7 Use what you have learned about negative exponents to rewrite each of these expressions with positive exponents and only one fraction bar.

a. $\frac{5^{-2}}{1}$ **b.** $\frac{1}{3^{-8}}$ **c.** $\frac{4x^{-2}}{z^2y^{-5}}$

Step 8 In one or two sentences, explain how to rewrite a fraction with a negative exponent in the numerator or denominator as a fraction with positive exponents.

This table supports what you have learned about negative exponents and zero exponents. To go down either column of the table, you divide by 3. Notice that each time you divide, the exponent decreases by 1. (Likewise, to go up either column of the table, you multiply by 3 and the exponent increases by 1.) In order to continue the pattern, 3^0 must have the value 1. As the exponents become negative, the base 3 appears in the denominator with a positive exponent.

Exponential form	Fraction form
3^3	27
3^2	9
3^1	3
3^0	1
3^{-1}	$\frac{1}{3}$
3^{-2}	$\frac{1}{9}$
3^{-3}	$\frac{1}{27}$

$$3^1 \div 3 = \frac{3^1}{3^1} = 3^{1-1} = 3^0 \qquad 3 \div 3 = \frac{3}{3} = 1$$

$$3^{-1} \div 3 = \frac{3^{-1}}{3^1} = 3^{-1-1} = 3^{-2} \qquad \frac{1}{3} \div 3 = \frac{1}{3} \cdot \frac{1}{3} = \frac{1}{3^2} = \frac{1}{9}$$

The values in the table represent the equation $y = 3^x$ when x values are -3, -2, -1, 0, 1, 2, and 3. Plotting the points $(-3, \frac{1}{27})$, $(-2, \frac{1}{9})$ $(-1, \frac{1}{3})$, (0, 1), (1, 3), (2, 9), and (3, 27) gives us this graph. Notice the shape the graph is starting to take.

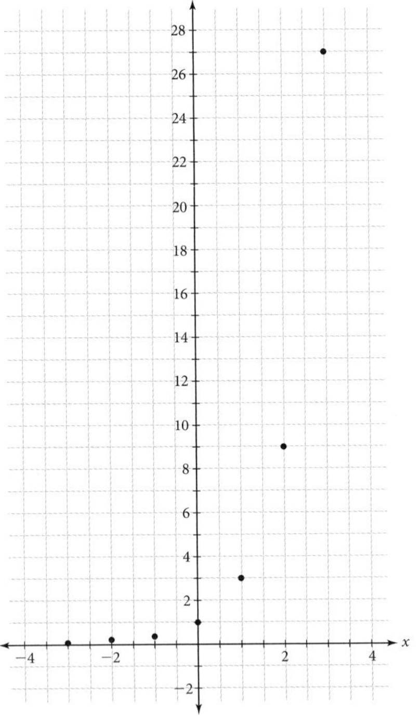

Negative Exponents and Zero Exponents

For any nonzero value of b and for any value of n,

$$b^{-n} = \frac{1}{b^n} \quad \text{and} \quad \frac{1}{b^{-n}} = b^n$$

$$b^0 = 1$$

EXAMPLE A

Use the properties of exponents to rewrite each expression without a fraction bar.

a. $\frac{3^5}{4^7}$

b. $\frac{25}{x^8}$

c. $\frac{5^{-3}}{2^{-8}}$

d. $\frac{3(17)^8}{17^8}$

Solution

a. $\frac{3^5}{4^7} = 3^5 \cdot \frac{1}{4^7}$ — Think of the original expression as having two separate factors.

$= 3^5 \cdot 4^{-7}$ — Use the definition of negative exponents.

b. $\frac{25}{x^8} = 25 \cdot \frac{1}{x^8} = 25 \cdot x^{-8} = 25x^{-8}$

c. $\frac{5^{-3}}{2^{-8}} = 5^{-3} \cdot \frac{1}{2^{-8}} = 5^{-3} \cdot 2^8$

d. $\frac{3(17)^8}{17^8} = 3 \cdot 17^0$ — Use the division property of exponents.

$= 3 \cdot 1$ — Use the definition of a zero exponent.

$= 3$ — Multiply.

You can also use negative exponents to look back in time with increasing or decreasing exponential situations.

EXAMPLE B

Solomon bought a used car for \$5,600. He estimates that it has been decreasing in value by 15% each year.

a. If his estimate of the rate of depreciation is correct, how much was the car worth 3 years ago?

b. If the car is 7 years old, what was the original price of the car?

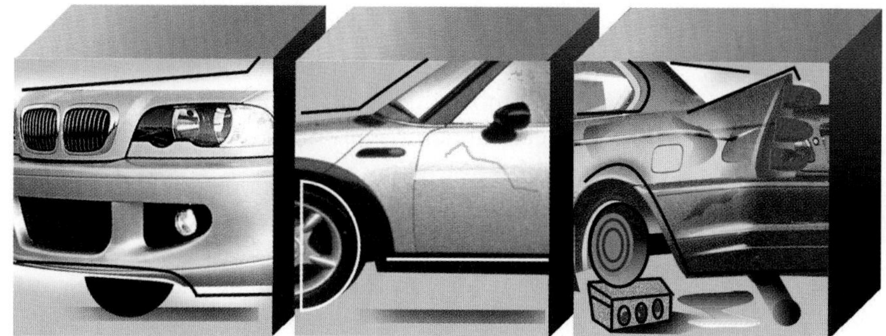

Solution

a. You can solve this problem by considering \$5,600 to be the starting value and then looking back 3 years.

$y = A(1 - r)^x$ — The general form of the equation.

$y = 5{,}600(1 - 0.15)^{-3}$ — Substitute the given information into the equation. -3 means you look back 3 years.

$y \approx 9{,}118.66$

The value of the car 3 years ago was approximately \$9,118.66.

b. The original price is the value of the car 7 years ago.

$$y = 5{,}600(1 - 0.15)^{-7}$$

$$y \approx 17{,}468.50$$

The original price was approximately \$17,468.50.

You can also use negative exponents to write numbers close to 0 in scientific notation. Just as positive powers of 10 help you rewrite numbers with lots of zeros, negative powers of 10 help you rewrite numbers with lots of zeros between the decimal point and a nonzero digit.

EXAMPLE C

Convert each number from scientific notation to standard notation, or vice versa.

a. A pi meson, an unstable particle released in a nuclear reaction, "lives" only 0.000000026 s.

b. The number 6.67×10^{-11} is the gravitational constant in the metric system used to calculate the gravitational attraction between two objects that have given masses and are a given distance apart.

c. The mass of an electron is 9.1×10^{-31} kg.

Solution

a. $0.000000026 = \frac{2.6}{100{,}000{,}000} = \frac{2.6}{10^8} = 2.6 \times 10^{-8}$

Notice that the decimal point in the original number was moved to the right eight places to get a number between 1 and 10, in this case, 2.6. To undo that, you must multiply 2.6 by 10^{-8}.

b. $6.67 \times 10^{-11} = \frac{6.67}{10^{11}} = \frac{6.67}{100{,}000{,}000{,}000} = 0.0000000000667$

Multiplying 6.67 by 10^{-11} moves the decimal point 11 places to the left, requiring 10 zeros after the decimal point—the first move of the decimal point changes 6.67 to 0.667.

c. Generalize the method in part b. To write 9.1×10^{-31} in standard notation you move the decimal point 31 places to the left, requiring 30 zeros after the decimal point.

$9.1 \times 10^{-31} = 0.00000000000000000000000000000091$

6.6 Exercises

You will need your graphing calculator for Exercise **13.**

Practice Your Skills

1. Rewrite each expression using positive exponents.

a. 2^{-3} @

b. 5^{-2}

c. 1.35×10^{-4} @

d. $\frac{(4^{-2})^0}{4^{-2}}$

e. $\frac{1}{3^{-2}}$

f. $\frac{1.4^{-3}}{1.4^5}$

2. Insert the appropriate symbol ($<$, $=$, or $>$) between each pair of numbers.

a. $6.35 \times 10^5 \square 63.5 \times 10^4$ @

b. $-5.24 \times 10^{-7} \square -5.2 \times 10^{-7}$

c. $2.674 \times 10^{-5} \square 2.674 \times 10^{-6}$

d. $-2.7 \times 10^{-4} \square -2.8 \times 10^{-3}$

e. $-4.7 \times 10^0 \square -4.7 \times 10^{-1}$

f. $3.25 \times 10^{-1} \square (-3x)^0$

3. Find the exponent of 10 that you need in order to write each expression in scientific notation.

a. $0.0000412 = 4.12 \times 10^{\square}$ @ b. $46 \times 10^{-5} = 4.6 \times 10^{\square}$ c. $0.00046 = 4.6 \times 10^{\square}$

4. The population of a town is currently 45,647. It has been growing at a rate of about 2.8% per year.

a. Write an expression in the form $45{,}647(1 + 0.028)^x$ for the current population. @

b. What does the expression $45{,}647(1 + 0.028)^{-12}$ represent in this situation? @

c. Write and evaluate an expression for the population 8 years ago. @

d. Write expressions without negative exponents that are equivalent to the exponential expressions in 4b and 4c. @

5. Juan says that 6^{-3} is the same as -6^3. Write an explanation of how Juan should interpret 6^{-3}, and then show him how each expression represents a different value.

Reason and Apply

6. Use the properties of exponents to rewrite each expression using only positive exponents, and simplify the result.

a. $(2x^3)^2(3x^4)$ b. $(5x^4)^0(2x^2)$ c. $3(2x)^3(3x)^{-2}$ @

d. $\left(\frac{2x^4}{3x}\right)^{-3}$ e. $\frac{9 \times 10^4}{3 \times 10^{-2}}$ f. $\frac{(x^3)^{-2}}{x \cdot x^{-1}}$

7. **APPLICATION** Suppose the annual rate of inflation is about 4%. This means that the cost of an item increases by about 4% each year. Write and evaluate an exponential expression to find the answers to these questions. (h)

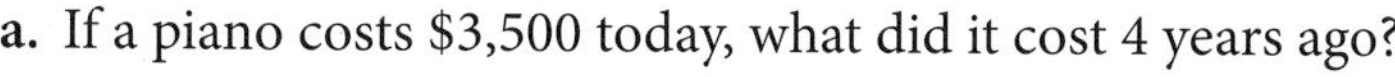

a. If a piano costs $3,500 today, what did it cost 4 years ago?

b. If a vacuum cleaner costs $250 today, what did the same model cost 3 years ago?

c. If tickets to a college basketball game cost $25 today, what did they cost 5 years ago?

d. The median price of a house in the United States in March 2013 was $184,300. What was the median price 30 years ago? (National Association of Realtors, *www.realtor.org*)

8. **APPLICATION** The population of Japan in 2012 was about 1.27×10^8. Japan has a land area of about 1.5×10^5 square miles. (Central Intelligence Agency, *www.cia.gov*)

a. On average, how much land, in square miles, is there per person in Japan? (*Note:* This is a different problem from the one you may have solved in Lesson 6.5.)

b. Convert your answer in 8a to square feet per person.

9. Decide whether each statement is true or false. Use expanded form to show either that the statement is true or what the correct statement should be.

a. $(2^3)^2 = 2^6$ b. $(3^0)^4 = 3^4$

c. $(10^{-2})^4 = -10^8$ @ d. $(5^{-3})^{-4} = 5^{12}$

10. A large ball of string originally held 1 mile of string. Abigail cut off a piece of string one-tenth that length. Barbara then cut a piece of string one-tenth as long as the piece Abigail had cut. Cruz came along and cut a piece one-tenth the length of what Barbara had cut.

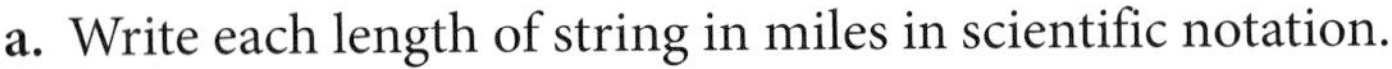

a. Write each length of string in miles in scientific notation.

b. If the process continues, how long a piece will the next person, Damien, cut off?

c. Do any of the people have a piece of string too short to use as a shoelace? ⓗ

11. Suppose $36(1 + 0.5)^4$ represents the number of bacteria cells in a sample after 4 hours of growth at a rate of 50% per hour. Write an exponential expression for the number of cells 6 hours earlier.

Review

12. APPLICATION A capacitor is charged with a 9-volt battery. The equation $y = 9.4(1 - 0.043)^x$ models the charge of a capacitor in volts as a function of the time in seconds since the capacitor was connected.

a. Is the voltage of the capacitor increasing or decreasing? Explain.

b. What are the meanings of the numbers 9.4 and 0.043 in the equation?

c. Draw a graph of this model for the first minute after disconnecting the battery.

d. When is y less than or equal to 4.7 volts? Explain how you found this answer.

13. Set your calculator to Scientific Notation mode for this problem.

a. Use your calculator to do each division.

i. $\dfrac{8 \times 10^8}{2 \times 10^3}$ ii. $\dfrac{9.3 \times 10^{13}}{3 \times 10^3}$ iii. $\dfrac{4.84 \times 10^9}{4 \times 10^4}$ iv. $\dfrac{6.2 \times 10^4}{3.1 \times 10^8}$

b. Describe how you could do the calculations in 13a without using a calculator.

c. Calculate the quotient $\frac{4.8 \times 10^7}{8 \times 10^2}$ without using your calculator.

IMPROVING YOUR Reasoning SKILLS

You have learned about scientific notation in this chapter. There is another convention for writing numbers called **engineering notation.**

Engineering notation	Not in engineering notation
2.5×10^9	2500×10^3
630×10^{-3}	630×10^{-2}
12×10^0	1.5×10^5
400×10^3	0.4×10^6
10.8×10^6	1.08×10^7

1. Write a definition of engineering notation based on the numbers in the lists. If your calculator has an Engineering Notation mode, you can enter more numbers to help support your definition.

2. Convert these numbers to engineering notation.

a. 78,000,000 b. 9,450

c. 130,000,000,000 d. 0.0034

e. 0.31 f. 1.4×10^8

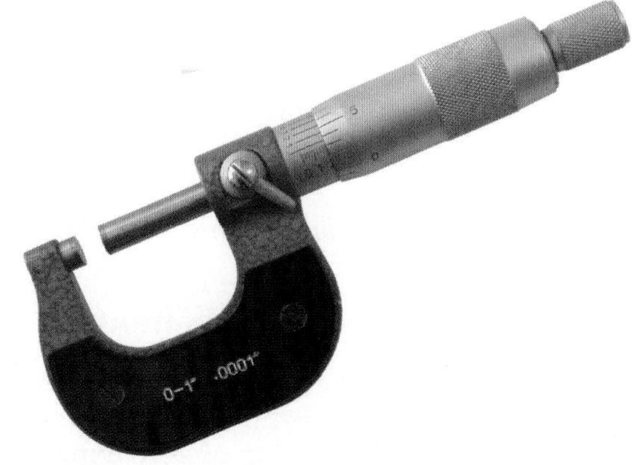

This tool, a micrometer, is used to accurately measure very small distances. Measurements made with it may be recorded in engineering notation.

3. You may have seen these symbols used as shorthand for numbers:

n ("nano," or times $\frac{1}{1,000,000,000}$)

μ ("micro," or times $\frac{1}{1,000,000}$)

k ("kilo," or times 1,000)

M ("mega," or times 1,000,000)

G ("giga," or times 1,000,000,000)

Explain how engineering notation is related to these symbols.

Practice with Properties of Exponents

You have been working with these exponent properties.

Properties of Exponents ($a \neq 0$ and $b \neq 0$)

Multiplication	$b^m \cdot b^n = b^{m+n}$
Power	$(b^m)^n = b^{mn}$ and $(ab)^n = a^n b^n$
Division	$\frac{b^n}{b^m} = b^{n-m}$

You have also been working with two definitions.

Exponent Definitions

Definition of negative exponents	$b^{-n} = \frac{1}{b^n}$ and $\frac{1}{b^{-n}} = b^n$
Definition of zero exponents	$b^0 = 1$

The examples and exercises will give you more practice working with exponents.

EXAMPLE A

Determine whether each expression is equivalent to b^8 for nonzero values of b. Explain your answer using the properties and definitions of exponents.

a. $b^4 + b^4$ b. $b^4 \cdot b^4$ c. $\frac{a^0 b^{16}}{b^8}$

d. $(b^2)^4$ e. $\left(\frac{b}{b^{-3}}\right)^2$ f. $\frac{(b^3)^2}{b^{-2}}$

Solution

a. You can combine the like terms $b^4 + b^4$ to get $2b^4$, which is not equivalent to b^8.

The other expressions are all equivalent to b^8.

b. $b^4 \cdot b^4 = b^{4+4} = b^8$

Two terms with the same base are multiplied, so use the multiplication property and add the exponents.

c. $\frac{a^0 b^{16}}{b^8} = 1 \cdot b^{16-8} = b^8$

By the definition of zero exponents, $a^0 = 1$. The fraction divides two terms with the same base, so use the division property and subtract the exponents.

d. $(b^2)^4 = b^{2 \cdot 4} = b^8$

An exponent is raised to a power, so use the power property and multiply the exponents.

e. $\left(\frac{b}{b^{-3}}\right)^2 = (b^{1-(-3)})^2 = (b^4)^2 = b^8$

The fraction divides two terms with the same base, so use the division property and subtract the exponents. The exponent is then raised to a power, so use the power property and multiply the exponents.

f. $\frac{(b^3)^2}{b^{-2}} = \frac{b^6}{b^{-2}} = b^{6-(-2)} = b^8$

The power property allows you to simplify the numerator to b^6, and the division property allows you to then simplify the fraction to b^8.

In the next example you will use the properties of exponents to find the missing value of x.

EXAMPLE B

Find the value of x in each expression, and name the properties and definitions of exponents that apply.

a. $2^x \cdot 2^7 = 2^{10}$

b. $(5^2)^x = \frac{1}{5^{-8}}$

c. $\frac{7^{-3}}{7^x} = 7^{-3}$

d. $(a^2b^3)^x = \frac{1}{a^6b^9}$

Solution

a.

$2^x \cdot 2^7 = 2^{10}$	Original equation.
$2^{x+7} = 2^{10}$	Multiplication property of exponents.
$x + 7 = 10$	Set the exponents equal.
$x = 3$	Subtract 7 from both sides of the equation.

Multiplication property

b.

$(5^2)^x = \frac{1}{5^{-8}}$	Original equation.
$5^{2x} = 5^8$	Power property of exponents. Definition of negative exponents.
$2x = 8$	Set the exponents equal.
$x = 4$	Divide both sides of the equation by 2.

Power property and definiton of negative exponents

c.

$\frac{7^{-3}}{7^x} = 7^{-3}$	Original equation.
$7^{-3-x} = 7^{-3}$	Division property of exponents.
$-3 - x = -3$	Set the exponents equal.
$-x = 0$	Add 3 to both sides of the equation.
$x = 0$	Divide both sides by -1.

Division property

d. $(a^2b^3)^x = \frac{1}{a^6b^9}$ — Original equation.

$a^{2x}b^{3x} = a^{-6}b^{-9}$ — Power property of exponents. Definition of negative exponents.

$2x = -6$ and $3x = -9$ — Set the exponents equal.

$x = -3$ — Solve both equations.

Power property and definition of negative exponents

Exercises

Practice Your Skills

1. Rewrite these expressions as a single term using only positive exponents.

a. $x \cdot x$

b. $x + x$

c. $\frac{x}{x}$

d. $\frac{1}{x} + \frac{1}{x}$

e. $x^{-1} \cdot x^0$

2. Find the x-value that makes each statement true.

a. $\frac{2^x}{2^5} = 2^1$

b. $\frac{2^5}{2^3} = 2^x$

c. $\frac{2^9}{2^x} = 2^7$

d. $\frac{2^{-3}}{2^x} = 2^9$

e. $\frac{2^3}{2^5} = 2^x$

3. Determine whether each expression is equivalent to $24x^5$? Explain your answer using the properties and definitions of exponents.

a. $3x^2 \cdot (2x)^3$

b. $\frac{6x^3}{(2x)^{-2}}$

c. $12x^2 + 12x^3$

d. $\frac{-8x(x^5)^0}{(-3x^4)^{-1}}$

e. $\frac{72x^7y^3}{3x^2y^3}$

4. Solve each equation for x.

a. $\frac{2^{-5} \cdot 2^{-3}}{2^{-4} \cdot 2^6} = 2^x$

b. $\frac{10^4 \cdot 10^2 \cdot 10^{-8}}{10^{-6} \cdot 10^5 \cdot 10^{-3}} = \frac{1}{10^x}$

c. $\frac{2^{-5} \cdot 2^{-3}}{2^{-4} \cdot 2^6} = \frac{1}{2^x}$

5. Use the distributive property to rewrite each expression without parentheses.

a. $x^3(2x^2 + 5x - 1)$

b. $3x^{-1}(4x^5 - 7x)$

c. $\frac{3}{x^2}\left(8x^9 + \frac{2}{x}\right)$

LESSON

6.7

Fitting Exponential Models to Data

"In broken mathematics
We estimate our prize
Vast—in its fading ratio
To our penurious eyes!"

EMILY DICKINSON

Over the past 10 years, Victoria Julian has been collecting data on changes in median house prices in her area. She plans to buy a house 5 years from now and wants to know how much money she needs to save each month toward the down payment. How can she make an intelligent prediction of what a house might cost in the future? What assumptions will she have to make?

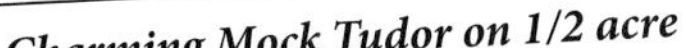

6 bedrms, 3 baths, stone fireplace, marquetry floors throughout, 2-car garage, huge landscaped lot. Best offer.

Lovely Westside Bungalow
Newly remodeled, 2 bedroom, 1.5 bath, off-street parking, laundry, porch, hdwd floors and fireplace, charming back patio

Affordable Brownstone

- 3 floors
- 3 bed/2 bath
- spacious
- charming details
- street parking
- needs only minor repairs
- walk to shops and park
- accepting offers starting Wed

In the real world, situations like population growth, price inflation, and the decay of substances often tend to approximate an exponential pattern over time. With an appropriate exponential model, you can sometimes predict what might happen in the future.

In Chapter 4, you learned about fitting linear models to data. In this lesson you'll learn how to find an exponential model to fit data.

INVESTIGATION

Radioactive Decay

YOU WILL NEED

- a paper plate
- a protractor
- a supply of small counters

The particles that make up an atom of some elements, such as uranium, are unstable. Over a period of time specific to the element, the particles change so that the atom eventually becomes a different element. This process is called **radioactive decay.**

In this investigation your counters represent atoms of a radioactive substance. Draw an angle from the center of your plate, as illustrated. Counters that fall inside the angle represent atoms that have decayed.

Step 1 Count the number of counters. Record this in a table as the number of "atoms" after 0 years of decay. Pick up all the counters.

Step 2 Drop the counters on the plate. Count and remove the counters that fall inside the angle—these atoms have decayed. Subtract from the previous value, and record the number remaining after 1 year of decay. Pick up the remaining counters.

Step 3 Repeat Step 2 until you have fewer than ten atoms that have not decayed. Each drop will represent another year of decay. Record the number of atoms remaining each time.

Procedure Note

Create a procedure for dropping counters randomly on the plate. Be sure that your method results in an approximately even distribution. Make a plan for handling counters that fall on the lines of your angle and those that miss the plate—they need to be accounted for too.

Step 4 Make a scatter plot of the number of atoms remaining as a function of elapsed time in years. What do you notice about the graph?

Step 5 Calculate the ratios of atoms remaining between successive years. That is, divide the number of atoms after 1 year by the number of atoms after 0 years, and then divide the number of atoms after 2 years by the number of atoms after 1 year, and so on. How do the ratios compare?

Step 6 Choose one representative ratio. Explain how and why you made your choice.

Step 7 At what rate did your atoms decay?

Step 8 Write an exponential equation that models the relationship between time elapsed and the number of atoms remaining.

Step 9 Graph your equation with the scatter plot. How well does it fit the data?

Step 10 If the equation does not fit well, which values could you try to adjust to give a better fit? Record your final equation when you are satisfied.

Step 11 Measure the angle on your plate. Describe a connection between your angle measure and the value of b in your exponential equation, $y = a \cdot b^x$.

Step 12 Based on what you've learned and the procedures outlined in this investigation, write an equation that would model the decay of 400 counters, using a central angle of 60°. What are some of the factors that might cause differences between actual data values and values predicted by your equation?

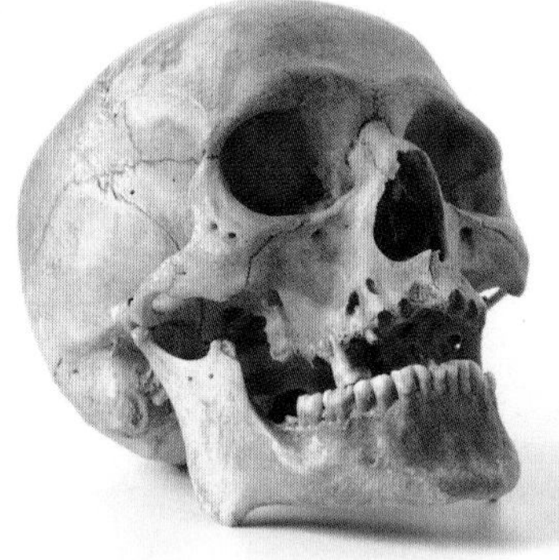

Archaeologists can approximate the age of artifacts with *carbon dating*. This process uses the rate of radioactive decay of carbon-14. Carbon is found in all living things, so the amount left in a bone, for example, is an indicator of the bone's age.

The steps in finding an equation in the investigation provide a good method for finding an exponential equation to model data that display an exponential pattern, either increasing or decreasing. These situations are often generated recursively by multiplying by a constant ratio. Thinking of the constant multiplier in the form $(1 + r)$ or $(1 - r)$ leads to these familiar equations:

$$y = A(1 + r)^x$$

$$y = A(1 - r)^x$$

You can fine-tune the fit of your model by slightly adjusting the values of A and r.

EXAMPLE

Every musical note has an associated frequency measured in hertz (Hz), or vibrations per second. The table shows the approximate frequencies of the notes in the octave from middle C up to the next C on a piano. (In this scale, E# is the same as F and B# is the same as C.)

Piano Notes

Note name	Note number above middle C	Frequency (Hz)
Middle C	0	262
C#	1	277
D	2	294
D#	3	311
E	4	330
F	5	349
F#	6	370
G	7	392
G#	8	415
A	9	440
A#	10	466
B	11	494
C above middle C	12	523

The arrangement of strings in a piano shows an exponential-like curve.

a. Find a model that fits the data.

b. Use your model to find the frequencies of the note two octaves above middle C (note 24) and the note one octave below middle C (note -12).

c. Is there a note on this piano with frequency 800 Hz?

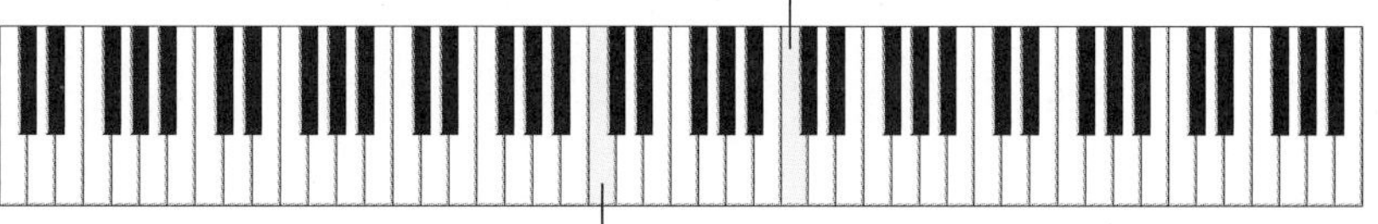

Solution

a. Let x represent the note number above middle C, and let y represent the frequency. A scatter plot shows the exponential-like pattern. To find an exponential model, first calculate the ratios between successive data points. The mean of the ratios is 1.0593. So the frequency of the notes increases by about 5.93% each time you move up one note on the keyboard. The starting frequency is 262 Hz. So an equation is

$$y = 262(1 + 0.0593)^x$$

The graph shows a very good fit.

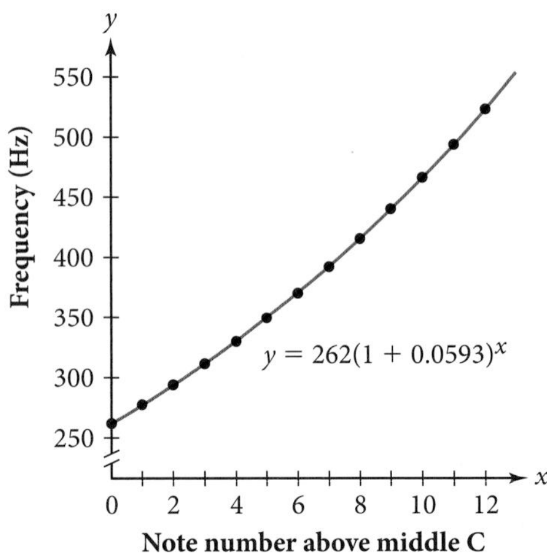

b. To find the frequency of each of these notes, substitute the note number for x in the model. To find the frequency of a note below middle C, you must use a negative number.

Note number	Frequency (Hz)
24	$262(1 + 0.0593)^{24} \approx 1044$
-12	$262(1 + 0.0593)^{-12} \approx 131$

c. To determine whether there is a note with frequency 800 Hz, extend the table of frequencies using your calculator.

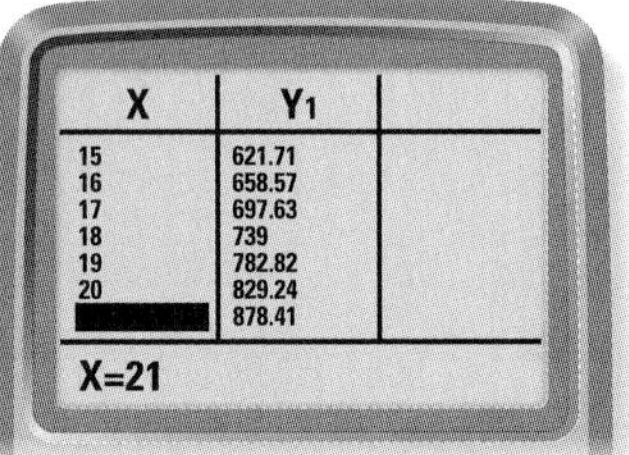

Because 800 falls between the frequencies for the nineteenth and twentieth notes, there is no note on this piano with frequency 800 Hz.

The frequencies found using the equation in the example will be fairly accurate because the data fit the equation so well. If the piano were very out of tune, the equation probably would not fit so nicely, and the model might be less valuable for predicting frequencies.

Music CONNECTION

Before the 17th century, there were many ways to tune an instrument. The most popular, developed by the ancient Greek philosopher Pythagoras, used different tuning ratios between each pair of adjacent notes. This made some scales, like the scale of C, sound good but others, like the scale of A-flat, sound bad. Modern Western tuning now uses *even temperament,* based on an equal tuning ratio between adjacent notes, which leads to an exponential model.

Exercises

You will need your graphing calculator for Exercises **5, 6, 8, 9, 10,** and **11.**

Practice Your Skills

1. Rewrite each value in the form of either $(1 + r)$ or $(1 - r)$. Then state the rate of increase or decrease as a percent.

a. 1.15 ⓐ
b. 1.08
c. 0.76 ⓐ
d. 0.998
e. 2.5

2. Use the equation $y = 47(1 - 0.12)^x$ to answer each question.

a. Does this equation model an increasing or a decreasing pattern? ⓗ

b. What is the rate of increase or decrease?

c. What is the y-value when x is 13?

d. What happens to the y-values as the x-values get very large?

3. Write an equation to model the growth of an initial deposit of \$250 in a savings account that pays 4.25% annual interest. Let B represent the balance in the account, and let t represent the number of years the money has been in the account. ⓐ

4. Use the properties of exponents to rewrite each expression using only positive exponents.

a. $4x^3 \cdot (3x^5)^3$
b. $\frac{60x^8y^4}{15x^3y}$ ⓐ
c. $3(2^x) \cdot 5(2^x)$
d. $\frac{(8x^3)^2}{(4x^2)^3}$ ⓐ
e. $x^{-3}y^4$
f. $(2x)^{-3}$
g. $(2^x)^3$
h. $2^{3x} \cdot 2^{4-3x}$

Reason and Apply

5. Mya placed a cup of hot water in a freezer. Then she recorded the temperature of the water each minute.

Water Temperature

Time (min) x	0	1	2	3	4	5	6	7	8	9	10
Temperature (°C) y	47	45	43	41.5	40	38.5	37	35.5	34	33	31.5

[Data sets: **FZTIM, FZTMP**]

a. Find the ratios between successive temperatures. ⓐ

b. Find the mean of the ratios in 5a. ⓐ

c. Write the mean ratio found in 5b in the form $(1 - r)$. ⓐ

d. Use your answer from 5c and the starting temperature to write an equation in the form $y = A(1 - r)^x$. ⓐ

e. Graph your equation with a scatter plot of the data. Adjust the values of A and r until you get a satisfactory fit.

f. Use your equation to predict how long it will take for the water temperature to drop below 5°C.

6. In science class Phylis used a light sensor to measure the intensity of light (in lumens per square meter, or lux) that passes through layers of colored plastic. The table shows her readings.

Light Experiment

Number of layers	0	1	2	3	4	5	6
Intensity of light (lux)	431	316	233	174	128	98	73

[Data sets: **LTLAY, LTINT**]

a. Write an exponential equation of the intensity of light in lux as a function of the number of layers of colored plastic to model Phylis's data. ⓗ

b. What does your r-value represent?

c. If Phylis's sensor cannot register readings below 30 lux, how many layers can she add before the sensor stops registering?

7. Suppose that on Sunday you see 32 mosquitoes in your room. On Monday you count 48 mosquitoes. On Tuesday there are 72 mosquitoes. Assume that the population will continue to grow exponentially.

a. What is the percent rate of growth? ⓐ

b. Write an equation that models the number of mosquitoes as a function of the number of days.

c. Graph your equation and use it to find the number of mosquitoes after 5 days, after 2 weeks, and after 4 weeks.

d. Name at least one real-life factor that would cause the population of mosquitoes to not grow exponentially.

8. Many stories in children's literature involve magic pots. An Italian variation goes something like this: A woman puts a pot of water on the stove to boil. She says some special words, and the pot begins filling with pasta. Then she says another set of special words, and the pot stops filling up.

Suppose someone overhears the first words, takes the pot, and starts it in its pasta-creating mode. Two liters of pasta are created. Then the pot continues to create more pasta because the impostor doesn't know the second set of words. The volume continues to increase at a rate of 50% per minute.

a. Write an equation that models the amount of pasta in liters as a function of time in minutes. ⓐ

b. How much pasta will there be after 30 seconds?

c. How much pasta will there be after 10 minutes?

d. How long, to the nearest second, will it be until the entire house, which can hold 450,000 liters, is full of pasta?

9. The equation $y = 262(1 + 0.0593)^x$ models the frequency in hertz of various notes on the piano, with middle C considered as note 0. The average human ear can detect frequencies between 20 and 20,000 hertz. If a piano keyboard were extended, the highest and lowest notes audible to the average human ear would be how far above and below middle C? ⓐ

10. MINI-INVESTIGATION In this exercise you will explore the equation $y = 10(1 - 0.25)^x$.

a. Find y for some large positive values of x, such as 100, 500, and 1000. What happens to y as x gets larger and larger?

b. The calculator will say y is 0 when x equals 10,000. Is this correct? Explain why or why not.

c. Find y for some negative values of x, such as -100, -500, and -1000. What happens to y as x moves farther and farther from 0 in the negative direction?

Review

11. APPLICATION Zoe must ship 532 tubas and 284 kettledrums from her warehouse to a store across the country. A truck rental company offers two sizes of trucks. A small truck will hold 5 tubas and 7 kettledrums. A large truck will hold 12 tubas and 4 kettledrums. If Zoe wants to fill each truck so that the cargo won't shift, how many small and large trucks should she rent?

a. Define variables and write a system of equations to find the number of small trucks and the number of large trucks Zoe needs to ship the instruments. (*Hint:* Write one equation for each instrument.) ⓗ

b. Solve the system symbolically.

c. Write a sentence describing the real-world meaning of the solution.

12. Very small amounts of time much less than a second have special names. Some of these names may be familiar to you, such as a millisecond, or 0.001 second. Have you heard of a nanosecond or a microsecond? A nanosecond is 1×10^{-9} second, and a microsecond is 1×10^{-6} second. How many nanoseconds are in a microsecond?

13. APPLICATION Lila researched tuition costs at several colleges she's interested in. The data are listed below. Costs are predicted to rise 3.7% each year. [Data set: **TUITN**]

{\$2,860, \$3,580, \$8,240, \$9,460, \$11,420, \$22,500, \$26,780}

a. What will the costs be next year?

b. Find the estimated cost for each school 5 years from now.

James Joule (1818–1889) was one of the first scientists to study how energy was related to heat. At the time of his experiments, many scientists thought heat was a gas that seeped in and out of objects. The SI (metric) unit of energy was named in Joule's honor.

14. One of the most famous formulas in science is

$$E = mc^2$$

This equation, formulated by Albert Einstein in 1905, describes the relationship between mass (m, measured in kilograms) and energy (E, measured in joules) and shows how each can be converted to the other. The variable c is the speed of light, 3×10^8 meters per second. How much energy could be generated by a 5-kilogram bowling ball? Express your answer in scientific notation.

LESSON 6.8

ACTIVITY DAY

Decreasing Exponential Models and Half-Life

In Lesson 6.7, you learned that data can sometimes be modeled using the exponential equation $y = A(1 - r)^x$. In this lesson you will do an experiment, write an equation that models the decreasing exponential pattern, and find the **half-life**—the amount of time needed for a substance or an activity to decrease to one-half its starting value. To find the half-life, approximate the value of x that makes y equal $\frac{1}{2} \cdot A$.

In the previous investigation, if your plate was marked with a 72° angle and you started with 200 "atoms," a model for the data could be $y = 200(1 - 0.20)^x$. This is because the ratio of the angle to the whole plate is $\frac{72}{360}$, or 0.20. To determine the half-life of your atoms, you would need to find out how many drops you would expect to do before you had 100 atoms remaining. Hence, you could solve the equation $100 = 200(1 - 0.20)^x$ for x using a graph or a calculator table. The x-value in this situation is approximately 3, which means your atoms have a half-life of about 3 years.

ACTIVITY

YOU WILL NEED

- a motion sensor
- a meterstick
- a ball
- string
- a soda can half-filled with water

Bouncing and Swinging

Two experiments are described in this activity. Each group should choose at least one, collect and analyze data, and prepare a presentation of results.

Step 1 Select one of these two experiments.

Experiment 1: Ball Bounce

Drop a ball from a height of about 1 m, and measure its rebound height for at least six bounces. You can collect data "by eye" using a meterstick, or you can use a motion sensor. [▶ Use the link in your ebook to download the program file BOUNCE. ◀] If you use a motion sensor, hold it $\frac{1}{2}$ m above the ball and collect data for about 8 s; trace the resulting scatter plot of data points to find the maximum rebound heights.

Experiment 2: Pendulum Swing

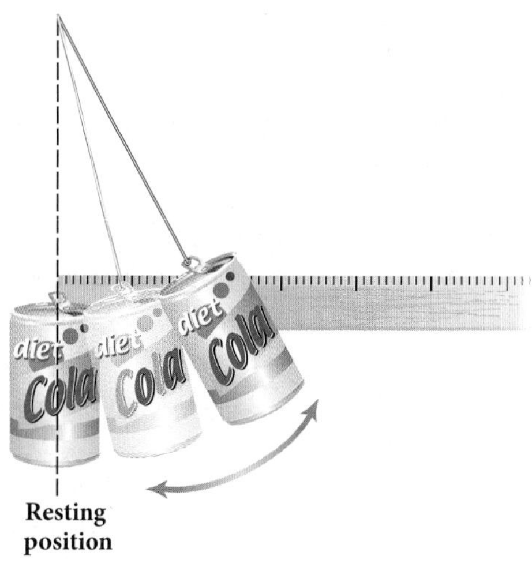

Resting position

Make a pendulum with a soda can half-filled with water tied to at least 1 m of string—use the pull tab on the can to connect it to the string. Pull the can back about $\frac{1}{2}$ m from its resting position, and then release it. Measure how far the can swings from the resting position for several swings. You can collect data "by eye" using a meterstick (you may have to collect data for every fifth swing in this case), or you can use a motion sensor. [▶ Use the link in your ebook to download the program file BOUNCE. ◀] If you use a motion sensor, position it 1 m from the can along the path of the swing; the program will collect the maximum distance from the resting position for 30 swings.

Step 2 Set up your experiment and collect data. Based on your results, you might want to modify your setup and repeat your data collection.

Step 3 Define variables and make a scatter plot of your data on your calculator. (If you used a motion sensor, you should have this already.) Draw the scatter plot accurately on your paper. Does the graph show an exponential pattern?

Step 4 Write an equation in the form $y = A(1 - r)^x$ that models your data. Graph this equation with your scatter plot and adjust the values if a better fit is needed.

Step 5 Find the half-life of your data. Explain what the half-life means for the situation in your experiment.

Step 6 Find the y-value after one half-life, two half-lives, and three half-lives. How do these values compare?

Step 7 Write a summary of your results. Include descriptions of how you found your exponential model, what the rate r means in your equation, and how you found the half-life. You might want to include ways you could improve your setup and data collection.

In the real world, eventually your ball will stop bouncing or your pendulum will stop swinging. Your exponential model, however, will never reach a y-value of 0. Remember that any mathematical model is, at best, an approximation and therefore will have limitations.

CHAPTER 6 REVIEW

You started this chapter by creating sequences that increase or decrease when you multiply each term by a constant factor. Repeated multiplication causes the rate of change between successive terms to increase or decrease. So the graphs of these sequences curve, getting steeper and steeper or less and less steep. You then discovered that these sequences are modeled by **exponential equations** in which the constant multiplier is the **base** and the number of the term in the sequence is the **exponent.**

By writing exponential expressions in both **expanded form** and **exponential form,** you learned the **multiplication, division,** and **power properties of exponents,** and you explored the meanings of zero and negative exponents. You applied these properties to **scientific notation,** a way to express numbers with powers of 10.

When modeling data, you can often use an equation to make predictions. You now have two kinds of models for real-world data—linear equations and exponential equations. Many real-world quantities that increase can be modeled as **exponential growth** with an equation in the form $y = A(1 + r)^x$. You can model many quantities that decrease, such as **radioactive decay,** with an equation in the form $y = A(1 - r)^x$.

Exercises

You will need your graphing calculator for Exercises **2, 3,** and **10.**

@ **Answers are provided for all exercises in this set.**

1. Write each number in exponential form with base 3.

a. 81 b. 27 c. 9

d. $\frac{1}{3}$ e. $\frac{1}{9}$ f. 1

2. Use the properties of exponents to rewrite each expression. Your final answer should have only positive exponents. Use a calculator table to check that your expression is equivalent to the original expression.

a. $\frac{x \cdot x \cdot x}{x}$ b. $2x^{-1}$ c. $\frac{6.273x^8}{5.1x^3}$ d. 3^{-x}

e. $3x^0$ f. $x^2 \cdot x^5$ g. $(3^4)^x$ h. $\frac{1}{x^{-2}}$

3. Consider this exponential equation:

$y = 300(1 - 0.15)^x$

a. Invent a real-world situation that you can model with this equation. Give the meaning of 300 and of 0.15 in your situation.

b. What would the inequality $75 \leq 300(1 - 0.15)^x$ mean for your situation in 3a?

c. Find all integer values of x such that $75 \leq 300(1 - 0.15)^x$.

4. Proaga says, "Three to the power zero must be zero. An exponent tells you how many times to multiply the base, and if you multiply zero times you would have nothing!" Give her a convincing argument that 3^0 equals 1.

5. For each table, find the value of the constants A and r such that $y = A(1 + r)^x$ or $y = A(1 - r)^x$. Then use your equations to find the missing values.

a.

x	y
0	200
1	280
2	392
3	548.8
4	768.32
5	1075.648
6	

b.

x	y
−2	
−1	
0	850
1	722.5
2	614.125
3	522.00625
4	

6. Convert each number from scientific notation to standard notation, or vice versa.

a. -2.4×10^6

b. 3.25×10^{-4}

c. 37,140,000,000

d. 0.00000008011

7. A person blinks about 9365 times a day. Each blink lasts about 0.15 second. If one person lives 72 years, how many years will be spent with his or her eyes closed while blinking? Write your answer in scientific notation.

8. APPLICATION In 2004, a bottle of juice cost $1.00 in a vending machine. If prices increase about 3% per year, in what year will the cost first exceed $2?

9. Classify each equation as true or false. If false, explain why and change the right side of the equation to make it true.

a. $(3x^2)^3 = 9x^6$

b. $3^2 \cdot 2^3 = 6^5$

c. $2x^{-2} = \dfrac{1}{2x^2}$

d. $\left(\dfrac{x^2}{y^3}\right)^3 = \dfrac{x^5}{y^6}$

10. APPLICATION A pendulum is pulled back 80 cm horizontally from its resting position and then released. The maximum distance of the swing from the resting position is recorded after each minute for 5 min.

Pendulum Swings

Time elapsed (min)	0	1	2	3	4	5
Maximum distance from resting position (cm)	80	66	55	46	38	32

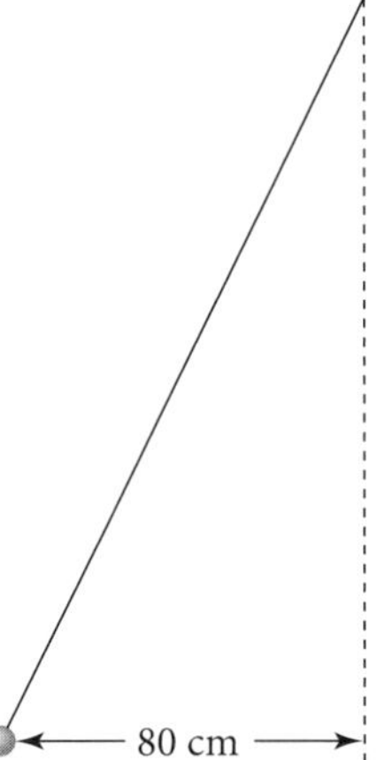

a. Write an equation that models the maximum distance of the swing as a function of time in minutes.

b. What is the maximum distance from the resting position after 9 min?

c. After how many minutes will the maximum distance from the resting position be less than 5 cm?

Take Another Look

Scientific notation gives scientists and mathematicians one way to express extremely large and extremely small numbers. Sometimes scientists focus on only the power of 10 to describe size or quantity, calling this the **order of magnitude.**

Consider that the average distance from Earth to the Sun is 9.29×10^7 mi. Unless a scientist is going to calculate with this figure, he or she may simply say the distance in miles from Earth to the Sun is *on the order of* 10^7. By stating only the power of 10, what range of values is the scientist including?

Order of magnitude is also used to compare numbers. Suppose a sample of bacteria grows from several hundred to several thousand cells overnight. How many times larger is the sample now? A scientist may say the number of cells in the sample *increased by one order of magnitude* because $\frac{10^3}{10^2}$ equals 10^1. What would the scientist say when the sample grows from several hundred cells to several hundred thousand cells? What fraction of cells would remain if the sample *decreased* by two orders of magnitude? (*Note:* The units must be equal to compare orders of magnitude.)

Think about the relative size of our universe as you answer these questions.

1. Explain what it means for the typical size of a cell in meters to be on the order of 10^{-6}.

2. Explain what it means for the length of a cow in meters to be on the order of 10^0.

3. The distance in meters from Earth to the nearest star (other than the Sun) is on the order of 10^{17}. Is it correct to compare the distance from Earth to the Sun and the distance from Earth to the nearest star as an increase by 10 orders of magnitude because $\frac{10^{17}}{10^7}$ equals 10^{10}?

4. The diameter in meters of the Milky Way galaxy is 10^{20}. Describe the increase in order of magnitude between the size of a cell and the size of the galaxy.

When something increases 100%, should it be described as an increase in order of magnitude? Give an example to support your conclusion.

Assessing What You've Learned

WRITE IN YOUR JOURNAL Add to your journal by considering one of these prompts:

- Why is scientific notation convenient for writing extremely large or extremely small numbers? Are there numbers that you find to be less convenient to write in scientific notation? Does scientific notation help you understand why our standard number system is called a "base 10" system?
- Compare and contrast linear and exponential data. How do the graphs differ? If you weren't specifically told to find either a linear or an exponential equation to fit a graph of data, how would you decide which to try? How do the methods of fitting linear and exponential models compare?

PERFORMANCE ASSESSMENT Show a classmate, a family member, or your teacher that you know how to find an exponential model in the form $y = A(1 + r)^x$. You may want to go back and use the data sets from Lesson 6.7 or Lesson 6.8. Explain why you think the data are exponential and when and why you would want to adjust the value of A or r.

GIVE A PRESENTATION Review the properties of exponents that you learned in this chapter. Think about the techniques you have used to remember these properties, or ask your peers, teachers, or family members how they remember these properties. Prepare a presentation for your class and demonstrate the memory methods you have learned. Your presentation will help your classmates remember the properties of exponents too!

CHAPTER

Functions and Transformations

The Dome of the Rock is a famous site in Jerusalem. Built in the 7th century, it is well known for its beautiful tile work. Moving a small design left, right, up, or down could create some of the large patterns you see. Flipping or turning a design could create yet other patterns. Moving, flipping, or turning a design is important in creating many art forms. As you will see, changes like these are equally important in mathematics.

OBJECTIVES

In this chapter you will

- learn about function notation and vocabulary
- learn the absolute-value and squaring functions
- learn about piecewise and step functions
- learn to change, or transform, graphs
- write a new equation to describe the transformed graph
- model real-world data with equations of transformations
- explore the relationship between factoring and the distributive property
- learn to add, subtract, multiply, divide, and simplify rational expressions

Translating Points

In computer animation, many individual points define each figure. You animate a figure by moving these points around the screen, little by little, through a series of frames. When you see the frames one after the other, the entire figure appears to move. This is the principle behind computer-animated movies and video games.

Every frame of an animation is a translation, rotation, reflection, or dilation of the one before it.

This computer-animated motorcycle was created with software called Maya. The software allows an animator to move the motorcycle by translating, rotating, reflecting, or dilating the points of an underlying skeleton of polygons that define its surfaces.

In this lesson you will create new polygons that are the result of translating the original polygons by moving their vertices left, right, up, or down, or by combinations of these movements. The figure that results from a translation is the **image** of the original figure. **Translations** move a figure horizontally, vertically, or both.

EXAMPLE

Sketch the image of this figure after a translation right 4 units and down 3 units. Define the coordinates of any point in the image using (x, y) as the coordinates of any point in the original figure.

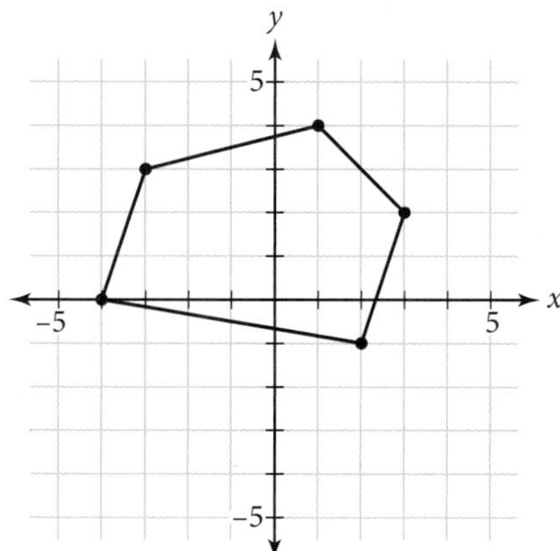

Solution

Translate every point right 4 units and down 3 units. For example, move the vertex at (1, 4) to (5, 1). This is the same as adding 4 to the x-coordinate and subtracting 3 from the y-coordinate. That is, $(1 + 4, 4 - 3)$ gives (5, 1).

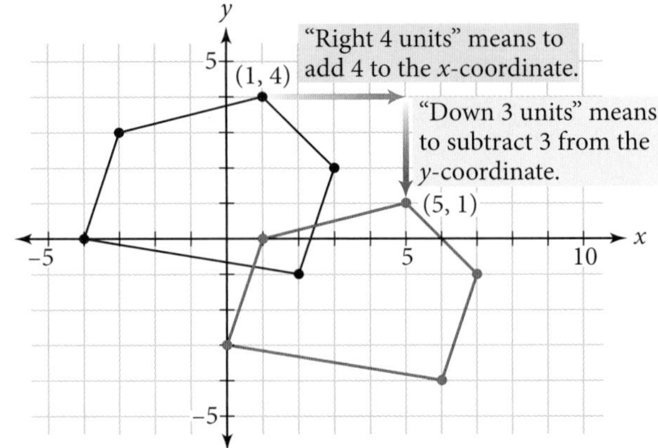

A definition for any point in the image is

$(x + 4, y - 3)$

On your calculator, you can list the x-coordinate of the vertices of the original pentagon in *list1*, and the y-coordinate of the vertices in *list2*. Then define the third list as *list3* = *list1* + 4 and the fourth list as *list4* = *list2* − 3 for the coordinates of the vertices of the image.

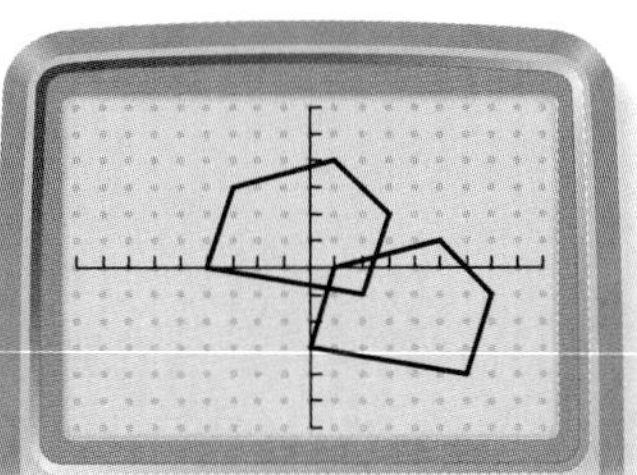

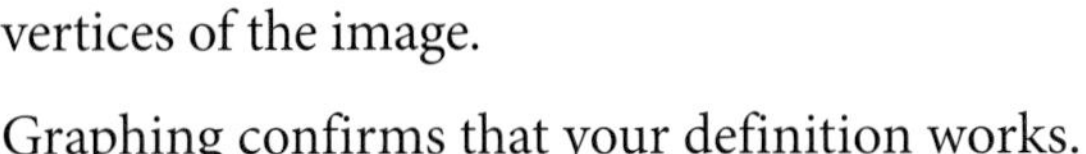

Graphing confirms that your definition works.

Exercises

You will need your graphing calculator for Exercise **6.**

1. Name the coordinates of the vertices of each figure.

a.

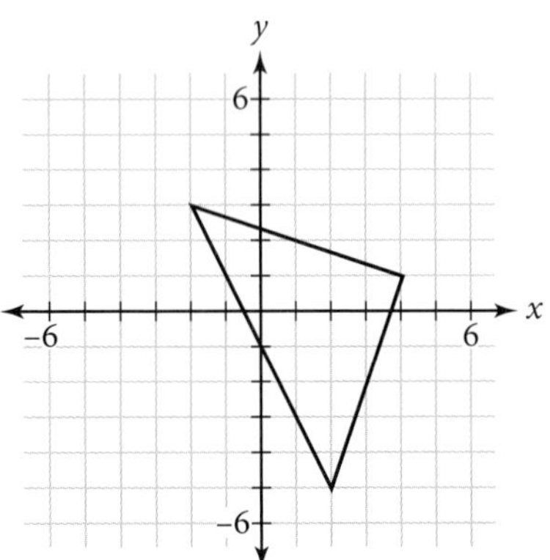

b.

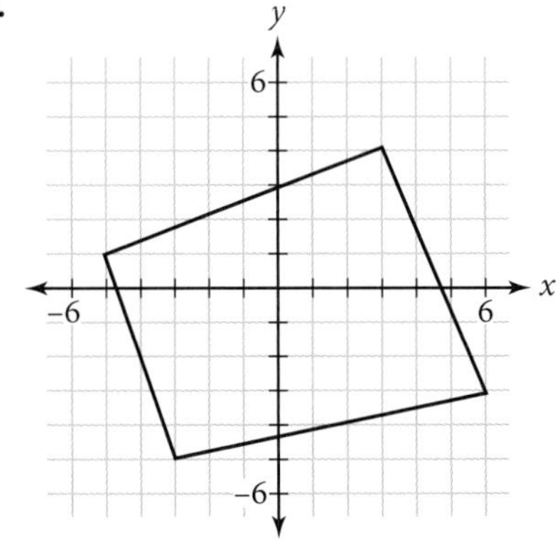

2. Consider this quadrilateral.

a. Name the coordinates of the vertices of the quadrilateral.

b. Sketch the image of the figure after a translation right 4 units and down 2 units.

c. Define the coordinates of the image using (x, y) as the coordinate of any point in the original figure.

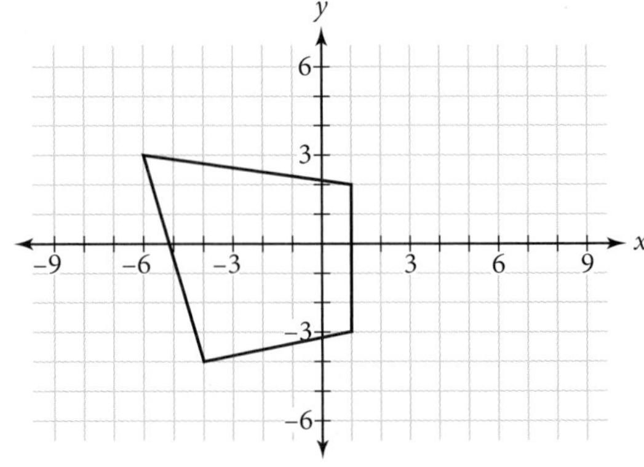

3. The red triangle at right is the image of the black triangle after a translation.

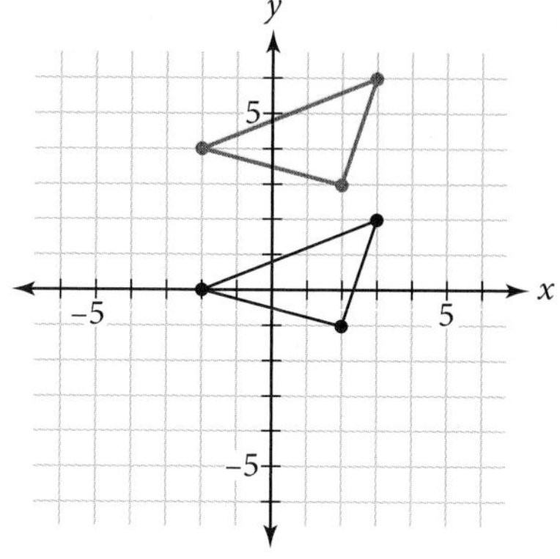

a. Describe the translation.

b. Describe how the x-coordinates of the vertices change between the original figure and the image.

c. Describe how the y-coordinates of the vertices change.

4. Consider the square at right.

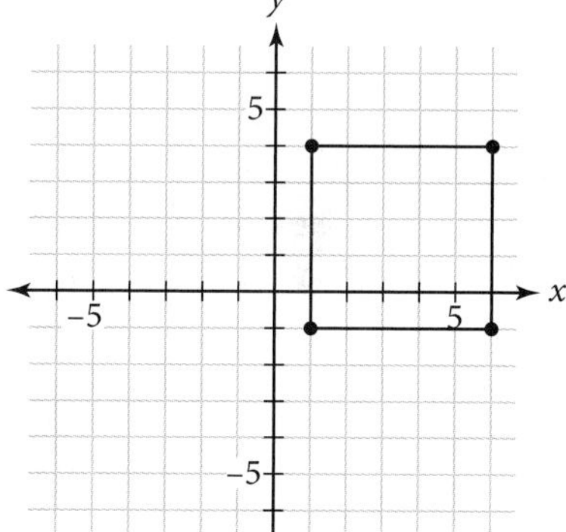

a. Sketch the image of the figure after a translation left 2 units.

b. Define the coordinates of any point in the image using (x, y) as the coordinates of any point in the original figure.

5. The "spider" in the upper left has its x-coordinates listed in *list1* and its y-coordinates listed in *list2*.

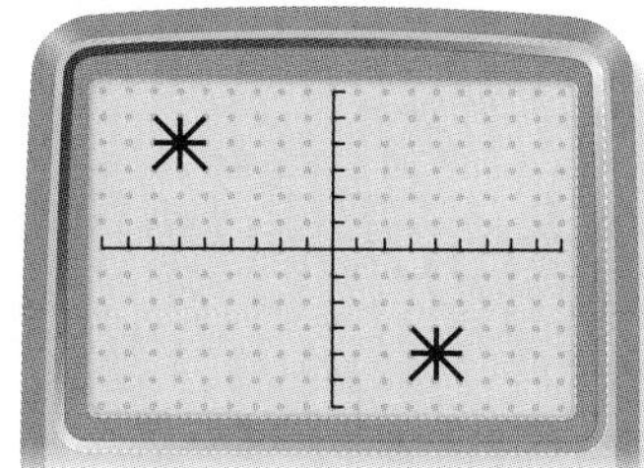

[−9.4, 9.4, 1, −6.2, 6.2, 1]

a. Describe the translations made to create the image in the lower right.

b. Write definitions for the x-coordinates listed in *list3* and the y-coordinates listed in *list4* in terms of *list1* and *list2*.

c. How would your answer to 5b change if the "spider" in the lower right were the original figure and the figure in the upper left were the image?

6. The coordinates of a polygon are $(-2, 1)$, $(4, 6)$, $(2, 2)$, and $(5, -1)$. A translation of the polygon is defined by the rule $(x - 4, y - 5)$.

a. Describe the translation.

b. Sketch the original polygon and its image on the same coordinate plane.

c. Use calculator lists and a graph to check your sketch in 6b.

LESSON

7.1

Function Notation

"The theory that has had the greatest development in recent times is without any doubt the theory of functions."

VITO VOLTERRA

As you learned in Chapter 4, every function defines a relationship between an input (independent) variable and an output (dependent) variable. **Function notation** uses parentheses to name the input, or independent, variable for the function. For instance, $y = f(x)$, which is read "y equals f of x," says "y is a function of x" or "y depends on x." (In function notation, the parentheses do *not* mean multiplication.)

Albert Einstein writes mathematical notation during a lecture to scientists in 1931.

You can show some functions with an equation. For example, the equation $y = 2x + 4$ represents a function, so you can write it as $f(x) = 2x + 4$. The notation $f(3)$ tells you to substitute 3 for x in the equation $y = 2x + 4$. So $f(3) = 2(3) + 4$. The value of $f(x)$ when $x = 3$ is 10. By itself, f is the name of the function. In this case, its rule is $2x + 4$.

Not all functions are expressed as equations. The graph below shows a new function, $f(x)$. No rule or equation is given, but you can still use function notation to find output values. For example, on the graph the point at $x = 4$ has coordinates $(4, f(4))$, or $(4, 1)$. The value of y when x is 4 is $f(4)$. So $f(4) = 1$. Check that $f(2)$ is 4. What is the value of $f(6)$? Can you find two x-values for which $f(x) = 1$?

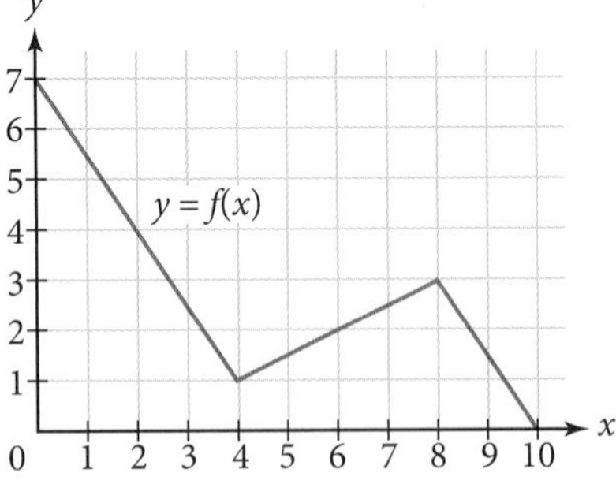

In the investigation you will learn more about using function notation with graphs.

INVESTIGATION

A Graphic Message

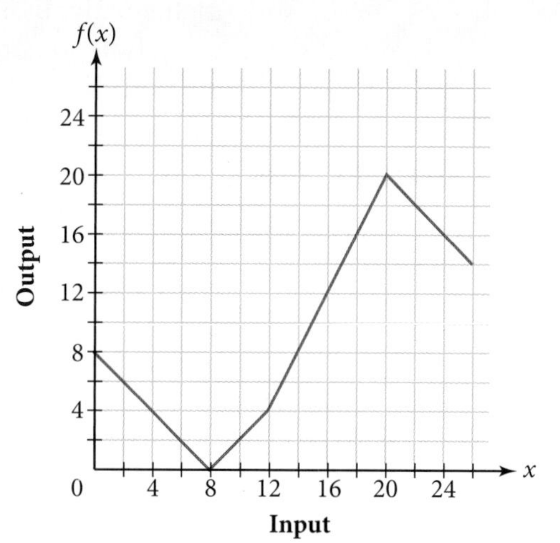

In this investigation you will apply function notation to learn the identity of the mathematician who introduced functions.

Step 1 Describe the domain and range of the function f in the graph.

Step 2 Use the graph to find each function value in the table. Then do the indicated operations.

Notation	Value
$f(3)$	
$f(18) + f(3)$	
$f(5) \cdot f(4)$	
$f(15) / f(6)$	
$f(20) - f(10)$	

Step 3 Use the rules for the order of operations to evaluate the expressions below involving function values. Do any operations inside parentheses first. Then use the graph to find the function values before doing the remaining operations. Write your answers in a table.

Notation	Value
$f(0) + f(1) - 3$	
$5 \cdot f(9)$	
x when $f(x) = 10$	
$f(9 + 8)$	
x when $f(x) = 0$	
$f(8 \cdot 3) - 5 \cdot f(11)$	
$f(4 \cdot 5 - 1)$	
$f(12)$	

Step 4 Think of the numbers 1 through 26 as the letters A through Z. Find the letters that match your answers in Step 2 to learn the mathematician's last name. Find the letters that match your answers in Step 3 to discover the first name.

The mathematician whose name you decoded was the inventor of much of the mathematical notation in use today. Function notation is used extensively in mathematics. It is important to be able to write, interpret, and evaluate expressions using function notation. This lesson will help you strengthen these skills before you are introduced to new functions.

EXAMPLE A You can use the function $f(x) = \frac{9}{5}x + 32$ to find the temperature $f(x)$ in degrees Fahrenheit for any given temperature x in degrees Celsius. Find the specified value.

a. $f(15)$

b. $f(-10)$

c. x when $f(x) = 41$

d. x when $f(x) = -4$

Solution In parts a and b, substitute the value in parentheses for x in the function. In parts c and d, substitute the given value for $f(x)$.

a. $f(15) = \frac{9}{5}(15) + 32$
$f(15) = 27 + 32$
$f(15) = 59$

b. $f(-10) = \frac{9}{5}(-10) + 32$
$f(-10) = -18 + 32$
$f(-10) = 14$

c. $41 = \frac{9}{5}x + 32$
$9 = \frac{9}{5}x$
$5 = x$

d. $-4 = \frac{9}{5}x + 32$
$-36 = \frac{9}{5}x$
$-20 = x$

EXAMPLE B Given $f(x) = 4x + 7$ and $g(x) = \frac{7}{x-1}$, evaluate $f(3) + g(3)$.

Solution Substitute the value in parentheses for x in the appropriate function. Evaluate $f(3)$ and $g(3)$ separately, and then add the results:

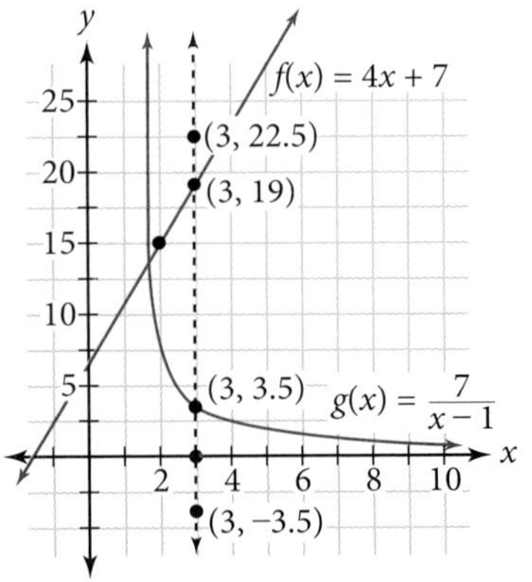

$f(3) = 4(3) + 7$
$= 19$

$g(3) = \frac{7}{3-1}$
$= \frac{7}{2}$

$f(3) + g(3) = 19 + \frac{7}{2}$
$= \frac{38}{2} + \frac{7}{2}$
$= \frac{45}{2}$

Notice that you get the same result if you add the y-values of the points on the graphs of the functions at $x = 3$.

You can also use function notation to describe points on a graph.

EXAMPLE C Use the graph of $f(x)$ to determine

a. $f(3)$

b. x when $f(x) = 4$

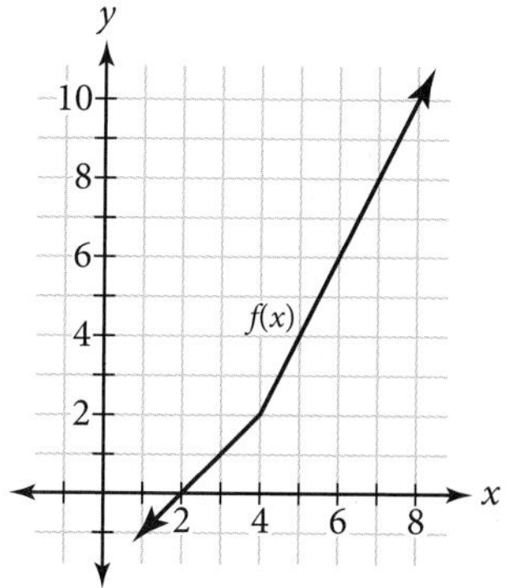

Solution All points on the graph have coordinates $(x, f(x))$.

a. $f(3)$ is the second coordinate of the point on the graph with x-coordinate 3. The point $(3, 1)$ is on the graph, so $f(3) = 1$.

b. Locate any point on the graph with second coordinate 4. The point $(5, 4)$ is the only one, so $f(x) = 4$ when $x = 5$.

[▶ See **Calculator Note: Function Notation** to learn how to evaluate functions on your calculator. ◀]

Note that you don't always have to call a function f, and the input doesn't have to be x. You can call a function $g(x)$, $h(t)$, or any letters you prefer. Sometimes you'll choose letters that represent the variables, such as t for time and h for height. But when you use your calculator, you'll usually need to translate your variables into x and y.

7.1 Exercises

You will need your graphing calculator for Exercises **1, 2, 13,** and **16.**

Practice Your Skills

1. Find each value for $f(x) = 3x + 2$ and $g(x) = x^2 - 1$ without using your calculator. Then use your calculator to check your answers. [▶ See **Calculator Note: Function Notation.** ◀]

a. $f(3)$ b. x when $f(x) = 2$ @ c. $g(5)$ d. $g(-3)$

e. $f(-4)$ f. $g(-2)$ g. x when $f(x) = 11$ h. x when $g(x) = -1$

2. Find the y-coordinate corresponding to each x-coordinate if the functions are $f(x) = -2x - 5$ and $g(x) = 3.75(2.5)^x$. Check your answers with your calculator.

a. $f(6)$ @ b. $f(0)$ c. $g(2)$ d. $g(-2)$

e. $f(-4)$ f. $g(-1)$ g. $f(3)$ h. $g(0)$

3. Use the given functions $f(x)$, $g(x)$, and $h(x)$ to find the requested values.

$f(x) = 4 + \frac{1}{2}(x - 3)$ $g(x) = \frac{x + 1}{3}$ $h(x) = 5 - 2x$

a. $f(11) + g(5)$ @ b. $g(8) - h(2)$ c. $f(3) \cdot g(2) \cdot h(1)$

d. $f(-1) - g(-1)$ e. $h(2) + g(2)$ f. $g(-4) + h(-4)$

4. Use the graph of $f(x)$ to find:

a. $f(1)$

b. $f(5)$

c. x when $f(x) = 0$

d. $f(2) + f(3)$

e. x when $f(x) = -1$ ⓐ

f. x when $f(x) = x$

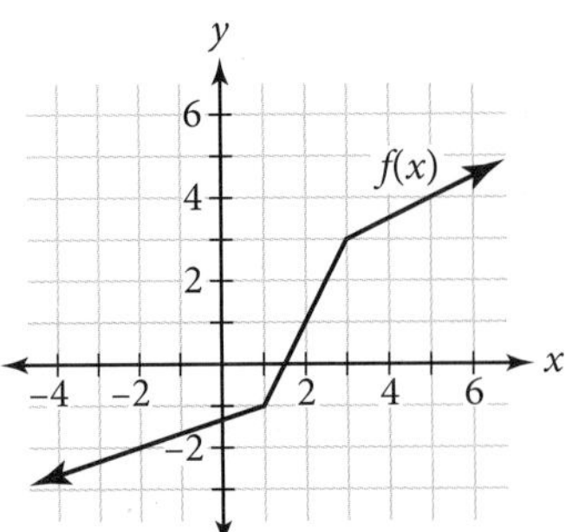

5. Use the graphs of $f(x)$ and $g(x)$ to find:

a. $f(2) + g(2)$

b. $f(4) \cdot g(4)$ ⓐ

c. x when $f(x) = g(x)$

d. x when $g(x) = 2 + f(x)$

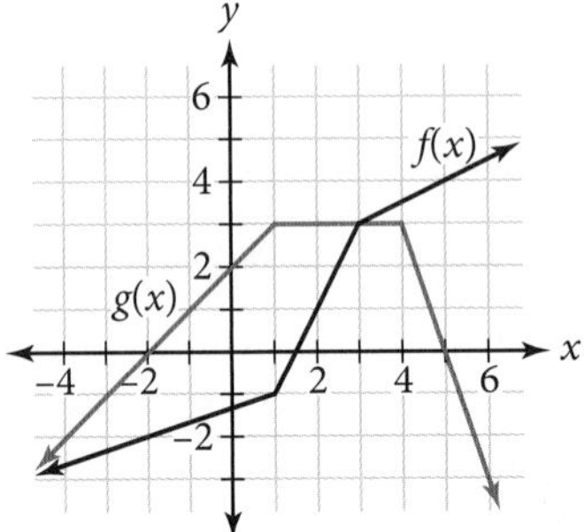

6. If $f(x)$ is a linear function with $f(2) = 5$ and $f(6) = 11$, write the equation for $f(x)$.

Reason and Apply

7. Draw the graph of a function that has all these features:

- $f(-2) = 3$
- $f(0) = 6$
- $f(2) = f(5)$
- The domain is all real numbers from -5 to 5, inclusive.
- The range is from -2 to 6, inclusive.

8. APPLICATION The graph of the function $y = f(x)$ shows the temperature, y, outside at different times, x, over a 24-hour period.

a. What are the dependent and independent variables? ⓐ

b. What are the domain and range shown on the graph? ⓐ

c. Use function notation to represent the temperature at 10 h. ⓐ

d. Use function notation to represent the time at which the temperature is 10°F. ⓐ

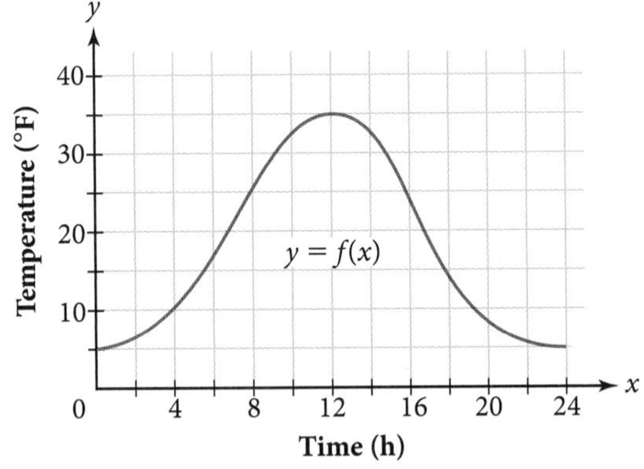

9. The function $f(x)$ gives the lake level over the past year, with x measured in days and y, the $f(x)$-values, measured in inches above last year's mean height. ⓗ

a. What is the real-world meaning of $f(60)$?

b. What is the real-world meaning of $f(x) = -3$?

c. What is an interpretation of $f(x) = f(150)$?

10. APPLICATION A population of bacteria decreases at the rate of 8.5% per hour. There are 650 bacteria present at the start.

a. Write an equation that describes this population decay. What domain and range values make sense for this situation?

b. On your calculator, graph the function you wrote in 10a.

c. The time it takes for the population to decrease to half its original size is called its half-life. Graph the horizontal line that represents half the starting amount of bacteria. Find the point of intersection of this line with the population decay function.

d. What is the real-world meaning of your answer in 10c?

11. Use the graph of $f(x)$ at right to evaluate each expression. Write your answers as a number sequence. Then think of the numbers 1 through 26 as the letters A through Z to decode a message.

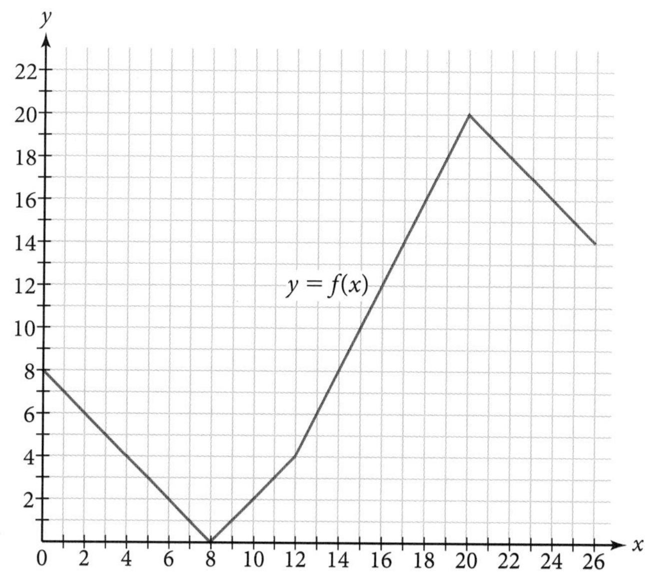

a. $f(8) + 6$ @

b. $f(20) + 1$

c. the sum of two x-values that give $f(x) = 8$ @

d. $f(0) - 4$

e. $f(7)$

f. x when x is an integer and $f(x) = 15$

g. $f(18) + f(5)$

h. (the sum of two x-values that give $f(x) = 16) \div 42$

i. (x when $f(x) = 12) - 8$

j. $\dfrac{f(25)}{3}$

k. $f(7) + f(8)$

l. the largest domain value − the largest range value − 2

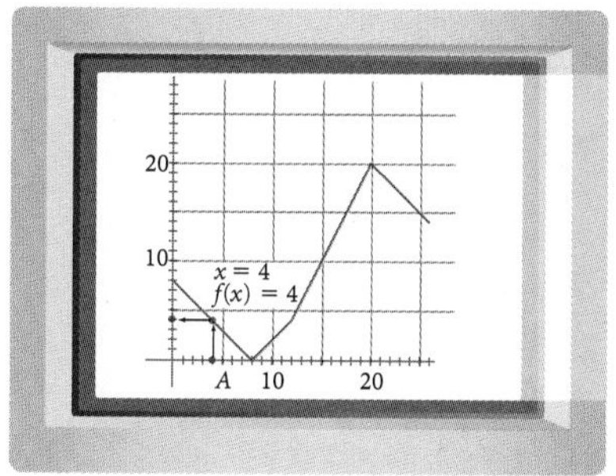

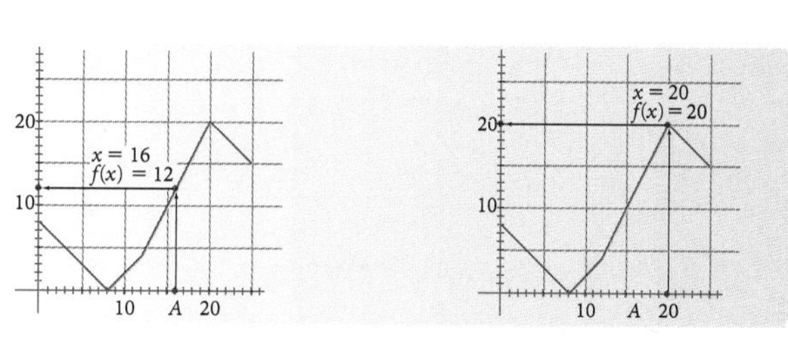

[▶ You can use the **Dynamic Algebra Exploration** in your ebook to explore input and output values of the function in Exercise 15. ◀]

12. The graph of $f(x)$ represents an object dropped straight down from the Tower of Pisa.

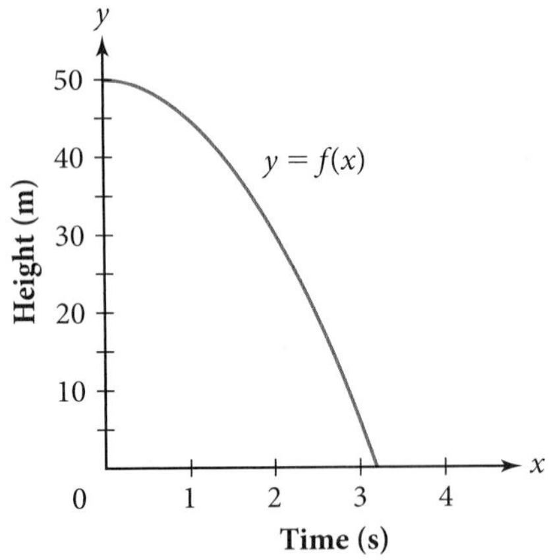

a. What are the domain and range of the function? ⓐ

b. Describe a real-world sequence of events for the graph. ⓐ

c. About how far does the ball drop in the 1st second (from $x = 0$ to $x = 1$)? ⓐ

d. About how far does the ball drop in the 2nd second (from $x = 1$ to $x = 2$)?

e. A dropped object has an initial velocity of 0 m/s. It accelerates as it falls. Sketch a graph of the velocity of the object dropped from the Tower of Pisa as a function of time. Describe your graph. How does your graph relate to the graph above? ⓗ

Review

13. Write each expression in exponential form using only positive exponents.

a. $(a^3)^{-3}$ b. $(b^2)^5$ c. $(a^4b^2)^3$ d. $(c^2d^3)^{-4}$

14. Find the slope of the line passing through each pair of points.

a. $(1, 3)$ and $(-2, 6)$ ⓐ b. $(-4, -5)$ and $(7, 0)$ c. $(-3, 6)$ and $(9, 6)$

15. Solve each equation.

a. $2x - 5 = 7x + 15$ b. $3(x + 6) = 12 - 5x$ c. $\dfrac{7(8 - x)}{4} = x + 3$

Creating New Functions

When you first encountered algebraic expressions, you were given expressions and asked to evaluate them by substituting some value for x. For example, to evaluate the expression $x^2 + 5$ when $x = 7$, you replaced x with 7 and calculated the value.

In Lesson 7.1, you saw function notation used as shorthand for "evaluate at this value." For example, given $f(x) = x^2 + 5$, find $f(7)$.

You can also use function notation when the given values are not numbers.

EXAMPLE A

Given $g(x) = \frac{x}{x + 10}$, find each function value.

a. $g(5)$

b. $g(\square)$

c. $g(t + 2)$

Solution

For each part, substitute the value in parentheses for x in the expression.

a. $$g(5) = \frac{5}{5 + 10} = \frac{5}{15} = \frac{1}{3}$$

b. $$g(\square) = \frac{\square}{\square + 10}$$

c. $$g(t + 2) = \frac{(t + 2)}{(t + 2) + 10} = \frac{t + 2}{t + 12}$$

You can also use function notation to describe new functions in terms of existing functions. These new functions are often called *transformations* of the original function. While they can have different forms, they are usually written without parentheses and with like terms combined.

EXAMPLE B

Given $f(x) = 3 + 1.5x$, define these new functions.

a. $g(x) = f(4x)$

b. $h(x) = f(x + 2)$

c. $j(x) = 6f(x)$

Solution To evaluate a function, you substitute the given value for the input variable. In this case, that value is an expression. Substitute the expression, and then simplify.

$$f(x) = 3 + 1.5x$$

a. $g(x) = f(4x)$
$= 3 + 1.5(4x)$
$= 3 + 6x$

b. $h(x) = f(x + 2)$
$= 3 + 1.5(x + 2)$
$= 3 + 1.5x + 3$
$= 6 + 1.5x$

c. $j(x) = 6f(x)$
$= 6(3 + 1.5x)$
$= 18 + 9x$

In this chapter you will learn how the new functions defined in Example B are related to the original functions in terms of their graphs, domains, ranges, and other properties.

EXAMPLE C Is it always, sometimes, or never true that $f(-x) = -f(x)$?

Solution To explore whether a statement is always, sometimes, or never true, look at a few examples using different types of functions.

Start with a simple function, such as $f(x) = 5x$.

$f(-x) = 5(-x)$ $\quad -f(x) = -(5x)$

$f(-x) = -5x$ $\quad -f(x) = -5x$

For this function, $f(-x)$ does equal $-f(x)$.

Now try a function that is a little more complex, such as $f(x) = 3 + 5x$.

$f(-x) = 3 + 5(-x)$ $\quad -f(x) = -(3 + 5x)$

$f(-x) = 3 - 5x$ $\quad -f(x) = -3 - 5x$

For this function, $f(-x)$ does *not* equal $-f(x)$.

Therefore the claim is sometimes true.

Exercises

1. Given $h(x) = \frac{5}{2} - 2x$, evaluate each expression. Write your answers without parentheses, and combine like terms.

a. $h(z)$ b. $h(2x)$ c. $h(x - 3)$ d. $h(x) + 2$

2. Given $f(x) = \frac{x + 5}{2x}$, define each new function. Write your answers without parentheses, and combine like terms.

a. $f(x + 1)$ b. $f(3x)$ c. $4f(x)$ d. $f(-x)$

3. Use different functions to explore whether each statement is always, sometimes, or never true. Give at least two functions that support each answer.

a. $f(2x) = 2f(x)$ b. $f(x) + 3 = f(x + 3)$

LESSON

7.2

Piecewise Functions and Absolute Value

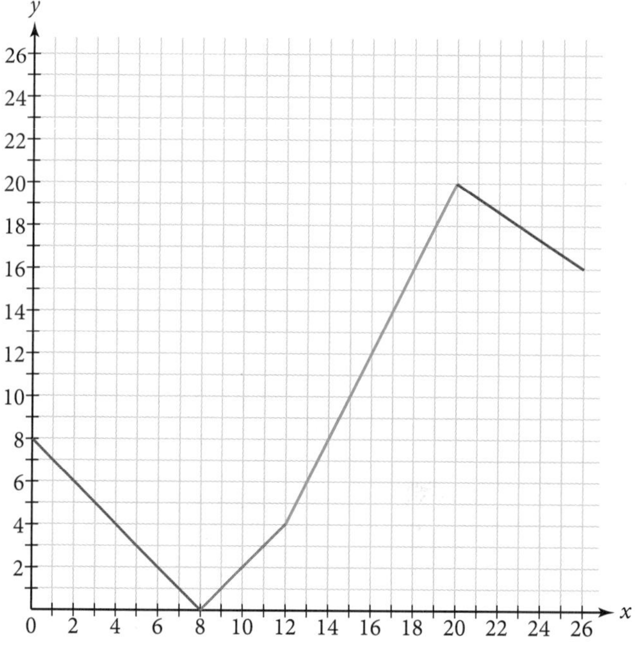

Recall this graph from the investigation in Lesson 7.1. In that investigation you used the graph to solve a code. But if you wanted a computer to do the decoding, it would need an equation rather than a graph. How would you write an equation to represent that code?

This graph represents a **piecewise function.** The equation of this function has four pieces, and each piece is defined for a specific domain. Working with piecewise functions is just like working with ordinary functions, except that you need to specify the domain. This piecewise function describes the graph:

$$f(x) = \begin{cases} 8 - x & 0 \le x < 8 \\ -8 + x & 8 \le x < 12 \\ 4 + 2(x - 12) & 12 \le x < 20 \\ 20 - \frac{2}{3}(x - 20) & 20 \le x < 26 \end{cases}$$

EXAMPLE A

Consider the piecewise function $f(x) = \begin{cases} 4 + x & x \le 3 \\ 13 - 2x & x > 3 \end{cases}$

a. Find each value.

i. $f(1)$ ii. $f(5)$

b. Graph $f(x)$.

Solution

a. To evaluate a piecewise function for a given input value, you must first determine which part of the piecewise function to apply.

i. Because $1 < 3$,

$$f(1) = \begin{cases} 4 + 1 & x \le 3 \\ \cancel{13 - 2x} & \cancel{x > 3} \end{cases} = 5$$

ii. Because $5 > 3$,

$$f(5) = \begin{cases} \cancel{4 + x} & \cancel{x \le 3} \\ 13 - 2(5) & x > 3 \end{cases} = 3$$

b. Find $f(x)$ for several values of x, including any points at the boundary of the domains—in this case, $x = 3$.

x	$f(x)$
−1	3
1	5
3	7
5	3
6	1

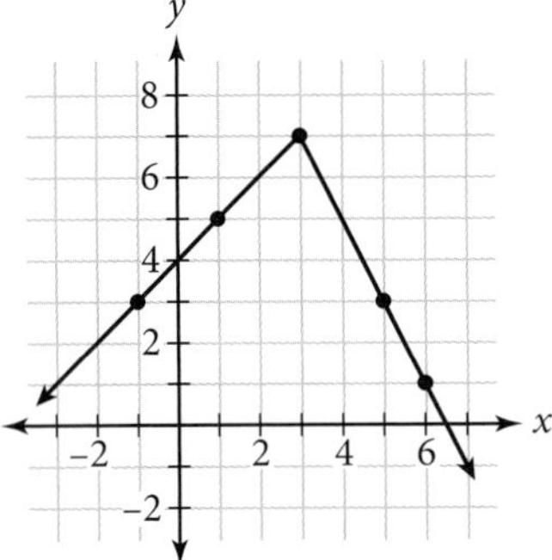

Plot the points and connect them to graph each piece of the graph in its domain.

INVESTIGATION

Valuable Pieces

In this investigation you will explore a special piecewise function.

Step 1 Complete the table for the piecewise function $f(x) = \begin{cases} x & x \geq 0 \\ -x & x < 0 \end{cases}$

Take care to use the correct piece of the function each time you evaluate $f(x)$.

x	$f(x) = -x$	x	$f(x) = x$
. . .		0	
−3		1	
−2		2	
−1		3	
		. . .	

Step 2 Plot the points and graph the piecewise function.

Step 3 Based on your graph, find these function values.

a. $f(7)$

b. $f(-5)$

c. $f(-2.5)$

Step 4 Use your graph to answer these questions.

a. What is x when $f(x) = 3$?

b. What is x when $f(x) = 6$?

c. What is x when $f(x) = -1$?

Step 5 The function defined and graphed here is the **absolute-value function.** The output is the **absolute value** of the input. Describe in your own words how to determine the absolute value of a number.

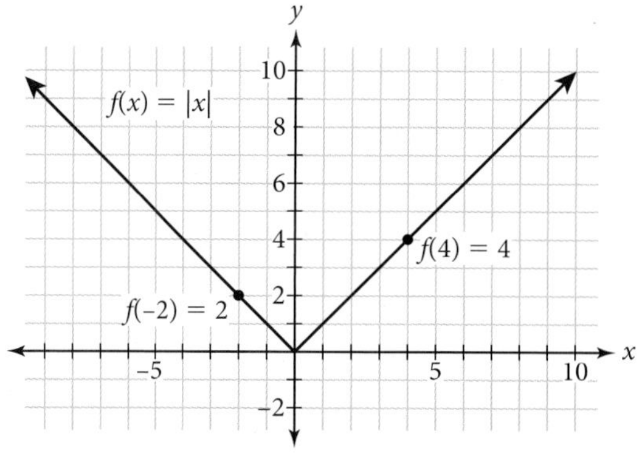

The absolute value of a number can be thought of as the distance that number is from zero on the number line. Because distance is never negative, the absolute value of a number is never negative. It is the size, or magnitude, of the number, without regard to whether the number is positive or negative.

For example, Cal and Al both live 3.2 miles from school but in opposite directions. If you assign the number 0 to the school, you can show that Cal and Al live in opposite directions from it by assigning $+3.2$ to Al's house and -3.2 to Cal's apartment. For both Cal and Al, the distance from school is 3.2 miles.

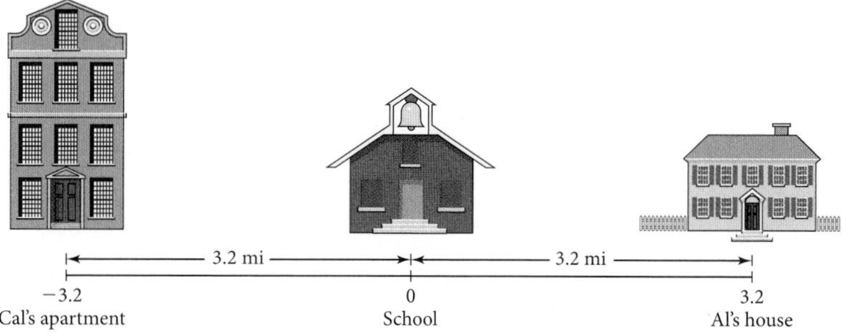

Because both x and $-x$ have the same absolute value, equations involving absolute values usually have more than one solution. To graph the absolute-value function on your calculator, input $y = \text{abs}(x)$. [▶ See **Calculator Note: Absolute-Value Function** for how to access the absolute value command ◀]

EXAMPLE B

Solve each equation or inequality.

a. $|x| + 7 = 12$ b. $|x - 2| + 7 = 12$ c. $|x - 2| + 7 \geq 12$

Solution

The process for symbolically solving equations and inequalities that involve absolute value is a bit different because there is no function for "undoing" the absolute value—and often there is more than one solution.

a. You might use a graph to estimate your solutions.

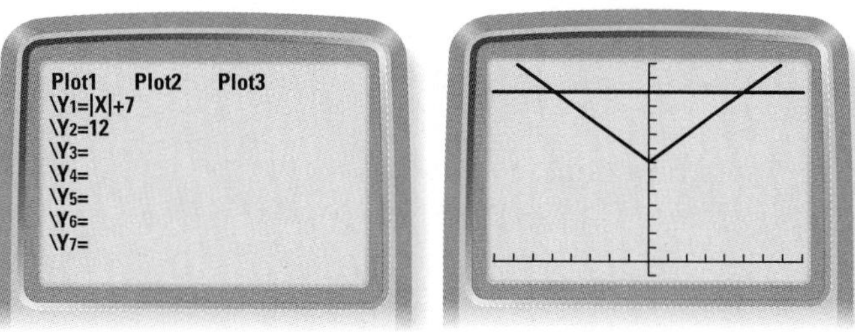

[−8, 8, 1, −1, 14, 1]

The graphs appear to intersect when $x = 5$ and $x = -5$.

Here's how to solve the equation symbolically:

$\lvert x\rvert + 7 = 12$	Original equation.
$\lvert x\rvert = 5$	Subtract 7 from both sides of the equation.
$x = 5$ and $x = -5$	The two numbers whose absolute value is 5.

b.

$\lvert x - 2\rvert + 7 = 12$	Original equation.
$\lvert x - 2\rvert = 5$	Subtract 7 from both sides of the equation.
$x - 2 = 5$ and $x - 2 = -5$	$x - 2$ is equal to both 5 and -5.
$x = 7$ and $x = -3$	Add 2 to both sides of each equation.

c. Again, you might use a graph to estimate your solution.

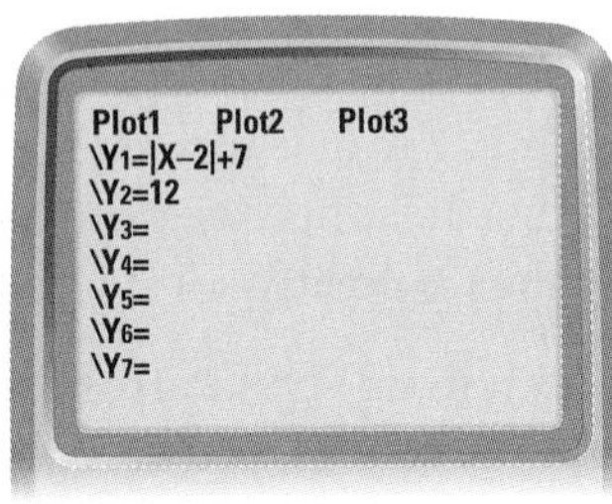

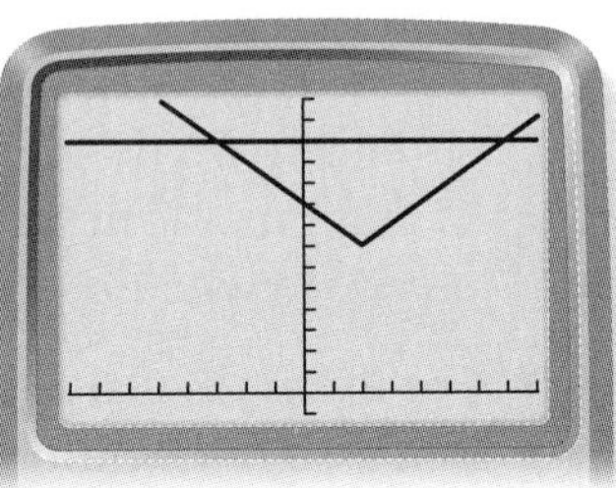

[−8, 8, 1, −1, 14, 1]

From part b, you know that $\lvert x - 2\rvert + 7 = 12$ when $x = 7$ and $x = -3$. The graph of $y = \lvert x - 2\rvert + 7$ is at or above the graph of $y = 12$ when $x \geq 7$ and when $x \leq -3$. So the solution is $x \geq 7$ and $x \leq -3$.

Whatever method you use to solve an absolute-value equation, you always have to be sure that you are finding all possible solutions. In general, an absolute-value equation has two solutions, one solution, or no solution.

If you're not sure how many solutions an equation should have, first look at the graph of the situation and then decide which method you want to use to solve the equation.

The absolute-value function is a special piecewise function. Another special piecewise-defined function is called the greatest integer, or floor, function. This function takes an input and rounds it down to an integer value. You probably use this function whenever someone asks how old you are. If you turned 14 on your last birthday, you probably answer "14," not "14 years 2 months 7 days." The most common notation for this function is $\lfloor x\rfloor$, although some mathematicians use $[\![x]\!]$. The graph looks like a series of steps, so functions that look like this are sometimes called **step functions.**

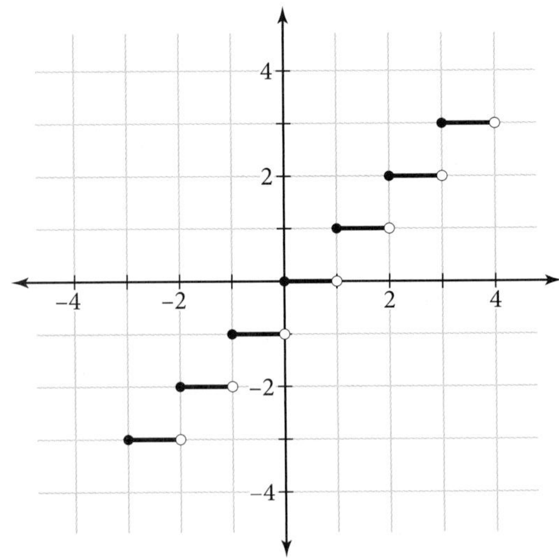

EXAMPLE C

Evaluate each of the following:

a. $\lfloor 3.7\rfloor$ **b.** $\lfloor -4.2\rfloor$ **c.** $\lfloor 2\rfloor$

Solution

a. Round 3.7 down to get $\lfloor 3.7 \rfloor = 3$.

b. Negative numbers can be a bit tricky. Just remember that you are rounding down to an integer. So you round -4.2 down to get $\lfloor -4.2 \rfloor = -5$.

c. Because 2 is an integer already, the greatest integer function does not change its value. So $\lfloor 2 \rfloor = 2$.

The greatest integer function would be tough to write as a piecewise function because it has an infinite number of pieces. Try to write a small part of the piecewise version of the greatest integer function.

7.2 Exercises

You will need your graphing calculator for Exercises **1, 3,** and **5.**

Practice Your Skills

1. Find the value of each expression without using a calculator. Check your results with your calculator. [▶ See **Calculator Note: Absolute-Value Function.** ◀]

a. $|-7|$

b. $|0.5|$

c. $|-7 + 2|$

d. $\lfloor -7.2 \rfloor + \lfloor 3.4 \rfloor$

e. $-|5|$

f. $-|-5|$ ⓐ

g. $\lfloor -4.1 \rfloor \cdot \lfloor 2.8 \rfloor$

h. $\dfrac{|-6|}{|2|}$

2. Find the x-values that satisfy each statement.

a. $|x| = 10$

b. $|x| > 4$

c. $|x + 1| = 8$

d. $|x - 2| = 4$

e. $|x| \leq 2$

f. $|x| > 0$

3. Evaluate both sides of each statement to determine whether to replace the box with $=$, $<$, or $>$. Use your calculator to check your answers.

a. $|5| + |7| \;\square\; |5 + 7|$

b. $|-5| \cdot |8| \;\square\; |-40|$

c. $\lfloor -5.2 - 4.5 \rfloor \;\square\; \lfloor -5.2 \rfloor - \lfloor 4.5 \rfloor$ ⓐ

d. $|-2 + 11| \;\square\; |-2| + |11|$

e. $\dfrac{|36|}{|-9|} \;\square\; \dfrac{|36|}{|-9|}$

f. $|4|^{|-2|} \;\square\; |4^{-2}|$

g. $|-2| + |3| + |-5| \;\square\; |-2 + 3 + -5|$

h. $\dfrac{|-2||6|}{|-4|} \;\square\; \dfrac{|-2 \cdot 6|}{|-4|}$

4. Consider the functions $f(x) = 3x - 5$ and $g(x) = |x - 3|$. Find each value.

a. $f(5)$ ⓐ

b. $f(-2.5)$

c. $g(-5)$ ⓐ

d. $g(1)$

5. Plot the function $y = |x|$ (or $y = \text{abs}(x)$ on some calculators). [▶ See **Calculator Note: Friendly Windows** to learn about friendly windows. ◀] Use the trace feature to evaluate $|2.8|$ and $|-1.5|$.

Reason and Apply

6. Consider the piecewise function $f(x) = \begin{cases} x - 2 & x < 2 \\ 2 - x & x \geq 2 \end{cases}$

a. Evaluate $f(-7)$.

b. Evaluate $f(7)$.

c. Graph $f(x)$.

7. Solve each system of equations.

a. $\begin{cases} y = |x| \\ y = 2.85 \end{cases}$ ⓐ

b. $\begin{cases} y = 3x - 5 \\ y = |x - 3| \end{cases}$ ⓗ

8. Solve each equation for x and check your answers.

a. $|x| = 12$

b. $10 = |x| + 4$

c. $10 = 2|x| + 6$ ⓐ

d. $4 = 2(|x| + 2)$

9. Write specific directions for the walk represented by this calculator graph. Include time, speed, position, and direction. Each mark on the x-axis represents 1 second, and each mark on the y-axis represents 1 meter.

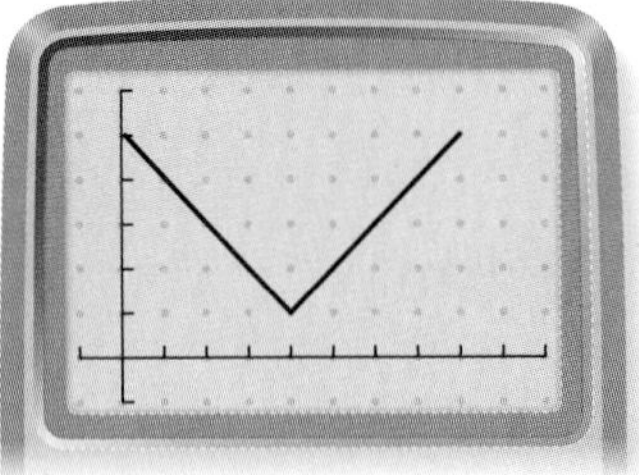

10. The graph in part a of Example B shows two solutions for x.

a. Replace $y = 12$ with a horizontal line that gives exactly one solution for x. ⓗ

b. Replace $y = 12$ with a horizontal line that gives no solution for x.

11. Identify which function, $f(x)$, $g(x)$, or $h(x)$, is represented by each (*input, output*) pair.

$f(x) = 7 + 4x$ $\qquad g(x) = |x| + 6$ $\qquad h(x) = 18(1 + 0.5)^x$

a. (5, 11) ⓐ

b. (1, 27)

c. (−2, 8)

d. (3, 19)

12. The solutions to the equation $|x - 4| + 3 = 17$ are $x = -10$ and $x = 18$.

a. Explain why the equation has two solutions.

b. What are the solutions to the inequality $|x - 4| + 3 \leq 17$? Explain. ⓐ

c. What are the solutions to the inequality $|x - 4| + 3 > 17$? Explain.

13. **APPLICATION** Write a piecewise function to describe this graph.

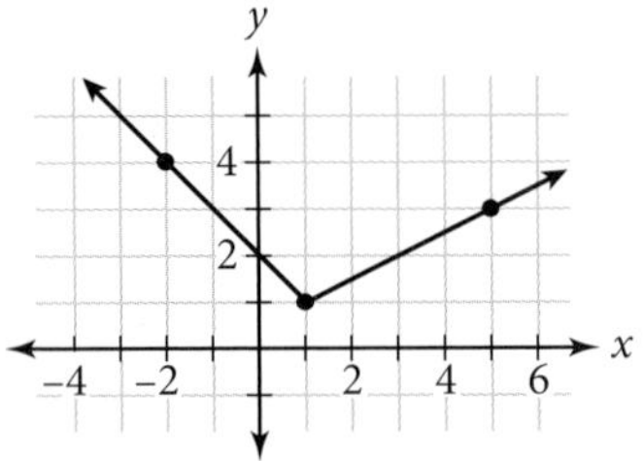

14. If possible, solve each equation for x. Check your answer by substituting the solution value or values into the original equation.

a. $|x + 1| = 7$ Ⓐ

b. $2|3x - 1| = 4$

c. $|2x - 4.2| - 3 = -3$

d. $3|x + 2| = -6$ Ⓗ

15. Consider $f(x) = \lfloor x \rfloor$ and $g(x) = \begin{cases} 3 & \text{when } x \leq 4 \\ 4 & \text{when } x > 4 \end{cases}$ on the interval $3 \leq x < 5$.

a. Find $f(3.5)$ and $g(3.5)$.

b. Find $f(4.7)$ and $g(4.7)$.

c. Are there any x-values in the interval $3 \leq x < 5$ where $f(x) \neq g(x)$?

Review

16. Solve each system of equations using the method of your choice. For each system tell which method you chose and why.

a. $\begin{cases} -2x + 3y = 12 \\ 4x - 3y = -21 \end{cases}$

b. $\begin{cases} 5x + y = 12 \\ 2x - 3y = 15 \end{cases}$

17. Solve each inequality, and graph the solution on a number line.

a. $-2 < 6x + 8$ Ⓐ

b. $3(2 - x) + 4 \geq 13$ Ⓐ

c. $-0.5 \geq -1.5x + 2(x - 4)$

IMPROVING YOUR Reasoning SKILLS

Consider this table of the squares of numbers between 0 and 50 that end in 5.

Number	5	15	25	35	45
Square	25	225	625	1225	2025

Do you notice a pattern that helps you mentally calculate these kinds of square numbers quickly? Can you square 65 in your head? When you think you have discovered the pattern, check your results with a calculator. Then try reversing the process to find the square root of 7225.

Practice this pattern, and then race someone who is using a calculator to see who is quicker at computing a square number ending in 5. Will this pattern work for all numbers ending in 5? Why or why not? Are there numbers for which this pattern is too difficult to use?

LESSON 7.3

Squares, Squaring, and Parabolas

Think of a number between 1 and 10. Multiply it by itself. What number did you get? Try it again with the opposite of your number. Did you get the same result? This result is called the **square** of a number. The process of multiplying a number by itself is called **squaring.** The square of a number x is "x squared," and you write it as x to the power 2, or x^2. When you calculate the area of a square, you multiply the length of a side by itself. If the side length of the square is x, the area of the square is x^2. When squaring numbers on your calculator, remember the order of operations. Try entering -3^2 and $(-3)^2$ into your calculator. Which result is the square of -3?

History **CONNECTION**

The mathematical process of squaring takes its name from the application of finding a square's area. From the Latin *quadrare,* which means to make square, we also have the word *quadratic* to describe x^2.

Many real-world situations, such as calculating the area of squares and circles, involve squaring. Do you think the rule for squaring is a function? To answer this question, you will graph the relationship between numbers and their squares.

Mosaic art has been around for centuries. Small pieces of stone or glass of different colors are *tessellated* to create a pattern or picture, often square tiles.

INVESTIGATION

Graphing a Parabola

In this investigation you will explore connections between any number x and its square by graphing the coordinate pairs (x, x^2).

Step 1 Make a table with column headings like the ones shown. Write the integers -10 through 10 in the first column, and then enter these numbers into the first list on your calculator.

Number x	Square x^2

Step 2 Without a calculator, find the square of each number and place it in the second column. Check your results by squaring the first list using the x^2 key. [▶ See **Calculator Note: Some Functions** to learn how to use the squaring function.◀] Store these numbers in the second list.

Step 3 How do the squares of numbers and their opposites compare?

Step 4 Choose an appropriate window and plot points in the form (*first number, second number*). [▶ See **Calculator Note: Scatter Plots** to review scatter plots. ◀] Graph $y = x^2$ on the same set of axes. What relationship does this graph show?

Step 5 Is the graph of $y = x^2$ the graph of a function? If so, describe the domain and range. If not, explain why not.

The graph of the **squaring function,** $y = x^2$, is a **parabola.** In Chapter 8, you will learn how to create other parabolas based on variations of this basic equation.

The parabolic shape of a radio telescope collects radio signals from space.

Step 6 In what quadrants are the points of the parabola representing $y = x^2$?

Step 7 What makes (0, 0) on your curve unique? Where is this point on the parabola?

Step 8 Draw a vertical line through (0, 0). How is this line like a mirror?

Step 9 Compare your parabola to the graph of the absolute-value function, $y = |x|$. How are they alike, and how are they different?

Step 10 Which x- and y-values on your parabola could represent side lengths and areas of squares?

What happens when you try to undo squaring while solving an equation? In the next example you will see what happens when you use the **square root** to undo squaring.

Square Root

A square root of a number is a value you multiply by itself to get that number.

Positive numbers have two square roots, one positive and one negative. The symbol $\sqrt{}$ refers to the nonnegative square root, or principle square root.

$\sqrt{25} = 5$**, because** $5^2 = 25$ **and 5 is nonnegative**

EXAMPLE A | Graph the function $f(x) = \sqrt{x^2}$. What other function has the same graph?

Solution Make a table of values, and connect the points to graph the function.

x	y
-3	3
-2	2
-1	1
0	0
1	1
2	2
3	3

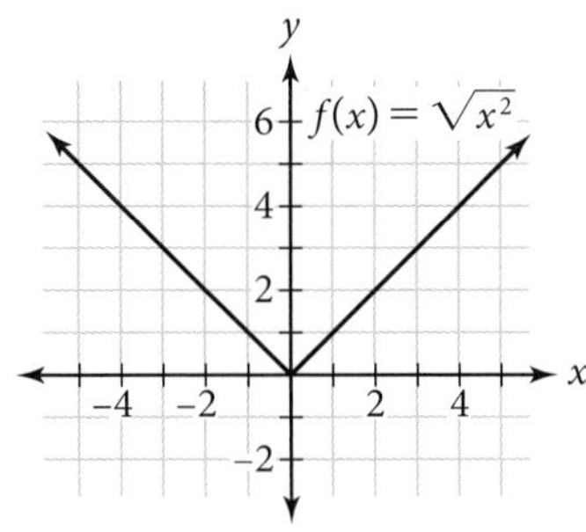

You can see that the graph is the same as the graph of the absolute-value function $y = |x|$, so it follows that $\sqrt{x^2} = |x|$. Recall that a square root always gives a positive result. You might at first think that $\sqrt{x^2} = x$, but x can be positive or negative. This is inconsistent with the definition of a square root, so it must be true that $\sqrt{x^2} = |x|$, which is always positive. [To apply the square root function using your graphing calculator, see **Calculator Note: Some Functions.**]

EXAMPLE B Solve the equation $x^2 = 16$.

Solution

$x^2 = 16$	Original equation.
$\sqrt{x^2} = \sqrt{16}$	Take the square root of both sides.
$|x| = 4$	Because $\sqrt{x^2} = |x|$.
$x = 4$ and $x = -4$	There are two solutions.

This solution makes sense because two values give 16 when squared, 4 and -4.

In some instances only one of the solutions will make sense. However, because the graph of the **square root function** $f(x) = \sqrt{x^2}$ is the same as the graph of the absolute-value function $f(x) = |x|$, whenever you solve by undoing a square you must remember to use the absolute value to get all possible solutions.

7.3 Exercises

You will need your graphing calculator for Exercise **4.**

Practice Your Skills

1. Complete the table by filling in the missing values for the side, perimeter, and area of each square.

Side (cm)	Perimeter (cm)	Area (cm^2)
1		
2		
	12	
		16
14		
	60	
		441
	100.8	
		2209

2. Solve each equation for x.

a. $|x| = 6$ @ b. $x^2 = 36$ @

c. $|x| = 3.8$ d. $x^2 = 14.44$

3. Solve each equation, if possible.

a. $4.7 = |x| - 2.8$ b. $-41 = x^2 - 28$ @

c. $11 = x^2 - 14$ d. $x^2 + 5 = 6$

e. $10 - x^2 = -15$ f. $x^2 + 11 = 7$

4. Solve each equation for x. Use a calculator graph to check your answers.

a. $|x - 2| = 4$ @   b. $(x - 2)^2 = 16$ @

c. $|x + 3| = 7$ d. $(x + 3)^2 = 49$

e. $|x + 4| = 3$ f. $(x + 4)^2 = 9$

Reason and Apply

5. For what values of x is $|x| \geq x^2$? To check your answer, graph $y = |x|$ and $y = x^2$ on the same set of axes.

6. For what values of y does the equation $y = x^2$ have

a. No real solutions? @   b. Only one solution?   c. Two solutions?

7. Look at the table of squares in the Investigation Graphing a Parabola. Use values from this table to explain why the equation $y = x^2$ is nonlinear.

8. MINI-INVESTIGATION Find the sum of each set of numbers in 8a–c.

a. The first five odd positive integers

b. The first 15 odd positive integers

c. The first n odd positive integers @

d. Use the diagram to explain the connection among the sum of odd integers, square numbers, and these square figures.

 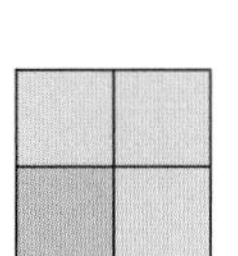 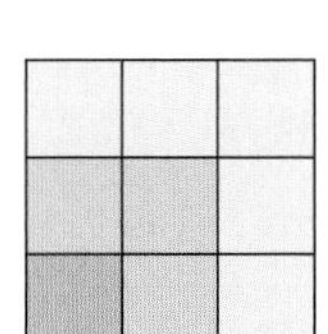 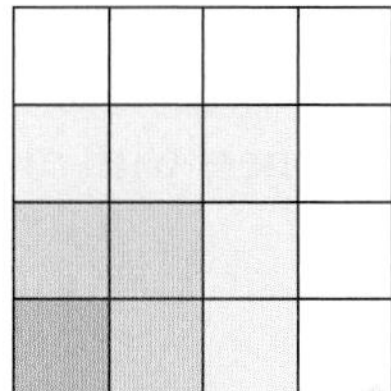

9. Write an equation to describe the function represented by each table. Use your calculator to check your answers.

a.

x	−3	−1	0	1	4	6
y	14	10	8	6	0	−4

b.

x	−3	−1	0	1	4	6
y	9	1	0	1	16	36

c.

x	−3	−1	0	1	4	6
y	3	1	0	1	4	6

d.

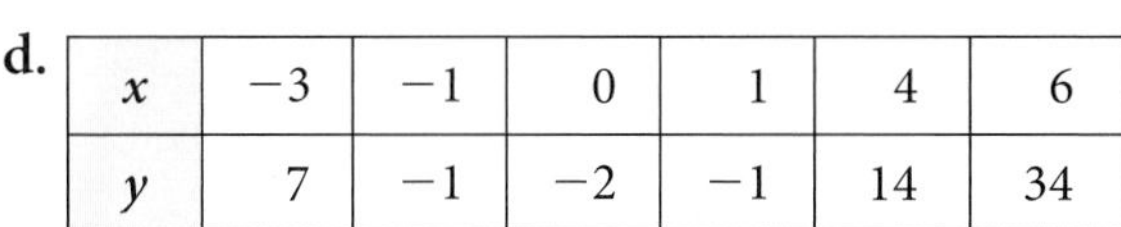

x	−3	−1	0	1	4	6
y	7	−1	−2	−1	14	34

10. This 4-by-4 grid contains squares of different sizes.

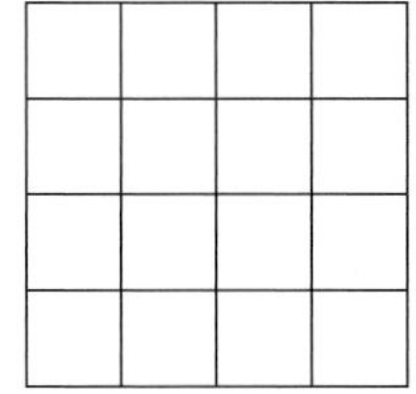

a. How many of each size square are there? Include overlapping squares. @

b. How many total squares would a 3-by-3 grid contain? A 2-by-2 grid? A 1-by-1 grid?

c. Find a pattern to determine how many squares an n-by-n grid contains. Use your pattern to predict the number of squares in a 5-by-5 grid.

11. Explain why the equation $x^2 = -4$ has no solutions. (h)

Review

x	y
0	
4	126.5625
3	168.75
1	
	1000

12. The table shows exponential data.

a. What equation in the form $y = ab^x$ can you use to model the data in the table? @

b. Use your equation to find the missing values.

13. Use properties of exponents to find an equivalent expression in the form ax^n.

a. $24x^6 \cdot 2x^3$ @

b. $(-15x^4)(-2x^4)$

c. $\dfrac{72x^{11}}{3x^2}$

d. $4x^2(2.5x^4)^3$

e. $\dfrac{15x^5}{-6x^2}$

f. $(-3x^3)(4x^4)^2$

g. $\dfrac{42x^{-6}y^2}{7y^{-4}}$

h. $3(5xy^2)^3$

14. Graph the functions $f(x) = 3x - 5$ and $g(x) = |x - 3|$. What do the two graphs tell you about the equation $3x - 5 = |x - 3|$?

IMPROVING YOUR Visual Thinking SKILLS

Square numbers are so named because they result from the geometric application of finding the area of a square. A square with side length 3 has area equal to 3^2, or 9. You can represent 9 and other *perfect square* numbers with diagrams like this:

1

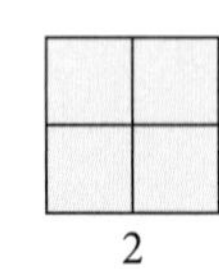
2

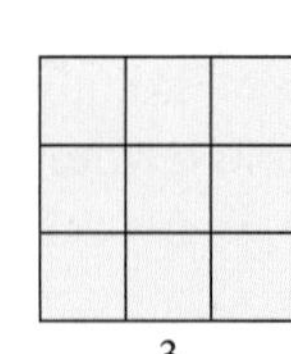
3

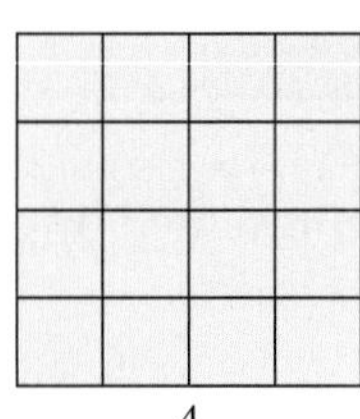
4

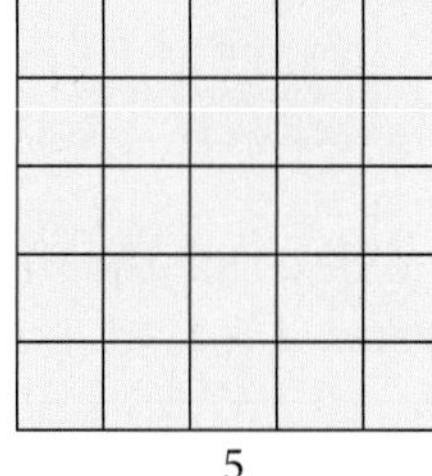
5

What numbers result when you represent them with cubes instead of squares? Use sugar cubes to make these shapes:

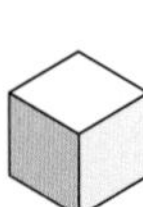

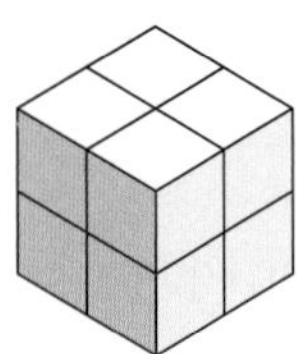

How many sugar cubes does it take to make each figure? What is the relationship between the side length (measured in sugar cubes) and the total number of cubes needed for each figure? How many times larger is the resulting volume of a cubic figure if you double the side length? If you triple the side length?

LESSON

7.4

Determining Rate of Change

You are in charge of ordering T-shirts for your club. The shirt company provides you with the price list below.

Number of Shirts	Cost
10	$250
20	$290
30	$325
40	$350
50	$370
60	$385

Your club only has 28 members, so you don't want to order 20 or 30 shirts. You only want to order 28 shirts. But you are not sure what that would cost.

You could look at the cost per shirt, but that cost is different at each point in the price list provided. For instance, if you order 20 shirts, the cost is $\frac{\$290}{20} = \$14.50$ for each shirt. What is the cost per shirt if you order 30 shirts?

What is more useful is the rate at which the cost of an order of shirts is increasing. If this were a linear function, then that rate would be called the slope. For a line the slope, or **rate of change,** is the same everywhere. Since this is not a linear function, the rate of change is not constant but instead depends on the interval you are looking at. So the rate of change is found by using the **average rate of change.**

Consider the interval from 20 to 30 shirts. The rate of change for the interval is $\frac{325 - 290}{30 - 20} = \frac{35}{10} = \$3.50$ per shirt. This is not the cost of the shirt; it is the rate at which the total cost is changing. Another way to think about it is that each additional shirt ordered between the total of 20 and 30 shirts will cost $3.50. Based on this rate, we can estimate the cost of ordering 28 shirts as 8 times $3.50, or $28, more than the cost of 20 shirts. So the cost of ordering 28 shirts is about $\$290 + \$28 = \$318$.

How would you estimate the cost of ordering 52 shirts?

Any continuous function will have an average rate of change that can help you understand and describe the behavior of that function. In the next example you will see that increasing the diameter of a rug rapidly changes the time it takes to make the rug for larger rugs.

EXAMPLE A

The time t, in hours, it takes the Round Rug Company to make a braided rug is equal to 7 times the square of the diameter of the rug d, in feet ($t = 7d^2$). Find the average rate of change between a rug with a 4-foot diameter and a rug with a 6-foot diameter, and explain what the value tells you. Then do the same for a rug with an 8-foot diameter and a rug with a 10-foot diameter.

Solution

A 4-foot-diameter rug takes $7(4)^2$ or 112 hours, while a 6-foot-diameter rug takes $7(6)^2$ or 252 hours. So the average rate of change is $\frac{252-112}{6-4} = 70$ hours per foot. The total time is increased an average of 70 hours per foot if you increase the diameter of a rug between 4 and 6 feet by an extra foot.

The average rate of change between 8-foot- and 10-foot-diameter rugs is $\frac{7(10)^2 - 7(8)^2}{10-8} = \frac{700-448}{2} = \frac{252}{2} = 126$ hours per foot. Adding an extra foot to an 8- to 10-foot-diameter rug could add about 126 hours to the project.

Another way to describe this average rate of change by using graphs is to give the slope of the **secant line.** This is a line that passes through any two points of your graph. You can visually see how the average rate of change depends on the interval you are interested in.

EXAMPLE B

The amount you owe on a $100,000 home loan for a 30-year mortgage is shown in the graph. The graph shows that after 20 years you still owe about $80,000. Estimate and compare the average rate of change between years 10 and 15 with the average rate of change between years 20 and 25.

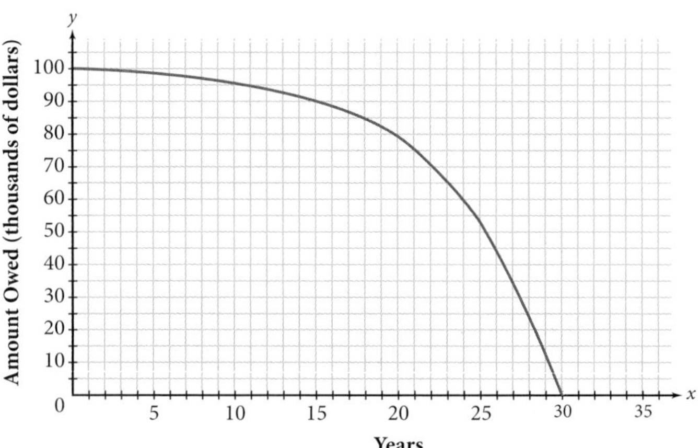

Solution

At year 10 you owe about $96,000, which drops to about $91,000 by year 15. So this average rate of change is $\frac{91{,}000 - 96{,}000}{15-10} = \frac{-5{,}000}{5} = -\$1{,}000$ per year. But in the interval between years 20 and 25 the rate is $\frac{53{,}000 - 79{,}000}{25-20} = \frac{-26{,}000}{5} = -\$5{,}200$ per year. So in this interval your mortgage is dropping at more than five times the rate it was in the other interval.

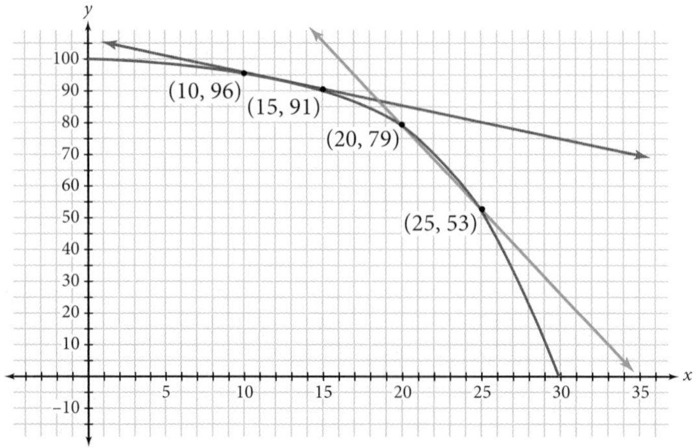

INVESTIGATION

Rate of Change

Over a four-week period, the number of weeds in Angelica's garden increased from 10 to 160. The average rate of change for the weeds during the four weeks is the slope between the two points (0, 10) and (4, 160).

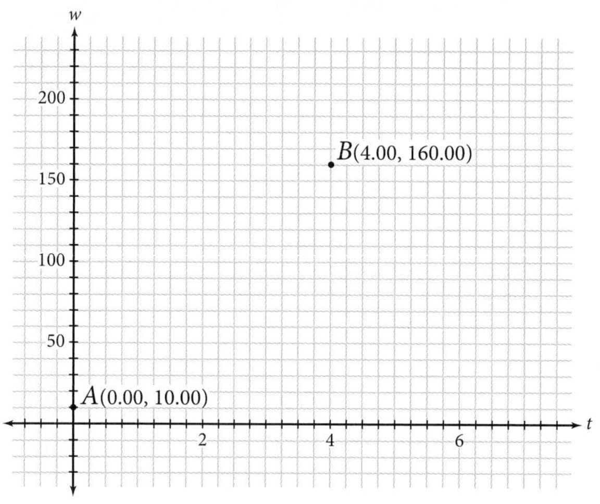

Here are three different models that fit these two data points:

$$w_1 = 10 + 37.5t$$
$$w_2 = 10(2^t)$$
$$w_3 = 10 + 75\sqrt{t}$$

Step 1 Calculate the number of weeds each week for each model, and record your answers in a table.

	Week				
Model	**0**	**1**	**2**	**3**	**4**
$w_1 = 10 + 37.5t$	10	47.5			

Step 2 Find the average rate of change in the number of weeds from each week to the next for each model. Record your answers in a table.

	Average Rate of Change			
Model	**Week 0 to Week 1**	**Week 1 to Week 2**	**Week 2 to Week 3**	**Week 3 to Week 4**
$w_1 = 10 + 37.5t$	37.5			

Step 3 Sketch a graph of each model over the interval $t = 0$ to $t = 4$.

Step 4 Look at the numbers in your table, and look at the shapes of the graphs.

a. For the first model, the rate of change should have been the same for each week. How does this show up in the graph?

b. For the second model, how does the rate of change vary from one week to the next? Does it increase or decrease? How does this show up in the graph?

c. For the third model, how does the trend in the rate of change differ from the second model? How does the shape of the graph show this difference?

Step 5 Graph the model $w_4 = -4.6875x^3 + 28.125x^2 + 10$. By looking at the graph, describe how you think the rate of change will vary over the four-week period.

Step 6 Sketch the graph of a function that meets each description:

a. The average rate of change is increasing.

b. The average rate of change is decreasing.

7.4 Exercises

Practice Your Skills

1. Find the slope of the line that passes through each pair of points.

a. (2, 7), (11, 20) b. (−3, 5), (6, −4) c. (0, 11), (8, 11) @

2. The slope of a line is $\frac{2}{3}$. If the point (6, 1) is on the line, name another point on the same line.

3. Consider the function $y = x^2 - 4$.

a. Find the average rate of change on the interval from $x = 1$ to $x = 3$. @

b. Find the average rate of change on the interval from $x = 3$ to $x = 7$.

c. Write the equation of the secant line containing the points for $x = 1$ and $x = 3$. @

d. Write the equation of the secant line containing the points for $x = 3$ and $x = 7$.

4. Akshay planted a garden and measured the height of one of his bean plants every day for a week. The data he collected are in the table below.

Day	1	2	3	4	5	6	7
Height (cm)	3	4.2	5.3	6.1	7.2	7.8	8.4

a. What is the average rate of change from day 1 to day 7?

b. What is the average rate of change from day 2 to day 5?

c. What is the average rate of change from day 4 to day 5? @

5. Use the graph to estimate values to answer the questions.

a. Estimate the average rate of change on the interval $0 \leq x \leq 4$. @

b. Estimate the average rate of change on the interval $-2 \leq x \leq 2$.

c. Estimate the average rate of change on the interval $-5 \leq x \leq 0$.

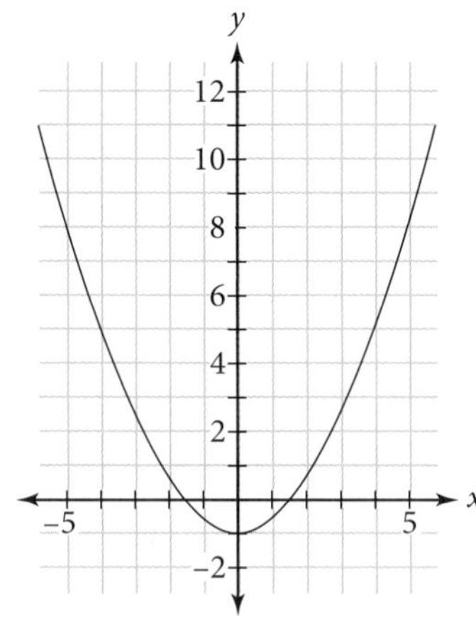

Reason and Apply

6. Consider the function $y = x^2 - 2$.

a. Graph this function, and draw the secant line between the points at $x = -3$ and $x = -1$. Then draw the secant line between the points at $x = 1$ and $x = 3$. ⓐ

b. Find the average rate of change for each of the secant lines in part a. How do they compare?

c. Find another pair of secant lines for this function that will have the same relationship.

d. What property of the function causes this relationship between the secant lines?

7. Some values for a continuous function are shown in the table.

x	1	3	4	8	11
y	23	26	28	37	56

a. What is the average rate of change on the interval $1 \leq x \leq 3$?

b. What is the average rate of change on the interval $4 \leq x \leq 11$?

c. Find an interval where the average rate of change is 2.2.

d. If x is measured in ounces and y is measured in dollars, then what are the units of the average rate of change?

8. Given this graph of a continuous function, estimate the values requested.

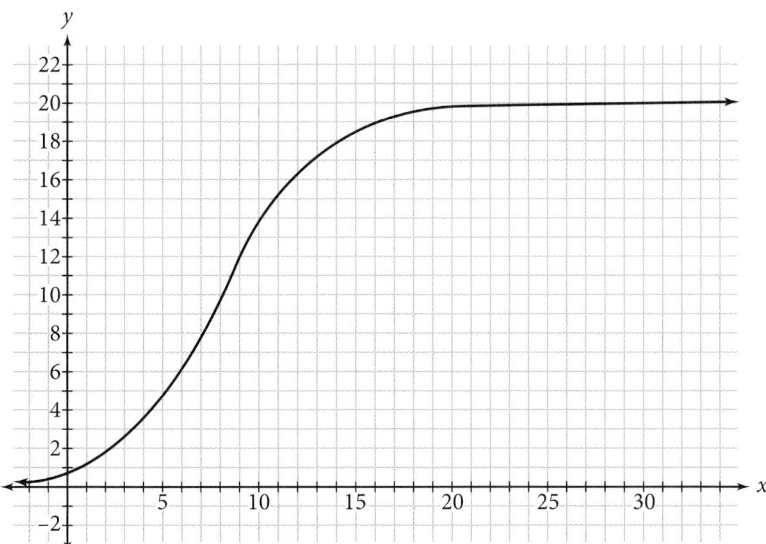

a. What is the average rate of change on the interval $4 \leq x \leq 10$?

b. What is the average rate of change on the interval $26 \leq x \leq 30$?

c. Find an interval where the average rate of change is 1.5.

d. How do you know there is no interval where the average rate of change is -2? ⓗ

e. Where would you find the greatest average rate of change?

9. Suppose the temperature T of a pizza is given by $T = 200 - 140(0.9^t)$, where t is the number of minutes after the pizza is placed in the oven.

a. Find the average rate of change over the first 2 minutes.

b. What is the real-world meaning of this average rate of change?

Review

10. Complete this table of values for $g(x) = |x - 3|$ and $h(x) = (x - 3)^2$.

x	0	1	2	3	4	5	6
$g(x)$							
$h(x)$							

11. Use $f(x) = 2 + 3x$ to find

a. $f(5)$ b. x when $f(x) = -10$ @ c. $f(x + 2)$ d. $f(2x - 1)$ @

12. Solve each equation for x.

a. $5 = -3 + 2x$ b. $-4 = -8 + 3(x - 2)$ c. $7 + 2x = 3 + x$

13. Write an equation to describe each graph.

a.

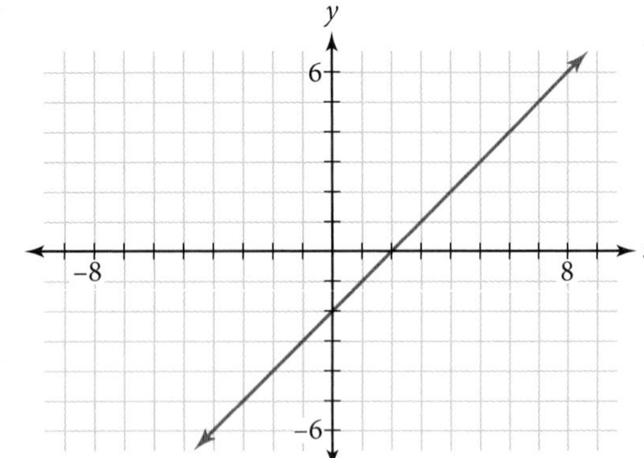

b.

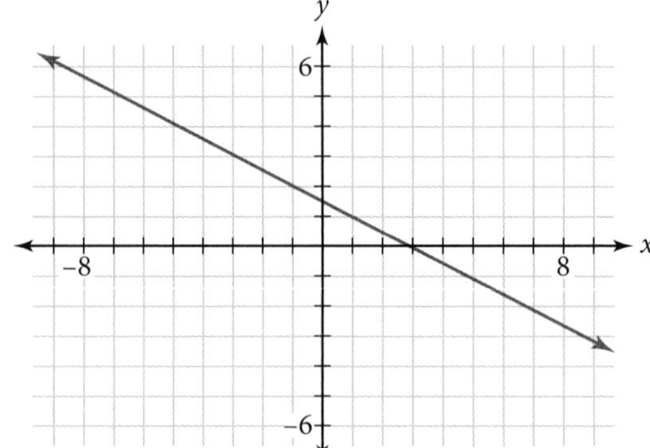

c.

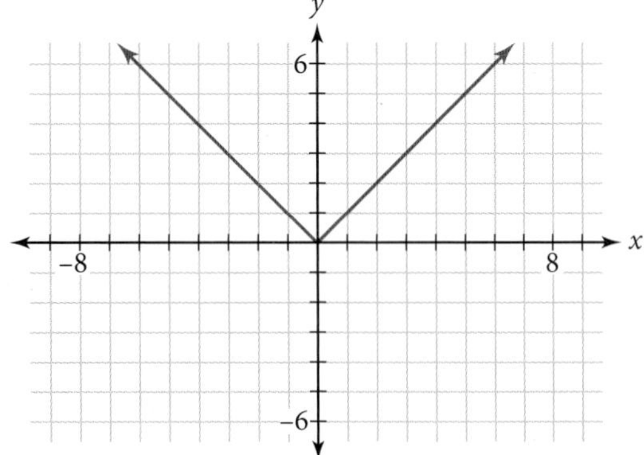

d.

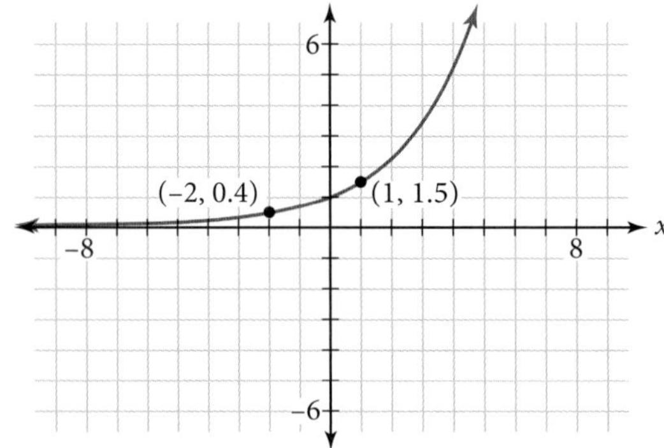

LESSON 7.5

Translating Graphs

"Poetry is what gets lost in translation."
ROBERT FROST

There are infinitely many linear and exponential functions. In previous chapters you wrote many of them "from scratch" using points, the y-intercept, the slope, the starting value, or the constant multiplier.

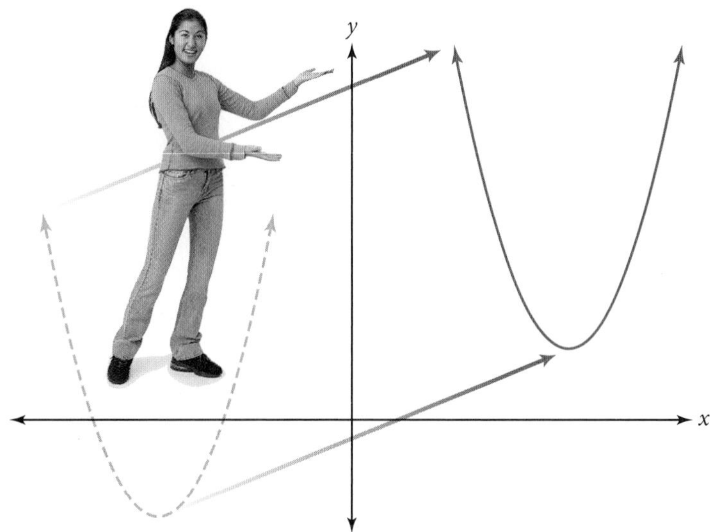

There are also infinitely many absolute-value and squaring functions. But rather than starting from scratch, you can transform $y = |x|$ and $y = x^2$ to create many different equations. In the investigation you will use what you know about translating points to translate functions. In mathematics, changing or moving a figure is called a **transformation.** If you discover any unexpected transformations along the way, make a note so that you can use them later in the chapter.

INVESTIGATION

Translations of Functions

Procedure Note

For this investigation use a screen with x and y scales of two units.

First you'll transform the absolute-value function by making changes to x.

Step 1 Graph $f(x) = |x|$ on your calculator.

Step 2 If you replace x with $x - 3$ in the function $f(x) = |x|$, you get $g(x) = |x - 3|$. Graph $g(x) = |x - 3|$ on the same screen as the graph of $f(x) = |x|$.

Step 3 Think of the graph of $f(x) = |x|$ as the original figure and the graph of $g(x) = |x - 3|$ as its image. How have you transformed the graph of $f(x) = |x|$?

The **vertex** of an absolute-value graph is the point where the function changes from decreasing to increasing or from increasing to decreasing.

Step 4 Name the coordinates of the vertex of the graph of $f(x) = |x|$. Name the coordinates of the vertex of the graph of $g(x) = |x - 3|$. How do these two points help verify the transformation you found in Step 3?

Step 5 Find a function for $h(x)$ that will translate the graph of $f(x) = |x|$ left 4 units. What is the function? What did you replace x with in the equation $f(x) = |x|$ to get your new function?

Step 6 Make a conjecture about the equation that will produce each translated graph below. Then write a function to model each translated graph. Check your work by graphing.

a.

b.

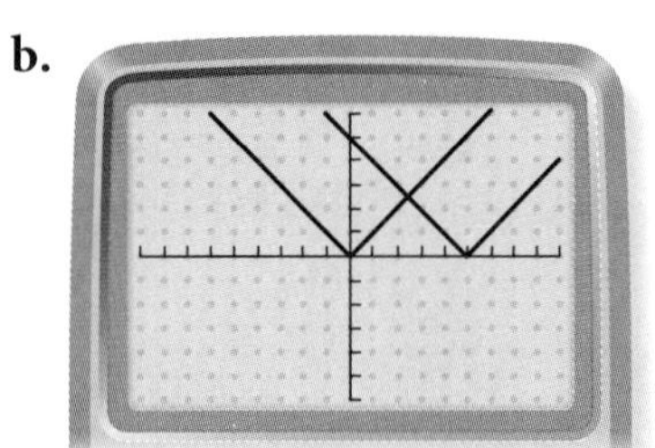

c.

Next you'll transform the absolute-value function by making changes to y.

Step 7 Clear all the functions in your graphing menu. Graph $f(x) = |x|$.

Step 8 If you replace $f(x)$ with $f(x) - 3$ in the function $f(x) = |x|$, you get $f(x) - 3 = |x|$. Solve for $f(x)$ and you get $f(x) = |x| + 3$. Name this new function $g(x)$ and graph it.

Step 9 Think of the graph of $f(x) = |x|$ as the original figure and the graph of $g(x) = |x| + 3$ as its image. How have you transformed the graph of $f(x) = |x|$?

Step 10 Name the coordinates of the vertex of the graph of $f(x) = |x|$. Name the coordinates of the vertex of the graph of $g(x) = |x| + 3$. How do these two points help verify the transformation you found in Step 9?

Step 11 Find a function for $g(x)$ that will translate the graph of $f(x) = |x|$ down 3 units. What is the function? What did you replace $f(x)$ with in the function $f(x) = |x|$ to get your new function?

Step 12 Make a conjecture about the equation that will produce each translated graph below. Then write a function to create each translated graph. Check your work by graphing.

a.

b.

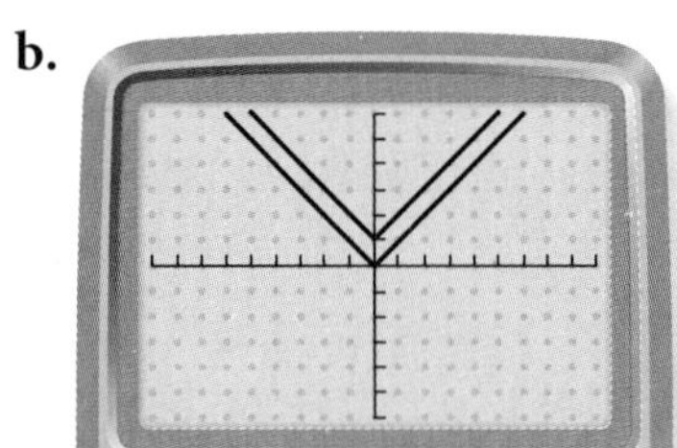

c.

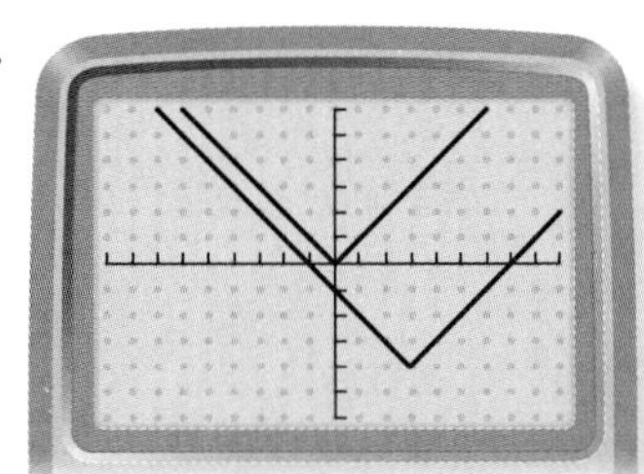

Step 13 Summarize what you have learned about translating the graph of the absolute-value function vertically and horizontally.

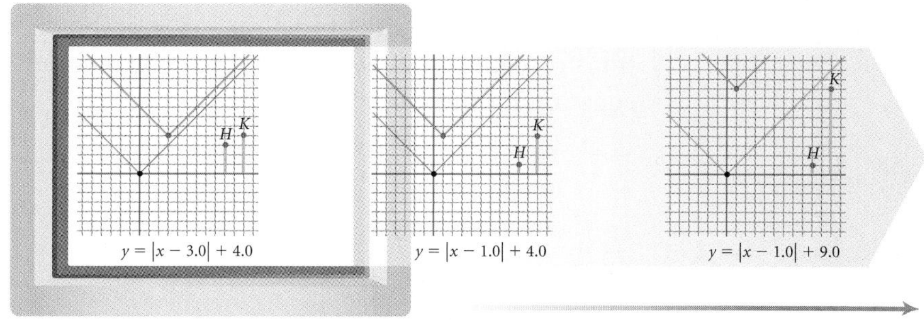

[▶ You can explore transformations interactively using the **Dynamic Algebra Exploration** in your ebook. ◀]

The most basic form of a function is often called a **parent function.** By transforming the graph of a parent function, you can create infinitely many new functions, or a **family of functions.** Functions like $y = |x - 3|$ and $y = |x + 3|$ are members of the absolute-value family of functions, with $y = |x|$ the parent function. Other families of functions include the linear family, with $y = x$ the parent; the squaring family, with $y = x^2$ the parent; and the base-3 exponential family, with $y = 3^x$ the parent.

Learning how to create a family of functions will help you see relationships between equations and graphs. The translations you learned in the investigation apply to any function.

Science CONNECTION

Earthquakes often translate Earth's crust along a *fault.* You can see faults most easily when buildings and other structures are translated too.

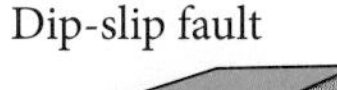

Dip-slip fault

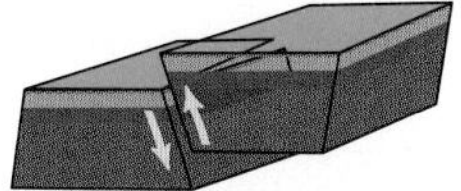

Strike-slip fault

EXAMPLE A The graph of the parent function $y = x^2$ is shown in black. Its image after a transformation is shown in red. Describe the transformation. Then write an equation for the image.

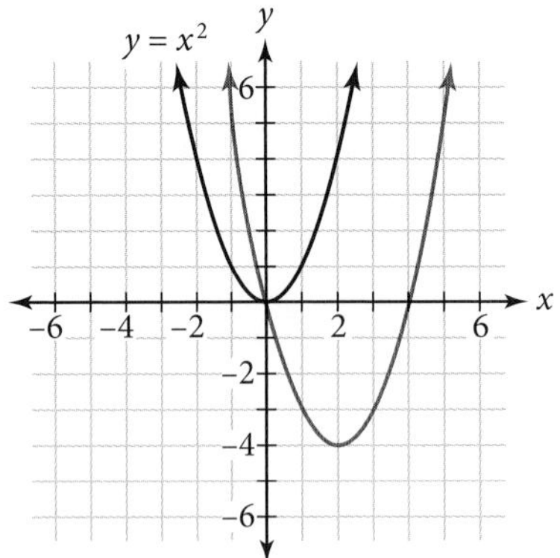

Solution The **vertex** of a parabola is the point where the squaring function changes from decreasing to increasing or from increasing to decreasing. The vertex of the graph of $y = x^2$ is at (0, 0). The vertex of the image is at (2, –4). So the graph of $y = x^2$ is translated right 2 units and down 4 units to create the red image. You can check this with any other point. For example, the image of (2, 4) is (4, 0), which is also a translation right 2 units and down 4 units.

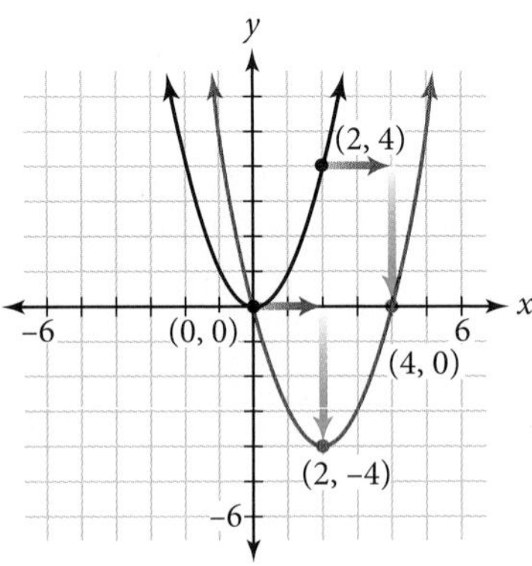

Every point on the graph of $y = x^2$ is translated right 2 units and down 4 units.

Use the translation to write an equation for the red image.

$y = x^2$	Equation of the original parabola.
$y = (x - 2)^2$	Replace x with $x - 2$ to translate the graph right 2 units.
$y - (-4) = (x - 2)^2$	Replace y with $y - (-4)$, or $y + 4$, to translate the graph down 4 units.
$y = (x - 2)^2 - 4$	Solve for y.

The equation of the image is $y = (x - 2)^2 - 4$. You can graph this on your calculator to check your work.

In the next example you'll see how to translate the graph of an exponential function. Later you'll use these skills to fit a function to a set of data.

EXAMPLE B

The starting number of bacteria in a culture dish is unknown, but the number grows by approximately 30% each hour. After 4 hours there are 94 bacteria present. Write an equation to model this situation. Then find the starting number of bacteria.

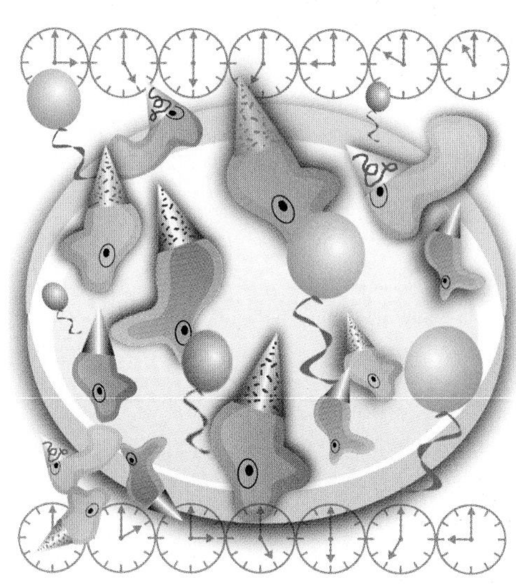

Solution

The starting number is not known, but you can find it by assuming that you're beginning with 94 bacteria and then shifting back in time. If you were beginning with 94 bacteria, the function would be $y = 94(1 + 0.30)^x$, where x represents time elapsed in hours and y represents the number of bacteria.

However, there were 94 bacteria after 4 hours, not at 0 hours. So translate (0, 94) right 4 units to (4, 94). To translate the whole graph right 4 units, replace x with $x - 4$ in the function. You get

$$y = 94(1 + 0.30)^{x-4}$$

The graph shows how the new function translates every point on the graph right 4 units.

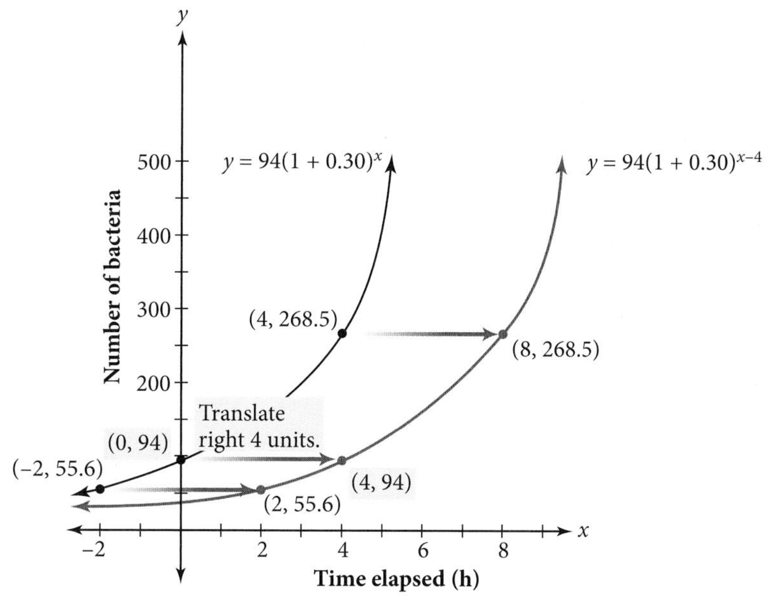

To find the starting number of bacteria, substitute 0 for x in the new function.

$$94(1 + 0.30)^{0-4} = 94(1 + 0.30)^{-4} \approx 33$$

The starting number was approximately 33 bacteria.

Using the starting value you found in Example B, you could now write the function as $y = 33(1 + 0.30)^x$. How can you use properties of exponents to show that $y = 94(1 + 0.30)^{x-4}$ is approximately equivalent to $y = 33(1 + 0.30)^x$? Do you think these functions would be considered members of the same family of functions? Why or why not?

Translations of Functions

To translate a function, $y = f(x)$, h units horizontally and k units vertically, replace x with $x - h$ and y with $y - k$.

$$y - k = f(x - h) \text{ or } y = f(x - h) + k$$

7.5 Exercises

You will need your graphing calculator for Exercises **4, 8, 11,** and **12.**

Practice Your Skills

1. Use $f(x) = 2|x + 4| + 1$ to find

a. $f(5)$ b. $f(-6)$ @ c. $f(-2) + 3$ d. $f(x + 2)$ @

e. $f(4) - 1$ f. $f(x) + 2$ g. $f(-1) + 1$ h. $f(x - 1) + 1$

2. In the first table *list1* and *list2* contain coordinates of three points on the graph of $f(x)$. In the second table *list3* and *list4* contain coordinates of the three points after a transformation of $f(x)$.

a. Write definitions for *list3* and *list4* in terms of *list1* and *list2*.

b. Describe the transformation.

list1 x	*list2* y
−1	3
3	5
2	4

list3 x	*list4* y
7	−1
11	1
10	0

3. Give the coordinates of the vertex for each graph.

a. 

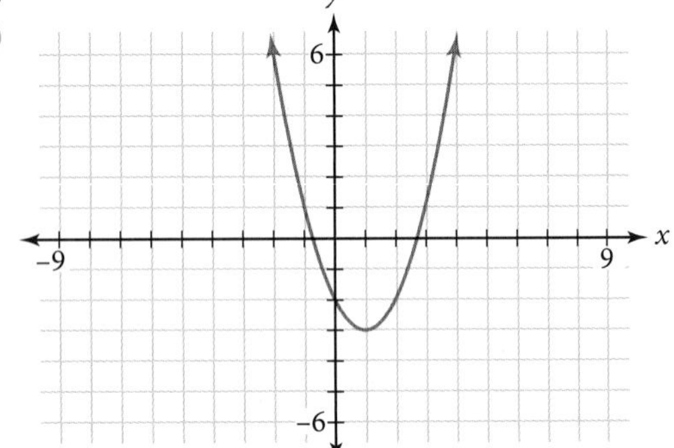

b.

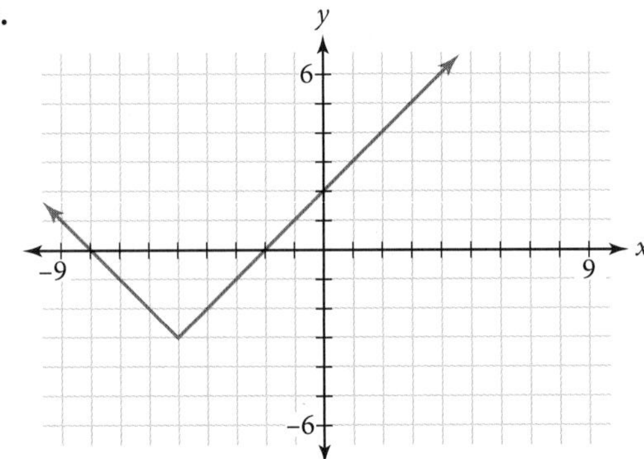

c.

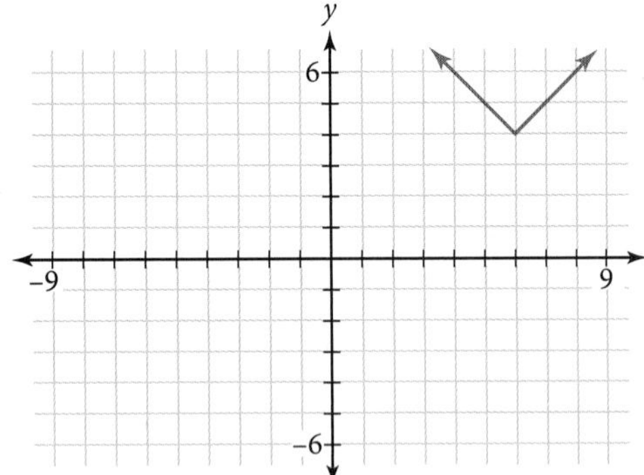

d.

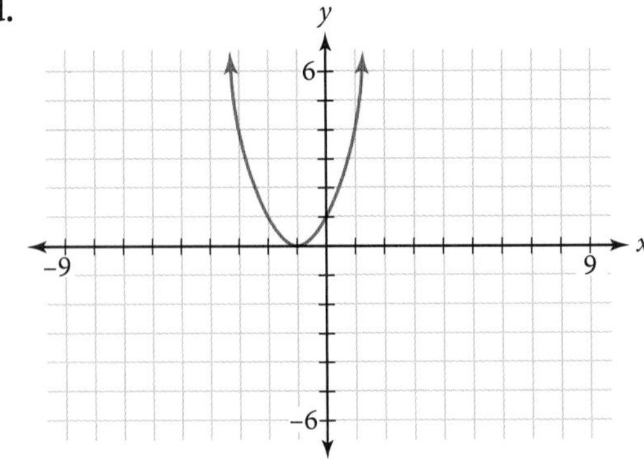

4. Graph each equation on your calculator. Describe the graph as a transformation of $y = |x|$, $y = x^2$, or $y = 3^x$.

a. $y + 2.5 = |x - 1.5|$ @ b. $y = (x + 3)^2$

c. $y - 3.5 = |x|$ d. $y - 2 = 3^{x+1}$ @

5. Write an equation to describe each transformation.

a. Translate the graph of $y = x^2$ down 2 units.

b. Translate the graph of $y = 4^x$ right 5 units. ⓐ

c. Translate the graph of $y = |x|$ left 4 units and up 1 unit.

Reason and Apply

6. Describe each graph in Exercise 3 as a transformation of $y = |x|$ or $y = x^2$. Then write its equation. Use your calculator to check your answers.

7. The graph at right shows Beth's distance from her teacher as she turns in her test.

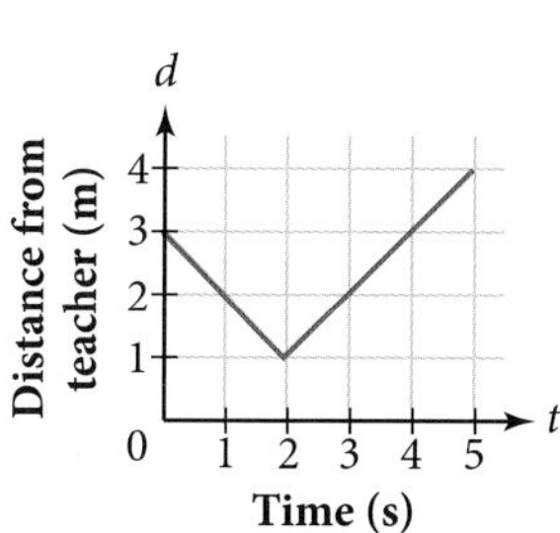

a. What are the input and output variables?

b. What are the units of the variables?

c. What are the domain and range shown in the graph?

d. Describe the situation.

e. Write a function that models this situation.

8. Graph $f(x) = |x|$ on your calculator. Predict what each graph in 8a and b will look like. Check by comparing the graphs on your calculator. [▶ See **Calculator Note: Transformations of Functions** for specific instructions for your calculator. ◀] ⓗ

a. $g(x) = f(x) - 4$

b. $g(x) = f(x - 4)$

9. Describe how the graph of $y = x^2$ will be transformed if you replace

a. x with $(x - 3)$

b. x with $(x + 2)$ ⓐ

c. y with $(y + 2)$ ⓐ

d. y with $(y - 3)$

e. x with $(x + 1)$ and y with $(y + 3)$

f. x with $(x - 4)$ and y with $(y - 1)$

10. APPLICATION The equation $y = a \cdot b^x$ models the decreasing voltage of a charged capacitor when connected to a load. Measurements for a particular capacitor are recorded in the table.

Time (s)	10	11	12	13	14	15	16
Voltage (volts)	6.579	6.285	5.992	5.738	5.484	5.230	4.995

[Data sets: **CAPTM, CAPVT**]

a. The voltages given begin at time $t = 10$ s rather than $t = 0$ s. How can the equation $y = a \cdot b^x$ be changed to account for this? ⓐ

b. To model the data, you need values of a and b. For the value of b, what is the average ratio between consecutive voltages?

c. Find the value of a and write the equation that models these data. ⓗ

d. Use your equation to predict the voltage at time $t = 0$ s.

e. Use your equation to predict when the voltage will be less than 1 volt.

11. MINI-INVESTIGATION Recall that an exponential equation in the form $y = A(1 - r)^x$ models some decreasing patterns. As you increase the value of x, the **long-run value** of y gets closer and closer to zero. Some situations, however, do not decrease all the way to zero. For example, as a cup of hot chocolate cools, the coolest it can get is the air temperature where it is cooling. The long-run value will not be 0°C. Consider this table of data.

Time (min)	0	1	2	3	4	5	6
Temperature (°C)	68	52	41	34	30	27	25

[Data sets: **HCTIM, HCTMP**]

a. Define variables and make a scatter plot of the data. What type of function would fit the data? ⓐ

b. Find the ratio of each temperature to the previous temperature. Do these ratios support your answer to 11a?

Assume that the air temperature of the room in this situation is 21°C. This means the long-run value of these data will also be 21°C.

c. Make a new table by subtracting 21 from each temperature. Then make a scatter plot of the changed data. How have the points been transformed? What will be the long-run value? ⓐ

d. For your data in 11c, find the ratios of temperatures between successive readings. How do the ratios compare? What is the mean of these ratios? ⓐ

e. Write an exponential equation in the form $y = A(1 - r)^x$ that models the data in 11c.

f. In 11c you subtracted 21 from each temperature. What transformation takes these data back to the original data? ⓐ

g. Your equation in 11e models translated data. Change that equation so that it models the original data. Check the fit by graphing on your calculator.

12. APPLICATION In 2004, the world population was estimated to be 6.4 billion, with an annual growth rate of 1.14%. (Central Intelligence Agency, *www.cia.gov*)

a. Define input and output variables for this situation.

b. Without finding an equation, sketch a graph of this situation for the years 1995 to 2015.

c. What one point on the graph do you know for sure?

d. Write a function that models this situation. Graph your function on your calculator and describe an appropriate window.

e. Use your graph to estimate the population to the nearest tenth of a billion in 1995 and 2015. (Assume a constant growth rate during this period.)

13. The graph of a linear equation in the form $y = bx$ passes through (0, 0).

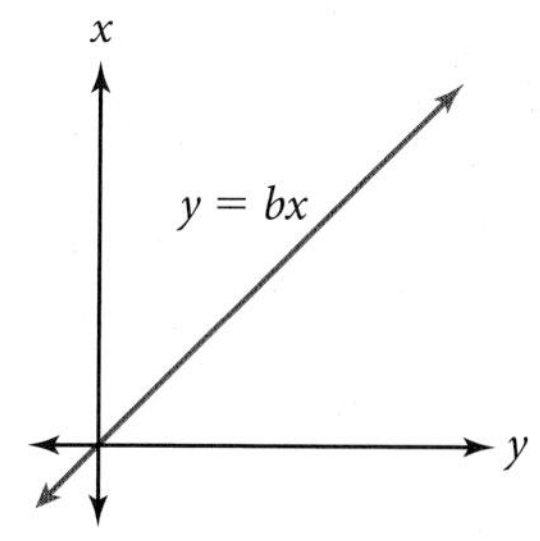

a. Suppose the graph of $y = bx$ is translated right 4 units and up 8 units. Name a point on the new graph.

b. Write an equation of the line in 13a after the transformation. @

c. Suppose the graph of $y = bx$ is translated horizontally H units and vertically V units. Name a point on the new graph. @

d. Write an equation of the line in 13c after the transformation.

Review

14. Drew's teacher gives skill-building quizzes at the start of each class.

a. On Monday Drew got 77 problems correct out of 85. What is her percent correct?

b. On Tuesday Drew got 100% on a quiz that had only 10 problems. Estimate her percent correct for the 2-day total.

c. Calculate her percent correct for the 2-day total.

15. Solve each system of equations.

a. $\begin{cases} y = 5 + 2x \\ y = 8 - 2x \end{cases}$

b. $\begin{cases} y = -2 + 3(x - 4) \\ y = 3 + 5(x - 2) \end{cases}$

c. $\begin{cases} 2x + 7y = 13 \\ 5x - 14y = 1 \end{cases}$

IMPROVING YOUR Visual Thinking SKILLS

Tammy and José are working on Exercise 13a in this lesson. They each decide to graph a linear equation in the form $y = bx$ to help them visualize the question. They translate their graphs right 4 units and up 8 units. Their results are surprisingly different.

José's Graph

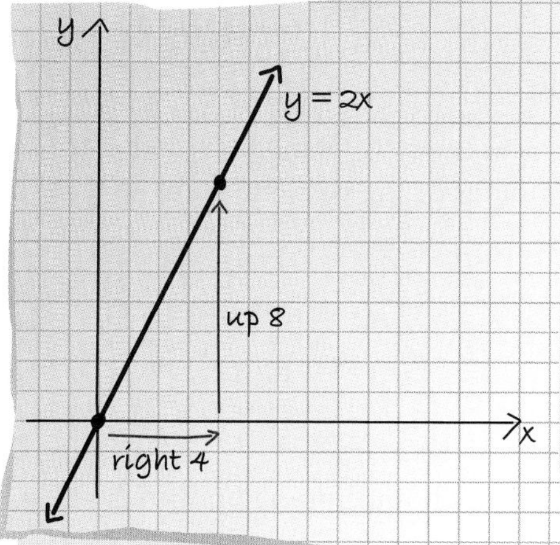

Tammy's Graph

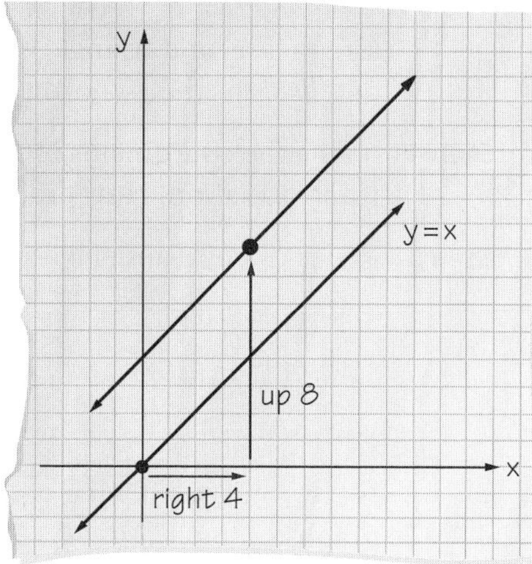

Why did José get the same graph after the translation?

If the graph of an equation in the form $y = bx$ is translated horizontally H units and vertically V units, when would you get the same graph after the translation?

LESSON 7.6

Reflecting Points and Graphs

"The art of a people is a true mirror to their minds."

JAWAHARLAL NEHRU

Translations move points and graphs around the coordinate plane. Have you noticed that the image of the translation always looks like the original figure? Although the image of a translation moves, it doesn't flip, turn, or change size. To get these changes you need other types of transformations.

INVESTIGATION

Flipping Graphs

In this investigation you will explore the relationships between the graph of an equation and its image when you flip it two different ways.

Step 1 Name the coordinates of the vertices of this triangle.

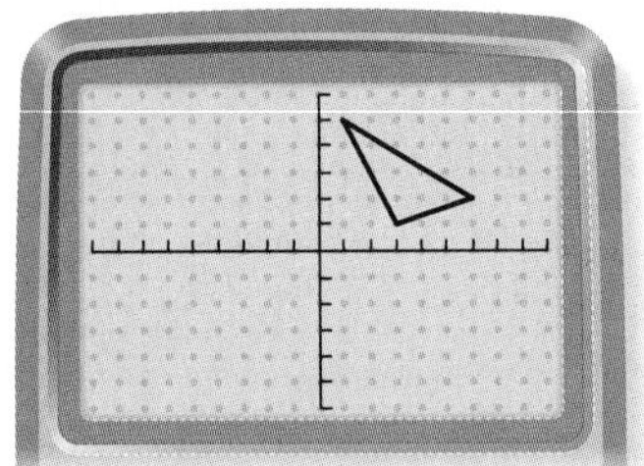

Procedure Note

For this investigation use a screen with *x* and *y* scales of two units.

Step 2 Graph the triangle on your calculator. List the *x*-coordinates of the vertices in *list1*, and list the *y*-coordinates of the vertices in *list2*.

Step 3 Define *list3* and *list4* as follows:

$list3 = -list1$

$list4 = list2$

Graph a second triangle using *list3* for the *x*-coordinates of the vertices and *list4* for the *y*-coordinates of the vertices.

Step 4 Name the coordinates of the vertices of the new triangle. Describe the transformation. How did the coordinates of the vertices change?

Step 5 Repeat Steps 3 and 4 with these definitions.

a. $list3 = list1$
$list4 = -list2$

b. $list3 = -list1$
$list4 = -list2$

Next, you'll see if what you have learned about flipping points is true for graphs of functions.

Step 6 Graph the function $y = 2^x$ on your calculator.

Step 7 Replace x with $-x$ in the function. Graph this second function. Describe how the second graph is related to the graph of $y = 2^x$.

Step 8 Now replace y with $-y$ in the function $y = 2^x$ and solve for y. Graph this third function. Describe how its graph is related to the graph of $y = 2^x$.

Step 9 Repeat Steps 6–8 with these functions. Make a note of anything unusual that you find.

a. $y = (x - 1)^2$

b. $y = |x|$

c. $y = x$

Step 10 Summarize what you have learned about flipping graphs.

In the investigation you saw *reflections* of figures and of functions. These reflections used the x- and y-axes as "mirrors."

Reflections

A **reflection** is a transformation that flips a figure to create a mirror image.

Point Reflections
A point is **reflected across the x-axis,** or *vertically reflected,* when you change the sign of its y-coordinate. A point is **reflected across the y-axis,** or *horizontally reflected,* when you change the sign of its x-coordinate.

Function Reflections
To reflect a graph of a function across the x-axis, replace y with $-y$ in the function equation. To reflect a graph of a function across the y-axis, replace x with $-x$.

You can combine reflections with other transformations. Sometimes, different combinations of transformations will give the same result.

EXAMPLE A

The graph of a parent function is shown in black. Its image after a transformation is shown in red. Describe the transformation, and then write a function to describe the image.

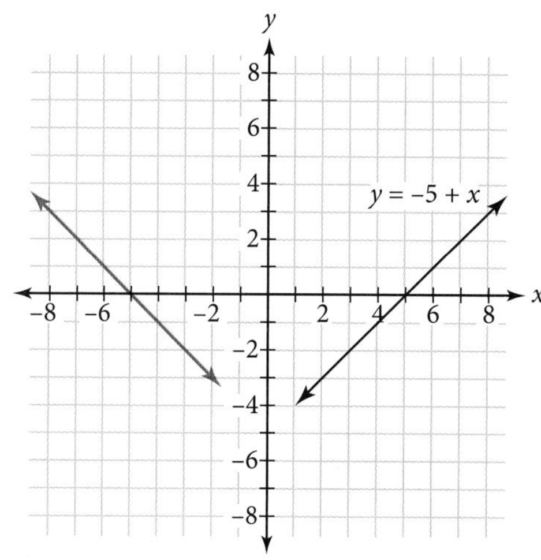

Solution

This is a reflection across the y-axis. The image is produced by replacing each x-value in the original function with $-x$.

$$y = -5 + (-x)$$

or

$$y = -5 - x$$

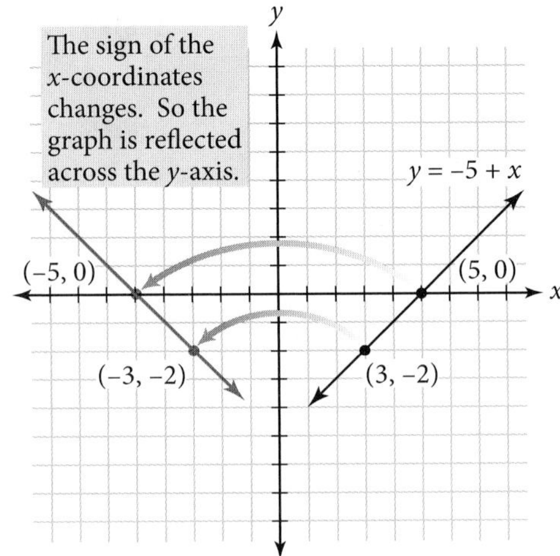

EXAMPLE B

The graph of a parent function is shown in black. Its image after a transformation is shown in red. Describe the transformation, and then write a function to describe the image.

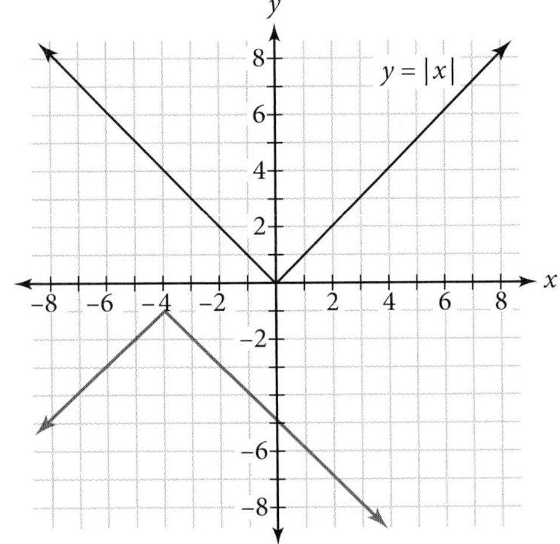

Solution

Here is one possible solution. Reflect the graph of the function across the x-axis, and then translate it left 4 units and down 1 unit. To write the equation of the image, change the original function in the same order.

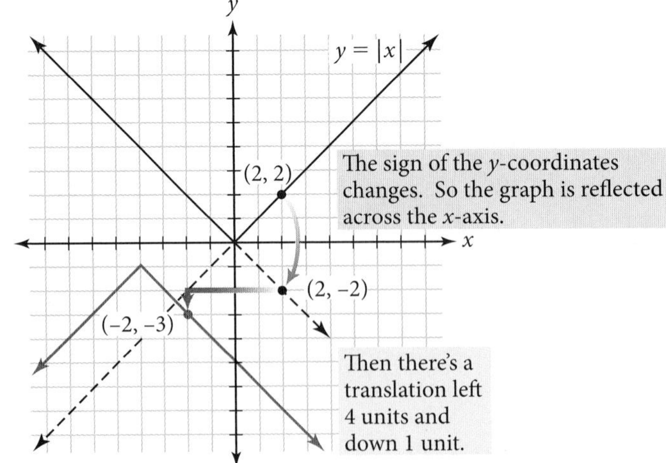

Technology CONNECTION

Many computer applications allow you to import and transform clip art. Most have commands like "reflect vertically" or "reflect horizontally." Because clip art doesn't normally have an x- or y-axis, these commands reflect the picture by flipping it top to bottom or left to right.

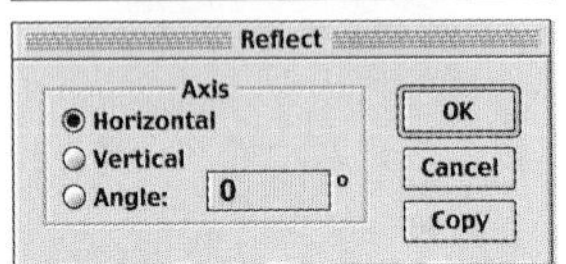

$$\begin{aligned} y &= |x| && \text{Original equation.} \\ -y &= |x| && \text{Replace } y \text{ with } -y \text{ to reflect across the } x\text{-axis.} \\ y &= -|x| && \text{Solve for } y. \\ y &= -|x+4| && \text{Replace } x \text{ with } x+4 \text{ to translate left 4 units.} \\ y+1 &= -|x+4| && \text{Replace } y \text{ with } y+1 \text{ to translate down 1 unit.} \\ y &= -|x+4|-1 && \text{Solve for } y. \end{aligned}$$

A function that describes the image is $y = -|x+4| - 1$.

[▶ You can practice writing a function to describe a translated and reflected graph, or graphing a translated and reflected function, using the **Dynamic Algebra Exploration** in your ebook. ◀]

EXAMPLE C

The graph of a parent function is shown in black. Its image after a transformation is shown in red.

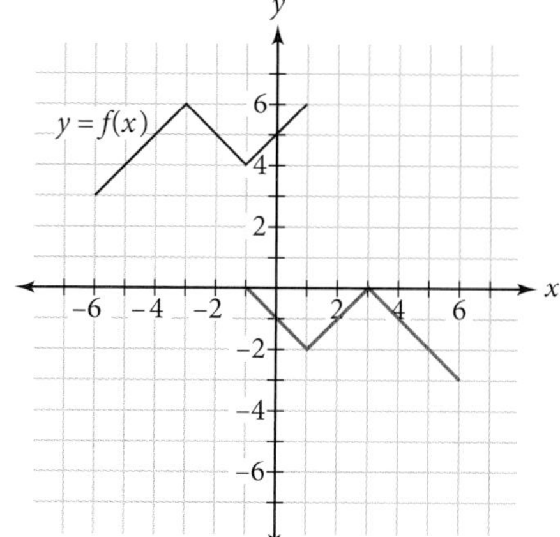

a. Describe two different combinations of transformations that could have created the image. Then write a function to describe the image in terms of the parent function.

b. Give the domain and range of the parent function and its image.

c. How are the changes in the domain and range related to the transformations?

Solution

You can sometimes use different combinations of transformations to get the same image. Two possible combinations are given here.

a. One solution is to translate the function graph down 6 units and then reflect it across the y-axis. Another approach is to first reflect the graph across the y-axis and then translate it down 6 units. In both cases, the equation of the transformed graph is $y = f(-x) - 6$. For example, to find the y-coordinate of the point on the new graph with x-coordinate 1, find $f(-1) - 6$, which is $4 - 6$ or -2.

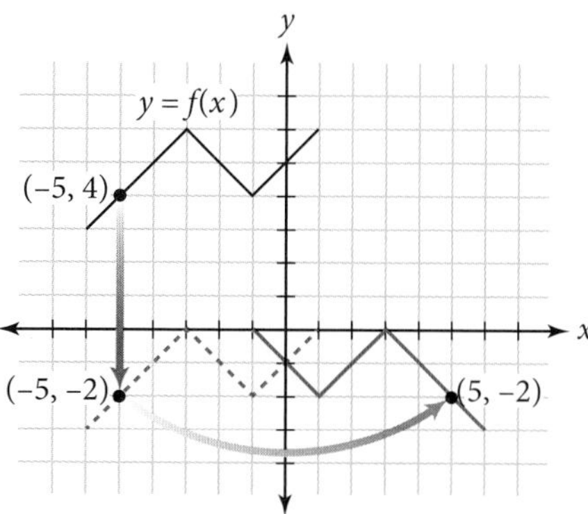

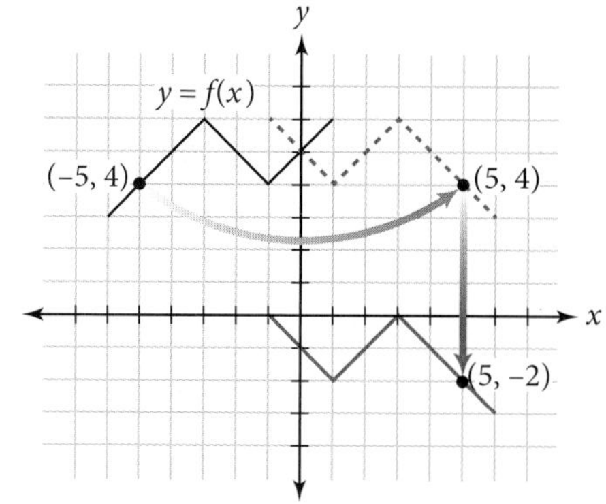

b. The parent function has domain $-6 \leq x \leq 1$ and range $3 \leq y \leq 6$. The image has domain $-1 \leq x \leq 6$ and range $-3 \leq y \leq 0$.

c. The domain of the image is a horizontal reflection (across the y-axis) of the domain of the function. The range of the image is a translation of the range of the function down 6 units. The domain and the range have been transformed the same as the function.

In the investigation you probably saw no change when you reflected the graph of $y = |x|$ across the y-axis. In Example C, a reflection across the y-axis has a result other than a horizontal translation. What do you notice about the graphs that could explain the difference in the results?

Many transformations of a single triangle were used to create this serigraph. Can you find some translations?

7.6 Exercises

You will need your graphing calculator for Exercises **4** and **12.**

Practice Your Skills

1. Use $f(x) = 0.5(x - 3)^2 - 3$ to find

a. $f(5)$ b. $f(-6)$ @ c. $4 \cdot f(2)$ d. $f(-x)$ e. $-f(x)$ @

2. Describe each graph as a transformation of the graph of $y = |x|$ or $y = x^2$. Then write its equation. Check your answers by graphing on your calculator.

a.

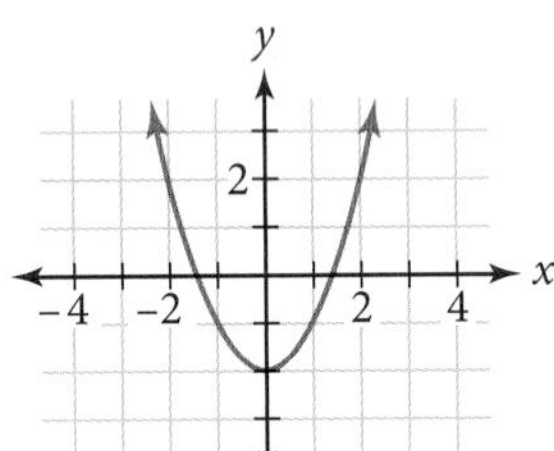

b.

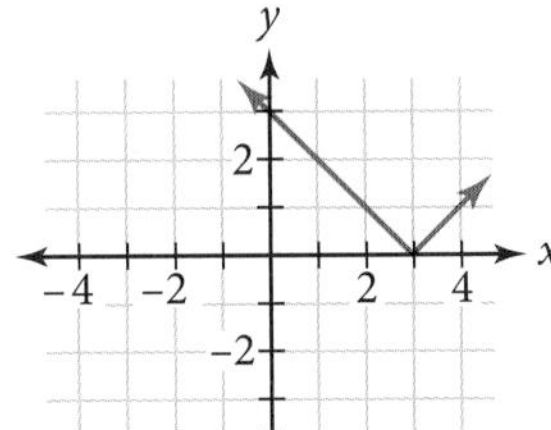

c.

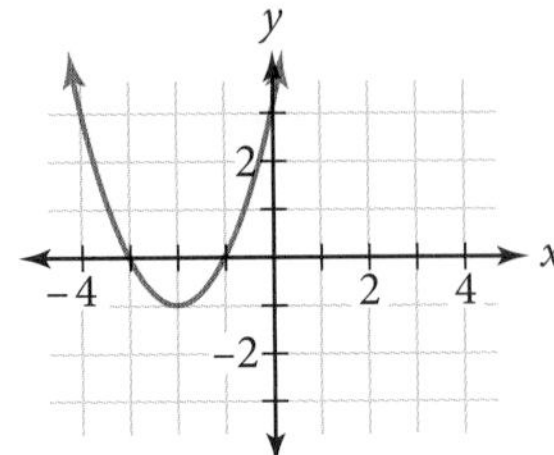

d.

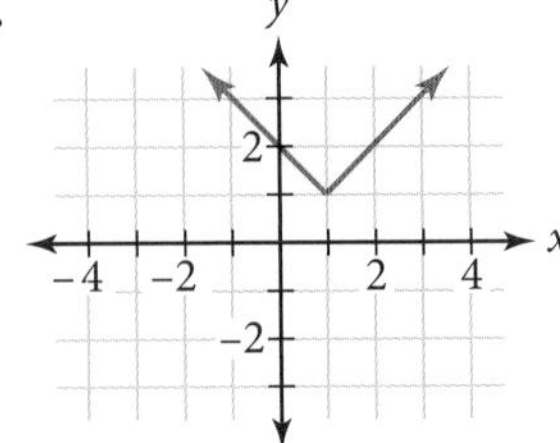

3. Graph $f(x) = 1 + 2.5x$ on your calculator. Predict what the graph of each transformation below will look like. Check by comparing graphs on your calculator. [▶ See **Calculator Note: Transformations of Functions** for specific instructions for your calculator. ◀]

a. $g(x) = f(-x)$ b. $g(x) = -f(x)$

4. Describe each graph below as a transformation of the graph of $y = |x + 3|$ at right.

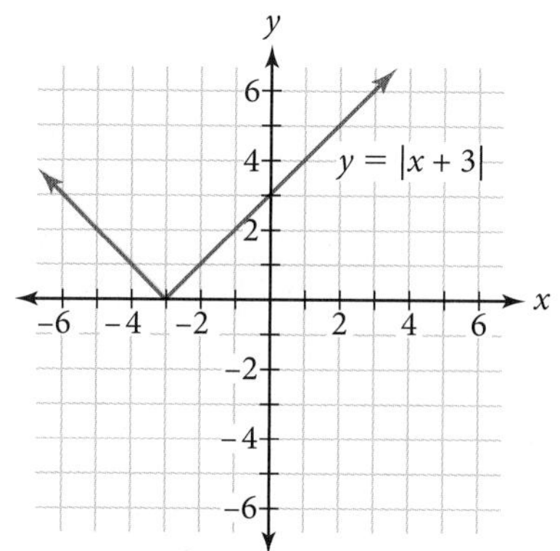

a.

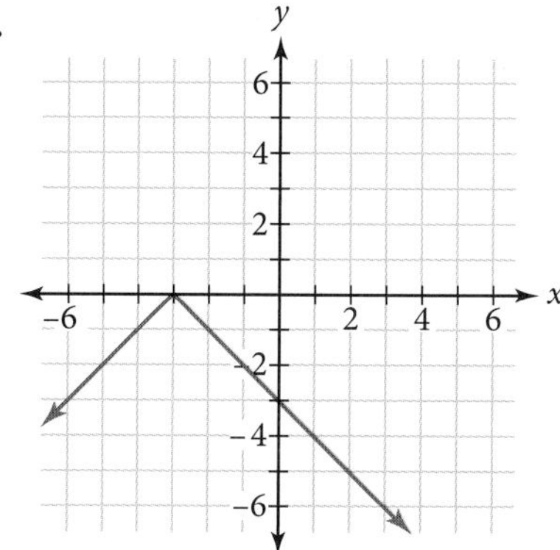

b. @

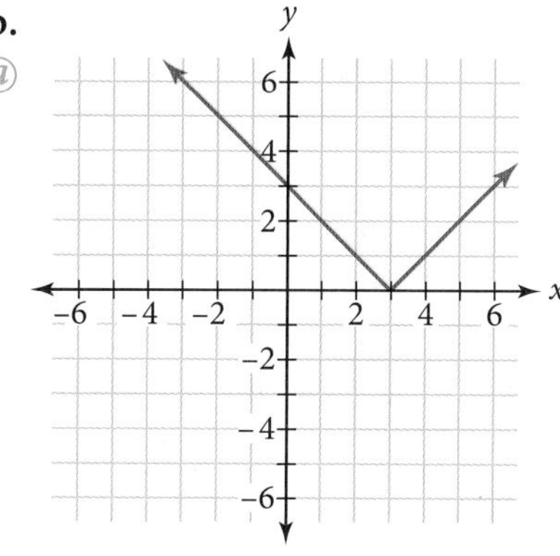

c.

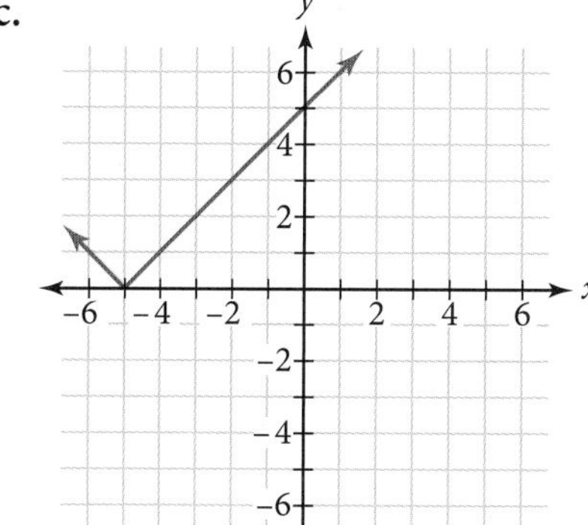

d. @

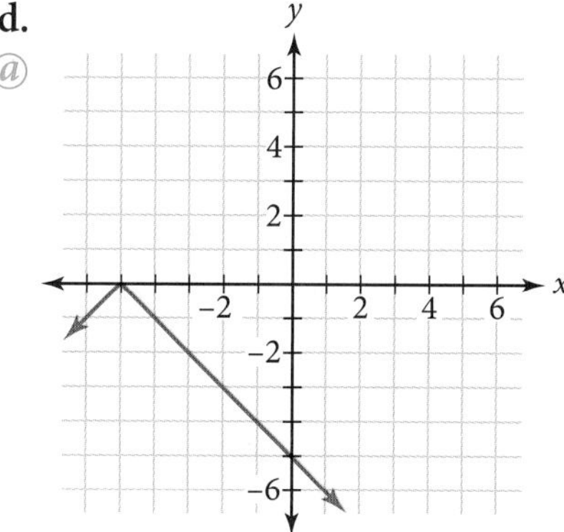

5. Describe the graph of each function below as a transformation of the graph of the parent function $y = x^2$. Check your answers by graphing on your calculator. (You'll need to solve for y first.)

a. $y = -x^2$

b. $-y = (x + 3)^2$

c. $y = -x^2 + 3$ @

d. $y - 3 = (-x)^2$ @

e. $y = (x - 2)^2$

f. $y = [-(x - 2)]^2$

g. $y - 2 = x^2$

h. $-(y - 2) = x^2$

Reason and Apply

6. APPLICATION Bo is designing a computer animation program. She wants the star on the left to move to the position of the star on the right using 11 frames. She also wants the star to flip top to bottom in each frame. Define the coordinates of each image in relation to the coordinates of the previous figure. @

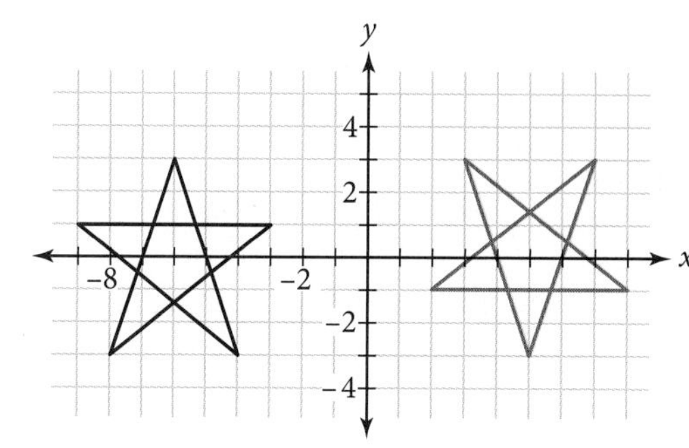

7. Consider the triangle at right.

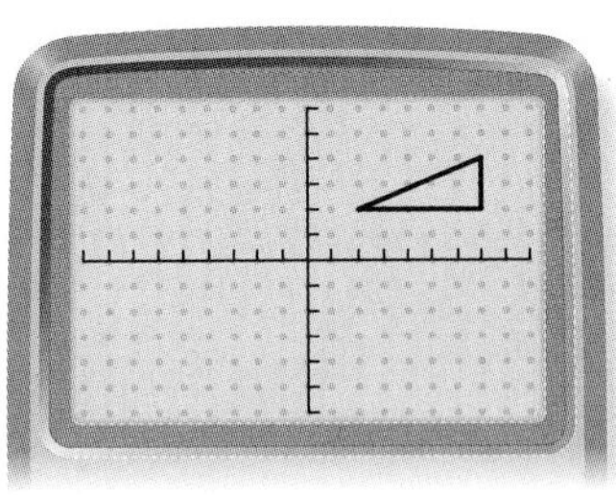

[−9.4, 9.4, 1, −6.2, 6.2, 1]

a. Describe how you can graph this triangle on your calculator.

b. Describe how you could graph these images.

i. ⓐ

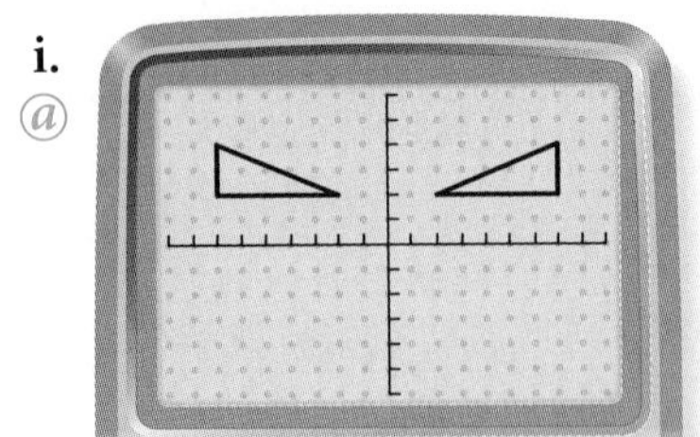

ii.

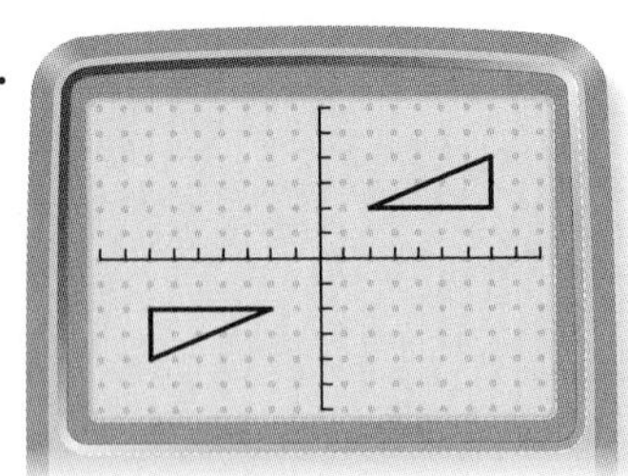

iii.

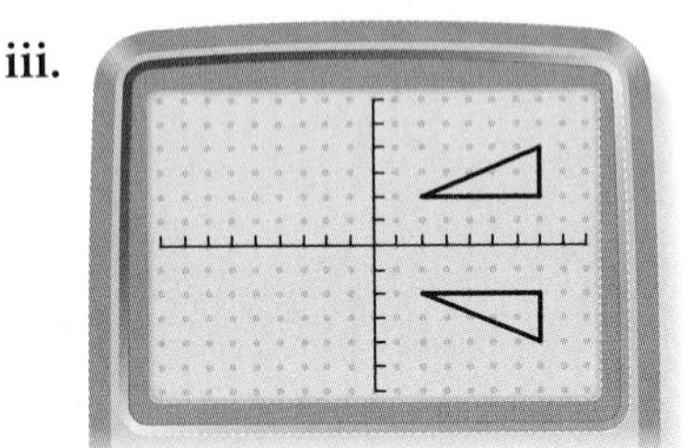

iv.

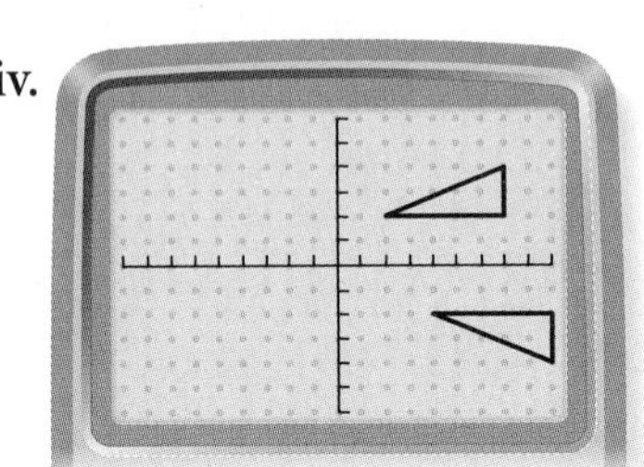

8. The points in the table form a star when you connect them in order. Describe the transformation that results when you change the points to

a. $(-x, y)$

b. $(x, -y)$

c. $(x - 8, -y)$

d. $(x + 2, y - 4)$ ⓐ

e. $(-x, -y)$ ⓐ

f. (y, x) ⓗ

x	y
6.0	2.0
2.4	3.2
4.6	0.1
4.6	3.9
2.4	0.8
6.0	2.0

9. Anthony and Cheryl are using a motion sensor for a "walker" investigation.

a. This graph models data that Cheryl collected when Anthony walked. Write an equation that models his walk.

Anthony's Walk

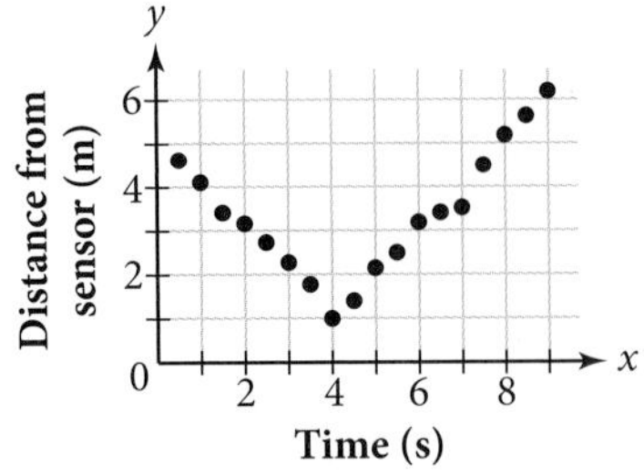

b. Here is a description of Cheryl's walk.

> Begin at a distance of 0.5 meter from the sensor. Walk away from the sensor at 1 meter per second for 3 seconds. Then walk toward the sensor at the same rate for 3 seconds.

Write an equation to model her walk. ⓗ

c. Give the domain and range of the function that models Cheryl's walk.

10. MINI-INVESTIGATION A line of reflection does not have to be the x- or y-axis. Consider this example in which the graph of $y = |x|$ is reflected across the line $x = 4$.

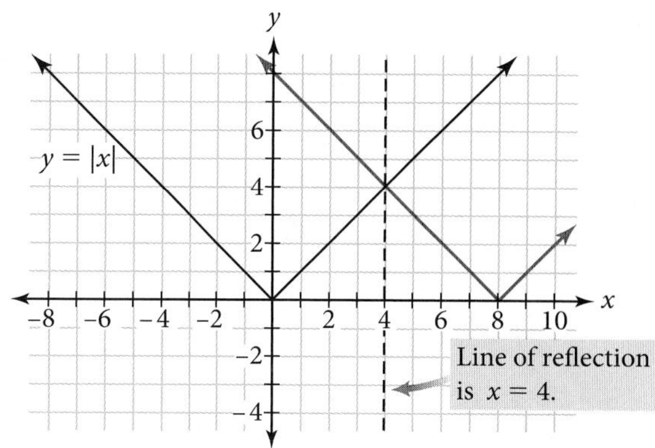

a. Write an equation of the red image in each graph. @

i.

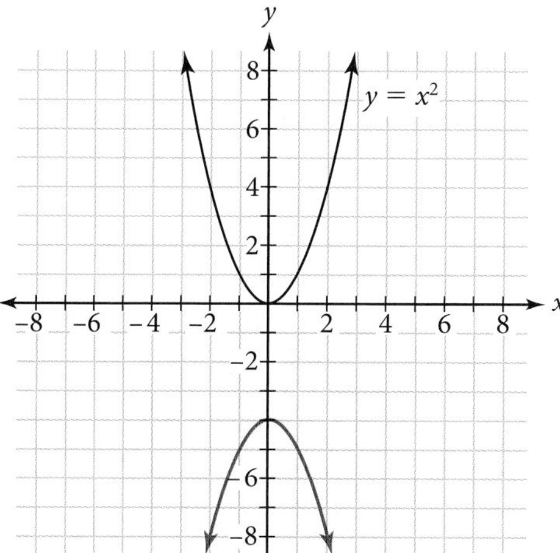

ii.

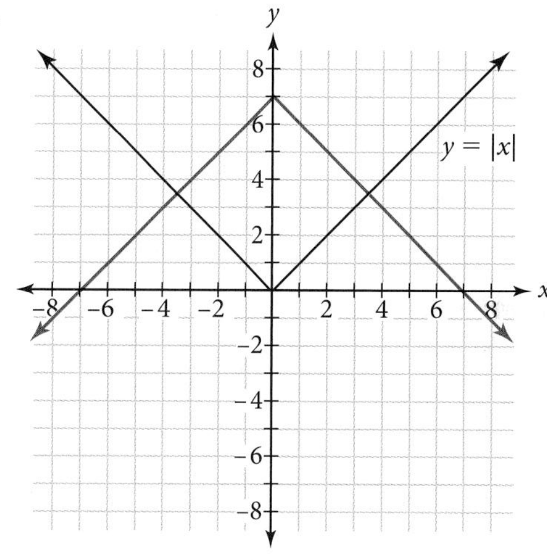

iii.

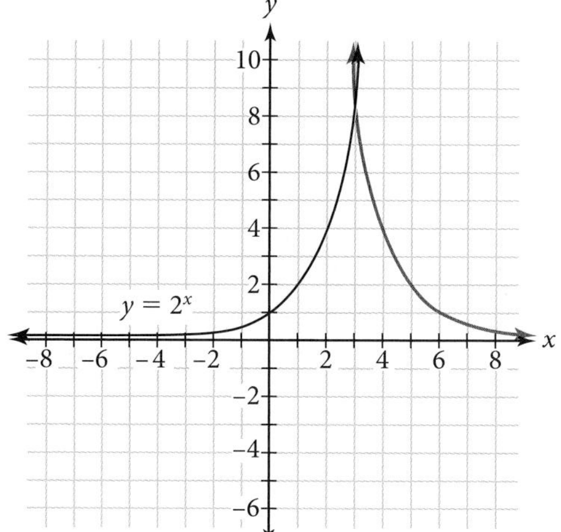

iv.

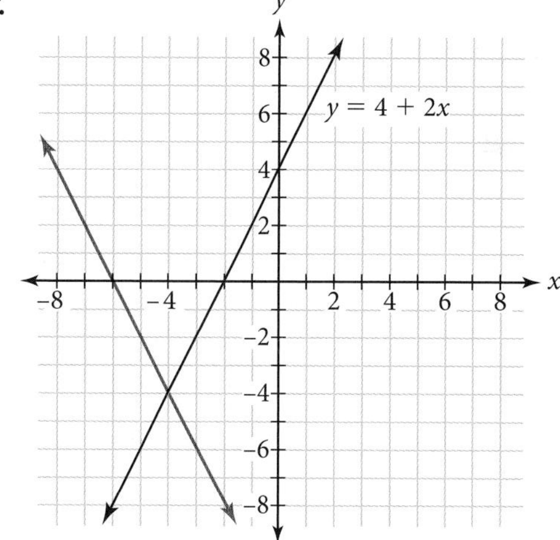

b. Think about each transformation in 10a as a single reflection. What is the line of reflection in each case? @

c. What is the relationship between the line of reflection and the translation in your equation?

d. The graph of $y = f(x)$ is reflected across the horizontal line $y = b$. What is the equation of the image? @

e. The graph of a function $y = f(x)$ is reflected across the vertical line $x = a$. What is the equation of the image?

11. For 11a and b the graph of a parent function is shown in black. Describe the transformation that creates the red image. Give the domain and range of the parent function and the image function. Then write a function to model the image.

a.

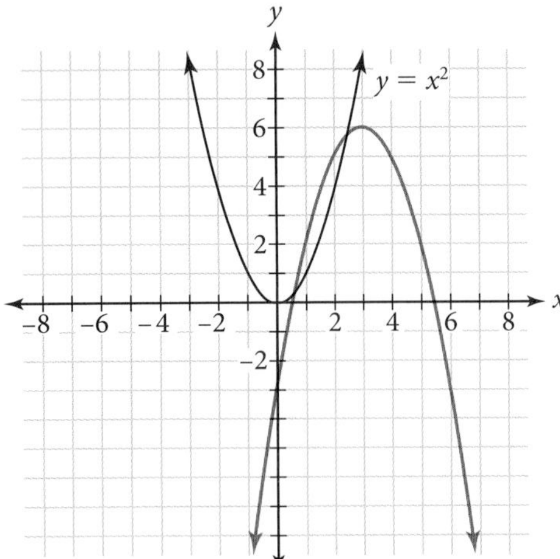

b. ⓐ

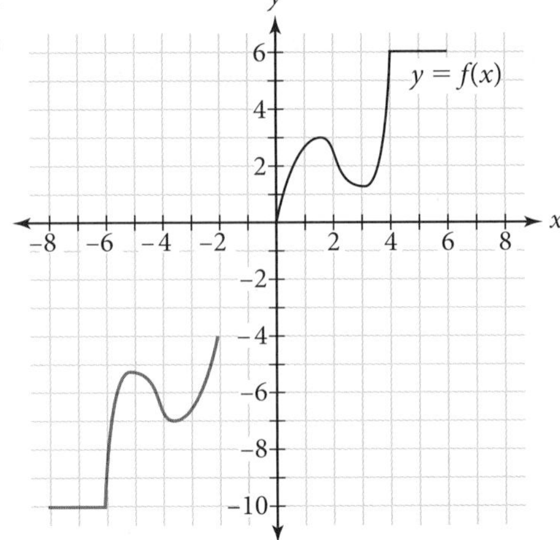

Review

12. A chemical reaction consumes 12% of the reactant per minute. A scientist begins with 500 grams of the reactant. So the equation $y = 500(0.88)^x$ gives the amount of reactant, y, remaining after x minutes.

a. What does the number 0.88 tell you?

b. What is the long-run value of y? What is the real-world meaning of this value?

c. What is the long-run value of y for the equation $y = 500(0.88)^x + 100$? What is the real-world meaning of this value?

d. Graph $y = 500(0.88)^x$ and $y = 500(0.88)^x + 100$ on your calculator. How are these graphs the same? How are they different?

13. Convert 47 tablespoons to quarts. (16 tablespoons = 1 cup; 1 quart = 4 cups) ⓗ

14. This table shows the temperature of water in a pan set on a stove.

a. Write the equation of a line that models these data.

b. How long will it take for the water to boil (100°C)?

Time (min)	0	2	4	6	8	10	12	14	16	18
Temperature (°C)	22	29	36	44	51	58	65	72	80	87

[Data sets: **PANTM, PANTP**]

IMPROVING YOUR Reasoning SKILLS

The ancient Mayan civilization occupied parts of Mexico and Central America as early as 1500 B.C.E. The Maya had a number system based on 20. They are also the earliest known civilization to use zero.

Below are the twenty numerals that make up the Mayan number system, like the digits 0–9 that make up our number system. Can you decode the numerals and label them with the numbers 0 to 19? A few are labeled to get you started.

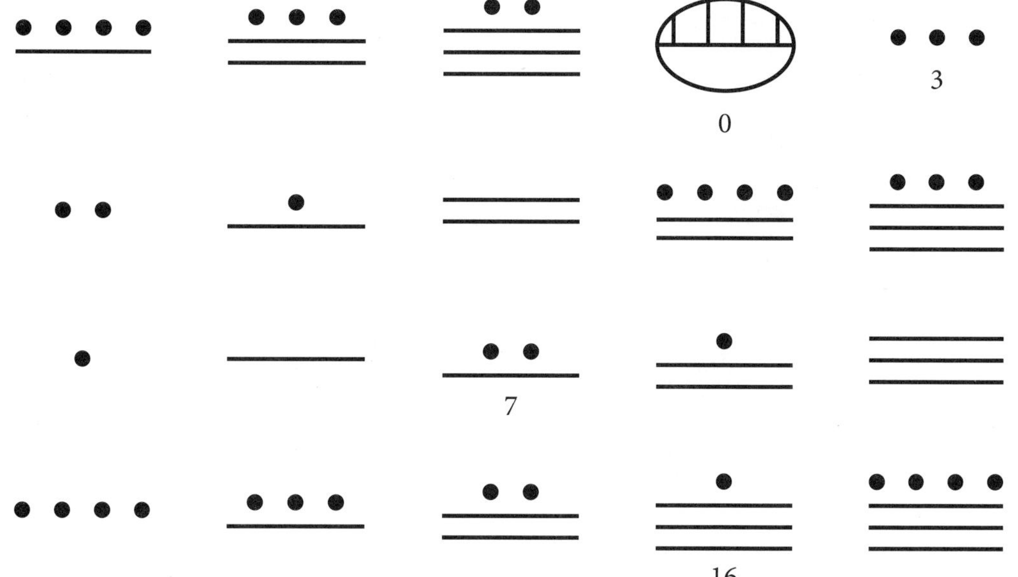

LESSON

7.7

Stretching and Shrinking Graphs

"There is no absolute scale of size in the Universe, for it is boundless towards the great and also boundless towards the small."

OLIVER HEAVISIDE

Imagine what happens to the shape of a picture drawn on a rubber sheet as you **stretch** the sheet vertically.

The width remains the same, but the height increases. You can also **shrink** a picture vertically. In this case, the width remains the same, but the height decreases.

You know how to translate and reflect graphs on a coordinate plane. Now you'll see how to change their shape.

The German painter Hans Holbein II (1497–1543) used a technique called anamorphosis to hide a stretched skull in his portrait *The Ambassadors* (1533). You can see the skull in the original painting if you look across the page from the lower left. The painting was originally hung above a doorway so that people would notice the skull as they walked through the door. Holbein may have been making a political statement about these two French ambassadors, who were members of England's court of King Henry VIII.

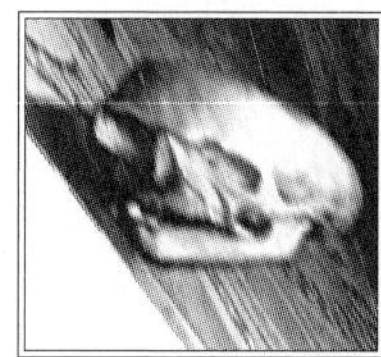

INVESTIGATION

Changing the Shape of a Graph

In this investigation you will learn how to stretch or shrink a graph vertically.

Procedure Note

For this investigation use a screen with x and y scales of two units.

Step 1 Name the coordinates of the vertices of this quadrilateral.

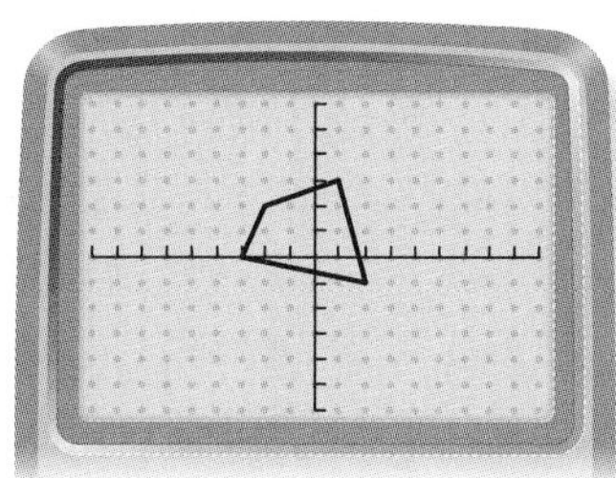

Step 2 Graph the quadrilateral on your calculator. List the x-coordinates of the vertices in *list1* and the y-coordinates of the vertices in *list2*.

Step 3 Each member of your group should choose one of these values of a: 2, 3, 0.5, or -2. Use your value of a to define two new lists, *list3* and *list4*, as follows:

list3 = *list1*

list4 = $a \cdot$ *list2*

Graph a second quadrilateral using *list3* for the x-coordinates of the vertices and *list4* for the y-coordinates of the vertices.

Step 4 Share your results from Step 3. For each value of a, describe the transformation of the quadrilateral in Step 2. What was the result for each vertex?

Step 5 Predict the location of each vertex if the value of a is 1.5. Describe how you think the overall appearance of the quadrilateral will change.

Step 6 Make a conjecture about how a graph will be affected when its y-values are multiplied by values greater than 1, between 0 and 1, and less than 0.

Step 7 Graph this triangle on your calculator. List the x-coordinates of the vertices in *list1* and the y-coordinates of the vertices in *list2*.

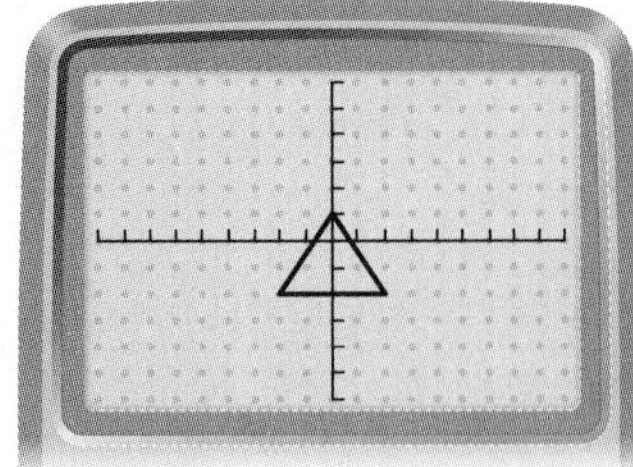

Step 8 Describe how the definitions below transform the triangle. List the x-coordinates of the vertices of the image in *list3* and the y-coordinates of the vertices of the image in *list4*. Check your answers by graphing on your calculator.

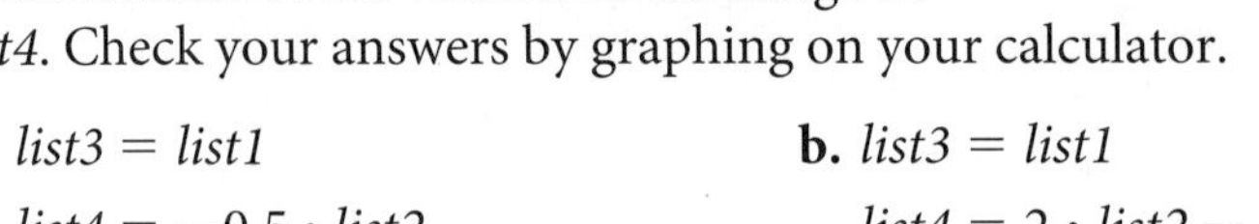

a. *list3* = *list1*

list4 = $-0.5 \cdot$ *list2*

b. *list3* = *list1*

list4 = $2 \cdot$ *list2* $- 2$

Step 9 Write definitions for *list3* and *list4* in terms of *list1* and *list2* to create each image below. Check your definitions by graphing on your calculator.

a.

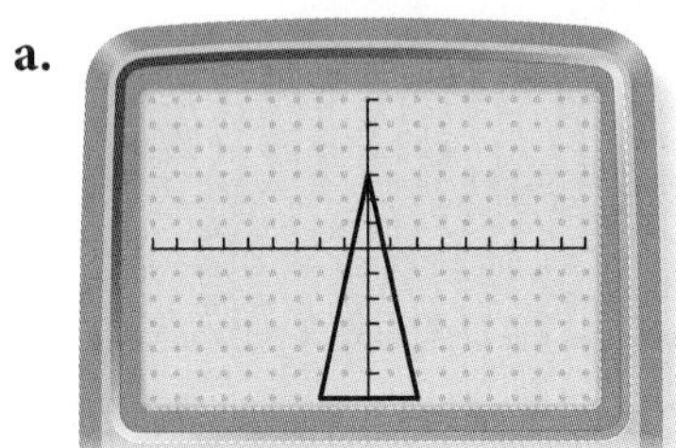

b.

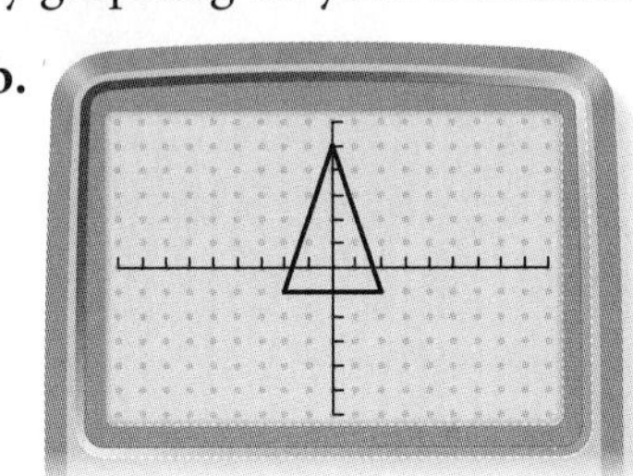

Next you'll see how you can stretch and shrink the graph of a function.

Step 10 Each member of your group should choose an equation from the list below. Enter your equation into your calculator and graph it.

$f(x) = -1 + 0.5x$ $\qquad$ $f(x) = |x| - 2$

$f(x) = -x^2 + 1$ $\qquad$ $f(x) = 1.4^x$

Step 11 Enter $g(x) = 2 \cdot f(x)$ and graph it on the same screen. [▶ See **Calculator Note: Transformations of Functions** for specific instructions for your calculator. ◀]

Step 12 Look at a table on your calculator and compare the y-values for $f(x)$ and $g(x)$.

Step 13 Repeat Steps 11 and 12, but use these equations for $g(x)$.

a. $g(x) = 0.5 \cdot f(x)$ $\qquad$ **b.** $g(x) = 3 \cdot f(x)$ $\qquad$ **c.** $g(x) = -2 \cdot f(x)$

Step 14 Write an equation for $R(x)$ in terms of $B(x)$. Then write an equation for $B(x)$ in terms of $R(x)$.

a.

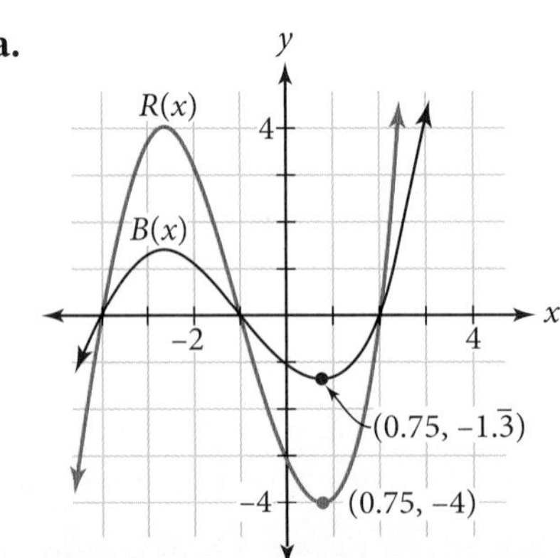

b.

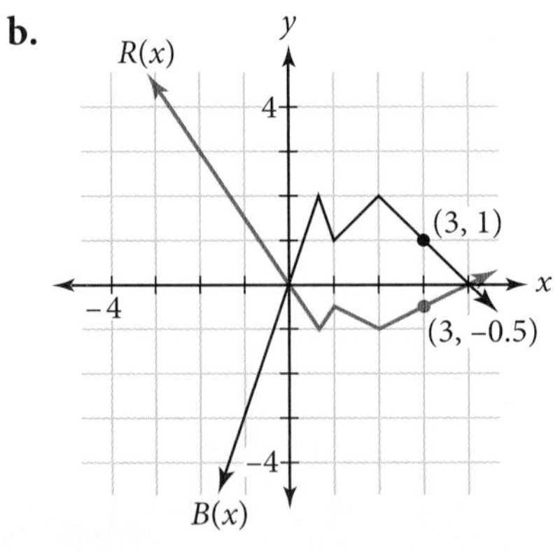

To vertically stretch or shrink a polygon, you multiply the y-coordinates of the vertices by a constant factor. To vertically stretch or shrink the graph of a function, you multiply the function by a factor.

EXAMPLE A

Describe how the graph of $y = 0.5\,|x|$ is related to the graph of $y = |x|$. Then graph both functions.

Solution

Tables of values for both functions show that $y = 0.5\,|x|$ is a vertical shrink of $y = |x|$. Each y-value for $y = 0.5\,|x|$ is one-half the corresponding y-value for $y = |x|$. Multiplying the function by 0.5 has the same effect as multiplying the y-coordinate of every point on the graph of $y = |x|$ by 0.5.

x	$y = \|x\|$	$y = 0.5\,\|x\|$
2	2	1
0	0	0
1	1	0.5
5	5	2.5

Graphing the functions together also shows a vertical shrink by a factor of 0.5. Each point on the graph of $y = 0.5\,|x|$ is one-half the distance from the x-axis of the corresponding point on the graph of $y = |x|$.

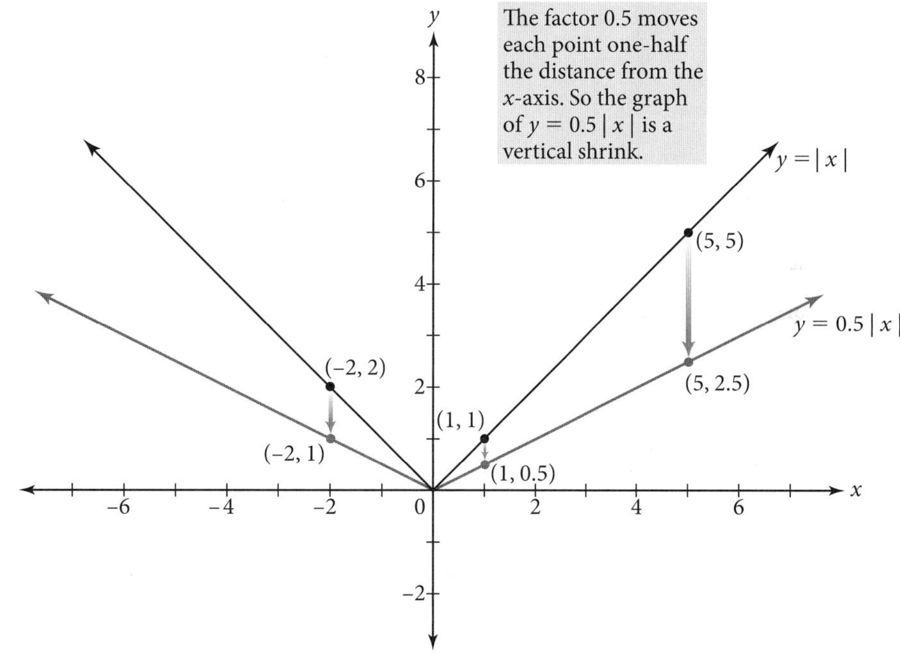

Many computer applications allow you to change the size and shape of clip art. Some applications have commands to change only the horizontal or the vertical scale. If you change only one scale, you distort the picture with a stretch or a shrink. If you change both scales by the same factor, you create a larger or smaller picture that is geometrically similar to the original.

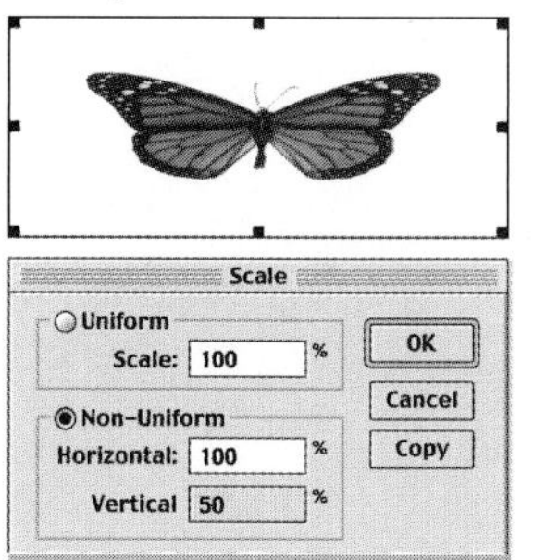

[▸ You can explore stretches and shrinks interactively using the **Dynamic Algebra Exploration** in your ebook. ◂]

Stretches and Shrinks

Given the function $y = f(x)$, the function $y = a \cdot f(x)$ stretches $y = f(x)$ vertically if $|a| > 1$ and shrinks $y = f(x)$ vertically if $|a| < 1$.

EXAMPLE B

Write an equation of the function in the graph at right.

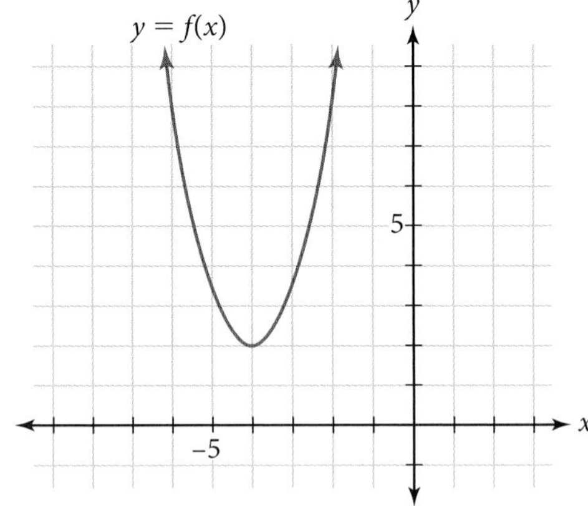

Solution

The graph is a parabola, so the parent function is $y = x^2$. First determine if a vertical stretch or shrink is necessary. An informal way to do this is to think about corresponding points on the graphs of $y = x^2$ and $y = f(x)$.

The parent function, $y = x^2$
When you move 1 unit left of the vertex, you move 1 unit up to find a point on the graph. When you move 2 units right of the vertex, you move 4 units up to find a point on the graph.

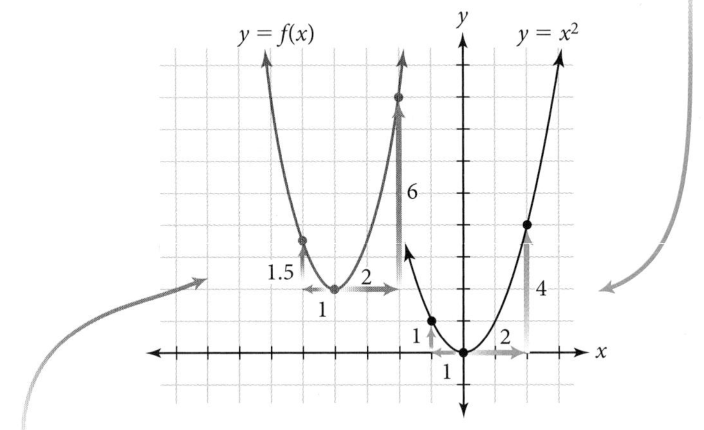

The image function, $y = f(x)$
When you move 1 unit left of the vertex, you move 1.5 units up to find a point on the graph. When you move 2 units right of the vertex, you move 6 units up to find a point on the graph.

For the same x-distances from the vertex of each graph, the corresponding y-distances from the vertex of the image graph, $y = f(x)$, are 1.5 times the y-distances from the vertex of the parent graph, $y = x^2$. So the stretch factor is 1.5.

x-distance from vertex	y-distance from vertex of parent function, $y = x^2$	y-distance from vertex of parent function, $y = f(x)$	Stretch factor calculation
1	1	1.5	$\frac{1.5}{1} = 1.5$
2	4	6	$\frac{6}{4} = 1.5$

$y = x^2$	Equation of the parent function.
$\downarrow$	
$y = 1.5x^2$	Multiply the parent function, x^2, by a factor of 1.5 for the vertical stretch.

The vertex of the graph of $y = f(x)$ is $(-4, 2)$. So you must now change the equation to show a translation left 4 units and up 2 units.

$y = 1.5(x + 4)^2$	Replace x with $x - (-4)$, or $x + 4$, to translate the graph left 4 units.
$\downarrow$	
$y - 2 = 1.5(x + 4)^2$	Replace y with $y - 2$ to translate the graph up 2 units.
$y = 1.5(x + 4)^2 + 2$	Solve for y.

The equation of the function is $y = 1.5(x + 4)^2 + 2$.

How can you check that this equation is correct?

Now that you've learned how to translate, reflect, and vertically stretch or shrink a graph, you can transform a function into many forms. This skill gives you a lot of power in mathematics. You can look at a complicated equation and see it as a variation of a simpler function. This skill also allows you to adjust the fit of mathematical models for many situations.

7.7 Exercises

You will need your graphing calculator for Exercises **4, 7,** and **12.**

Practice Your Skills

1. Ted and Ching-I are using a motion sensor for a "walker" investigation. They find that the graph at right models the data for Ted's first walk. Write an equation to describe this graph. ⓐ

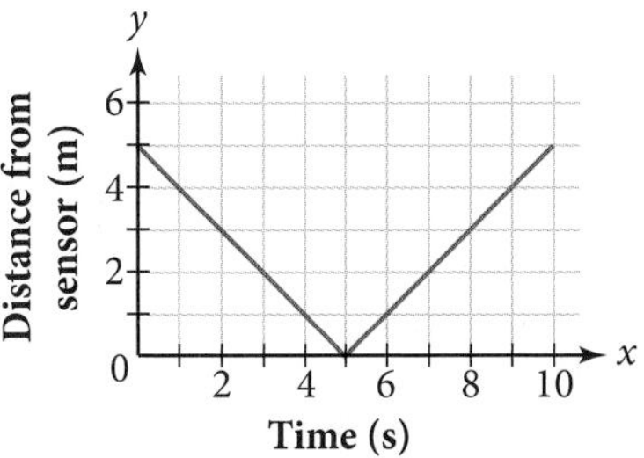

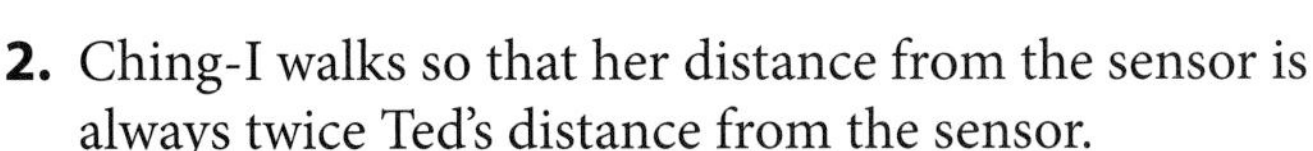

2. Ching-I walks so that her distance from the sensor is always twice Ted's distance from the sensor.

a. Sketch a graph that models Ching-I's walk. ⓐ

b. Write an equation to describe the graph in 4a.

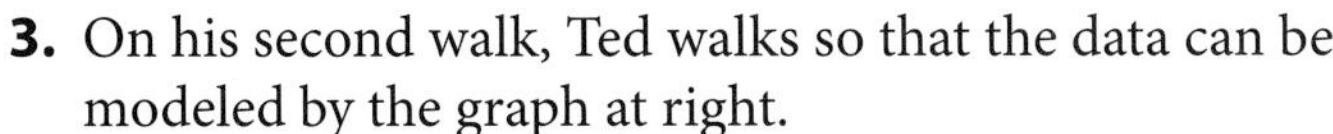

3. On his second walk, Ted walks so that the data can be modeled by the graph at right.

a. Write an equation to describe this graph. ⓐ

b. Describe how Ted walked to create this graph.

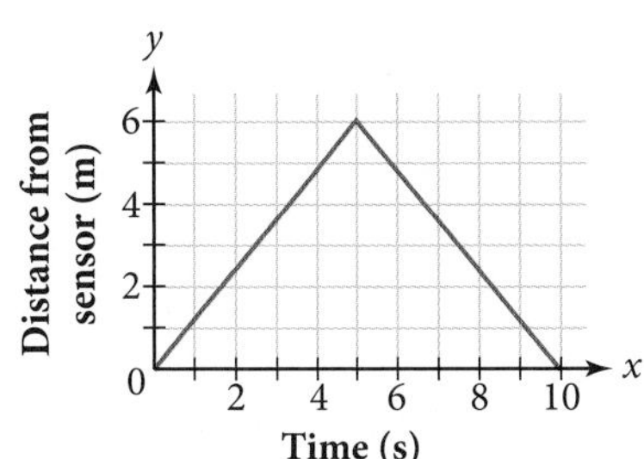

4. Describe each graph in 4a–d as a transformation of the graph of the parent function $y = |x|$ or $y = x^2$. Then write the equation of the image. (For more practice writing equations from graphs, run the ABS program and the PARAB program. [▶ Use the link in your ebook to download the program files ABS and PARAB. ◀])

a.

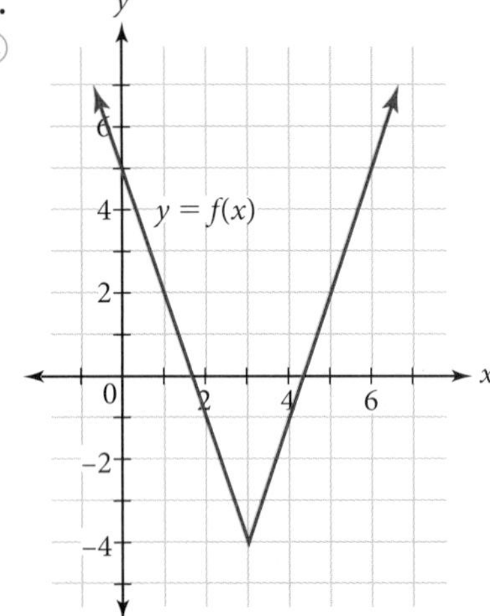

b.

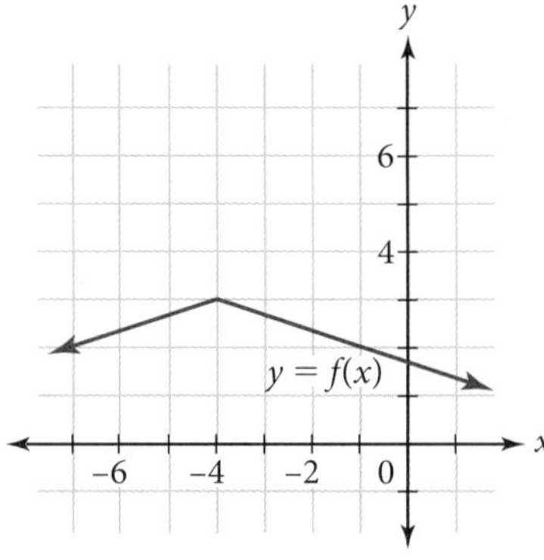

c.

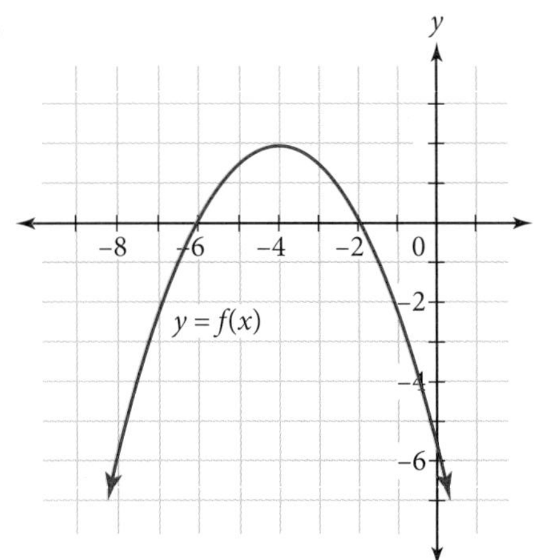

d.

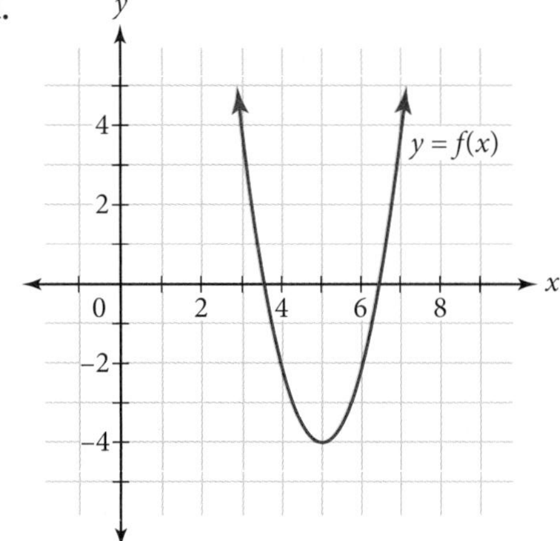

5. Consider the graphs of $y = x^2$ and $y = 3x^2$. For the graph of the parent function, $y = x^2$, the point on the graph 1 unit to the right of the vertex is up 1 unit. For the graph of $y = 3x^2$, that point is up 3 units. For each equation in 5a–f, give the coordinates of the vertex of its graph. Then find the coordinates of the point on the graph whose x-coordinate is 1 unit to the right of the x-coordinate of the vertex.

a. $y = 3|x|$

b. $y = 0.25x^2$

c. $y - 1 = 2|x + 3|$

d. $y + 4 = 5(x - 2)^2$

e. $y = -|x - 2| + 1$

f. $y = -0.5x^2 - 3$

g. What do you notice about the relationship between the y-value of the second point in 5a–f and the corresponding y-value on the parent graph?

Reason and Apply

x	y
2	0
4	2
0	1

6. The table at right lists the vertices of a triangle. Name the vertex or vertices that will not be affected by a vertical stretch. ⓗ

7. Graph each function on your calculator. Then describe how each graph is related to the graph of $y = |x|$ or $y = x^2$. Use the words *translation, reflection, vertical stretch,* and *vertical shrink.*

a. $y = 2x^2$

b. $y = 0.25|x - 2| + 1$ ⓐ

c. $y = -(x + 4)^2 - 1$

d. $y = -2|x - 3| + 4$

8. In previous lessons you have seen "replace" language used to describe a transformation of an equation, such as "replace x with $x - 3$ to shift the graph right 3 units." What is the effect of replacing y with $\frac{y}{3}$ in the equation $y = |x|$? ⓐ

9. Each row of this table describes a single transformation of the parent function $y = |x|$. Copy and complete the table.

Change to the equation $y = \|x\|$	New equation in y-equals form	Transformation of the graph of $y = \|x\|$
Replace x with $x - 3$.	$y = \|x - 3\|$	Translation right 3 units
		Translation down 2 units
	$y = -\|x\|$	
Replace y with $y - 2$.		
Replace y with $\frac{y}{0.5}$.		Vertical shrink by a factor of 0.5
		Translation left 4 units
	$y = 1.5\|x\|$	
		Translation right 1 unit
Replace y with $\frac{y}{3}$.		

10. Describe the order of transformations of the graph of $y = x^2$ represented by

a. $y = -(x + 3)^2$ ⓗ

b. $y = 0.5(x - 2)^2 + 1$ ⓗ

11. Draw this J on graph paper or on your calculator. Then draw the image defined by each definition in 11a–c. Describe how each image is related to the original figure. (If you use graph paper, give yourself a lot of room or make five individual graphs. If you use a calculator, adjust your window so that you can see both figures at the same time.)

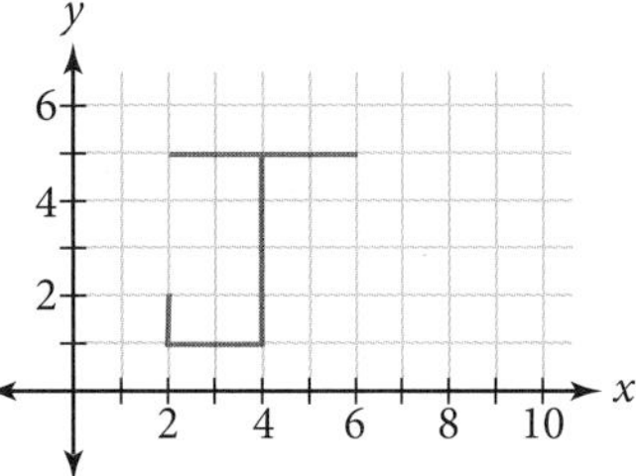

a. $(3x, y)$

b. $(3x, 3y)$

c. $(0.5x, 0.5y)$

d. Explain why the transformations in 11b and c are often called "size transformations."

12. Graph $f(x) = |x|$ on your calculator. Predict what the graph of each equation below will look like. Check by comparing the graphs on your calculator. [▶ See **Calculator Note: Transformations of Functions** for specific instructions for your calculator. ◀]

a. $g(x) = -0.5f(x)$

b. $g(x) = 2f(x - 4)$

c. $g(x) = -3f(x + 2) + 4$

13. In Interlochen, Michigan, it begins to snow in early November. The depth of snow increases over the winter. When winter ends the snow melts and the depth decreases. This table shows data collected in Interlochen.

Snow in Interlochen

Date	Nov 1	Dec 1	Jan 1	Feb 1	Mar 1	Apr 1
Depth of snow (cm)	25	50	70	60	35	10

a. Plot the data. For the dependent variable, let Nov 1 = 1, Dec 1 = 2, and so on. Find a function that models the data. @

b. Use your function to find $f(2.5)$. Explain what this value represents.

c. Find x if $f(x) = 47$. Explain what this x-value represents.

d. According to your model, when was the snow deepest? How deep was it at that time?

14. APPLICATION Deshawn is designing a computer animation program. She has a set of coordinates for the tree shown on the right side of the grid. She wants to use 13 frames to move the tree from the right to the left. In each frame she wants the tree height to shrink by 80%. How should she define the coordinates of each image in relation to the coordinates from the previous frame? @

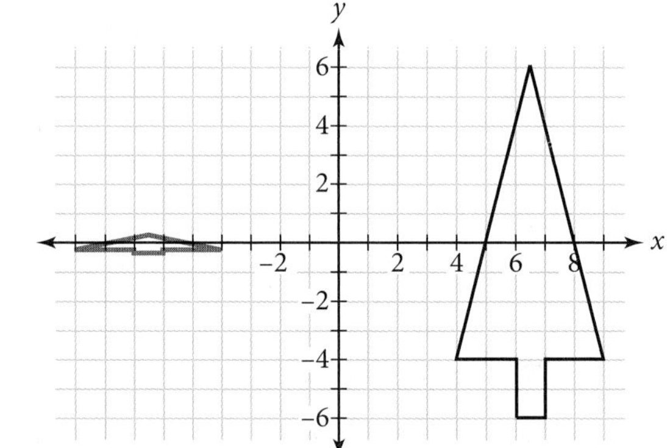

15. Byron says,

> If the graph of a function is stretched vertically but not translated, the factor a is the same as the y-value when x equals 1.

Does Byron's conjecture work for every function in the forms below? Explain why or why not.

a. $y = a \cdot x^2$ @

b. $y = a \cdot |x|$

c. $y = a \cdot f(x)$

Review

16. Use the properties of exponents to rewrite each expression using only positive exponents.

a. $(2^3)^{-3}$ @

b. $(5^2)^5$

c. $(2^4 \cdot 3^2)^3$

d. $(3^2 \cdot x^3)^{-4}$

17. The equation $y = -29 + 1.4x$ approximates the wind chill temperature in degrees Fahrenheit for a wind speed of 40 miles per hour.

a. Which variable represents the actual temperature? Which variable represents the wind chill temperature?

b. What x-value gives the y-value -15? Explain what your answer means in the context of this problem.

18. Solve each equation for x. Substitute your answer into the original equation to verify your solution.

a. $\frac{1}{x+3} = \frac{1}{2x}$

b. $\frac{20}{x} = \frac{15}{x-4}$

c. $\frac{5}{2x} + \frac{1}{2} = \frac{9}{4}$

d. $-95 = \frac{5}{x-10} - 100$

IMPROVING YOUR Reasoning SKILLS

In this lesson you learned how to transform points and functions with a vertical stretch or shrink. In Exercise 11 in the exercise set, you also saw how to transform points with a horizontal stretch or shrink. It is also possible to change the equation of a function to show a horizontal stretch or shrink.

Consider the graph of $y = x^2$ and its image after a horizontal stretch by a factor of 2. Write an equation of the image.

Describe the image in terms of a vertical stretch or shrink. Write an equation that shows this transformation. Is this equation equivalent to the one that shows a horizontal stretch?

When you vertically stretch or shrink the graph of $y = f(x)$ by a factor of a, you get a graph of $y = a \cdot f(x)$. If you horizontally stretch or shrink the graph of $y = f(x)$ by a factor of b, you will get a graph of what equation?

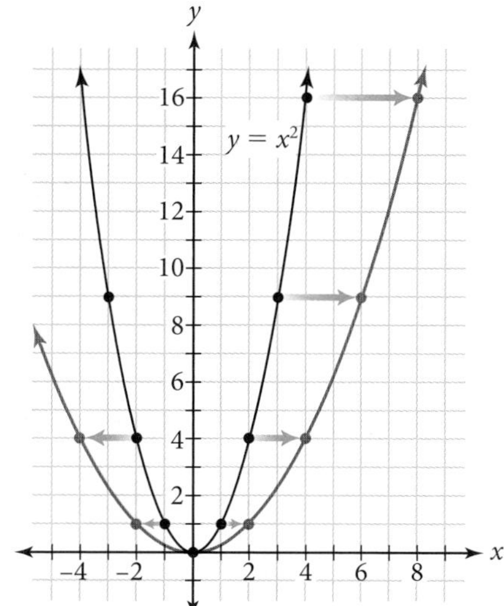

LESSON

7.8

ACTIVITY DAY

Using Transformations to Model Data

In this lesson you'll do experiments to gather data, and then you'll find a function to model the data. To fit the model, you'll first need to identify a parent function. Then you'll transform the parent function and fit the image function to the data.

There are three experiments to choose from. Your group should choose one experiment. Do the other experiments if time permits.

ACTIVITY

Roll, Walk, or Sum

YOU WILL NEED

- a large marble
- tape
- one sheet of paper
- four books
- a sheet of poster board
- a paper cup
- a meterstick or yardstick
- a table and chair
- a motion sensor
- a stopwatch or a watch with a second hand

Experiment 1: The Rolling Marble

In this experiment you'll write an equation to model the path of a falling marble. Then you'll catch the marble at a point you calculate using your equation.

Procedure Note

Use the books and poster board to build a ramp whose bottom is about 30 cm from the edge of the table. Fold the sheet of paper into fan pleats—the smaller the pleats, the better. This paper, when unfolded, will help you locate where the marble hits the floor.

Step 1 Do a trial run. Roll the marble from the top edge of the ramp. Let it roll down the ramp and across the table and drop to the floor. Spot the place where it hits the floor (approximately). Tape the folded paper to the floor in this area.

Step 2 Now collect data to identify the drop point more precisely. Roll the marble two or three times, and mark the point where it hits the paper each time. Each roll should be as much like the other rolls as you can make it. Start each roll at the same place, and release the marble the same way each time.

Step 3 Next find the coordinates of points for a graph. Let x represent horizontal distance, and let y represent vertical distance. Locate the point on the floor directly below the *edge* of the table. Call this point (0, 0). Measure from (0, 0) up to the point at the edge of the table where the marble rolls off. Name the coordinates of this point. Then measure from (0, 0) to each point where the marble hit the floor. Find the average coordinates for these points on the floor.

Step 4 As your marble falls it will follow the path of a parabola. The point where it leaves the table is the vertex of the parabola. Define variables and write an equation in the form $y = ax^2 + b$ that fits your two points.

Next you'll test your model by using it to calculate a point on the path of the marble. See if you can catch the marble at that point.

Step 5 Measure the height of the chair seat. Put the chair next to the table, and place a small cup on the chair. Use your calculations to adjust the position of the cup so that when you roll the marble, it will land in the cup.

Step 6 You have only one chance to land a marble in the cup. Release the marble as you did in Step 2. Good luck!

Experiment 2: Walking

In this experiment you'll walk past a motion sensor and model the data you collect.

> **Procedure Note**
>
> Aim the sensor at the walker. The walker should start about 3 meters away and then walk quickly toward the sensor, aiming just to the side of it. As the walker passes, the student holding the motion sensor should turn it so that it is always directed at the walker. [Use **Calculator Note: Collecting Distance Data Using the EasyData App** to learn how to collect your data.]

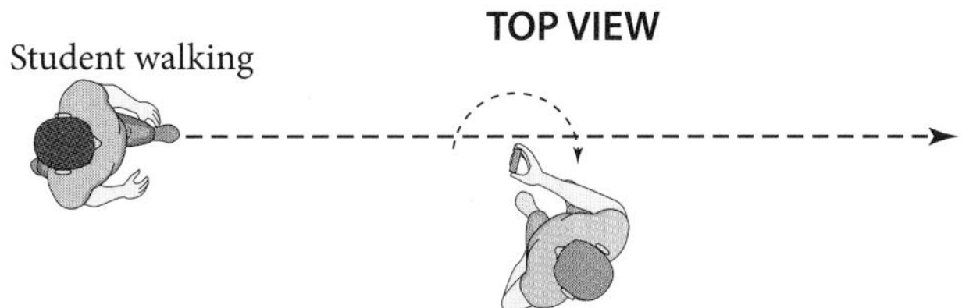

Step 1 Walk steadily in the same direction toward the sensor. Pass it and go about 3 meters farther. Record data for the entire walking time.

Step 2 Download the data to each person's calculator. You should expect some erratic data points when the walker is close to the sensor.

Step 3 Fit the data using function transformations. If the vertex is "missing" from the data, estimate its location.

Step 4 Write walking instructions for each function below. In your instructions say where to start, how fast to go, and when to pass the sensor.

a. $f(x) = 1.5\,|x - 1.2|$ **b.** $f(x) = 2.1\,|x - 0.85|$

Step 5 If time permits, try following your instructions in Step 4 to see if your data fit the graph.

Experiment 3: Calculating

Who is the fastest calculator operator (CO) in your group? The COs had better warm up their fingers!

Procedure Note

You must start with $1 + 2 + 3 \ldots$ each time. It is not fair to use the last result!

Step 1 The CO should carefully calculate sums a–g. Record the answers.

a. $1 + 2 + 3 + \cdots + 8 + 9 + 10$

b. $1 + 2 + 3 + \cdots + 13 + 14 + 15$

c. $1 + 2 + 3 + \cdots + 18 + 19 + 20$

d. $1 + 2 + 3 + \cdots + 23 + 24 + 25$

e. $1 + 2 + 3 + \cdots + 28 + 29 + 30$

f. $1 + 2 + 3 + \cdots + 33 + 34 + 35$

g. $1 + 2 + 3 + \cdots + 38 + 39 + 40$

Step 2 Next the CO calculates the first sum, 1 to 10, again *while being timed.* (Record the time only if the CO gets the correct answer. Otherwise, run the trial again.)

Step 3 Repeat Step 2 for sums b–g, that is, 1 to 15, 1 to 20, . . . , 1 to 40. You should have seven data points in the form (*number of numbers added, time*).

Step 4 Write an equation to model the data. Transform it as needed for a better fit.

Step 5 Use your model to predict the time it would take to sum the numbers from 1 to 47. Test your prediction and record the results.

Step 6 What is the y-intercept of your model? Does this value have any real-world meaning? If so, what is the meaning? If not, why not?

Discuss your results with the class. How were the experiments alike? How were they different? How could you recognize the parent function in the data?

LESSON

7.9

Introduction to Rational Functions

In Chapter 2, you learned that some relationships are modeled by inverse variation. The simplest inverse variation equation is $y = \frac{1}{x}$. Look at the graph of this equation.

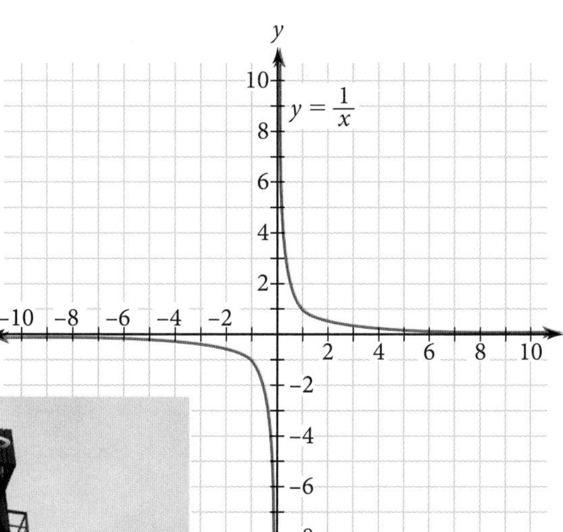

Notice that the graph of $y = \frac{1}{x}$ has two parts. One part is in Quadrant I, and the other is in Quadrant III. In Chapter 2, you wrote inverse variation equations to model countable and measurable quantities, such as number of nickels and distance in inches. Because these quantities are always positive, you worked only with the part of the graph in Quadrant I.

Notice that as the x-values get closer and closer to 0, the value of y gets larger and larger approaching the y-axis. As the x-values get larger and larger, the value of y gets closer and closer to 0, or nearer to the x-axis. The same is true on the negative side. We call these lines **asymptotes,** a line that the graph approaches as you move further and further along the line but never reaches. The graph of $y = \frac{1}{x}$ has two asymptotes: the lines $x = 0$ and $y = 0$. Can you explain why the x- and y-axes are asymptotes for this graph?

Also notice that $y = \frac{1}{x}$ is a function because it passes the vertical line test. You can use the inverse variation function as a parent function to help you understand many other functions.

Some amusement parks have free-fall rides shaped like a first-quadrant inverse variation graph. The Demon Drop at Cedar Point Amusement Park in Ohio is one of them.

INVESTIGATION

I'm Trying to Be Rational

In this investigation you will explore transformations of the parent function $y = \frac{1}{x}$.

Procedure Note

For this investigation use a screen with x and y scales of two units.

Step 1 Graph the parent function $y = \frac{1}{x}$ on your calculator.

Step 2 Use what you have learned about transformations to predict what the graphs of these functions will look like.

a. $\frac{y}{-3} = \frac{1}{x}$ **b.** $\frac{y-3}{2} = \frac{1}{x}$ **c.** $y = \frac{1}{x-2}$ **d.** $y + 2 = \frac{1}{x+1}$

Step 3 Graph each equation in Step 2 on your calculator along with $y = \frac{1}{x}$. Compare the graph to your prediction in Step 2. How can you tell where asymptotes occur on your calculator screen?

Step 4 Without graphing, describe what the graphs of these functions will look like. Use the words *linear, nonlinear, increasing,* and *decreasing.* Define the domain and range. Write equations of the asymptotes.

a. $y = \frac{5}{x - 4}$ **b.** $y = \frac{-1}{x + 3} - 5$ **c.** $y = \frac{a}{(x - h)} + k$

Step 5 A function is an inverse variation when the product of x and y is constant. Do you think the equations in Step 2 and Step 4 are inverse variations? Explain.

Step 6 Write a function that has asymptotes at $x = -2$ and $y = 1$. Sketch its graph, and describe its domain.

The functions you explored in the investigation are called **rational functions.** An equation like $y = \frac{5}{x - 4}$ is an example of a rational function because it shows a ratio between two polynomial expressions, 5 and $x - 4$. (Recall that a polynomial expression can be written as a sum of terms in which the variable is raised only to nonnegative integer exponents.)

Rational functions model many real-world applications. Structural engineers use rational functions to determine properties of support beams, designers use them to help determine where they should place light sources, and businesses use them to track the ratio of total cost to the total number of units produced. The next example shows how a chemist might use a rational function.

EXAMPLE A

A salt solution is made from salt dissolved in water. A bottle contains 1 liter of a 20% salt solution. This means that the concentration of salt is 20%, or 0.2, of the whole solution.

a. Show what happens to the concentration of salt as you add water to the bottle in half-liter amounts.

b. Write an equation that models the concentration of salt as you add water.

c. How much water should you add to get a 2.5% salt solution?

Mono Lake is a natural saltwater lake located near Lee Vining, California. The tufa columns in the background are rock formations created as trickles of calcium-rich water from springs in the lake encounter the salty lake water. The combination of minerals forms rock, which grows the tufa columns. These columns were underwater until water diversion caused the lake level to drop.

(www.sherpaguides.com)

Solution

a. Use a table to show what happens. The bottle originally contains 20% salt, or 0.2 liter. As you add water, the amount of salt stays the same, but the amount of whole solution increases. Each time you add water, recalculate the concentration of salt by finding the ratio of salt to whole solution.

Added amount of water (L)	0	0.5	1.0	1.5	2.0	2.5	3.0	3.5	4.0	4.5	5.0
Amount of salt (L)	0.2	0.2	0.2	0.2	0.2	0.2	0.2	0.2	0.2	0.2	0.2
Whole solution (L)	1.0	1.5	2.0	2.5	3.0	3.5	4.0	4.5	5.0	5.5	6.0
Concentration of salt	0.2	0.133	0.1	0.08	0.067	0.057	0.05	0.044	0.04	0.036	0.033

b. As the amount of whole solution increases, the concentration of salt decreases, but the *amount* of salt stays the same. This is an inverse variation, and the constant of variation is the amount of salt.

$$\textit{concentration} = \frac{\textit{salt}}{\textit{whole solution}}$$

The equation you write should show a relationship between the amount of water you add, x, and the concentration of salt, y. From the table you can see that the amount of whole solution starts at 1 liter and increases by the amount of water you add. The equation is

$$y = \frac{0.2}{1 + x}$$

Concentration of salt → y

Constant amount of salt → 0.2

Added amount of water → x; Starting amount of solution → 1; together: Whole solution

A graph of both the data points and the equation confirms that this equation is a perfect model.

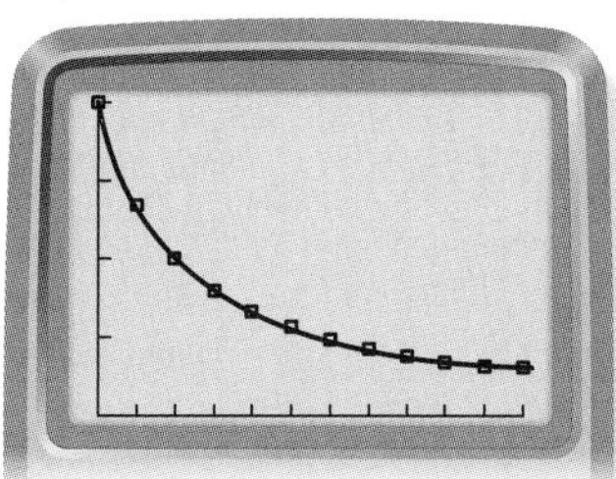

[0, 5.5, 0.5, 0, 0.2, 0.05]

This equation is not an inverse variation because the product of x and y is not constant. It is, however, a transformation of the parent inverse variation function.

c. Use the equation to find the amount of water that you should add. A 2.5% salt solution has a concentration of salt of 0.025.

$0.025 = \frac{0.2}{1 + x}$ Substitute 0.025 for y.

$0.025 + 0.025x = 0.2$ Multiply both sides by $(1 + x)$ and distribute.

$x = 7$ Solve for x.

You would need to add 7 liters of water to have a 2.5% salt solution.

Mathematicians often explore similarities in patterns. **Rational expressions** look similar to fractions, but they include variables as well as numbers. When you studied fractions, you simplified and did arithmetic. Can you do the same thing with rational expressions? In the next example you'll perform operations with rational expressions the same way you've performed them with fractions, and you'll use your graphing calculator to provide evidence that the same methods apply.

EXAMPLE B

A rational expression is simplified to **lowest terms** when the numerator and denominator have no factors in common other than 1.

a. Express these rational expressions in lowest terms.

i. $\dfrac{45x^2}{60x}$ ii. $\dfrac{5x^2 - 100x}{35x}$

b. Perform the indicated operation, and express the results in lowest terms.

i. $\dfrac{6}{x} \cdot \dfrac{4x^3}{15}$

ii. $\dfrac{2x^5}{5y^2} \div \dfrac{6x^4}{20y}$

iii. $\dfrac{2x}{3} + \dfrac{5}{2}$

iv. $\dfrac{x-2}{4} - \dfrac{x-5}{2x}$

Solution

a. You can express a rational expression in lowest terms in the same way you simplified a numerical fraction to lowest terms. Find the common factors in the numerator and denominator that would represent 1 and simplify.

i. $\dfrac{45x^2}{60x} = \dfrac{3 \cdot 3 \cdot 5 \cdot x \cdot x}{3 \cdot 4 \cdot 5 \cdot x}$ Rewrite each expression as a product of its factors.

$= \dfrac{\cancel{3} \cdot 3 \cdot \cancel{5} \cdot \cancel{x} \cdot x}{\cancel{3} \cdot 4 \cdot \cancel{5} \cdot \cancel{x}}$ Pair fractions in the numerator and denominator equal to 1: $\frac{3}{5}$, $\frac{5}{5}$, and $\frac{x}{x}$ and simplify.

$= \dfrac{3x}{4}$ Combine the remaining factors to write as a rational expression in lowest terms.

You can check this answer by looking at table values for your original and final expressions.

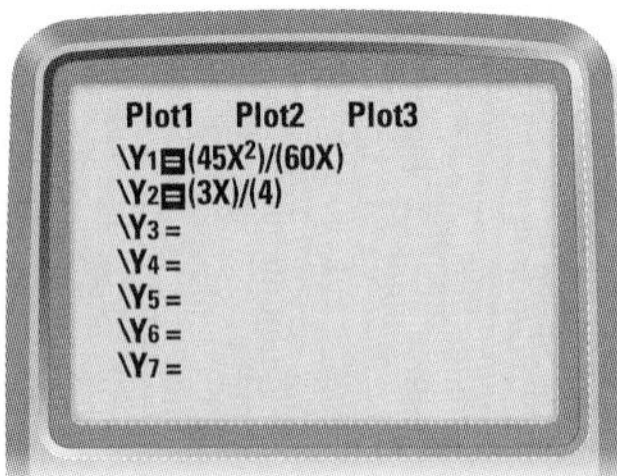

X	Y1	Y2
0	ERR	0
1	.75	.75
2	1.5	1.5
3	2.25	2.25
4	3	3
5	3.75	3.75
6	4.5	4.5

X = 0

Notice that all x-values except 0 give the same y-values. The expression $\frac{45x^2}{60x}$ is undefined when $x = 0$ because you can't divide by 0. However, x can be equal to 0 in the expression $\frac{3x}{4}$. So $\frac{45x^2}{60x}$ is equal to $\frac{3x}{4}$ for all values of x except 0. This value is called an **excluded value** or a **restriction on the variable.** You can write $\frac{45x^2}{60x} = \frac{3x}{4}$, where $x \neq 0$.

ii. $\dfrac{5x^2 - 100x}{35x} = \dfrac{5 \cdot x \cdot (x - 20)}{5 \cdot 7 \cdot x}$

Rewrite each expression as a product of its factors. In the numerator you'll need to identify factors that are common to both terms.

$= \dfrac{\cancel{5} \cdot \cancel{x} \cdot (x - 20)}{\cancel{5} \cdot 7 \cdot \cancel{x}}$

Simplify fractions equal to 1.

$= \dfrac{x - 20}{7}$, where $x \neq 0$

Write as a rational expression in lowest terms.

Again, be sure to note any values of x for which the original expression is undefined. These values must also be excluded from the domain of the reduced expression. In this case $x \neq 0$.

b. You can add, subtract, multiply, and divide rational expressions following the same procedures you use with fractions.

i. $\dfrac{6}{x} \cdot \dfrac{4x^3}{15} = \dfrac{6 \cdot 4x^3}{x \cdot 15}$

Multiply the numerators and denominators.

$= \dfrac{3 \cdot 2 \cdot 2 \cdot 2 \cdot x \cdot x \cdot x}{x \cdot 3 \cdot 5}$

Rewrite each expression as a product of its factors.

$= \dfrac{8x^2}{5}$, where $x \neq 0$

Simplify fractions equal to 1 and write as a rational expression in lowest terms. You can use the multiplication and division properties of exponents that you learned in Chapter 6 to help you. State restrictions on the variable.

Again, you can check table values for the original and final expressions. This table suggests that all defined x-values give the same y-values.

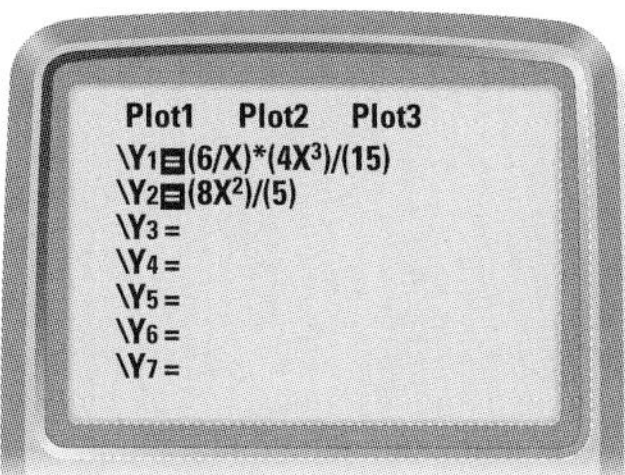

X	Y1	Y2
0	ERR	0
1	1.6	1.6
2	6.4	6.4
3	14.4	14.4
4	25.6	25.6
5	40	40
6	57.6	57.6

X = 0

ii. $\dfrac{2x^5}{5y^2} \div \dfrac{6x^4}{20y} = \dfrac{2x^5}{5y^2} \cdot \dfrac{20y}{6x^4}$

Rewrite the division as multiplication by a reciprocal.

You may now be able to eliminate common factors by observation, or you might prefer to combine the numerators and denominators and write them as products of factors.

$= \dfrac{2 \cdot 2 \cdot 2 \cdot 5 \cdot x^5 \cdot y}{2 \cdot 3 \cdot 5 \cdot x^4 \cdot y^2}$

$= \dfrac{4x}{3y}$, where $x \neq 0$ and $y = 0$

Write as a rational expression in lowest terms, and state restrictions on the variables.

The restrictions must include $x \neq 0$ because the divisor, $\frac{6x^4}{20y}$, is zero when $x = 0$.

iii. To add fractions or rational expressions, first find a common denominator.

$$\frac{2x}{3} + \frac{5}{2} = \frac{2}{2} \cdot \frac{2x}{3} + \frac{3}{3} \cdot \frac{5}{2}$$

The least common denominator is 6, so multiply the first and second expressions by 1, in the form $\frac{2}{2}$ and $\frac{3}{3}$.

$$= \frac{4x}{6} + \frac{15}{6}$$

Multiply. Now that you have a common denominator, you can combine the numerators.

$$= \frac{4x + 15}{6}$$

There are no restrictions on the variable.

iv. To subtract fractions or rational expressions, you also begin by finding a common denominator.

$$\frac{x-2}{4} - \frac{x-5}{2x} = \frac{x}{x} \cdot \frac{x-2}{4} - \frac{2}{2} \cdot \frac{x-5}{2x}$$

The least common denominator is $4x$, so multiply each expression by an appropriate fraction equal to 1.

$$= \frac{x^2 - 2x}{4x} - \frac{2x - 10}{4x}$$

Multiply.

$$= \frac{(x^2 - 2x) - (2x - 10)}{4x}$$

Combine the fractions.

$$= \frac{x^2 - 4x + 10}{4x}, \text{ where } x \neq 0$$

Combine like terms. State restrictions on the variable.

7.9 Exercises

Practice Your Skills

1. Describe each graph as a transformation of the graph of the parent function $y = |x|$ or $y = x^2$. Then write its equation.

a.

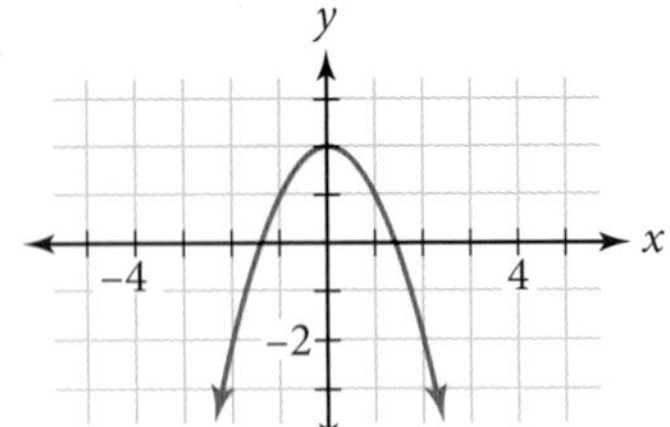

b. 

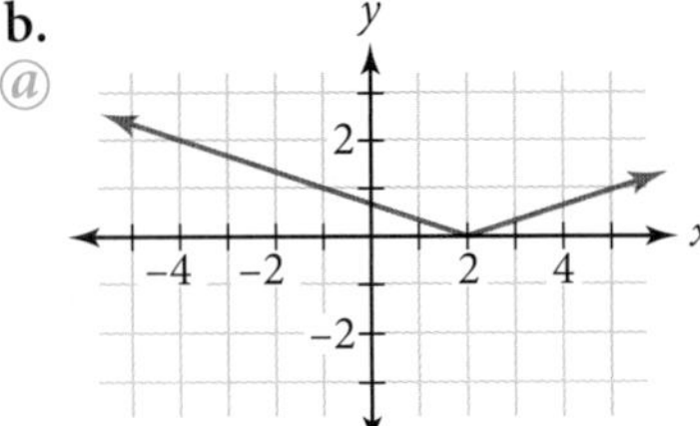

c.

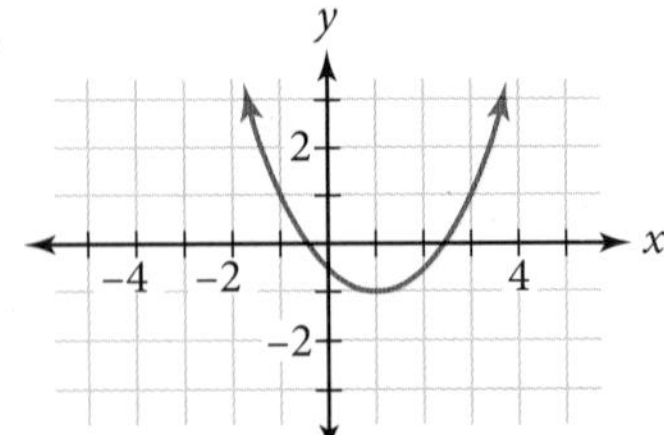

d.

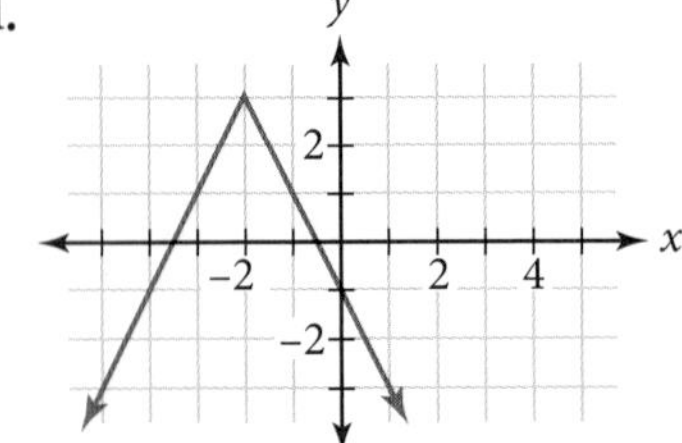

2. Write an equation that generates this table of values. @

x	-4	-3	-2	-1	0	1	2	3	4
y	$-\frac{1}{2}$	$-\frac{2}{3}$	-1	-2	Undefined	2	1	$\frac{2}{3}$	$\frac{1}{2}$

3. Write an equation to model this graph in the form $y = \frac{a}{x}$. @

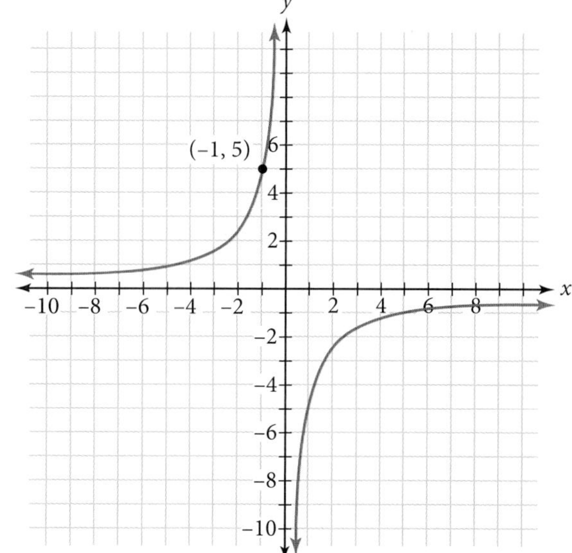

4. The two curves at right are graphs of $f(x) = \frac{4}{x}$ and $g(x) = \frac{8}{x}$. Which equation describes the red curve? The blue curve? Explain.

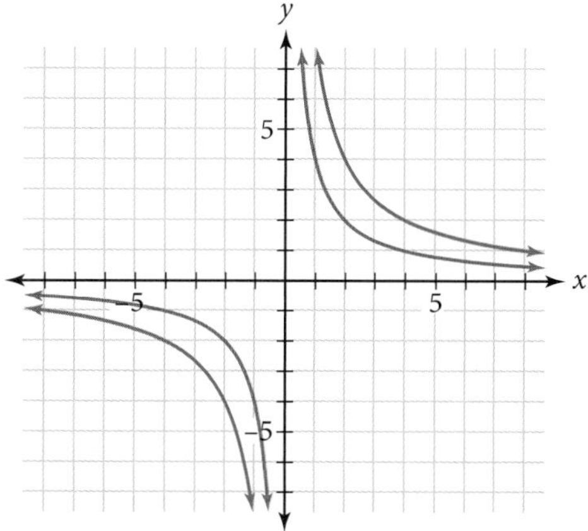

5. Describe each function as a transformation of the graph of the parent function $y = \frac{1}{x}$. Then sketch a graph of each function, and list any values that are not part of the domain.

a. $y = \frac{4}{x}$ @

b. $y = \frac{1}{x - 5} - 2$

c. $y = \frac{0.5}{x} + 3$

d. $y = \frac{-3}{x + 3}$

e. $y + 1 = \frac{2}{x}$

f. $y = -\frac{5}{x - 1}$

g. $y = \frac{6}{x - 2} - 3$

h. $y + 5 = \frac{8}{x + 3}$

Reason and Apply

6. Imelda simplified the rational expression $\frac{3x + 7}{x + 7}$ like this:

$$\frac{3x + 7}{x + 7} = \frac{3\cancel{x} + \cancel{7}}{\cancel{x} + \cancel{7}} = 3$$

She then graphed $f(x) = \frac{3x + 7}{x + 7}$ and $g(x) = 3$ to verify that the two expressions are equivalent. Her graph is shown. How does the graph show that $\frac{3x + 7}{x + 7}$ is not equal to 3? What did Imelda do incorrectly?

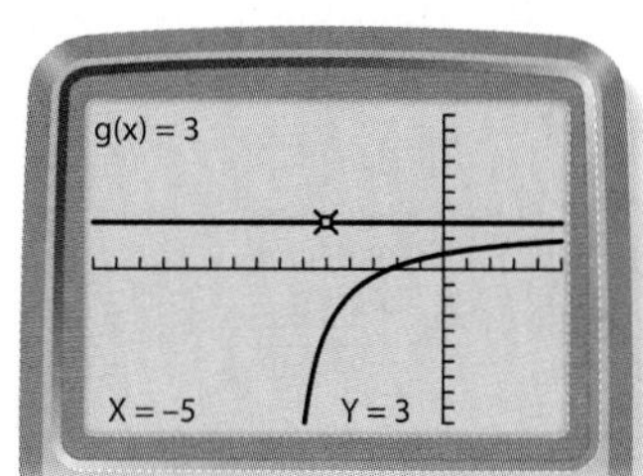

7. Write an equation for each graph. Each calculator screen shows a screen with x and y scales of one unit.

a. @

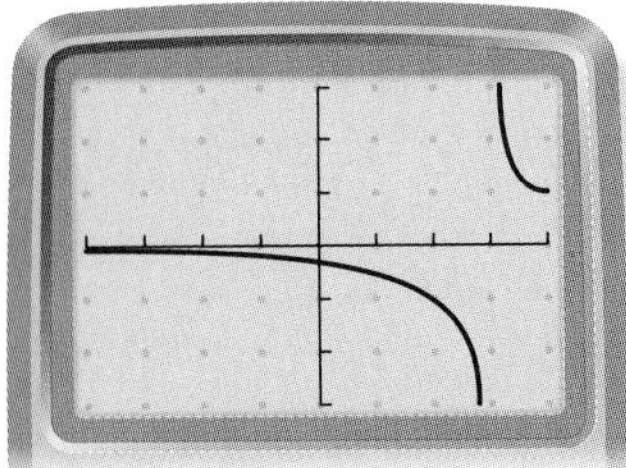

b.

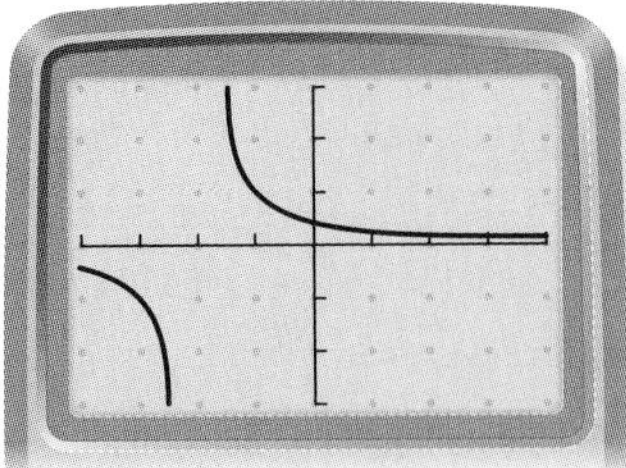

c. @

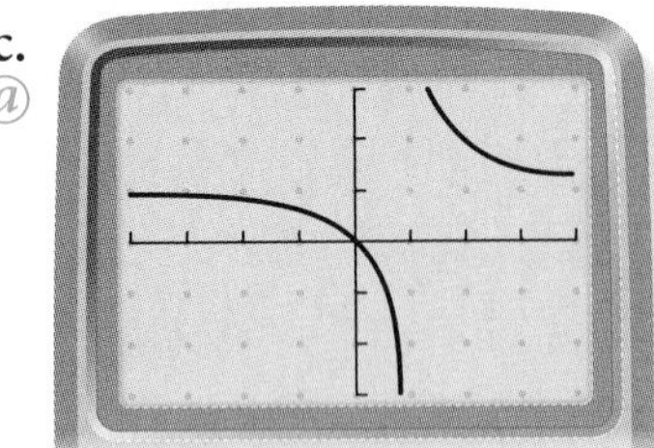

d.

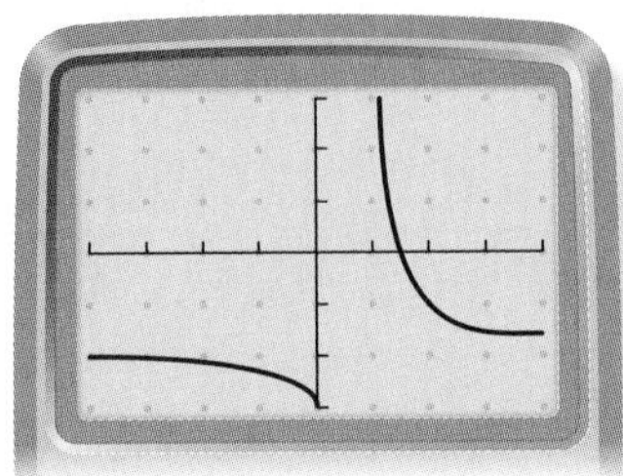

8. Consider the graph of the inverse variation function $f(x) = \frac{1}{x}$.

a. Write an equation that reflects the graph across the x-axis. Sketch the image.

b. Write an equation that reflects the graph across the y-axis. Sketch the image.

c. Compare your sketches in 8a and b. Explain what you find.

9. APPLICATION A nurse needs to treat a patient's eye with a 1% saline solution (salt solution). She finds only a half-liter bottle of 5% saline solution. Write an equation and use it to calculate how much water the nurse should add to create a 1% solution. @

The saline solution that is used to clean contact lenses is usually a 1% salt solution.

10. APPLICATION A business group wants to rent a meeting hall for its job fair during the week of spring break. The rent is \$3,500, which will be divided among the businesses that agree to participate. So far only five businesses have signed up.

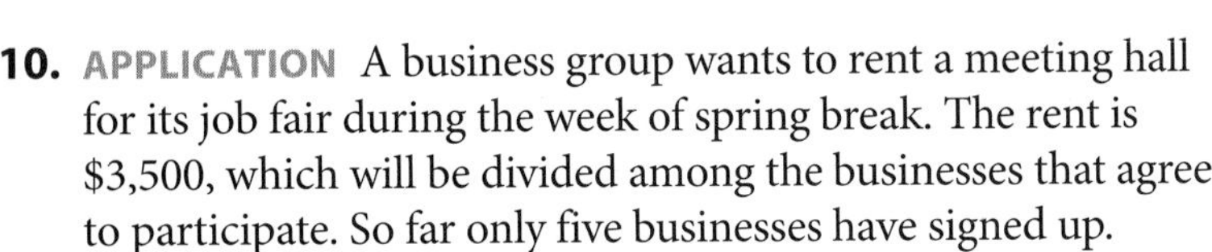

a. At this time what is the cost for each business?

b. Make a table to show what happens to the cost per business as additional businesses agree to participate.

c. Write a function that relates the cost per business to the number of additional businesses that agree to participate.

d. How many additional businesses must agree to participate before the cost per business is less than \$150?

11. Simplify each rational expression by dividing out common factors, and state any restrictions on the variable. Use your calculator's table feature to verify your answer.

a. $\frac{120x^4}{24x^5}$

b. $\frac{(5x^3)(16x^2)}{80x^3}$

c. $\frac{24x^3}{8x^5}$

d. $\frac{4 + 20x}{20x}$

e. $\frac{5x - 15x^4}{5x}$ @

f. $\frac{12x^2}{9x^4 - 3x^3}$

g. $\frac{7x^2 - 7x}{21x^5}$

h. $\frac{6x^2}{x^2 - 2x}$

i. $\frac{8x + 16}{16x + 8}$

Review

12. Solve each inequality for x.

a. $4 - 2x > 8$ @ b. $-8 + 3(x - 2) \geq -20$ c. $7 + 2x \leq 3 + 3x$

13. Name the coordinates of the vertex of the graph of $y = 2(x - 3)^2 + 1$. Without graphing, name the points on the parabola whose x-coordinates are 1 unit more or less than the x-coordinate of the vertex. Check your answers by graphing on your calculator.

14. Jack lives in a cabin at the bottom of a hill. At the top of the hill, directly behind his cabin, is an observation tower. There is a creek at the bottom of the hill on the side opposite Jack's cabin.

Observation tower
Cabin
Creek

Match each description in 14a–c to one of the graphs below. Then answer 14d. The horizontal axis shows time, and the vertical axis shows distance from the *top* of the hill.

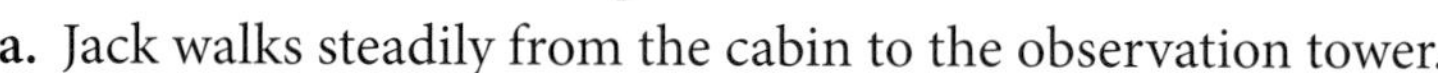

a. Jack walks steadily from the cabin to the observation tower.

b. Jack walks steadily from the observation tower to the creek.

c. Jack walks steadily from the cabin to the creek.

d. Create a walking context and story for the unmatched graph.

i. Distance / Time

ii. Distance / Time

iii.
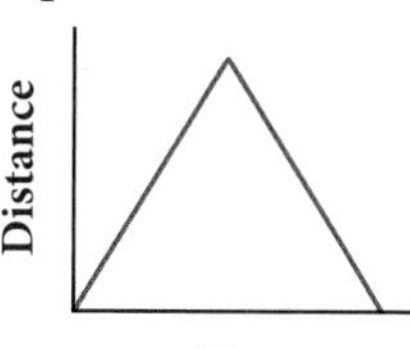

iv.
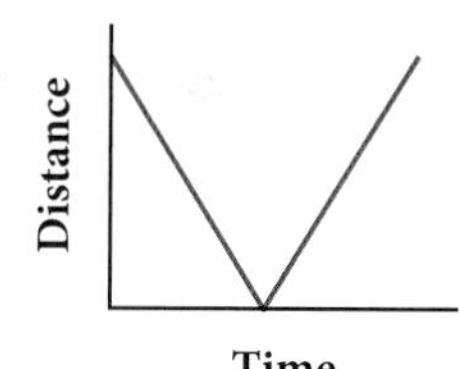

IMPROVING YOUR Visual Thinking SKILLS

Describe each striped or plaid fabric pattern as a set of transformations. Which patterns are translations? Which are reflections?

Fabric A

Fabric B

Fabric C

Fabric D

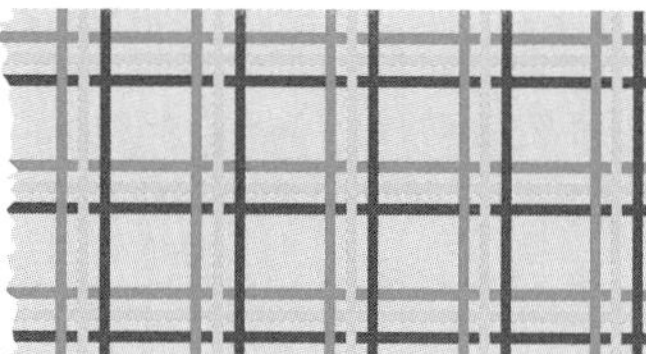

What is the smallest rectangular "unit" that repeats throughout each pattern? Can there be more than one "unit" for a pattern? Suppose a tailor is making a shirt from each fabric pattern and knows that it is easier to make shirts from a pattern made up of reflections. Which shirt should be most expensive? Why?

Rational Expressions

In Lesson 7.9, you worked with simple rational expressions. More complex problems require the use of more complex operations.

In this lesson you will use the properties of exponents and identify least common denominators as you simplify more complex rational expressions. You can use your calculator to compare two expressions at any step in your solution.

EXAMPLE A | Find $\dfrac{x+5}{(x-3)(x+3)} + \dfrac{x-2}{(x+2)(x+3)}$.

Solution | As with adding fractions, you must find a common denominator and rewrite each rational expression with that denominator. In this case the least common denominator must have the factors $(x-3)$, $(x+3)$, and $(x+2)$. This means that you should multiply the first term by 1 in the form $\frac{(x+2)}{(x+2)}$ and the second term by 1 in the form $\frac{(x-3)}{(x-3)}$.

$$\frac{x+5}{(x-3)(x+3)} + \frac{x-2}{(x+2)(x+3)} =$$

$$= \frac{(x+2)}{(x+2)} \cdot \frac{x+5}{(x-3)(x+3)} + \frac{(x-3)}{(x-3)} \cdot \frac{x-2}{(x+2)(x+3)}$$

$$= \frac{(x+5)(x+2)}{(x+2)(x-3)(x+3)} + \frac{(x-2)(x-3)}{(x-3)(x+2)(x+3)}$$

Now the terms have the same denominator, so you can combine the fractions.

$$= \frac{(x+5)(x+2) + (x-2)(x-3)}{(x-3)(x+3)(x+2)}$$

If you expand the numerator, you can combine like terms to get a simpler expression.

$$= \frac{(x^2+7x+10) + (x^2-5x+6)}{(x-3)(x+3)(x+2)}$$

$$= \frac{2x^2+2x+16}{(x-3)(x+3)(x+2)}$$

You can then factor the numerator to see whether it has any factors in common with the denominator. Don't forget to state any restrictions on the variables.

$$= \frac{2(x^2+x+8)}{(x-3)(x+3)(x+2)}, \text{ where } x \neq -3, -2, \text{ or } 3$$

The numerator factors no further, so the expression is in simplest form.

EXAMPLE B | Find $\frac{8x+16}{5x-15} \div \frac{10x^2-20x}{6x^3-18x^2}$.

Solution | As with dividing fractions, you can multiply by the reciprocal of the dividend.

$$\frac{8x+16}{5x-15} \div \frac{10x^2-20x}{6x^3-18x^2} = \frac{8x+16}{5x-15} \cdot \frac{6x^3-18x^2}{10x^2-20x}$$

You can often save time and steps if you next factor each part of the expression.

$$= \frac{8(x+2)}{5(x-3)} \cdot \frac{6x^2(x-3)}{10x(x-2)}$$

Now several common factors can be divided out because multiplication and the division indicated by the fraction bar undo each other.

$$= \frac{8(x+2)}{5} \cdot \frac{3x}{5(x-2)}$$

This expression can be rewritten as a single fraction.

$$= \frac{24x(x+2)}{25(x-2)}, \text{ where } x \neq 0, 2, \text{ or } 3$$

Exercises

1. Factor the numerator and denominator of each rational expression, and divide out any common factors. Leave your answers in factored form. State any restrictions on the variable.

a. $\frac{12x^3-4x^2}{9x^2-3x}$ b. $\frac{(x-2)(x+2)}{x^2-2x}$ c. $\frac{(x-2)(x-5)}{(x+3)(x-2)}$

d. $\frac{(x+4)^2}{(x+2)(x+4)}$ e. $\frac{x(x+5)(x-1)}{3x^3(x-1)^2}$ f. $\frac{(x-11)(x+4)}{9x^2+36x}$

g. $\frac{4(x+2)(x+3)}{6x(x+2)(x-3)}$ h. $\frac{4(x+2)(x-2)}{16x^2+32x}$ i. $\frac{28x^2(x-5)}{7(x-5)^2}$

2. Perform the indicated operation. State any restrictions on the variable.

a. $\frac{6x}{5} - \frac{x}{5}$ b. $\frac{5}{12x} + \frac{1}{6x}$ c. $\frac{5}{2x} - \frac{5}{3}$

d. $\frac{5}{x-5} + \frac{2}{x+2}$ e. $\frac{5}{8x^2} + \frac{3}{10x}$ f. $\frac{-x}{x-3} + \frac{x+1}{x+2}$

g. $\frac{8x+16}{16x+8} + \frac{3x+1}{2x+1}$ h. $\frac{x^2}{(x+3)(x-1)} - \frac{x-1}{(x+3)(x+1)}$

3. Perform the indicated operation. Leave your answers in factored form. State any restrictions on the variable.

a. $\frac{4x^3}{24x^6} \cdot \frac{12x^4}{15x}$ b. $\frac{3(x-6)}{18} \cdot \frac{4(x+6)}{8(x-6)}$ c. $\frac{4xy^3}{(2x)^3} \div \frac{2y^2}{1}$

d. $\frac{3(x+4)}{5x} \cdot \frac{20x^2}{6x^2+24x}$ e. $\frac{18x^3}{4x^5} \cdot \frac{10x}{15}$ f. $\frac{x-4}{3x^2-3x} \cdot \frac{6x^3}{2x-8}$

g. $\frac{6x^2}{x^2-4x} \div \frac{9x}{2x-8}$ h. $\frac{8x+16}{5x-15} \div \frac{10x^2+20x}{6x^3-18x^2}$

CHAPTER 7 REVIEW

In this chapter you learned how to use function notation $f(x)$ and some new vocabulary. You explored the **piecewise function** and its special case, the **step function.** You also explored the **absolute-value function,** $f(x) = |x|$, and the **squaring function,** $f(x) = x^2$, and their graphs. You learned that equations modeling these two functions can have zero, one, or two solutions. You learned how to graph the equation of a **parabola.** You also used the **square root function** to undo the squaring function. And you investigated how to find the **average rate of change** of a nonlinear function.

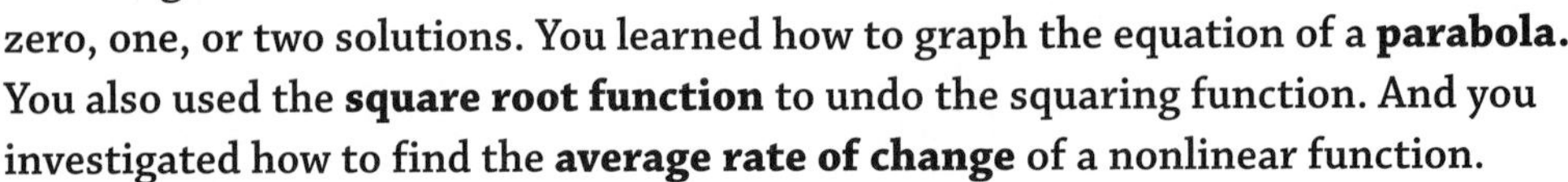

You moved individual points, polygons, and graphs of functions with **transformations.** You learned to **translate, reflect, stretch,** and **shrink** a **parent function** to create a **family of functions** based on it. For example, if you know what the graph of $y = x^2$ looks like, understanding transformations gives you the power to know what the graph of $y = 3(x + 2)^2 - 4$ looks like.

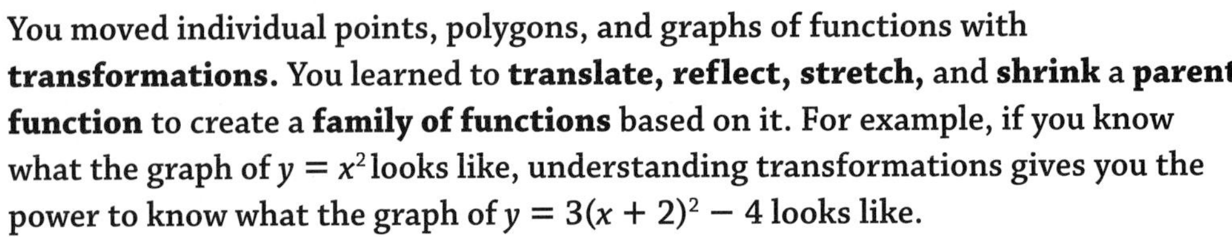

You transformed the graphs of the parent functions $y = |x|$ and $y = x^2$ to create many different absolute-value and squaring functions. You can now apply the same transformations to the graphs of other functions, such as $y = x$ or $y = 2^x$, to create many different linear or exponential functions. You can even fit an equation to data by transforming a simple graph.

You learned that the inverse variation function, $y = \frac{1}{x}$, is one type of **rational function.** The graphs of transformations of the parent function $y = \frac{1}{x}$ have one vertical **asymptote** and one horizontal asymptote—understanding transformations helps you know where asymptotes will occur. You then learned how to perform operations with **rational expressions.**

Exercises

You will need your graphing calculator for Exercises **2** and **11.**

@ **Answers are provided for all exercises in this set.**

1. Consider the function $f(x) = |x|$.

a. Find $f(-3)$.

b. Find $f(2)$.

c. For what x-value(s) does $f(x)$ equal 10?

2. Use your calculator for 2a–c.

a. Graph the functions $y = \sqrt{x}$ and $y = x^2$.

b. Compare the graphs. How are they similar? How are they different?

c. Explain why the graph of $y = \sqrt{x}$ has only one "branch."

d. Sketch the graph of $y^2 = x$. Is this the graph of a function? Explain why or why not.

3. **APPLICATION** A recent catalog price for tennis balls was $4.25 for a can containing three balls. The shipping charge per order was $1.00.

   a. Write an equation that you can use to project the cost of ordering different numbers of cans.

   b. Draw a graph showing this relationship.

   c. How does raising the shipping charge by 50¢ affect the graph?

   d. What equation models the cost equation in 3c?

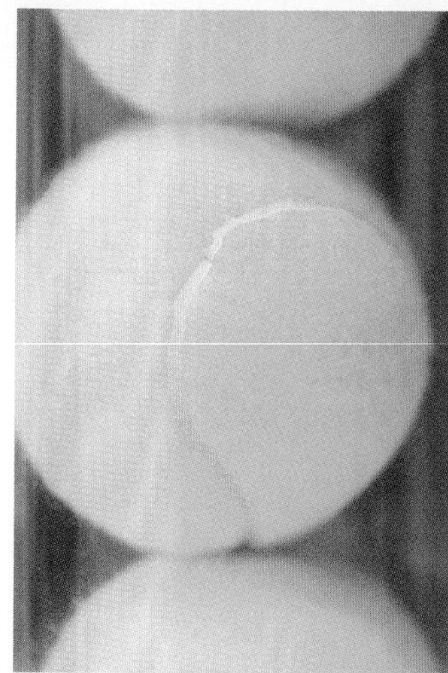

4. Draw a graph to fit each description.

   a. A function that has domain $-5 \le x \le 1$, range $-4 \le y \le 4$, and $f(-2) = 1$.

   b. A relation that is not a function and that has inputs on the interval $-6 \le x \le 4$ and outputs on the interval $0 \le y \le 5$.

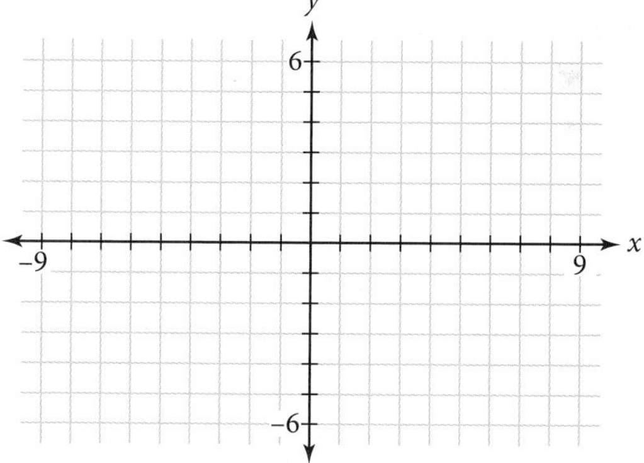

For Exercises 5 and 6, consider the black pentagon in Exercise 5 the original figure.

5. The image of the black pentagon after a transformation is shown in red.

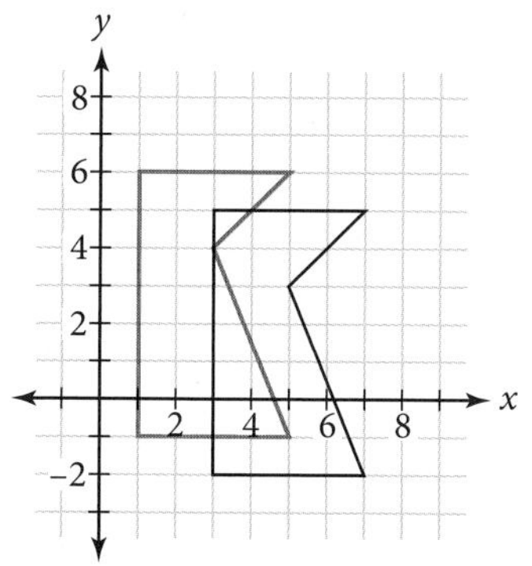

   a. Describe the transformation.

   b. Define the coordinates of any point in the image using (x, y) as the coordinates of any point in the original figure.

6. Here are three more transformations of the black pentagon from Exercise 5.

i.

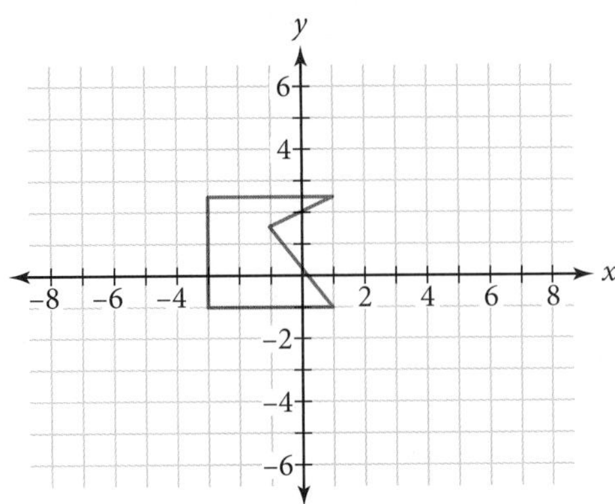

ii.

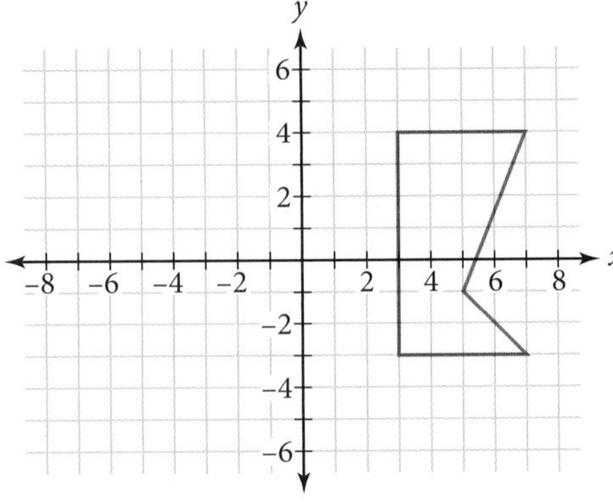

iii.

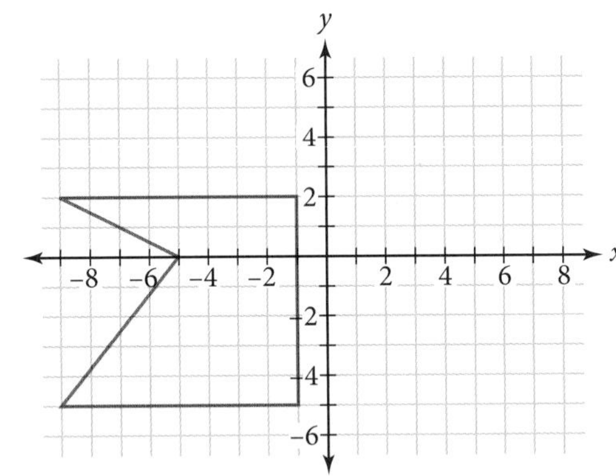

a. Describe the transformations.

b. Patty plots the original pentagon on her calculator. She lists the x-coordinates of the vertices in *list1*, and she lists the y-coordinates in *list2*. Explain to Patty how to define *list3* and *list4* for the x- and y-coordinates of each image above.

7. You can create the figure at right on a calculator by connecting four points. Assume that the x-coordinates of each point are entered into *list1* and the corresponding y-coordinates are entered into *list2*. Explain how to make an image that is

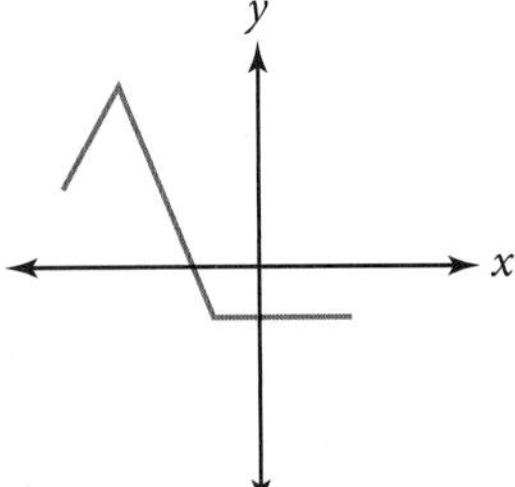

a. A reflection across the x-axis.

b. A reflection across the y-axis.

c. A reflection across the x-axis and a translation right 3 units.

8. Describe each function as a transformation of the graph of the parent function $y = |x|$ or $y = x^2$. Then sketch a graph of each function. Check your answers by graphing on your calculator.

a. $y = 2|x| + 1$

b. $y = -|x + 2| + 2$

c. $y = 0.5(-x)^2 - 1$

d. $y = -(x - 2)^2 + 1$

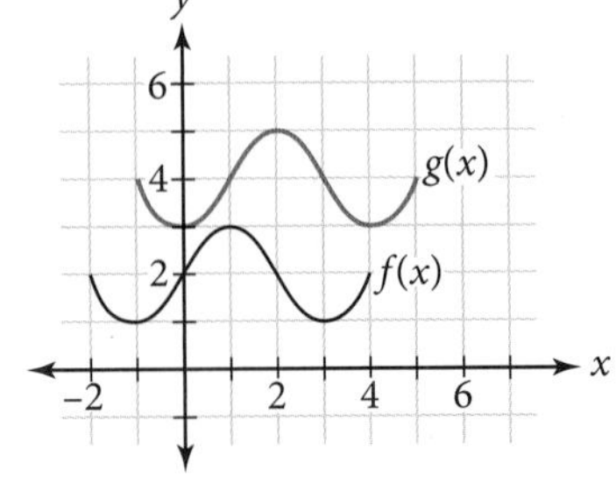

9. The graph of $g(x)$ at right is a transformation of the graph of $f(x)$. Write an equation of $g(x)$ in terms of $f(x)$.

10. Write an equation for each graph.

a.

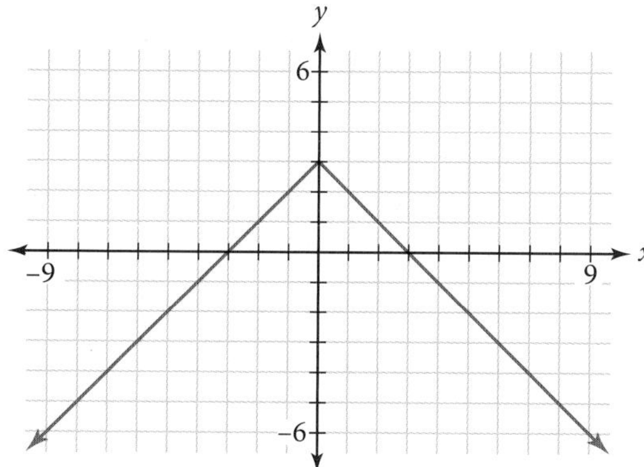

b.

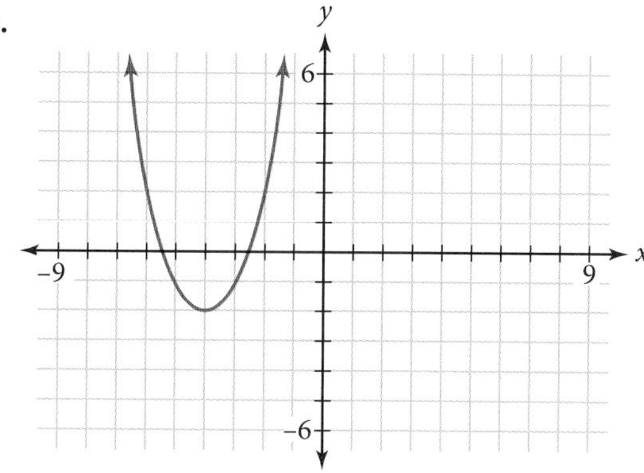

c.

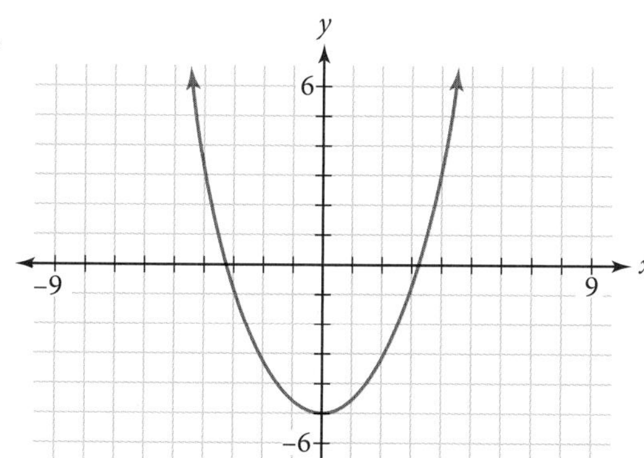

d.

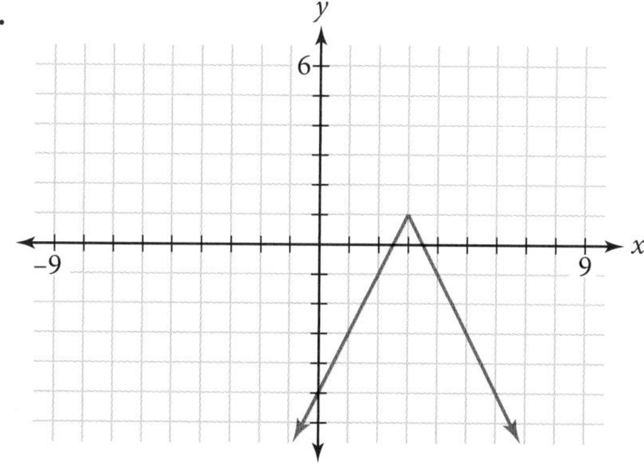

11. Consider the graph of $f(x)$ at right.

a. Sketch the graph of $-f(x)$.

b. Enter a linear function, $g(x)$, into your calculator to create a graph like $f(x)$. Enter $h(x) = -g(x)$ and graph it too. Describe your results.

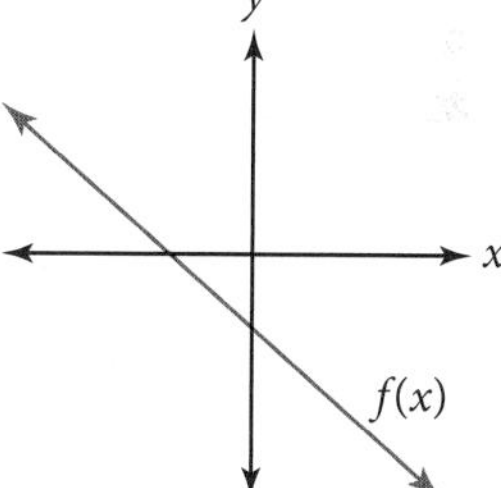

12. Describe each function as a transformation of the graph of the parent function, $y = \frac{1}{x}$. Write the equations of the asymptotes.

a. $y = \frac{1}{x - 3}$

b. $y = \frac{3}{x + 2}$

c. $y = \frac{1}{x - 5} - 2$

13. APPLICATION The intensity, I, of a 100-watt light bulb is related to the distance, d, from which it is measured. This rational function shows the relationship when intensity is measured in lux (lumens per square meter) and distance is measured in meters.

$$I = \frac{90}{d^2}$$

a. Find the intensity of the light 4 meters from the bulb.

b. Find the distance from the bulb if the intensity of the light measures 20 lux.

14. Describe each graph as a transformation of the graph of the parent function $y = 2^x$ or $y = \frac{1}{x}$. Then write an equation for each graph.

a.

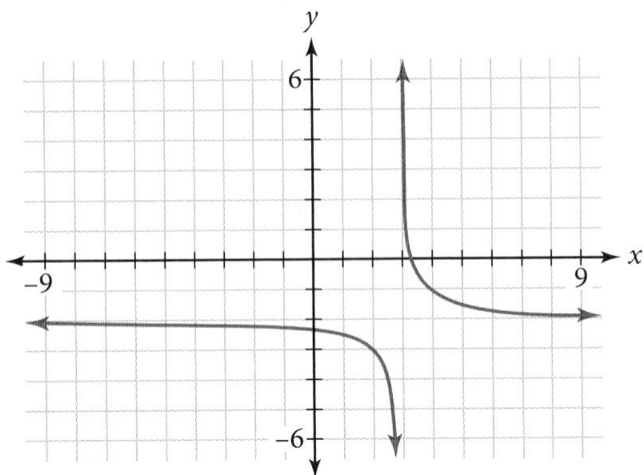

b.

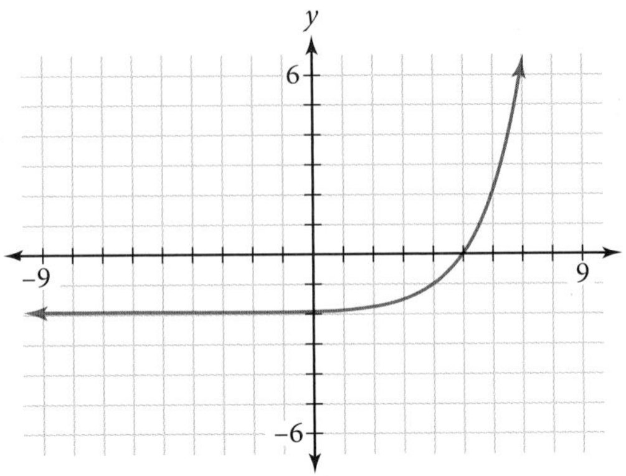

c.

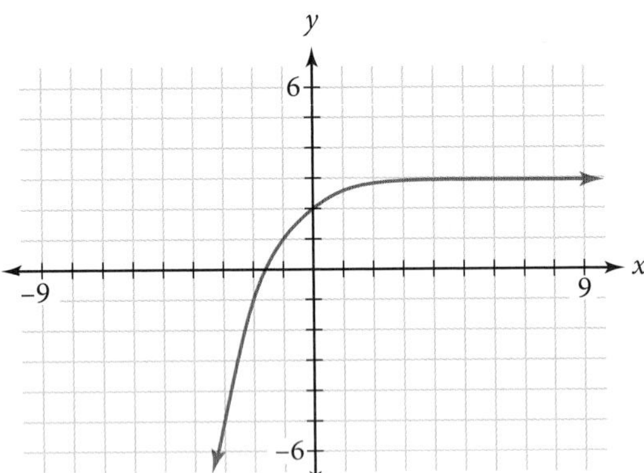

d.

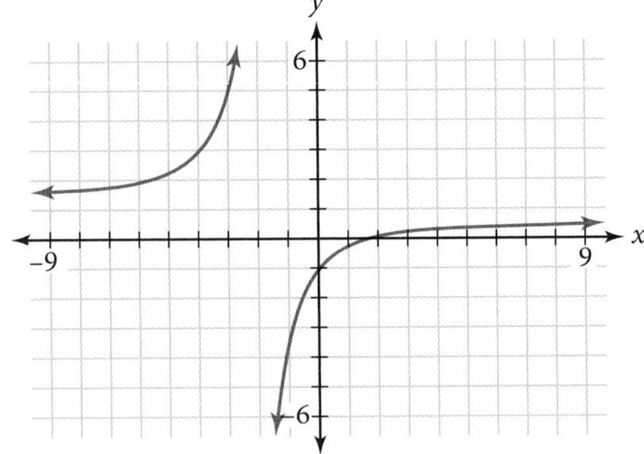

15. Perform the indicated operation, and simplify the result to lowest terms. State any restrictions on the variable.

a. $\frac{x}{2x - 3} - \frac{2x + 3}{8x - 12}$

b. $\frac{42x^2}{x - 3} \div \frac{3}{2x - 6}$

c. $\frac{3x + 3}{12x - 5} \cdot \frac{6}{2x + 2}$

d. $\frac{x}{x + 7} + \frac{1}{x - 2}$

16. Factor the numerator and denominator of each expression, and divide out any common factors. Leave your answers in factored form. State any restrictions on the variable.

a. $\frac{2x^2 + 4x}{3x + 6}$

b. $\frac{(15x + 21)(x + 3)}{(3x + 9)(x + 1)}$

17. Let $f(x) = 3x^2 - 5$. Find the average rate of change over the given intervals.

a. $x = 0$ and $x = 1$

b. $x = 3$ and $x = 7$

Take Another Look

In this chapter you saw reflections across the x-axis and across the y-axis. You also saw reflections across other vertical and horizontal lines (see Exercise 10 in Lesson 7.6). Let's examine another very important line of reflection.

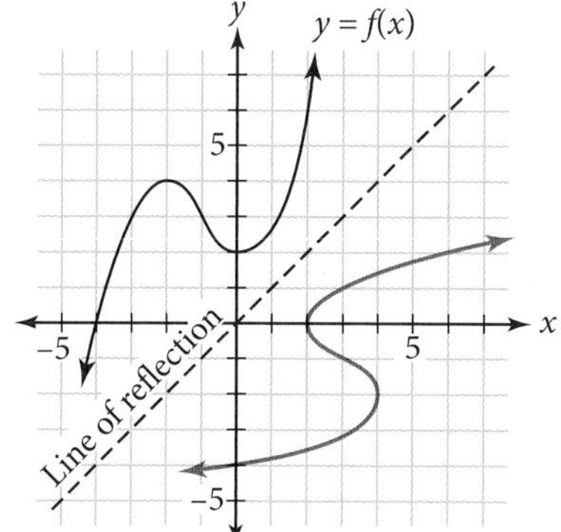

Here is the graph of a function in black. The red image was created by a reflection across the dotted line. What is the equation of the line of reflection?

Identify at least three points on the graph of $y = f(x)$. Then name the image of each point after the reflection. How would you define the coordinates of the image based on the coordinates of the original graph?

The image that results from this type of reflection is called an **inverse**. Is the inverse of a function necessarily a function too? Find an example of a function whose inverse is also a function. Find an example of a function whose inverse is not a function.

Reflection of the Glasgow Arc Bridge, often called the Squinty Bridge because of its unique design, across the River Clyde in Scotland.

Assessing What You've Learned

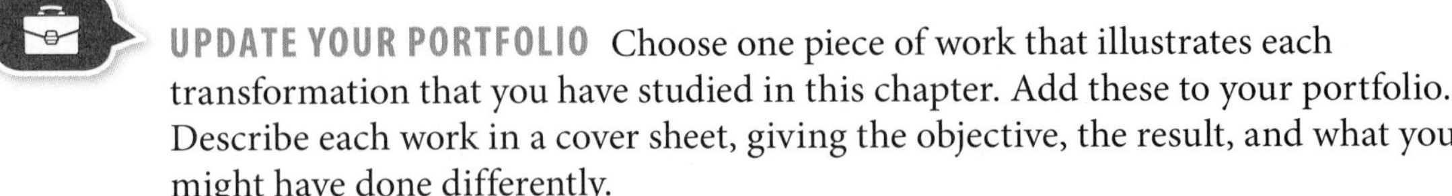

UPDATE YOUR PORTFOLIO Choose one piece of work that illustrates each transformation that you have studied in this chapter. Add these to your portfolio. Describe each work in a cover sheet, giving the objective, the result, and what you might have done differently.

ORGANIZE YOUR NOTEBOOK Organize your notes on each type of transformation that you have learned about. Review how each transformation affects individual points and how it changes the equation of a function. Then create a table that summarizes your notes. Use rows for the type of transformation and columns to show effects on points and equations. You can use subrows and subcolumns to further organize the information. For example, you might want to use one row for reflections across the x-axis and another row for reflections across the y-axis. You might want to use one column for changes to the function $y = f(x)$ and other columns for changes to specific functions such as $y = x^2$, $y = |x|$, or $y = \frac{1}{x}$.

PERFORMANCE ASSESSMENT Show a classmate, a family member, or your teacher how you can transform a single parent function into a whole family of functions. Explain how you can write a function to represent a graph by identifying the transformations. In contrast, show how you can sketch a graph simply by looking at the equation.

CHAPTER 8

Quadratic Functions

Buckingham Fountain in Chicago's Grant Park contains 1.5 million gallons of water. When pumped through one of the fountain's 133 jets, the water forms the shape of a parabola as it falls back into the pool. The central spout shoots 135 feet in the air. The relationship between time and the height of free-falling objects in the air is described by quadratic equations.

OBJECTIVES

In this chapter you will

- review factoring and using the distributive property
- model applications with quadratic functions
- compare features of parabolas to their quadratic equations
- learn strategies for solving quadratic equations
- learn how to combine and factor polynomials
- make connections between some new polynomial functions and their graphs

Factoring and Multiplying

As you work with new types of equations in this chapter, you'll extend your skills of factoring and using the distributive property. Here you'll review some skills you probably already have.

EXAMPLE A

In earlier grades you learned to factor whole numbers. For example, when you find factors of the number 12, you list whole numbers of which 12 is a multiple. You could also write 12 as a product of integers. List the integer pairs whose product is 12; then do the same for −12 and 7.

Solution

x	y	Product
1	12	12
−1	−12	12
2	6	12
−2	−6	12
3	4	12
−3	−4	12

x	y	Product
1	−12	−12
−1	12	−12
2	−6	−12
−2	6	−12
3	−4	−12
−3	4	−12

x	y	Product
1	7	7
−1	−1	7

The tables for 12 and −12 are similar, but they differ because multiplying a positive number by a positive number or a negative number by a negative number results in a positive number and multiplying a negative number by a positive number results in a negative number. There are only two pairs of integers whose product is 7, because 7 is a prime number.

EXAMPLE B

Rectangle diagrams are useful graphic organizers for finding products and factors. Use the distributive property to factor the sums or multiply the products.

a. $4x(150x + 8)$ **b.** $24x - 12x^2$

Solution

Multiply the number outside by each term in the parentheses, or factor out the greatest common factor.

a. This expression is the product of $4x$ and $150x + 8$. Applying the distributive property you multiply $4x$ by $150x$ and by 8. This rectangle diagram shows a picture of the distribution of $4x$ over $150x$ and 8; the product is $600x^2 + 32x$.

	$150x$	8
$4x$	$600x^2$	$32x$

b. There are many ways to factor the expression $24x - 12x^2$. The rectangle diagram shows the preferred solution, $12x(2 - x)$, because $12x$ is the greatest common factor (GCF) of $24x$ and $12x^2$.

	2	$-x$
$12x$	$24x$	$-12x^2$

This is an example of the distributive property in reverse, or factoring. The factor $12x$ is the GCF of the two terms $24x$ and $-12x^2$. The $12x$ goes on one side of the rectangle, making the other side $(2 - x)$. That is, $24x - 12x^2 = 12x(2 - x)$. You could have chosen the common factor 2, to get $24x - 12x^2 = 2(12x - 6x^2)$, but mathematicians tend to *factor completely,* using the GCF rather than any other common factor.

EXAMPLE C

Use the distributive property to factor the sums or multiply the products without using rectangle diagrams.

a. $-3(2 - x - x^2)$

b. $x^2y(2x^2 - xy + 3y^2)$

c. $2k^2 - 4k$

d. $-w^2z^3 + wz^2 - 3wz$

Solution

a. The -3 must be multiplied by each term inside the parentheses, so

$$-3(2 - x - x^2) = -3 \cdot 2 - (-3) \cdot x - (-3) \cdot x^2$$
$$= -6 + 3x + 3x^2$$

b. The x^2y must be multiplied by each term inside the parentheses, so

$$x^2y(2x^2 - xy + 3y^2) = (x^2y) \cdot 2x^2 - (x^2y) \cdot xy + (x^2y) \cdot 3y^2$$
$$= 2x^4y - x^3y^2 + 3x^2y^3$$

c. The GCF is $2k$, so $2k^2 - 4k = 2k(k - 2)$

d. The GCF is wz, so $-w^2z^3 + wz^2 - 3wz = wz(-wz^2 + z - 3)$

EXAMPLE D

Solve the equation $\dfrac{2x^3 - 4x^2 - 6x}{2x} = \dfrac{3x^2 - 12x + 15}{3}$

Solution

First see if the fractions on each side of the equation can be simplified. In the numerator on the left side of the equation, $2x$ is the GCF of $2x^3 - 4x^2 - 6x$, so the numerator can be factored. In the numerator on the right side of the equation, 3 is the GCF of $3x^2 - 12x + 15$, so the numerator can be factored. The equation can be written as

$$\frac{2x(x^2 - 2x - 3)}{2x} = \frac{3(x^2 - 4x + 5)}{3}$$

$x^2 - 2x - 3 = x^2 - 4x + 5$	Simplify
$-2x - 3 = -4x + 5$	Subtract x^2 from both sides
$2x - 3 = 5$	Add $4x$ to both sides
$2x = 8$	Add 3 to both sides
$x = 4$	Divide both sides by 2

Exercises

1. Write an equation that describes each rectangle diagram.

a.

	$3x$	1
$6x$		

b.

$21x^3$	$-28x^2$

2. Use the distributive property to write these products as sums or differences.

a. $9(100 - 1)$

b. $18(3x + 5)$

c. $2x(1 - 3x)$

d. $xy^2(2x + 3y)$

e. $-2km^3(3k - 4m + 5km - k^2m^2)$

f. $(p^2 - 3pq - 2q^2)(-2pq)$

g. $3e(e^2 - 9ed + 4d^2) - 2d(5e - 3d)$

h. $x^3y(x^2 - y) + xy(x^4 + x^2y)$

3. Use the distributive property to write these expressions as a product of two factors. One factor should be the GCF of the original expression.

a. $24 - 3x$

b. $27x^2 - 6x$

c. $30xy^2 + 25xy^2 + 25xy$

d. $x + x + y + y$

e. $12x - 12x^2$

f. $2x^2 + 72x^3 + 14x^2$

g. $6xy - 10xy^2$

h. $8 + 4x$

i. $a^3c^3 - a^2c^2 - ac$

j. $9vw^3 + 12v^2w^2 + 15v^3w$

k. $-18xy^4 - 12xy^3 - 24xy^2$

l. $42h^2k - 35h^2k^2 + 14h^2k^3$

4. What are all the possible integer pairs that could be the dimensions of this rectangle? How do you know you have them all?

y	$A = 100$ square units
	x

5. Solve these equations.

a. $2(b - 2) + 3 = 9$

b. $2(y + 3) = 3(2y - 2)$

c. $-4d + 3(1 - 2d) = 3(5 - 2d)$

d. $2a + 3[2(2a - 1) + 3(1 - a)] = 2(2a + 5)$

LESSON

8.1

Quadratic Models

"We especially need imagination in science; it is not all mathematics, nor all logic, but it is somewhat beauty and poetry."

MARIA MITCHELL

When you throw a ball straight up into the air, its height depends on three major factors: its starting position, the velocity at which it leaves your hand, and the force of **gravity.** Earth's gravity causes objects to accelerate downward, gathering speed every second. This acceleration due to gravity, called g, is 32 ft/s^2. It means that the object's downward speed increases 32 ft/s *for each second* in flight. If you plot the height of the ball at each instant of time, the graph of the data is a parabola.

EXAMPLE A

A baseball batter pops a ball straight up. The ball reaches a height of 68 ft before falling back down. Roughly 4 s after it is hit, the ball bounces off home plate. Look at the graph that models the ball's height in feet during its flight time in seconds. When is the ball 68 ft high? How many times will it be 20 ft high? What are the domain and range of the function modeling the ball's height? What are the intercepts, and what do they represent?

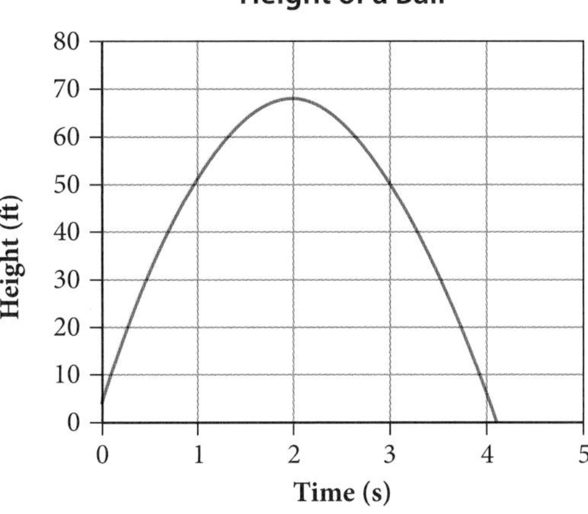

Solution

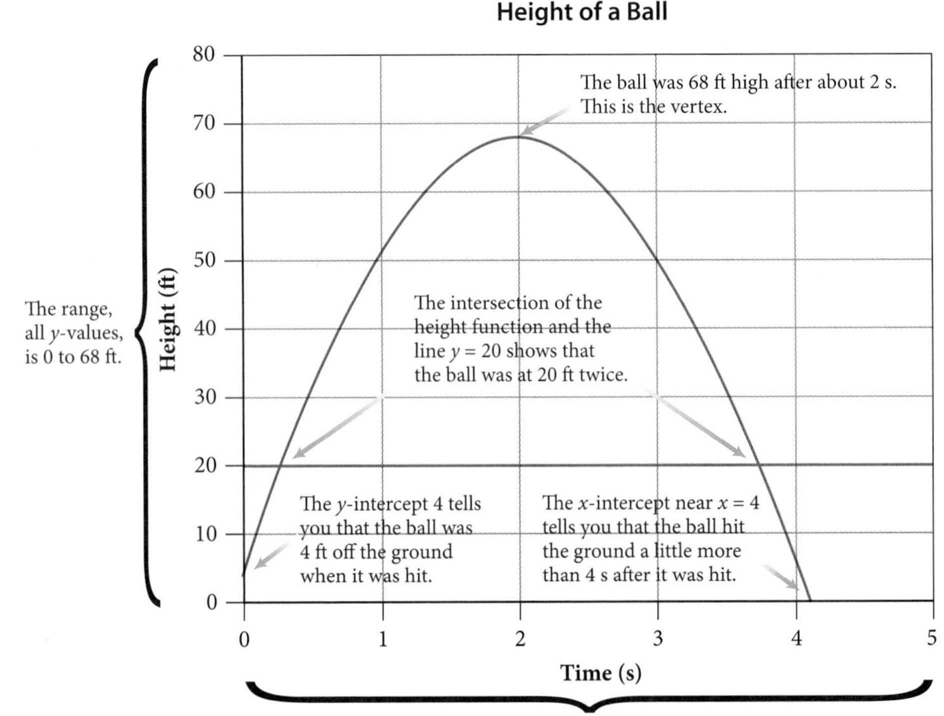

The parabola in Example A is a transformation of the equation $y = x^2$. The function $f(x) = x^2$ and transformations of it are called **quadratic functions** because the highest power of x is x-squared. The Latin word meaning "to square" is *quadrare.* The function that describes the motion of a ball, and of many other projectiles, is a quadratic function. You will learn more about this function in the investigation.

INVESTIGATION

Rocket Science

A model rocket blasts off, and its engine shuts down when it is 25 m above the ground. Its velocity at that time is 50 m/s. Assume that it travels straight up and that the only force acting on it is the downward pull of gravity. In the metric system, the acceleration due to gravity is 9.8 m/s². The quadratic function $h(t) = \frac{1}{2}(-9.8)t^2 + 50t + 25$ describes the rocket's **projectile motion.**

Known as the father of rocketry, Robert Hutchings Goddard fired the first successful liquid-fueled rocket in 1926.

Step 1 Define the function variables and their units of measure for this situation.

Step 2 What is the real-world meaning of $h(0) = 25$?

Step 3 How is the acceleration due to gravity, g, represented in the equation? How does the equation show that this force is *downward*?

Next you'll make a graph to represent the situation.

Step 4 Graph the function $h(t)$. What viewing window shows all the important parts of the parabola?

Step 5 How high does the rocket fly before falling back to Earth? When does it reach this point?

Step 6 How much time passes while the rocket is in flight, after the engine shuts down?

Step 7 What domain and range values make sense in this situation?

Step 8 Write the equation you must solve to find when $h(t) = 60$.

Step 9 When is the rocket 60 m above the ground? Use a calculator table to approximate your answers to the nearest tenth of a second.

Step 10 Describe how to answer Step 8 graphically.

Throughout the text you have used tables and graphs to find approximate solutions to equations. Previously you saw how to use undoing or balancing to find exact solutions to linear equations. In the next example you will see how to find exact solutions to a quadratic equation.

EXAMPLE B

Find the two exact solutions to the quadratic equation $5(x + 2)^2 - 10 = 47$. Then give approximate solutions to the nearest 0.01 and check your answers with a graph.

Solution

Undo each operation as you would when solving a linear equation. To undo the squaring operation, take the square root of both sides. You will get two possible answers.

$5(x + 2)^2 - 10 = 47$	Original equation.
$5(x + 2)^2 = 57$	Add 10 to undo the subtraction.
$(x + 2)^2 = 11.4$	Divide by 5 to undo the multiplication.
$\sqrt{(x + 2)^2} = \sqrt{11.4}$	Take the square root to undo the squaring.
$\lvert x + 2 \rvert = \sqrt{11.4}$	Definition of square root.
$x + 2 = \pm\sqrt{11.4}$	Definition of absolute value.
$x = -2 \pm \sqrt{11.4}$	Subtract 2.

The two solutions are exactly $-2 + \sqrt{11.4}$ and $-2 - \sqrt{11.4}$, or approximately 1.38 and -5.38.

The calculator screens of the graph support each solution.

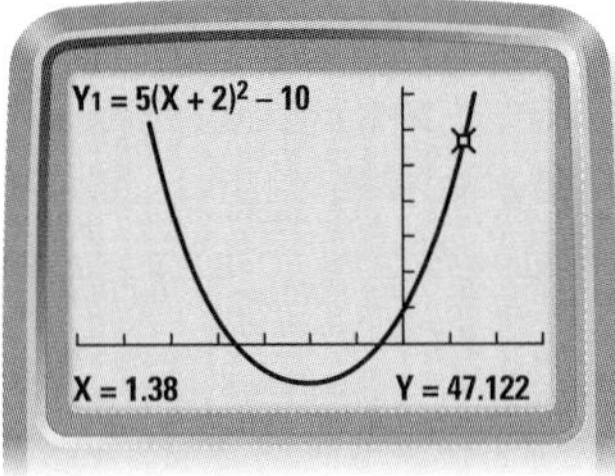

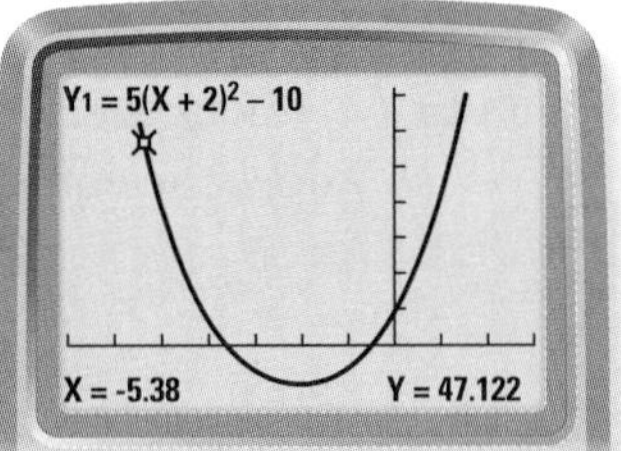

[−7, 3, 1, −10, 70, 10]

You can also confirm your answer by using your calculator to evaluate $y = 5(x + 2)^2 - 10$ for each solution and verifying that the result is 47. [▶ See **Calculator Note: Function Notation** to review how to evaluate a function. ◀]

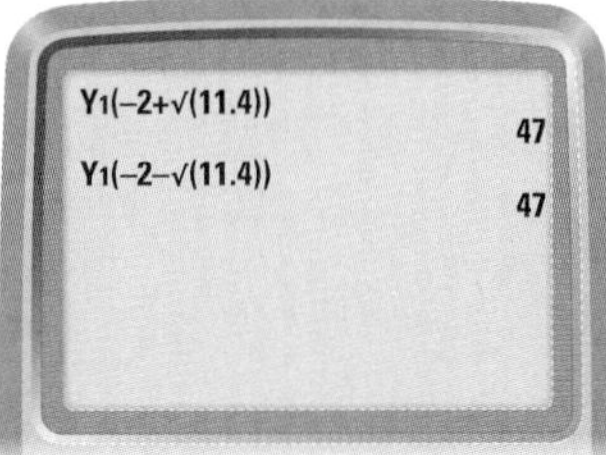

As you practice solving quadratic equations symbolically, first think about the order of operations. Then concentrate on how to undo this order. In some situations only one of the solutions you find has a real-world meaning. Always ask yourself whether the answers you find make sense in real-world situations.

A symbolic approach allows you to find exact solutions rather than using the approximations from a table or a graph. Exact solutions such as $x = -2 \pm \sqrt{11.4}$ are called **radical expressions** because they contain the square root symbol, $\sqrt{\ }$, and "radical" comes from the Latin word for "root."

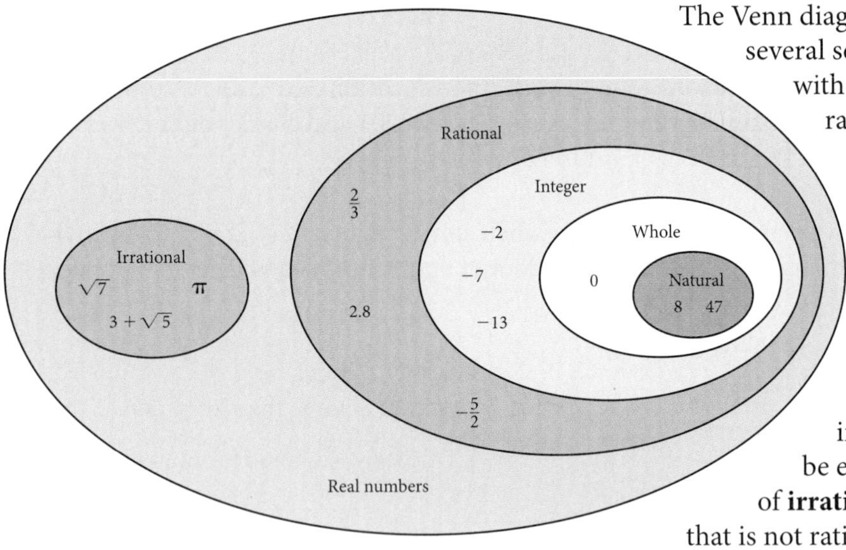

Rational
Integer
Whole
Natural
Irrational
$\sqrt{7}$ π $3 + \sqrt{5}$
$\frac{2}{3}$ 2.8 $-\frac{5}{2}$
−2 −7 −13
0
8 47
Real numbers

The Venn diagram at left shows the relationship among several sets of numbers that you may be familiar with. The set of **real numbers** includes all rational and irrational numbers. The inner region of rational numbers is the set of *natural* or *counting numbers*—1, 2, 3, and so on. The set of *whole numbers* includes the natural numbers and zero. The set of numbers that includes the whole numbers and their negatives is the *integers.* The set of *rational numbers* includes all the integers and any other number that can be expressed as a ratio of integers. The set of **irrational numbers** includes any number that is not rational, that is, any number that cannot be expressed as a ratio of two integers. Most numbers that, when simplified, contain the square root symbol are irrational numbers.

Every real number can be plotted on the x- or y-axis, and every point on the axis can be identified with a real number. When you draw a number line or the x- or y-axis of a graph, you are drawing a line that represents all real numbers. The location of values on a number line depends on the number's sign (+ or −) and relative size. While you can't represent an irrational number exactly with a fraction or a decimal, you can use a close decimal approximation and find the irrational number's position relative to rational numbers.

EXAMPLE C

Use approximation to match points A, B, C, and D on the number line with these numbers. Explain your answer.

i. π **ii.** $\sqrt{11.4}$ **iii.** $\sqrt{7}$ **iv.** $\frac{3\sqrt{2}}{2}$

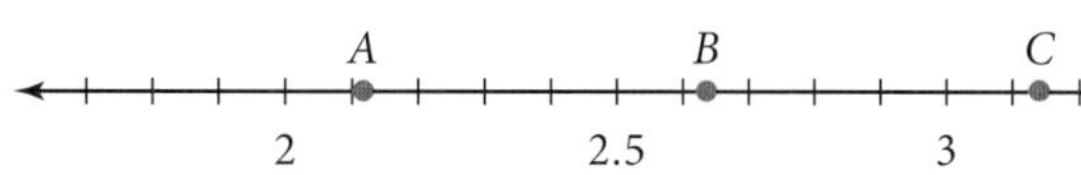

Solution

i. Point C, because π is approximately 3.14.

ii. Point D, because $\sqrt{11.4}$ is between $\sqrt{9}$, or 3, and $\sqrt{16}$, or 4.

iii. Point B, because $\sqrt{7}$ is between $\sqrt{4}$, or 2, and $\sqrt{9}$, or 3. You also know that it must be to the left of $\sqrt{11.4}$ because 7 is less than 11.4.

iv. Point A, because $\sqrt{2}$ is between $\sqrt{1}$, or 1, and $\sqrt{4}$, or 2, but closer to 1. You can estimate it as a little less than 1.5, or $\frac{3}{2}$. You want a little less than $\frac{3}{2}$ of $\frac{3}{2}$: $\frac{3}{2} \cdot \frac{3}{2} = \frac{9}{4} = 2.25$. Point A is closest to this estimate.

8.1 Exercises

Practice Your Skills

1. Use a graph and a table to approximate solutions to each equation, to the nearest hundredth.

a. $x^2 + 3x - 7 = 11$

b. $-x^2 + x + 4 = 7$ @

c. $x^2 - 6x + 14 = 5$

d. $-3x^2 - 5x - 2 = -5$ @

2. Classify each number by specifying all the number sets of which it is a member. Consider these sets: real, irrational, rational, integer, whole, and natural numbers.

a. $-\frac{17}{4}$

b. -8 @

c. $\sqrt{\frac{5}{4}}$

d. 2047

e. $\sqrt{16}$

f. 0.33

g. $0.\overline{33}$

h. $-2 + \sqrt{11.4}$

3. Use a symbolic method to solve each equation. Show each solution exactly as a rational or a radical expression.

a. $x^2 = 18$

b. $x^2 + 3 = 52$

c. $(x - 2)^2 = 25$

d. $2(x + 1)^2 - 4 = 10$ @

e. $x^2 = -18$

f. $-(x - 1)^2 = -17$

g. $-3(x - 2)^2 + 5 = 2$

h. $-16(x - 2)^2 + 5 = 2$

4. Sketch the graph of a quadratic function with

a. One x-intercept.

b. Two x-intercepts.

c. Zero x-intercepts.

d. The vertex in the first quadrant and two x-intercepts.

5. Use approximation to answer each question. Explain your answer.

a. Between what two integers is $\sqrt{12}$?

b. Which is larger, $3\sqrt{3}$ or 6?

Reason and Apply

6. A baseball is dropped from the top of a very tall building. The ball's height, in meters, as a function of time, in seconds after it has been released, is represented by the equation $h(t) = -4.9t^2 + 147$.

a. Find $h(0)$ and give a real-world meaning for this value.

b. Solve $h(t) = 20$ symbolically and graphically.

c. Does your answer to 6b mean the ball is 20 m above the ground twice? Explain your reasoning.

d. During what interval of time is the ball less than 20 m above the ground? @

e. When does the ball hit the ground? Justify your answer with a graph. @

7. **APPLICATION** An arrow is fired into the air from the ground. It reaches its highest point, 108 m, at 4.70 s. It falls back to the ground at 9.40 s.

a. Name three points that the graph goes through.

b. Name a graphing window that lets you see the three points in 7a.

c. What are the coordinates of the vertex of this parabola?

d. Write an equation in the form $y = a(x - h)^2 + k$ that fits the three known points. You may need to guess-and-check to find the value of a. (h)

e. Find $h(3)$ and give a real-world meaning for this value.

f. Find the t-values for $h(t) = 47$, and describe the real-world meaning for these values.

8. Solve the equation $4 = -2(x - 3)^2 + 4$ using

a. A graph. b. A table. c. A symbolic method.

9. **APPLICATION** The graph at right shows the graph of the function $h(t) = -4.9t^2 + 50t - 97.5$. The variable t represents time in seconds, and $h(t)$ represents the height in meters of a projectile.

[0, 10, 1, −5, 35, 5]

a. What is a real-world meaning for the x-intercepts in the graph? @

b. Find the x-intercepts to the nearest 0.01 second. @

c. How can you use your answer in 9b to find the vertex of this parabola? (h)

d. What is a real-world meaning for the vertex in the graph?

e. What does $h(3.2)$ tell you?

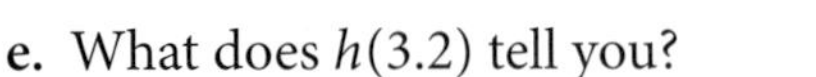

f. When is the projectile 12.5 m high? Explain how to find these solutions on a graph.

10. **MINI-INVESTIGATION** Each equation represents the height of a projectile as a function of time.

a. $y = -16(x - 3)^2 + 20$ b. $y = -4.9(x - 4.2)^2 + 12$

For each equation:

i. Describe the transformations of $y = x^2$. (h)

ii. Name the vertex of the parabola representing the equation.

iii. What is the real-world meaning of each number in the equation?

11. MINI-INVESTIGATION When you add any two natural numbers, the solution is always a natural number. Another way to say this is that the set of natural numbers is closed under addition. When you subtract two natural numbers, sometimes the solution is a natural number and sometimes it is not. For example, 7 minus 4 is 3 (a natural number), but 4 minus 7 is -3 (not a natural number). So the set of natural numbers is not closed under subtraction.

a. Fill in the table by determining whether each of these sets of numbers is closed under the given operation. If the set is not closed, give a counterexample.

	Addition	Subtraction	Multiplication	Division
Natural Numbers	Yes	No $4 - 7 = -3$ (an integer)	Yes	No $1 \div 2 = 0.5$ (a rational number)
Whole Numbers				
Integers				
Rational Numbers				
Irrational Numbers				
Real Numbers				

b. In 11a you investigated whether systems of numbers were closed for addition, subtraction, multiplication, and division. But what happens when the two numbers are from different systems? For example, is the result of multiplying a whole number times a natural number always, sometimes, or never a natural number? How do you know? The product of a whole number and a natural number is sometimes a natural number. The product of zero (a whole number) and any natural number is zero, a whole number. Decide whether these statements are always, sometimes, or never true and explain why.

i. The sum of a rational number and an irrational number is irrational.

ii. The product of a nonzero rational number and an irrational number is irrational.

Review

12. Show a step-by-step symbolic solution of the inequality $-3x + 4 > 16$. @

13. The solid line in the graph passes through (0, 6) and (6, 1). Write an inequality to describe the shaded region.

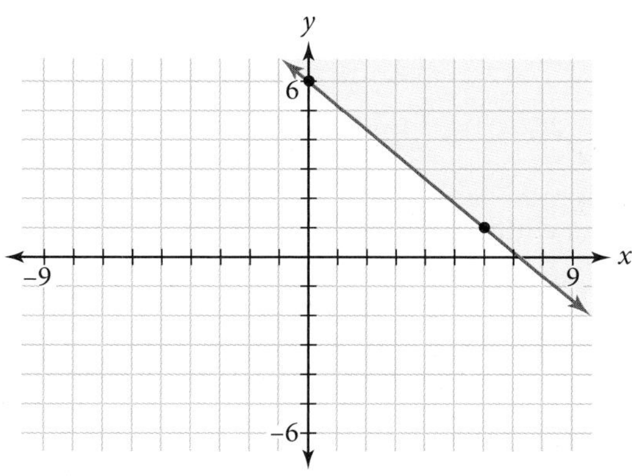

LESSON 8.2

Finding the Roots and the Vertex

In this lesson you will discover that quadratic functions can model relationships other than projectile motion. You will explore relationships between parabolas and their equations. You will practice writing equations, finding x-intercepts, and determining real-world meanings for the x-intercepts and the vertex of a parabola.

INVESTIGATION

YOU WILL NEED

- graph paper

Making the Most of It

Suppose you have 24 meters of fencing material and you want to use it to enclose a rectangular space for your vegetable garden. Naturally you want to have the largest area possible for your vegetables. What dimensions should you use for your garden?

Step 1 Find the dimensions of at least eight different rectangular regions, each with perimeter 24 meters. You must use all of the fencing material for each garden.

Step 2 Find the area of each garden. Make a table to record the width, length, and area of the possible gardens. It's okay to have widths that are greater than their corresponding lengths.

Width (m)	Length (m)	Area (m^2)

Step 3 Enter the data for the possible widths into a calculator list. Enter the area measures into a second list. Which garden width values would give no area? Add these points to your lists.

Step 4 Label a set of axes and plot points in the form (x, y), with x representing width in meters and y representing area in square meters. Describe as completely as possible what the graph looks like. Does it make sense to connect the points with a smooth curve?

Step 5 Where does your graph reach its highest point? Which rectangular garden has the largest area? What are its dimensions?

Next you'll write an equation to describe this relationship.

Step 6 Create a graph of length as a function of width for your data. What is the length of the garden that has width 2 meters? Width 4.3 meters? Write an expression for length y in terms of width x.

Step 7 Using your expression for the length from Step 6, write an equation to model the area of the garden. Graph this equation. Does the graph confirm your answer in Step 5?

Step 8 Locate the points where the graph crosses the x-axis. What is the real-world meaning of these points?

Step 9 Do you think the general shape of a garden with maximum area would change for different perimeters? Explain your answer.

In the investigation you found three important points on the graph. The two points on the x-axis are the x-intercepts. The x-values of those points are the solutions to the equation $y = f(x)$ when the function value is equal to zero. These solutions are the **roots** of the equation $f(x) = 0$.

In the investigation the roots are the widths that make the garden area equal to zero. The roots help you find a third important point—the vertex of the parabola.

In Lesson 8.1, you symbolically solved quadratic equations written in the form $y = a(x - h)^2 + k$. In the next example you will learn to approximate roots of the quadratic equation $0 = ax^2 + bx + c$.

EXAMPLE A

Use a graph and your calculator's table function to approximate the roots of the equation

$$0 = x^2 + 3x - 5$$

Solution

Graph $y = x^2 + 3x - 5$ and find the x-intercepts. On the graph you can see that there are two roots—one appears to have a value a little less than -4 and the other a value a little greater than 1.

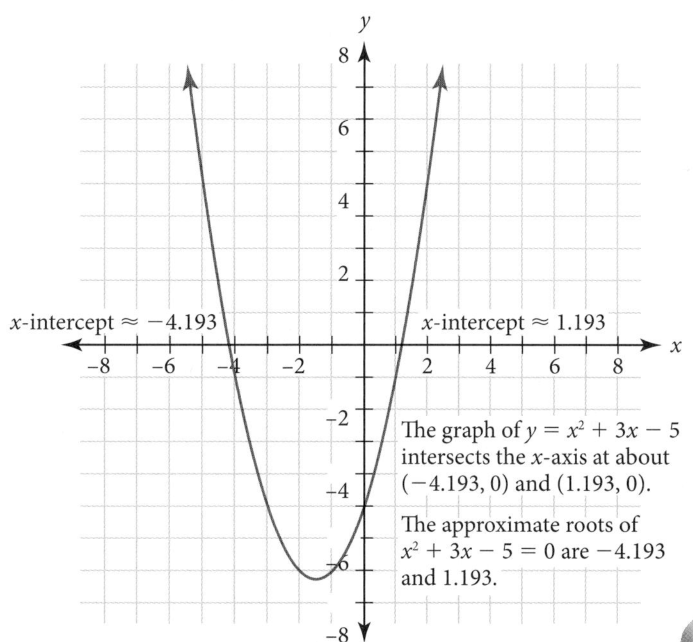

Use the Ask command with your calculator table to find an x-value just above 1 that gives a y-value close to 0. Continue to try different numbers for x until you get fairly close to the output $y = 0$. An x-value of about 1.193 for the positive root is close enough. [See **Calculator Note: Ask Command** to learn how to use the Ask command in a table.] Repeat this process for the negative root, which you'll find to be about -4.193.

X	Y_1
1	-1
2	5
1.1	-.49
1.15	-.2275
1.19	-.0139
1.195	.01303
1.192	-.0031
1.193	.00225

X = 1.193

The line through the vertex that cuts a parabola into two mirror images is called the **line of symmetry.** If you know the roots, you can find the vertex and the line of symmetry.

EXAMPLE B Find the equation of the line of symmetry of the parabola modeled by $y = x^2 + 3x - 5$, and find the coordinates (h, k) of the vertex. Then write the equation in the form $y = a(x - h)^2 + k$.

Solution This parabola crosses the x-axis twice and has a vertical line of symmetry. The x-coordinate of the vertex lies on the line of symmetry, halfway between the roots. From Example A, you know that the two roots are approximately 1.193 and -4.193. Averaging the two roots gives -1.5. The graph shows that the line of symmetry passes through this x-value. The equation of the line of symmetry is $x = -1.5$.

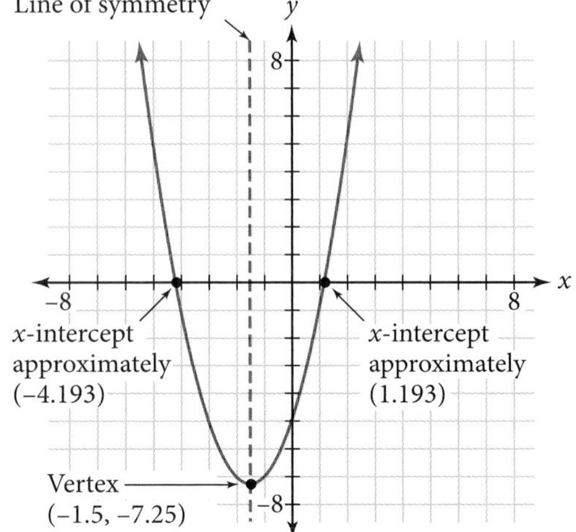

The x-coordinate of the vertex is -1.5. Now use the equation of the parabola, $y = x^2 + 3x - 5$, to find the y-coordinate of the vertex.

$y = x^2 + 3x - 5$	Equation of the parabola.
$= (-1.5)^2 + 3(-1.5) - 5$	Substitute -1.5 for x.
$= 2.25 - 4.5 - 5$	Multiply.
$= -7.25$	Subtract.

The vertex is $(-1.5, -7.25)$. Sometimes you can find the vertex and see the symmetry in a table of values.

In the table, this point appears to be the lowest point on the parabola.

X	Y1
-1.8	-7.16
-1.7	-7.21
-1.6	-7.24
-1.5	-7.25
-1.4	-7.24
-1.3	-7.21
-1.2	-7.16

Y1 = -7.25

The symmetry of the curve shows up in the repeated y-values on either side of the vertex.

The graph is a transformation of the parent function $f(x) = x^2$. The vertex, (h, k), is $(-1.5, -7.25)$, so there is a translation left 1.5 units and down 7.25 units. Substitute the values h and k into the equation to get $y = (x + 1.5)^2 - 7.25$. Graph this equation along with $y = x^2 + 3x - 5$. Describe the two graphs.

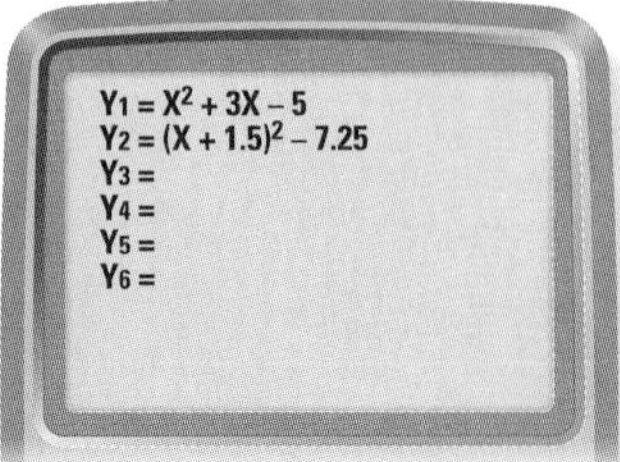

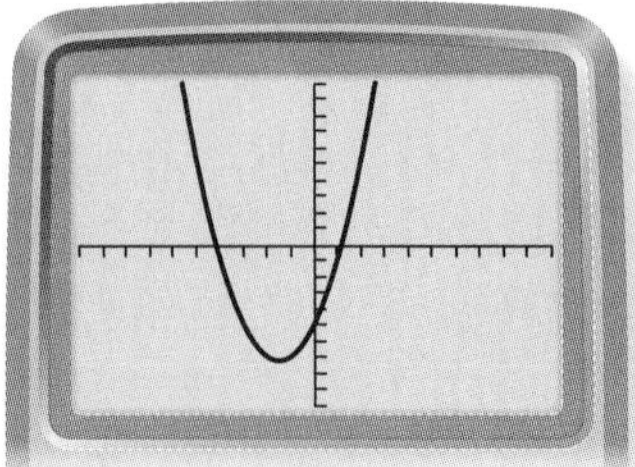

[−10, 10, 1, −10, 10, 1]

X	Y1	Y2
-1.5	-7.25	-7.25
-1	-1	-1
-.5	-6.25	-6.25
0	-5	-5
.5	-3.25	-3.25
1	-1	-1
1.5	1.75	1.75

You can see from the graph and the table that the equations $y = x^2 + 3x - 5$ and $y = (x + 1.5)^2 - 7.25$ are equivalent. So the value of a is 1. The equation $y = 1(x + 1.5)^2 - 7.25$ is in **vertex form.** It tells you that the point $(-1.5, -7.25)$ is the vertex of the parabola.

Vertex Form of a Quadratic Equation

$y = a(x - h)^2 + k$

The parabola has vertex (h, k).

8.2 Exercises

You will need your graphing calculator for Exercises **4, 6, 8,** and **11.**

Practice Your Skills

1. This parabola has x-intercepts 3 and -2. What is the equation of the line of symmetry? What is the x-coordinate of the vertex? ⓐ

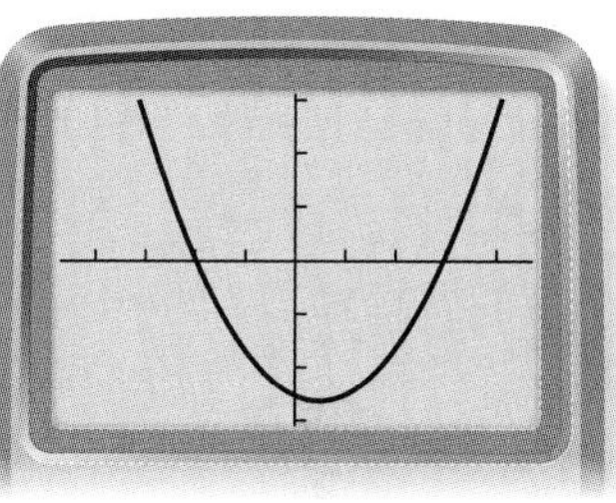

$[-4.7, 4.7, 1, -3.1, 3.1, 1]$

2. The equation of the parabola in Exercise 1 is $y = 0.4x^2 - 0.4x - 2.4$. Use the x-coordinate you found in Exercise 1 to find the y-coordinate of the vertex.

3. Solve $0 = (x + 1.5)^2 - 7.25$ symbolically. Show each step. Compare your solutions to the approximations from Examples A and B. ⓐ

4. Find the roots of each equation to the nearest thousandth by looking at a graph, zooming in on a table, or both.

a. $0 = x^2 + 2x - 2$ ⓐ

b. $0 = -3x^2 - 4x + 3$

5. Solve each equation symbolically and check your answer.

a. $(x + 3)^2 = 7$

b. $(x - 2)^2 - 8 = 13$

c. $x^2 - 16 = 0$

d. $x^2 - 14 = 3$

e. $2(x + 5)^2 - 10 = 0$

f. $x^2 + 16 = 1$

6. Graph $y = (x + 3)^2$ and $y = 7$. What is the relationship between your solution to Exercise 5a and these graphs? ⓐ

Reason and Apply

7. The height of a golf ball in feet is a function of time in seconds, modeled by the equation $h = -16t^2 + 48t$.

a. At what times is the golf ball on the ground?

b. At what time is the golf ball at its highest point?

c. How high does the golf ball go?

d. What domain and range values make sense in this situation?

8. APPLICATION Taylor hits a baseball, and its height in the air in feet is a function of time in seconds, modeled by the equation $y = -16x^2 + 58x + 3$. Use your calculator to help you answer these questions.

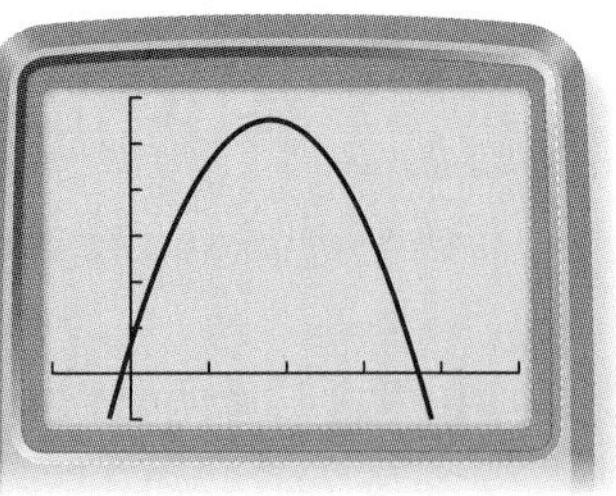

$[-1, 5, 1, -10, 60, 10]$

a. When does the ball hit the ground?

b. Find the answer to 8a to three decimal places. ⓐ

c. Find the vertex using the method in the examples.

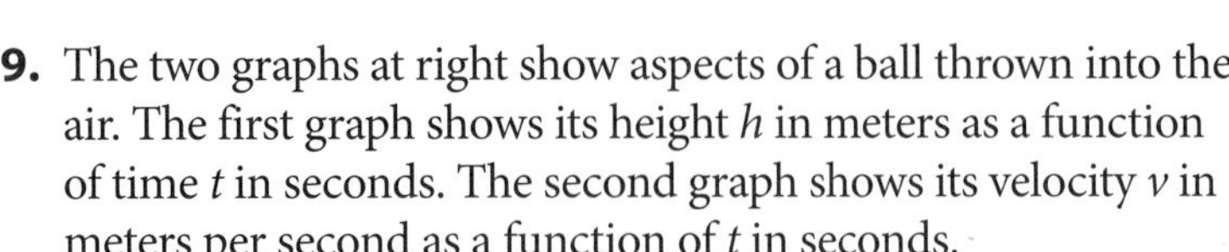

9. The two graphs at right show aspects of a ball thrown into the air. The first graph shows its height h in meters as a function of time t in seconds. The second graph shows its velocity v in meters per second as a function of t in seconds.

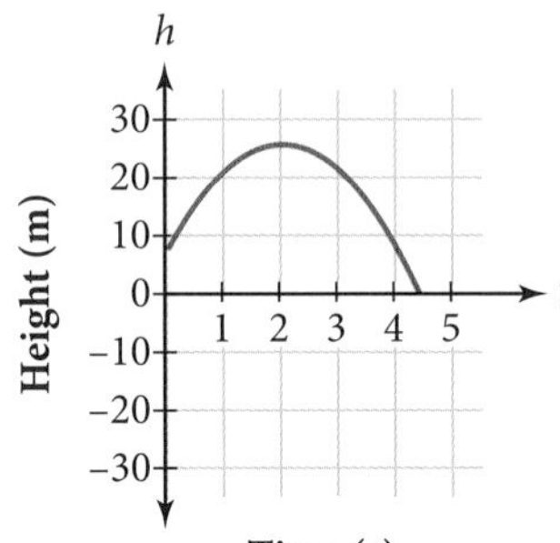

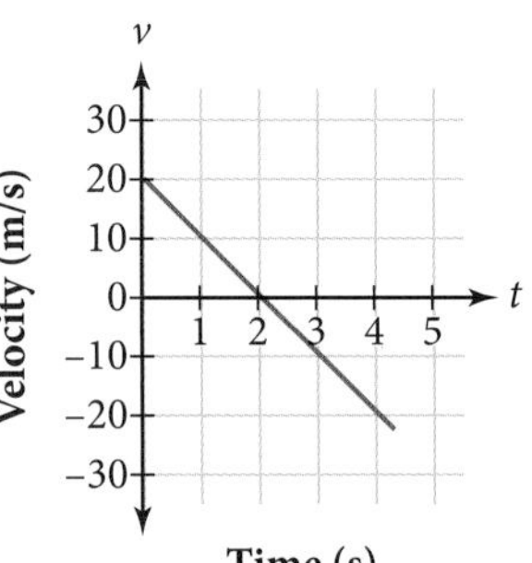

a. What does the first graph tell you about the situation? Use numbers to be as specific as you can.

b. What does the second graph tell you about the situation? Use numbers to be as specific as you can. ⓗ

c. Give a real-world meaning in this context for the negative values on the second graph. ⓐ

d. What can you say about the ball when the graph of the velocity intersects the x-axis? ⓐ

e. What can you say about the height of the ball when the velocity is ± 10 meters per second?

f. What are realistic domain and range intervals for the graphs?

10. Bo and Gale are playing golf. Bo hits his ball, and it is in flight for 3.4 seconds. Gale's ball is in flight for 4.7 seconds.

a. At what time does each ball reach its highest point? ⓗ

b. Can you tell whose ball goes farther or higher? Explain.

11. The table at right shows the coordinates of a parabola.

a. On your calculator, plot the points shown in the table.

b. What is the equation of the line of symmetry for this graph?

c. Name the vertex of this graph.

d. Use your knowledge of transformations to write the equation of this parabola in the vertex form, $y = a(x - h)^2 + k$. Check your answer graphically.

x	y
1.5	−8
2.5	7
3.5	16
4.5	19
5.5	16
6.5	7
7.5	−8

[Data sets: **PARAX, PARAY**]

12. The graph of the height of a small projectile as a function of time, modeled by the equation, $y = a(x - h)^2 + k$, contains the vertex (2, 67) and the points (0, 3) and (4, 3). You can find the particular equation of this graph by substituting (2, 67) for (h, k) in the equation and then finding the value of a by substituting the coordinates of one of the other points for x and y. What is the particular equation? ⓐ

Review

13. Write an equation in the form $y = a + bx$ for each of these graphs. One tick mark represents 1 unit.

a.

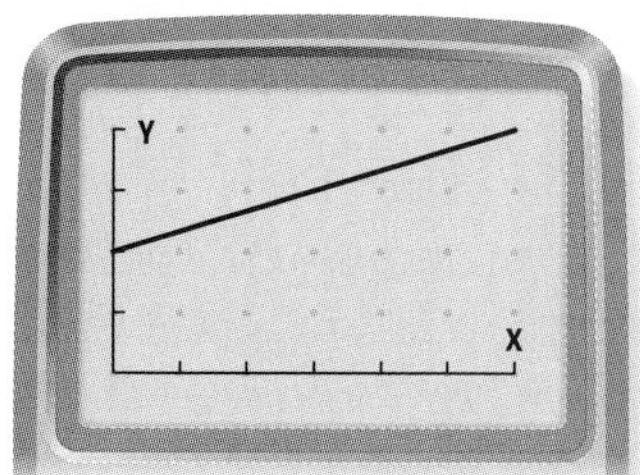

b.

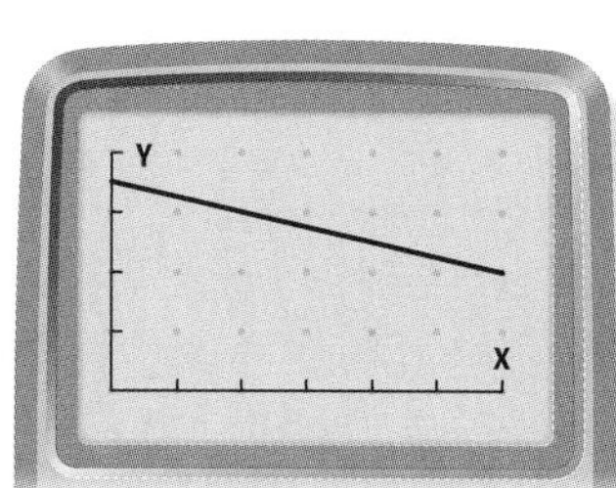

IMPROVING YOUR Visual Thinking SKILLS

A parabola is an example of a **conic section.** The Greek geometer Apollonius (255–170 B.C.E.) defined conic sections by intersecting a double cone with a plane.

Plane section

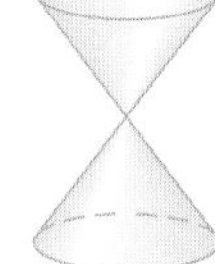

Double cone

The plane is a flat surface that extends into infinity. Likewise, both halves of the double cone widen infinitely in opposite directions. To form a parabola, Apollonius sliced the cone with a plane parallel to the cone's edge.

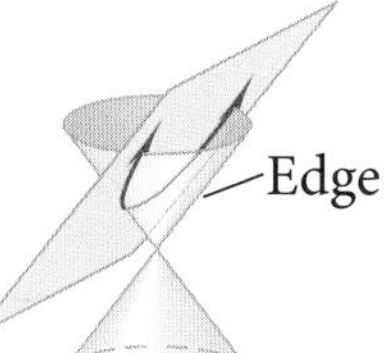

Parabolic section

Other examples of conic sections are circles, ellipses, and hyperbolas. How can you intersect a plane with a cone to form these shapes? How can a plane intersect a double cone in a point? A line? A pair of intersecting lines?

Circle

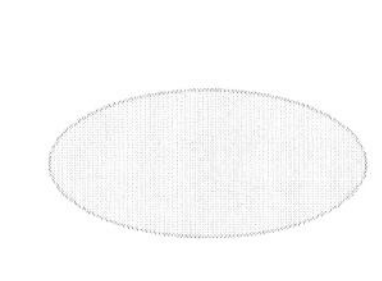

Ellipse

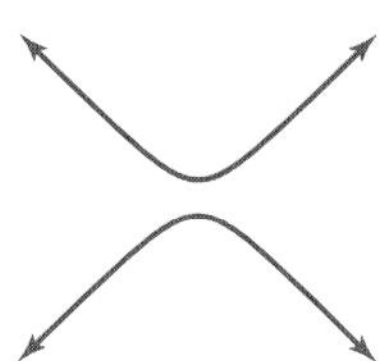

Hyperbola

Make a drawing that shows how to form each conic section. Can you form any other shapes? If so, describe them.

LESSON

8.3

From Vertex to General Form

"Attempt the impossible in order to improve your work."

BETTE DAVIS

You have learned two forms of a quadratic equation. The vertex form, $y = a(x - h)^2 + k$, gives you information about transformations of the parent function, $y = x^2$. You used the **general form,** $y = ax^2 + bx + c$, to model many projectile motion situations. In this lesson you will learn how to convert an equation from the vertex form to the general form.

General Form of a Quadratic Equation

$y = ax^2 + bx + c$

The parabola has y-intercept c.

The general form, $y = ax^2 + bx + c$, is the sum of three terms: ax^2, bx, and c. A **term** is an algebraic expression that represents only multiplication and division between variables and constants. Recall that a sum of terms with nonnegative integer exponents is called a **polynomial.** Variables cannot appear as exponents in a polynomial.

Here are some examples of polynomials:

$17x$ $\qquad 4.7x^3 + 3x$ $\qquad x^2 + 3x + 7$ $\qquad 47x^4 - 6x^3 + 0.28x + 7$

The expression $17x$ has only one term, so it is called a **monomial.** The second expression has two terms and is called a **binomial.** The third expression is a **trinomial** because it has three terms. If there are more than three terms, the expression is generally referred to as a polynomial.

Recall that terms whose variable parts are identical, such as $3x$ and $2x$, are *like terms.* Terms such as $2x^2$ and x^4 are not like terms because their variable components are different.

EXAMPLE A

Is each algebraic expression a polynomial? If so, combine like terms and state how many terms it has. If not, give a reason why it is not a polynomial.

a. $3x^2 + 4x^{-1} + 7$ b. $2^x - 7.5x + 18$

c. $\frac{47}{x} + 28$ d. $3x + 1 + 2x$

e. $x^2 - x^{10}$ f. $-2x^3 \cdot 3x^2$

Solution

Expression	Is it a polynomial?
a. $3x^2 + 4x^{-1} + 7$	No, because the term $4x^{-1}$ has a negative exponent.
b. $2^x - 7.5x + 18$	No, because 2^x has a variable as the exponent.
c. $\frac{47}{x} + 28$	No, because the term $\frac{47}{x}$ is equivalent to $47x^{-1}$.
d. $3x + 1 + 2x$	Yes, it is a polynomial. It is equivalent to the binomial $1 + 5x$, which has two terms.
e. $x^2 - x^{10}$	Yes. It has two terms and is a binomial.
f. $-2x^3 \cdot 3x^2$	Yes. It involves only multiplication of constants and varibles. It is equivalent to the monomial $-6x^5$.

In the investigation you will combine like terms when you convert an equation from the vertex form to the general form.

INVESTIGATION

YOU WILL NEED

- graph paper

Sneaky Squares

There are many different, yet equivalent, expressions for a number. For example, 7 is the same as $3 + 4$ and $10 - 3$. In this investigation you will use equivalent expressions to model squaring binomials with rectangle diagrams.

Step 1 The rectangle diagram at right shows how to express 7^2 as $(3 + 4)^2$. Find the area of each inner rectangle. What is the sum of the rectangular areas? What is the area of the overall square? What conclusions can you draw?

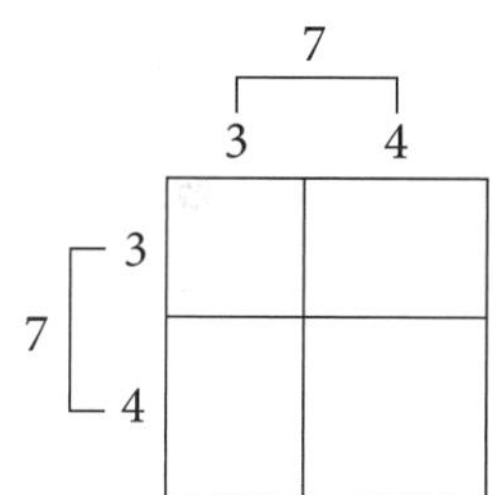

Step 2 For each of these expressions, draw a rectangle diagram on your graph paper like the one in Step 1. Label the area of each rectangle, and find the total area of the overall square.

a. $(5 + 3)^2$ **b.** $(4 + 2)^2$ **c.** $(10 + 3)^2$ **d.** $(20 + 5)^2$

Even though lengths and areas are not negative, you can use the same kind of rectangle diagram to square an expression involving subtraction. You can use different colors, such as red and blue, to distinguish between the negative and the positive numbers. For example, this diagram shows 7^2 as $(10 - 3)^2$.

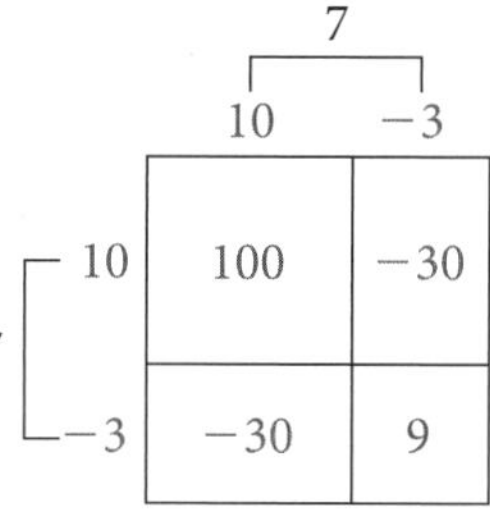

Step 3 Draw a rectangle diagram representing each expression. Label each inner rectangle and find the sum.

a. $(5 - 2)^2$ **b.** $(7 - 3)^2$ **c.** $(20 - 2)^2$ **d.** $(50 - 3)^2$

You can make the same type of rectangle diagram to square an expression involving variables.

Step 4 Draw a rectangle diagram for each expression. Label each inner rectangle and find the total sum. Combine any like terms, and express your answer as a trinomial.

a. $(x + 5)^2$ **b.** $(x - 3)^2$ **c.** $(x + 11)^2$ **d.** $(x - 13)^2$

Now use what you have learned to create a rectangle diagram for a trinomial.

Step 5 Make a rectangle diagram for each trinomial. What must you do with the middle term? The diagram at right provides a hint for Step 5a. Label each side of the overall square in your diagram, and write the equivalent expression in the form $(x + h)^2$.

	?	?
?	x^2	?
?	?	9

a. $x^2 + 6x + 9$ **b.** $x^2 - 10x + 25$

c. $x^2 + 8x + 16$ **d.** $x^2 - 12x + 36$

Step 6 Use your results from Step 5 to solve each new equation symbolically. Remember that quadratic equations can have two solutions.

a. $x^2 + 6x + 9 = 49$ **b.** $x^2 - 10x + 25 = 81$

c. $x^2 + 8x + 16 = 121$ **d.** $x^2 - 12x + 36 = 64$

Numbers like 49 are called **perfect squares** because they are the squares of integers, in this case 7 or -7. The trinomial $x^2 + 6x + 9$ is the square of $x + 3$, so it is also called a perfect square.

Step 7 Which of these trinomials are perfect squares?

a. $x^2 + 14x + 49$

b. $x^2 - 18x + 81$

c. $x^2 + 20x + 25$

d. $x^2 - 12x - 36$

Step 8 Explain how you can recognize a perfect-square trinomial when the coefficient of x^2 is 1. What is the connection between the middle term and the last term?

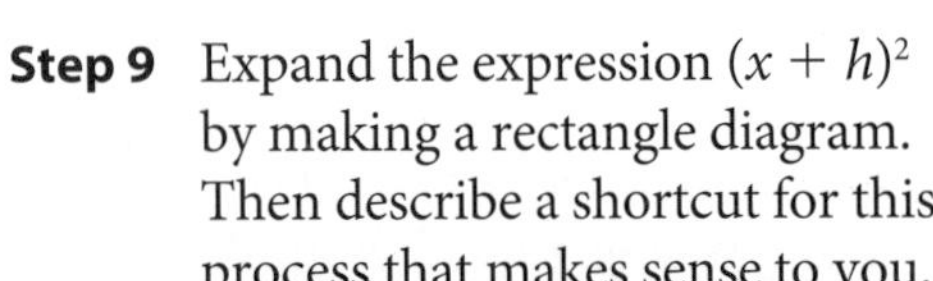

Step 9 Expand the expression $(x + h)^2$ by making a rectangle diagram. Then describe a shortcut for this process that makes sense to you.

Knowing how to square a binomial is a useful skill. It allows you to convert equations from vertex form to general form.

EXAMPLE B | Rewrite $y = 2(x + 3)^2 - 5$ in general form, $y = ax^2 + bx + c$.

Solution

$y = 2(x + 3)^2 - 5$ Original equation.

$y = 2(x^2 + 6x + 9) - 5$ Square the binomial using a rectangle diagram, as shown.

$y = 2x^2 + 12x + 18 - 5$ Apply the distributive property.

$y = 2x^2 + 12x + 13$ Combine like terms.

	x	3
x	x^2	$3x$
3	$3x$	9

You can use a graph or a table on your calculator to verify that the vertex form and the general form of this equation are equivalent. [▶ See **Calculator Note: Equivalent Equations** to review checking different forms of an equation. ◀]

In Example B, you **expand** $(x + 3)^2$ when you rewrite it as $x^2 + 6x + 9$ in finding the general form. The vertex form tells you about translations, reflections, stretches, and shrinks of the graph of the parent function, $y = x^2$. The general form tells you the initial position, the velocity, and the acceleration due to gravity in projectile motion applications. Later in this chapter you will learn to convert the general form to the vertex form. Then you'll be able to solve all forms of quadratic equations symbolically.

8.3 Exercises

You will need your graphing calculator for Exercises **2, 4, 8, 11,** and **16.**

Practice Your Skills

1. Is each algebraic expression a polynomial? If so, how many terms does it have? If not, give a reason why it is not a polynomial.

a. $x^2 + 3x - 8$

b. $2x - \frac{4}{5}$ @

c. $5x^{-1} - 2x^2$

d. $\frac{3}{x^2} - 5x + 2$ @

e. $6x$

f. $\frac{x^2}{3^{-2}} + 5x - 8$ (h)

g. $10x^3 + 5x^2$

h. $3(x - 2)$ @

2. Expand each expression. Use your calculator to check that both forms are equivalent.

a. $(x + 5)^2$ @

b. $(x - 7)^2$

c. $3(x - 2)^2$

d. $\left(x + \frac{3}{2}\right)^2$

e. $\left(x - \frac{3}{2}\right)^2$

f. $4\left(x - \frac{3}{2}\right)^2$

3. Copy each rectangle diagram and fill in the missing values. Then write a squared binomial and an equivalent trinomial that both represent the sum of the inner rectangles of each diagram.

a. @

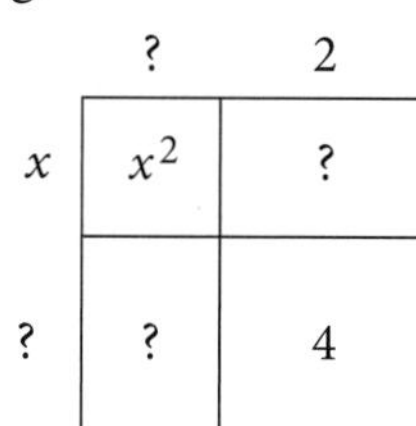

b.

	x	?
?	?	$12x$
12	?	144

c.

	x	?
?	x^2	$-7x$
-7	?	?

4. Convert each equation from the vertex form to the general form. Use your calculator to check that both forms are equivalent.

a. $y = (x + 5)^2 + 4$

b. $y = 2(x - 7)^2 - 8$

c. $y = -3(x + 4)^2 + 1$ @

d. $y = 0.5(x - 3)^2 - 4.5$

e. $y = -5(x - 2)^2 + 10$

f. $y = -16(x - 3)^2 + 5$

g. $y = -4.9(x - 4)^2 + 1$

h. $y = -0.5(x + 0.5)^2 - 0.5$

Reason and Apply

5. Draw a rectangle diagram to represent each expression. Then write an equation showing the product of the two binomials and the equivalent polynomial in general form.

a. $(x + 2)(x + 4)$ b. $(x + 3)(x + 5)$

c. $(x + 2)(x - 5)$ d. $x(x - 3)$ ⓐ

e. $(x + 2)(2x + 5)$ ⓐ f. $(3x - 1)(2x + 3)$

6. Consider the graph of $y = x^2 - 4x + 7$.

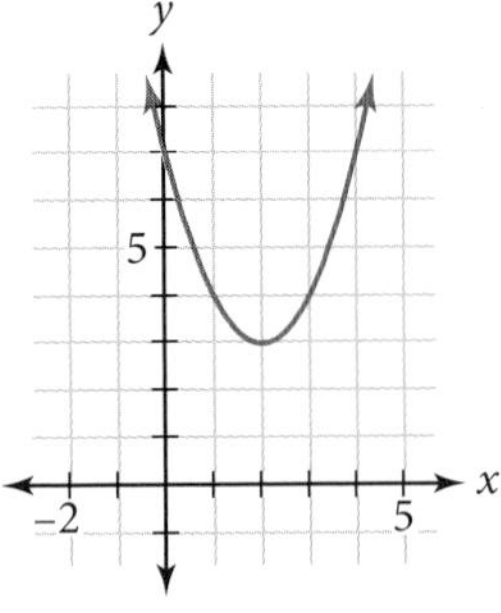

a. What are the coordinates of the vertex?

b. Write the equation in vertex form.

c. Check that the equation you wrote in 6b is correct by expanding it to general form.

7. Heather thinks she has found a shortcut to the rectangle diagram method of squaring a binomial. She says that you can just square everything inside the parentheses. That is, $(x + 8)^2$ would be $x^2 + 64$. Is Heather's method correct? Explain.

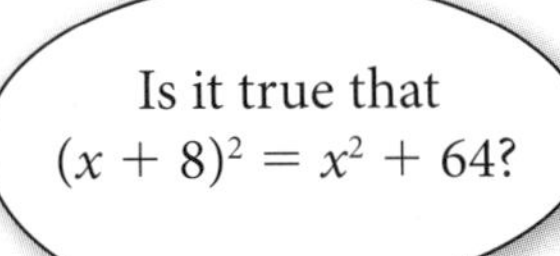

8. APPLICATION The quadratic equation $y = 0.0056x^2 + 0.14x$ represents a vehicle's stopping distance as a function of the vehicle's speed in kilometers per hour.

a. Find the stopping distance for a vehicle traveling 100 km/h.

b. Write an equation to find the speed of a vehicle that took 50 m to stop. Use a calculator graph or table to solve the equation.

9. The function $h(t) = -4.9(t - 0.4)^2 + 2.5$ describes the height of a softball thrown by a pitcher, in meters as a function of time in seconds.

a. How high does the ball go? ⓗ

b. What is an equivalent function in general form?

c. At what height did the pitcher release the ball when t was 0 s? ⓐ

d. What domain and range values make sense in this situation?

Saskatchewan pitcher Haley Volk competes in women's softball at the 2013 Canada Games.

10. Is the expression on the right of the equal sign equivalent to the expression on the left? If not, correct the expression on the right to make it equivalent.

a. $(x + 7.5)^2 - 3 \stackrel{?}{=} x^2 + 15x + 53.25$

b. $2(x - 4.7)^2 + 2.8 \stackrel{?}{=} 2x^2 - 9.4x - 41.38$

c. $-3.5(x + 1.6)^2 - 2.04 \stackrel{?}{=} -3.5x^2 + 11.2x - 11$

d. $-4.9(x - 5.6)^2 + 8.9 \stackrel{?}{=} -4.9x^2 + 54.88x - 144.764$

11. APPLICATION The Yo-yo Warehouse uses the equation $y = -85x^2 + 552.5x$ to model its income as a function of the selling price for one of its top-selling yo-yos.

a. Graph this relationship on your calculator, and describe a meaningful domain and range for this situation. @

b. What is the real-world meaning of the two x-intercepts of the graph?

c. Interpret the meaning of this model if $x = 5$.

d. Describe a method for finding the vertex of the graph of this relationship. What is the vertex?

e. What are the real-world meanings of the coordinates of the vertex?

12. Use a three-by-three rectangle diagram to square each trinomial.

a. $(x + y + 3)^2$ @

b. $(2x - y + 5)^2$

c. $(x + y + 1)^2$

d. $(3x + 2y - 5)^2$

13. What is the general form of $y = (x + 4)^2$? Write a paragraph describing several ways to rewrite this equation in general form.

Review

14. Is this parabola a graph of a function? Explain your answer.

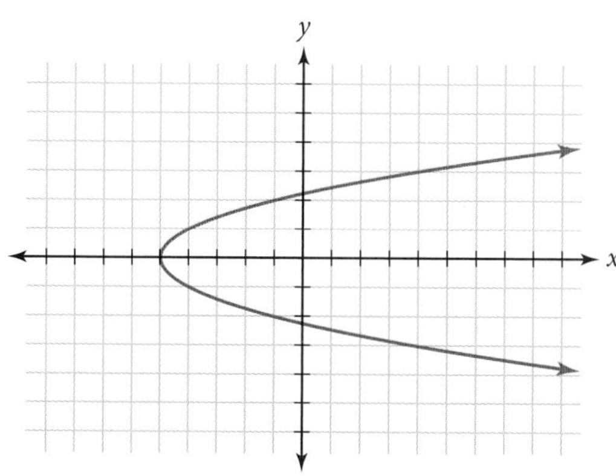

15. Use the graph of $f(x)$ to evaluate each expression. Then substitute the letters A through Z for the numbers 1 through 26 to decode a message.

a. $f(18)$

b. $3 \cdot f(3)$

c. $f(4^2)$ @

d. $[f(3)]^2$

e. the greater x-value when $f(x) = 8$

f. $f(25)$

g. $f(5) + f(15)$

h. the greater x-value when $f(x) = 1$ @

i. $f(1) - f(2)$

j. $f(4) \cdot f(5)$

k. $f(5^2 - 2^2)$

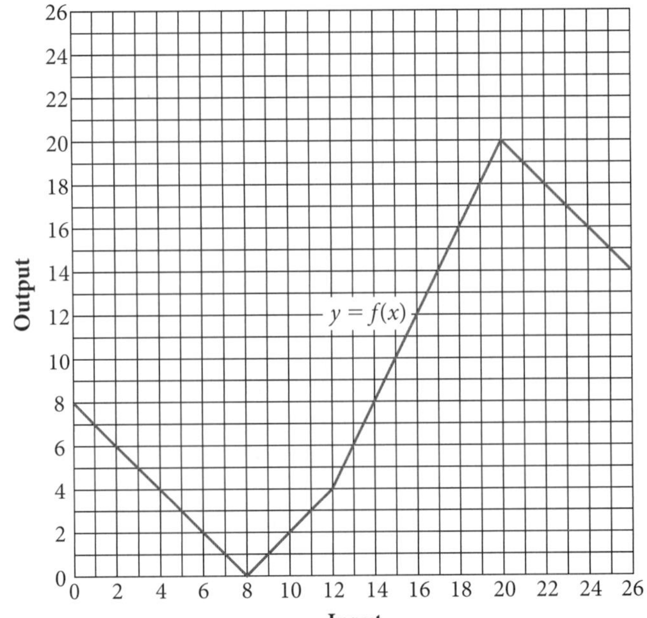

16. The equation $y = -0.0024x^2 + 0.81x + 2.0$ models the height of a golf ball above the ground in yards as a function of the horizontal distance from the tee in yards.

a. Name a graphing window that allows you to see the entire path of the ball.

b. What domain values make sense in this situation?

c. What range values make sense in this situation?

LESSON

8.4

Factored Form

So far you have worked with quadratic equations in vertex form and general form. This lesson will introduce you to another form of quadratic equation, the **factored form.**

"Mathematicians assume the right to choose, within the limits of logical contradiction, what path they please in reaching their results."
HENRY ADAMS

Factored Form of a Quadratic Equation

$y = a(x - r_1)(x - r_2)$

This quadratic equation has roots r_1 and r_2. The x-intercepts of the parabola it defines are at $x = r_1$ and $x = r_2$.

In the investigation you'll discover connections between the equation in factored form and its graph. You'll also use rectangle diagrams to convert the factored form to the general form and vice versa. Then you'll learn how to use a special property to find the roots of an equation.

INVESTIGATION

YOU WILL NEED
- graph paper

Getting to the Root of the Matter

First you'll find the roots of an equation in factored form from its graph.

Step 1 On your calculator, graph the equations $y = x + 3$ and $y = x - 4$ at the same time.

Step 2 What is the x-intercept of each equation you graphed in Step 1?

Step 3 Graph $y = (x + 3)(x - 4)$ on the same set of axes as in Step 1. Describe the graph. Where are the x-intercepts of this graph?

Step 4 Use the rectangle diagram at right to expand $y = (x + 3)(x - 4)$ to general form. Graph the equation in general form on the same set of axes. What do you notice about this parabola and its x-intercepts? Is the graph of $y = (x + 3)(x - 4)$ a parabola?

	x	-4
x	?	?
3	?	?

Now you'll learn how to find the roots from the general form.

Step 5 Complete the rectangle diagram whose sum is $x^2 + 5x + 6$. A few parts on the diagram have been labeled to get you started.

	x	
x	x^2	
		6

Step 6 Write the multiplication expression of the rectangle diagram in factored form. Use a graph or table to check that this form is equivalent to the original expression.

Step 7 Find the roots of the equation $0 = x^2 + 5x + 6$ from its factored form.

Step 8 Rewrite each equation in factored form by completing a rectangle diagram. Then find the roots of each. Check your work by making a graph.

a. $0 = x^2 - 7x + 10$ **b.** $0 = x^2 + 6x - 16$

c. $0 = x^2 + 2x - 48$ **d.** $0 = x^2 - 11x + 28$

Now you have learned three forms of a quadratic equation. You can enter each of these forms into your calculator to check that they are equivalent. Here are three equivalent equations that describe the height in meters, y, of an object in motion for the number of seconds, x, after being thrown upward. Each equation gives different information about the object.

Vertex form	$y = -4.9(x - 1.7)^2 + 15.876$
General form	$y = -4.9x^2 + 16.66x + 1.715$
Factored form	$y = -4.9(x + 0.1)(x - 3.5)$

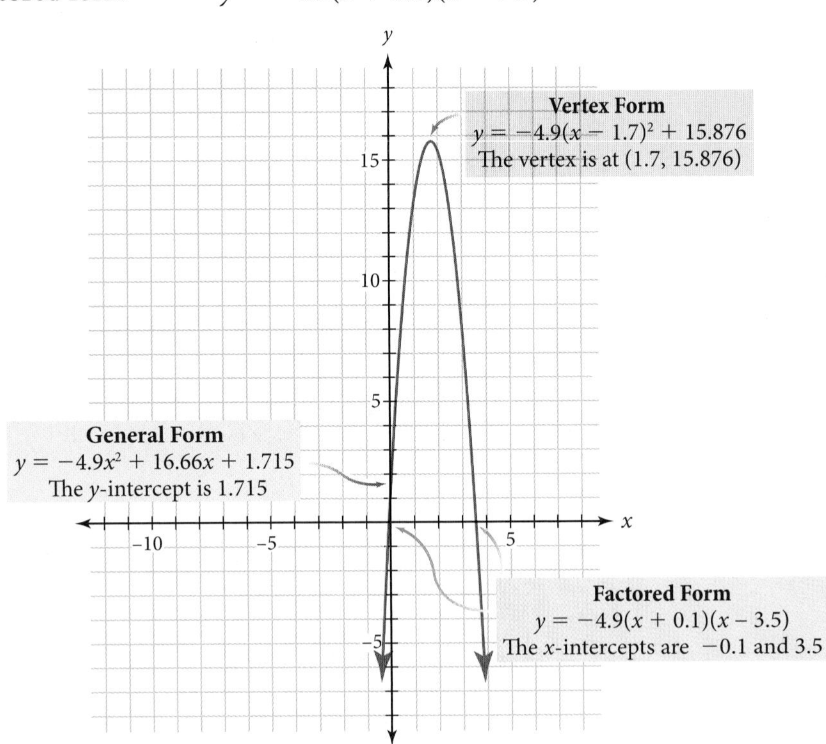

Which form is best? The answer depends on what you want to know. The graph shows you what information you can get directly from each form of the equation.

You have already learned how to convert to and from the general form of a quadratic equation. In Example A, you will learn how to write quadratic equations from the information on a graph.

EXAMPLE A

Write the equation for this parabola in vertex form, factored form, and general form.

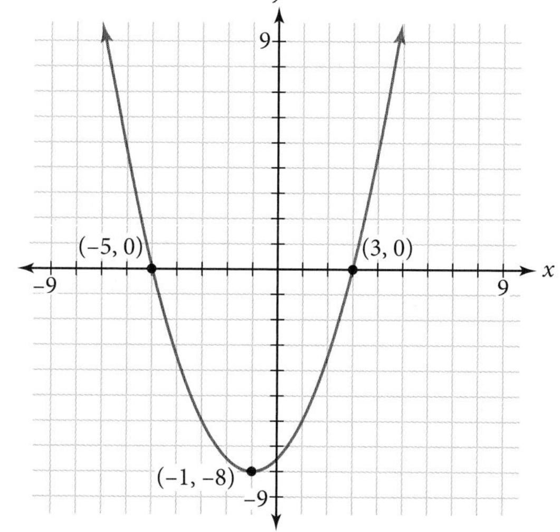

Solution

From the graph you can see that the x-intercepts are 3 and -5. So the factored form contains the binomial expressions $(x - 3)$ and $(x + 5)$.

If you graph $y = (x - 3)(x + 5)$ on your calculator, you'll see that it has the same x-intercepts as the graph shown here but a different vertex. The new vertex is $(-1, -16)$.

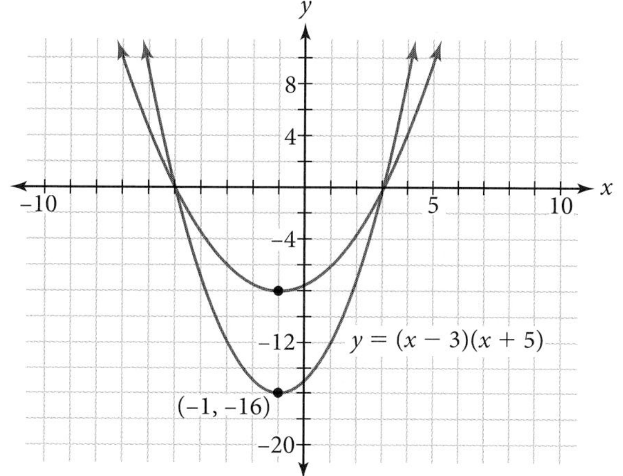

The new vertex needs to be closer to the x-axis, so you need to find the vertical shrink factor a.

The original vertex of the graph shown is $(-1, -8)$. So the graph of the function must have a vertical shrink by a factor of $\frac{-8}{-16}$, or 0.5. The factored form is $y = 0.5(x - 3)(x + 5)$. A calculator graph of this equation shows the desired parabola.

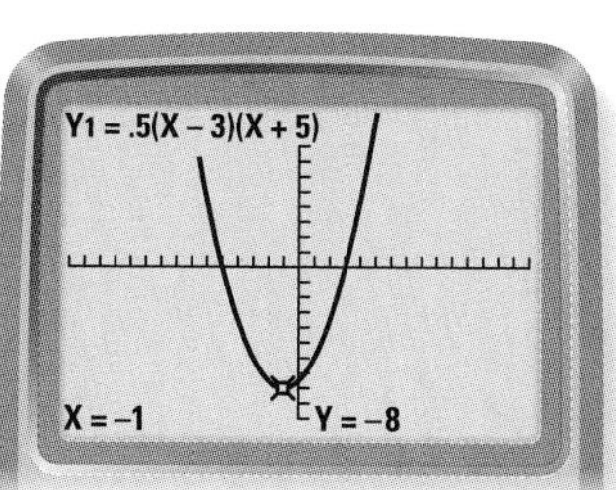

$[-15, 15, 1, -10, 10, 1]$

Now you know that the value of a is 0.5 and that the vertex is $(-1, -8)$. Substitute this information into the vertex form to get $y = 0.5(x + 1)^2 - 8$.

Expand either form to find the general form.

$y = 0.5(x - 3)(x + 5)$	Original equations.	$y = 0.5(x + 1)^2 - 8$
$y = 0.5(x^2 - 3x + 5x - 15)$	Expand using rectangle diagrams.	$y = 0.5(x^2 + 1x + 1x + 1) - 8$

	x	-3
x	x^2	$-3x$
5	$5x$	-15

	x	1
x	x^2	$1x$
1	$1x$	1

$y = 0.5(x^2 + 2x - 15)$	Combine like terms.	$y = 0.5(x^2 + 2x + 1) - 8$
$y = 0.5x^2 + x - 7.5$	Distribute and combine.	$y = 0.5x^2 + x - 7.5$

So the three forms of the quadratic equation are

Vertex form	$y = 0.5(x + 1)^2 - 8$
General form	$y = 0.5x^2 + x - 7.5$
Factored form	$y = 0.5(x - 3)(x + 5)$

When finding roots it is helpful to use the factored form. The only way the product of two numbers can equal 0 is if at least one of the numbers is 0. In Example A, the equation $0 = (x - 3)(x + 5)$ indicates that either $x - 3$ equals 0 or $x + 5$ equals 0. One root of the equation is 3, because 3 is the value that makes $(x - 3)$ equal 0. The other root is -5, because -5 makes $(x + 5)$ equal 0.

Zero-Product Property

If $ab = 0$, then a or b must equal 0.

[▶ You can further explore the relationship between factored form, roots, and x-intercepts using the **Dynamic Algebra Exploration** in your ebook. ◀]

The roots of an equation are sometimes called the **zeros** of a function. The values 3 and 5 are the roots of the equation $(x - 3)(x + 5) = 0$ and the zeros of the function $y = (x - 3)(x + 5)$.

EXAMPLE B

Use rectangle diagrams to factor each quadratic expression.

a. $x^2 + 2x - 24$

b. $x^2 + 7x + 6$

Solution

a. To factor $x^2 + 2x - 24$:

	x	
x	x^2	
		-24

b. To factor $x^2 + 7x + 6$:

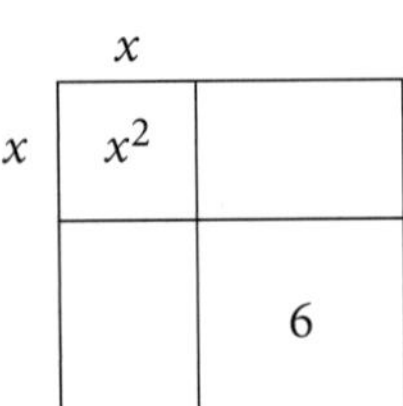

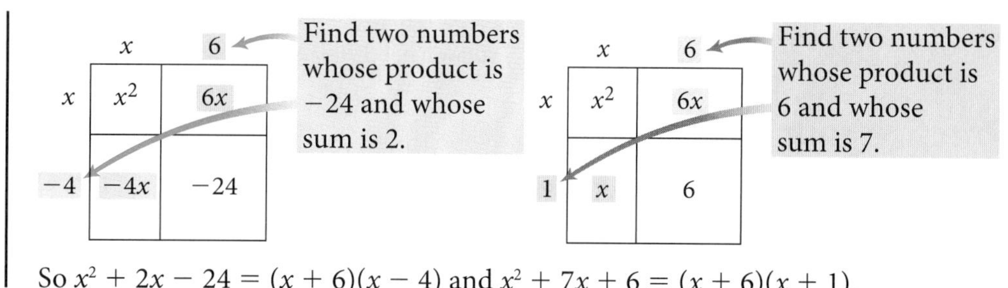

So $x^2 + 2x - 24 = (x + 6)(x - 4)$ and $x^2 + 7x + 6 = (x + 6)(x + 1)$.

The ability to factor polynomials is also useful in simplifying rational expressions, as you'll see in the next example. When a **polynomial equation** is in factored form, and simplified, it's much easier to predict or identify characteristics such as x-intercepts and asymptotes.

EXAMPLE C

A rational expression can be simplified if there is a common factor in both the numerator and the denominator. Simplify the expression $\frac{x^2 + 2x - 24}{x^2 + 7x + 6}$ by factoring. Then check your answer with a graph.

Solution

First factor the quadratic expressions in the numerator and denominator. See Example B.

Next simplify the rational expression. Be sure to state any restrictions on the variable.

$$\frac{x^2 + 2x - 24}{x^2 + 7x + 6} = \frac{(x + 6)(x - 4)}{(x + 6)(x + 1)}$$

$$= \frac{\cancel{(x + 6)}(x - 4)}{\cancel{(x + 6)}(x + 1)}$$

$$= \frac{x - 4}{x + 1}, \text{ where } x \neq -6 \text{ and } x \neq -1$$

You can check your work by graphing $y = \frac{x^2 + 2x - 24}{x^2 + 7x + 6}$ and $y = \frac{x - 4}{x + 1}$. If the expressions are equivalent, the graphs should be the same, except for any points that may be undefined in one graph but defined in the other.

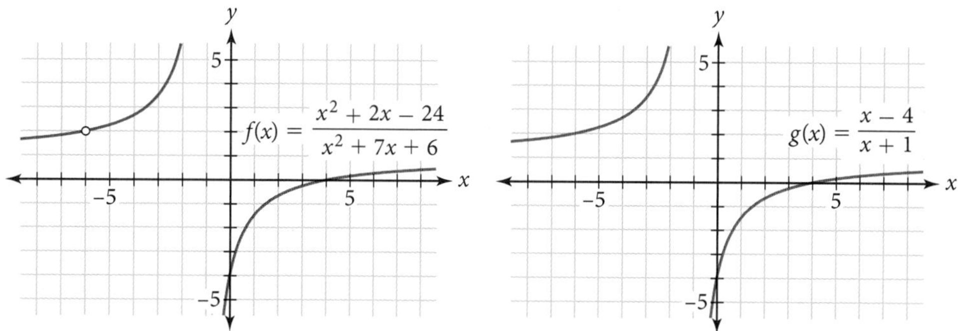

Notice that both graphs have an asymptote at $x = -1$. The only difference in the graphs is that the first graph is missing the point, or has a **hole** at the point, $(-6, 2)$. So the simplified expression is equivalent to the original expression.

8.4 Exercises

You will need your graphing calculator for Exercises **2, 3, 9, 12,** and **16.**

Practice Your Skills

1. Use the zero-product property to solve each equation.

a. $(x + 4)(x + 3.5) = 0$ @

b. $2(x - 2)(x - 6) = 0$

c. $(x + 3)(x - 7)(x + 8) = 0$

d. $x(x - 9)(x + 3) = 0$

2. Graph each equation, and then rewrite it in factored form.

a. $y = x^2 - 4x + 3$ @

b. $y = x^2 + 5x - 24$

c. $y = x^2 + 12x + 27$

d. $y = x^2 - 7x - 30$

3. Name the x-intercepts of the parabola described by each quadratic equation. Then check your answers with a graph.

a. $y = (x - 7)(x + 2)$ @

b. $y = 2(x + 1)(x + 8)$

c. $y = 3(x - 11)(x + 7)$

d. $y = (0.4x + 2)(x - 9)$

4. Write an equation of a quadratic function that corresponds to each pair of x-intercepts. Assume there is no vertical stretch or shrink.

a. 2.5 and -1 @

b. -4 and -4

c. -2 and 2

d. r_1 and r_2

5. Consider the equation $y = (x + 1)(x - 3)$.

a. How many x-intercepts does the graph of this equation have?

b. Find the vertex of this parabola.

c. Write the equation in vertex form. Describe the transformations of the parent function, $y = x^2$.

Reason and Apply

6. Is the expression on the left side of the equal sign equivalent to the expression on the right? If not, change the expression on the right to make it equivalent.

a. $x^2 + 7x + 12 \stackrel{?}{=} (x + 3)(x + 4)$

b. $x^2 - 11x + 30 \stackrel{?}{=} (x + 6)(x + 5)$

c. $2x^2 - 5x - 7 \stackrel{?}{=} (2x - 7)(x + 1)$ @

d. $4x^2 + 8x + 4 \stackrel{?}{=} (x + 1)^2$

e. $x^2 - 25 \stackrel{?}{=} (x + 5)(x - 5)$

f. $x^2 - 36 \stackrel{?}{=} (x - 6)^2$

g. $x^2 + 25 \stackrel{?}{=} (x + 5)^2$

h. $3x^2 - 6x + 3 \stackrel{?}{=} (3x - 3)(x - 1)$

7. Factor each expression.

a. $x^2 + 7x + 6$ @

b. $x^2 + 7x + 10$

c. $x^2 + x - 42$ @

d. $x^2 - 3x - 18$

e. $x^2 - 10x + 24$ @

f. $x^2 + 8x - 48$

g. $x^2 + 4x - 21$

h. $x^2 + 2x - 8$

i. $x^2 + 4x$

8. MINI-INVESTIGATION The sum and product of the roots of a quadratic equation are related to b and c in the general form $y = x^2 + bx + c$. The first row in the table below will help you recognize this relationship.

a. Complete the table.

Factored form	Roots	Sum of roots	Product of roots	General form
$y = (x + 3)(x - 4)$	-3 and 4	$-3 + 4 = 1$	$(-3)(4) = -12$	$y = x^2 - 1x - 12$
	5 and -2			
		-5	6	
$y = (x - 5)(x + 5)$		0	-25	

b. Use the values of b and c to find the roots of the equation $0 = x^2 + 2x - 8$.

9. MINI-INVESTIGATION In this exercise you will discover whether knowing the x-intercepts determines a unique quadratic equation. Work through the steps in 9a–e to find an answer. Graph each equation to check your work.

a. Write an equation of a parabola with x-intercepts at $x = 3$ and $x = 7$.

b. Name the vertex of the parabola in 9a.

c. Modify your equation in 9a so that the graph is reflected across the x-axis. Where are the x-intercepts? Where is the vertex?

d. Modify your equation in 9a to apply a vertical stretch by a factor of 2. Where are the x-intercepts? Where is the vertex? @

e. How many quadratic equations do you think there are with x-intercepts at $x = 3$ and $x = 7$? How are they related to one another?

10. Write a quadratic equation of a parabola with x-intercepts -3 and 9 and vertex $(3, -9)$. Express your answer in factored form. @

11. APPLICATION The school Ecology Club wants to fence in an area along the riverbank to protect endangered wildflowers that grow there. The club has enough money to buy 200 feet of fencing. It decides to enclose a rectangular space. The fence will form three sides of the rectangle, and the riverbank will form the fourth side.

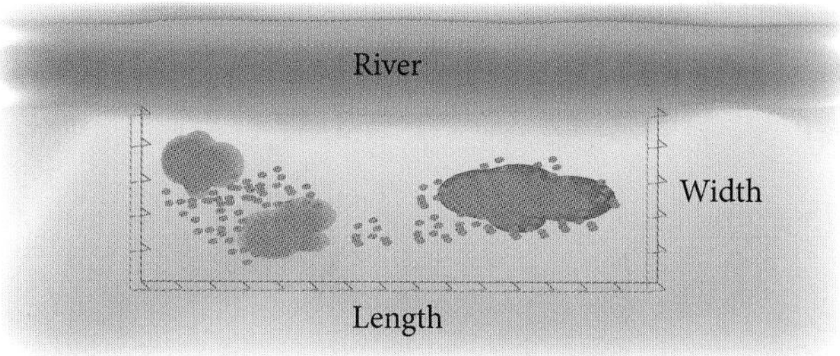

a. If the width of the enclosure is 30 feet, how much fencing material is available for the length? Sketch this situation. What is the area? @

b. If the width is w, how much fencing material remains for the length, l?

c. Use your answer from 11b to write an equation of the area of the rectangle in factored form. Check your equation with your width and area from 11a.

d. Which two different widths would give an area equal to 0? @

e. Which width will give the maximum area? What is that area?

12. MINI-INVESTIGATION Consider the equation $y = x^2 - 9$.

a. Graph the equation. What are the x-intercepts?

b. Write the factored form of the equation.

c. How are the x-intercepts related to the original equation?

d. Write each equation in factored form. Verify each answer by graphing.

i. $y = x^2 - 49$ ii. $y = 16 - x^2$

iii. $y = x^2 - 47$ iv. $y = x^2 - 28$

e. An expression in the form $a^2 - b^2$ is called a **difference of two squares.** Based on your work in 12a–d, make a conjecture about the factored form of $a^2 - b^2$.

f. Graph the equation $y = x^2 + 4$. How many x-intercepts do you see?

g. Explain the difficulty in trying to write the equation in 12f in factored form.

13. Kayleigh says that the roots of $0 = x^2 + 16$ are 4 and -4 because $(4)^2 = 16$ and $(-4)^2 = 16$. Derek tells Kayleigh that this equation has no roots. Who is correct and why?

The roots of $0 = x^2 + 16$ are 4 and -4 because $(4)^2 = 16$ and $(-4)^2 = 16$.

There are no roots for this equation.

14. Simplify the rational expressions by dividing out common factors from the numerator and the denominator. State any restrictions on the variable. (h)

a. $\dfrac{(x-2)(x+2)}{(x+2)(x+3)}$ (a)

b. $\dfrac{x^2+3x+2}{(x-4)(x+2)}$

c. $\dfrac{x^2-3x-10}{x^2-5x}$ (a)

d. $\dfrac{x^2+2x-3}{x^2+5x+6}$

e. $\dfrac{x^2+x-6}{x^2+6x+9}$

f. $\dfrac{(x-1)^2}{x^2-2x+1}$

g. $\dfrac{5x+5}{x^2+2x+1}$

h. $\dfrac{x^2-4x-5}{x^2-6x-7}$

Review

15. Multiply and combine like terms.

a. $(x - 21)(x + 2)$ b. $(3x + 1)(x + 4)$ c. $2(2x - 3)(x + 2)$

16. Edward is responsible for keeping the stockroom packed with the best-selling merchandise at the Super Store. He has collected data on sales of the new video game "Math-a-Magic."

Week	1	2	3	4	5	6	7	8	9	10
Games sold	0	186	366	516	636	727	789	821	825	798

[Data sets: **GMWK, GMSLD**]

a. Find a quadratic model in vertex form that fits the data. Let w represent the week number, and let s represent the number of games sold.

b. If the pattern continues, in what week will people stop buying the game?

c. How many total games will have been sold when people stop buying the game? (h)

d. There are 1000 games left in the stockroom at the start of week 11. How many more games should Edward buy?

LESSON

8.5

ACTIVITY DAY

Projectile Motion

You have already learned that quadratic equations model projectile motion. In this lesson you'll do an experiment with projectile motion and find a quadratic function to model the data. If you choose the first experiment, you'll collect parabolic data and then find an equation in vertex form that matches the graph. If you choose the second experiment, you'll collect data for the x-intercepts of a parabola and then find an equation in factored form that matches the graph. Read the steps of each experiment, and then choose one experiment for your group to do.

ACTIVITY

Jump or Roll

YOU WILL NEED

- a motion sensor
- an empty coffee can
- a long table

Each experiment in this activity requires a calculator program. Be sure you have this program in your calculator before you begin. [► See **Calculator Note: Collecting Jump and Roll Data Using the EasyData App** for the required programs. ◄]

Experiment 1: Rolling Along

The object of this experiment is to write a quadratic equation from experimental data.

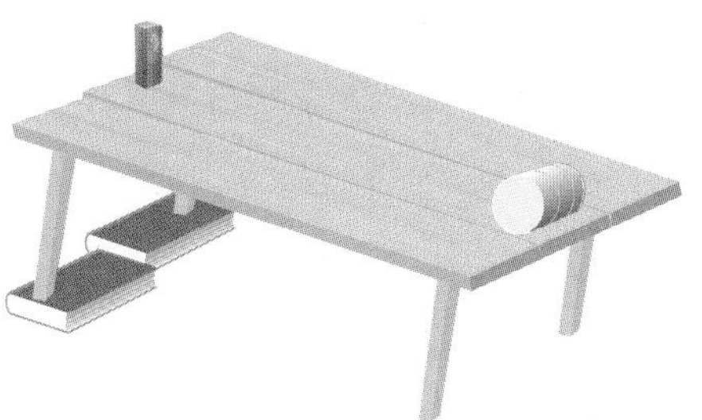

Procedure Note

Prop up one end of the table slightly. Make sure each leg of the table is raised by the same amount. Position the motion sensor at the high end of the table, and aim it toward the low end.

Step 1 Practice rolling the can up the table directly in front of the sensor. The can should roll up the table, stop about 2 feet from the sensor, and then roll back down. Give the can a short push so that it rolls up the table under its own momentum. Then the force of gravity should cause the can to reverse direction as it rolls back down the slanted table.

Step 2 Set up the program to collect the data. When the sensor begins, gently roll the can up the table. Catch it as it falls off the table.

Step 3 The data collected by the sensor will have the form (*time, distance*). If you do the experiment correctly, the graph should show a parabolic pattern. Sketch this graph.

Step 4 Write the equation of a parabola that fits your data. Which points did you use to write the equation? In which form is it? Sketch a parabola that represents this equation onto the graph from Step 3.

Step 5 Rewrite your equation from Step 4 in general form. Use your calculator to verify that the equations are equivalent.

Experiment 2: How High?

The object of this experiment is to find how high you jump. You will collect data for the zeros of a projectile motion function.

Procedure Note

Place the motion sensor on the floor. The jumper stands 2 ft or 0.5 m in front of it. There should be a wall or another object about 4 ft or 1 m from the sensor. When the jumper's feet leave the ground, the motion sensor should register a change in distance at a specific instant in time.

Step 1 Set up the program to collect data. Jump straight up, without bending your knees while you're in the air. Be sure to land in front of the sensor again. The sensor will record the times your feet left the ground and landed.

Step 2 The data measured by the motion sensor have the form (*time, distance*), where the distance is that between the motion sensor and the object nearest to it. Here is a calculator screen showing sample data. Why does the scatter plot look like this? From your data, approximate the times when the jumper's feet left the ground and when they landed back on the ground.

[0, 1.2, 0.1, 0, 4, 0.5]

Step 3 If you want to graph the height of your jump over time, what are the variables for the quadratic function in this situation? Substitute the two roots you found in Step 2 for r_1 and r_2 into the equation $h = -192(t - r_1)(t - r_2)$. Use it to calculate the height of your jump in inches. (Or use the equation $h = -490(t - r_1)(t - r_2)$ to find this height in centimeters.) At what time did you reach this height? Explain how you got your answer.

Step 4 Repeat the experiment with each member of your group as a jumper.

CHAPTER 8 SHARPENING YOUR SKILLS

Factoring or Expanding to Write Equivalent Expressions

Algebra often involves changing algebraic expressions to different but equivalent forms. You've done this with linear forms such as $y = a + bx$ and $y = y_1 + b(x - x_1)$. Here you'll practice writing equivalent expressions by expanding or factoring. These skills allow you to rewrite $x^2 + 7x + 6$ as a product, $(x + 6)(x + 1)$. Remember that you can use your calculator to see whether expressions are equivalent.

EXAMPLE A | Expand the product $(3x + 4)(3x + 4)$, and factor the expression $4x^2 - 20x + 25$.

Solution | You have used rectangle diagrams to expand the product of binomials. A rectangle diagram is a graphic organizer for the distributive property. When multiplying a binomial times a binomial, you multiply each term in the first parentheses by each term in the second parentheses.

	$3x$	4
$3x$	$9x^2$	$12x$
4	$12x$	16

$$(3x + 4)(3x + 4) = 3x(3x + 4) + 4(3x + 4)$$
$$= 9x^2 + 12x + 12x + 16$$
$$= 9x^2 + 24x + 16$$

How does this strategy compare to the rectangle diagram above?

Looking at the lower left and upper right, notice that $12x$ plus $12x$ is our middle term $24x$. In addition the product $(12x)(12x) = 144x^2$ is equal to the product of first and last terms. $(9x^2)(16) = 144x^2$. This can be useful when finding numbers to put in the rectangles when factoring.

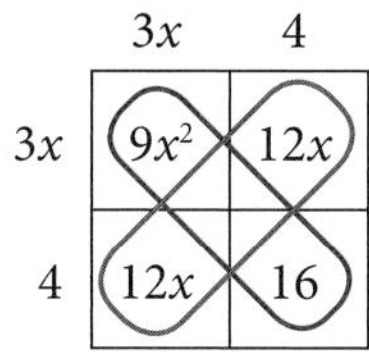

You can also use a rectangle diagram to factor $4x^2 - 20x + 25$. The first and third terms, $4x^2$ and 25, go in the upper-left and lower-right cells.

$4x^2$	
	25

To fill the rectangles in this problem, you must find two terms that will have a sum of $-20x$ and a product of $(4x^2)(25) = 100x^2$. The factors of 100 lead us to consider (1, 100)(2, 50)(4, 25)(5, 20) and (10, 10). The pair with a sum of 20 tells you that the missing values need to be $-10x$ and $-10x$.

$4x^2$	$-10x$
$-10x$	25

Now you can look for the GCF for each row and each column.

Multiply to confirm your answer.

So $4x^2 - 20x + 25 = (2x - 5)(2x - 5)$.

How would you factor this trinomial without using rectangle diagrams?

	$2x$	-5
$2x$	$4x^2$	$-10x$
-5	$-10x$	25

The two expressions in Example A are perfect squares, which have the form $(a + b)^2 = a^2 + 2ab + b^2$.

EXAMPLE B Factor the expression $a^2 - b^2$, the difference of two squares.

Solution The first term, a^2, equals $a \cdot a$, so enter these values into the rectangle diagram. In this case the product of the lower-left and upper-right entries is $-b^2$, and their sum is 0. The only possibility is b and $-b$, so $a^2 - b^2 = (a + b)(a - b)$.

	a	$-b$
a	a^2	$-ab$
b	ab	$-b^2$

Sometimes general expressions like $x^2 + bx + c$ or $ax^2 + bx + c$ can be factored quickly by using guess-and-check. Start by looking for common factors in the expression. You might need repeated trials to find factors whose products provide the first and last term and whose sum will give you the middle, or linear, term.

EXAMPLE C Factor the expression $5x^2 + 7x - 6$.

Solution The coefficient of x, 5, is positive and the constant term, -6, is negative. So one of the factors of 6 must be negative. The possible factors of $5x^2$ are x and $5x$. The possible factor pairs of -6 are 1 and -6, -1 and 6, 2 and -3, and -2 and 3.

Look at all possibilities to find the one that will give a linear term of $7x$:

$(5x + 6)(x - 1)$; the linear term is x

$(5x + 1)(x - 6)$; the linear term is $-29x$

$(5x + 2)(x - 3)$; the linear term is $-13x$

$(5x + 3)(x - 2)$; the linear term is $-7x$

$(5x - 3)(x + 2)$; the linear term is $7x$

So $5x^2 + 7x - 6 = (5x - 3)(x + 2)$

You can verify that your answer is correct by using a graphing calculator. Set both expressions equal to y and graph to see that the expressions are equivalent.

Exercises

1. Use the information in each rectangle diagram to find the factors and their product.

a.

	?	?
?	x^2	$2x$
?	x	2

b.

	?	?
?	$3x^2$	$-x$
?	$12x$	-4

2. Complete the rectangle diagram to factor each expression.

a. $x^2 - 9x - 36$

x^2	
$3x$	-36

b. $6x^2 + 13x - 15$

$6x^2$	$18x$
	-15

3. Factor each expression.

a. $x^2 - 17x + 72$

b. $x^2 + 3x - 28$

c. $2x^2 - 72$

d. $4x^3 - 4x$

e. $x^2 - 3x - 10$

f. $-2x^2 + 28x - 98$

g. $x^2 - 121$

h. $3x^3 - 18x^2 + 27x$

i. $2x^2 + 3x - 2$

j. $4x^2 + 12x + 9$

k. $x^2 + 144$

l. $x^2 + 7x + 10$

m. $25x^2 - 4y^2$

n. $81k^2 + 36k + 4$

o. $(a + b)^2 - (c + d)^2$

p. $9(w^2 - 2wv + v^2) - 16z^2$

q. $4t^2(2t - 1) - 4t(2t - 1) + (2t - 1)$

r. $2xy^3 - 8x^3y$

LESSON

8.6

Completing the Square

"For every problem there is one solution which is simple, neat, and wrong."

H. L. MENCKEN

Quadratic equations, such as those modeling projectile motion, are often in the form $y = ax^2 + bx + c$. Often you'll want to find the zeros—the times when the object hits the ground. You can always find approximate zeros of quadratic equations by using tables and graphs. If you can convert the equation to the factored form, $y = a(x - r_1)(x - r_2)$, or the vertex form, $y = a(x - h)^2 + k$, then you can use symbolic methods to find exact zeros. In this lesson you'll learn a symbolic method to find exact zeros of equations in the general form, $y = ax^2 + bx + c$.

Recall that rectangle diagrams help you factor expressions to find exact roots of some quadratic equations in the form $ax^2 + bx + c = 0$.

Perfect-square trinomial

$x^2 + 6x + 9$

	x	3
x	x^2	$3x$
3	$3x$	9

Factorable trinomial

$x^2 + x - 6$

	x	3
x	x^2	$3x$
-2	$-2x$	-6

Because these quadratic expressions can be factored easily, you can find the roots of the quadratic equations.

$x^2 + 6x + 9 = 0$	**General form**	$x^2 + x - 6 = 0$
$(x + 3)(x + 3) = 0$	**Factored form**	$(x + 3)(x - 2) = 0$
$-3, -3$	**Roots**	$-3, 2$

How do you find the roots of an equation such as $0 = x^2 + x - 1$? It is not a perfect-square trinomial, nor is it easily factorable. For such equations you can use a method called **completing the square.**

INVESTIGATION

YOU WILL NEED

- graph paper

Searching for Solutions

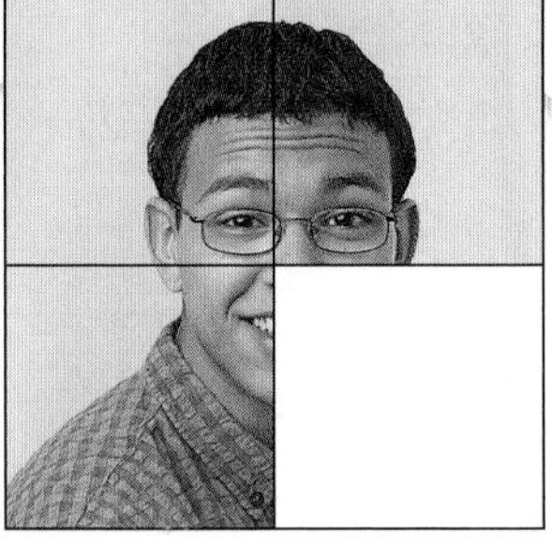

To understand how to complete the square with quadratic equations, you'll first work with rectangle diagrams.

Step 1 Complete each rectangle diagram so that it is a square. How do you know which number to place in the lower-right corner?

a.

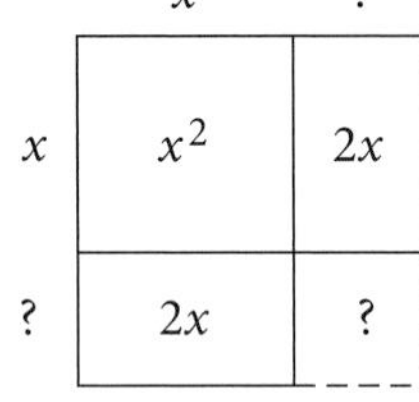

b.

	x	?
x	x^2	$-3x$
?	$-3x$	?

c.

	x	?
x	x^2	$-2.5x$
?	$-2.5x$	?

d.

	x	?
x	x^2	$\frac{b}{2}x$
?	$\frac{b}{2}x$	?

Step 2 The diagram in Step 1a represents the equation $x^2 + 4x + \underline{?} = (x + \underline{?})^2$. For each diagram in Step 1, write an equation in the form $x^2 + bx + c = (x + h)^2$. On which side of the equation can you isolate x by undoing the order of operations?

Step 3 Suppose the area of each diagram in Step 1a–c is 100 square units. For each square, write an equation that you can solve for x by undoing the order of operations.

Step 4 Solve each equation in Step 3 symbolically. You will get two values of x.

The solutions for x in the equations from Step 4 are rational numbers. This means you could have factored the equations with rational numbers. Next you'll consider the solution of an equation that you cannot factor with rational numbers.

Step 5 Consider the equation $x^2 + 6x - 1 = 0$. Describe what's happening in each stage of the solution process.

Stage	Equation	Description
1	$x^2 + 6x - 1 = 0$	Original equation.
2	$x^2 + 6x = 1$	
3	$x^2 + 6x + 9 = 1 + 9$	

	x	3
x	x^2	$3x$
3	$3x$	9

Stage	Equation	Description
4	$(x + 3)^2 = 10$	
5	$x + 3 = \pm\sqrt{10}$	
6	$x = -3 \pm \sqrt{10}$	

Step 6 Use your calculator to find decimal approximations of $-3 + \sqrt{10}$ and $-3 - \sqrt{10}$. Then enter the equation $y = x^2 + 6x - 1$ into your calculator, and use a graph or table to check that your solutions are the x-intercepts of the equation.

Step 7 Repeat the solution stages in Step 5 to find the solutions to $x^2 + 8x - 5 = 0$.

In Step 5 of the investigation, you solved an equation by expressing one side as a perfect-square trinomial and then solving for x. This process is called completing the square. In the investigation the equations are in the form $y = 1x^2 + bx + c$. Note that the coefficient of x^2, called the **leading coefficient,** is 1. However, there are other perfect-square trinomials. An example is shown at right.

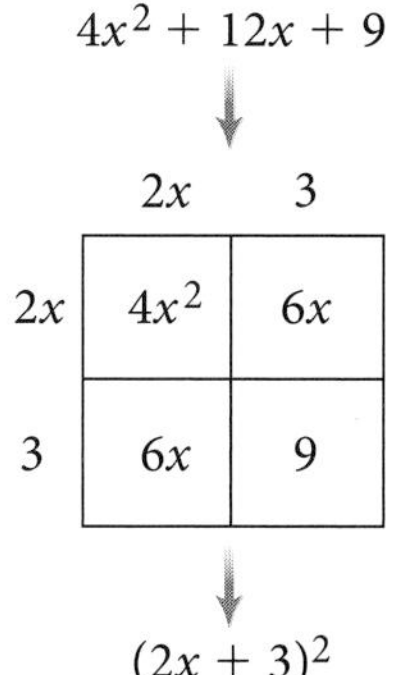

In these cases the leading coefficient is a perfect-square number. In Example A, you'll learn to complete the square for any quadratic equation in general form.

EXAMPLE A | Solve the equation $3x^2 + 18x - 8 = 22$ by completing the square.

Solution

First transform the equation so that you can write the left side as a perfect-square trinomial in the form $x^2 + 2hx + h^2$.

$3x^2 + 18x - 8 = 22$	Original equation.
$3x^2 + 18x = 30$	Add 8 to both sides of the equation.
$x^2 + 6x = 10$	Divide both sides by 3.

Now you need to decide what number to add to both sides to get a perfect-square trinomial on the left side: $x^2 + 6x + \underline{?} = (x + \underline{?})^2$.

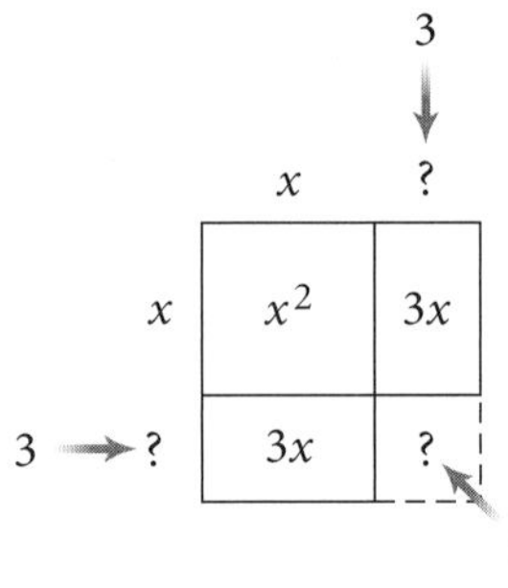

$x^2 + 6x + 9 = 10 + 9$	Add 9 to both sides to complete the square.
$(x + 3)^2 = 19$	Write the perfect-square trinomial as a squared binomial, and combine any like terms.
$x + 3 = \pm\sqrt{19}$	Take the square root of both sides.
$x = -3 \pm \sqrt{19}$	Add -3 to both sides.

The two solutions are $-3 + \sqrt{19}$ and $-3 - \sqrt{19}$, or approximately 1.36 and -7.36.

You can also complete the square to convert the general form of a quadratic equation to the vertex form.

EXAMPLE B | Find the vertex form of the equation $y = -2x^2 + 12x - 21$. Then identify the vertex of the parabola and any x-intercepts.

Solution

To convert $y = -2x^2 + 12x - 21$ to the form $y = a(x - h)^2 + k$, complete the square. When you complete the square of a function with a leading coefficient other than 1, an efficient approach is to isolate the x-terms on one side of the equation and divide to make the coefficient of x^2 equal 1.

$y = -2x^2 + 12x - 21$	Original equation.
$y + 21 = -2x^2 + 12x$	Add 21 to both sides to isolate the x-terms.
$\frac{y + 21}{-2} = x^2 - 6x$	Divide by -2 so the leading coefficient is 1.

Now you can complete the square by adding 9 to both sides.

$\frac{y + 21}{-2} + 9 = x^2 - 6x + 9$	Add 9 to both sides of the equation.
$\frac{y + 21}{-2} + \frac{-18}{-2} = (x - 3)^2$	Express 9 as $\frac{-18}{-2}$ so you can add the terms on the left. Express the right side as a perfect square.
$\frac{y + 3}{-2} = (x - 3)^2$	Combine fractions.
$y = -2(x - 3)^2 - 3$	Solve for y by undoing.

So the vertex is (3, −3). To find any x-intercepts, you can set y equal to 0 in the vertex form of the equation and then solve symbolically.

$$-2(x-3)^2 - 3 = 0$$ Substitute 0 for y in the original equation.

$$(x-3)^2 = \frac{3}{-2}$$ Add 3 and then divide both sides by −2.

$$x = 3 \pm \sqrt{\frac{3}{-2}}$$ Take the square root, and then add 3 to both sides.

If you try to evaluate $3 \pm \sqrt{\frac{3}{-2}}$, your calculator may give you an error message about a nonreal answer. These roots are not real numbers because the number under the square root sign is negative, and no real number can be squared to produce a negative number. The set of numbers that includes real numbers and numbers containing even roots of negative numbers is the **complex numbers.** The number-set diagram at the end of Lesson 8.1 can be expanded to include the complex numbers.

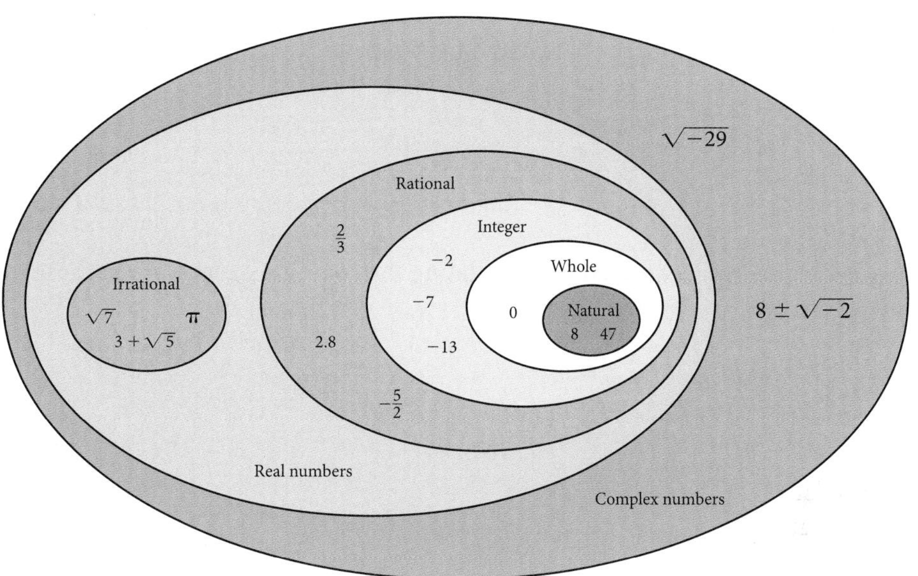

Only real numbers appear on a number line, so $y = -2(x-3)^2 - 3$ has no x-intercepts. The graph confirms this result. Note that the vertex is below the x-axis and the parabola opens downward. So the graph does not cross the x-axis.

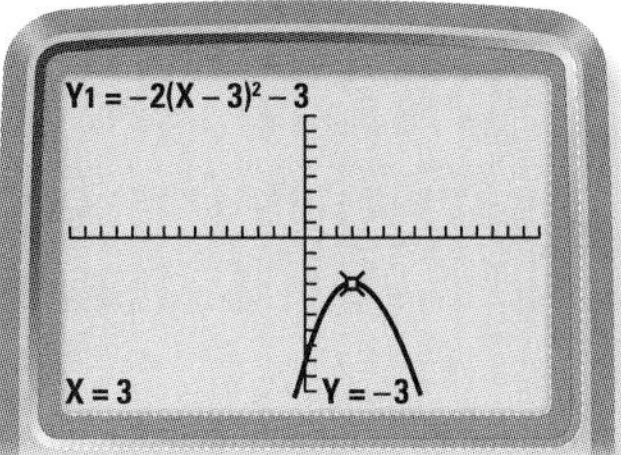

[10, 10, 1, 10, 10, 1]

You can now solve any quadratic equation in general form by completing the square. This process leads to a general formula that you will learn in the next lesson.

8.6 Exercises

You will need your graphing calculator for Exercises **7, 8, 10, 11,** and **12.**

Practice Your Skills

1. Solve each quadratic equation.

a. $(x + 2)^2 = 6$

b. $3(x - 4)^2 - 9 = 0$

c. $2(x + 3)^2 - 4 = 0$ @

d. $-2(x - 5)^2 + 7 = 3$ @

e. $3(x + 8)^2 - 7 = 0$

f. $-5(x + 6)^2 - 3 = -10$

2. Solve each equation.

a. $(x - 5)(x + 3) = 0$ @

b. $(2x + 6)(x - 7) = 0$

c. $(3x + 4)(x + 1) = 0$

d. $x(x + 6)(x + 9) = 0$

e. $(3x - 2)(2x + 3) = 0$

f. $4(3x + 5)(4x - 1) = 0$

3. Decide what number must be added to each expression to make a perfect-square trinomial. Then rewrite the trinomial as a squared binomial.

a. $x^2 + 8x$

b. $x^2 + 4x$

c. $x^2 + 16x$

d. $x^2 + 18x$ @

e. $x^2 - 10x$

f. $x^2 + 3x$

g. $x^2 - x$

h. $x^2 + \frac{2}{3}x$

i. $x^2 - 1.4x$

4. Solve each quadratic equation by completing the square. Leave your answer in radical form.

a. $x^2 + 2x = 1$

b. $x^2 - 4x - 3 = 0$

c. $x^2 - 4x - 8 = 0$ @

d. $x^2 + 2x - 1 = -5$

e. $x^2 + 10x - 9 = 0$

f. $5x^2 + 10x - 7 = 28$ @

Reason and Apply

5. If you know the vertex and one other point on a parabola, you can find its quadratic equation. The vertex (h, k) of this parabola is $(2, -31.5)$, and the other point is $(5, 0)$.

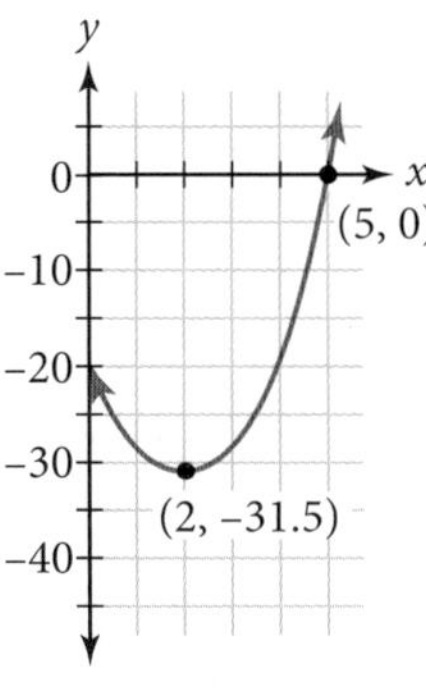

a. Substitute the values of h and k into the equation $y = a(x - h)^2 + k$.

b. To find the value of a, substitute 5 for x and 0 for y. Then solve for a.

c. Use the a-value you found in 5b to write the equation of the graph in vertex form.

d. Use what you learned in 5a–c to write the equation of the graph whose vertex is $(2, 32)$ and that passes through $(5, 14)$.

6. The length of a rectangle is 4 meters more than its width. The area is 12 square meters.

a. Define variables and write an equation for the area of the rectangle in terms of its width. @

b. Solve your equation in 6a by completing the square.

c. Which solution in 6b makes sense for the width of the rectangle? What is the corresponding length?

7. Consider the equation $y = x^2 + 6x + 10$.

a. Convert this equation to vertex form by completing the square.

b. Find the vertex. Graph both equations.

c. Find the roots of the equation $0 = x^2 + 6x + 10$. What happens and why?

8. APPLICATION A professional football team uses computers to describe the projectile motion of a football when punted. After compiling data from several games, the computer models the height of an average punt with the equation

$$h(t) = \frac{-16}{3}(t - 2.2)^2 + 26.9$$

where t is the time in seconds and $h(t)$ is the height in yards. The punter's foot makes contact with the ball when $t = 0$.

a. When does the punt reach its highest point? How high does the football go? ⓐ

b. Find the zeros of the equation $h(t) = \frac{-16}{3}(t - 2.2)^2 + 26.9$. Which solution is the hang time—that is, the time it takes until the ball hits the ground?

c. How high is the ball when the punter kicks it? ⓐ

d. Graph the equation. What are the real-world meanings of the vertex, the y-intercept, and the x-intercepts? ⓐ

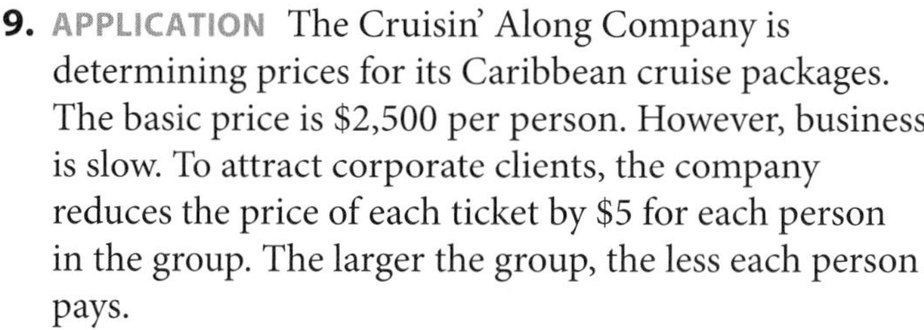

9. APPLICATION The Cruisin' Along Company is determining prices for its Caribbean cruise packages. The basic price is \$2,500 per person. However, business is slow. To attract corporate clients, the company reduces the price of each ticket by \$5 for each person in the group. The larger the group, the less each person pays.

a. Define variables and write an equation to model the price of a single ticket. ⓐ

b. Write an equation to model the total price the company charges for a group package. ⓐ

c. Convert the equation in 9b to vertex form.

d. What is the total price of a cruise for a group of 20 people?

e. The company accountant reports that the cost of running a cruise is \$200,000. Solve the equation

$$x(2500 - 5x) = 200{,}000$$

by completing the square.

f. What limitations should the cruise company place on group size in order to make a profit? ⓗ

10. APPLICATION The rate at which a bear population grows in a park is given by the equation $R(b) = 0.001b(100 - b)$. The function value $R(b)$ represents the rate at which the population is growing in bears per year, and b represents the number of bears.

a. Find $R(10)$ and provide a real-world meaning for this value. @

b. Solve $R(b) = 0$ and provide real-world meanings for the solutions. @

c. For what size bear population would the population grow fastest?

d. What is the maximum number of bears the park can support?

e. What does it mean to say $R(120) < 0$?

Review

11. Find each product. Check your answers by using calculator tables or graphs.

a. $(x + 1)(2x^2 + 3x + 1)$ b. $(2x - 5)(3x^2 + 2x - 4)$

12. Combine like terms in each polynomial. Check your results by using calculator tables or graphs.

a. $(x + 1) + (2x^2 + 3x + 1)$ b. $(2x - 5) + (3x^2 + 2x - 4)$

c. $(x + 1) - (2x^2 + 3x + 1)$ @ d. $(2x - 5) - (3x^2 + 2x - 4)$

13. Solve each equation by converting it to the form $ax^2 + bx + c = 0$, if necessary, and then factoring and using the zero-product property. Verify your answers by using substitution.

a. $x^2 - 4x = 0$ b. $x^2 + 2x - 3 = 0$

c. $x^2 - 3x = 4$ d. $2x^2 - 11x + 15 = 0$

e. $5x^2 - 13x + 8 = 0$ f. $3x^2 - 8 = -5x$ @

14. Use all these clues to find the equation of the one function that they describe.

- The graph of the equation is a parabola that crosses the x-axis twice.
- If you write the equation in factored form, one of the factors is $x + 7$.
- The graph of the equation has y-intercept 14.
- The axis of symmetry of the graph passes through the point $(-4, -2)$.

15. Ibrahim Patterson is planning to expand his square deck. He will add 3 feet to the width and 2 feet to the length to get a total area of 210 square feet. Find the dimensions of his original deck. Show your work.

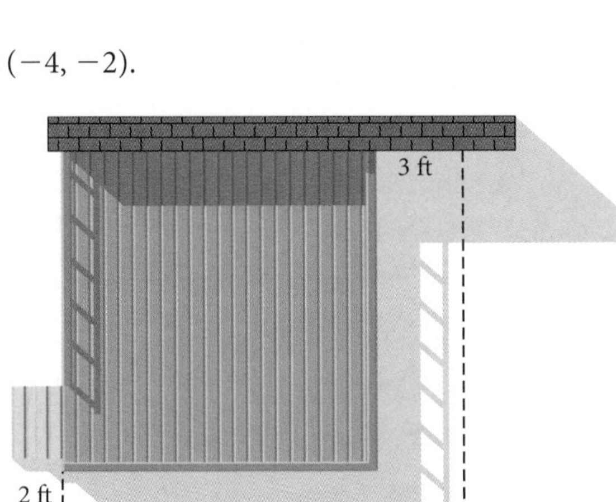

LESSON

8.7

The Quadratic Formula

"Most people are more comfortable with old problems than with new solutions."

ANONYMOUS

You have learned several methods for solving quadratic equations symbolically. Completing the square is particularly useful because it can be used for any quadratic equation. But if your equation is something like $y = 0.2x^2 + \frac{365}{17}x + \frac{2}{19}$, completing the square will be very messy! In this lesson you'll find a formula for solving any quadratic equation in the form $ax^2 + bx + c = 0$ directly, using only the values of a, b, and c. It is called the **quadratic formula.**

Recall that you can solve some quadratic equations symbolically by recognizing their forms:

Vertex form	$-4.9(t-5)^2 + 75 = 0$
Factored form	$0 = w(200 - 2w)$
Perfect-square trinomial	$x^2 + 6x + 9 = 0$

You can also undo the order of operations in other quadratic equations when there is no x-term or when the equation is a perfect square, as in these:

$x^2 = 10$

$(x+5)^2 = 0$

$x^2 - 0.36 = 0$

If the quadratic expression is in the form $x^2 + bx + c$, you can complete the square by using a rectangle diagram.

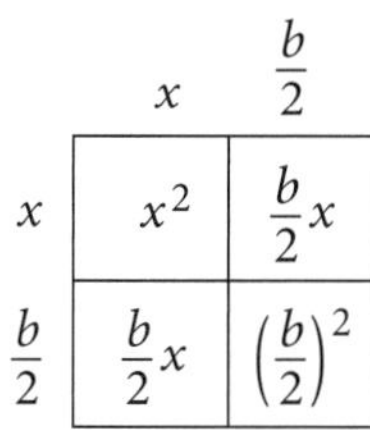

	x	$\frac{b}{2}$
x	x^2	$\frac{b}{2}x$
$\frac{b}{2}$	$\frac{b}{2}x$	$\left(\frac{b}{2}\right)^2$

In the investigation you'll use the completing-the-square method to derive the quadratic formula.

INVESTIGATION

Deriving the Quadratic Formula

You'll solve the quadratic equation $2x^2 + 3x - 1 = 0$ and develop the quadratic formula for the general case in the process.

Step 1 Identify the values of a, b, and c in the general form, $ax^2 + bx + c = 0$, for the equation $2x^2 + 3x - 1 = 0$.

Step 2 Group all the variable terms on the left side of your equation so that it is in the form

$$ax^2 + bx = -c$$

Step 3 It's easiest to complete the square when the coefficient of x^2 is 1. So divide your equation by the value of a. Write it in the form

$$x^2 + \frac{b}{a}x = \frac{-c}{a}$$

Step 4 Use a rectangle diagram to help you complete the square. What number must you add to both sides? Write your new equation in the form

$$x^2 + \frac{b}{a}x + \left(\frac{b}{2a}\right)^2 = \left(\frac{b}{2a}\right)^2 - \frac{c}{a}$$

Step 5 Rewrite the trinomial on the left side of your equation as a squared binomial. On the right side, find a common denominator. Write the next stage of your equation in the form

$$\left(x + \frac{b}{2a}\right)^2 = \frac{b^2}{4a^2} - \frac{4ac}{4a^2}$$

Step 6 Take the square root of both sides of your equation, like this:

$$x + \frac{b}{2a} = \pm\frac{\sqrt{b^2 - 4ac}}{\sqrt{4a^2}}$$

Step 7 Rewrite $\sqrt{4a^2}$ as $2a$. Then get x by itself on the left side:

$$x = -\frac{b}{2a} \pm \frac{\sqrt{b^2 - 4ac}}{2a}$$

Step 8 There are two possible solutions:

$$x = \frac{-b + \sqrt{b^2 - 4ac}}{2a} \text{ and } x = \frac{-b - \sqrt{b^2 - 4ac}}{2a}$$

Write your two solutions in radical form.

Step 9 Write your solutions in decimal form. Check them with a graph and a table.

Step 10 Consider the expression $\frac{-b \pm \sqrt{b^2 - 4ac}}{2a}$. What restrictions should there be so that the solutions exist and are real numbers?

The quadratic formula gives the same solutions as completing the square or factoring. You don't need to derive the formula each time. All you need to know are the values of a, b, and c. Then substitute these values into the formula.

Quadratic Formula

When a quadratic equation is written in the general form, $ax^2 + bx + c = 0$, the roots are

$$x = \frac{-b + \sqrt{b^2 - 4ac}}{2a} \text{ and } x = \frac{-b - \sqrt{b^2 - 4ac}}{2a}.$$

The roots can be written together as

$$x = \frac{-b \pm \sqrt{b^2 - 4ac}}{2a}.$$

In the example you'll learn how to use the formula for quadratic equations in general form. You can even use it when the values of a, b, and c are decimals or fractions.

EXAMPLE | Use the quadratic formula to solve the equation $3x^2 + 5x - 7 = 0$.

Solution The equation is already in general form, so identify the values of a, b, and c. For this equation, $a = 3$, $b = 5$, and $c = -7$. Here is one way to use the formula:

$x = \dfrac{-b \pm \sqrt{b^2 - 4ac}}{2a}$	The quadratic formula.
$= \dfrac{-(\ ) \pm \sqrt{(\ )^2 - 4(\ )(\ )}}{2(\ )}$	Replace each letter in the formula with a set of parentheses.
$= \dfrac{-(5) \pm \sqrt{(5)^2 - 4(3)(-7)}}{2(3)}$	Substitute the values of a, b, and c into the appropriate places.
$= \dfrac{-5 \pm \sqrt{25 - (-84)}}{6}$	Simplify.
$x = \dfrac{-5 \pm \sqrt{109}}{6}$	Subtract.

The two exact roots of the equation are $\dfrac{-5 + \sqrt{109}}{6}$ and $\dfrac{-5 - \sqrt{109}}{6}$.

You can use your calculator to calculate the approximate values, 0.907 and -2.573, respectively.

To make the formula simpler, think of the expression under the square root sign as one number. This expression, $b^2 - 4ac$, is called the **discriminant.**

The Discriminant

When a quadratic equation is written in the general form $ax^2 + bx + c = 0$, the discriminant, d, is

$$d = b^2 - 4ac$$

The discriminant is the value found under the square root sign in the quadratic formula.

$$x = \frac{-b \pm \sqrt{b^2 - 4ac}}{2a}$$

In the example the discriminant is 109. Let $d = b^2 - 4ac$. Then the formula becomes

$$x = \frac{-b \pm \sqrt{d}}{2a}$$

If you store these values in your calculator as shown, then you can use the formula directly on your calculator.

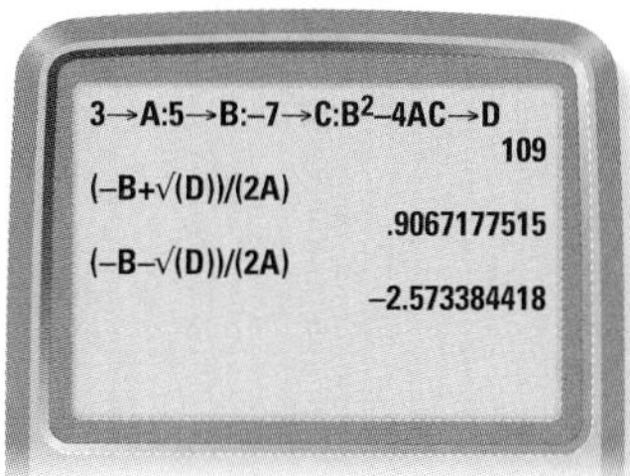

The discriminant, $b^2 - 4ac$, gives you information about the roots of a quadratic equation in the form $ax^2 + bx + c = 0$ and about the number of x-intercepts on the graph of the quadratic function $y = ax^2 + bx + c$.

Discriminant	Roots	Number of x-intercepts
positive and not a perfect square	irrational	two
positive and a perfect square	rational	two
negative	not real	none
zero	equal and rational	one

8.7 Exercises

You will need your graphing calculator for Exercises **4, 11, 12,** and **14.**

Practice Your Skills

1. Without using a calculator, evaluate the expression $b^2 - 4ac$ for the given values. Then check your answers using a calculator.

a. $a = 3, b = 5, c = 2$ @

b. $a = 1, b = -3, c = -3$

c. $a = -2, b = -6, c = -3$ @

d. $a = 9, b = 9, c = 0$

2. For each equation identify the values of a, b, and c. Rewrite each quadratic equation in general form if necessary.

a. $2x^2 + 3x - 7 = 0$

b. $x^2 + 6x = -11$ @

c. $-3x^2 - 4x + 12 = 0$

d. $18 - 4.9x^2 + 47x = 0$ @

e. $-16x^2 + 28x + 10 = 57$

f. $5x^2 - 2x = 7 + 4x$

g. $-4 + 5x^2 = 3x$

h. $2x + 3(4 - 5x^2) = 5x + 1$

3. Solve each quadratic equation. Which equations can you solve readily by completing the square? Which equation has no real solutions?

a. $2x^2 - 3x + 4 = 0$ @

b. $-2x^2 + 7x = 3$

c. $x^2 - 6x - 8 = 0$

d. $3x^2 + 2x - 1 = 5$

e. $3x^2 - 12 = 0$

f. $-2(x + 2)(3 - x) = 0$

Reason and Apply

4. Consider the quadratic equation $y = x^2 + 3x + 5$.

a. How can you use the discriminant to tell whether the equation has any real roots? @

b. How can you use your answer to 4a (or the discriminant) to determine the number of x-intercepts?

c. Confirm your answers to 4a and b with a graph.

5. Match each quadratic equation to its graph. Then explain how to use the discriminant, $b^2 - 4ac$, to find the number of x-intercepts.

a. $y = x^2 + x + 1$ ⓐ

b. $y = x^2 + 2x + 1$

c. $y = x^2 + 3x + 1$

i. 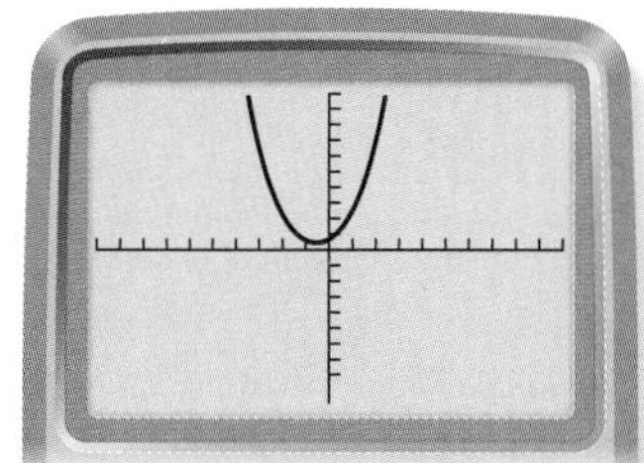

ii. 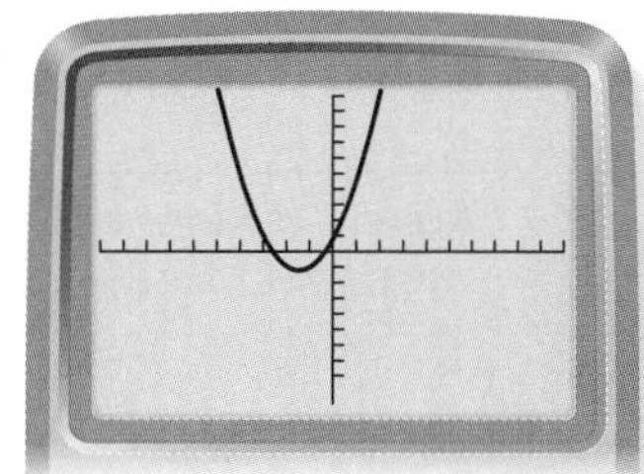

iii. 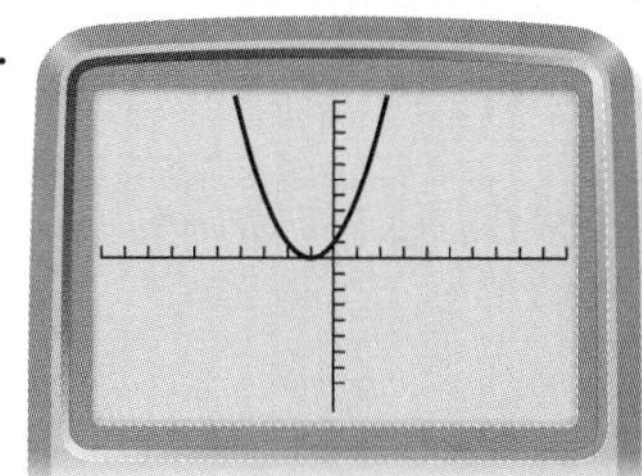

6. The equation $h = -4.9t^2 + 6.2t + 1.9$ models the height of a soccer ball after Brandi hits it with her head. The variable t represents the time in seconds, and h represents the height in meters. Write an equation that describes each event in 6a–c. Then use the quadratic formula to solve it. Explain the real-world meanings of your solutions.

a. The ball hits the ground. ⓐ

b. The ball is 3 meters above the ground. ⓐ

c. The ball is 4 meters above the ground. ⓐ

Brandi Chastain of the USA team heads a soccer ball during the 2003 Women's World Cup at RFK Stadium.

7. Evaluate each expression to the nearest tenth. Assuming each expression gives the solutions to a quadratic equation, write each equation, sketch the parabola, and identify the x-intercepts. ⓗ

a. $\dfrac{14 \pm \sqrt{(-14)^2 - 4(1)(49)}}{2(1)}$ ⓐ

b. $\dfrac{3 \pm \sqrt{(-3)^2 - 4(2)(2)}}{2(2)}$

c. $\dfrac{3 \pm \sqrt{(-3)^2 - 4(2)(-2)}}{2(2)}$

8. **MINI-INVESTIGATION** The quadratic formula gives two roots of an equation:

$$x = \frac{-b + \sqrt{b^2 - 4ac}}{2a} \quad \text{and} \quad x = \frac{-b - \sqrt{b^2 - 4ac}}{2a}$$

What is the average of these two roots? How does averaging the roots help you find the vertex?

9. The equation $h = -4.9t^2 + 17t + 2.2$ models the height of a stone thrown into the air, where t is time in seconds and h is height in meters. Use the quadratic formula to find how long the stone is in the air. ⓗ

10. APPLICATION A shopkeeper is redesigning the rectangular sign on her store's rooftop. She wants the largest area possible for the sign. When she considers adding an amount to the width, she subtracts that same amount from the length. Her original sign has width 4 m and length 7 m.

a. Complete the table. (h)

Increase (x) (m)	Width (m)	Length (m)	Area (m^2)	Perimeter (m)
0	4	7		
0.5				
1.0				
1.5				
2.0				

b. How do the changes in width and length affect the perimeter?

c. How do the changes in width and length affect the area?

d. Write an equation in factored form to model the area A of the rectangle in terms of x, the amount the shopkeeper adds to the width.

e. What are the dimensions of the rectangle with the largest area?

11. Solve the system of equations

$$\begin{cases} y = x^2 + 4x + 2 \\ y = 0.5x + 4 \end{cases}$$

a. By graphing both equations on the same screen to find where they intersect.

b. Algebraically, using substitution. (a)

12. Solve the system of equations

$$\begin{cases} y = -3x - 2 \\ y = x^2 + 3x + 6 \end{cases}$$

a. By graphing.

b. Using tables.

c. Algebraically, using substitution.

Review

13. Simplify each rational expression by factoring and then dividing out common factors. State any restrictions on the variable.

a. $\dfrac{x^2 - 5x + 6}{x - 3}$ @ b. $\dfrac{x^2 + 7x + 6}{x + 1}$ c. $\dfrac{2x^2 - x - 1}{2x + 1}$

d. $\dfrac{x^2 - 2x - 15}{x^2 - 3x - 10}$ e. $\dfrac{x^2 + 10x + 24}{x^2 + 2x - 24}$ f. $\dfrac{2x^2 - 18}{2x^2 + 18}$

14. On graph paper, sketch graphs of these equations. Then use your calculator to check your sketches.

a. $y - 2 = (x - 3)^2$ b. $y - 2 = -2|x - 3|$

IMPROVING YOUR Reasoning SKILLS

In Chapter 2, you may have done the project The Golden Ratio. Now you have the tools to calculate this number. One way to calculate the golden ratio is to add 1 to square it. The symbolic statement of this rule is $x^2 = x + 1$ (or $x = \sqrt{x + 1}$).

You can approximate this value using a recursive rule on your calculator.

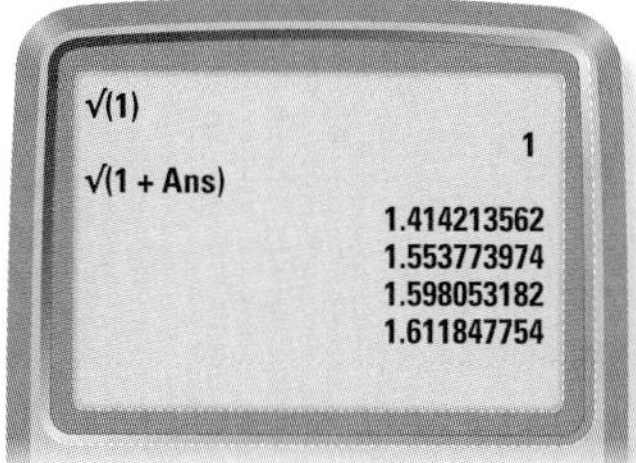

This is the same as calculating $\sqrt{1 + \sqrt{1 + \sqrt{1 + \sqrt{1 + \ldots}}}}$

You can also divide both sides of $x^2 = x + 1$ by x to get $x = 1 + \frac{1}{x}$.

You can use another recursive rule to approximate x in this case.

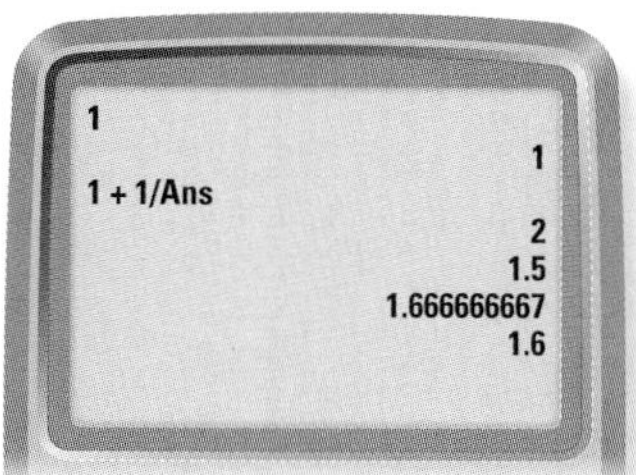

This is the same as calculating $1 + \cfrac{1}{1 + \cfrac{1}{1 + \cfrac{1}{1 + \ldots}}}$

Try different starting values for these recursive rules. Do they always result in the same number? Use one of the methods you learned in this chapter to solve the equation $x^2 = x + 1$ symbolically. What are the solutions in radical form? Can you write a recursive rule for the negative solution?

Solving Quadratic Equations

You have solved equations using graphs, tables, your calculator, and symbolic methods. Here you will focus on the symbolic methods of factoring and using the quadratic formula to solve quadratic equations.

With coefficients that are real numbers, the possible outcomes are two different real solutions, as shown by parabola l; two identical real solutions, or one unique solution, as shown by parabola m; or two nonreal solutions, as shown by parabola n.

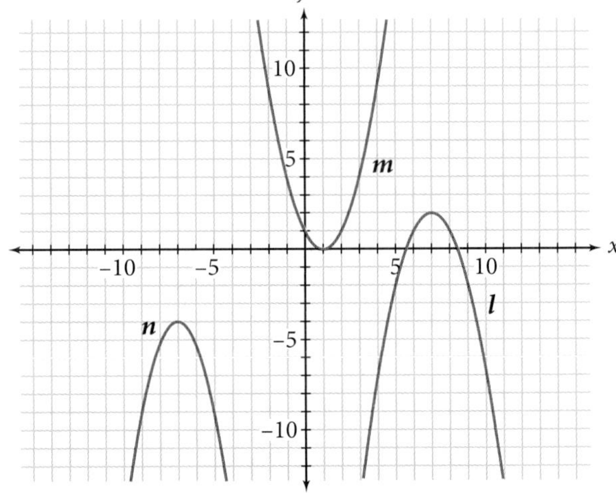

No one symbolic method of solving a quadratic equation is always best or quickest. To determine which method to use in a situation, think about the form of the equation and perhaps test the discriminant.

EXAMPLE

Determine the quickest way to solve each quadratic equation. Then find the solution.

a. $-2(x-9)(x+7)=0$ **b.** $5x^2-11=0$ **c.** $x(x+11)=12$

d. $2(x-3)^2+3=21$ **e.** $x^2-16=5x$

Solution

a. You can solve the equation $-2(x-9)(x+7)=0$ by looking at it. The equation is already factored, and because the product equals 0, the two roots are 9 and -7.

b. The variable x appears only once in this equation, so you can use undoing to solve it.

$$5x^2-11=0$$
$$5x^2=11$$
$$x^2=\frac{11}{5}=2.2$$
$$x=\pm\sqrt{2.2}$$

c. If the product $x(x + 11)$ were 0, this solution would be simple; but the product is 12. So first expand the expression, and move all the terms to one side to get $x^2 + 11x - 12 = 0$. Perhaps you will see immediately how the expression on the left factors—you're looking for two numbers whose product is -12 and whose sum is 11. But if you don't see this, check the discriminant, $b^2 - 4ac$, which equals $11^2 - 4(1)(-12)$, or 169. Because 169 is a perfect square, 13^2, you know that this equation has two rational roots. Look for a way to factor the expression, or use the quadratic formula.

$$x^2 + 11x - 12 = 0$$
$$(x + 12)(x - 1) = 0$$
$$x = -12 \text{ and } x = 1$$

d. In this equation x appears only once, so you can use undoing to solve it.

$$2(x - 3)^2 + 3 = 21$$
$$2(x - 3)^2 = 18$$
$$(x - 3)^2 = 9$$
$$x - 3 = -3 \text{ and } x - 3 = 3$$
$$x = 0 \text{ and } x = 6$$

e. Group the terms of $x^2 - 16 = 5x$ on one side of the equal sign to get an equation in general form, $x^2 - 5x - 16 = 0$. To see whether the expression $x^2 - 5x - 16$ can be factored, check the discriminant: $b^2 - 4ac = (-5)^2 - 4(1)(-16) = 89$. Because 89 is not a perfect square, the equation does not have factors with integer coefficients, so use the quadratic formula. The quadratic formula can be used to solve any quadratic equation, but often it is not the quickest method.

$$x^2 - 5x - 16 = 0$$
$$a = 1, b = -5, c = -16, \text{ and } d = 89$$
$$x = \frac{5 + \sqrt{89}}{2} \text{ and } x = \frac{5 - \sqrt{89}}{2}$$

To summarize, if the equation is equal to zero and is already factored, or if the factors are clearly visible, then use the factors to solve the equation. If the variable x occurs only once, then you can undo to find the solutions. If the equation is in general form and the discriminant is not a perfect square, then factoring will be difficult and you should use the quadratic formula. The value of the discriminant, $b^2 - 4ac$, determines whether you will have one, two, or no real roots.

Exercises

1. The discriminants, $b^2 - 4ac$, of two quadratic equations are given. What are the equations? What are the exact roots?

a. $(-8)^2 - 4(2)(8)$

b. $(-1.5)^2 - 4(7)(-1)$

2. Solve each equation. Give the exact answers.

a. $2x^2 - 18 = 0$

b. $6x^2 = 6x$

c. $4x^2 + 12x + 9 = 0$

d. $4x^2 + x - 3 = 0$

e. $x^2 + 5x = 24$

f. $x^2 + 3x - 5 = 0$

g. $2x^2 - 6x - 22 = 0$

h. $x^2 - x + 3 = 0$

i. $(x - 4)^2 - 2 = 0$

j. $(x - 1)^2 - 4 = 0$

k. $2x^2 - 3x = 10$

l. $-2x^2 + 14x - 20 = 0$

m. $x^2 = 144$

n. $x^2 = 14 - 3x$

o. $14 + 2x^2 = 0$

p. $x^4 - 6x^2 + 9 = 0$ (Hint: let $y = x^2$ and rewrite the equation.)

LESSON

8.8

Operations with Polynomials

You probably recall that the terms of a polynomial are separated with plus and minus signs. The linear expressions $2x$ and $3x + 1$ are examples of one- and two-term polynomials, respectively. The quadratic expression $x^2 + 4x - 3$ is a polynomial with three terms. A polynomial can have any number of terms. In this lesson you will concentrate on polynomials of up to five terms.

Polynomial	Number of terms	Degree	Description
$ax^4 + bx^3 + cx^2 + dx + e$	5	4	quartic, polynomial
$ax^3 + bx^2 + cx + d$	4	3	cubic, polynomial
$ax^2 + bx + c$	3	2	quadratic, polynomial
$ax + b$	2	1	linear, binomial, polynomial
kx	1	1	linear, monomial, polynomial
c	1	0	constant, monomial, polynomial

In each polynomial in the table, the exponent of x decreases as you move to the next term. This is the **general form** of a polynomial. The exponent of the variable is the **degree** of the term. The degree of a polynomial is the largest degree of the individual terms in the polynomial.

In the next example you'll review how to add or subtract two polynomials even when their degrees differ.

EXAMPLE A Find the sum and difference of the polynomials $2x^3 + 5x^2 - 11x - 4$ and $2x^2 + x - 3$.

Solution Terms of the same degree, called *like terms,* can be combined.

$$(2x^3 + 5x^2 - 11x + 4) + (2x^2 + x - 3) = 2x^3 + 7x^2 - 10x + 1$$

$$\begin{aligned}(2x^3 + 5x^2 - 11x + 4) - (2x^2 + x - 3) &= (2x^3 + 5x^2 - 11x + 4) + (-2x^2 - x + 3)\\ &= 2x^3 + 3x^2 - 12x + 7\end{aligned}$$

Note that the subtraction was rewritten as addition by changing the sign of every term being subtracted.

When multiplying polynomials, the degree of the product might be different from the degree of either factor. You can use exponent properties to predict the degree of the product.

EXAMPLE B | Find the product of the polynomials $2x^3 + 5x^2 - 11x + 4$ and $2x^2 + x - 3$.

Solution

The 12 individual term-by-term products are shown in this rectangle diagram.

	$2x^3$	$5x^2$	$-11x$	4
$2x^2$	$4x^5$	$10x^4$	$-22x^3$	$8x^2$
x	$2x^4$	$5x^3$	$-11x^2$	$4x$
-3	$-6x^3$	$-15x^2$	$33x$	-12

Leading coefficient and term

You can see that like terms are lined up along diagonals from the lower left to the upper right. Combining like terms gives

$$(2x^3 + 5x^2 - 11x + 4)(2x^2 + x - 3) = 4x^5 + 12x^4 - 23x^3 - 18x^2 + 37x - 12$$

The Multiplication Property of Exponents allows you to conclude that the degree of the product, 5, is the sum of the degrees of the polynomials being multiplied.

You can verify that your work is correct by checking that graphs or calculator table entries are the same for the functions on the left and right sides of the equal sign.

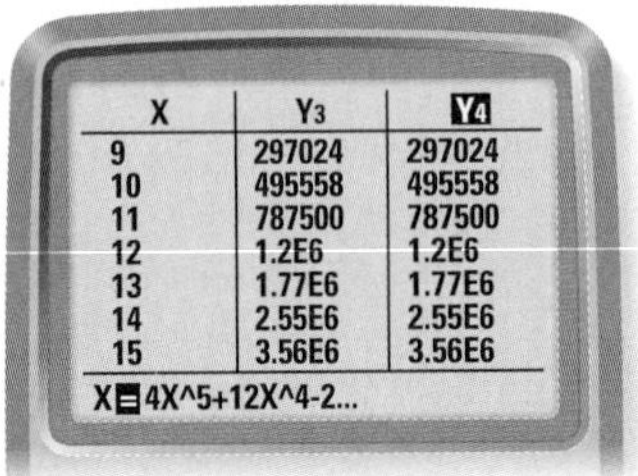

This example, like those throughout the chapter, uses a rectangle diagram to multiply polynomials. You can also use the distributive property to multiply polynomials. Choose the method that works best for you.

In the investigation you will discover connections between the graphs of cubic equations and their factored form.

INVESTIGATION

Rooting for Factors

In this investigation you'll discover relationships between the graphs and equations of polynomial functions.

Step 1 List the x-intercepts for each of these graphs.

Graph A

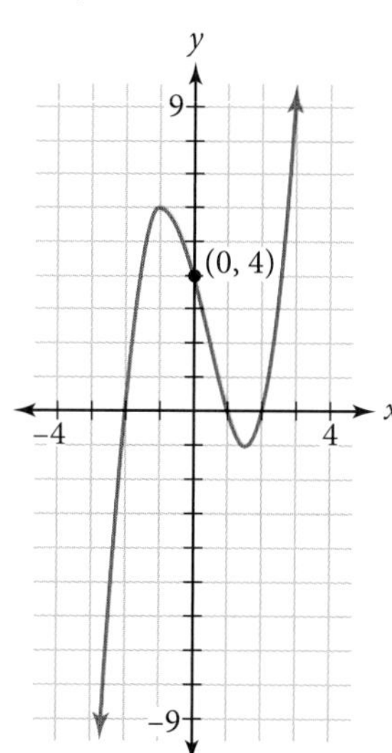

Graph B

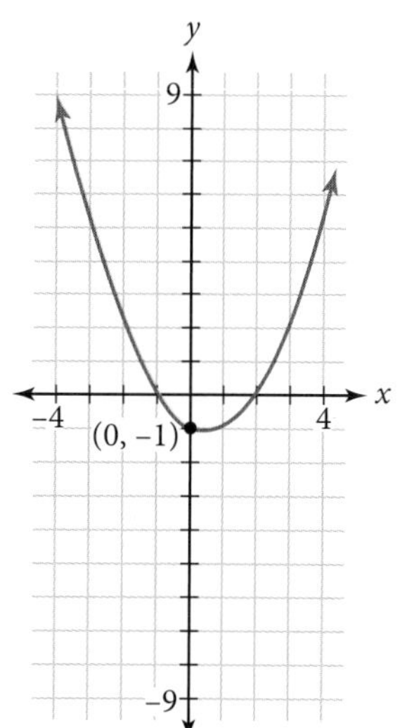

Graph C

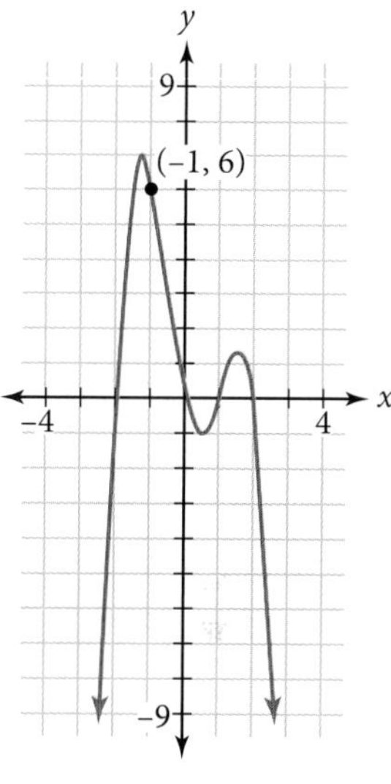

Graph D

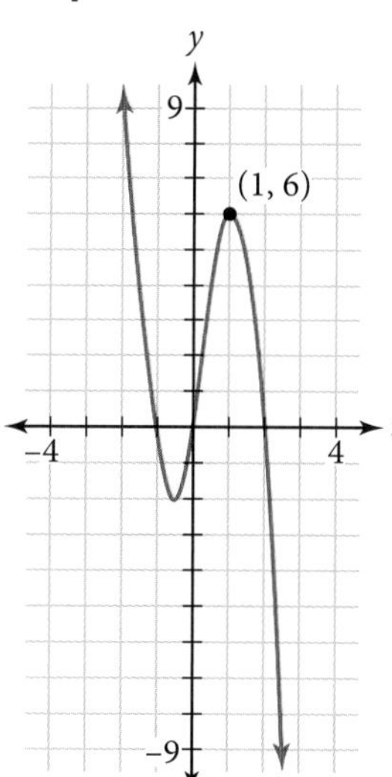

Graph E

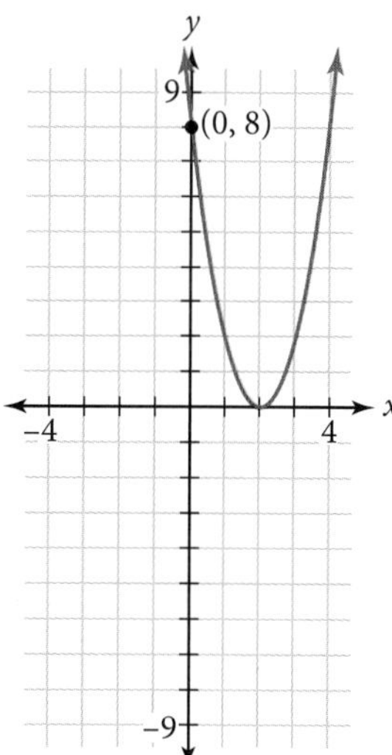

Graph F

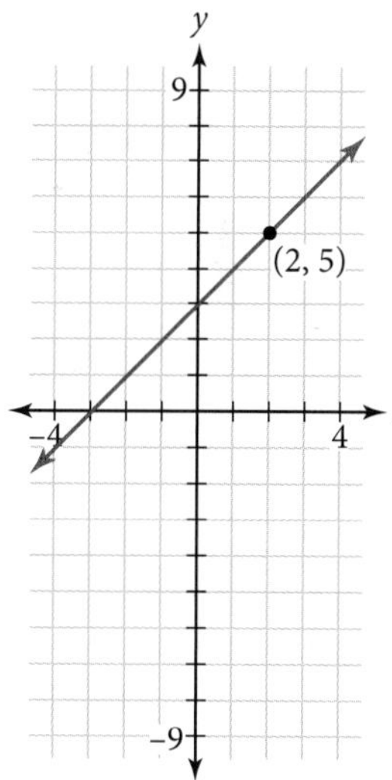

Step 2 Each equation below matches exactly one graph in Step 1. Use graphs and tables to match each equation to its graph.

a. $y = x + 3$

b. $y = 0.5(x + 1)(x - 2)$

c. $y = (x + 2)(x - 1)(x - 2)$

d. $y = -x(x - 1)(x + 2)(x - 2)$

e. $y = -3x(x + 1)(x - 2)$

f. $y = 2(x - 2)(x - 2)$

Step 3 Describe how the x-intercepts you found in Step 1 relate to the factored form of the equations in Step 2.

Now you'll write an equation from a graph.

Step 4 Use what you discovered in Steps 1–3 to write an equation with the same x-intercepts as those on the graph at right.

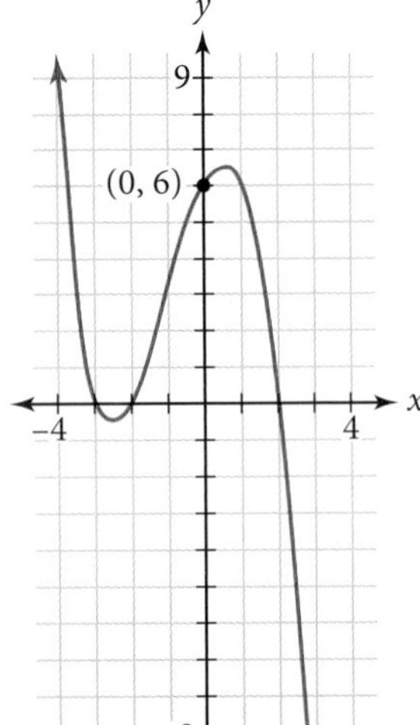

Step 5 Use the equation you wrote in Step 4 and the point given on the graph to write the exact equation of the graph. Check your equation by graphing it on your calculator.

Is there a way to determine the shape of the graph from its equation?

EXAMPLE C

Determine the degree of each equation, and describe generally what each graph will look like.

a. $y = (x + 2)(x - 1)$

b. $y = x(x - 3)(x + 1)$

c. $y = -2(x + 2)(x - 1)(x - 2)(x + 3)$

Solution

Expand each equation and combine like terms.

a. The equation $y = x^2 + x - 2$ has degree 2. The graph of a quadratic function is a parabola. This parabola has the a-value 1, so it opens upward. Its x-intercepts are -2 and 1. Its y-intercept is -2.

b. The equation $y = x^3 - 2x^2 - 3x$ has degree 3. You saw polynomials with degree 3 in Step 2c and e of the investigation. If a is positive, the graph of the cubic function starts in Quadrant III. If a is negative, the graph starts in Quadrant II. This graph starts in Quadrant III and has x-intercepts 0, 3, and -1, with y-intercept -3.

c. The equation $y = -2x^4 - 4x^3 + 14x^2 + 16x - 24$ has degree 4. You saw a polynomial with degree 4 in Step 2d of the investigation. Just as with a parabola, if a is positive, the graph of the quartic function opens upward. In this case, $a = -2$, so it opens downward and is stretched. It has x-intercepts -2, 1, 2, and -3 and y-intercept -24.

How can you find the roots of an equation when you can't identify the exact x-intercepts on a graph? Example D will show you a way to factor a cubic expression if you know only one x-intercept.

EXAMPLE D | Find the exact x-intercepts of $y = x^3 + 2x^2 - 7x - 2$.

Solution

The graph shows that 2 is an x-intercept of the function. This means that $(x - 2)$ is a factor. You can approximate the other two roots by tracing, but to find exact algebraic solutions you need to factor. You can do this by using a rectangle diagram.

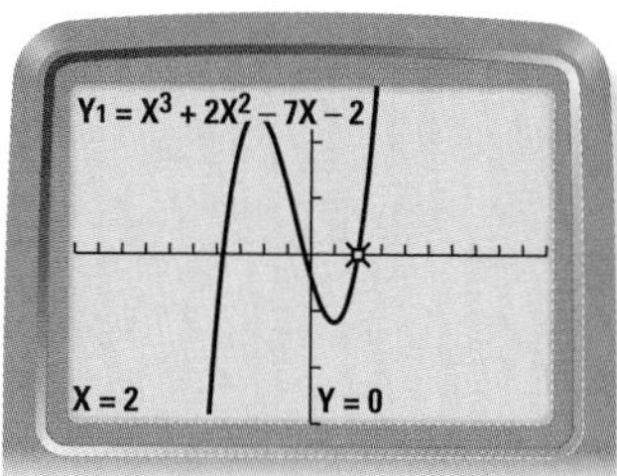

[−10, 10, 1, −15, 15, 5]

x	x^3		
-2			-2

Enter the factor $x - 2$ on the left. Enter the cubic term of the cubic expression in the upper-left rectangle and the number, or constant term, in the lower-right rectangle.

	x^2		
x	x^3		
-2	$-2x^2$		-2

You can now determine that x^2 is the width of the left rectangles because $x \cdot x^2 = x^3$. Next, $-2 \cdot x^2 = -2x^2$, so enter $-2x^2$ in the lower-left rectangle.

	x^2		
x	x^3	$4x^2$	
-2	$-2x^2$		-2

The original equation contains $2x^2$. Because there is already $-2x^2$ in the rectangle diagram, the entry in another rectangle must be $4x^2$ so that their sum is $2x^2$. Enter $4x^2$ in the upper-middle rectangle.

	x^2	$4x$	
x	x^3	$4x^2$	
-2	$-2x^2$	$-8x$	-2

You can now determine that $4x$ is the term above the middle rectangles because $x \cdot 4x = 4x^2$. Next, $-2 \cdot 4x = -8x$, so enter $-8x$ in the lower-middle rectangle.

	x^2	$4x$	1
x	x^3	$4x^2$	$1x$
-2	$-2x^2$	$-8x$	-2

The original equation contains $-7x$. Because there is already $-8x$ in the rectangle diagram, another rectangle must be $1x$ so that their sum is $-7x$. Enter $1x$ in the upper-right rectangle. You can now determine that the term above the right rectangles is 1.

This rectangle diagram shows that $x^2 + 4x + 1$ is another factor of the cubic equation. The values that make this expression equal zero are the remaining two x-intercepts. The expression doesn't factor easily, so use the quadratic formula to solve the equation $x^2 + 4x + 1 = 0$.

$$\frac{-4 \pm \sqrt{(4^2 - 4 \cdot 1 \cdot 1)}}{2 \cdot 1} = \frac{-4 \pm \sqrt{12}}{2} \approx -0.268 \text{ and } -3.732$$

So the exact x-intercepts are 2, $\frac{-4 + \sqrt{12}}{2}$, and $\frac{-4 - \sqrt{12}}{2}$. You can use the approximate values of the radical expressions to confirm the location of the x-intercepts on the graph.

Exercises

You will need your graphing calculator for Exercises **1, 6, 8, 10, 14, 15,** and **16.**

Practice Your Skills

1. The **cubing function,** $f(x) = x^3$, gives the volume of a cube with edge length x. When given the volume of a cube, to solve for the edge length you must find the **cube root** of the volume. For example, the edge length of a cube with a volume of 64 is 4. So you can write $\sqrt[3]{64} = 4$ and conversely $4^3 = 64$. You can evaluate cubes and cube roots with your calculator. [► See **Calculator Note: Cubes and Cube Roots.** ◄] Write and solve an equation to find the value of the variable in each figure.

a. @

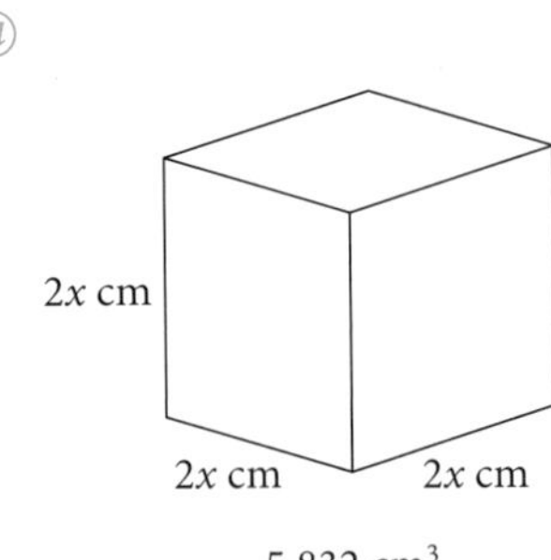

5,832 cm³

b.

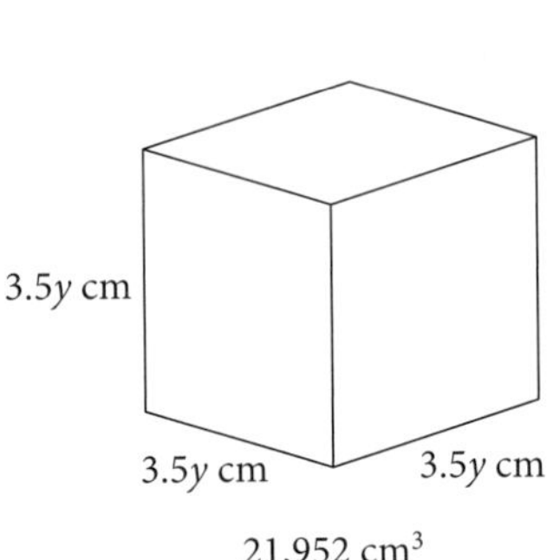

21,952 cm³

c. @

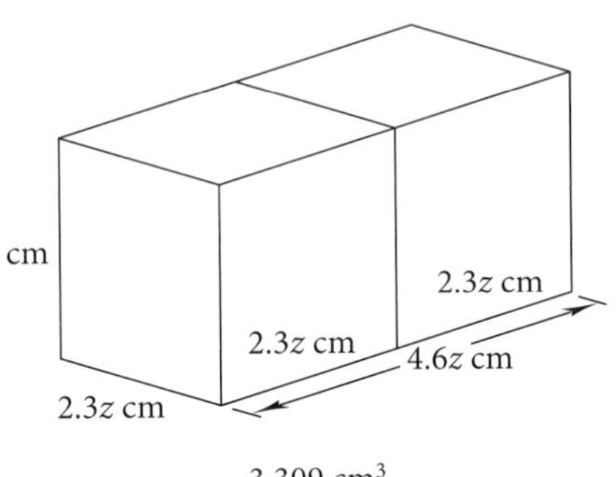

3,309 cm³

2. The greatest common factor (GCF) of a polynomial's terms is the monomial with the highest degree and the largest coefficient that is a factor of all the terms. Factor each expression by removing the GCF from all the terms.

a. $4x^2 + 12x$ @ b. $6x^2 - 4x$ c. $14x^4 + 7x^2 - 21x$ @ d. $12x^5 + 6x^3 + 3x^2$

3. Identify the leading coefficient and the degree of each polynomial.

a. $x^3 - 4x + 3$ b. $3 + x - 2x^2 + 5x^3$ c. $3x - 5x^4 + 7 - x^2$

4. Combine like terms by expanding, if necessary, and then adding or subtracting. Write your answers in general form.

a. $4x^3 - 2x + 5x^4 + 12 + 4x - x^2$

b. $x^2 - 3x^3 + 6x^2 + 2x - 4 - x^3$

c. $5x - 2(1 + 2x^2) + 4x^3$

d. $-2x^4 - 3x + 12x^2$

5. Perform the indicated operations. Write your answers in general form.

a. $(3x^2 + x + 5) + (4x^2 - 3x + 1)$

b. $(3x^2 + x + 5) - (4x^2 - 3x + 1)$

c. $(x^3 + 4x - 12) + (2x^2 - 5x + 2x^3 - 7)$

d. $(x^3 + 4x - 12) - (2x^2 - 5x + 2x^3 - 7)$

e. $(8x^3 - 5x) + (3x^3 + 2x^2 + 7x + 12)$

f. $(8x^3 - 5x) - (3x^3 + 2x^2 + 7x + 12)$ @

g. $(2x^2 - 6x + 11) + (-8x^2 - 7x + 9)$

h. $(2x^2 - 6x + 11)(-8x^2 - 7x + 9)$

Reason and Apply

6. A box is made so that its length is 6 cm more than its width. Its height is 2 cm less than its width.

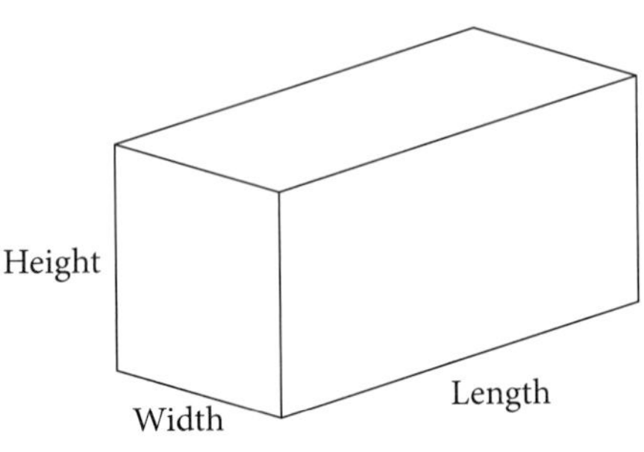

a. Use the width as the independent variable, and write an equation to model the volume of the box. @

b. Suppose you want to ensure that the volume of the box is greater than 47 cm³. Use a graph and a table to describe all possible widths, to the nearest 0.1 cm, of such boxes.

7. Determine whether each statement about the equation $0 = 2x^3 + 4x^2 - 10x$ is true or false.

a. The equation has three real roots.

b. One of the roots is at $x = 2$.

c. There is one positive root.

d. The graph of $y = 2x^3 + 4x^2 - 10x$ passes through $(1, -4)$.

8. Convert each equation from factored form to general form. Use a graph or a table to compare the original factored form to your final general form.

a. $(x + 1)(x + 2)(x + 3) = 0$ @

b. $(x + 2)(x - 2)(x - 3) = 0$

9. Use rectangle diagrams to find the missing expressions.

a. $(3x - 4)(x^2 + 4x + 5) = (?)$ @

b. $(3x + 5)(?) = 6x^2 - 2x - 20$

c. $(x - 5)(?) = 2x^2 - 7x - 15$ @

d. $(x + 5)(?) = 2x^3 + 14x^2 + 17x - 15$

10. Using the x-intercepts and the given point, write an equation for this graph in factored form. Check your equation by graphing it on your calculator.

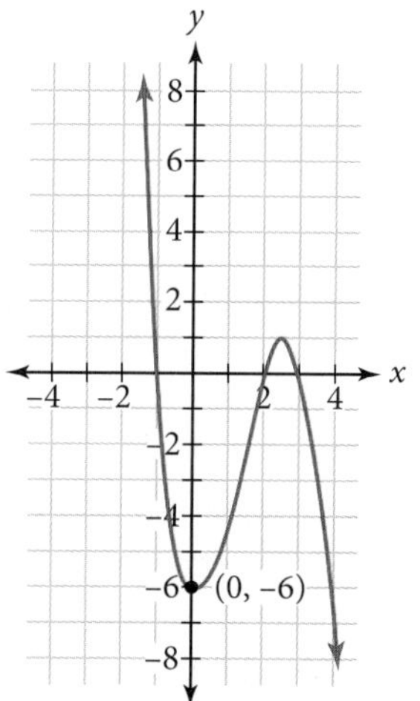

11. Give the degree of each equation, describe generally what each graph will look like, and list all intercepts.

a. $y = -(x + 2)(x - 1)(x - 2)(x + 3)$

b. $y = 2(x + 2)(x - 1)$

c. $y = (x + 2)(x - 5)(x + 1)$

12. One factor of $4x^5 + 12x^4 - 23x^3 - 18x^2 + 37x - 12$ is $2x^2 + x - 3$. Use a rectangle diagram to find the other factor.

13. Write an equation in factored form to represent this cubic function, which touches the x-axis only twice, at $x = -2$ and $x = 1$, and includes $(2, 4)$. The root at $x = 1$ is called a *double root.*

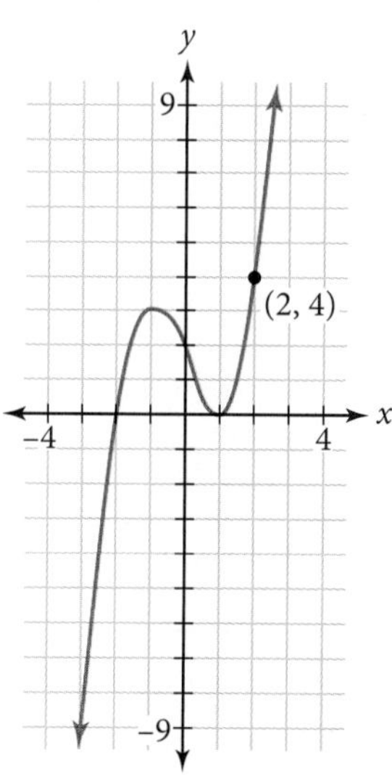

14. Determine whether each table represents a linear function, an exponential function, a cubic function, or a quadratic function. ⓗ

a.

x	y
2	4
5	25
8	64
11	121
14	196

b.

x	y
2	7
5	11
8	15
11	19
14	23

c.

x	y
2	4
5	32
8	256
11	2,048
14	16,384

d.

x	y
2	8
5	125
8	512
11	1,331
14	2,744

Review

15. Perform the indicated operation, and write the result in lowest terms. State any restrictions on the variable. Verify your answers by using your calculator to compare graphs or tables of values.

a. $\frac{x+4}{x+2} \cdot \frac{x^2+4x+4}{x^2-16}$ ⓐ

b. $\frac{x^2+2x}{x^2-4} \div \frac{x^2}{x^2-6x+8}$

c. $\frac{x}{x^2+6x+9} + \frac{1}{x+3}$ ⓐ

d. $\frac{x-1}{x^2-1} - \frac{4}{x+1}$

16. The table shows hourly compensation costs in 15 countries for 1980, 1990, and 2000. Use the list commands on your calculator to do this statistical analysis.

a. Choose at least three countries and graph the hourly compensation costs for those countries over time. Write a paragraph describing the trends you notice and the conclusions you draw.

b. Which of the 15 countries had the largest increase in compensation costs from 1980 to 2000? Which country had the smallest?

c. Create three box plots that compare the compensation costs for the three years. Write a brief paragraph analyzing your graph.

Hourly Compensation Costs (in U.S. dollars) for Production Workers

Country	1980	1990	2000
Australia	8.47	13.24	14.47
Canada	8.67	15.95	16.05
Denmark	10.83	18.04	21.49
France	8.94	15.49	15.66
Germany	12.21	21.81	22.99
Hong Kong	1.51	3.23	5.63
Israel	3.79	8.55	12.86
Italy	8.15	17.45	14.01
Japan	5.52	12.80	22.00
Luxembourg	11.54	16.04	17.70
Mexico	2.21	1.58	2.08
Spain	5.89	11.38	10.78
Sri Lanka	0.22	0.35	0.48
Taiwan	1.02	3.90	5.85
United States	9.87	14.91	19.72

(U.S. Bureau of Labor Statistics, in *The New York Times Almanac 2004*, p. 510) [Data sets: **HCC80, HCC90, HCC00**]

17. In Lesson 8.1, Exercise 11, you learned about closure. Is the set of polynomials closed under addition? Subtraction? Multiplication? Division? In complete sentences, explain what your answers mean.

18. The *girth* of a box is the distance completely around the box in one direction—that is, the length of a string that wraps around the box. Shippers put a maximum limit on the girth of a box rather than trying to limit its length, width, and height. Suppose you must ship a box with girth 120 cm in one direction and 160 cm in another direction.

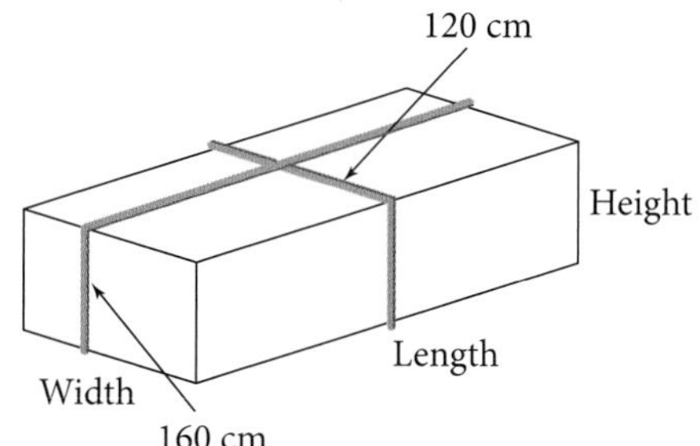

a. If the height of the box is 10 cm, what is the width of the box? @

b. If the height of the box is 10 cm, what is the length of the box?

c. What is the volume of the box described in 18a and b?

d. If the height is 15 cm, what are the other two dimensions and what is the volume of the box?

e. If the height is x cm, find an expression for the width of the box. @

f. If the height is x cm, find an expression for the length of the box.

g. Using your answers to 18e and f, write an equation for the volume of the box. @

h. What are the roots of the equation you wrote in 18g, and what do they tell you?

i. Find the dimensions of a box with volume 48,488 cm^3.

CHAPTER 8 REVIEW

In this chapter you learned about **quadratic functions.** You learned that they model **projectile motion** and the acceleration due to **gravity.** You discovered important connections between the **roots** and the ***x*-intercepts** of quadratic equations and graphs. You learned how to use the three different forms of quadratic equations:

General form	$y = ax^2 + bx + c$
Vertex form	$y = a(x - h)^2 + k$
Factored form	$y = a(x - r_1)(x - r_2)$ or $y = ax(x - r_2)$ if $r_1 = 0$

The quadratic expression $ax^2 + bx + c$ is a type of **polynomial** because it is the sum of many **terms** or **monomials.** The vertex form gives you information about the **line of symmetry** of the parabola. The factored form shows you the roots of the equation. The **zero-product property** tells you that if the polynomial equals zero, then one of the **binomial** factors, $(x - r_1)$ or $(x - r_2)$, must equal zero. The roots r_1 and r_2 are also called **zeros** of the quadratic function. You learned to expand the vertex and factored forms to the general form by combining like terms.

You first learned to locate solutions to quadratic equations using calculator tables and graphs. You then learned to solve equations symbolically by one of three methods: factor with rectangle diagrams, **complete the square,** or use the **quadratic formula.**

To use the quadratic formula, $x = \frac{-b \pm \sqrt{b^2 - 4ac}}{2a}$, you identified the values of a, b, and c for the **trinomial** $ax^2 + bx + c$. You also learned to calculate the **discriminant,** $b^2 - 4ac$, and saw that it gives information about the number of solutions to the equation.

You saw that solutions to quadratic equations often contain **radical expressions.** You learned that the square root of a negative number does not result in a **real number.** In the last lesson you studied the graphs of higher degree polynomials and operations with polynomials.

Exercises

You will need your graphing calculator for Exercises **9** and **10.**

@ **Answers are provided for all exercises in this set.**

1. State whether each statement is true or false. If it is false, change the right side to make it true, but keep it in the same form. That is, if the statement is in factored form, write your corrected version in factored form.

a. $x^2 + 5x - 24 \stackrel{?}{=} (x + 3)(x - 8)$

b. $2(x - 1)^2 + 3 \stackrel{?}{=} 2x^2 + x + 1$

c. $(x + 3)^2 \stackrel{?}{=} x^2 + 9$

d. $(x + 2)(2x - 5) \stackrel{?}{=} 2x^2 - x - 10$

2. The equation of the graph at right is

$y = -2(x + 5)^2 + 4$

Describe the transformations of the parent function $y = x^2$ that give this parabola.

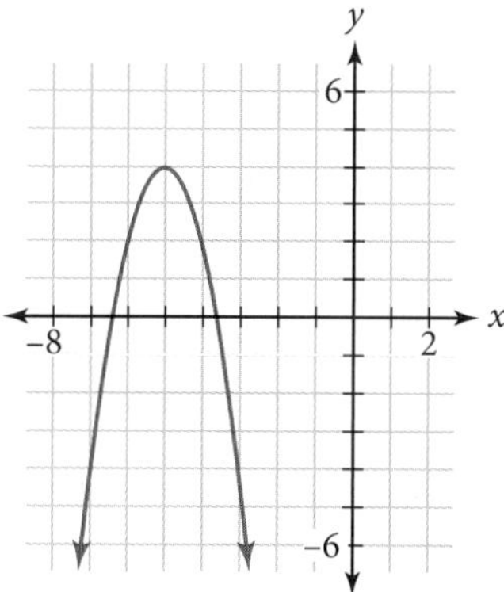

3. Write an equation for each graph. Choose the form that best fits the information given.

a.

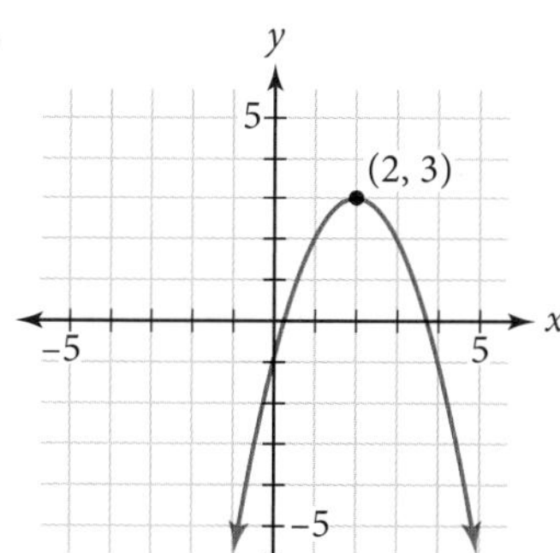

b.

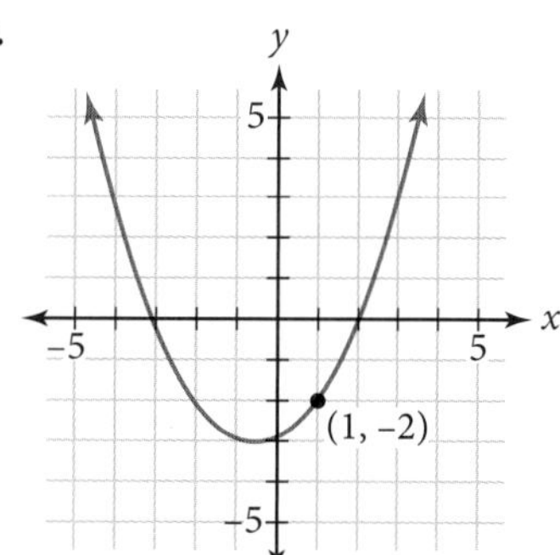

4. Write an equation in the form $y = a(x - h)^2 + k$ for each graph.

a.

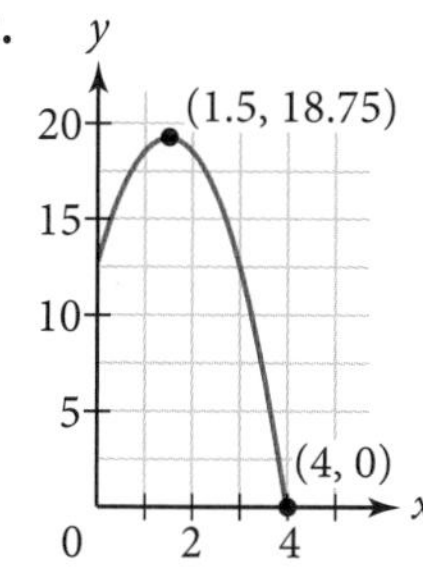

b.

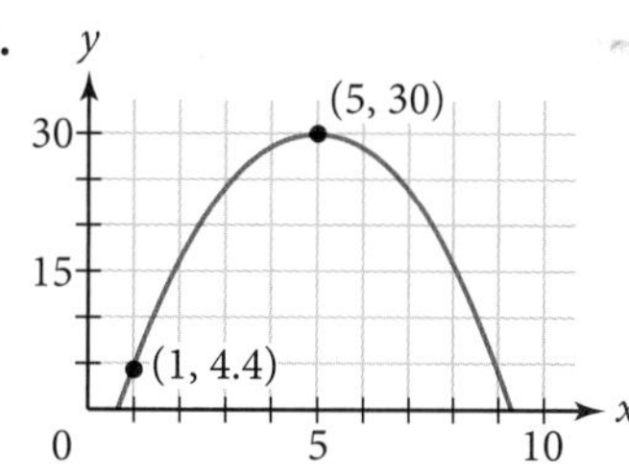

5. Use the zero-product property to solve each equation.

a. $(2w + 9)(w - 3) = 0$

b. $(2x + 5)(x - 7) = 0$

6. Write an equation of a parabola that satisfies the given conditions.

a. The vertex is $(1, -4)$, and one of its x-intercepts is 3.

b. The x-intercepts are -1.5 and $\frac{1}{3}$.

7. Solve each equation by completing the square. Show each step. Leave your answer in radical form.

a. $x^2 + 6x - 9 = 13$

b. $3x^2 - 24x + 27 = 0$

8. Solve each equation by using the quadratic formula. Determine whether there are real-number solutions. Leave your answer in radical form.

a. $5x^2 - 13x + 18 = 0$

b. $-3x^2 + 7x + 9 = 0$

9. Given the equation $-\frac{1}{2}x + 1 = x^2 + 2x + 1$

a. Write a system of equations related to the equation.

b. Solve the system of equations by graphing.

c. Solve the system of equations algebraically.

10. APPLICATION The function $f(x) = 0.0015x(150 - x)$ models the rate at which the population of fish grows in a large aquarium. The x-value is the number of fish, and the $f(x)$-value is the rate of increase in the number of fish per week.

a. Find $f(60)$, and give a real-world meaning for this value.

b. For what values of x does $f(x) = 0$? What do these values represent?

c. How many fish are there when the population is growing fastest?

d. What is the maximum number of fish the aquarium can support?

e. Graph this function.

11. A toy rocket blasts off from ground level. After 0.5 s it is 8.8 ft high. It hits the ground after 1.6 s. Write an equation in factored form to model the height of the rocket as a function of time.

12. Name values of c so that $y = x^2 - 6x + c$ satisfies each condition given. Use the discriminant, $b^2 - 4ac$, or translate the graph of $y = x^2 - 6x$ to help you.

a. The graph of the equation has no x-intercepts.

b. The graph of the equation has exactly one x-intercept.

c. The graph of the equation has two x-intercepts.

13. Use the quadratic formula to find the roots of each equation.

a. $x^2 + 10x - 6 = 0$

b. $3x^2 - 8x + 5 = 0$

14. Perform the indicated operations. Write your answers in general form.

a. $(5x^2 + 2x + 1) + (3x^2 - 4x + 1)$

b. $(x^2 + 2x + 3) - (6x^2 - x^2 + 3)$

c. $(2x^3 + 4x^2 - 11) + (2x^2 + 5x + 2x^3 - 9)$

d. $(x^2 + 7x^3 - 10) - (3x^2 - 5x + 2 - 7x^3)$

15. Use a rectangle diagram to factor each expression.

a. $x^2 + 7x + 12$

b. $x^2 - 14x + 49$

c. $x^2 + 3x - 28$

c. $x^2 - 81$

Take Another Look

In this chapter you have encountered many equations, such as $x^2 = -4$, that have no real solution. The solutions to these equations exist in another set of numbers called **imaginary numbers.** To find the solution to $x^2 = -4$, mathematicians write $x = 2i$ or $x = -2i$. The symbol i represents the imaginary unit.

Express i as a square root of a negative number. (*Hint*: If $2i = \sqrt{-4}$ and $3i = \sqrt{-9}$, what does $1i$ equal?) What happens if you multiply i by itself to find i^2? Use this result to find i^3 and i^4. What happens if you keep multiplying by i?

Use the pattern you discovered to calculate i^{10}, i^{25}, and i^{100}.

Assessing What You've Learned

WRITE IN YOUR JOURNAL Add to your journal by answering one of these prompts:

- There are many ways to solve quadratic equations—calculator tables and graphs, factoring, completing the square, and the quadratic formula. Which method do you like best? Do you always use the same method?
- Compare each form of a quadratic equation—general, vertex, and factored. What information does each form tell you? How can you convert an equation from one form to another?

ORGANIZE YOUR NOTEBOOK Choose your best graph of a parabola from this chapter. Label the vertex, roots, line of symmetry, and y-intercept. Show the equation for the graph in each quadratic form—general, vertex, and factored.

GIVE A PRESENTATION Work with a partner or in a group to create your own problem about projectile motion. It can be about the height of a ball, the path of a rocket, or some other motion. If possible, conduct an experiment to collect data. Decide which information will be given and which form of quadratic equation to use. Make up a question about your problem. Put the problem and its solution on a poster, and make a presentation to the class.

PERFORMANCE ASSESSMENT Show a classmate, a family member, or your teacher that you can solve any quadratic equation. Demonstrate how to find solutions with a calculator (graph or table) and by hand (factoring, completing the square, or using the quadratic formula).

Selected Hints and Answers

This section contains hints and answers for exercises marked with ⓗ or ⓐ in each set of Exercises.

LESSON 0.1

2a. $\frac{1}{8}$; $\frac{1}{16} + \frac{1}{16}$ or $2 \times \frac{1}{16}$

2d. $\frac{7}{625}$; $\frac{1}{625} + \frac{1}{625} + \frac{1}{625} + \frac{1}{625} + \frac{1}{625} + \frac{1}{625} + \frac{1}{625}$ or $7 \times \frac{1}{625}$

3a. $\frac{1}{4} + \frac{1}{16} = \frac{5}{16}$ **3c.** $9 \times \frac{1}{81} = \frac{1}{9}$

4a.

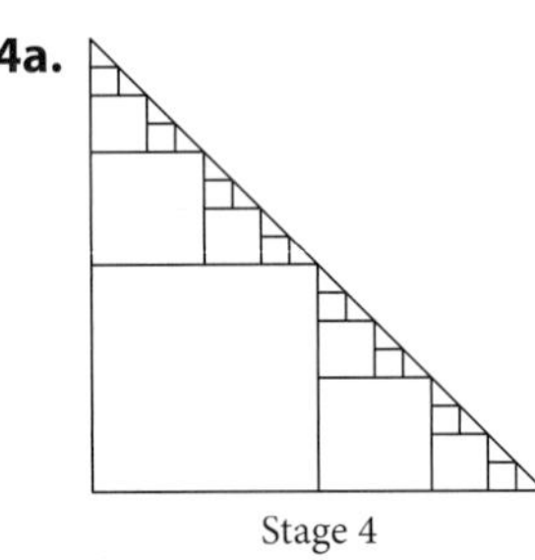

Stage 4

4b. *Hint:* The length of the side of the square is half the length of the base. The area of a triangle is $\frac{1}{2}b \cdot h$, or $\frac{1}{2}b^2$, because $b = h$ in this case.

4c. 48

5b. *Hint:* The smallest triangle shown is $\frac{1}{64}$. Shade only triangles that are $\frac{1}{16}$ of the area.

7a. $\frac{1}{4} \times \frac{1}{4} \times 32 = \frac{32}{16} = 2$

10a. $8 \div 4 = 2$ **10b.** $8 \times \frac{1}{4} = 2$

10c. Essentially, they are the same.

10d. $8 \times \frac{3}{4} = 6$

12. *Hint:* Draw a picture.

LESSON 0.2

1a. 5^4

2a. $3 \times 3 \times 3 \times 3$; $3 \cdot 3 \cdot 3 \cdot 3$; $3(3)(3)(3)$

3a. 3^3

6a. 25 or 5^2

7a. 10

7d. *Hint:* Look at the number of branches in each stage.

11b. $\frac{29}{64}$

LESSON 0.3

1b. $\frac{25}{9}$; 2.78

5a. *Hint:* For Stage 1, the length is the total number of segments, 5, times the length of each segment, $\frac{1}{4}$. Continue this pattern recursively.

11a. 4

LESSON 0.4

6b. Subtract the number with the smaller absolute value from the number with the larger absolute value. The sign of the answer is the sign of the number with the larger absolute value.

7a. In the first recursion, he should get $-0.2 \cdot 2 = -0.4$, not $+0.4$. His arithmetic when evaluating $0.4 - 4$ was correct. In the second recursion, he used the wrong value (-3.6 instead of -4.4) because of his previous error. His arithmetic was also incorrect, because $-0.2 \cdot -3.6 = +0.72$, not -0.72. His arithmetic when evaluating $-0.72 - 4$ was correct.

8a.

Starting value	2	−1	10
First recursion	−1.8	−2.1	−1
Second recursion	−2.18	−2.21	−2.1
Third recursion	−2.218	−2.221	−2.21
⋮			

8b. yes; about -2.222

9c. The result is $\frac{1}{3}$. The value $\frac{1}{3}$ is a fixed point for this expression.

12b. 0.2 **12d.** 3

CHAPTER 0 REVIEW

1a. iii **1b.** v **1c.** ii

1d. iv **1e.** i

2a. 72 **2b.** 290 **2c.** -10

2d. 312 **2e.** $2.1\overline{6}$ **2f.** -34

3a. $\frac{1}{3} \times \frac{1}{3} \times \frac{1}{3}$

3b. $\frac{2}{3} \times \frac{2}{3} \times \frac{2}{3} \times \frac{2}{3}$

3c. 1.2×1.2

3d. $16 \times 16 \times 16 \times 16 \times 16$

3e. $2 \times 2 \times 2 \times 2 \times 2 \times 2 \times 2$

4a. $\frac{1}{16} + \frac{1}{16} + \frac{1}{16} = \frac{3}{16}$

4b. $\frac{1}{9} + \frac{1}{9} + \frac{1}{81} + \frac{1}{81} = \frac{20}{81}$

4c. $\frac{1}{4} + \frac{1}{16} + \frac{1}{64} + \frac{1}{64} = \frac{11}{32}$

5a. 10 **5b.** 17 **5c.** $\frac{-1}{15}$

5d. 11 **5e.** 16 **5f.** 19

5g. $-6\frac{1}{2}$

6a.

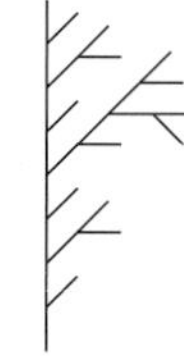

Stage 3

A branch is added at the midpoint of each of the newest segments, with half the length, at a 45° clockwise rotation.

6b.

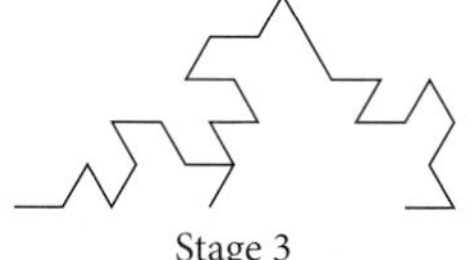

Stage 3

A "bottomless" equilateral triangle is built on the "right" half of segments.

6c.

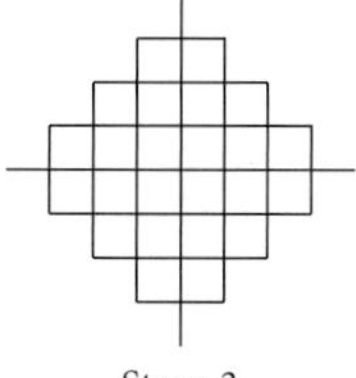

Stage 3

Each new segment is crossed at its midpoint by a centered perpendicular segment of equal length.

6d.

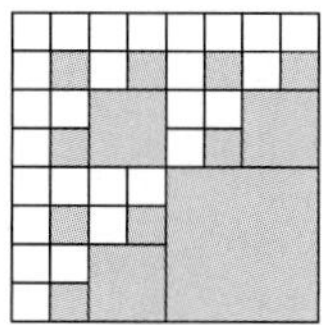

Stage 3

Each unshaded square is divided horizontally and vertically to create four congruent squares; the bottom-right square is shaded.

7. The attractor is 5.

8a. See below.

8b. $\left(\frac{7}{5}\right)^{20} \approx 836.68$

LESSON 1.1

1. *Hint:* Begin by ordering the numbers from least to greatest.

4a. **Travel Time to School**

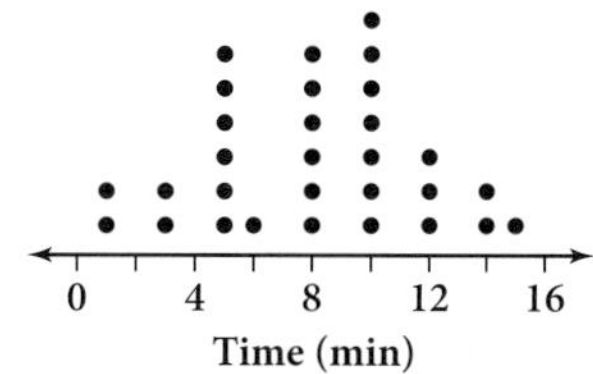

4c. *Hint:* Multiply each time value by the number of students.

6d. i

8. a bar graph; because the information falls into categories, is not numerical data, and cannot be scaled on a number line

9a. possible answer: Jonesville's Varsity Basketball Team

11d. -1

12a. 18;

Doubles of 225	450	900	1800	3600	7200
Doubles of 1	2	4	8	16	32

LESSON 1.2

1a. mean and median: 6; mode: 5

1c. mean: 10.25; median: 9; no mode

4a. mean: 262.2 ft; median: 215 ft

7. *Hint:* $\frac{53 + 53 + 53 + x + x}{5} = 50$

8a. *(Chapter 0 Review)*

	Total length		
Stage number	**Multiplication form**	**Exponent form**	**Decimal form**
0	1	1	1
1	$7 \cdot \left(\frac{1}{5}\right)$	$7^1 \cdot \left(\frac{1}{5}\right)^1 = \left(\frac{7}{5}\right)^1 = \frac{7}{5}$	1.4
2	$7 \cdot 7 \cdot \left(\frac{1}{5}\right) \cdot \left(\frac{1}{5}\right)$	$7^2 \cdot \left(\frac{1}{5}\right)^2 = \left(\frac{7}{5}\right)^2 = \frac{49}{25}$	1.96

10a. Multiply the mean by 10; together they weigh approximately 15,274 lb.

10b. Five of the fish caught weigh 1449 lb or less, and five weigh 1449 lb or more.

11a. *Hint:* The data set has five values, with the middle value equal to 12.

13a. A dot plot may be most appropriate for the numeric data. However, if each value was translated into years (divide by 12), you could make a bar graph or pictograph with ages as categories.

LESSON 1.3

1a. 5, 10, 23, 37, 50

1c. 14, 22.5, 26, 41, 47

2b. i. 0, 1, 1.5, 3, 7; ii. 64, 75, 80, 86, 93

5a. Quartiles are the boundaries dividing a data set into four groups, or quarters, with the same number of values.

5b. the range

6c. 2.4

8b. 23 points

9a. For men, the mean salary is approximately \$943.19, and the five-number summary is 427, 655, 828, 1248, 1696; for women, the mean salary is approximately \$722.56, and the five-number summary is 376, 490, 766, 935.5, 1088.

Median Weekly Earnings, 2008

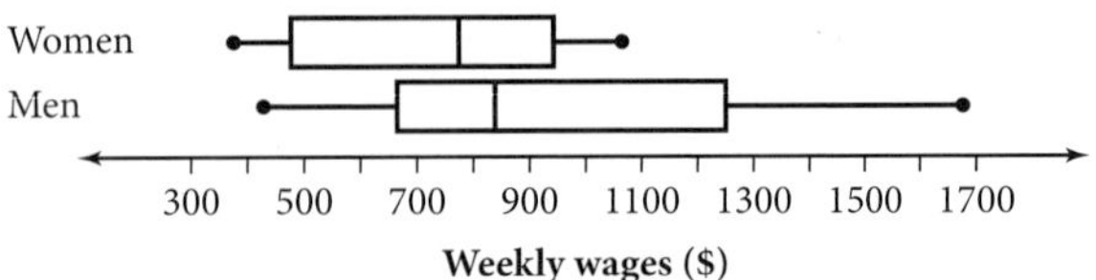

13a. 65 in., 3 in., 68 in.

13g. 3.240 in., 1.414 in., 3.536 in.

15a. 76 million

15c. $10\frac{1}{2}$ pawprints

LESSON 1.4

1a. *Hint:* Find the sum of the bin heights.

1c. none

3a. 80

3b. Approximately $\frac{1}{4}$ of the countries had a life expectancy between approximately 71 yr and 75 yr.

5b. Ring Finger Length

6	0 5 5
7	0 0 0 5
8	5

Key

6 | 0 means 6.0 cm

7a. The bin heights should be about the same, with about 16 or 17 in each of six bins.

8a. *Hint:* The median, Q_1, and Q_2 are all equal to 7.

8d. *Hint:* The minimum and Q_1 are the same value. The maximum and Q_3 are the same value.

10a. \$1.50

11a. Ida weighed the apples from the market, which are more uniform in weight, and Mac weighed the backyard apples, whose weights vary more widely.

12a. Hospital A's histogram is mounded toward the left. Hospital B's histogram is mounded toward the right. Hospital C's histogram has all bins of equal height. Hospital D's histogram is mounded in the middle.

LESSON 1.5

1. Type AB = 3,750; Type B = 9,000; Type A = 30,000; Type O = 32,250

2. *Hint:* Find the sum of each data set, then compare each data point to the sum.

3. No; the total height of all the bars must be 100%.

5b. **Comparing Chloe's Candy with the Manufacturer's**

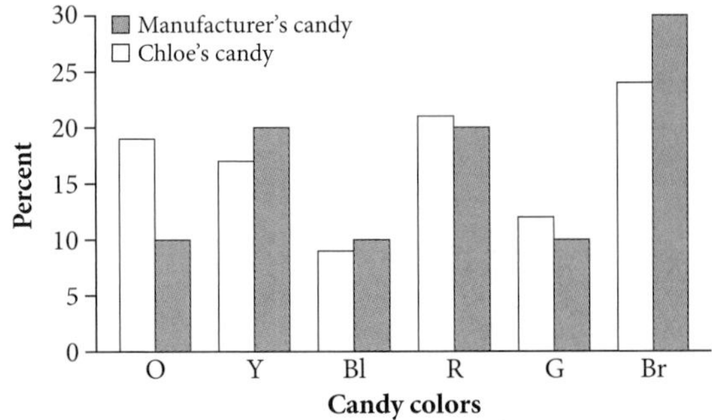

Chloe's bag of candy had the same dominant color as the graph from the manufacturer, and her least common color was one of the least manufactured. But the distributions are not very close.

6a. *Hint:* You must first find the total number of students.

7b. i

13. *Hint:* Range = Maximum − Minimum

LESSON 1.7

1.

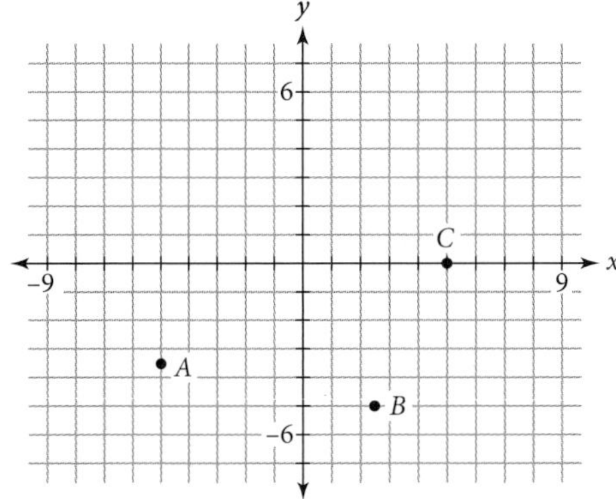

4a. about 2 m

4b. about 5 s

4c. about 2.7 m

4d. between 0 and 1 s, and between 4.5 and 5.5 s

10a. 8:06

10c. 12 min

LESSON 1.8

5. *Hint:* Plot the points and compare them to the line where *actual temperature* = *estimated temperature.*

7a. (12, 16)

7b. (18, 13)

7d. **Estimated Prices vs. Actual Prices**

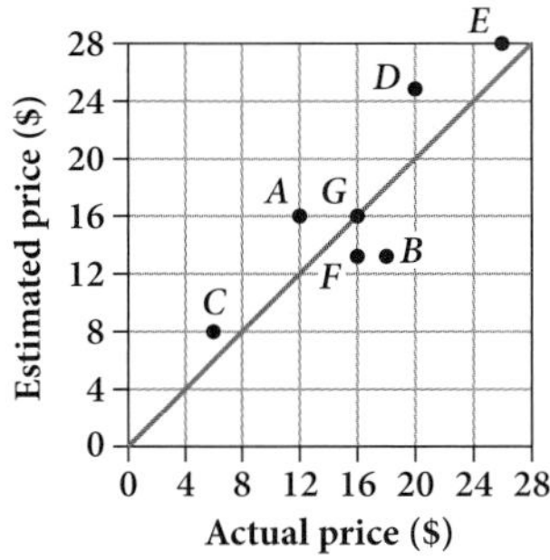

9b. These states also have high verbal scores. The verbal scores are not as high as the math scores.

11a. Answers will vary. The mean of the values is 125.0 cm, and the median is 125.3 cm.

11c. Answers will vary. The range of measures is 123.3 to 126.5. This could be written 124.9 ± 1.6 cm.

12a. {1, 3, 3, 3, 4, 5, 6}

CHAPTER 1 REVIEW

1. possible answer: {9, 11, 14, 16, 19, 21, 22}

2a. Mean: 41.5; divide the sum of the numbers by 14. Median: 40; list the numbers in ascending order and find the mean of the two middle numbers. Mode: 36; find the most frequently occurring number.

2b. 27, 36, 40, 46, 58

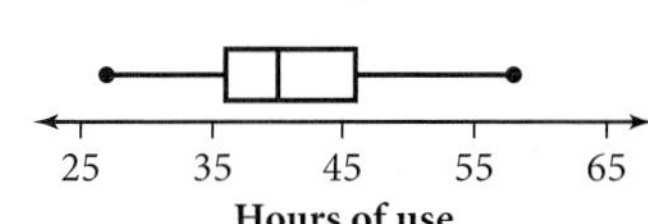

3a.

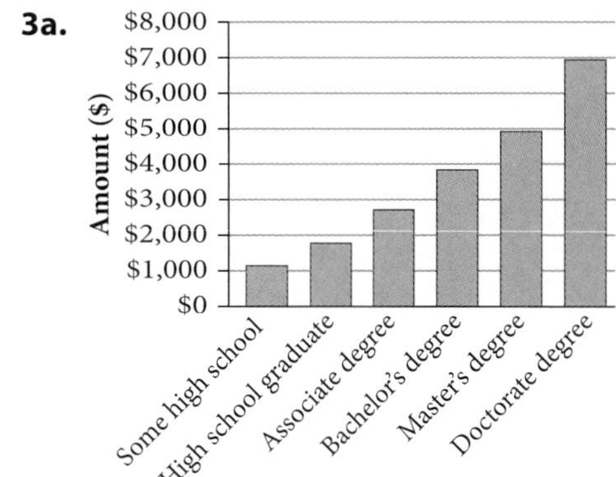

3b. greatest jump: from a master's degree to a doctorate ($1993); smallest difference: from not finishing high school to a high school diploma ($612)

4a. **2009 NCAA Women's Tournament Top Scorers**

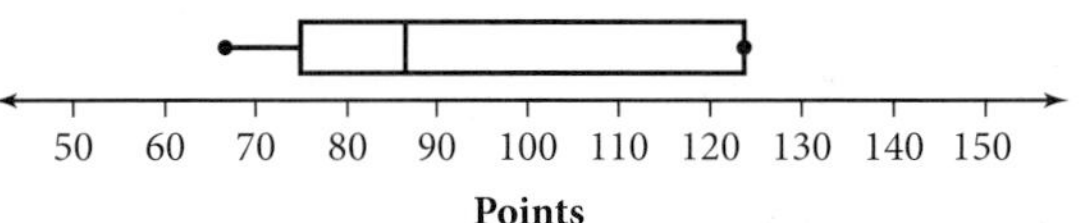

4b. No real outlier. Possible answer 68 pts. (Prince)

4c. Choices will vary; mean: 96; median: 87; modes: 124.

5a. Mean: approximately 154; median: 121; there is no mode.

5b. Bin widths may vary.

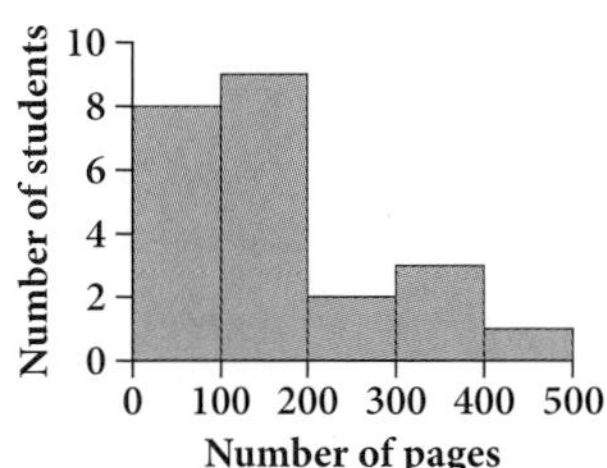

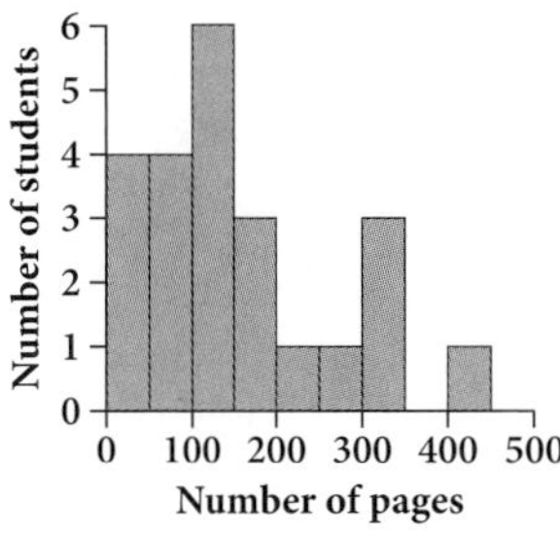

Selected Hints and Answers

5c. **Pages Read in Current Book**

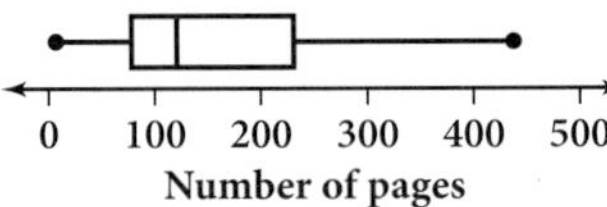

5d. Possible answer: Most of the students questioned had read fewer than 200 pages, with a fairly even distribution between 0 and 200.

6a. **Invention Dates**

Estimated year: 1900, 1920, 1940, 1960, 1980, 2000

Actual year: 1860, 1880, 1900, 1920, 1940, 1960, 1980, 2000

6b. (1952, 1945), (1985, 1980)

6c. $y = x$, where x represents actual year and y represents estimated year

7a. Degrees for each sector, rounded to the nearest degree: China 75°, India 60°,United States 16°, Indonesia 13°, Brazil 10°, Other 185°; degrees add up to less than 360° because of rounding.

7b.

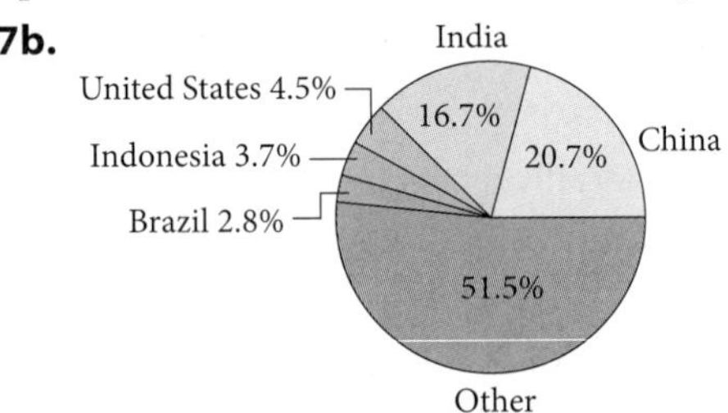

8a. between points A and B

8b. Kayo was not moving; perhaps she was resting.

8c. Possible answer: Kayo started out jogging fast but had to rest for a few minutes. Then she jogged much slower until she had to rest again. She finally got the energy to jog all the way home at a steady pace without stopping.

9a. 2,850,000

9b. See below.

9c. **The Ten Most Populated U.S. Cities, 2000**

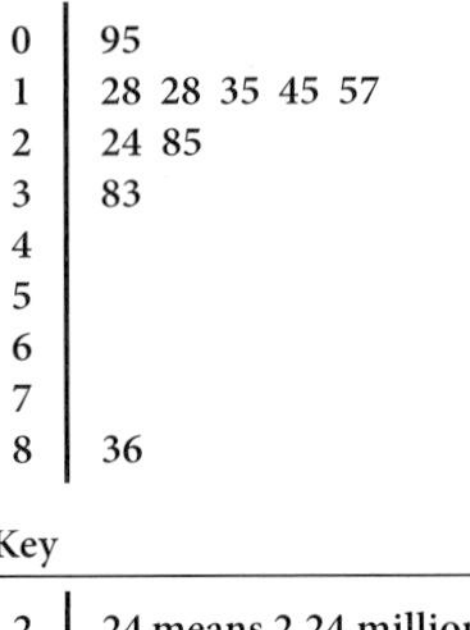

Stem	Leaf
0	95
1	28 28 35 45 57
2	24 85
3	83
4	
5	
6	
7	
8	36

Key

2 | 24 means 2.24 million

9d. **The Ten Most Populated U.S. Cities, 2008**

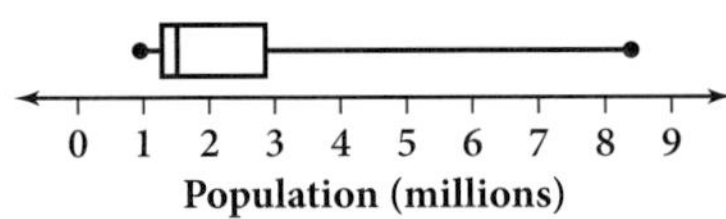

9e. The bar graph helps show how each city compares with the others, because they remain identified by name. The stem plot shows distribution but also shows actual values. The box plot shows distribution and a clustering between 1 and 1.4 million but does not show individual city names or populations.

10a. 416.875 min

10b. 425 min

10c. 480 min

9b. *(Chapter 1 Review)*

Ten Most Populated U.S. Cities, 2008

Population (millions): 0, 2, 4, 6, 8, 10

City: Chicago, Dallas, Houston, Los Angeles, New York, Philadelphia, Phoenix, San Antonio, San Diego, San Jose

11. Answers will vary.

11a. Entries in the body of the table are joint frequencies. Any of the numbers below are joint frequencies. A sample description is the number of males (or females) that use a particular mode of transportation, such as 24 males walk to school.

	Male	Female	Totals
Walk	24	17	
Car	35	38	
Bus	58	45	
Cycle	22	8	
Totals			

11b. Marginal frequencies are the Totals rows and columns. Any of the numbers below are marginal frequencies. A sample description is that 41 of the students surveyed walk to school.

	Male	Female	Totals
Walk			41
Car			73
Bus			103
Cycle			30
Totals	139	108	247

11c. The relative frequencies in the body of the table compared to the total of the survey are the conditional frequencies. Any of the numbers below are conditional frequencies. A sample description is that one-tenth of those surveyed were males who walk to school.

	Male	Female	Totals
Walk	.10	.07	
Car	.14	.15	
Bus	.23	.18	
Cycle	.09	.03	
Totals			

11d. If we look only at the marginal frequencies in the Totals row, we might observe that the majority of students ride the bus or ride in a car to get to school. The joint frequencies show a small percentage of females who cycle to school.

12a. median = 75 packages; IQR = 19 packages

12b. mean ≈ 80.9 packages; standard deviation ≈ 24.6 packages

12c. **Hot Chocolate Mix**

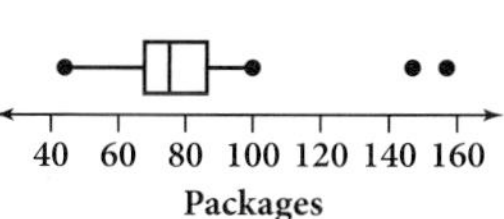

five-number summary: 44, 67.5, 75, 86.5, 158; outliers: 147, 158

12d. **Hot Chocolate Mix**

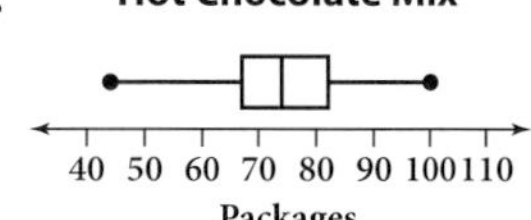

five-number summary: 44, 67, 74, 82, 100

12e. median = 74 packages; IQR = 15 packages; mean ≈ 74.7 packages; standard deviation ≈ 12.4 packages

12f. The mean and standard deviation are calculated from all data values, so outliers affect these statistics significantly. The median and IQR, in contrast, are defined by position and not greatly affected by outliers.

LESSON 2.1

1a. $\frac{9}{14}$ **1c.** $\frac{4}{3}$

2. *Hint:* To write a rate like 9.6 miles per gallon as a fraction, separate the units. "Per" and "of every" indicate division. So 9.6 miles per gallon can be written $\frac{9.6 \text{ miles}}{1 \text{ gallon}}$.

2a. $\frac{257 \text{ mi}}{1 \text{ h}}$

2b. $\frac{10 \text{ parts capsaicin}}{1{,}000{,}000 \text{ parts water}}$, or $\frac{1 \text{ part capsaicin}}{100{,}000 \text{ parts water}}$

2c. $\frac{350 \text{ women-owned firms}}{1000 \text{ firms}}$, or $\frac{7 \text{ women-owned firms}}{20 \text{ firms}}$

3a. 30 **3c.** 16

4a. *Hint:* Multiply by 30 to undo the division.

4c. $S = 73.5$

5a. *Hint:* Solve the proportion $\frac{1.5}{4} = \frac{55}{x}$.

6b. *Hint:* Solve the proportion $\frac{85}{100} = \frac{x}{7.38}$.

7. $\frac{1}{8} = \frac{3000}{P}$; $P = 24{,}000$

9a. 3 carbon, 6 hydrogen, 1 oxygen

9b. You will need 3(470), or 1410 atoms of carbon and 6(470), or 2820 atoms of hydrogen.

9c. 500 molecules; use all the hydrogen atoms, 1500 atoms of carbon, and 500 atoms of oxygen.

LESSON 2.2

1a. 32% of what number is 24?

3a. $\frac{80}{d} = \frac{125}{100}$

5a. *Hint:* Solve the proportion $\frac{5}{75} = \frac{250}{x}$.

6a. Marie should win over half the games.

6b. $\frac{\text{28 games won by Marie}}{\text{28 + 19 total games}} = \frac{M}{12}$; $M = 7.15$ or 7 games

6c. $\frac{19}{47} = \frac{30}{G}$; $G \approx 74$ games

9b. $\frac{5}{8}$

10b. 9

10c. younger than 42, 44, 45, 66, 67, and older than 69

LESSON 2.3

1a. $x = 49.4$

2. 227 g

3. 1.76 oz

5. 159 cm

7. 4.72 in.

8c. *Hint:* Multiply: $\frac{50\text{ m}}{1\text{ s}} \cdot \frac{1\text{ km}}{1000\text{ m}} \cdot \frac{60\text{ s}}{1\text{ min}} \cdot \frac{60\text{ min}}{1\text{ h}}$.

9. *Hint:* First find the total number of seconds in 3 minutes 53.43 seconds.

10a. $\frac{3\text{ lb}}{30\text{ days}} = 0.1$ lb per day

10c. *Hint:* Find a common denominator and compare ratios.

11b. 90 m

13a. fifteen 12 oz cans to make 960 oz

13c. $\frac{\textit{number of ounces of concentrate}}{\textit{number of ounces of lemonade}} = \frac{12}{64}$

14. If the profits are divided in proportion to the number of students in the clubs, the Math Club would get \$288, leaving \$192 for the Chess Club.

LESSON 2.4

1a. 40

2a. 88

3. The first missing value in the table is 2.8.

4a. Divide by 3.5 to undo the multiplication; $x = 4$.

9b. *Hint:* The cost of corn at Market A can be described by the equation $y = 0.179x$.

10b. $y = 2.2x$ **10c.** 2.95 kg **10d.** 7920 lb

10e. 100 lb = $45.\overline{45}$ kg; 100 kg = 220 lb

11a. *Hint:* Evaluate the ratio $\frac{150}{93}$.

13a. *Hint:* Solve the proportion $\frac{3\text{ mi}}{1.5\text{ h}} = \frac{x}{1\text{h}}$.

13e. 2 mi/h; this represents the constant walking speed.

13f. $d = 2t$, where d is distance traveled in miles and t is travel time in hours.

14a. $D = 5t$, where D is the distance traveled in inches and t is the time elapsed in minutes.

14d. 163.2 min, or 2.72 h

16a. 81.25 mi/h

17a. \$2.49 per box, 42¢ per bar, \$2.99 per box, 25¢ per ounce

17c. 1.495 oz per bar

LESSON 2.5

1a. $y = \frac{15}{x}$

2a. *Hint:* Solve $4 = \frac{k}{3}$ for k, then substitute $(4, y)$ and k into $y = \frac{k}{x}$.

5a. 3 h

6a. *Hint:* Solve $65 \cdot 4 = 2.5 \cdot x$.

7a. inverse variation; $y = \frac{24}{x}$ or $xy = 24$

8a. $62.\overline{3}$ N, 93.5 N, and 187 N

9b. $15 \cdot M = 20 \cdot 7$; $M \approx 9.3$ kg

12a. 2 atm **12c.** 0.1 L

LESSON 2.7

1. 6 Across: 143/42

1. 10 Down: $40 \cdot 529$

3a. First multiply 16 by 4.5, then add 9.

5a. See bottom of page 599.

5b. At Stages 6 and 7; the original number has been subtracted.

5d. $\frac{2(n-3)+4}{2} - n + 4$ or $-3\left[\frac{2(n-3)+4}{2} - n\right]$

6a. See bottom of page 599.

LESSON 2.8

1a. Subtract 32.

4b. 5

7a. 3

7b. Start with 3 and see if you get the answer 3.

7d. The final result is always the original number no matter what number you choose.

10a. -2.6 **10d.** 75

12a. *Hint:* Substitute $t = 60$.

14d. 35 **14g.** -19

CHAPTER 2 REVIEW

1a. $n = 8.75$

1b. $w = 84.6$

1c. $k = 5\frac{1}{6}$, or $5.1\overline{6}$

2. possible answers:

$\frac{7\text{ bh}}{5\text{ h}} = \frac{30\text{ bh}}{x\text{ h}}$; $\frac{7\text{ bh}}{30\text{ bh}} = \frac{5\text{ h}}{x\text{ h}}$; $\frac{5\text{ h}}{7\text{ bh}} = \frac{x\text{ h}}{30\text{ bh}}$; $\frac{30\text{ bh}}{7\text{ bh}} = \frac{x\text{ h}}{5\text{ h}}$

3a. Possible points include (2, 1), (3, 1.5), (4, 2), (5, 2.5), (6, 3), (7, 3.5), (8, 4).

3b. All points appear to lie on a line.

4a. 75 ft

4b. 0.52 ft/mo

5. 1365 shih rice; 169 shih millet

6a. If x represents the weight in kilograms and y represents weight in pounds, one equation is $y = 2.2x$ where 2.2 is the data set's mean ratio of pounds to kilograms.

6b. about 13.6 kg

6c. 55 lb

7a. about 7.5 cm

7b. approximately 17 days

7c. $H = 1.5 \cdot D$, where H represents height in centimeters and D represents time in days

8a. Because the product of the x- and y-values is approximately constant, it is an inverse relationship.

8b. One possibility: $y = \frac{45.5}{x}$; the constant 45.5 is the mean of the products.

8c. $y = \frac{45.5}{32}$, $y \approx 1.4$

9a. directly; $d = 50t$

9b. directly; $d = 1v$, or $d = v$

9c. inversely; $100 = vt$, or $t = \frac{100}{v}$

10a. 2.1875 L

10b. $2.\overline{3}$ atm

10c. $y = \frac{1.75}{x}$

5a. (*Lesson 2.7*)

Stage	Picture	Description
1	n	Pick a number.
2	n -1 -1 -1	Subtract 3.
3	n n -1 -1 -1 -1 -1 -1	Multiply your result by 2.
4	n n -1 -1	Add 4.
5	n -1	Divide by 2.
6	-1	Subtract the original number.
7	$+1$ $+1$ $+1$	Add 4 or multiply by -3.

6a. (*Lesson 2.7*)

Description	Jack's sequence	Nina's sequence
Pick the starting number.	5	3
Multiply by 2.	10	6
Multiply by 3.	30	18
Add 6.	36	24
Divide by 3.	12	8
Subtract your original number.	7	5
Subtract your original number again.	2	2

10d.

11a. Start with a number. Double it. Subtract 1. Multiply by 3. Add 1.

11b. x; $2x$; $2x - 1$; $3(2x - 1)$; $3(2x - 1) + 1$

11c. 4.5, 9, 8, 24, 25 **11d.** The starting value is 4.

12. Start with 1. Add 4, to get 5. Multiply by -3, to get -15. Add 12, to get -3. Divide by 6, to get -0.5. Add 5, to get 4.5.

13.

Equation: $\frac{12 - 3(x + 4)}{6} + 5 = 4$		
Description	**Undo**	**Result**
Pick x.		2
+ (4)	− (4)	6
• (−3)	/ (−3)	− 18
+ (12)	− (12)	− 6
/ (6)	• (6)	− 1
+ (5)	− (5)	4

3

LESSON 3.1

3. $-14.2, -10.5, -6.8, -3.1, 0.6, 4.3$

5a.

Figure number	Perimeter
1	5
2	8
3	11
4	14
5	17

5c. 32

7a. Possible explanation: The smallest square has an area of 1. The next larger white square has an area of 4, which is 3 more than the smallest square. The next larger gray square has an area of 9, which is 5 more than the 4-unit white square.

7b. The recursive routine is 1 ENTER, Ans + 2 ENTER, ENTER, and so on.

7c. 17, the value of the 9th term in the sequence

10a. *Hint:* What do you add to get from -4 to 8? What do you multiply by to get from -4 to 8?

11a. $17 \cdot 7$, or 119 **11b.** 14

11c. Possible answer: There are 14 multiples between 100 and 200. There are also 14 multiples of 7 between 200 and 300, but there are 15 between 300 and 400.

11d. Possible answer: The 4th multiple of 7 is $4 \cdot 7$, or 28; the 5th multiple of 7 is $5 \cdot 7$, or 35; and so on. Recursively, you start with 7 and then continue adding 7.

13a. Press 1 ENTER, Ans · 3 ENTER, ENTER . . . ; the 9th term is 6561.

13b. Press 5 ENTER, Ans · (−1) ENTER, ENTER . . . ; the 123rd term is 5.

LESSON 3.2

2a. {0.5, 1, 1.5, 2, 2.5, 3}; 0.5, Ans + 0.5

2b. {4, 3, 2, 1, 0}; 4, Ans − 1

4d. In 4a, the y-coordinates increase by 7. In 4b, the y-coordinates decrease by 6.

8a. *Hint:* The perimeters of the pentagon tile arrangements for 1–10 tiles are 5, 8, 11, 14, 17, 20, 23, 26, 29, 32.

8f. *Hint:* Can you arrange a design with 1.5 tiles?

9a. Possible answer: {1, 1.38} ENTER, {Ans(1) + 1, Ans(2) + 0.36} ENTER, ENTER, ... The recursive routine keeps track of time and cost for each minute. Apply the routine until you get {7, 3.54}. A 7 min call costs $3.54.

10a. Answers will vary. The graph starts at (0, 5280). The points (0, 5280), (1, 4680), (2, 4080), and (3, 3480) will appear to lie on a line. From (3, 3480) to (8, −1520), the points will appear to lie on a steeper line. The bicyclist ends up 1520 ft past you.

10b. **Bicyclist**

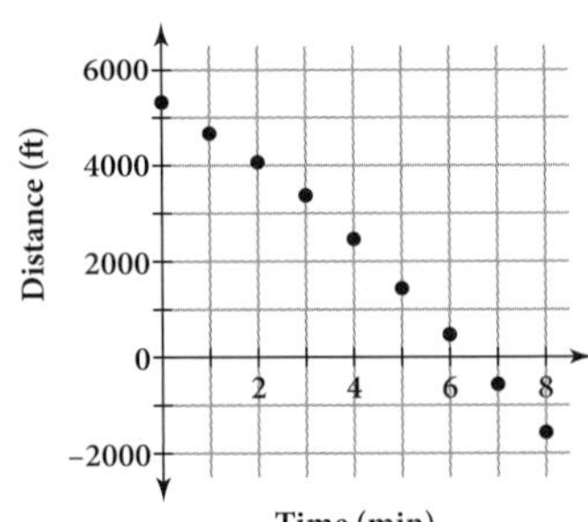

13a. $\frac{9(C + 40)}{5} - 40$

13b. Add 40, multiply by 5, divide by 9, then subtract 40.

LESSON 3.3

1. {0, 4.0} and {Ans(1) + 1, Ans (2) − 0.4}

3. Start at the 0.8 m mark and walk away from the sensor at a constant rate of 0.2 m/s.

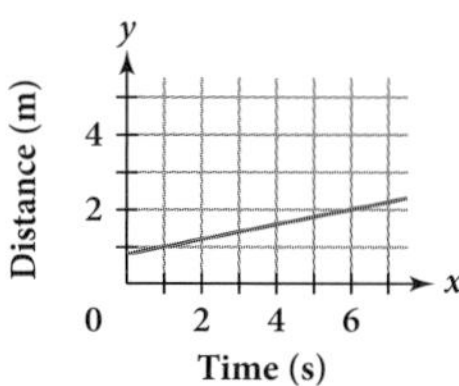

4a. iii, i, iv, ii

6. *Hint:* Convert 1 mi/h to ft/s.

7a. The rate is negative, so the line slopes down to the right.

8b. away; the distance is increasing

8d. *Hint:* Divide the distance Carol traveled by 4 seconds. Include units in your answer.

8e. $\frac{5.5\text{ m}}{0.6\text{ m/s}} = 9.1\bar{6}$ s, or approximately 9 s

8f. The graph is a straight line.

10a. ii

13a. Not possible; the walker would have to be at more than one distance from the sensor at the 3 s mark.

14b. $x = \frac{22}{9}$, or $2.\bar{4}$

15a. *Hint:* To find the total number of days, calculate $2 \cdot 365 + 2 \cdot 30.4 + 2$.

16a. *Hint:* Consumption rate is best measured in gallons/mile.

LESSON 3.4

1a. ii

4a. See below.

6a. $t \approx 0.18$ h

6c. 24 represents the initial number of miles the driver is from his or her destination.

8a. *Hint:* For calories burned per minute, find the common difference between consecutive actual workout calories burned entries.

8b. 400 (ENTER), Ans + 20.7 (ENTER)

8d. $y = 700 + 0x$ or $y = 700$

10a. $s = 5 + 9.8t$ or $s = 9.8t + 5$

10c. 8 s

10d. It doesn't account for air resistance and terminal speed.

13a. $\frac{8}{n} = \frac{15}{100}$, $n \approx 53.3$

14b.

Time (s)	Distance (m)
1	14
2	28
3	42
4	56
5	70
6	84
7	98
8	112
9	126
10	140

17a. The expression equals −4.

Ans − 8	−3
Ans · 4	−12
Ans/3	−4

17b. $y = 14$

4a. *(Lesson 3.4)*

Equation $3(x - 5.2) + 7.8 = 14$			
Description	**Undo**	**Result**	**Equation**
Pick x		≈7.267	$x \approx 7.267$
Subtract 5.2	+5.2	≈2.067	$x - 5.2 \approx 2.067$
Multiply by 3	/3	6.2	$3(x - 5.2) = 6.2$
Add 7.8	−7.8	14	$3(x - 5.2) + 7.8 = 14$

Selected Hints and Answers

LESSON 3.5

1a.

Input x	Output y
20	100
-30	-25
16	90
15	87.5
-12.5	18.75

2b. $t = 15°F$

2c. The wind chill temperature changes by 1.4° for each 1° change in actual temperature.

3a. The rate is negative, so the line goes from the upper left to the lower right.

5a. i. 3.5

5b. *Hint:* For table iii, use the rate of change to work backward from the data pair (2, 20.2) to (0, ?).

5b. i. -6

5c. i. $y = -6 + 3.5x$

5d. i.

X	Y1
0	-6
1	-2.5
2	1
3	4.5
4	8

Y1 = -6+3.5X

7a. The input variable x is the temperature in °F, and the output variable y is the wind chill in °F.

7b. The rate of change is 1.4°. For every 10° increase in temperature, there is a 14° increase in wind chill.

7c. $y = -28 + 1.4x$

8a. *Hint:* To find the rate of change, calculate $\frac{3.4 - 4.0}{2 - 0}$ or $\frac{2.2 - 3.4}{6 - 2}$.

14a. *Hint:* Find the total number of yards in 72 lengths, then convert to feet. How does this compare to the number of feet in a mile, 5280?

15a. $y = 6 + 1.25x$

LESSON 3.6

1a. $2x = 6$

3a.
$$\begin{aligned} 0.1x + 12 - 12 &= 2.2 - 12 \\ 0.1x &= -9.8 \\ \frac{0.1x}{0.1} &= \frac{-9.8}{0.1} \\ x &= -98 \end{aligned}$$

5a. $-\frac{1}{5}$

6a. $\frac{1}{12}$

11a.
$$\begin{aligned} 3 + 2x &= 17 \\ 3 - 3 + 2x &= 17 - 3 \\ 2x &= 14 \\ \frac{2x}{2} &= \frac{14}{2} \\ x &= 7 \end{aligned}$$

11e.
$$\begin{aligned} \frac{4 + 0.01x}{6.2} - 6.2 &= 0 \\ \frac{4 + 0.01x}{6.2} - 6.2 + 6.2 &= 0 + 6.2 \\ \frac{4 + 0.01x}{6.2} &= 6.2 \\ \frac{4 + 0.01x}{6.2} \cdot 6.2 &= 6.2 \cdot 6.2 \\ 4 + 0.01x &= 38.44 \\ 4 - 4 + 0.01x &= 38.44 - 4 \\ 0.01x &= 34.44 \\ \frac{0.01x}{0.01} &= \frac{34.44}{0.01} \\ x &= 3444 \end{aligned}$$

12a. $r = \frac{C}{2\pi}$

12c. $l = \frac{P}{2} - w$

13a. See bottom of page 603.

LESSON 3.7

1a. 2

2a. $\frac{3}{2}$, or 1.5; one possible point is (6, 10).

3a. (1, 7), (−1, 1)

5a. i. The x-values don't change, so the slope is undefined.

5b. i. Using the points (4, 0) and (4, 3), the slope is $\frac{3 - 0}{4 - 4} = \frac{3}{0}$. You can't divide by 0, so the slope is undefined.

5c. i. $x = 4$

7a. Use the slope to move backward from (40, 16.55): $(40 - 10, 16.55 - 0.29 \cdot 10) = (30, 13.65)$, or \$13.65 for 30 h; $(30 - 10, 13.75 - 0.29 \cdot 10) = (20, 10.75)$, or \$10.75 for 20 h.

7b. Continuing the process in 7a leads to (0, 4.95), or \$4.95 for 0 h. This is the flat monthly rate for Hector's Internet service.

9b. m/min; the hot-air balloon rises at a rate of 30 m/min.

9d. 254 m

LESSON 3.8

3c. The lengths calculated may be as much as 0.5 cm off from the true length.

4a. Rope A: $y = 93.7 - 4.6x$;
Rope B: $y = 111.6 - 10.4x$

7b. Between 9.36 s and 9.50 s

9a. $y = (0.5 \pm 0.1) + 0.2x$

14. -46.5 cm. This is impossible even though predicted by the model. Ropes can't have a negative length.

CHAPTER 3 REVIEW

1a. $x = -7$

1b. $x = -23.4$

2a. 1; 3; add 1; $y = 3 + x$

2b. 0.01; 0; add 0.01; $y = 0.01x$

2c. 2; 5; add 2; $y = 5 + 2x$

2d. $-\frac{1}{2}$; 3; subtract $\frac{1}{2}$; $y = 3 - \frac{1}{2}x$

3a. iii **3b.** i **3c.** ii

4a. $y = -68.99$ **4b.** $y = 4289.83$

4c. $y = 0.14032$ **4d.** $y = 238{,}723$

5a. $y = x$ **5b.** $y = -3 + x$

5c. $y = -4.3 + 2.3x$ **5d.** $y = 1$

6a. 0 represents no bookcases sold; -850 represents fixed overhead, such as start-up costs; Ans(1) represents the previously calculated number of bookcases sold; Ans(1) + 1 represents the current number of bookcases sold, one more than the previous; Ans(2) represents the profit for the previous number of bookcases; Ans(2) + 70 represents the profit for the current number of bookcases—the company makes \$70 more profit for each additional bookcase sold.

6b.

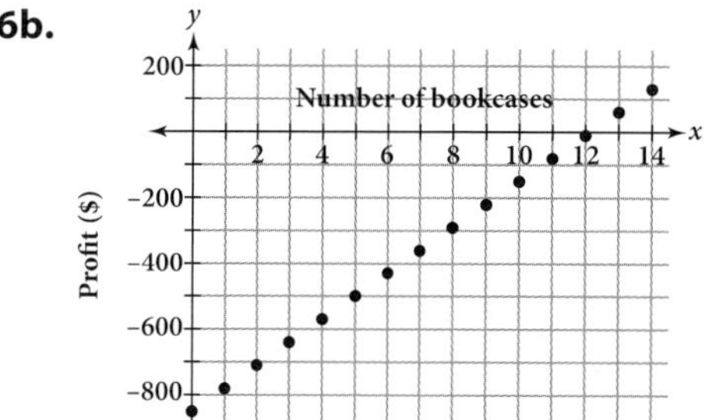

6c. Sample answer: The graph crosses the x-axis at approximately 12.1 and is positive after that; the company needs to make at least 13 bookcases to make a profit.

6d. -850, the profit if the company makes zero bookcases, is the y-intercept; 70, the amount of additional profit for each additional bookcase, is the rate of change; y goes up by \$70 each time x goes up by one bookcase.

6e. No; partial bookcases cannot be sold.

7a. Let v represent the value in dollars and y represent the number of years; $v = 5400 - 525y$.

7b. The rate of change is -525; in each additional year, the value of the computer system decreases by \$525.

7c. The y-intercept is 5400; the original value of the computer system is \$5,400.

13a. (*Lesson 3.6*)

Picture	Action taken	Equation
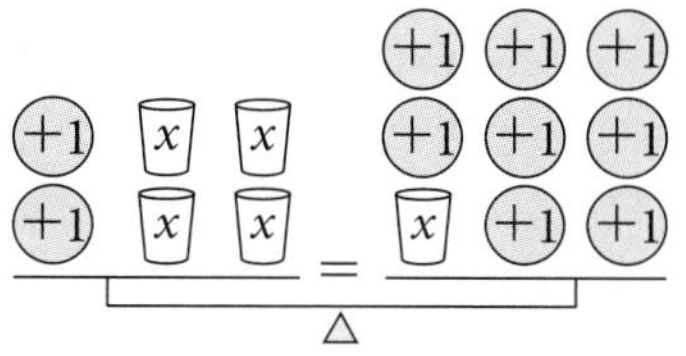	Original equation.	$2 + 4x = x + 8$
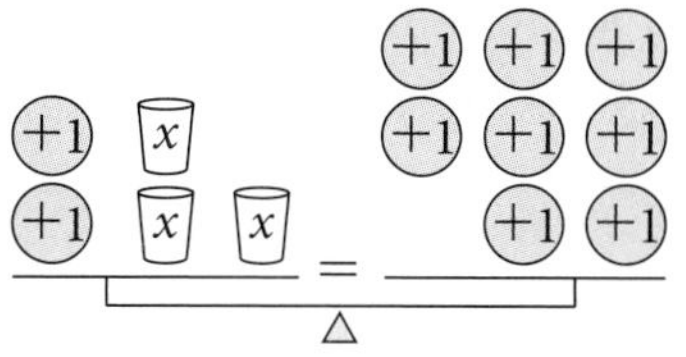	Subtract 1x from both sides.	$2 + 3x = 8$
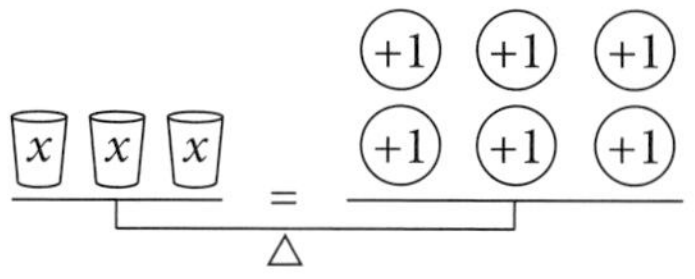	Subtract 2 from both sides.	$3x = 6$
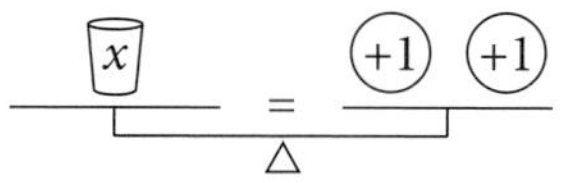	Divide both sides by 3.	$x = 2$

8a. 3

8b.

Number of sections	1	2	3	4	...	30	...	50
Number of logs	4	7	10	13	...	91	...	151

8c. 4 ENTER, Ans + 3 ENTER, ENTER, . . .

8d. 216 m

9a. $50 = 7.7t$

$t = \frac{50}{7.7} \approx 6.5$ s

9b. $50 = 5 + 6.5t$

$t = \frac{50 - 5}{6.5} \approx 6.9$ s

9c. Andrei wins; when Andrei finishes, his younger brother is $50 - [5 + 6.5(6.5)] \approx 2.8$ m from the finish line.

10a. $x = 4.5$

10b. $x = -4.1\overline{3}$

10c. $x = 0.\overline{6}$

10d. $x = 12.8$

10e. $x = 6.\overline{3}$

10f. $x = \frac{13}{7} \approx 1.857$

10g. $x = -\frac{6}{5} = -1.2$

10h. $x = -\frac{1}{2} = -0.5$

10i. $x = 9$

11a. $y = -5.7 + 2.3x$

11b. $y = -5 - 8x$

11c. $y = 12 + 0.5x$

12a. $y = 1 + \frac{1}{2}x$; the output value is half the input value plus 1.

x	y
0	1
1	1.5
2	2
3	2.5
4	3

12b. $y = -x$; the output value is the additive inverse (or opposite) of the input value, or the sum of the input value and the output value is 0.

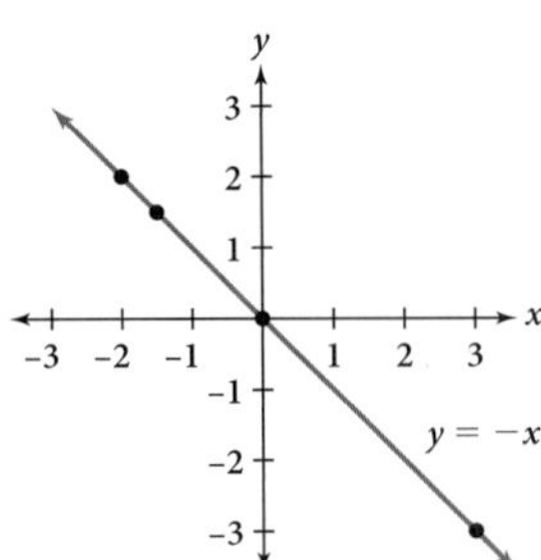

13a. -1

13b. undefined

13c. $-\frac{5}{2}$

13d. 0

14. $x_2 = 4$

15a. $\frac{\textit{change in } y}{\textit{change in } x} = -\frac{1.5}{3} = -0.5$

15b. $\frac{\textit{change in } y}{\textit{change in } x} = -\frac{3}{6} = -0.5$

15c. Possible answers: The slope triangle side lengths for 15b are twice as long, but the slopes are equal.

15d. Possible answer: You would get a larger triangle, but the ratio of the side lengths would equal -0.5, giving a slope of -0.5

16a. $0.5(18.3)(7.4) = 67.7$ cm^2

16b. $0.5(18.2)(7.3) = 66.4$ cm^2

16c. $0.5(18.4)(7.5) = 69.0$ cm^2

16d. 67.7 ± 1.3 cm^2

LESSON 4.1

1a. SBOHF

2c. RELATIONSHIP

3a. SECRET CODES

5a. {1:00, 2:00, 3:00, 4:00, 5:00, 6:00, 7:00, 8:00, 9:00, 10:00, 11:00, 12:00} or {1:00 A.M., 1:00 P.M., . . . , 12:00 A.M., 12:00 P.M.}

5b. range: {0000, 0100, 0200, 0300, 0400, 0500, 0600, 0700, 0800, 0900, 1000, 1100, 1200, 1300, 1400, 1500, 1600, 1700, 1800, 1900, 2000, 2100, 2200, 2300}

5c. It is not a function because each standard time designation has two military time designations. If students distinguish A.M. from P.M. times, then it is a function.

9a. Yes, this does represent a function because each input codes to exactly one output.

10a. Domain: {0, 1, −1, 2, −2}; range: {0, 1, 2}; the relationship is a function because each input is coded to exactly one output.

12. Yes, it could represent a function even though different inputs have the same output; domain: {−2, 0, 1, 3}; range: {−2, 3}.

14a. Subtract the input letter's position from 27 to get the output letter's position.

LESSON 4.2

1c.

Input x	Output y
−4	1
−1	3.4
1.5	5.4
6.4	9.32
9	11.4

4. Answers will vary. In each table, every input value produces exactly one output value. All four graphs in Exercises 2 and 3 pass the vertical line test. All four rules are functions.

5. Sample answer: Start at the 2 m mark and stand still for 2 s. Walk toward the 4 m mark at 2 m/s for 1 s. Stand still for another second. Walk toward the 8 m mark at 4 m/s for 1 s. Then stand still for 3 s. Yes, the graph represents a function.

6c. *Hint:* Notice that the second segment is vertical.

7a. *Hint:* Large cities have multiple ZIP Codes.

7c. No; the same last name will correspond to many different first names.

10. Graphs must pass the vertical line test, have the correct domain and range, and pass through the points $(-2, 3)$ and $(3, -2)$.

12a.

x	2	8	-4	-1	0	5
y	-1	1	-3	-2	$-\frac{5}{3}$	0

The graph is a line. This is a function; each x-value is paired with only one y-value.

13b. domain: $0 \leq x \leq 360$; range: $-1 \leq y \leq 1$

14a. *Hint:* The capital letter *A* does not represent a function because it does not pass the vertical line test.

16b. *Hint:* First invert both fractions.

LESSON 4.3

1a.

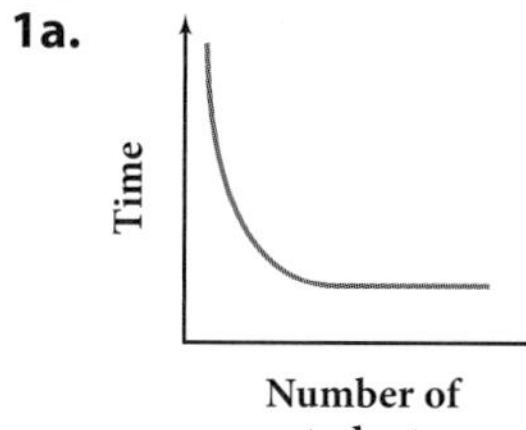

The graph shows an inverse relationship. It is not possible to take 0 hr to decorate, no matter how many students help.

2b.

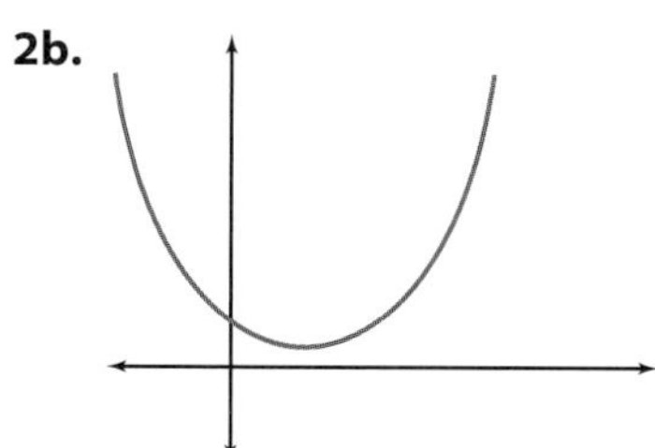

2d.

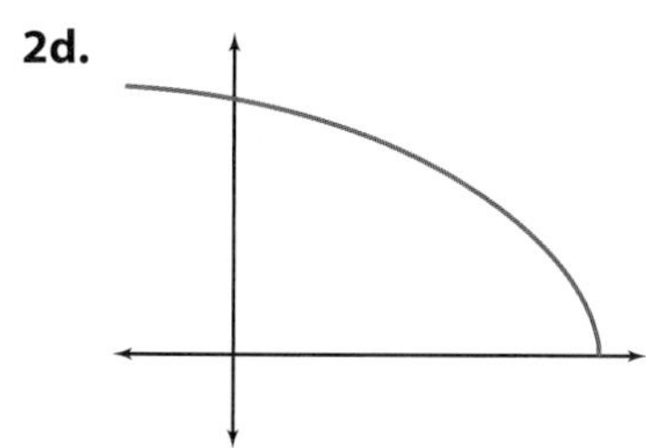

3a. $0 \leq x < 4$

4a.

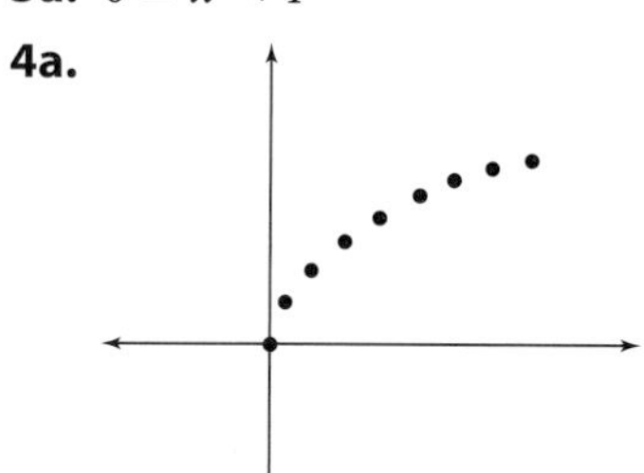

7. *Hint:* Your graph should include three segments.

10a. Erica won in about 13.5 s.

10b. Eileen

10c. They were tied at approximately 3 s, at 5.5 s, from 10 to 10.5 s, and just before the end of the race.

10d. from approximately 0 to 3 s, from 5.5 to 10 s, and from 10.5 to about 13.2 s.

12a. Answers will vary. A sample graph is shown. It should be made up of at least three horizontal segments at heights 0, 2, and -2.

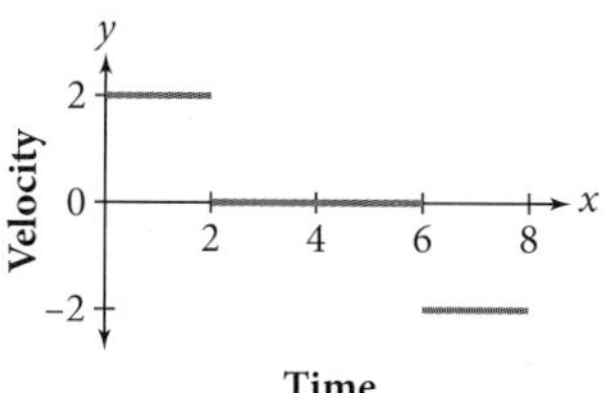

13a. i. moving away **13a.** ii. speeding up

LESSON 4.4

1b. No; although the slope of the line shows the general direction of the data, too many points are below the line.

1d. No; although the same number of points are above the line as below the line, the slope of the line doesn't show the direction of the data.

3c. Slope $= -\frac{4}{5}$; y-intercept $= \frac{1}{4}$

4a. $y = -2 + \frac{2}{3}x$

5a. The number of representatives depends on the population.

5b. Let x represent population in millions, and let y represent the number of representatives.

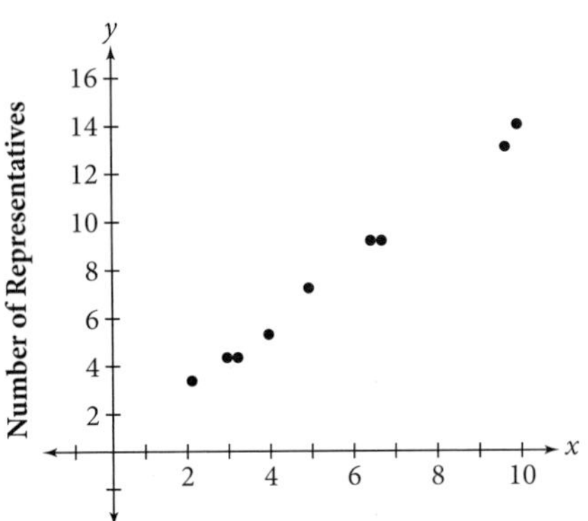

5c. Answers will vary. Two possible points are (3.0, 4) and (6.4, 9). The slope between these points is approximately 1.5. The equation $y = 1.5x$ appears to fit the data with a y-intercept of 0. The slope represents the number of representatives per 1 million people. The y-intercept means that a state with no population would have no representatives.

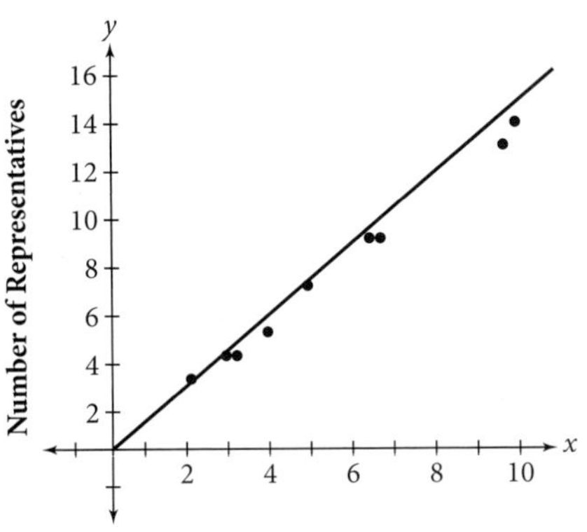

7b. *Hint:* Use the points (2, 3.4) and (4.5, 4.4) to find the slope.

9a. All lines have a slope of 3; they are all parallel.

10a. neither

10b. inverse variation; $y = \dfrac{100}{x}$

LESSON 4.5

1a. 4; (5, 3)

1c. −3.47; (7, −2)

3a. 2

3b. $y = -1 + 2(x + 2)$

6. *Hint:* The first of the three equations is $y = 1 + x$.

7b. The slopes are the same; the coordinates of the points are different.

7c. *ABCD* appears to be a parallelogram because each pair of opposite sides is parallel; the equal slopes in 7b mean that $\overline{AD}$ and $\overline{BC}$ are parallel. $\overline{AB}$ and $\overline{DC}$ are parallel because they both have slope 2.

9b. \$0.17/oz; this is the cost per additional ounce after the first.

9e. *Hint:* Think about what the column header for the x-values means. A 3.5 oz letter costs \$1.73 to mail, not \$165.

9f. Answers will vary. A continuous line includes points whose x-values are not whole numbers and whose y-values are not possible rates.

10a. $y = 239 + 2.2(x - 2000)$ or $y = 250 + 2.2(x - 2005)$

10b and 10c. See below.

10f. *Hint:* Try to adjust the slope value first.

12.

$4x + 3 = 2x + 7$	Original equation.
$4x - 2x + 3 = 2x - 2x + 7$	Subtract $2x$ from both sides.
$2x + 3 = 7$	Combine like terms.
$2x + 3 - 3 = 7 - 3$	Subtract 3 from both sides.
$2x = 4$	Combine like terms.
$\dfrac{2x}{2} = \dfrac{4}{2}$	Divide both sides by 2.
$x = 2$	Simplify.

10b and 10c. (*Lesson 4.5*)

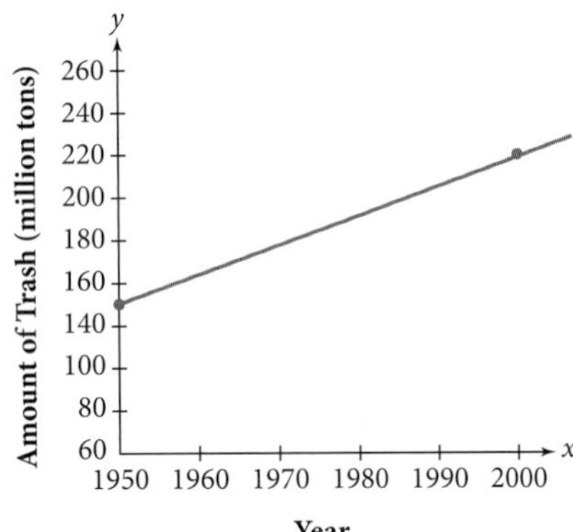

The point (2007, 254) is somewhat close to the line, but the predicted value is too low.

LESSON 4.6

1a. not equivalent; $-3x - 9$

2b. $y = -15 - 2x$

3b. $-x = 92$; addition property; $x = -92$; multiplication property

5a. $3(x - 4)$

5b. $-5(x - 4)$

7c. The y_1-value is missing, which means it is zero; $y = 0 + 5(x + 2)$.

7d. $(-2, 0)$; this is the x-intercept.

8a. Equations i and ii are equivalent.

9a. $y = 59.24 + 0.45(x - 265)$ or $y = 80.39 + 0.45(x - 312)$

10a. The possible answers are $y = 568 + 4.6(x - 5)$; $y = 591 + 4.6(x - 10)$; $y = 614 + 4.6(x - 15)$; $y = 637 + 4.6(x - 20)$.

10c. *Hint:* Use the units in your description of the real-world meaning.

13a. possible answer: (0, 15); \$0.45/min

LESSON 4.7

1a. $y = 1 + 2(x - 1)$ or $y = 5 + 2(x - 3)$

2. *Hint:* For the graph in Exercise 1a, you might estimate a y-intercept of -0.5. If you convert the point-slope equation to intercept form, you get $y = -1 + 2x$, so the y-intercept is actually -1.

3a. 3

5a.

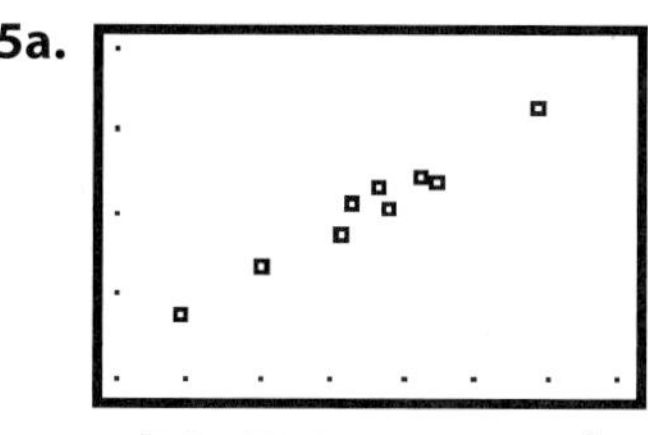

[10, 45, 5, 40, 120, 20]

5b. Using the points (20, 67) and (31.2, 88.6), the slope is approximately 1.9 and a possible equation is $y = 67 + 1.9(x - 20)$.

5d. $y = 32 + 1.8(x - 0)$ or $y = 212 + 1.8(x - 100)$

5e. The sample equation in 5b gives $y = 29 + 1.9x$; the equations in 5d both give $y = 32 + 1.8x$.

6a. $y = 30 + 1.4(x - 67)$

6c. Equations will vary. The graph with a larger y_1-value is parallel but higher, and the graph with a smaller y_1-value is parallel but lower.

8d. *Hint:* Subtract the y-intercepts.

9a. *Hint:* Remember that slope is a rate of change. What rate was given in the problem?

10. See below.

LESSON 4.8

1b. $Q_1 = 50.5$; $Q_3 = 62$

1c. $Q_1 = 29$; $Q_3 = 41$

2d. Increasing

3c. $y = 19.2 + 0.25(x - 40)$ or $y = 24.2 + 0.25(x - 60)$

5a. (5, 4), (10, 9)

6b.

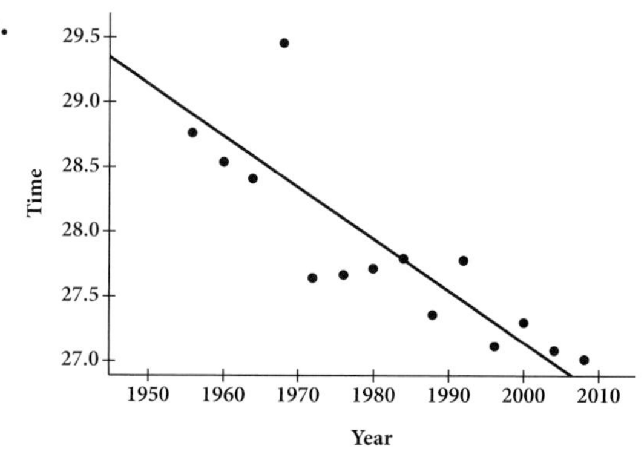

7. *Hint:* Separate the coordinates of one point and use each part to make a new point. The point with the smaller x should have the larger y.

9a. $y = 1.3 + 0.625(x - 4)$ or $y = 6.3 + 0.625(x - 12)$

9b. The elevator is rising at a rate of 0.625 s per floor.

9c. 36.3 s after 2:00, or at approximately 2:00:36

9d. almost at the 74th floor

---

10. (*Lesson 4.5*)

Description	Undo	Equation
Pick y.		$y =$
$+1$	-1	
$\cdot(-3)$	$/(-3)$	
$+2x$	$-2x$	

$y = \frac{12 - 2x}{-3} - 1$, or $y = -5 + \frac{2x}{3}$

$y + 1 = \frac{12 - 2x}{-3}$, or $y + 1 = -4 + \frac{2x}{3}$

$-3(y + 1) = 12 - 2x$

$2x - 3(y + 1) = 12$

13a. Start with 370, then use the rule Ans -54.

Time (h)	Distance from Mt. Rushmore (mi)
0	370
1	316
2	262
3	208
4	154
5	100
6	46

14. *Hint:* Look at the ratio of cost to size.

LESSON 4.9

1a. ii

3d. There is a positive relationship between the semester of language and the SAT score.

4a. 1.5

6b. Mean of the residual values $= -20$

Average of the absolute values of the residuals $= 71.6$

7a. A linear equation appears to be a good model as there appears to be no pattern to the residuals.

CHAPTER 4 REVIEW

1. The domain of the 26 letters is coded to a range of the 13 even-number-positioned letters—{B, D, F, . . . , Z}. The code is a function because every original letter is coded to a unique single letter. The rule for decoding is not a function because there are two choices for every letter in the coded message. For example, the letter B could be decoded to either A or N.

2a. $-2 \leq x \leq 4$

2b. $1 \leq f(x) \leq 3$

2c. 1

2d. -1 and 3

3a. A function; each x-value corresponds to only one y-value.

3b. Not a function; the input $x = 3$ has two different output values, 5 and 7.

3c. A function; each x-value corresponds to only one y-value.

4. The graph is a horizontal line segment at 0.5 m/s.

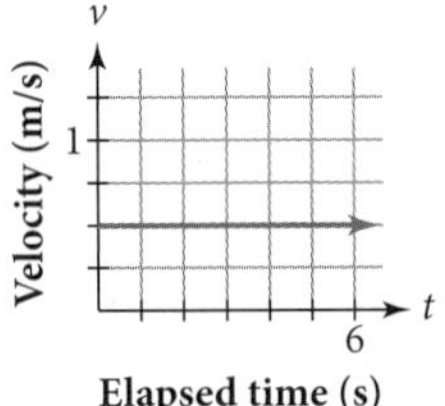

5a. DESCARTES

5b. HYPATIA

5c. EUCLID

5d. This code shifts 20 spaces forward, or 6 spaces back, in the alphabet.

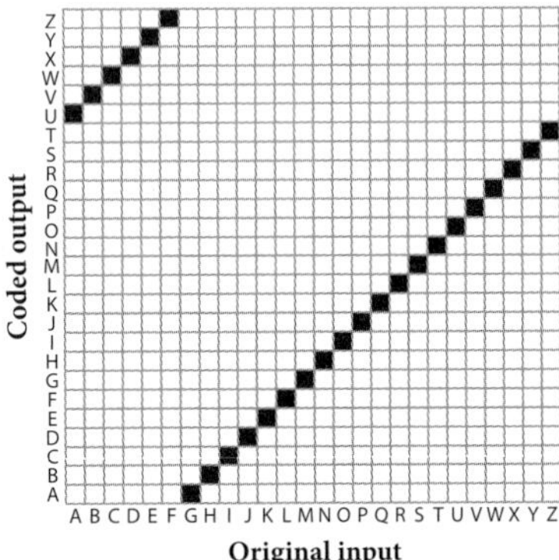

6a. Stories will vary. At the 20 s mark, each girl is moving at the same velocity. Bea's velocity increases steadily in a linear fashion. Caitlin's velocity increases very slowly at first and then becomes faster and faster. Abby's velocity increases very quickly at first and then increases at a slower rate.

6b. No; because Abby starts out moving faster than both Bea and Caitlin, even when she slows down to their speed she stays ahead.

7a. slope: -3; y-intercept: -4

7b. slope: 2; y-intercept: 7

7c. slope: 3.8; y-intercept: -2.4

7d. slope 5; y-intercept 7.

8. Line a has slope -1, y-intercept 1, and equation $y = 1 - x$. Line b has slope 2, y-intercept -2, and equation $y = -2 + 2x$.

9a. $y = 13.6x - 25{,}709$

9b. $y = -37 - 5.2(x - 10)$

9c. $y = \frac{1}{2}x + 4$

10a. $(-4.5, -3.5)$

10b. $y = 2x + 5.5$

10c. $y = 2(x + 2.75)$; the x-intercept is -2.75.

10d. The x-coordinate is 5.5; $y = 16.5 + 2(x - 5.5)$.

10e. Answers will vary. Possible methods are graphing, using a calculator table, and putting all equations in intercept form.

11a. $4 + 2.8 = 51$

$$2.8x = 51 - 4 = 47$$

$$x = \frac{47}{2.8} \approx 16.8$$

11b. $38 - 0.35x = 27$

$$-0.35x = 27 - 38 = -11$$

$$x = \frac{-11}{-0.35} \approx 31.4$$

11c. $11 + 3(x - 8) = 41$

$$3(x - 8) = 41 - 11 = 30$$

$$x - 8 = \frac{30}{3} = 10$$

$$x = 10 + 8 = 18$$

11d. $220 - 12.5(x - 6) = 470$

$$-12.5(x - 6) = 470 - 220 = 250$$

$$x - 6 = \frac{250}{-12.5} = -20$$

$$x = -20 + 6 = -14$$

12a. Let x represent the number of years Karl owns the car, and let y represent the value of the car in dollars. $y = 12{,}600 - 1{,}350x$

12b. $-1{,}350$; the car's value decreases by \$1,350 each year.

12c. 12,600; Karl paid \$12,600 for the car.

12d. $9\frac{1}{3}$; in $9\frac{1}{3}$ years the car will have no monetary value.

13a. $43 = 30 + 0.375(x - 36)$

13b. $x \approx 71$ s

X	Y1	Y2
68	42	43
69	42.375	43
70	42.75	43
71	43.125	43
72	43.5	43
73	43.875	43
74	44.25	43

X=71

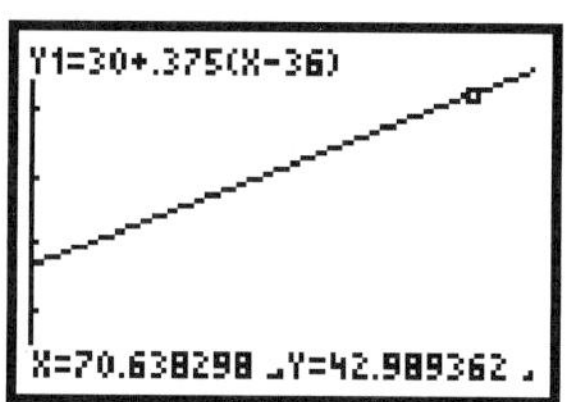

[0, 80, 10, 0, 50, 10]

13c. $x = \frac{43 - 30}{0.375} + 36 = 70.\overline{6}$

14a. 1960, 1970, 1984, 1998, 2008; 1.82, 1.91, 2.01, 2.04, 2.06

14b. The Q-points are (1970, 1.91) and (1998, 2.04)

14c. $y = 1.91 + 0.00464(x - 1970)$ or $y = 2.04 + 0.00464(x - 1998)$

14d.

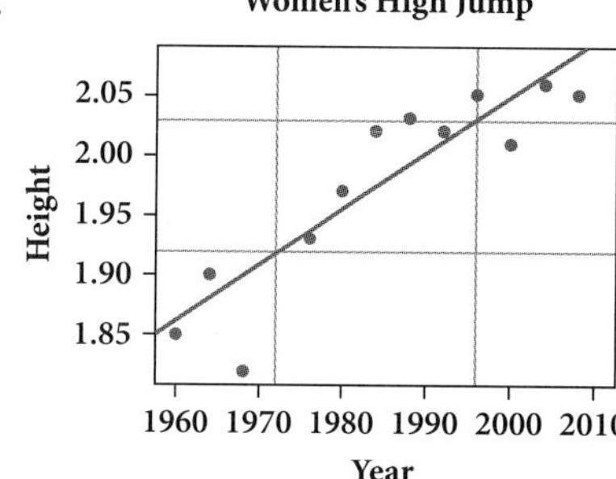

Answers will vary. Yes, it is a good model for the data, because there is the same number of points above the line as below it.

14e. Using $y = 1.91 + 0.00464(x - 1970)$ the prediction is 2.10 m; the predicted height is 0.05 m greater than the actual winning height.

15a. $y = 2.475 + 0.127(x - 1977.5)$ or $y = 4.50 + 0.127(x - 1993.5)$

15b. The slope means the minimum hourly wage increased approximately \$0.13 per year.

15c. Using the equation $y = 2.475 + 0.127(x - 1977.5)$, the prediction is \$7.24; using the equation $y = 4.50 + 0.127(x - 1993.5)$, the prediction is \$7.23.

15d. Using either equation from 15a, the prediction is 1966.

16a. In an equation written as $y = a + bx$, b is the slope and a is the y-intercept.

16b. If the points are (x_1, y_1) and (x_2, y_2), then the slope of the line is given by the equation $\frac{y_2 - y_1}{x_2 - x_1} = b$. The equation of the line is $y = y_1 + b(x - x_1)$.

5

LESSON 5.1

1c. No, because $12.3 \neq 4.5 + 5(2)$; furthermore, the lines are parallel, so the system has no solution.

2a. (8, 7)

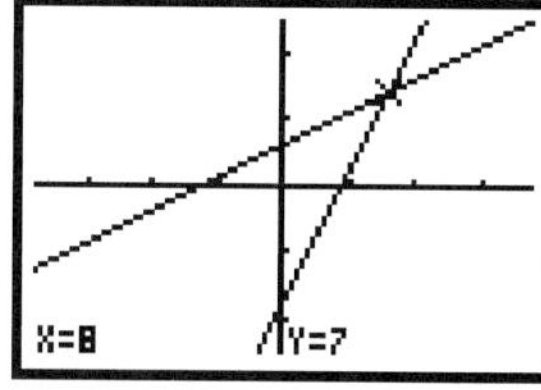

3b. $(-2.9, 4.3)$

5. $\begin{cases} y = 2 + \frac{3}{2}x \\ y = 1 - \frac{2}{3}(x - 2) \end{cases}$

6a. Let P represent profit in dollars and N represent the number of hits; $P = -12{,}000 + 2.5N$.

6b. *P* represents profit, *N* represents hits. Widget.kom's start-up costs are $5,000, and its advertisers pay $1.60 per hit. Because Widget.kom spent less in start-up costs, its website might be less attractive to advertisers, hence the lower rate.

6c. When $N \approx 7778$, $P \approx 7445$ in both equations.

7c. *Hint:* What does it mean if two profit equations have parallel graphs?

8a. $y = 25 + 30x$, where y is tuition for x credits at University College; $y = 15 + 32x$, where y is tuition for x credits at State College

8b. (5, 175); check: $175 = 25 + 30(5)$, $175 = 15 + 32(5)$

8d. When a student takes 5 credit hours, the tuition at either college is $175.

9d. $\begin{cases} y = 109.2882 - 0.0411x \\ y = 109.289 - 0.0411x \end{cases}$

The graph in 9c appears to show one line; however, the y-values are 0.0008 unit apart. While the two lines are not identical, they are well within the accuracy of the model, so you could say they are the same model.

13.

$2x + 9 = 6x + 1$	Original equation.
$2x - 2x + 9 = 6x - 2x + 1$	Subtract $2x$ from both sides.
$9 = 4x + 1$	Combine like terms.
$9 - 1 = 4x + 1 - 1$	Subtract 1 from both sides.
$8 = 4x$	Combine like terms.
$\frac{8}{4} = \frac{4x}{4}$	Divide both sides by 4.
$x = 2$	Simplify.

LESSON 5.2

1c. -1.25

1e. $\frac{3}{2}$

1g. $\frac{3}{2}$

2. *Hint:* Make sure that your calculator window is square so that you can identify perpendicular lines.

4a. $\frac{-1}{1.2} = -\frac{5}{6} = -0.8\overline{3}$

4b. -1

6a. The slope of the first equation is 3 and the slope of the second equation is 3. Because the lines have different slopes, the system has a unique solution.

9. The other diagonal is $\overline{BD}$, the segment with endpoints $(-4, 0)$ and $(3, 1)$. $y = \frac{1}{7}(x + 4)$ or $y = 1 + \frac{1}{7}(x - 3)$ with $-4 \leq x \leq 3$.

LESSON 5.3

2. *Hint:* Substitute the point into each equation and check for equality.

3a. $2x + 3x = 4 - 14$

$5x = -10$

$x = -2$

3b. $-2y + y = -3 - 7$

$-y = -10$

$y = 10$

4. *Hint:* Using your calculator with the equations $Y_1 = 25 + 20x$ and $Y_2 = 15 + 32x$, you could check your answer by looking at the intersection point or table values.

5b. $7x - 2(4 - 3x) = 7x - 8 + 6x = 13x - 8$

7a. See below.

7b. The approximate solution, $N \approx 7778$ and $P \approx 7444$, is more meaningful because there cannot be a fractional number of website hits.

9a. $A + C = 200$

9b. $8A + 4C = 1304$

10a. $\begin{cases} d = 35 + 0.8t \\ d = 1.1t \end{cases}$

$1.1t = 35 + 0.8t$; $\left(116\frac{2}{3}, 128\frac{1}{3}\right)$

The pickup passes the sports car roughly 128 mi from Flint after approximately 117 min.

7a. *(Lesson 5.3)*

Answers will vary. A sample solution:

$-12{,}000 + 2.5N = -5{,}000 + 1.6N$	Set equations equal to each other.
$-12{,}000 + 0.9N = -5{,}000$	Subtract $1.6N$ from both sides.
$0.9N = 7{,}000$	Add 12,000 to both sides.
$N = \frac{70{,}000}{9} = 7{,}777\frac{7}{9}$	Divide both sides by 0.9.

$$P = -12{,}000 + 2.5\left(\frac{70{,}000}{9}\right) = 7{,}444\frac{4}{9}$$

10d. *Hint:* Write an equation with one distance equal to twice another distance.

11a. women: $y = 71.16 - 0.17125(x - 1976)$ or $y = 67.05 - 0.17125(x - 2000)$;
men: $y = 63.44 - 0.12417(x - 1976)$ or $y = 60.46 - 0.12417(x - 2000)$

11b. $x \approx 2139, y \approx 43.25$

11d. The solution means that in the year 2140 (a little more than 100 years from now), both men and women will swim this race in 43.08 s. This is not likely. The model may be a good fit for the data, but extrapolating that far into the future produces unlikely predictions.

13. 5 lb of sour cherry worms and 15 lb of sour lime bugs

16a. 12.1 ft/s

16b. 50 s

16c. $y = 100 + 12.1x$, where x represents the time in seconds and y represents her height above ground level. To find out how long her ride to the observation deck is, solve the equation $520 = 100 + 12.1x$.

LESSON 5.4

1a. x-intercept 2, y-intercept 5.

1b. x-intercept 2, y-intercept 5. The graph is the same as the graph for 1a. Both equations have the same intercepts.

2a. *Hint:* Substitute 6 for x and a for y, then solve for a.

2b. $(-4, -15)$

5a. Multiply the first equation by -5 and the second equation by 3, or multiply the first equation by 5 and the second equation by -3.

6. The solution is $(2, -2)$. You can

(1) solve for y and graph, then look for the point where the lines intersect;
(2) solve for y, create tables, and zoom in to where the y-values are equal;
(3) solve one equation for y (or x) and substitute into the other; or
(4) multiply the equations and add them to eliminate x or y.

8a. $y = -3 + 0.5x$ **8b.** $y = 2 - 0.75x$

8c. $y = 7 - 2x$

8d. The solution of the system is also a solution of the sum of the equations.

9b. $2y = 130, y = 65$

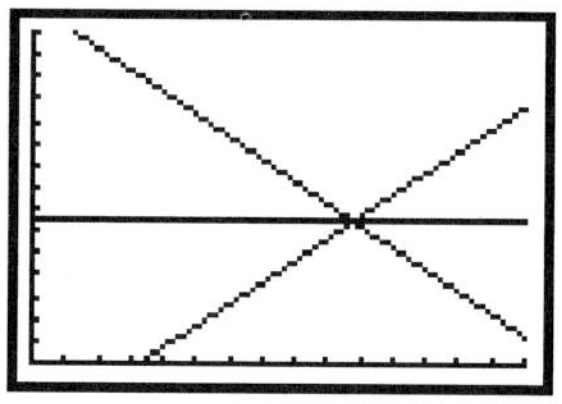

10. *Hint:* The missing equation will be in the form $4x + by = c$.

13a. $\begin{cases} w + p = 10 \\ 3.25w + 10.50p = 61.50 \end{cases}$

14a. Let c represent gallons burned in the city and h represent gallons burned on the highway.

$\begin{cases} c + h = 11 \\ 17c + 25h = 220 \end{cases}$

14b. (6.875, 4.125); 6.875 gal in the city, 4.125 gal on the highway

14c. $\frac{17 \text{ mi}}{\text{gal}} \cdot 6.875 \text{ gal} \approx 117$ city mi, $\frac{25 \text{ mi}}{\text{gal}} \cdot 4.125 \text{ gal} \approx 103$ hwy mi

14d. check: $\begin{cases} 6.875 + 4.125 = 11 \\ 17(6.875) + 25(4.125) = 220 \end{cases}$
and $117 + 103 = 220$

LESSON 5.5

1a. Multiply by 4; $12 < 28$.

1c. Add -10; $-14 \geq x - 10$.

1e. Divide by 3; $8d < 10\frac{2}{3}$.

2a. Answers will vary, but the values must be > 8.

3a. $x \leq -1$ **3d.** $-2 < x < 1$

4b. $y \geq -2$

6a. $x > 4.34375$, or $\frac{139}{32}$

7b. $x < -2$

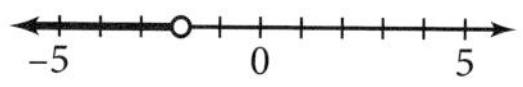

8. *Hint:* Will this solution be continuous or discrete?

9a. Add 3 to both sides; $4 < 5$.

11a. The variable x drops out of the inequality, leaving $-3 > 3$, which is never true. So the original inequality is not true for any number x. The graph would be an empty number line, with no points filled in.

13. *Hint:* Consider whether the boundary value makes the statement true. For 13a, if you spend exactly \$30, is the statement true?

LESSON 5.6

1c. i

2a. $0 \geq 70$, so the point (0, 0) is in the solution set.

3c.

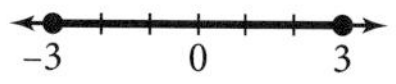

4a–c.

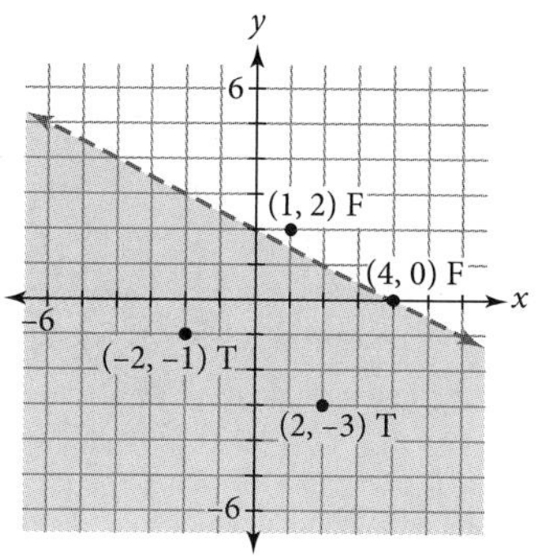

6a.

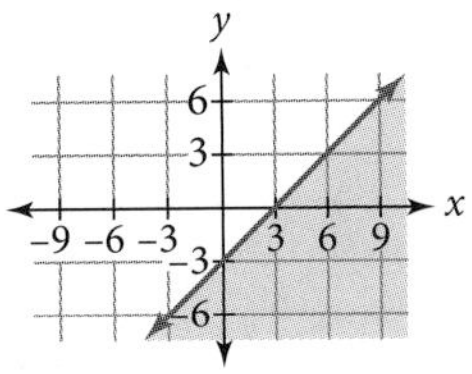

7. *Hint:* First find the equation of the line. Is the line dashed or solid?

7a. $y \le 1 - 2x$ **7e.** $y \le 2$

9a.

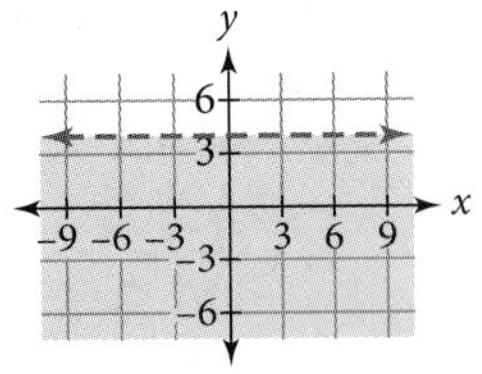

10a. $F + 2S < 84$

10b. $F + 2S = 84$

12a. Exactly one of the following is true: $a < b$, $a = b$, or $a > b$.

14. *Hint:* Recall that the distance is equal to the average speed times the time taken.

LESSON 5.7

2a. Yes; (1, 2) satisfies both inequalities.

3a. $y \ge -x + 2$; $y \ge x - 2$

5. *Hint:* You need three inequalities for this system.

6a. $y \ge -1250 + 0.40x$, $y \le -1250 + 1.00x$, $x \ge 0$

6b.

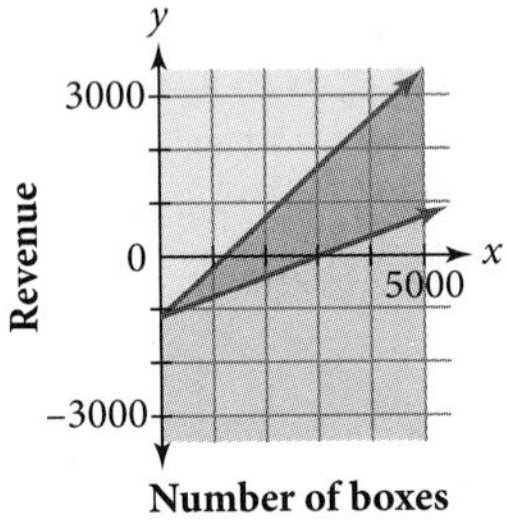

7a. $\begin{cases} A \le C \\ A + C \le 75 \\ A \ge 0 \\ C \ge 0 \end{cases}$

10. *Hint:* The equation for the half-plane below line AB is $y \le 3 + \frac{2}{3}(x - 2)$.

12. *Hint:* Region 1 is defined by $y \ge 3$, $y \ge x - 2$, and $y \le \frac{1}{3}x + \frac{8}{3}$.

13a. \$713.15

13b. *Hint:* You don't need to use the 15% for this equation.

CHAPTER 5 REVIEW

1. line *a*: $y = 1 - x$; line *b*: $y = 3 + \frac{5}{2}x$; intersection: $\left(-\frac{4}{7}, \frac{11}{7}\right)$

2. The lines meet at the point (4, 1); the equations $3(4) - 2(1) = 10$ and $(4) + 2(1) = 6$ are both true.

3.

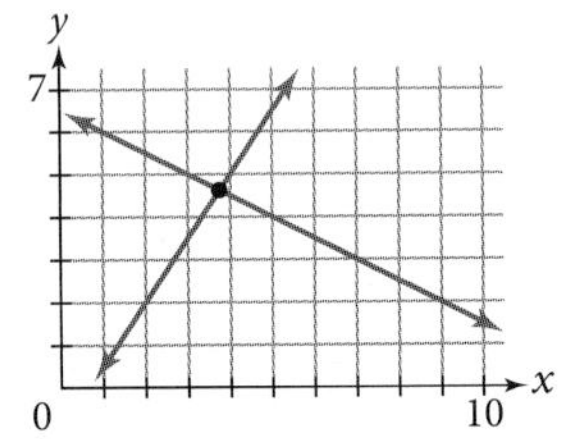

The point of intersection is (3.75, 4.625).

4. See below.

5a. . . . the slopes are the same but the intercepts are different (the lines are parallel).

5b. . . . the slopes are the same and the intercepts are the same (the lines coincide).

5c. . . . the slopes are different (the lines intersect in a single point).

6a. $x > -1$ **6b.** $x < 2$ **6c.** $-2 \le x < 1$

7. $x \le -1$

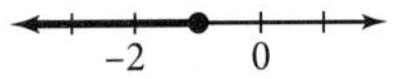

8. $\begin{cases} y \le x + 4 \\ y \le -1.25x + 8.5 \\ y \ge 1 \end{cases}$

9a. 10 m^2/min; 7 m^2/min

9b. No; he will cut 156 m^2, and the lawn measures 396 m^2.

9c. $10h + 7l = 396$ **9d.** $\frac{1}{30}$ L/min; $\frac{3}{200}$ L/min

---

4. (*Lesson 5 Review*)

$16 + 4.3(x - 5) = -7 + 4.2x$	Set the right sides of the two equations equal to each other.
$16 + 4.3x - 21.5 = -7 + 4.2x$	Apply the distributive property.
$-5.5 + 4.3x = -7 + 4.2x$	Subtract.
$0.1x = -1.5$	Add $-4.2x$ and 5.5 to both sides.
$x = -15$	Divide both sides by 0.1.
$y = -7 + 4.2(-15)$	Substitute -15 for x to find y.
$y = -70$	Multiply and add.

The solution is $x = -15$ and $y = -70$.

9e. $\frac{h}{30} + \frac{3l}{200} = 1.2$

9f. $l = 14.4$ min, $h = 29.52$ min; if Harold cuts for 29.52 min at the higher speed and 14.4 min at the lower speed, he will finish Mr. Fleming's lawn and use one full tank of gas.

10a. Lines i and iii have the same slope, so they are parallel.

10b. Lines i and ii have opposite reciprocal slopes, so they are perpendicular. Lines ii and iii also have opposite reciprocal slopes, so they are also perpendicular.

10c. $y = 7 + \frac{2}{3}(x - 4)$ **10d.** $y = 11 - \frac{3}{2}(x - 7)$

LESSON 6.1

1a. starting value: 16; multiplier: 1.25; 7th term: 61.035

3c. $\frac{1125}{1000}$, or $\frac{112.5}{100}$; $1 + 0.125$

3d. $\frac{9,375}{10,000}$, or $\frac{93.75}{100}$; $1 - 0.0625$

4b. $1000(1 - 0.18)$, or $1000(0.82)$

4c. $P(1 + r)$

5. *Hint:* To find the constant multiplier, find the ratio of shaded triangles to total triangles in Stage 1.

6a. Start with 20,000, then apply the rule Ans $\cdot$ $(1 - 0.04)$.

6b. 5th term: 16,986.93; \$16,982.93 is the selling price of the car after four price reductions.

7a. Start with 7.1, then apply the rule Ans $\cdot$ $(1 + 0.117)$.

9a. 1.7 m

9b. Start with 2, then apply the rule Ans $\cdot$ 0.85.

9d. *Hint:* Modify your recursive rule in 9b.

10. *Hint:* $75 + 75(0.02)$ represents an increasing situation that starts with a value of \$75 and increases 2% per year.

11a. See below.

12c. *Hint:* The answer is not \$7.50.

16a. Let x represent minutes of use and y represent cost; $y = 50$.

16b. $y = 50 + 0.35(x - 500)$

16d. First plan: \$67.50; second plan: \$45.00 (she pays only the flat rate of \$45.00). She should sign up for the second plan.

16f. The plans cost the same for 800 min of use. A new subscriber who will use more than 800 min should choose the first plan. If she will use 800 min or less, then the second plan is better.

LESSON 6.2

1c. $(1 + 0.12)^4$

2a. $450(1 + 0.2) = 540$ bacteria

5b. $y = 500 \cdot 0.2^x$

8. $100(1 + 0.0175)(1 + 0.0175)(1 + 0.0175) \cdot (1 + 0.0175) = 100(1 + 0.0175)^4$; about \$107.19

10c. $2(3)^3$

13a. $y = 5000(1 + 0.05)x$

13b.

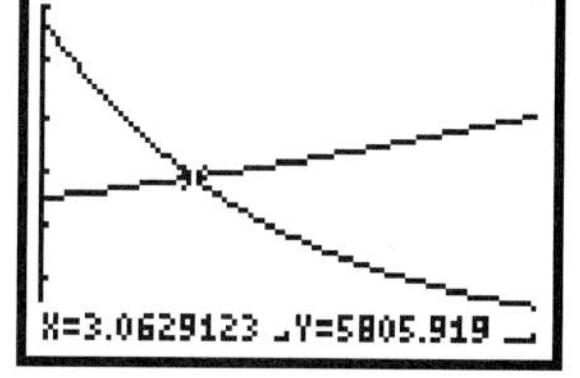

[0, 10, 1, 0, 12000, 2000]

The intersection point represents the time and the value of both cars when their value will be the same. By tracing the graph shown, you should see that both cars will be worth approximately \$5,800 after a little less than 3 years 1 month.

16a.

Number of steps x	1	2	3	4
Perimeter (cm) y	4	8	12	16

LESSON 6.3

1a. $5x^4$

1f. $3x^4$

2b. $(7 \cdot 7 \cdot 7)(7 \cdot 7 \cdot 7 \cdot 7) = 7^7$

5. *Hint:* Student 1 is proposing $(2 \cdot 3)^2$. Student 2 is proposing $2(3^2)$. Does multiplication or exponentiation come first in the order of operations?

10a. 28

12a. $500(1 + 0.015)^6$; \$546.72

12b. \$46.72

11a. (*Lesson 6.1*)

	Jan	Feb	Mar	Apr	May	June	July	Aug	Sep	Oct	Nov	Dec
Option 1	\$50	\$25	\$25	\$25	\$25	\$25	\$25	\$25	\$25	\$25	\$25	\$25
Option 2	\$1	\$2	\$4	\$8	\$16	\$32	\$64	\$128	\$256	\$512	\$1,024	\$2,048

14. *Hint:* a is a constant.

15a. *Hint:* Compare the equation to $y = y_1 + b(x - x_1)$. What are the values of x_1 and y_1?

17b. approximately (3.095, 0.762)

LESSON 6.4

1a. 3.4×10^{10}

2a. 74,000

4. 1.674×10^{25}

8a. yes, because they are both equal to 51,800,000,000

8b. Al's answer

8c. possible answer: 518×10^8

8d. Rewrite the digits before the 10 in scientific notation, then use the multiplication property of exponents to add the exponents on the 10's. In this case, $4.325 \times 10^2 \times 10^3 = 4.325 \times 10^5$.

9b. *Hint:* Address why the expression in part ii requires an additional step.

11a. *Hint:* Write a proportion.

14b. $7y^{16}$

15b. $81y^{12}$

16a. 3.8 is the population (in millions) in 1900; 0.017 is the annual growth rate; t is the elapsed time in years since 1900; P is the population (in millions) t years after 1900.

16b. Answers will vary depending on the current year; $0 \leq t \leq (\textit{current year} - 1900)$.

16d. approximately 8.8 million

16e. *Hint:* How many years have passed since 1990? (You may round to the nearest whole year, or give a decimal or fraction value if you wish.) Substitute this value for t.

LESSON 6.5

2a. 7^8

2c. $4x^3$

3. *Hint:* Write $\frac{3^6}{3^2}$ using expanded notation, then cancel.

4a. A represents the starting value.

4b. $10{,}000 = A(1 + 0.1)^{20}$

4c. $10{,}000 = A(1 + 0.1)^{20}$

$$\frac{10{,}000}{(1 + 0.1)^{20}} = A$$

$$1486.43 \approx A$$

The furniture was worth about $1,486 twenty years ago.

5c. $-4x^2$

6a. about 146 people per square mile

7a. 0.25%

8. *Hint:* Recursively work backward from the present by dividing, or create a table for an equation that uses 864 and 3^x.

10a. approximately 76 yr

12. *Hint:* Convert tons to ounces and write a proportion.

14a. *Hint:* Write a proportion for each plant.

LESSON 6.6

1a. $\frac{1}{2^3}$

1c. $\frac{1.35}{10^4}$

2a. =

3a. -5

4a. $45{,}647(1 + 0.028)^0$

4b. the population 12 yr ago

4c. $45{,}647(1 + 0.028)^{-8} \approx 36{,}599$

4d. $\frac{45{,}647}{(1 + 0.028)^{12}}; \frac{45{,}647}{(1 + 0.028)^8}$

6c. $\frac{8x}{3}$

7. *Hint:* This exercise is about inflation, so the constant multiplier is more than 1, but the situation calls for thinking back in time, so the exponent is negative.

9c. false; $(10^{-2})^4 = \left(\frac{1}{10^2}\right)^4 =$

$$\left(\frac{1}{10 \cdot 10}\right)\left(\frac{1}{10 \cdot 10}\right)\left(\frac{1}{10 \cdot 10}\right)\left(\frac{1}{10 \cdot 10}\right) = \frac{1}{10^8} = 10^{-8}$$

10c. *Hint:* Would you use inches, feet, or miles to measure a shoelace?

LESSON 6.7

1a. $1 + 0.15$; rate of increase: 15%

1c. $1 - 0.24$; rate of decrease: 24%

2a. *Hint:* Is the multiplier more than 1 or less than 1?

3. $B = 250(1 + 0.0425)^t$

4b. $4x^5y^3$

4d. 1

5a. The ratios are 0.957, 0.956, 0.965, 0.964, 0.963, 0.961, 0.959, 0.958, 0.971, and 0.955.

5b. approximately 0.96

5c. $1 - 0.04$

5d. $y = 47(1 - 0.04)^x$

6a. *Hint:* Follow steps similar to those in Exercise 5a–d to help find the equation.

7a. 50%

8a. $y = 2(1 + 0.5)^x$

9. Note 75 above middle C (a D#) would be the highest audible note; note -44 (an E 44 notes below middle C) would be the lowest audible note.

11a. Hint: The equation for tubas is $5s + 12L = 532$, where s = number of small trucks and L = number of large trucks.

CHAPTER 6 REVIEW

1a. 3^4 **1b.** 3^3 **1c.** 3^2 **1d.** 3^{-1}

1e. 3^{-2} **1f.** 3^0

2a. x^2 **2b.** $\frac{2}{x}$ **2c.** $1.23x^5$ **2d.** $\frac{1}{3^x}$

2e. 3 **2f.** x^7 **2g.** 3^{4x} **2h.** x^2

3a. Possible answer: A $300 microwave depreciates at a rate of 15% per year.

3b. the years (x) for which the depreciating value of the microwave is at least $75

3c. Answers will vary given the context of 3a. $x \leq 8$ or $0 \leq x \leq 8$ (some integers may be excluded by the real-life situation).

4. Answers will vary. Possible answer: $\frac{3^x}{3^x} = 3^{x-x} = 3^0$. The result of any number divided by itself is 1.

5a. $y = 200(1 + 0.4)^x$

x	y
0	200
1	280
2	392
3	548.8
4	768.32
5	1075.648
6	1505.9072

5b. $y = 850(1 - 0.15)^x$

x	y
−2	1176.4706
−1	1000.0000
0	850
1	722.5
2	614.125
3	522.00625
4	443.7053

6a. −2,400,000

6b. 0.000325

6c. 3.714×10^{10}

6d. 8.011×10^{-8}

7. approximately 1.17×10^0 yr

8. after 24 yr, or in 2028

9a. False; 3 to the power of 3 is not 9; $27x^6$.

9b. False; you can't use the multiplication property of exponents if the bases are different; $9^2 \cdot 8^3$, or 72.

9c. False; the exponent −2 applies only to x; $\frac{2}{x^2}$.

9d. False; the power property of exponents says to multiply exponents; $\frac{x^6}{y^9}$.

10a. Possible answer: $y = 80(1 - 0.17)^x$, where x is the time elapsed in minutes and y is the maximum distance in centimeters; $(1 - 0.17)$ is derived from the mean ratio of approximately 0.83.

10b. approximately 15.0 cm

10c. 15 min

LESSON 7.1

1b. $3x + 2 = 2, x = 0; f(0) = 2$

2a. $-2(6) - 5 = -17$

3a. 10

4e. 1

5b. 10.5

8a. The dependent variable, y, is temperature in degrees Fahrenheit; the independent variable, x, is time in hours.

8b. domain: $0 \leq x \leq 24$; range: $5 \leq y \leq 35$

8c. $f(10)$

8d. $f(x) = 10$

9. *Hint:* Draw a possible graph of $f(x)$ and use it to look at each situation.

11a. 6 **11c.** 14

12a. for $f(x)$: domain $0 \leq x \leq 3.2$, range $0 \leq y \leq 50$

12b. Answers will vary. For the graph of $f(x)$, the ball is dropped from an initial height of 50 m. It hits the ground after about 3.2 s. At the moment the ball is dropped, its velocity is 0 m/s.

12c. In the 1st second, the ball falls about 5 m, from 50 m at $x = 0$ to about 45 m at $x = 1$.

12e. *Hint:* Think about the relationship of speed and velocity and whether the graph of constant acceleration is linear or quadratic.

14a. −1

LESSON 7.2

1f. −5

3c. $-10 = -10$

4a. 10

4c. 8

7a. The solutions are (2.85, 2.85) and (−2.85, 2.85).

[−4.7, 4.7, 1, −3.2, 3.2, 1]

7b. *Hint:* Try graphing both equations on the same set of axes.

8c. $x = 2$ and $x = -2$

10a. *Hint:* What horizontal line would touch the graph only once?

11a. $g(5) = |5| + 6 = 11$

12b. $-10 \le x \le 18$; when $-10 \le x \le 18$, the graph of $y = |x - 4| + 3$ is at or below the graph of $y = 17$.

13. *Hint:* You need more than just the range. Compare plots of the data or the set of deviations.

14a. $x = 6$ and $x = -8$

14d. *Hint:* First divide both sides by 3 to isolate the absolute value.

17a. $-1\frac{2}{3} < x$, or $x > -1\frac{2}{3}$

17b. $x \le -1$

LESSON 7.3

2a. $x = \pm 6$

2b. $x = \pm 6$

3b. no real solution

4a. $x = 6$ and $x = -2$

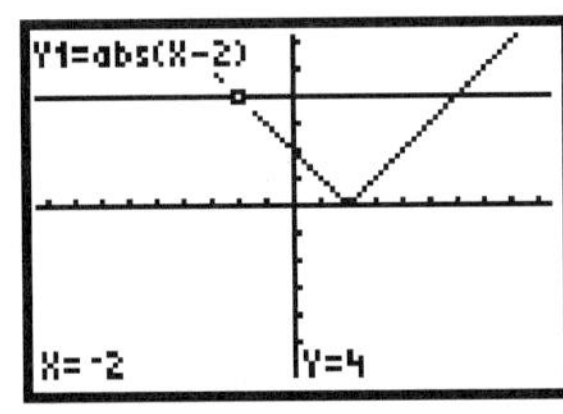

[−9.4, 9.4, 1, −6.2, 6.2, 1]

4b. $x = 6$ and $x = -2$

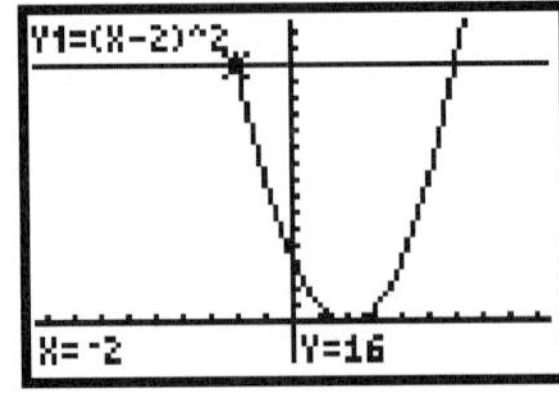

[−9.4, 9.4, 1, −2.2, 18.6, 1]

6a. $y < 0$

8c. The sum of the first n positive odd integers is n^2.

10a. sixteen 1-by-1 squares, nine 2-by-2 squares, four 3-by-3 squares, and one 4-by-4 square

11. *Hint:* Why is it impossible for the product of a number multiplied by itself to be negative?

12a. $y = 400(0.75)^x$

13a. $48x^9$

LESSON 7.4

1c. Slope is 0.

3a. Average rate of change is 4.

3c. $y = 4(x - 3) + 5$ or $y = -3 + 4(x - 1)$

4c. 1.1 cm per day

5a. Average rate of change $\approx \frac{3}{2}$

6a.

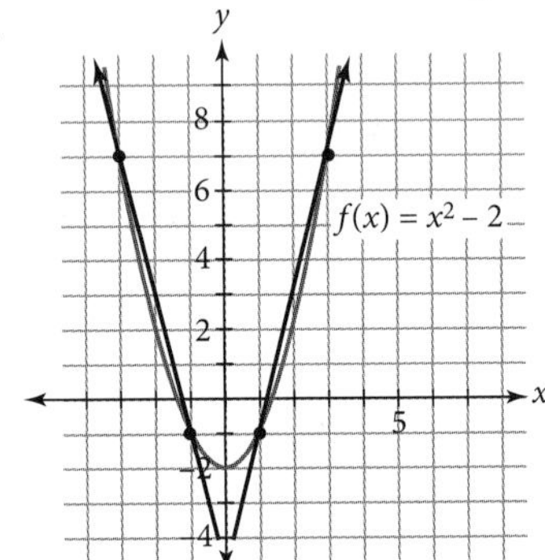

8d. *Hint:* How is average rate of change related to slope of a line?

11b. $x = -4$

11d. $-1 + 6x$

LESSON 7.5

1b. 5

1d. $2|x + 6| + 1$

3a. $(1, -3)$

4a. a translation of $y = |x|$ right 1.5 units and down 2.5 units

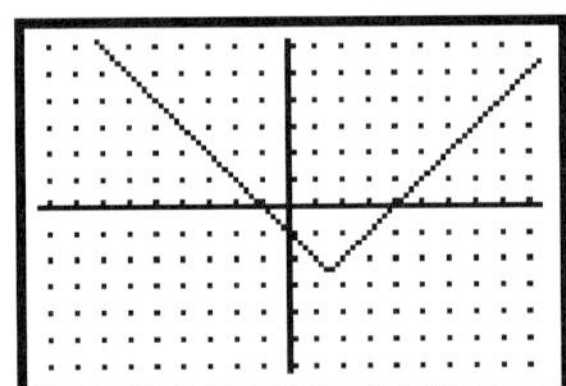

4d. a translation of $y = 3^x$ left 1 unit and up 2 units

5b. $y = 4^{x-5}$

8. *Hint:* Remember that $f(x)$ does not mean f times x!

9b. a translation left 2 units

9c. a translation down 2 units

10a. $y = a \cdot b^{x-10}$

10c. *Hint:* Use one point (x, y) and the average ratio to solve for a.

11a. Let x represent time in minutes, and let y represent temperature in degrees Celsius. The scatter plot suggests an exponential function.

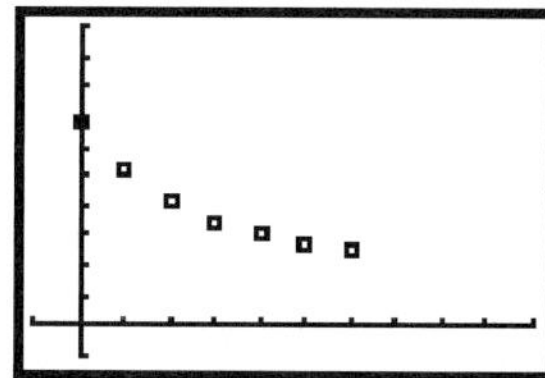

$[-1, 10, 1, -10, 100, 10]$

11c.

Time (min)	Temperature (°C)
0	47
1	31
2	20
3	13
4	9
5	6
6	4

A translation down 21 units; the long-run value will now be 0°C.

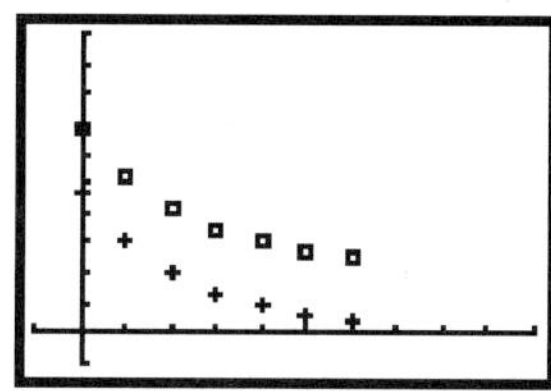

11d. Ratios to the nearest thousandth: 0.660, 0.645, 0.65, 0.692, 0.667, 0.667; the ratios are approximately constant; the mean is approximately 0.66.

11f. a translation up 21 units

13b. $y = b(x - 4) + 8$ **13c.** (H, V)

LESSON 7.6

1b. 37.5 **1e.** $-0.5(x - 3)^2 + 3$

4b. a translation right 6 units or a reflection across the y-axis

4d. a translation left 2 units and a reflection across the x-axis

5c. a reflection across the x-axis followed by a translation up 3 units

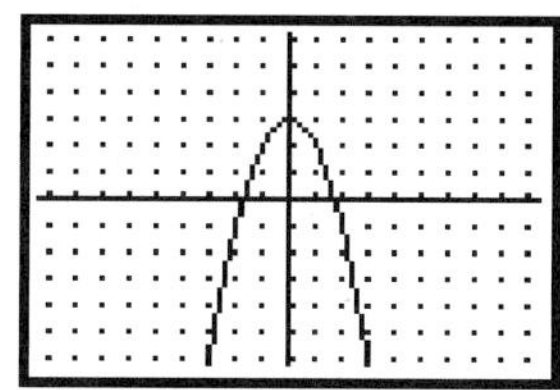

5d. a reflection across the y-axis and a translation up 3 units

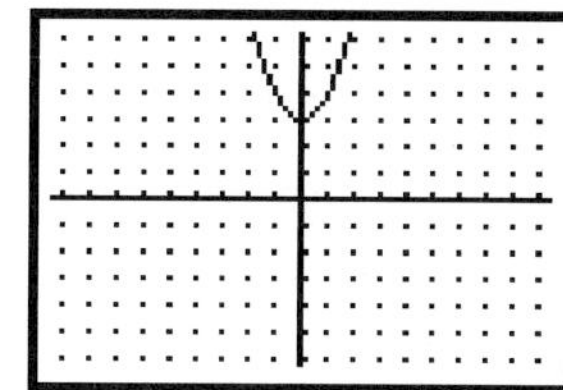

6. $(x + 1, -y)$

7b. i. Define *list3* = − *list1* and *list4* = *list2*.

8d. a translation right 2 units and down 4 units

8e. a reflection across the x- and y-axes

8f. *Hint:* Try graphing this.

9b. *Hint:* Try making a sketch of this situation, similar to the one in 9a.

10a. i. $y = -x^2 - 4$

ii. $y = -|x| + 7$

iii. $y = 2^{-(x-6)}$

iv. $y = 2[-(x + 8)] + 4$;
$y = [4 + 2(-x)] - 16$;
$y = -(4 + 2x) - 8$; or
$y = -[4 + 2(x + 4)]$

10b. i. $y = -2$

ii. $y = 3.5$

iii. $x = 3$

iv. $x = -4$ or $y = -4$

10d. $y = -f(x) + 2b$

11b. possible answer: $y = -f(-(x + 2)) - 4$

13. *Hint:* Use dimensional analysis.

LESSON 7.7

1. $y = |x - 5|$

2a.

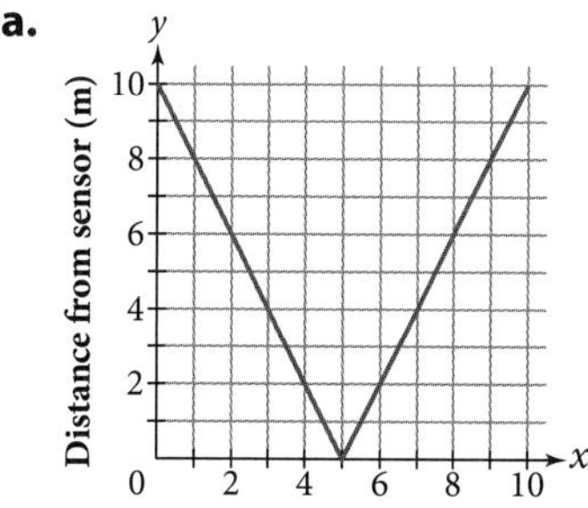

3a. $y = -1.2|x - 5| + 6$

4a. The equation of the image is $y = 3|x - 3| - 4$

6. *Hint:* Sketch the triangle.

Selected Hints and Answers

7b. a vertical shrink of $y = |x|$ by a factor of 0.25, then a translation right 2 units and up 1 unit

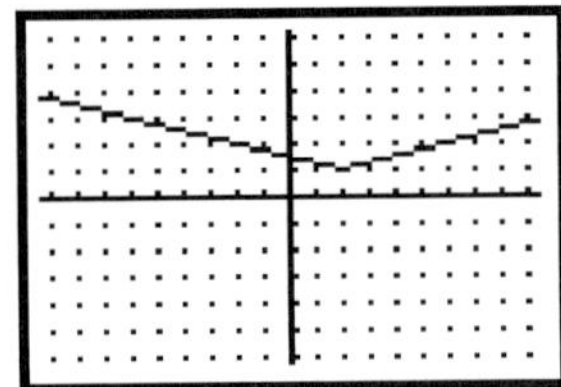

8. The absolute-value graph is stretched vertically by a factor of 3. Its vertex remains at (0, 0).

10a, b. *Hint:* Reflections and dilations can be performed in either order, but both must occur before translations.

13a. possible answer: $f(x) = -25|x - 3.2| + 80$

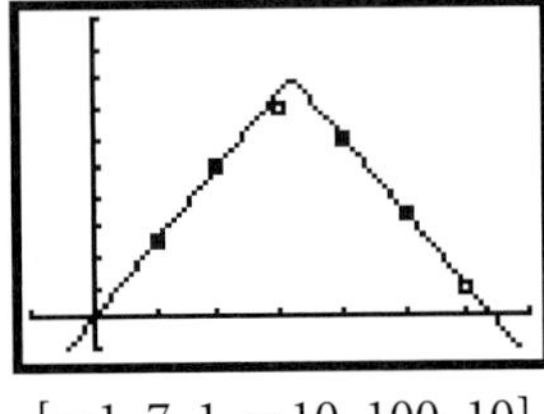

[−1, 7, 1, −10, 100, 10]

14. $(x - 1, 0.8y)$

15a. Yes; when you substitute 1 for x, you get $y = a \cdot 1^2 = a$.

16a. $\frac{1}{2^9}$

LESSON 7.9

1b. a vertical shrink of the graph of $y = |x|$ by a factor of $\frac{1}{3}$ and a translation right 2 units; $y = \frac{1}{3}|x - 2|$

2. $y = \frac{2}{x}$

3. $y = -\frac{5}{x}$

5a. a vertical stretch by a factor of 4; domain: $x \neq 0$

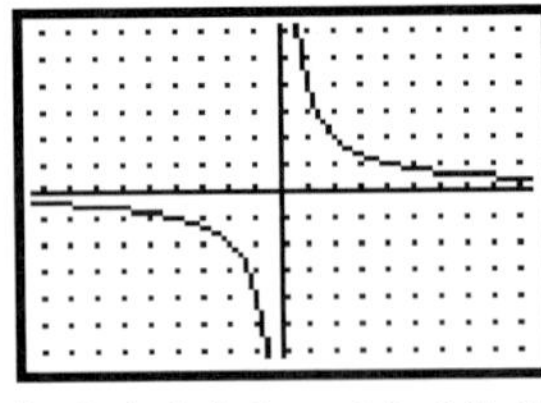

[−9.4, 9.4, 1, −6.2, 6.2, 1]

7a. $y = \frac{1}{x - 3}$ **7c.** $y = \frac{1}{x - 1} + 1$

9. Let x represent the amount of water to add and y represent the concentration of salt. The amount of salt is 0.05(0.5).

$y = \frac{0.025}{0.5 + x}$; $0.01 = \frac{0.025}{0.5 + x}$; $x = 2$; 2 L

11e. $1 - 3x^3$, where $x \neq 0$

12a. $x < -2$

CHAPTER 7 REVIEW

1a. $f(-3) = |-3| = 3$ **1b.** $f(2) = |2| = 2$

1c. 10 and −10

2a.

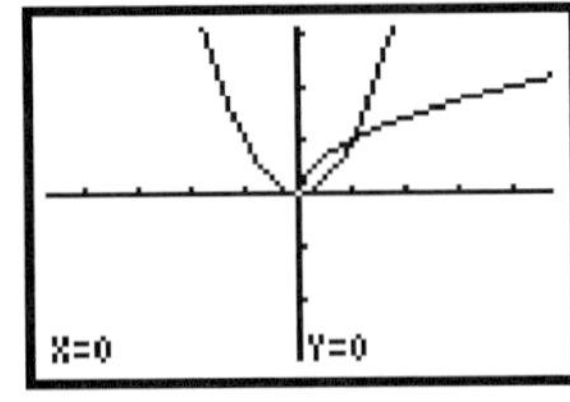

[−4.7, 4.7, 1, −3.1, 3.1, 1]

2b. The graph of $y = \sqrt{x}$ looks like half of the graph of $y = x^2$ lying on its side.

2c. The graph of $y = \sqrt{x}$ has only one branch because it gives only positive solutions.

2d. This equation does not represent a function, because a given input can have two different outputs. For example, if $x = 4$, then $y = 2$ or $y = -2$.

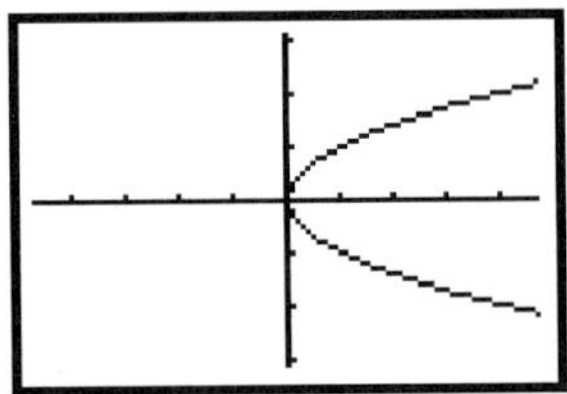

3a. $y = 4.25x + 1.00$

3b.

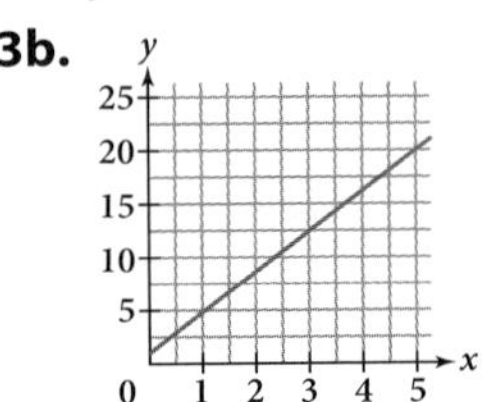

3c. It shifts the graph up 0.50 unit on the y-axis.

3d. $y = 4.25x + 1.50$

4a. Answers will vary. The graph will pass the vertical line test.

4b. Answers will vary. The graph will fail the vertical line test.

5a. a translation left 2 units and up 1 unit

5b. $(x - 2, y + 1)$

6a. i. a vertical shrink by a factor of 0.5 and a translation left 6 units

6a. ii. possible answer: a reflection across the x-axis, then a translation up 2 units

6a. iii. possible answer: a horizontal stretch by a factor of 2 and a reflection across the y-axis, then a translation right 5 units and down 3 units

6b. i. $list3 = list1 - 6$, $list4 = 0.5 \cdot list2$

6b. ii. possible answer: $list3 = list1$, $list4 = -list2 + 2$

6b. iii. possible answer: $list3 = -2list1$, $list4 = list2 - 3$

7. Answers will vary. For these possible answers, *list3* and *list4* are used for the x- and y-coordinates, respectively, of each image.

7a. $list3 = list1$, $list4 = -list2$

7b. $list3 = -list1$, $list4 = list2$

7c. $list3 = list1 + 3$, $list4 = -list2$

8a. a vertical stretch of the graph of $y = |x|$ by a factor of 2, then a translation up 1 unit

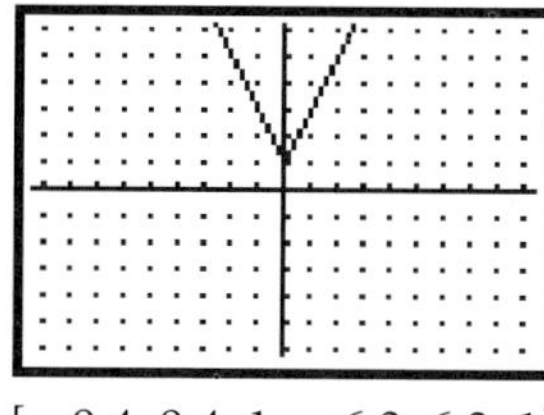

[−9.4, 9.4, 1, −6.2, 6.2, 1]

8b. a reflection of the graph of $y = |x|$ across the x-axis, then a translation left 2 units and up 2 units

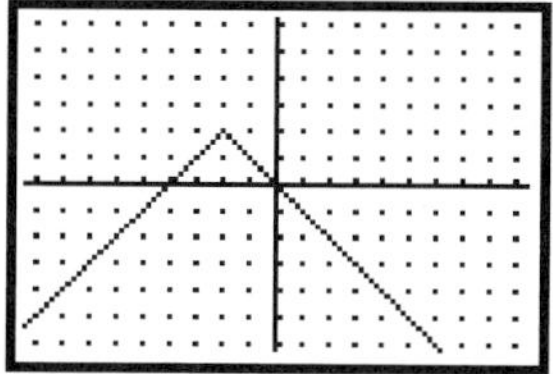

8c. possible answer: a vertical shrink of the graph of $y = x^2$ by a factor of 0.5, then a reflection across the y-axis, then a translation down 1 unit

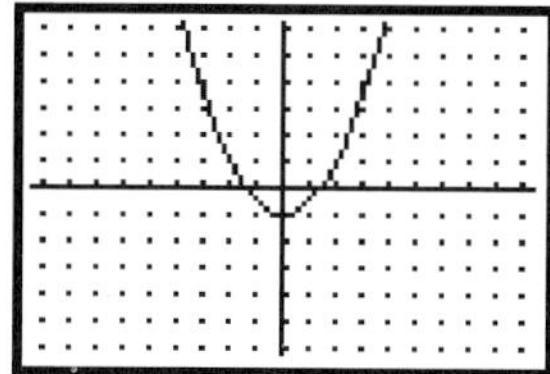

8d. possible answer: a reflection of the graph of $y = x^2$ across the x-axis, then a translation right 2 units and up 1 unit

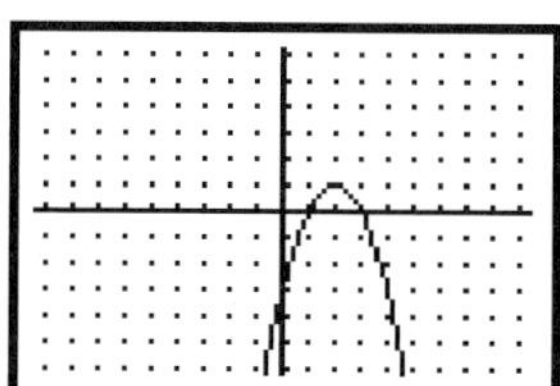

9. $g(x) = f(x - 1) + 2$

10a. $y = -|x| + 3$

10b. $y = (x + 4)^2 - 2$

10c. $y = 0.5x^2 - 5$

10d. $y = -2|x - 3| + 1$

11a. The graph should have the same x-intercept as $f(x)$. The y-intercept should be the opposite of that for $f(x)$.

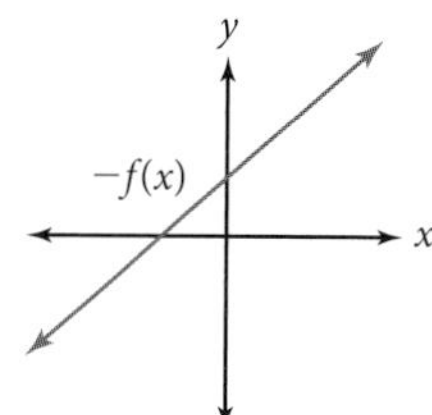

11b. Answers will vary. Possible answer for a friendly window with a factor of 1: If $Y_1 = -x - 2$, then $Y_2 = -Y_1$ reflects the graph across the x-axis (because the calculator interprets $-Y_1$ as $-(-x - 2)$, or $(x + 2)$; this supports the answer to 7a.

12a. a translation right 3 units; asymptotes: $x = 3$, $y = 0$

12b. a vertical stretch by a factor of 3 and then a translation left 2 units; asymptotes: $x = -2$, $y = 0$

12c. a translation right 5 units and down 2 units; asymptotes: $x = 5$, $y = -2$

13a. 5.625 lumens

13b. approximately 2.12 m

14a. a translation of the graph of $y = \frac{1}{x}$ right 3 units and down 2 units; $y = \frac{1}{x-3} - 2$

14b. a translation of the graph of $y = 2^x$ right 4 units and down 2 units; $y = 2^{(x-4)} - 2$

14c. possible answer: a reflection of the graph of $y = 2^x$ across the x-axis and across the y-axis, followed by a translation up 3 units (or a reflection across the x-axis, followed by a translation up 3 units, followed by a reflection across the y-axis); $y = -2^{(-x)} + 3$

14d. possible answer: a vertical stretch of the graph of $y = \frac{1}{x}$ by a factor of 4 and a reflection across the x-axis, followed by a translation up 1 unit and left 2 units; $y = -\frac{4}{x+2} + 1$

15a. $\frac{1}{4}$, where $x \neq \frac{3}{2}$

15b. $28x^2$, where $x \neq 3$

15c. $\frac{9}{12x-5}$, where $x \neq \frac{5}{12}$ or -1

15d. $\frac{x^2 - x + 7}{(x+7)(x-2)}$, where $x \neq -7$ or 2

16a. $\frac{2x}{3}$, where $x \neq -2$

16b. $\frac{5x+7}{x+1}$, where $x \neq -3$ or -1

17a. 3 **17b.** 30

8

LESSON 8.1

1b. no solution

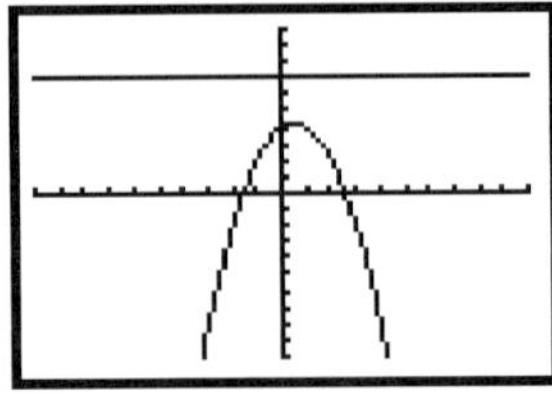

[−10, 10, 1, −10, 10, 1]

1d. $x \approx -2.14$ or $x \approx 0.47$

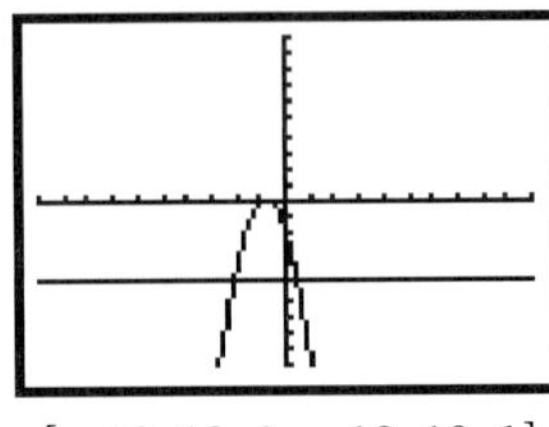

[−10, 10, 1, −10, 10, 1]

2b. real, rational, integer

3d.
$$2(x+1)^2 = 14$$
$$(x+1)^2 = 7$$
$$x+1 = \pm\sqrt{7}$$
$$x = -1 \pm\sqrt{7}$$

6d. $t > 5.09$ s

6e. The ball hits the ground when $t \approx 5.48$ s because the positive x-intercept is near the point (5.48, 0).

7d. *Hint:* You could also substitute a known pair of (x, y) values and solve for a.

9a. The x-intercepts indicate when the projectile is at ground level.

9b. 2.63 s and 7.58 s

9c. *Hint:* Think about the symmetry in your parabola.

10a. i. *Hint:* For $y = -16(x-3)^2 + 20$, the parent graph $y = x^2$ is translated right 3 units, vertically stretched by a factor of 16 and reflected across the x-axis, and translated up 20 units.

12.

$-3x + 4 > 16$	The given inequality.
$-3x > 12$	Subtract 4 from both sides.
$x < -4$	Divide both sides by −3 and reverse the inequality symbol.

LESSON 8.2

1. The average of 3 and −2 is $\frac{3+(-2)}{2}$, or 0.5. So the axis of symmetry is $x = 0.5$, and the vertex has an x-coordinate of 0.5.

3.
$$0 = (x+1.5)^2 - 7.25$$
$$7.25 = (x+1.5)^2$$
$$\pm\sqrt{7.25} = x + 1.5$$
$$-1.5 \pm\sqrt{7.25} = x$$
$$x \approx 1.192582404 \quad \text{or}$$
$$x \approx -4.192582404$$

4a. $x \approx -2.732$ and $x \approx 0.732$

6. Answers will vary. The graph of $y = (x+3)^2$ intersects the graph of $y = 7$ at (−5.646, 7) and (−0.354, 7).

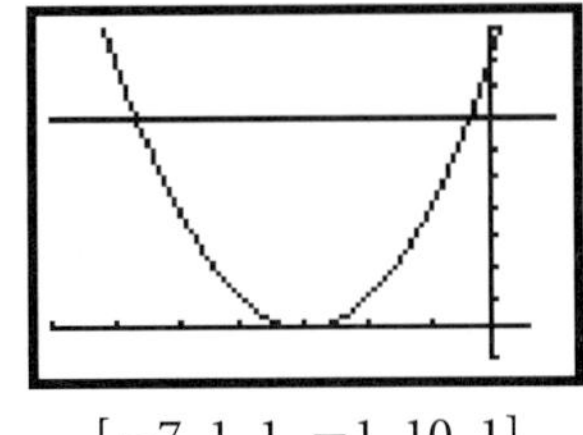

[−7, 1, 1, −1, 10, 1]

8b. Starting the table at 3.67 and setting ΔTbl equal to 0.001 gives the answer 3.676 s.

9b. *Hint:* Recall that velocity includes both speed and direction.

9c. When the velocity is negative, the ball is falling.

9d. This is when the ball is at its maximum height and not moving. Its velocity is zero.

10a. *Hint:* Visualize the symmetry of the parabolas.

12. $y = -16(x-2)^2 + 67$

LESSON 8.3

1b. yes; two terms (binomial)

1d. No; the first term is equivalent to $3x^{-2}$, which has a negative exponent.

1f. *Hint:* Rewrite the first term so that it has only positive exponents.

1h. Not a polynomial as written, but it is equivalent to $3x - 6$, a binomial.

2a. $x^2 + 10x + 25$

3a. $(x+2)^2 = x^2 + 4x + 4$

4c. $y = -3x^2 - 24x - 47$

5d.

	x
x	x^2
-3	$-3x$

$x(x-3) = x^2 - 3x$

Selected Hints and Answers

5e.

	x	2
$2x$	$2x^2$	$4x$
5	$5x$	10

$(x + 2)(2x + 5) = 2x^2 + 9x + 10$

9a. *Hint:* Find the vertex.

9c. The pitcher released the ball at a height of 1.716 m.

11a. meaningful domain: $0 \leq x \leq 6.5$; meaningful range: $0 \leq y \leq 897.81$

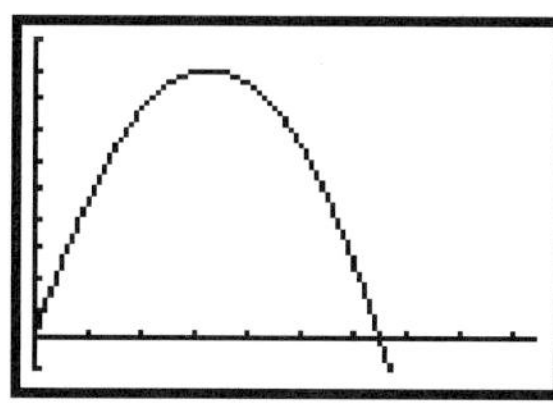

$[0, 9.4, 1, -100, 1000, 100]$

12a.

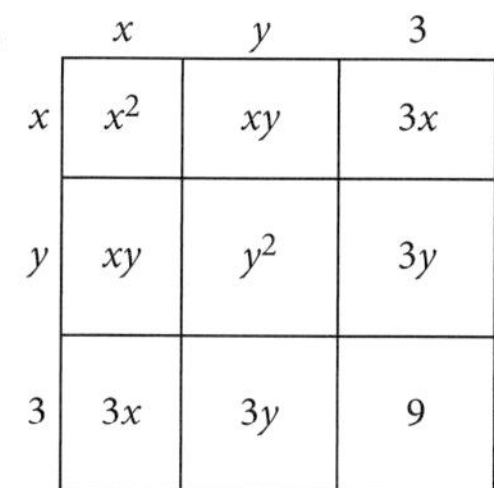

	x	y	3
x	x^2	xy	$3x$
y	xy	y^2	$3y$
3	$3x$	$3y$	9

$x^2 + y^2 + 2xy + 6x + 6y + 9$

15c. 12; L

15h. 9; I

LESSON 8.4

1a. $x + 4 = 0$ or $x + 3.5 = 0$, so $x = -4$ or $x = -3.5$

2a.

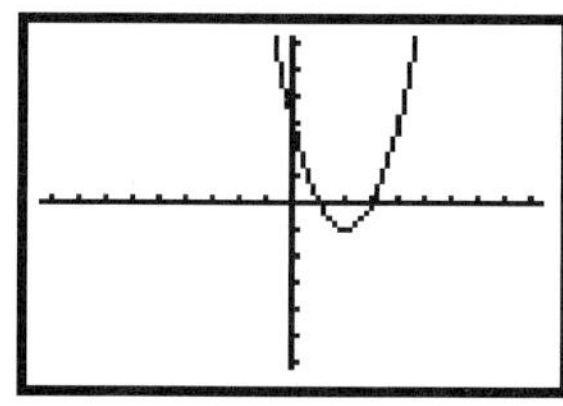

$[-9.4, 9.4, 1, -6.2, 6.2, 1]$

$y = (x - 3)(x - 1)$

3a. $x = 7$ and $x = -2$

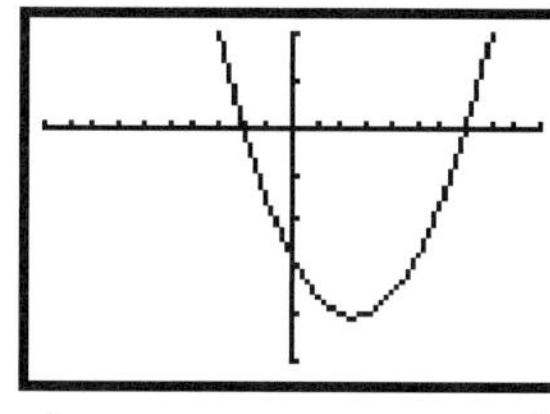

$[-10, 10, 1, -25, 10, 5]$

4a. $y = (x - 2.5)(x + 1)$

6c. yes

7a. $(x + 6)(x + 1)$

	x	6
x	x^2	$6x$
1	x	6

7c. $(x + 7)(x - 6)$

	x	7
x	x^2	$7x$
-6	$-6x$	-42

7e. $(x - 4)(x - 6)$

	x	-4
x	x^2	$-4x$
-6	$-6x$	24

9d. $y = 2(x - 3)(x - 7)$; x-intercepts: $x = 3$ and $x = 7$; vertex: $(5, -8)$

10. $y = 0.25(x + 3)(x - 9)$

11a. length: 140 ft; area: 4200 ft^2

11d. $w = 0$ ft and $w = 100$ ft

14. *Hint:* Factor the numerators and denominators if they are not factored already.

14a. $\frac{x-2}{x+3}$, where $x \neq -2$ and $x \neq -3$

14c. $\frac{x+2}{x}$, where $x \neq 0$ and $x \neq 5$

16c. *Hint:* Sum the numbers for each of the 16 weeks.

LESSON 8.6

1c. $x = -3 \pm \sqrt{2}$

1d. $x = 5 \pm \sqrt{2}$

2a. $x = 5$ or $x = -3$

3d. $\left(\frac{18}{2}\right)^2$; $x^2 + 18x + 81 = (x + 9)^2$

4c.
$$\begin{aligned} x^2 - 4x - 8 &= 0 \\ x^2 - 4x &= 8 \\ x^2 - 4x + 4 &= 12 \\ (x - 2)^2 &= 12 \\ x - 2 &= \pm\sqrt{12} \\ x &= 2 \pm \sqrt{12} \end{aligned}$$

4f. $x = -1 \pm \sqrt{8}$

6a. Let w represent the width in meters. Let l represent the length in meters. Then $l = w + 4$. The area equation is $w(w + 4) = 12$.

8a. 2.2 s; 26.9 yd (80.7 ft)

8c. The general form is $\frac{-16}{3}t^2 + 23.4\overline{6}t + 1.08\overline{6}$, so the football is about 1 yd high.

8d. The vertex is the maximum height of the ball. The y-intercept is the height of the ball when the punter kicks it. The positive x-intercept is the hang time. The other x-intercept has no real-world meaning.

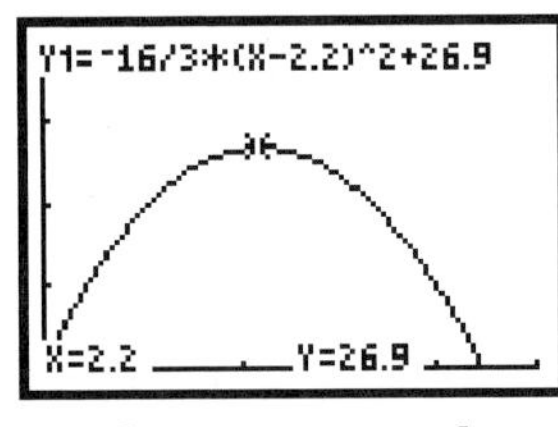

[0, 5, 1, 0, 40, 10]

9a. $p = 2500 - 5x$, where p represents the price in dollars of a single ticket and x represents the number of tickets sold.

9b. Let C represent the total price of the group package. $C = xp = x(2500 - 5x)$

9f. *Hint:* Use the equation in 9e.

10a. $R(10) = 0.9$; this means that when there are 10 bears in the park, the population grows at a rate of 0.9 bear per year.

10b. $R(b) = 0$ when $b = 0$ or $b = 100$; when there are no bears, the population does not grow, and when there are 100 bears, the population does not grow but remains at that level.

12c. $-2x^2 - 2x$

13f. $x = 1$ or $x = -\frac{8}{3}$

LESSON 8.7

1a. $25 - 24 = 1$

1c. $36 - 24 = 12$

2b. $x^2 + 6x + 11 = 0$; $a = 1$, $b = 6$, $c = 11$

2d. $-4.9x^2 + 47x + 18 = 0$; $a = -4.9$, $b = 47$, $c = 18$

3a. $x = \frac{3 \pm \sqrt{-23}}{4}$; there are no real solutions.

4a. If the discriminant is negative, there are no real roots. If it is positive or zero, there are real roots.

5a. i; $1^2 - 4(1)(1) = -3$; no x-intercept

6a. $-4.9t^2 + 6.2t + 1.9 = 0$; $t \approx -0.255$ s or $t \approx 1.52$ s; the ball hits the ground 1.52 s after Brandi heads it.

6b. $-4.9t^2 + 6.2t + 1.9 = 3$; $t \approx 0.21$ s or $t \approx 1.05$ s; the ball is 3 m above the ground after 0.21 s (on the way up) and after 1.05 s (on the way down).

6c. $-4.9t^2 + 6.2t + 1.9 = 4$; $t \approx \frac{-6.2 \pm \sqrt{-2.72}}{-9.8}$; this equation has no real solution, so the ball is never 4 m high.

7. *Hint:* To sketch the graphs, you can use the x-intercepts, or substitute the values of a, b, and c into the standard form of a quadratic equation.

7a. Sample answers: $y = x^2 - 14x + 49$. The x-intercept is 7.

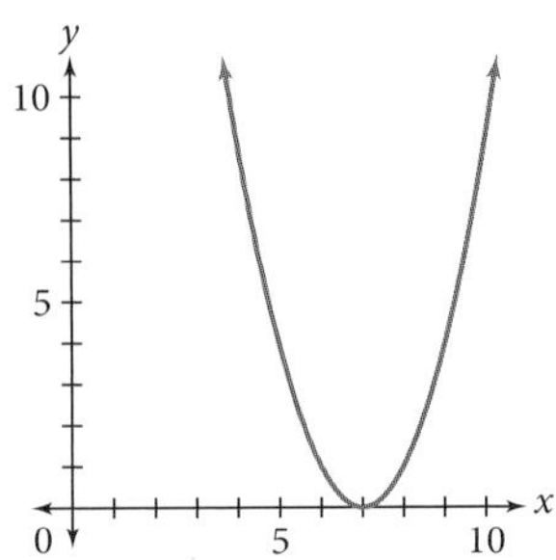

9. *Hint:* What is the height of the stone when it hits the ground? Substitute this value for h.

10a. *Hint:* For an increase of 0, the area is 28 m^2 and the perimeter is 22 m. For an increase of 0.5, the width is 4.5 m and the length is 6.5 m.

11. (0.5, 4.25) and (−4, 2)

13a. $x - 2$; $x \neq 3$

LESSON 8.8

1a. $(2x)^3 = 5{,}832$; $2x = 18$; $x = 9$ cm

1c. $2(2.3x)^3 = 3{,}309$; $2.3x \approx 11.83$; $x \approx 5.14$

2a. $4x(x + 3)$

2c. $7x(2x^3 + x - 3)$

5f. $5x^3 - 2x^2 - 12x - 12$

6a. If the width is w, the length is $w + 6$ and the height is $w - 2$, so the volume is given by the equation $V = w(w + 6)(w - 2)$.

8a. $x^3 + 6x^2 + 11x + 6$

9a. $3x^3 + 8x^2 - x - 20$

9c. $2x + 3$

14. *Hint:* Look at the graphs of each table.

15a. $\frac{x + 2}{x - 4}$; $x \neq -2$, $x \neq 4$, and $x \neq -4$

15c. $\frac{2x + 3}{(x + 3)^2}$; $x \neq -3$

18a. 50 cm

18e. $w = \frac{120 - 2x}{2} = 60 - x$

18g. $V = x(60 - x)(80 - x)$

CHAPTER 8 REVIEW

1a. false; $(x - 3)(x + 8)$ **1b.** false; $2x^2 - 4x + 5$

1c. false; $x^2 + 6x + 9$ **1d.** true

Selected Hints and Answers

2. Sample response: There is a reflection across the x-axis ($y = -x^2$) and a vertical stretch by a factor of 2 ($y = -2x^2$). Finally, there is a translation left 5 units and up 4 units ($y = -(x + 5)^2 + 4$).

3a. $y = -(x - 2)^2 + 3$; vertex form

3b. $y = 0.5(x - 2)(x + 3)$; factored form

4a. $y = -3(x - 1.5)^2 + 18.75$

4b. $y = -1.6(x - 5)^2 + 30$

5a. $2w + 9 = 0$ or $w - 3 = 0$; $w = -4.5$ or $w = 3$

5b. $2x + 5 = 0$ or $x - 7 = 0$; $x = -2.5$ or $x = 7$

6a. $y = (x - 1)^2 - 4$

6b. sample answers:

$y = (x + 1.5)\left(x - \frac{1}{3}\right)$,

$y = (2x + 3)(3x - 1)$

7a.
$$\begin{aligned} x^2 + 6x - 9 &= 13 \\ x^2 + 6x &= 22 \\ x^2 + 6x + 9 &= 22 + 9 \\ (x + 3)^2 &= 31 \\ x + 3 &= \pm\sqrt{31} \\ x &= -3 \pm \sqrt{31} \end{aligned}$$

7b.
$$\begin{aligned} 3x^2 - 24x + 27 &= 0 \\ 3x^2 - 24x &= -27 \\ x^2 - 8x &= -9 \\ x^2 - 8x + 16 &= -9 + 16 \\ (x - 4)^2 &= 7 \\ x - 4 &= \pm\sqrt{7} \\ x &= 4 \pm \sqrt{7} \end{aligned}$$

8a. $x = \frac{13 \pm \sqrt{-191}}{10}$; no real number solutions

8b. $x = \dfrac{-7 \pm \sqrt{157}}{-6}$

9a. One possibility:

$y = -\frac{1}{2}x + 1$

$y = x^2 + 2x + 1$

9b.

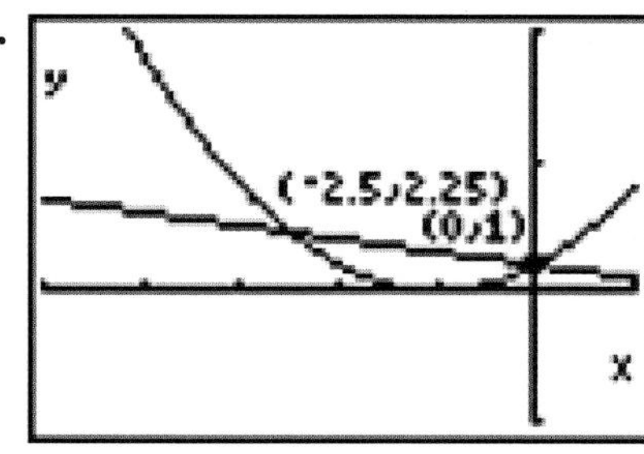

9c. Substitute $-\frac{1}{2}x + 1$ for y in the quadratic equation, and solve for x.

$$\begin{aligned} -\frac{1}{2}x + 1 &= x^2 + 2x + 1 \\ -x + 2 &= 2x^2 + 4x + 2 \\ 0 &= 2x^2 + 5x \\ 0 &= x(2x + 5) \\ x &= 0 \text{ or } 2x + 5 = 0 \\ x &= 0 \text{ or } x = -\frac{5}{2} \quad \text{Solve each linear equation.} \end{aligned}$$

Substituting 0 for x in the equation $y = -\frac{1}{2}x + 1$ gives $y = 1$.

Substitution $-\frac{5}{2}$ for x in the equation $y = -\frac{1}{2}x + 1$ gives $y = \frac{9}{4}$.

Therefore, the system has two solutions, (0, 1) and $\left(-\frac{5}{2}, \frac{9}{4}\right)$.

10a. $f(60) = 8.1$; when there are 60 fish in the tank, the population is growing at a rate of about 8 fish per week.

10b. $f(x) = 0$ for $x = 0$ and $x = 150$; when there are no fish, the population does not grow; when there are 150 fish, the number of fish hatched is equal to the number of fish that die, so the total population does not change.

10c. When there are 75 fish, the population is growing fastest.

10d. The population no longer grows once there are 150 fish, so that is the maximum number of fish the tank has to support.

10e.

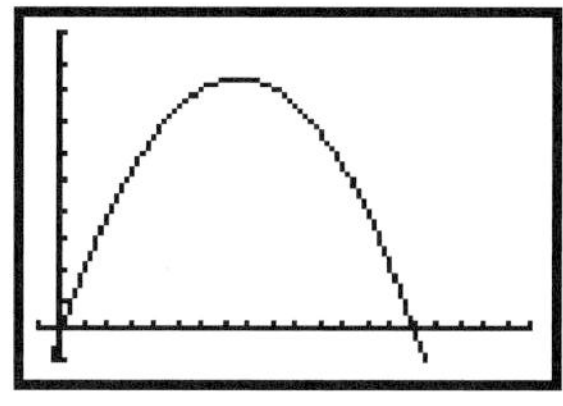

$[-10, 200, 10, -1, 10, 1]$

11. The roots are at 0 s and 1.6 s, so start with the equation $y = x(x - 1.6)$. Then reflect the graph across the x-axis. When $x = 0.5$, $y = 0.55$. You need the value of y to be 8.8, so apply a vertical stretch with a factor of $\frac{8.8}{0.55}$, or 16. The final equation is $y = -16x(x - 1.6)$.

12a. No x-intercepts means taking the square root of a negative number. So $(-6)^2 - 4(1)(c) < 0$; $-4c < -36$; $c > 9$. Or translate the graph of $y = x^2 - 6x$ vertically to see that for $c > 9$, the parabola does not cross the x-axis.

Selected Hints and Answers

12b. One x-intercept implies a double root, so $x^2 - 6x + c$ must be a perfect-square trinomial. Make a rectangle diagram to find $\left(\frac{-6}{2}\right)^2 = 9$, so $x^2 - 6x + 9$ is a perfect-square trinomial, and $c = 9$. The graph touches the x-axis once. You can also solve $b^2 - 4ac = 36 - 4c = 0$ to get $c = 9$.

12c. For $c < 9$, $b^2 - 4ac > 0$, so the discriminant gives two real roots. The parabola $y = x^2 - 6x + c$ crosses the x-axis twice for values of c less than 9.

13a. $x = -5 + \sqrt{31}$ and $x = -5 - \sqrt{31}$

13b. $x = 1$ and $x = \frac{5}{3}$

14a. $8x^2 - x + 2$

14b. $-4x^2 + 2x$

14c. $4x^3 + 6x^2 + 5x - 20$

14d. $14x^3 - 2x^2 + 5x - 12$

15a. $(x + 3)(x + 4)$

	x	3
x	x^2	$3x$
4	$4x$	12

15b. $(x - 7)^2$

	x	-7
x	x^2	$-7x$
-7	$-7x$	49

15c. $(x + 7)(x - 4)$

	x	-4
x	x^2	$-4x$
7	$7x$	-28

15d. $(x - 9)(x + 9)$

	x	-9
x	x^2	$-9x$
9	$9x$	-81

Glossary

The number in parentheses at the end of each definition gives the page where each word or phrase is introduced in the text. Some words and phrases have multiple page numbers listed, either because they have different applications in different chapters or because they first appeared within features such as Take Another Look.

abscissa The x-coordinate in an ordered pair (x, y), measuring horizontal distance from the y-axis on a coordinate plane. (78)

absolute deviation The positive value of the deviation—that is, the distance from the mean without the direction from the mean. (54)

absolute value A number's distance from 0 on the number line. The absolute value of a number gives its size, or magnitude, whether the number is positive or negative. The absolute value of a number x is shown as $|x|$. For example, $|-9| = 9$ and $|4| = 4$. (459)

absolute-value function The function $f(x) = |x|$, which gives the absolute value of a number. The absolute-value function is defined by two rules: If $x \geq 0$, then $f(x) = x$. If $x < 0$, then $f(x) = -x$. (459)

accuracy The degree of closeness with which a measurement approaches the actual value. For instance, a rope with actual length 12.2524 inches measured accurate to the nearest 0.01 inch would be measured at 12.25 inches. (86)

addition property of equality If $a = b$, then $a + c = b + c$ for any number c. (242)

additive identity property of zero For any real number a, $a + 0 = 0 + a = a$. (286)

additive inverse The opposite of a number. The sum of a number and its additive inverse equals zero. For any value of a, the additive inverse is $-a$, and $a + (-a) = 0$. (205)

algebraic expression A symbolic representation of mathematical operations that can involve both numbers and variables. (143)

associative property of addition For any values of a, b, and c, $a + (b + c) = (a + b) + c$. (286)

associative property of multiplication For any values of a, b, and c, $a(bc) = (ab)c$. (286)

asymptote A line that a graph approaches more and more closely, but never actually reaches. (507)

attractor A number that the results get closer and closer to when an expression is evaluated recursively. (23)

average The number obtained by dividing the sum of the values in a data set by the number of values. Formally called the mean. (45)

average rate of change The slope of the secant line between $x = a$ and $x = b$ on the graph of a function. (469)

axis One of two perpendicular number lines used to locate points in a coordinate plane. The horizontal axis is often called the x-axis, and the vertical axis is often called the y-axis. The plural of axis is axes. (39, 78)

balancing method A method of solving an equation that involves performing the same operation on both sides until the variable is isolated on one side. (204)

bar graph A data display in which bars are used to show measures or counts for various categories. (38)

base A number or an expression that is raised to a power. For example, $x + 2$ is the base in the expression $(x + 2)^3$, and 5 is the base in the expression 5^y. (397)

biased A sample is biased if the values in the sample are not like those in the population. (40)

bimodal Used to describe a data set that has two modes. (45)

binomial A polynomial with exactly two terms. Examples of binomials include $-3x + x^4$, $x = 12$, and $x^3 - x^{12}$. (542)

bins Intervals on the horizontal axis of a histogram that data values are grouped into. Boundary values fall into the bin to the right. (60)

box plot A one-variable data display that shows the five-number summary of a data set. A box plot is drawn over a horizontal number line. The ends of the box indicate the first and third quartiles. A vertical segment inside the box indicates the median. Horizontal segments, called whiskers, extend from the left end of the box to the minimum value and from the right end of the box to the maximum value. (52)

box-and-whisker plot See **box plot.**

category A group of data with the same attribute. For example, data about people's eye color could be grouped into three categories: blue, brown, and green. (39)

causation A relationship in which changes in one variable, called the *explanatory* or *predictor* variable, cause changes in another variable, called the *response* variable. Causation is difficult to prove. (300, 306)

coefficient A number that is multiplied by a variable. For example, in a linear equation in intercept form $y = a + bx$, b is the coefficient of x. (187)

collinear A set of points that can be connected by a single straight line. (237)

common monomial factor A monomial that is a factor of every term in an expression. For example, $3x$ is a common monomial factor of $12x^3 - 6x^2 + 9x$. (270, 584)

commutative property of addition For any values of a and b, $a + b = b + a$. (286)

commutative property of multiplication For any values of a and b, $ab = ba$. (286)

completing the square Adding a constant term to an expression in the form $x^2 + bx$ to form a perfect-square trinomial. For example, to complete the square in the expression $x^2 + 12x$, add 36. This gives $x^2 + 12x + 36$,which is equivalent to $(x + 6)^2$. To solve a quadratic equation by completing the square, write it in the form $x^2 + bx = c$, complete the square on the left side (adding the same number to the right side), rewrite the left side as a binomial squared, and then take the square root of both sides. (562)

complex number A number with a real part and an imaginary part. A complex number can be written in the form $a + bi$, where a and b are real numbers and i is the imaginary unit, $\sqrt{-1}$. (565)

compound inequality A combination of two inequalities. For example, $-5 < x \leq 1$ is a compound inequality that combines the inequalities $x > 5$ and $x \leq 1$. (358)

conclusion The result of a deductive argument. (336)

conditional relative frequency Compares data with respect to one specific condition, the ratio of the relative frequency for a condition to the marginal frequency of that condition (71)

conic section Any curve that can be formed by the intersection of a plane and a double cone. Parabolas, circles, ellipses, and hyperbolas are examples of conic sections. (541)

conjecture A statement that might be true but that has not been proven. Conjectures are usually based on data patterns or on experience. (76)

constant A value that does not change. (121)

constant multiplier In a sequence that grows or decreases exponentially, the number each term is multiplied by to get the next term. The value of $1 + r$ in the exponential equation $y = A(1 + r)^x$. (388, 391)

constant of variation The constant ratio in a direct variation or the constant product in an inverse variation. The value of k in the direct variation equation y^{kx} or in the inverse variation equation $y = \frac{k}{x}$. (121, 129)

constraint A limitation on the values of the variables in a situation. A system of inequalities can model the constraints in many real-world situations. (371)

continuous function A function that has no breaks in the domain or range. The graph of a continuous function is a line or curve with no holes or gaps. (263)

conversion factor A ratio used to convert measurements from one unit to another. (114)

coordinate plane A plane with a pair of scaled, perpendicular axes allowing you to locate points with ordered pairs and to represent lines and curves by equations. (78)

coordinates An ordered pair of numbers in the form (x, y) that describes the location of a point on a coordinate plane. The x-coordinate describes the point's horizontal distance and direction from the origin, and the y-coordinate describes its vertical distance and direction from the origin. (78)

correlation An association between two variables that may or may not imply causation. (300, 306)

counterexample An example that shows that a given conjecture is not true. (257)

counting number See **natural number.**

cube (of a number) A number raised to the third power. The cube of a number x is "x cubed" and is written x^3. For example, the cube of 4 is 4^3,which is equal to 64. (584)

cube root The cube root of a number a is the number b such that $a = b^3$. The cube root of a is denoted $\sqrt[3]{a}$. For example, $\sqrt[3]{64}$ and $\sqrt[3]{-125} = -5$. (584)

cubing function The function $f(x) = x^3$,which gives the cube of a number. (584)

data A collection of information, numbers, or pairs of numbers, usually measurements for a real-world situation. (38)

data analysis The process of calculating statistics and making graphs to summarize a data set. (76)

decreasing A term used to describe the behavior of a function. A function is decreasing on an interval of its domain if the y-values decrease as the x-values increase. Visually, the graph of the function goes down as you read from left to right for that part of the domain. (261)

decreasing function A function that is always decreasing. (263)

deductive reasoning A way of reasoning in which a statement is accepted as logical from agreed-upon assumptions and proven facts. (336)

degree In a one-variable polynomial, the power of the term that has the greatest exponent. In a multivariable polynomial, the greatest sum of the powers in a single term. (579)

dependent variable A variable whose values depend on the values of another variable (called the independent variable). In a graph of the relationship between two variables, the values on the vertical axis usually represent values of the dependent variable. (260)

design The strategy used for the collection, measurement, and analysis of data. (108)

deviation from the mean A data value minus the mean of its data set. The deviations of the data values from the mean give an idea of the spread of the data values. (54)

difference of two squares An expression in the form $a^2 - b^2$, in which one squared number is subtracted from another. A difference of two squares can be factored as $(a + b)(a - b)$. (556)

dimensional analysis A strategy for converting measurements from one unit to another by multiplying by a string of conversion factors. (114)

direct variation A relationship in which the ratio of two variables is constant. That is, a relationship in which two variables are directly proportional. A direct variation has an equation in the form $y = kx$, where x and y are the variables and k is a number called the constant of variation. (121)

directly proportional Used to describe two variables whose values have a constant ratio. (121)

discrete function A function whose domain and range are made up of distinct values rather than intervals of real numbers. The graph of a discrete function is made up of distinct points. (263)

discrete solutions A solution set in which all points in the solution set are whole-numbers (374)

discriminant The expression under the square root symbol in the quadratic formula. If a quadratic equation is written in the form $ax^2 + bx + c = 0$, then the discriminant is $b^2 - 4ac$. If the discriminant is greater than 0, the quadratic equation has two solutions. If the discriminant equals 0, the equation has one real solution. If the discriminant is less than 0, the equation has no real solutions. (571)

distance formula The distance, d, between points (x_1, y_1) and (x_2, y_2) is given by the formula $d = \sqrt{(x_2 - x_1)^2 + (y_2 - y_1)^2}$. (213)

distributive property of multiplication over addition For any values of a, b, and c, $a(b + c) = a(b) + a(c)$. (284, 286)

division property of equality If $a = b$, then $\frac{a}{c} = \frac{b}{c}$ for any nonzero number c. (242)

division property of exponents For any nonzero value of b and any values of m and n, $\frac{b^m}{b^n} = b^{m-n}$. (417)

domain The set of input values for a function. (247)

dot plot A one-variable data display in which each data value is represented by a dot above that value on a horizontal number line. (39)

elimination method A method for solving a system of equations that involves adding or subtracting the equations to eliminate a variable. In some cases, both sides of one or both equations must be multiplied by a number before the equations are added or subtracted. For example, to solve $\begin{cases} 3x - 2y = 5 \\ -6x + y = 11 \end{cases}$, you could multiply the first equation by 2 and then add the equations to eliminate x. (347)

engineering notation A notation in which a number is written as a number greater than or equal to 1 but less than 1000, multiplied by 10 to a power that is a multiple of 3. For example, in engineering notation, the number 10,800,000 is written 10.8 × 106. (427)

equation A statement that says the value of one number or algebraic expression is equal to the value of another number or algebraic expression. (151)

equivalent equations Equations that have the same set of solutions. (283)

error The difference between a measurement and the actual value. (86)

evaluate (an expression) To find the value of an expression. If an expression contains variables, values must be substituted for the variables before the expression can be evaluated. For example, if $3x^2 - 4$ is evaluated for $x = 2$, the result is $3(2)^2 - 4$, or 8. (22)

excluded value See **restriction on the variable.**

expand (an algebraic expression) To rewrite an expression by multiplying factors and combining like terms. For example, to expand $(x + 8)(x - 2)$, rewrite it as $x^2 + 6x - 16$. (545)

expanded form (of a repeated multiplication expression) The form of a repeated multiplication expression in which every occurrence of each factor is shown. For example, the expanded form of the expression $3^2 \cdot 5^4$ is $3 \cdot 3 \cdot 5 \cdot 5 \cdot 5 \cdot 5$. (397)

exponent A number or variable written as a small superscript of a number or variable, called the base, that indicates how many times the base is being used as a factor. For example, in the expression y^4, the exponent 4 means four factors of y, so $y^4 = y \cdot y \cdot y \cdot y$. (10)

exponential equation An equation in which a variable appears in the exponent. (397)

exponential form The form of an expression in which repeated multiplication is written using exponents. For example, the exponential form of $3 \cdot 3 \cdot 5 \cdot 5 \cdot 5 \cdot 5$ is $32 \cdot 54$. (397)

exponential growth A growth pattern in which amounts increase by a constant percent. Exponential growth can be modeled by the equation $y = A(1 + r)^x$, where A is the starting value, r is the rate of growth written as a decimal or fraction, x is the number of time periods elapsed, and y is the final value. (398)

factor One of the numbers, variables, or expressions multiplied to obtain a product. (10)

factored form An expression written as a product of expressions, rather than as a sum or difference. For example, $3(x + 2)$ and $y(4 - w)$ are in factored form. See **factoring.** (335)

factored form (of a quadratic equation) The form $y = a(x - r_1)(x - r_2)$, where $a \neq 0$. The values r_1 and r_2 are the zeros of the quadratic function. (549, 550)

factoring The process of rewriting an expression as a product of factors. For example, to factor $7x - 28$, rewrite it as $7(x - 4)$. To factor $x^2 + x - 2$, rewrite it as $(x - 1)(x + 2)$. (288)

family of functions A group of functions with the same parent function. For example, $y = |x - 5|$ and $y = -2|x| + 3$ are both members of the family of functions with parent function $y = |x|$. (477)

feasible region In a linear programming problem, the set of points that satisfy all the constraints. If the constraints are given as a system of inequalities, the feasible region is the solution to the system. (381)

first quartile (Q_1) The median of the values less than the median of a data set. (51)

first-quadrant graph A coordinate graph in which all the points are in the first quadrant. (80)

five-number summary The minimum, first quartile, median, third quartile, and maximum of a data set. The five-number summary helps show how the data values are spread. (51)

fixed point A number that, when substituted into an expression, results in the same number. For example, -4 is a fixed point for $0.5x - 2$, because $0.5(-4) - 2 = -4$. (23)

fractal The result of infinitely many applications of a recursive procedure to a geometric figure. The resulting figure has self-similarity. From the Latin word *fractus,* meaning broken or irregular. (2, 4, 5, 15)

frequency The number of times a value appears in a data set. (60)

function A rule or relationship in which there is exactly one output value for each input value. (247)

function reflections To reflect a graph of a function across the x-axis, replace y with $-y$ in the function equation. To reflect a graph of a function across the y-axis, replace x with $-x$. (485)

function notation A notation in which a function is named with a letter and the input is shown in parentheses after the function name. For example, $f(x) = x^2 + 1$ represents the function $y = x^2 + 1$. The letter f is the name of the function, and $f(x)$ (read "f of x") stands for the output for the input x. The output of this function for $x = 2$ is written $f(2)$, so $f(2) = 5$. (448)

general equation An equation that represents a whole family of equations. For example, the general equation $y = kx$ represents the family of equations that includes $y = 4x$ and $y = -3.4x$. (160)

general form (of a polynomial) A polynomial is in general form when the exponent of x decreases as you move to the next term. (579)

general form (of a quadratic equation) The form $y = ax^2 + bx + c$, in which $a \neq 0$. (549)

gravity The force of attraction between two objects. Gravity causes objects to accelerate toward Earth at a rate of 32 ft/s^2, or 9.8 m/s^2. (536)

greatest value See **maximum.**

half-life The time needed for an amount of a substance to decrease by one-half. (448)

half-plane The points on a plane that fall on one side of a boundary line. The solution of a linear inequality in two variables is a half-plane. (363)

histogram A one-variable data display that uses bins to show the distribution of values in a data set. Each bin corresponds to an interval of data values; the height of a bin indicates the number, or frequency, of values in that interval. (60)

hole (in a graph) A missing point in a graph where a variable is undefined. (553)

horizontal axis The horizontal number line on a coordinate graph or data display. Also called the ***x*-axis.** (78, 190)

horizontally reflected See **reflection across the *y*-axis.**

hypothesis The starting statement, which is assumed to be true, in a deductive argument. (336)

image The figure or graph of a function that is the result of a transformation of an original figure or graph of a function. (445)

image function The function that results when a transformation or series of transformations are performed upon an original function. (498)

imaginary number A number that includes the square root of a negative number. In the set of imaginary numbers, $\sqrt{-1}$ is represented by the letter *i*. For example, the solution to $x^2 = -4$ is the imaginary number $\sqrt{-4}$, or $2i$. (591)

increasing Used to describe the behavior of a function. A function is increasing on an interval of its domain if the *y*-values increase as the *x*-values increase. Visually, the graph of the function goes up as you read from left to right for that part of the domain. (261)

increasing function A function that is always increasing. (263)

independent variable A variable whose values affect the values of another variable (called the dependent variable). In a graph of the relationship between two variables, values on the horizontal axis usually represent values of the independent variable. (260)

inductive reasoning The process of observing data, recognizing patterns, and making conjectures about generalizations. (336)

inequality A statement that one quantity is less than or greater than another. For example, $x + 7 \geq -3$ and $6 + 2 < 11$ are inequalities. (355)

infinitely many solutions Two equations in a system represent the same line, then all solutions of one are solutions of the system (336)

integer A number expressed in the form a or $-a$ for some whole number *a*. For example, any one of the numbers . . . , −3, −2, −1, 0, 1, 2, 3, ... (532)

intercept form The form $y = a + bx$ of a linear equation. The value of *a* is the *y*-intercept, and the value of *b*, the coefficient of *x*, is the slope of the line. (187, 285)

interquartile range (IQR) The difference between the third quartile and the first quartile of a data set. (53)

interval The set of numbers between two given numbers, or the distance between two numbers on a number line or axis. (39)

inverse Reversed in order or effect. In an inverse mathematical relationship, as one quantity increases, the other decreases. (88, 123)

inverse (of a function) The relationship that reverses the inputs and outputs of a function. For example, the inverse of the function $y = x + 2$ is $y = x - 2$. (319, 494)

inverse variation A relationship in which the product of two variables is constant. That is, a relationship in which two variables are inversely proportional. An inverse variation has an equation in the form $xy = k$, or $y = \frac{k}{x}$, in which *x* and *y* are the variables and *k* is a number called the constant of variation. (129)

inversely proportional Used to describe two variables whose values have a constant product. (128, 129)

IQR See **interquartile range.**

irrational number A number that cannot be expressed as the ratio of two integers. In decimal form, an irrational number has an infinite number of digits and doesn't show a repeating pattern. Examples of irrational numbers include π and $\sqrt{2}$. (99, 539)

joint frequency Value in each cell of a two-way frequency table . . .(71)

joint relative frequency The ratio of the value in a cell of a frequency table to the table total (71)

key A guide for interpreting the values in a data display. For example, a stem plot has a key that shows how to read the stem and leaf values. (62)

leading coefficient In a polynomial, the coefficient of the term with the highest power of the variable. For example, in the polynomial $3x^2 - 7x + 4$, the leading coefficient is 3. (571)

least value See **minimum.**

like terms Terms that have the same variables raised to the same exponents. For example, $3x^2y$ and $8x^2y$ are like terms. You can add or subtract like terms—this process is sometimes called *combining like terms.* For example, in the expression $4x + 2x^2 - x + 5 + 7x^2$ you can combine the like terms $4x$ and $-x$ and the like terms $2x^2$ and $7x^2$ to get $3x + 9x^2 + 5$. (206)

line of fit A line used to model a set of data. A line of fit shows the general direction of the data and has about the same number of data points above and below it. (268)

line of symmetry A line that divides a figure into mirror-image halves. In a parabola that opens up or down, the line of symmetry is the vertical line through the vertex. (545)

line segment Two points on a line (endpoints) and all the points between them on the line. Also called a **segment.** (2)

linear In the shape of a line or represented by a line. (174, 260)

linear equation An equation that can be represented with a straight-line graph. A linear equation has variables raised only to the power of 1. For example, $y = 1 + 3x$ is a linear equation. (186)

linear function A function characterized by a constant rate of change—that is, as the x-values change by a constant amount, the y-values also change by a constant amount. The graph of a linear function is a straight line. (260)

linear programming A process that applies the concepts of constraints, points of intersection, and≈algebraic expressions to solve application problems. (381)

linear relationship A relationship that you can represent with a straight-line graph. A linear relationship is characterized by a constant rate of change—that is, as the value of one variable changes by a constant amount, the value of the other variable also changes by a constant amount. (86)

long-run value The value that the y-values approach as the x-values increase. (494)

lowest terms The form of a fraction or rational expression in which the numerator and denominator have no common factors except 1. (523)

margin of error A way of describing the precision of predictions made from data or equations. (226)

marginal frequency The totals of each row and column in a frequency table. (71)

marginal relative frequency a ratio of the marginal total of a row or column to the table total. (71)

maximum The greatest value in a data set or the greatest value of a function. (39, 406)

mean A measure of center obtained by dividing the sum of the values in a data set by the number of values. Often called the **average.** (45)

mean absolute deviation Average of the positive values of the deviations from the mean. (54)

measure of center A single number used to summarize a one-variable data set. The mean, median, and mode are measures of center. (45)

measure of central tendency See **measure of center.**

median (of a data set) A measure of center in a set of numerical data. The median of a list of values is the value appearing at the center of a sorted version of the list—or the mean of the two central values, if the list contains an even number of values (45)

midpoint formula If the endpoints of a segment are (x_1, y_1) and (x_2, y_2), then the midpoint of the segment is $\frac{x_1 + x_2}{2}, \frac{y_1 + y_2}{2}$. (603)

minimum The least value in a data set or the least value of a function. (39, 406)

mixture problem A problem that involves mixtures and usually requires a system of two or more equations to be solved. (342)

mode The value or values that occur most often in a data set. A data set may have more than one mode or no mode. (45)

monomial A polynomial with only one term. Examples of monomials include $-3x$, x^4, and $7x^2$. (549)

multiplication property of equality If $a = b$, then $ac = bc$ for any number c. (286)

multiplication property of exponents For any values of b, m, and n, $b^m \cdot b^n = b^{m+n}$. (415)

multiplicative identity property of 1 For any values of a, b, and c, $a \cdot 1 \cdot 1 \cdot a \cdot a$ (286)

multiplicative inverse The product of a number and its multiplicative inverse is 1. For any number a, the multiplicative inverse is $\frac{1}{a}$. (210)

natural number Any one of the numbers 1, 2, 3, 4, ... (539)

negative exponent For any nonzero value of b and any value of n, $b^{-a} = \frac{1}{b^a}$ and $\frac{1}{b^{-n}} = b$. (432)

nonlinear Not in the shape of a line or not able to be represented by a line. In mathematics, a nonlinear equation or expression has variables raised to powers other than 1. For example, $x^2 + 5x$ is a nonlinear expression. (260)

nonlinear function A function characterized by a nonconstant rate of change—that is, as the x-values change by a constant amount, the y-values change by varying amounts. (260)

null set A set with no elements, also called the empty set (335)

number line A straight line on which every point is assumed to correspond to a real number and every real number to a point. One of the simplest graphs, a number-line graph allows you to order numbers. The values of the numbers increase as you move along the line from left to right. (21)

one-variable data Data that measure only one trait or quantity. A one-variable data set consists of single values, not pairs of data values. (78)

order of magnitude A way of expressing the size of an extremely large or extremely small number by giving the power of 10 associated with the number. For example, the number 6.01×10^{26} is on the order of 10^{26} and the number 2.43×10^{-11} is on the order of 10^{-11}. (452)

order of operations The agreed-upon order in which operations are carried out when evaluating an expression: (1) evaluate all expressions within parentheses or other grouping symbols, (2) evaluate all powers, (3) multiply and divide from left to right, and (4) add and subtract from left to right. (24, 140)

ordered pair A pair of numbers named in an order that matters. For example, (3, 5) is different from (5, 3). The coordinates of a point are given as an ordered pair in which the first number is the x-coordinate and the second number is the y-coordinate. (78)

ordinate The y-coordinate in an ordered pair (x, y), measuring vertical distance from the x-axis on a coordinate plane. (78)

origin The point on a coordinate plane where the x- and y-axes intersect. The origin has coordinates (0, 0). (78)

outlier A value that is far outside the range of most of the other values in a data set. As a general rule, a data value is considered an outlier if the distance from the value to the first quartile or third quartile (whichever is nearest) is more than 1.5 times the interquartile range. (47)

parabola The graph of a function in the family of functions with parent function $y = x^2$. The set of all points whose distance from a fixed point, the focus, is equal to the distance from a fixed line, the directrix. (476, 524)

parallel lines Lines in the same plane that never intersect. They are always the same distance apart. Lines with equal slopes are parallel. (333)

parent function The most basic form of a function. A parent function can be transformed to create a family of functions. For example, $y = x^2$ is a parent function that can be transformed to create a family of functions that includes $y = x^2 + 2$ and $y = 3(x - 4)^2$. (489, 511)

perfect cube A number that is equal to the cube of an integer. For example, -125 is a perfect cube because $-125 = (-5)3$. (537)

perfect square A number that is equal to the square of an integer, or a polynomial that is equal to the square of another polynomial. For example, 64 is a perfect square because it is equal to 8^2, and $x^2 - 10x + 25$ is a perfect-square trinomial because it is equal to $(x - 5)^2$. (428, 551)

perpendicular lines Lines that meet at a right angle. Lines with opposite reciprocal slopes are perpendicular. (333)

pictograph A data display with symbols showing the number of data items in each category. Each symbol in a pictograph stands for a specific number of data items. (38)

piecewise function A function that consists of two or more functions defined on different intervals. (468)

point reflections A point is reflected across the x-axis, or *vertically reflected,* when you change the sign of its y-coordinate. A point is reflected across the y-axis, or *horizontally reflected,* when you change the sign of its x-coordinate. (485)

point-slope form The form $y = y_1 + b(x - x_1)$ of a linear equation, in which (x_1, y_1) is a point on the line and b is the slope. (278, 285)

polynomial A sum of terms that have positive integer exponents. For example, $-4x^2 + x$ and $x^3 - 6x^2 + 9$ are polynomials. (549)

polynomial equation An equation in which a polynomial expression is set equal to a second variable, such as y or $f(x)$. (560)

population A complete set of people or things being studied. (40)

population density The number of people per square mile. (429)

power properties of exponents For any values a, b, m, and n, $(b^m)^n = bmn$ and $(ab)^n = a^n b^n$. (416)

precision The smallest unit in which a measurement is expressed. For instance, if a measurement is determined as 12.25 inches, then its precision is 0.01 inch, or one-hundredth of an inch. (86)

premise A statement, such as a definition, property, or proven fact, used to prove further conclusions in a deductive argument. (336)

projectile motion The motion of a thrown, kicked, fired, or launched object—such as a ball—that has no means of propelling itself. (537)

properties of equality All real numbers, variables, and algebraic expressions follow certain properties relationship between two quantities or, more generally two mathematical expressions, asserting that the quantities have the same value or that the expressions represent the same mathematical object. (242)

properties of exponents Properties of the behavior of exponential expressions under the basic operations (438)

properties of operations All real numbers, variables, and algebraic expressions will behave in a certain way under the basic operations (286)

proportion An equation stating that two ratios are equal. For example, $\frac{34}{72} = \frac{x}{18}$ is a proportion. (101)

Q-points On a scatter plot, the vertices of the rectangle formed by drawing vertical lines through the first and third quartiles of the x-values and horizontal lines through the first and third quartiles of the y-values. If the points show an increasing linear trend, then the line through the lower-left and upper-right Q-points is a line of fit. If the points show a decreasing linear trend, then the line through the upper-left and lower-right Q-points is a line of fit. (299)

quadrant One of the four regions that a coordinate plane is divided into by the two axes. The quadrants are numbered I, II, III, and IV, starting in the upper right and moving counterclockwise. (78)

quadratic formula If a quadratic equation is written in the form $ax^2 + bx + c = 0$, then the solutions to the equation are given by $x = \frac{-b \pm \sqrt{b^2 - 4ac}}{2a}$. (578)

quadratic function Any function in the family with parent function $f(x) = x^2$. Examples of quadratic functions are $f(x) = 1.5x^2 + 2$, $f(x) = (x - 4)^2$, and $f(x) = 5x^2 - 3x + 12$. (537)

quadrilateral A polygon with exactly four sides. (280)

quantitative data A categorical measurement expressed in terms of numbers (78)

qualitative data A categorical measurement expressed not in terms of the description of a quality (78)

radical expression An expression containing a square root symbol, $\sqrt{}$. Examples of radical expressions are $\sqrt{x + 4}$ and $3 \pm \sqrt{19}$. (539)

radioactive decay The process by which an unstable chemical element loses mass or energy, transforming it into a different element or isotope. (441)

raised to the power A term used to connect the base and the exponent in an exponential expression. For example, in the expression 7^4, the base 7 is raised to the power of 4. (416)

random Not ordered, unpredictable. (28, 564)

range (of a data set) The difference between the maximum and minimum values in a data set. (40)

range (of a function) The set of output values for a function. (247)

rate A comparison, or ratio, between two quantities with different units. (115, 188)

rate of change The difference between two output values divided by the difference between the corresponding input values. For a linear relationship, the rate of change is constant. (198)

rate problem A problem involving a rate or rates, which is usually solved using the equation $d = rt$. (304)

ratio A comparison of two quantities, often written in fraction form. (101)

rational expression A ratio of two polynomial expressions with a non-zero denominator, such as $\frac{3}{x+2}$ or $\frac{x+1}{(x+3)(x-1)}$. (523)

rational function A function, such as $f(x) = \frac{3}{x+2}$ or $f(x) = \frac{x-1}{(x+3)(x-1)}$, that is expressed as the ratio of two polynomial expressions. (521)

rational number A number that can be written as a ratio of two integers. (104, 539)

real number Any number that can be represented on a number line. The real numbers include integers, rational numbers, and irrational numbers. The real numbers do *not* include imaginary numbers. (499, 539)

reciprocal The multiplicative inverse. The reciprocal of a given number is the number you multiply it by to get 1. To find the reciprocal of a number, you can write the number as a fraction and then invert the fraction. For example, the reciprocal of $\frac{3}{4}$ is $\frac{4}{3}$. (102, 334)

recursive Describes a procedure that is applied over and over again, starting with a number or geometric figure, to produce a sequence of numbers or figures. Each stage of a recursive procedure builds on the previous stage. The resulting sequence is said to be generated recursively, and the procedure is called recursion. (2)

recursive rule The instructions for producing each stage of a recursive sequence from the previous stage. (3)

recursive sequence An ordered list of numbers defined by a starting value and a recursive rule. You generate a recursive sequence by applying the rule to the starting value, then applying the rule to the resulting value, and so on. (166)

reflection A transformation that flips a figure or graph over a line, creating a mirror image. (498)

reflection across the *x*-axis A transformation that flips a figure or graph across the x-axis. Reflecting a point across the x-axis changes the sign of its y-coordinate. (498)

reflection across the *y*-axis A transformation that flips a figure or graph across the y-axis. Reflecting a point across the y-axis changes the sign of its x-coordinate. (498)

reflexive property For any real number a, $a = a$ (286)

relation A set of ordered pair. (247)

relative frequency The ratio of the number of times a particular outcome occurred to the total number of trials. Also called observed probability. (71)

relative frequency graph A data display (usually a bar graph or a circle graph) that compares the number in each category to the total for all the categories. Relative frequency graphs show fractions or percents, rather than actual values. (68)

repeating decimal A decimal number with a digit or group of digits after the decimal point that repeats infinitely. (99)

residual For a two-variable data set, the difference between the y-value of a data point and the y-value predicted by the equation of fit. (308)

residual plot A statistical graph that plots residuals versus the x-values of data points. (309)

restriction on the variable A statement of values that are excluded from the domain of an expression or equation. Any value of a variable that results in a denominator of 0 must be excluded from the domain. (523)

right angle An angle that measures 90°. (333)

roots The solutions to an equation in the form $f(x) = 0$. The roots are the x-intercepts of the graph of $y = f(x)$. For example, the roots of $(x - 2)(x + 1) = 0$ are 2 and -1. These roots are the x-intercepts of the graph of $y = (x - 2)(x + 1)$. (544)

sample A part of a population selected to represent the entire population. Sampling is the process of selecting and studying a sample from a population in order to make conjectures about the whole population. (40, 108)

scatter plot A two-variable data display in which values on a horizontal axis represent values of one variable and values on a vertical axis represent values of the other variable. The coordinates of each point represent a pair of data values. (78)

scientific notation A notation in which a number is written as a number greater than or equal to 1 but less than 10, multiplied by an integer power of 10. For example, in scientific notation, the number 32,000 is written 3.2×10^4. (419)

secant line A line that goes through any two points of a graph (481)

segment Two points on a line (endpoints) and all the points between them on the line. Also called a **line segment.** (3)

self-similar Describes a figure in which part of the figure is similar to—that is, has the same shape as—the whole figure. (6)

sequence An ordered list of numbers (166)

shrink A transformation that decreases the height or width of a figure. A vertical shrink decreases the height but leaves the width unchanged. A horizontal shrink decreases the width but leaves the height unchanged. A vertical shrink by a factor of a multiplies the y-coordinate of each point on a figure or graph by a. A horizontal shrink by a factor of b multiplies the x-coordinate of each point on a figure by b. (507, 510)

simulate To model an experiment with another experiment, called a *simulation,* so that the outcomes of the simulation have the same probabilities as the corresponding outcomes of the original experiment. For example, you can simulate tossing a coin by randomly generating a string of 0's and 1's on your calculator. (108)

slope The steepness of a line or the rate of change of a linear relationship. If (x_1, y_1) and (x_2, y_2) are two points on a line, then the slope of the line is $\frac{y_2 - y_1}{x_2 - x_1}$. The slope is the value of b when the equation of the line is written in intercept form, $y = a + bx$, and it is the value of m when the equation of the line is written in slope-intercept form, $y = mx + b$. (216, 219)

slope formula The formula for the **slope** of the line passing through point 1 with coordinates (x_1, y_1) and point 2 with coordinates (x_2, y_2) is $slope = \frac{\text{change in } y}{\text{change in } x} = \frac{y_2 - y_1}{x_2 - x_1}$ (219)

slope triangle A right triangle formed by drawing arrows to show the vertical and horizontal change from one point to another point on a line. (217)

slope-intercept form The form $y = mx + b$ of a linear equation. The value of m is the slope and the value of b is the y-intercept. (269, 272, 285)

solution The value(s) of the variable(s) that make an equation or inequality true. (151)

solve an equation To determine the value(s) of the variable(s) that make an equation true. (151)

spread A property of one-variable data that indicates how the data values are distributed from least to greatest and where gaps or clusters occur. Statistics such as the range, the interquartile range, and the five-number summary can help describe the spread of data. (39)

square (of a number) The product of a number and itself. The square of a number x is "x squared" and is written x^2. For example, the square of 6 is 6^2, which is equal to 36. (475)

square root The square root of a number a is a number b so that $a = b^2$. Every positive number has two square roots. For example, the square roots of 36 are -6 and 6 because 62 = 36 and $(-6)^2 = 36$. The square root symbol, $\sqrt{\ }$, means the positive square root of a number. So, $\sqrt{36} = 6$. (476)

square root function The function that undoes squaring, giving only the positive square root (that is, the positive number that, when multiplied by itself, gives the input). The square root function is written $f(x) = \sqrt{x}$. For example, $\sqrt{144} = 12$. (477)

squaring The process of multiplying a number by itself. See **square** (of a number). (475)

squaring function The function $f(x) = x^2$, which gives the square of a number. (476, 429)

standard deviation A measurement of how widely dispersed a set of data is from its mean. (55)

standard form The form $ax + by = c$ of a linear equation, in which a and b are not both 0. (285)

statistics Numbers, such as the mean, median, and range, used to summarize or represent a data set. Statistics also refers to the science of collecting, organizing, and interpreting information. (40)

stem plot A one-variable data display used to show the distribution of a fairly small set of data values. Generally, the left digit(s) of the data values, called the stems, are listed in a column on the left side of the plot. The remaining digits, called the leaves, are listed in order to the right of the corresponding stem. A key is usually included. (62)

stem-and-leaf plot See **stem plot.**

step function A function whose graph consists of a series of horizontal line segments. (471)

stretch A transformation that increases the height or width of a figure. A vertical stretch increases the height but leaves the width unchanged. A horizontal stretch increases the width but leaves the height unchanged. A vertical stretch by a factor of a multiplies the y-coordinate of each point on a figure or graph by a. A horizontal stretch by a factor of b multiplies the x-coordinate of each point on a figure by b. (507, 510)

substitution method A method for solving a system of equations that involves solving one of the equations for one variable and substituting the resulting expression into the other equation. For example, to find the solution to $\begin{cases} y + 2 = 3x \\ y - 1 = x + 3 \end{cases}$ you can solve the first equation for y to get $y = 3x - 2$ and then substitute $3x - 2$ for y in the second equation. (339)

subtraction property of equality For any values of a, b, and c, if $a = b$, then $a - c = b - c$ (286)

symbolic manipulation Applying mathematical properties to rewrite an equation or expression in equivalent form. (343)

symmetric property For any values of a and b, if $a = b$, then $b = a$ (286)

system of equations A set of two or more equations with the same variables. (325, 328)

system of inequalities A set of two or more inequalities with the same variables. (371)

term (of a polynomial) An algebraic expression that represents only multiplication and division between variables and constants. For example, inthe polynomial $x^3 - 6x^2 + 9$, the terms are x^3, $-6x^2$, and 9. (549)

term (of a sequence) Each number in a sequence. (168)

terminating decimal A decimal number with a finite number of nonzero digits after the decimal point. (99)

third quartile (Q_3) The median of the values greater than the median of a data set. (51)

transformation A change in the size or position of a figure or graph. Translations, reflections, stretches, shrinks, and rotations are types of transformations. (487)

transitive property of equality For any values of a, b, and c, if $a = b$ and $b = c$, then $a = c$. (286, 341)

translation A transformation that slides a figure or graph to a new position. (455)

translation of functions To translate a function, $y = f(x)$, h units horizontally and k units vertically, replace x with $x - h$ and y with $y - k$. So $y - k = f(x - h)$ or $y = f(x - h) + k$ (492)

trinomial A polynomial with exactly three terms. Examples of trinomials include $x + 2x^3 + 4$, $x^2 - 6x + 9$, and $3x^3 + 2x^2 + x$. (549)

two-variable data set A collection of data that measures two traits or quantities. A two-variable data set consists of pairs of values. (78)

undoing method A method of solving an equation that involves working backward to reverse each operation until the variable is isolated on one side of the equation. (151)

unit rate A rate with a denominator of 1. (115)

unique solution Exactly one solution to a system of equations (335)

value of an expression The numerical result of evaluating an expression. (22)

variable A trait or quantity whose value can change, or vary. In algebra, letters often represent variables. (78, 102, 136)

variance (s^2) A measure of spread for a one-variable data set that uses squaring to eliminate the effect of the different signs of the individual deviations. The variance of the data is the sum of the squares of the deviations, divided by one less than the number of values. (55)

vertex The point where the graph changes direction from increasing to decreasing or from decreasing to increasing. (490)

vertex form (of a quadratic equation) The form $y = a(x - h)^2 + k$, where $a \neq 0$. The point (h, k) is the vertex of the parabola. (546)

vertical axis The vertical number line on a coordinate graph or data display. Also called the ***y*-axis.** (39, 70)

vertical line test A method for determining whether a graph on the xy-coordinate plane represents a function. If all possible vertical lines cross the graph only once or not at all, the graph represents a function. If even one vertical line crosses the graph in more than one point, the graph does not represent a function. (254)

vertically reflected See **reflection across the *x*-axis.**

whole number Any one of the numbers 0, 1, 2, 3, ... (539)

work problem A problem involving a task, a rate of work for the task, and the total time necessary to complete the task. Work problems usually involve the equation *rate of work* · *time* = *part of work.* (297)

***x*-intercept** The x-coordinate of a point where a graph meets the x-axis. For example, the graph of $y = x + 2$ has x-intercept -2, and the graph of $y = (x + 2)(x - 4)$ has two x-intercepts, -2 and 4. (, 270)

***y*-intercept** The y-coordinate of the point where a graph crosses the y-axis. The value of y when x is 0. The y-intercept of a line is the value of a when the equation of the line is written in intercept form, $y = a + bx$, and it is the value of b when the equation for the line is written in slope-intercept form, $y = mx + b$. (187)

zero exponent For any nonzero value of b, $b^0 = 1$. (432)

zero-product property If the product of two or more factors equals zero, then at least one of the factors equals zero. For example, if $x(x + 2)(x - 3) = 0$, then $x = 0$ or $x + 2 = 0$ or $x - 3 = 0$. (559)

zeros (of a function) The values of the independent variable (the x-values) that make the corresponding values of the function (the $f(x)$-values) equal to zero. For example, the zeros of the function $f(x) = (x - 1)(x + 7)$ are 1 and -7 because $f(1) = 0$ and $f(-7) = 0$. See **roots.** (559)

Index

F

O

P

R

T

Photo Credits

Chapter 0

1: © 2014 Reinhold Leitner. Used under license from Shutterstock, Inc.; **4:** Ken Karp Photography; **5:** © Roger Ressmeyer/Corbis; **12:** © 2014 Janet Faye Hastings. Used under license from Shutterstock, Inc.; **15 (*l*):** © 2014 Craig Levers. Used under license from Shutterstock, Inc.; **15 (*r*):** Ken Karp Photography; **20:** © 2014 Yuri Arcurs. Used under license from Shutterstock, Inc.; **22:** Ken Karp Photography; **24:** Ken Karp Photography; **29 (*l*):** © 2014 Front page. Used under license from Shutterstock, Inc.; **29 (*r*):** © 2014 Corepics VOF. Used under license from Shutterstock, Inc.; **30 (*tl*):** Ken Karp Photography; **30 (*bl*):** Ken Karp Photography

Chapter 1

34: © David Robinson/CORBIS; **38:** Ken Karp Photography; **39 (*l*):** © 2014 Candy Box Images. Used under license from Shutterstock, Inc.; **39 (*r*):** Ken Karp Photography; **42:** © 2014 Pixel 4 Images. Used under license from Shutterstock, Inc.; **45:** Cheryl Fenton; **46:** © 2014 Deklofenak. Used under license from Shutterstock, Inc.; **48:** © 2014 Paul Brennan. Used under license from Shutterstock, Inc.; **49:** © 2014 Photobank gallery. Used under license from Shutterstock, Inc.; **50:** © 2014 holbox. Used under license from Shutterstock, Inc. **51:** © Bettmann/CORBIS; **53:** © James L. Amos/Photo Researchers; **57:** © Bettmann/CORBIS; **59:** Ken Karp Photography; **61:** Ken Karp Photography; **64 (*tl*):** © 2014 Saurabhbphoyar. Used under license from Shutterstock, Inc.; **64 (*tr*):** © 2014 Andrey Armyagov. Used under license from Shutterstock, Inc.; **64 (*ml*):** © 2014 Anna Omelchenko. Used under license from Shutterstock, Inc.; **64 (*mr*):** © 2014 Brian Eichhorn. Used under license from Shutterstock, Inc.; **64 (*bl*):** © 2014 Piyato. Used under license from Shutterstock, Inc.; **64 (*br*):** © 2014 Kailash K Soni. Used under license from Shutterstock, Inc.; **72:** © 2014 vladm. Used under license of Shutterstock, Inc.; **76:** Ken Karp Photography; **77:** Ken Karp Photography; **80:** © 2014 bikerriderlondon. Used under license from Shutterstock, Inc.; **81:** © 2014 Geoffrey Kuchera. Used under license from Shutterstock, Inc.; **83:** © 2014 miker. Used under license from Shutterstock, Inc.; **85:** © 2014 Auremar. Used under license from Shutterstock, Inc.; **90 (*l*):** © 2014 holbox. Used under license from Shutterstock, Inc.; **90 (*r*):** © 2014 Pixel 4 Images. Used under license from Shutterstock, Inc.; **91:** © 2014 Doug James. Used under license from Shutterstock, Inc.;

Chapter 2

97: © 2014 Christian Carollo. Used under license from Shutterstock, Inc.; **101 (*t*):** Ken Karp Photography; **101 (*b*):** © 2014 f9 photos. Used under license from Shutterstock, Inc.; **105 (*t*):** Ken Karp Photography; **105 (*b*):** © 2014 Ryan M. Bolton. Used under license from Shutterstock, Inc.; **107 (*t*):** © 2014 Joe Seer. Used under license from Shutterstock, Inc.; **107 (*b*):** www.nps.gov (National Park Service); **108 (*t*):** Source: Aaron Delonay, USGS; **108 (*b*):** Source: USGS; **109:** © 2014 Evok20. Used under license from Shutterstock, Inc.; **111:** Ken Karp Photography; **113:** © 2014 iofoto. Used under license from Shutterstock, Inc.; **115 (*tl*):** © 2014 photosphobos. Used under license from Shutterstock, Inc.; **115 (*m*):** Cheryl Fenton; **116:** © 2014 Natursports. Used under license from Shutterstock, Inc.; **117:** © 2014 Dima Sobko. Used under license from Shutterstock, Inc.; **118 (*l*):** © 2014 feathercollector. Used under license from Shutterstock, Inc.; **118 (*ml*):** © 2014 drsuth48. Used under license from Shutterstock, Inc.; **118 (*m*):** © 2014 Steve Byland. Used under license from Shutterstock, Inc.; **118 (*mr*):** © 2014 Sue Robinson. Used under license from Shutterstock, Inc.; **118 (*r*):** © 2014 Gualberto Becerra. Used under license from Shutterstock, Inc. **120:** © 2014 meunierd. Used under license from Shutterstock, Inc.; **121:** © 2014 Zaboo. Used under license from Shutterstock, Inc.; **123 (*t*):** © Regis Bossu/Sygma/Corbis; **123 (*b*):** © Bettmann/CORBIS; **125:** © 2014 Bjorn Hoglund. Used under license from Shutterstock, Inc.; **126:** © 2014 Ikonoklast Fotografie. Used under license from Shutterstock, Inc.; **129:** Cheryl Fenton; **131:** ©2014 Pavel L. Photo and Video. Used under license from Shutterstock, Inc.; **132:** © 2014 BW Folsom. Used under license from Shutterstock, Inc.; **133:** Ken Karp Photography; **134 (*t*):** Courtesy of Library of Congress; **134 (*b*):** © 2014 Steve Heap. Used under license from Shutterstock, Inc.; **137:** Ken Karp Photography; **139:** © 2014 Ant Clausen. Used under license from Shutterstock, Inc.; **147:** © 2014 Warren Goldswain. Used under license from Shutterstock, Inc.; **148:** Ken Karp Photography; **154:** © 2014 Pavel Vakhrushev. Used under license from Shutterstock, Inc.; **155:** Cheryl Fenton; **156:** © 2014 Joy Brown. Used under license from Shutterstock, Inc.; **157:** © 2014 BaLL LunLa. Used under license from Shutterstock, Inc.; **159:** © Burstein Collection/CORBIS

Chapter 3

162 (*t*): © Alison Wright/Corbis; **162 (*b*):** © 2014 lynnette. Used under license from Shutterstock, Inc.; **166:** © 2014 ruigsantos. Used under license from Shutterstock, Inc.; **170:** © Swim Ink 2, LLC/CORBIS; **171:** © Nate Allred. Used under license from Shutterstock, Inc.; **172:** © 2014 joyfull. Used under license from Shutterstock, Inc.; **178:** U.S. Navy photo by Mass Communication Specialist 1st Class Jeffrey Jay Price. **187:** © 2014 wavebreakmedia. Used under license from Shutterstock, Inc.; **189:** © 2014 lightpoet. Used under license from Shutterstock, Inc.; **194:** © 2014 Perspectives - Jeff Smith. Used under license from Shutterstock, Inc.; **195:** © 2014 svetlovskiy. Used under license from Shutterstock, Inc.; **196:** © Bettmann/CORBIS; **198:** © 2014 djandre77. Used under license from Shutterstock, Inc.; **203:** © 2014 Rido. Used under license from Shutterstock, Inc.; **204:** © James P. Blair/CORBIS; **216:** © 2014 IM Photo. Used under license from Shutterstock, Inc.; **223:** © 2014 M. M. Used under license from Shutterstock, Inc.; **225:** Ken Karp Photography; **226:** © 2014 vjom. Used under license from Shutterstock, Inc.; **229:** © 2014 bikeriderlondon. Used under license from Shutterstock, Inc.; **234:** © 2014 Perspectives - Jeff Smith. Used under license from Shutterstock, Inc.; **236:** Ken Karp Photography; **238:** © 2014 Jarno Gonzalez Zarraonandia. Used under license from Shutterstock, Inc.

Chapter 4

241: Scala/Art Resource, NY; **245 (*t*):** © Archivo Iconografico, SA/CORBIS; **245 (*b*):** Ken Karp Photography; **248:** © 2014 mark higgins. Used under license from Shutterstock, Inc.; **252:** © 2014 Steve Byland. Used under license from Shutterstock, Inc.; **253:** Private Collection/Photo © Christie's Images/The Bridgeman Art Library. © 2013 Estate of Pablo Picasso/Artists Rights Society (ARS), New York.; **256:** © 2014 Christina Richards. Used under license from Shutterstock, Inc.; **259:** © 2014 oliveromg. Used under license from Shutterstock, Inc.; **264:** © Gail Mooney/Corbis; **268:** © 2014 Miao Liao. Used under license from Shutterstock, Inc.; **270 (*t*):** © 2014 spirit of america. Used under license from Shutterstock, Inc.; **270 (*b*):** © 2014 Nayashkova Olga. Used under license from Shutterstock, Inc.; **274:** © Patsy Lynch/Retna Ltd./Corbis; **282 (*t*):** © 2014 vadim kozlovsky. Used under license from Shutterstock, Inc.; **282 (*b*):** © 2014 Christopher Elwell. Used under license from Shutterstock, Inc.; **283:** Private Collection/Photo © Christie's Images/The Bridgeman Art Library. © 2013 The Andy Warhol Foundation for the Visual Arts, Inc./Artists Rights Society (ARS), New York.; **289:** © 2014 Maridav. Used under license from Shuttrestock, Inc.; **290:** © 2014 Giuseppe_R. Used under license from Shutterstock, Inc.; **293:** © 2014 Khamidulin Sergey. Used under license from Shutterstock, Inc.; **295 (*t*):** © 2014 col. Used under license from Shutterstock, Inc.; **295 (*b*):** © 2014 Wildnerdpix. Used under license from Shutterstock, Inc.; **300:** © Annie Griffiths Belt/Corbis; **305 (*t*):** © 2014 Ffooter. Used under license from Shutterstock, Inc.; **305 (*b*):** © 2014 TACstock1. Used under license from Shutterstock, Inc.; **306:** © 2014 Artisticco. Used under license from Shutterstock, Inc.; **310:** © 2014 CandyBox Images. Used under license from Shutterstock, Inc.; **311:** © 2014 Sergey Karpov. Used under license from Shutterstock, Inc.; **312:** © 2014 Jiri Sebesta. Used under license from Shutterstock, Inc.; **313:** Ken Karp Photography; **316:** © 2014 Pavel Tops. Used under license from Shutterstock, Inc.; **318:** © KERIM OKTEN/ epa/Corbis

Chapter 5

321: © 2014 gualtiero boffi. Used under license from Shutterstock, Inc.; **326 (*l*):** © Tom Bean/CORBIS; **326 (*r*):** © Tom Bean/ CORBIS; **331:** © 2014 Darren Brode. Used under license from Shutterstock, Inc.; **333:** © Philadelphia Museum of Art/CORBIS; **334 (*t*):** © 2014 Videowokart. Used under license from Shutterstock, Inc.; **334 (*b*):** © 2014 B Calkins. Used under license from Shutterstock,Inc.; **338:** © 2014 DM7. Used under license from Shutterstock,Inc.; **339:** © 2014 Paul Fleet. Used under license from Shutterstock, Inc.; **341:** © 2014 Vasiliy Koval. Used under license from Shutterstock, Inc.; **343 (*l*):** © Tom Bean/ CORBIS; **343 (*r*):** © Tom Bean/CORBIS; **344 (*t*):** Photofest; **344 (*l*):** Photofest; **344 (*r*):** Photofest; **346 (*t*):** © 2014 Maxisport. Used under license from Shutterstock, Inc.; **346 (*b*):** © 2014 Gleb Tarro. Used under license from Shutterstock, Inc.; **351:** © 2014 bikeriderlondon. Used under license from Shutterstock, Inc.; **352:** © 2014 nouseforname. Used under license from Shutterstock, Inc.; **357:** © James L.Amos/Corbis; **360:** © 2014 Jason Stitt. Used under license from Shutterstock, Inc.; **362:** © 2014 archideaphoto. Used under license from Shutterstock, Inc.; **368:** © Morgan Hill/ Demotix/Corbis; **371:** © John Gress/Corbis; **373:** © 2014 Johann Helgason. Used under license from Shutterstock, Inc.; **378:** © 2014 Josef Hanus. Used under license from Shutterstock, Inc.; **379:** © 2014 Maxisport. Used under license from Shutterstock, Inc.; **381:** © 2014 Maxim Blinkov. Used under license from Shutterstock, Inc.

Chapter 6

383: © Bettmann/CORBIS; **387:** Ken Karp Photography; **392:** © 2014 Monkey Business Images. Used under license from Shutterstock, Inc.; **394:** © 2014 Peter Bernik. Used under license from Shutterstock, Inc.; **395:** © 2014 arka38. Used under license from Shutterstock, Inc.; **399:** © 2014 grebcha. Used under license from Shutterstock, Inc.; **401 (*t*):** © 2014 Werner Stoffberg. Used under license from Shutterstock, Inc.; **401 (*b*):** © 2014 Sarah Fields Photography. Used under license from Shutterstock, Inc.; **402:** © 2014 Dmitrijs Dmitrijevs. Used under license from Shutterstock, Inc.; **403:** © 2014 Tupungato. Used under license from Shutterstock, Inc.; **404:** © 2014 NatalieJean. Used under license from Shutterstock, Inc.; **409:** © 2014 molekuul.be. Used under license from Shutterstock, Inc.; **410 (*t*):** © CORBIS; **410 (*b*):** © Bettmann/CORBIS; **411:** © 2014 Susan Montgomery. Used under license from Shutterstock, Inc.; **412:** © Bettmann/ CORBIS; **413:** © 2014 Gunnar Pippel. Used under license from Shutterstock, Inc.; **419:** © 2014 Pojoslaw. Used under license from Shutterstock, Inc.; **420:** © 2014 CreativeNature.nl. Used under license from Shutterstock, Inc.; **427:** © 2014 Charles Neal. Used under license from Shutterstock, Inc.; **431 (*l*):** © 2014 Paul D. Smith. Used under license from Shutterstock, Inc.; **431 (*m*):** © 2014 Robert Crum. Used under license from Shutterstock, Inc.; **431 (*r*):** © 2014 rSnapshotPhotos. Used under license from Shutterstock, Inc.; **432:** © 2014 Ivancovlad. Used under license from Shutterstock, Inc.; **433:** © 2014 James Steidl. Used under license from Shutterstock, Inc. **437:** © Hulton-Deutsch/CORBIS; **440 (*l*):** © 2014 CreativeNature.nl. Used under license from Shutterstock, Inc.; **440 (*r*):** © 2014 Tupungato. Used under license from Shutterstock, Inc.; **441:** © 2014 Mark Herreid. Used under license from Shutterstock, Inc.

Chapter 7

444: © 2014 Jelle vd Wolf. Used under license from Shutterstock, Inc.; **448:** © Bettmann/CORBIS; **454:** © 2014 Fedor Selivanov. Used under license from Shutterstock, Inc.; **464:** © 2014 ermess. Used under license from Shutterstock, Inc.; **465:** © 2014 Mpanchenko. Used under license from Shutterstock, Inc.; **469:** © 2014 Africa Studio. Used under license from Shutterstock, Inc.; **477:** © 2014 NigelSpiers. Used under license from Shutterstock, Inc.; **482:** Ken Karp Photography; **488:** © 2014 HotVector. Used under license from Shutterstock, Inc.; **492:** © 2014 Eugene Sergeev. Used under license from Shutterstock, Inc.; **493:** © 2014 Hannamariah. Used under license from Shutterstock, Inc.; **495:** © National Gallery, London/Art Resource, NY; **502:** © 2014 Adam Gryko. Used under license from Shutterstock, Inc.; **507:** © Jim Sugar/Corbis; **508:** © 2014 Tung Tran. Used under license from Shutterstock, Inc.; **514:** © 2014 Sergey Dubrov. Used under license from Shutterstock, Inc.; **515:** © 2014 Oleg Begunenco. Used under license from Shutterstock, Inc.; **518:** © 2014 Tung Tran. Used under license from Shutterstock, Inc.; **519:** © 2014 AdStock RF. Used under license from Shutterstock, Inc.; **521:** © 2014 Eky Studio. Used under license from Shutterstock, Inc.; **523:** © 2014 Craig Burrows. Used under license from Shutterstock, Inc.

Chapter 8

525: © 2014 Songquan Deng. Used under license from Shutterstock, Inc.; **530:** © Bettmann/CORBIS; **536:** © 2014 Scott Norsworthy. Used under license from Shutterstock, Inc.; **546:** © 2014 Aspen Photo. Used under license from Shutterstock, Inc.; **548:** © 2014 Tony Bowler. Used under license from Shutterstock, Inc.; **567:** © Todd Kirkland/Icon SMI/Corbis; **568:** © 2014 Erik Mandre. Used under license from Shutterstock, Inc.; **573:** © Paul J. Sutton/Duomo/Corbis; **586:** © 2014 nikkytok. Used under license from Shutterstock, Inc.; **588:** © 2014 Scott Norsworthy. Used under license from Shutterstock, Inc.